Andrew Streitwieser, Jr.
Clayton H. Heathcock

Introduction to Organic Chemistry

Third Edition

Solutions Manual and Study Guide

prepared by

Paul A. Bartlett

University of California, Berkeley

Macmillan Publishing Company

NEW YORK

Collier Macmillan Publishers

LONDON

Macmillan Publishing Company
866 Third Avenue, New York, New York 10022

Collier Macmillan Canada, Inc.

ISBN 0-02-418150-1

Printing: 4 5 6 7 8   Year: 7 8 9 0 1 2 3 4 5

ACKNOWLEDGMENT

This Study Guide, like most endeavors, is the product
of the efforts of several individuals. For creating
the outstanding parent text, "Introduction to Organic
Chemistry", my colleagues Andy Streitwieser and Clay
Heathcock deserve ultimate credit for the existence
of the Study Guide. I put most of it together and can
therefore take credit for its shortcomings and failings.
The person who deserves top honors, though, is
Wendy Zukas, for it is her artistry and craftsmanship
which are most evident on the pages of this book.

CONTENTS

Introduction to Organic Chemistry

Third Edition

Solutions Manual and Study Guide

NOTES ON STUDYING

If you ask a group of college students which course is the most difficult, they will probably say "organic chemistry". This is intimidating to say the least, especially if you are about to start the course. There is no denying that a course in organic chemistry contains a great deal of material, including many names and facts and an extensive framework of basic principles. However, many students discover the logical foundation to the subject and thoroughly enjoy learning it. It requires work, but so do many other skills worth knowing and doing.

Learning organic chemistry requires logical reasoning as well as memorization. The importance of memorization is great, because the framework of organic chemistry rests on a foundation of facts, but you will find that memorization alone is not going to be enough. (If it were, organic chemistry would not have the reputation it has. Sheer memorization is easy -- dull perhaps, but basically easy.) To be able to discern a general principle from a collection of facts (reason deductively) and then to be able to predict the behavior of an unknown system (reason inductively) is really what is required to learn organic chemistry beyond the level of simple memorization. The subject can be compared to the game of chess: the chemical behavior of each class of compounds is the counterpart of the moves that different chess pieces are allowed to make. Each chess game becomes intricate and unique, but it always develops within the logical framework of the rules. Similarly, although the range and variety of chemical reactions is often bewildering, they too arise from a finite set of logical principles. We derive a great deal of satisfaction from organic chemistry, as do many of our friends from the game of chess. Hopefully we can help you to learn and enjoy the game of organic chemistry as well.

Learning organic chemistry is not easy: it requires you to commit both time and intellectual effort. Learning anything requires reinforcement through repetition, especially repetition in different contexts. In a typical chemistry course repetition is provided in several different ways in order to involve the whole brain. Among these are:

Lectures. The lecture is often an underrated or misunderstood part of the learning process, but it shows you what aspects of the subject the instructor feels are most important, which reactions or mechanisms should receive emphasis, and what should be considered background information. Moreover, the lecturer will present the material in a different way than the text, provide different examples and thereby complement the text. Finally, you listen to a lecturer, and involve a different part of your brain than you do when reading.

Lecture Notes. Because the material that the lecturer presents both orally and and on the blackboard is clearly important, it is necessary to recall it while studying. Many students in this electronic age use tape recorders for this purpose, but we feel that these are only a poor supplement to taking notes. Unless you videotape the lecture, you lose the blackboard material. Moreover, you can review a 50-minute lecture more effectively and quickly from notes than you can by spending 50 minutes listening to it again. All of which is to say that lecture notes are important. They help you focus your attention on the lecturer and the material (an important aid on Monday mornings if you or the lecturer is not at peak performance...), they force you to process the information (providing another form of repetition), and they make you use a different brain function as well.

Taking good notes does not end with the lecture. You should transcribe the rough notes into a more organized, legible, and complete form as soon as possible after the lecture. This further processing of information (more repetition...) should be done while the lecture is still fresh in your mind and before the short term memory has started to fade.

Textbook Study. As pointed out above, learning organic chemistry requires an intellectual commitment on top of the time commitment of studying. Mere reading is not study: study is work and requires self-discipline. It requires reading with concentration and thought. For instance, you should constantly ask yourself questions and formulate examples on your own as you proceed through the text. In studying a new reaction, run through specific examples in your mind, using those provided in the text as a guide. Interspersed throughout the text are exercises that ask you to do just this. You will find additional specific suggestions on what to look for and how to learn new reactions in this Study Guide.

Most reactions fall into a very few categories such as proton transfer, displacement, addition, elimination, etc. In studying each reaction, see how these categories apply, and see how the mechanism of that reaction compares with similar ones of that class. The most important thing you should remember about a reaction is that it exists: that is, that a given functional group transformation or interconversion can be accomplished. It is secondarily useful, although still important, to know the overall reaction conditions and reagents required and any structural limitations involved. It is generally sufficient to know these aspects in general terms, such as the need for heating or cooling the reaction mixture, having acid or base present, etc., rather than memorizing a host of specific details.

Many students find it useful to construct "flash cards" for learning reactions. If you use this technique, be sure to make your own. Remember that the process of writing out the flash cards helps you to learn what's on them.

Problem Sets. Except for the first and last chapters, each chapter in the text is followed by a number of problems. **Working these problems is the most important way to learn organic chemistry.** Working a problem forces you to think, points out the things you don't know, and is good practice for exams. When you review your notes, or go back over the text, it is only human nature to say to yourself, "I know that reaction...I've seen that mechanism before...I'll remember that tomorrow morning..." But your professor is not going to be very sympathetic if you write, "I understood that yesterday" as an answer to an exam question. Working problems is really the only way to probe your mind to find out if you know something when you don't have it right in front of you. Multistep syntheses for example provide an excellent test of knowledge. You have to know each reaction, but that alone is not enough; you have to be able to put them together in the proper sequence.

It should be obvious that you have to work the problems on your own; that is, without thumbing back through the text to find the answer, or worse, simply looking it up in this Study Guide. You should make a serious attempt to work a problem before you look for the answer; if you honestly can't, then use the text and your notes to help you. Only when you are completely stymied by a problem, or you have solved it, should you look up the answer in this Study Guide. It will be a valuable check to see if you got the right answer, and it shows you how to solve the problem if you didn't. If you look the answer up right away, you'll just say to yourself, "Oh, I knew that", or "I'll remember that tomorrow" (when you probably didn't and won't).

If the answer given in the Study Guide doesn't make sense to you, check back through the text and your notes again. If you still are confused, by all means see your professor and/or teaching assistant. That is what they are paid for, and most organic chemistry classes are too large for the instructor to come to you. Most instructors like to teach, and they will be pleased if you use their office hours judiciously.

Laboratory. Most introductory organic chemistry courses have a laboratory associated with them. The primary purpose of the laboratory part of the course is for you to learn the experimental operations of organic chemistry and to gain facility in the associated physical manipulations. It takes actual practice to set up an experimental apparatus and carry out the preparation of a compound, just as it takes dexterity and practice to play the piano or make a sauce béarnaise. Moreover, your laboratory experience provides still another reinforcement route to learning organic chemistry. Organic compounds are stuff that melt, boil, smell, have colors and crystalline form; modern organic chemistry has many abstract theories and principles, but they apply to real physical substances. This character of organic compounds is emphasized in the text, but will be reinforced by your laboratory work.

Further Suggestions. Finally, but most importantly, you should study frequently and in continuous pieces. If you limit your study to "cramming" for examinations, you will not learn organic chemistry. There is a great deal of structural hierarchy in the science, and you should understand each level thoroughly before you go on to the next one.

WHAT THIS STUDY GUIDE CONTAINS

The Study Guide is organized in chapters which parallel those of the text. Each chapter contains the following sections:

A. Outline of the chapter in the text, with keywords (bold-faced terms), important ideas introduced, a brief equation illustrating each reaction discussed in the chapter, and where appropriate the major points to keep in mind for these reactions.

B. A discussion section which: 1) provides an overview of the chapter and a look at the important reactions from a different point of view, and 2) gives specific hints on how to approach certain topics and how to solve certain types of problems.

C. Answers to the exercises which are interspersed throughout the chapter in the text.

D. Answers and explanations to the problems at the end of the chapter in the text.

E. Supplementary problems to provide you with additional practice. These problems tend to be a bit harder than those in the text, and they often incorporate ideas from previous chapters as well. This can be valuable from the point of view of review, of course.

F. Answers to the supplementary problems. Although these are very near the questions themselves, don't look until you've worked the problems!

The Study Guide concludes with two Appendices:

Appendix I is a glossary of terms, and contains definitions and comments on the vocabulary and concepts which are important in organic chemistry. It is arranged alphabetically and is cross-referenced both among the terms themselves and to the section of the text where the terms are introduced.

Appendix II is a summary of Functional Group Preparations, listing essentially every reaction in the text. It is organized according to the type of product formed, and it gives the page(s) where specific examples can be found.

We hope that this Study Guide is useful to you in learning organic chemistry. Even more importantly, we hope that it helps you to appreciate the beauty and excitement of this area of science, and that you will be one of the many students who enjoy the subject. We would appreciate any comments or suggestions that you might have for this Study Guide; we apologize for any mistakes and will be grateful if you bring them to our attention.

2. ELECTRONIC STRUCTURE AND BONDING

2.C   Important Concepts and Hints

    The topics of electronic structure and bonding are presented from two different points of view in Chapter 2. The first is concerned with the accounting of electrons, predicting how many co-valent bonds an atom will make, and assigning formal charges. All of this falls under the heading of **Lewis**, or "electron dot", structures. Being familiar with this accounting procedure is impor-tant, because as you progress in organic chemistry, you will be expected to keep track mentally of the information which Lewis structures provide, although you will write the simpler Kekule struc-tures primarily. Another important concept in the accounting of electrons and bonds is that of **resonance**, which enables you to understand the structure and reactivity of a molecule which does not conform to any single Lewis structure.

    In parallel with an understanding of Lewis structures and resonance, you will also need to be familiar with the concept of an **orbital**, and many of the topics pertaining to it. Because modern organic chemists describe almost all reaction mechanisms in terms of the orbitals involved, you should understand

1) what an orbital is
2) why it can be filled or empty
3) how a covalent bond is formed from the overlap of two atomic orbitals
4) what **molecular** and **bonding** orbitals are
5) what **hybridized** orbitals are, how and why they are formed, and what their shape and orientation are
6) how the geometry of a molecule depends on this hybridization.

We don't exaggerate when we say that these concepts are the foundation of the modern approach to understanding organic chemistry. You would be wise, therefore, to understand them from the start.

HINTS: For determining the hybridization of an atom, a convenient approach is to count up the number of things attached to that atom. By "things" we mean other atoms <u>and</u> unshared electron pairs. For example, methane, ammonia, and water all have four things attached to the central atom; they are all, therefore, sp^3-hybridized.

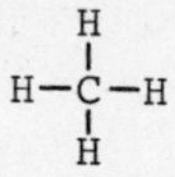

$$H-\underset{\underset{H}{|}}{\overset{\overset{H}{|}}{C}}-H \qquad H-\underset{\underset{\cdot\cdot}{|}}{\overset{\overset{H}{|}}{N}}-H \qquad H-\overset{\cdot\cdot}{\underset{\cdot\cdot}{O}}-H$$

$$\textit{methane} \qquad\qquad \textit{ammonia} \qquad\qquad \textit{water}$$

The carbon in methyl cation, the carbon and oxygen in formaldehyde, the nitrogens in diimide, and the boron in borane are all connected to only three things and are sp^2-hybridized. The carbons and boron in these examples are bonded to three atoms only, although in formaldehyde the carbon still has four bonds. Each nitrogen in diimide is attached to a hydrogen, another nitrogen, and a lone pair. The oxygen in formaldehyde is attached to a carbon and two lone pairs.

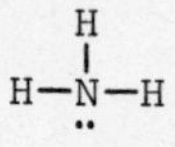

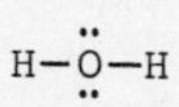

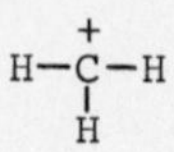

$$H-\overset{\overset{+}{|}}{\underset{\underset{H}{|}}{C}}-H \qquad \overset{H}{\underset{H}{\diagup}}C=\overset{\cdot\cdot}{\underset{\cdot\cdot}{O}} \qquad H-\overset{\cdot\cdot}{N}=\underset{\underset{\cdot\cdot}{}}{N}-H \qquad H-\overset{\overset{H}{\diagup}}{\underset{\underset{H}{\diagdown}}{B}}$$

$$\textit{methyl cation} \qquad \textit{formaldehyde} \qquad \textit{diimide} \qquad \textit{borane}$$

Using these criteria, it is clear why all the non-hydrogen atoms in the structures below are sp-hybridized:

$$H-Be-H \qquad H-C\equiv N: \qquad {}^{-}:C\equiv C-H \qquad {}^{+}:O\equiv N:$$

The only difficulties arise in attempting to predict the hybridization of the halogens, and of elements below the second row of the periodic table. We would predict by the method outlined above that the halogens are sp^3-hybridized. Because the significance of evaluating hybridization lies in the prediction of bond angles, the hybridization of the monovalent halogens is unimportant. Nevertheless, in some instances (e.g., the fluorine in HF), they are considered to be unhybridized (see Section 8.1 later on in the text). For elements in the third row of the periodic table and below, the question of hybridization can become more complicated (see the discussion at the end of Section 2.4 in the text, as well as Exercise 2.6).

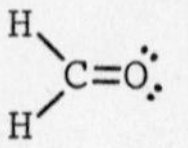

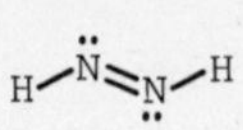

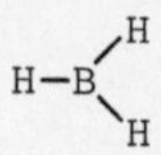

2.D   Answers to Exercises

2.1

(a) :C̈l:⁻
$\qquad$
Number of valence electrons for the neutral atom (which corresponds to column in periodic table), plus corrections for negative and positive charges.

$$
\begin{array}{rr}
\text{Cl:} & 7 \text{ valence electrons} \\
-\text{ charge:} & 1 \\ \hline
\text{Sum:} & 8
\end{array}
$$

(b) H:Ö:H

$$
\begin{array}{rr}
2\text{H:} & 2 \\
\text{O:} & 6 \\ \hline
\text{Sum:} & 8
\end{array}
$$

(c) H:Ö:⁻

$$
\begin{array}{rr}
\text{H:} & 1 \\
\text{O:} & 6 \\
-\text{ charge:} & 1 \\ \hline
\text{Sum:} & 8
\end{array}
$$

You can arrive at the structure of the hydroxide ion by combining a hydrogen atom, an oxygen atom, and the negative charge, or by taking the structure of the water molecule and subtracting a proton, H^+.

(d) :C̈l:Ö:⁻

$$
\begin{array}{rr}
\text{Cl:} & 7 \\
\text{O:} & 6 \\
-\text{ charge:} & 1 \\ \hline
\text{Sum:} & 14
\end{array}
$$

To make an octet for each atom using only 14 electrons, one pair has to be shared between the atoms. The oxygen has the negative charge because it controls seven electrons (6 + 1/2 of the 2 shared = 7), one more than in a free oxygen atom.

(e) H:N̈:H
$\quad$ H

$$
\begin{array}{rr}
3\text{ H:} & 3 \\
\text{N:} & 5 \\ \hline
\text{Sum:} & 8
\end{array}
$$

(f) :F̈:C:::N:

$$
\begin{array}{rr}
\text{C:} & 4 \\
\text{N:} & 5 \\
\text{F:} & 7 \\ \hline
\text{Sum:} & 16
\end{array}
$$

In this case, with 16 electrons to make octets for three atoms, (3 x 8) - 16 = 4 pairs of electrons have to be shared. This is accomplished by putting one pair between F and C (single bond) and three pairs between C and N (triple bond). All of the atoms are neutral since they control the same number of electrons as they do in the atomic state (F: 6 + 1/2 of 2 = 7; C: 1/2 of 8 = 4; N: 2 + 1/2 of 6 = 5).

(g) :N::Ö:

$$
\begin{array}{rr}
\text{N:} & 5 \\
\text{O:} & 6 \\ \hline
\text{Sum:} & 11
\end{array}
$$

With an odd number of valence electrons, it is impossible to have an octet for each atom. The best that can be achieved is to share two pairs to give oxygen an octet and nitrogen 7 electrons in the valence shell.

(h) H:Ö:⁺H
$\quad$ H

$$
\begin{array}{rr}
3\text{ H:} & 3 \\
\text{O:} & 6 \\
+\text{ charge:} & -1 \\ \hline
\text{Sum:} & 8
\end{array}
$$

Note that you can get this structure by adding a proton, H^+, to the water molecule. Oxygen has the positive charge because it controls only five electrons (2 + 1/2 of the 6 shared).

(i) Na⁺

$$
\begin{array}{rr}
\text{Na:} & 1 \\
+\text{ charge:} & -1 \\ \hline
\text{Sum:} & 0 \text{ electrons in valence shell}
\end{array}
$$

The next shell lower in energy than the valence shell has a complete octet; the sodium cation in fact has the same number of electrons as neon.

(j) He:

(k) H:Ö:Ö:H

(l) :O::C::O:

$$
\begin{array}{rr}
\text{C:} & 4 \\
2\text{ O:} & 12 \\ \hline
\text{Sum:} & 16
\end{array}
$$

Three octets from 16 electrons requires four pairs to be shared.

2.2   :N::O: The Lewis dot structure indicates that two pairs of electrons are shared and that nitric oxide has a double bond. As indicated in the text, the N=O double bond distance is 1.15 Å (0.115 nm); the experimentally determined value for nitric oxide is in fact 1.15 Å.

2.3

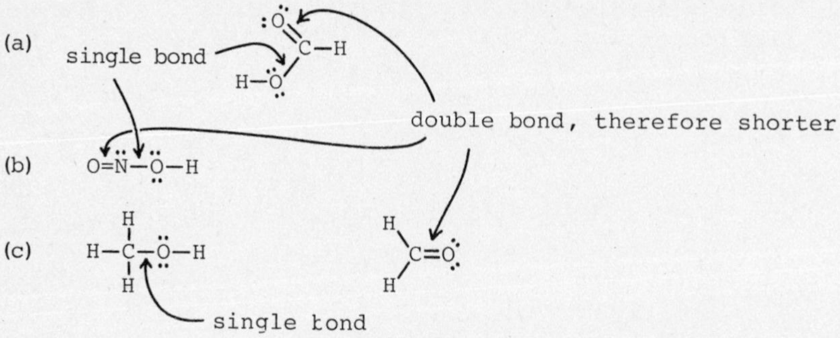

(a)

single bond

double bond, therefore shorter

(b)   O=N—O—H

(c)

single bond

2.4

Ozone:    Hydrogen peroxide: H:O:O:H

Each O-O bond in ozone is 50% a single bond and 50% a double bond. These bonds are therefore shorter than the O-O bond in H-O-O-H, which is 100% a single bond.

2.5

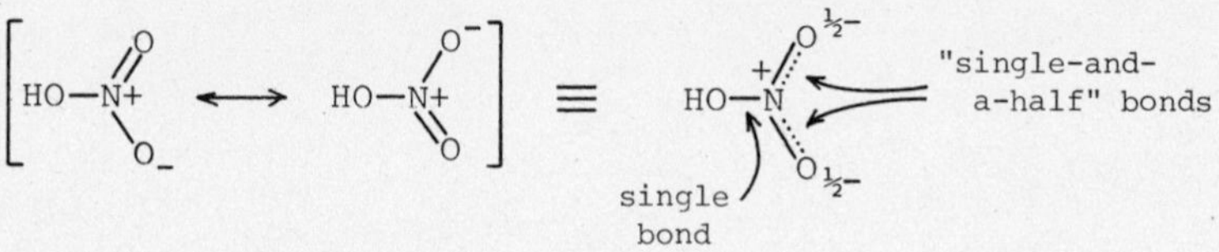

Resonance Structures   Hybrid

nitric acid:

"single-and-a-half" bonds

single bond

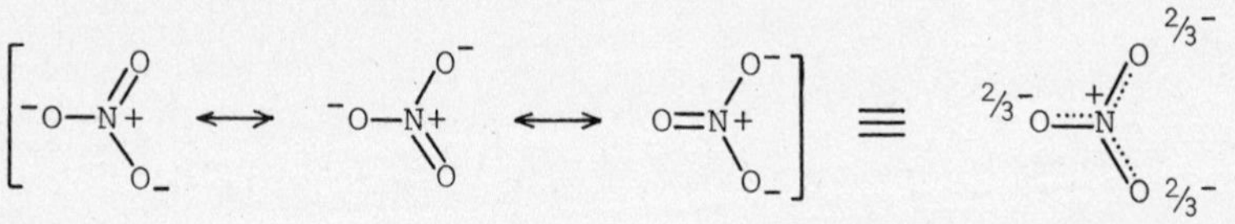

nitrate ion:

each N-O bond is a "single-and-a-third"

The single bond in nitric acid is the longest, and the "single-and-a-half" bonds in nitric acid are the shortest.

2.6   The fact that the H-S-H angle is closer to 90° than to 109° suggests that the sulfur atom uses unhybridized p orbitals to bond to the hydrogens, rather than sp^3 orbitals.

2.E   Answers and Explanations for Problems

1(a)

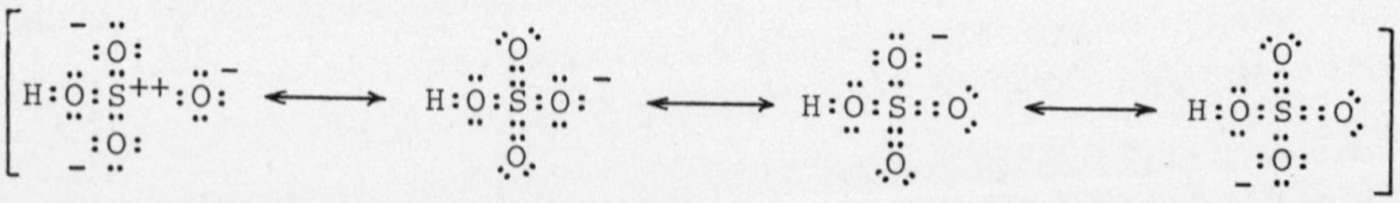

See the Lewis structure of the sulfate ion given in Section 2.2 of the text, and the discussion of resonance hybrids with expanded valence shells in Section 2.4. Note the equivalence of the three resonance structures at the right above.

(b)   H:N:H   Nitrogen contributes five valence electrons, each hydrogen contributes one, and the negative charge represents one more for a total of eight.

(c) $[\; :\!\ddot{O}::\!\ddot{N}\!:\!\ddot{O}\!:^- \quad \longleftrightarrow \quad {}^-:\!\ddot{O}\!:\!\ddot{N}::\!\ddot{O}: \;]$

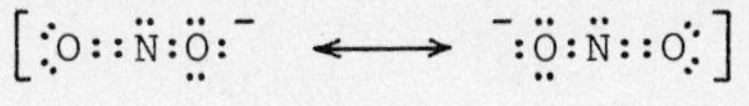

Nitrogen contributes five valence electrons, the two oxygens contribute twelve, and the negative charge adds one for a total of eighteen.

Incorrect:

6 electrons around N ⟶ $:\!\ddot{O}\!:\!\overset{+}{\underset{..}{N}}\!:\!\ddot{O}\!:^-$ and $:\!\ddot{O}::\!\overset{-}{N}::\!\ddot{O}:$ ⟵ 10 electrons around N

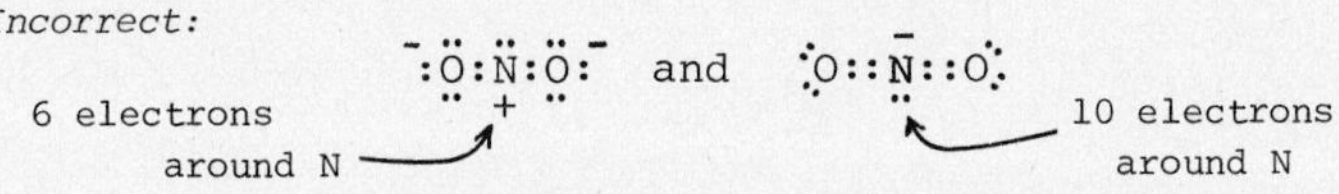

These structures are wrong because nitrogen should not have less or more than an octet.

(d) $:\!\ddot{O}::\!\ddot{N}\!:\!\ddot{O}\!:\!\ddot{N}::\!\ddot{O}:$ (e) ${}^-:\!\ddot{N}::\!\overset{+}{N}::\!\ddot{O}: \quad \longleftrightarrow \quad :N:::\!\overset{+}{N}\!:\!\ddot{O}\!:^-$ (f) ${}^-:\!\ddot{O}\!:\!\overset{+}{N}\!:\!H$
                                                                                                                                                                               $\quad\quad\quad\quad H$

(g) $:\!\ddot{O}::\!\overset{+}{N}::\!\ddot{O}:$ Compare with nitrite ion (ONO⁻, 1(c)), which has two more electrons.

(h) $\overset{\textstyle H}{\underset{\textstyle ..}{H\!:\!\ddot{N}\!:\!C\!:::\!N:}}$ (i) $:N:::\!\overset{+}{O}:$ Note the NO triple bond. Compare with N_2, in Section 2.2 of the text.

(j) $H\!:\!\ddot{N}\!:\!\overset{+}{N}\!:\!\ddot{N}\!:^-$ (k) ${}^-:\!\ddot{N}\!:\!\overset{+}{N}::\!\ddot{N}\!:^- \quad \longleftrightarrow \quad :N:::\!\overset{+}{N}\!:\!\ddot{N}\!:^= \quad \longleftrightarrow \quad {}^=:\!\ddot{N}\!:\!\overset{+}{N}:::\!N:$

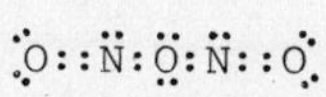

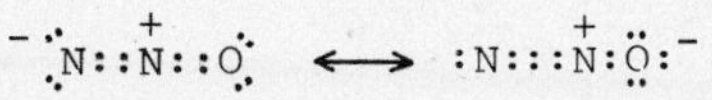

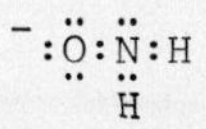

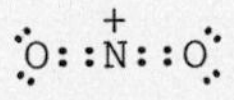

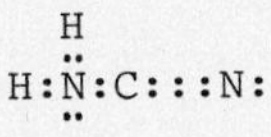

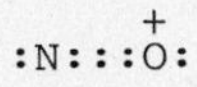

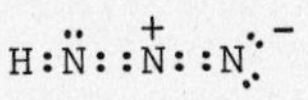

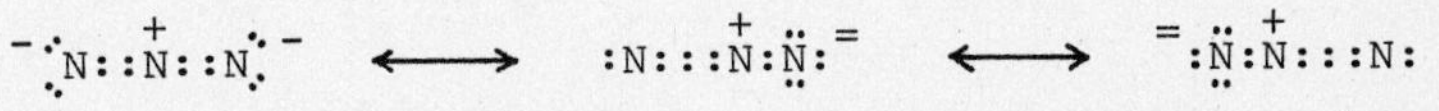

Note that two of the possible resonance structures put two formal charges on one nitrogen.

(1) $\left[\; {}^-:\!\ddot{O}\!:\!\overset{\textstyle :\!\ddot{O}\!:^-}{C}\!:\!\ddot{O}\!: \quad \longleftrightarrow \quad :\!\ddot{O}::\!\overset{\textstyle :\!\ddot{O}\!:^-}{C}\!:\!\ddot{O}\!:^- \quad \longleftrightarrow \quad {}^-:\!\ddot{O}\!:\!\overset{\textstyle :\!\ddot{O}:}{C}\!:\!\ddot{O}\!:^- \;\right]$ (m) $:\!\ddot{O}::\!C::\!\ddot{N}\!:\!H$

2(a) $\overset{\textstyle H\;\;H}{\underset{\textstyle H\;\;H}{H\!:\!\ddot{C}\!:\!\ddot{C}{}^+}} \;\equiv\; \overset{\textstyle H\;\;H}{\underset{\textstyle H\;\;H}{H\!-\!\overset{|}{\underset{|}{C}}\!-\!\overset{|}{\underset{|}{C}}{}^+}}$ (b) $\overset{\textstyle H\;\;H}{\underset{\textstyle H\;\;H}{H\!:\!\ddot{C}\!:\!\ddot{C}\!\cdot}} \;\equiv\; \overset{\textstyle H\;\;H}{\underset{\textstyle H\;\;H}{H\!-\!\overset{|}{\underset{|}{C}}\!-\!\overset{|}{\underset{|}{C}}\!\cdot}}$ (c) $\overset{\textstyle H\;\;H}{\underset{\textstyle H\;\;H}{H\!:\!\ddot{C}\!:\!\ddot{C}\!:^-}} \;\equiv\; \overset{\textstyle H\;\;H}{\underset{\textstyle H\;\;H}{H\!-\!\overset{|}{\underset{|}{C}}\!-\!\overset{|}{\underset{|}{C}}{}^-}}$

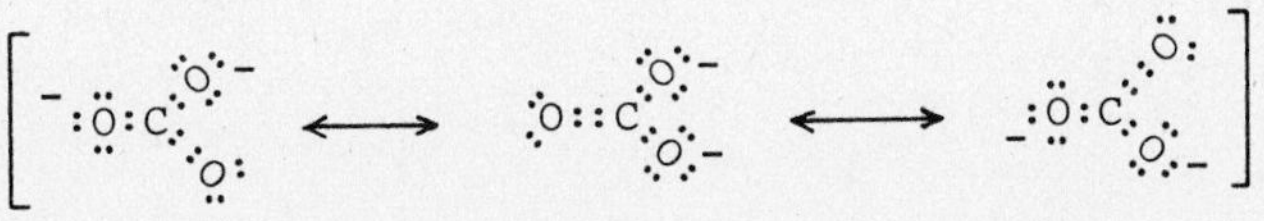

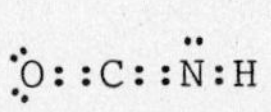

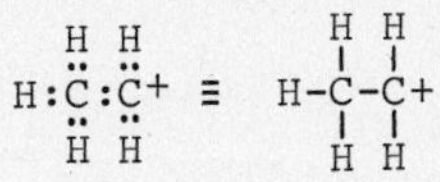

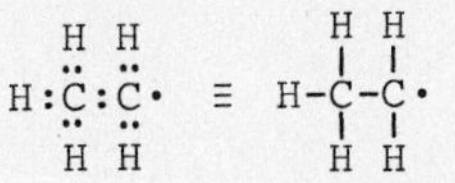

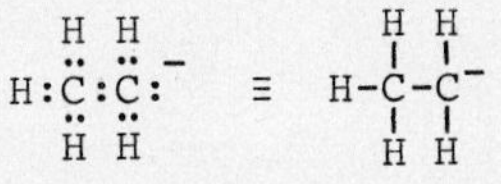

Note the change in charge on carbon as it goes from six (2a) to seven (2b) to eight (2c) valence electrons.

(d) $\overset{\textstyle H}{\underset{\textstyle H}{H\!:\!\ddot{C}\!:\!C\!:::\!C\!:\!H}} \;\equiv\; \overset{\textstyle H}{\underset{\textstyle H}{H\!-\!\overset{|}{\underset{|}{C}}\!-\!C\!\equiv\!C\!-\!H}}$ (e) $\overset{\textstyle :\!\ddot{O}:}{\underset{\textstyle H\;\;H\;\;H}{H\!:\!\ddot{C}\!:\!C\!:\!\ddot{C}\!:\!C\!:\!H}} \;\equiv\; \overset{\textstyle H\;\;O\;\;H\;\;H}{\underset{\textstyle H\;\;\;\;\;H\;\;H}{H\!-\!\overset{|}{\underset{|}{C}}\!-\!\overset{||}{C}\!-\!\overset{|}{\underset{|}{C}}\!-\!\overset{|}{\underset{|}{C}}\!-\!H}}$

(f) $\overset{\textstyle H\;\;\;\;\;\;H}{\underset{\textstyle H\;\;\;\;\;\;H}{H\!:\!\ddot{C}\!:\!\ddot{O}\!:\!\ddot{C}\!:\!H}} \;\equiv\; \overset{\textstyle H\;\;\;\;\;\;H}{\underset{\textstyle H\;\;\;\;\;\;H}{H\!-\!\overset{|}{\underset{|}{C}}\!-\!O\!-\!\overset{|}{\underset{|}{C}}\!-\!H}}$ (g) $\overset{\textstyle H\;\;H}{\underset{\textstyle H\;\;H}{H\!:\!\ddot{C}\!:\!\ddot{N}:}} \;\equiv\; \overset{\textstyle H\;\;H}{\underset{\textstyle H\;\;H}{H\!-\!\overset{|}{\underset{|}{C}}\!-\!N}}$ Compare with ethyl anion (2c).

(h) $\overset{\textstyle H\;\;H}{\underset{\textstyle H\;\;H}{H\!:\!\ddot{C}\!:\!\overset{+}{N}\!:\!H}} \;\equiv\; \overset{\textstyle H\;\;H}{\underset{\textstyle H\;\;H}{H\!-\!\overset{|}{\underset{|}{C}}\!-\!\overset{+}{\underset{|}{N}}\!-\!H}}$ (i) $\overset{\textstyle H}{\underset{\textstyle H}{H\!:\!\ddot{C}\!:\!\ddot{O}\!:^-}} \;\equiv\; \overset{\textstyle H}{\underset{\textstyle H}{H\!-\!\overset{|}{\underset{|}{C}}\!-\!O^-}}$

(j) $\overset{\textstyle H\;\;H}{\underset{\textstyle H\;\;H}{H\!:\!\ddot{C}\!:\!\ddot{O}\!:^+}}$ Compare the electronic arrangement in the series: ethyl anion (2c), methylamine (2g), and methyl oxonium ion (2j).

(k) $\overset{\textstyle H_{..}\;\;\;\;\ddot{Cl}}{\underset{\textstyle H\;\;\;\;\;\;H}{C::C}} \;\equiv\; \overset{\textstyle H\quad\quad Cl}{\underset{\textstyle H\quad\quad H}{C\!=\!C}}$

(ℓ) $[\; H\!:\!C\!:::\!O: \quad \longleftrightarrow \quad H\!:\!C\!::\!\ddot{O}\!: \;]$

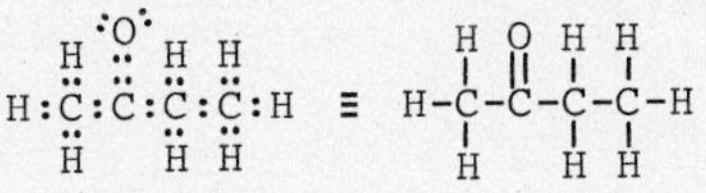

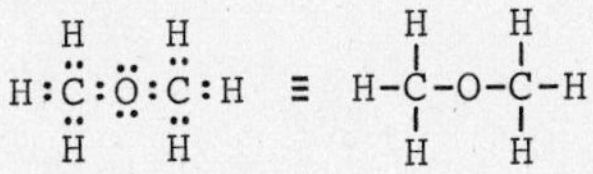

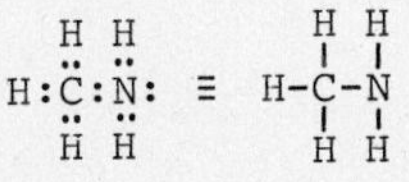

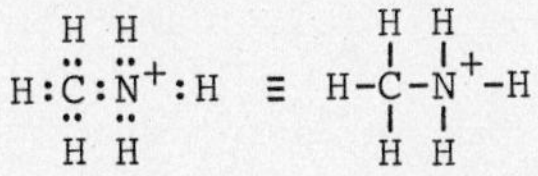

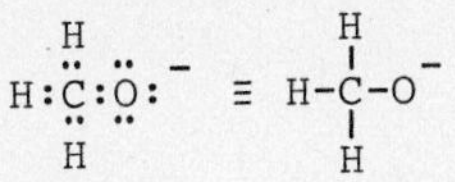

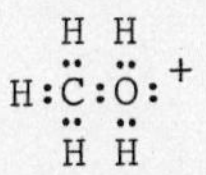

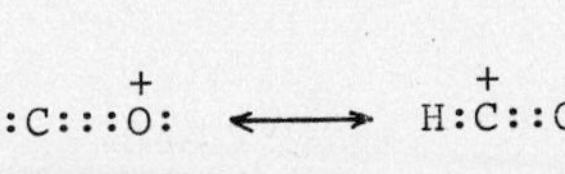

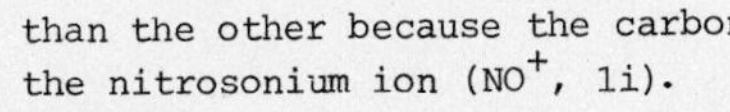

Note the non-equivalent resonance structures. The one on the right is less important than the other because the carbon has only six electrons around it. Compare with the nitrosonium ion (NO⁺, 1i).

NOTE: for many applications it is convenient to use lines to indicate electron-pair bonds and dots to show lone pairs; for instance:

2(c) 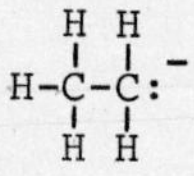   2(e) 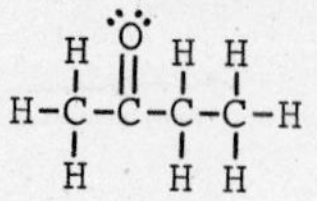   2(j)

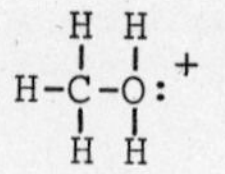

3(a)

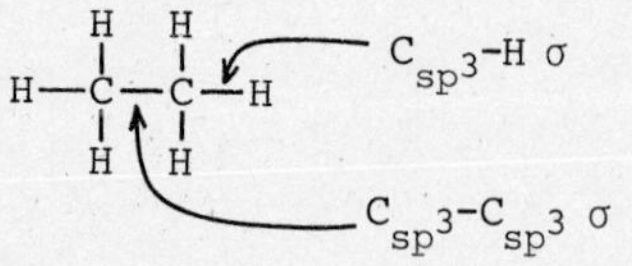

$C_{sp^3}-H$ σ

$C_{sp^3}-C_{sp^3}$ σ

(b)

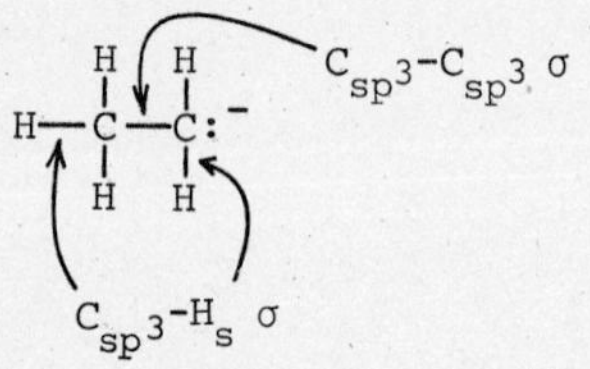

$C_{sp^3}-C_{sp^3}$ σ

$C_{sp^3}-H_s$ σ

Each carbon has four things bonded to it, and therefore is sp^3-hybridized.

(c)

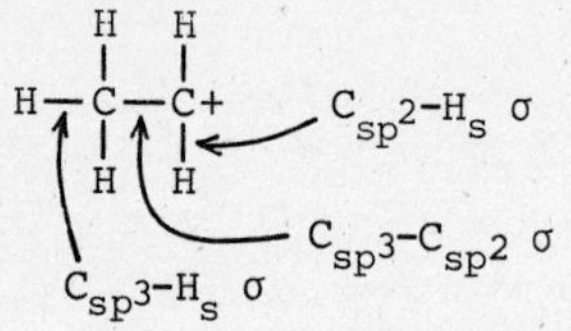

$C_{sp^2}-H_s$ σ

$C_{sp^3}-C_{sp^2}$ σ

$C_{sp^3}-H_s$ σ

The carbon with only three things bonded to it is planar, sp^2-hybridized.

(d)

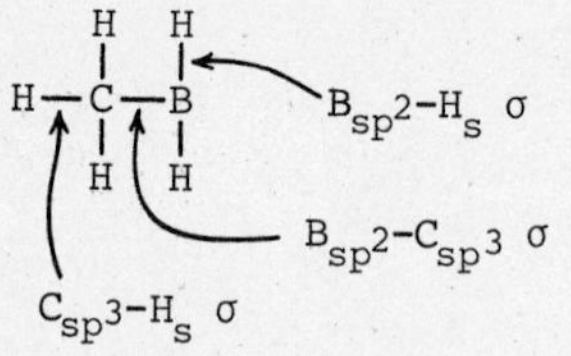

$B_{sp^2}-H_s$ σ

$B_{sp^2}-C_{sp^3}$ σ

$C_{sp^3}-H_s$ σ

Methylborane has the same arrangement of electrons as ethyl cation (3c).

(e)

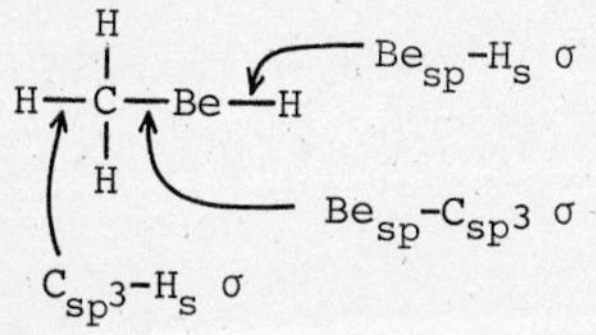

$Be_{sp}-H_s$ σ

$Be_{sp}-C_{sp^3}$ σ

$C_{sp^3}-H_s$ σ

Beryllium, bonded to only two other atoms, is linear, sp-hybridized.

(f)

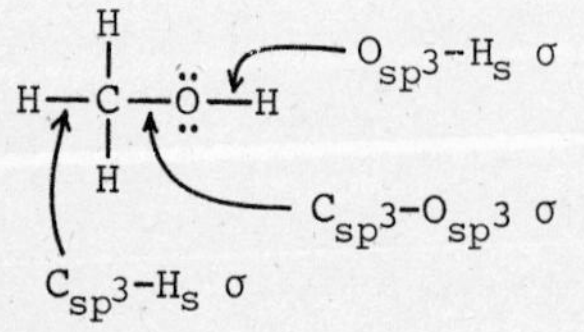

$O_{sp^3}-H_s$ σ

$C_{sp^3}-O_{sp^3}$ σ

$C_{sp^3}-H_s$ σ

Oxygen, with four things bonded to it (a carbon, a hydrogen, and two lone electron pairs), is approximately sp^3-hybridized.

4. Resonance structures involve a shift in the position of electrons only. They do not involve changes in the positions of the atomic nuclei. Therefore, (b), (c), (f), (g), (j), and (k) are not pairs of resonance structures because one or more atoms change position.

5(a)

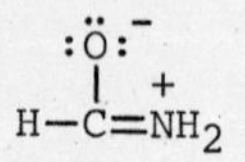

is less important because charge separation leads to higher energy.

(b)

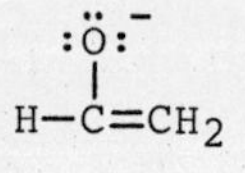

is more important (lower energy) because the negative charge is on a more electronegative atom (oxygen rather than carbon).

(c)

$$\overset{\overset{\displaystyle :\ddot{O}:^-}{|}}{H-C\equiv NH}$$

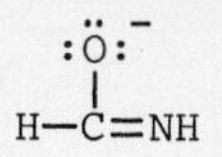

is more important for the same reason given in 5(b): oxygen is more electronegative than nitrogen.

(d)

$$\overset{\overset{\displaystyle :O:}{||}}{CH_2=CH-CH}$$

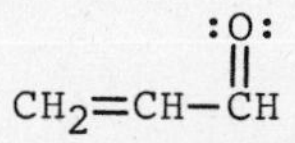

is the most important because of the absence of charge separation.

$$\overset{\overset{\displaystyle :O:^+}{|}}{{}^-\!:CH_2-CH=CH}$$

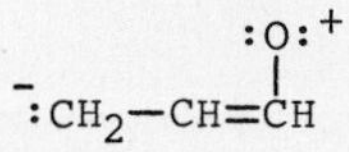

is the least important (highest energy) because an electronegative atom (oxygen) is forced to accept only six valence electrons, while a much less electronegative atom (carbon) must carry a negative charge.

(e)   These two structures are exactly equivalent, and therefore contribute equally to the resonance hybrid.

(f)   These two structures are also equivalent.

(g) $CH_3-\overset{+}{N}\equiv C-O^-$ is more important than $CH_3-\overset{-}{N}-C\equiv O^+$ because oxygen is more electronegative than nitrogen. Neither resonance structure is as important as $CH_3-\overset{..}{N}=C=\overset{..}{O}:$, which has no charge separation.

(h)   O=O=O is of much higher energy (is less important) because the central oxygen atom has ten valence electrons around it, as can be seen by drawing the full Lewis dot structure: $:\overset{..}{O}::\overset{..}{O}::\overset{..}{O}:$ (three oxygens $\times$ 6 = 18 valence electrons)

NOTE that *no* octet structure can be written for ozone which does not involve charge separation.

(i)   N=O is more important because it has no charge separation and $^-N=O\cdot^+$ does.

(j) $H-\overset{..}{\underset{..}{O}}-\overset{..}{N}=C:$ is less important because there are only six electrons around the carbon. There is charge separation in $H-\overset{..}{\underset{..}{O}}-\overset{+}{N}\equiv C:^-$, but all of the atoms have a filled octet.

(k)   In both structures, the atoms all have filled octets. However, $CH_2=C=O$ is more important because there is no charge separation.

6. $Na\cdot \longrightarrow Na^+ + e^-$ *requires* 118.0 kcal/mole

   $Cl\cdot + e^- \longrightarrow Cl^-$ *liberates* 83.3 kcal/mole

   _____

   $Na\cdot + Cl\cdot \longrightarrow Na^+ + Cl^-$ requires 34.7 kcal/mole energy *input*

Electrostatic energy is proportional to $\dfrac{1}{r}$; therefore if a positive and negative charge separated by 1 Å have an energy of 330 kcal/mole, Na^+ and Cl^- at a distance of 2.36 Å will have an energy of roughly $\dfrac{1}{2.36} \times 330 = 140$ kcal/mole. This is more than sufficient to overcome the unfavorable ionization energy calculated above.

2.F   Supplementary Problems

S1. (a) Write Lewis structures for BH_4^-, CH_4, and NH_4^+. Do you expect
     the structures of these molecules to be similar or different?

     (b) Do the same for AlH_4^- and GaH_4^-. How should these structures
     compare to BH_4^-? to PH_4^+?

     (c) Write the Lewis structures of BH_3 and NH_3. Do these molecules
     have similar structures?

S2. Write Lewis structures for the following molecules.

     (a) CH_3F (c) $ClNO$ (e) H_2CCCH_2

     (b) O_2^- (d) CH_3CHNH (f) H_3BNH_3 (assign formal
                                                               charges)

S3. For each of the compounds in problem #S2 above, show the hybridiza-
     tion of all atoms except hydrogen or halogens.

S4. Write out the Lewis structures and corresponding Kekulé structures
     for at least two resonances structures of each of the following
     compounds. Circle the one which represents the most important con-
     tributor to the structure of each compound, and justify your choice.

     (a) $[CH_2CHNH_2]$ (b) $[CH_2NO]^-$ (c) $[CH_2NCH_2]^+$ (d) $[CH_2C\overset{O}{\underset{OCH_3}{}}]^-$

2.G   Answers to Supplementary Problems

S1.   (a)
$$\begin{array}{ccc}
\text{H} & \text{H} & \text{H} \\
\ddot{} & \ddot{} & \ddot{} \\
\text{H:B}^-\text{:H} & \text{H:C:H} & \text{H:N}^+\text{:H} \\
\ddot{} & \ddot{} & \ddot{} \\
\text{H} & \text{H} & \text{H}
\end{array}$$

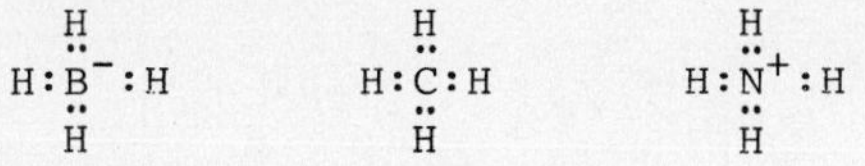

Since the electronic structure is the same for all three molecules (they are isoelectronic), the structures will be similar: they are tetrahedral with sp^3-hybridized central atoms.

(b)
$$\begin{array}{cc}
\text{H} & \text{H} \\
\ddot{} & \ddot{} \\
\text{H:Al}^-\text{:H} & \text{H:Ga}^-\text{:H} \\
\ddot{} & \ddot{} \\
\text{H} & \text{H}
\end{array}$$

Aluminum and gallium are in the same column of the periodic table as boron, hence their valence shells are similar. BH_4^-, AlH_4^-, and GaH_4^- are all tetrahedral in shape (sp^3-hybridized), although the molecules get bigger on going from B → Al → Ga. PH_4^+ is isoelectronic with AlH_4^- and is tetrahedral as well.

(c)
$$\begin{array}{cc}
\text{H} & \ddot{} \\
\text{H:B}\cdot & \text{H:N:H} \\
\cdot\text{H} & \ddot{} \\
 & \text{H}
\end{array}$$

BH_3 has six valence electrons, the boron is sp^2-hybridized and the molecule is therefore planar; NH_3 has eight valence electrons, the nitrogen is sp^3-hybridized, and the molecule is therefore pyramidal.

S2,3.   (a)
$$
\begin{array}{c}
\text{H} \\
\text{H:C:F:} \\
\text{H}
\end{array}
\quad sp^3 \;,\; sp^2
$$

(b) $\;^-:\!\ddot{O}\!:\!\ddot{O}\!:\quad sp^3$

(c) $\;:\!\ddot{Cl}\!:\!\ddot{N}\!:\!:\!\ddot{O}\quad sp^2$

(d)
$$
\begin{array}{c}
\text{H} \quad sp^2 \\
\text{H:C:C::N:H} \\
\text{H} \qquad sp^2 \\
sp^3
\end{array}
$$

(e)
$$
\begin{array}{c}
sp \\
\text{H} \quad\quad \text{H} \\
\cdot\text{C::C::C}\cdot \\
\text{H} \quad\quad \text{H} \\
sp^2
\end{array}
$$

(f)
$$
\begin{array}{c}
^- \text{H} \;\; \text{H} \;^+ \\
\text{H:B:N:H} \\
\text{H} \;\; \text{H} \\
sp^3
\end{array}
$$

S4. (a)
$$
\left[
\begin{array}{c}
\text{H:C::C:N:H} \\
\text{H} \;\; \text{H} \;\; \text{H}
\end{array}
\right]
\longleftrightarrow
\left[
\begin{array}{c}
\text{H:}\overset{-}{\text{C}}\text{:C::}\overset{+}{\text{N}}\text{:H} \\
\text{H} \;\; \text{H} \;\; \text{H}
\end{array}
\right]
$$

||| |||

$$
\left[
\begin{array}{c}
\text{H–C=C–N–H} \\
\text{H} \; \text{H} \; \text{H}
\end{array}
\right]
\longleftrightarrow
\left[
\begin{array}{c}
\overset{-}{\text{H–C}}\text{–C=}\overset{+}{\text{N}}\text{–H} \\
\text{H} \; \text{H} \; \text{H}
\end{array}
\right]
$$

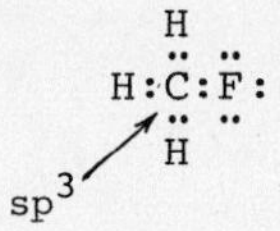

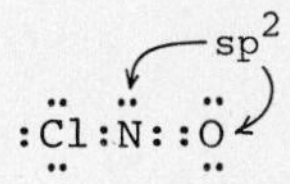

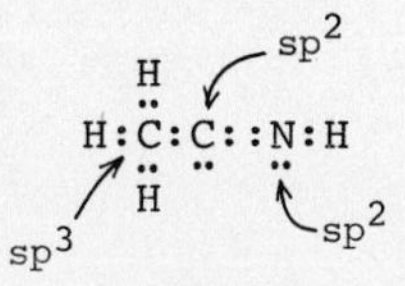

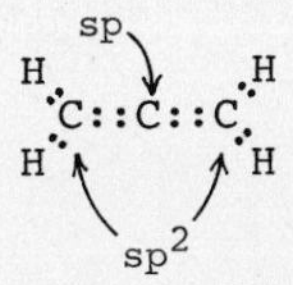

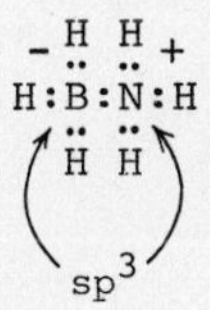

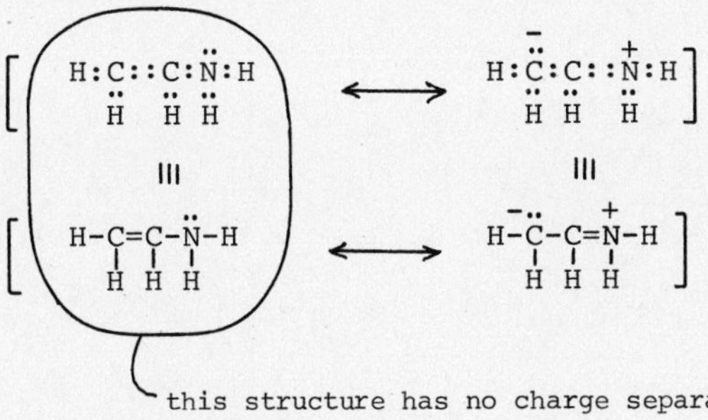

this structure has no charge separation

(b)
$$
\left[
\begin{array}{c}
\text{H:C::N:}\ddot{O}\text{:}^- \\
\text{H}
\end{array}
\right]
\longleftrightarrow
\left[
\begin{array}{c}
\overset{-}{\text{H:C:N::}}\ddot{O}\text{:} \\
\text{H}
\end{array}
\right]
$$

||| |||

$$
\left[
\begin{array}{c}
\text{H–C=N–O}^- \\
\text{H}
\end{array}
\right]
\longleftrightarrow
\left[
\begin{array}{c}
\text{H–}\overset{-}{\text{C}}\text{–N=O} \\
\text{H}
\end{array}
\right]
$$

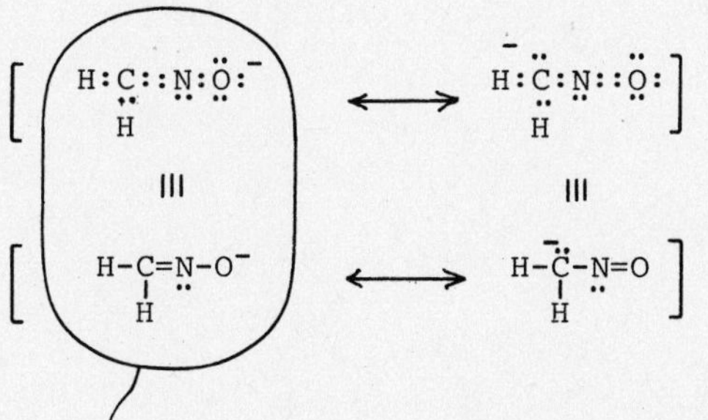

in this structure, the more electronegative atom carries the negative charge

(c)

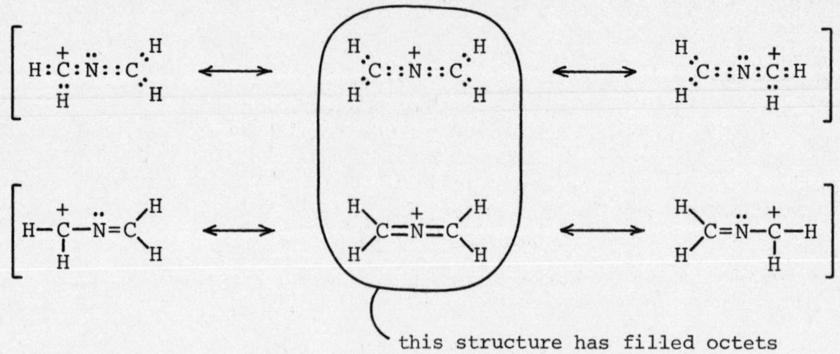

$$\left[\begin{array}{ccc} H\overset{+}{\underset{H}{:}}\overset{..}{C}:\overset{..}{N}::\overset{H}{C}\overset{H}{:} & \longleftrightarrow & \overset{H}{\underset{H}{:}}\overset{..}{C}::\overset{+}{N}:\overset{..}{C}\overset{H}{:} & \longleftrightarrow & \overset{H}{\underset{H}{:}}\overset{..}{C}::\overset{..}{N}:\overset{+}{C}H \end{array} \right]$$

$$\left[\begin{array}{ccc} H-\overset{+}{\underset{H}{C}}-\overset{..}{N}=\overset{H}{\underset{H}{C}} & \longleftrightarrow & \overset{H}{\underset{H}{C}}=\overset{+}{N}=\overset{H}{\underset{H}{C}} & \longleftrightarrow & \overset{H}{\underset{H}{C}}=\overset{..}{N}-\overset{H}{\underset{H}{C}}H \end{array} \right]$$

this structure has filled octets

(d)

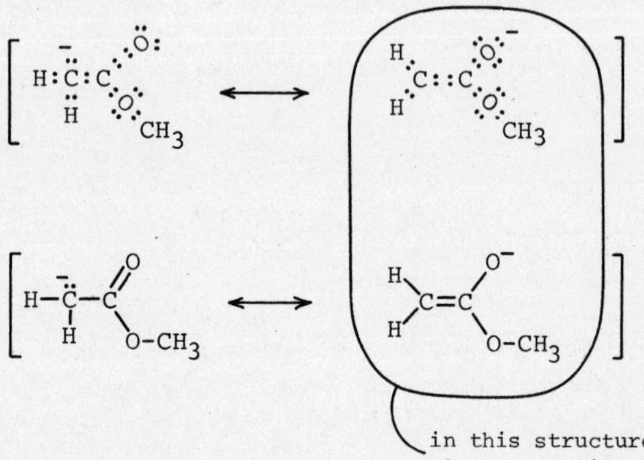

$$\left[\begin{array}{cc} H\overset{-}{\underset{H}{:}}\overset{..}{C}:C\overset{\overset{..}{O}:}{\underset{\overset{..}{O}:}{}} & \longleftrightarrow & \overset{H}{\underset{H}{:}}\overset{..}{C}::C\overset{\overset{..}{O}:^{-}}{\underset{\overset{..}{O}:}{}} \\ & & CH_3 \end{array} \right]$$

$$\left[\begin{array}{cc} H-\overset{-}{\underset{H}{C}}-C\overset{O}{\underset{O-CH_3}{\parallel}} & \longleftrightarrow & \overset{H}{\underset{H}{}}C=C\overset{O^{-}}{\underset{O-CH_3}{}} \end{array} \right]$$

in this structure, the more electronegative
element carries the negative charge

3. ORGANIC STRUCTURES

3.A Chapter Outline and Important Terms Introduced

3.1 Introduction (historical)

- isomerism
- structural formulas
- condensed formulas

3.2 Functional Groups (commonly-encountered subunits)

- hydrocarbons (alkanes, alkenes, alkynes, cyclo-)
- alcohols
- ethers
- aldehydes
- ketones
- carboxylic acids
- (all other functional groups)
- aromatic compounds
- aliphatic compounds

3.3 The Shape of Molecules (their three-dimensionality)

- molecular models

3.4 The Determination of Organic Structure (how to figure out the formula)

- characterization
- combustion analysis
- empirical formula
- molecular formula
- spectroscopy

3.5 n-Alkanes, the Simplest Organic Compounds (the backbone of organic structure)

- homologous series
- saturated and unsaturated hydrocarbons

3.6 Systematic Nomenclature (naming compounds)

- IUPAC system
- isomers
- common names (iso-, neo-)
- chemical literature

3.B Important Reactions Introduced: still none yet

3.C Important Concepts and Hints

Chapter 3 continues to discuss structure, but emphasizes the molecular level as opposed to the electronic aspects which are presented in Chapter 2. A good way to organize your thoughts on this topic is to consider the chart on the following page, in which each level down the scheme corresponds to a more specific or detailed description of the structure of a molecule. You should know the difference between empirical and molecular formulas, and understand the concept of **isomerism**. For instance, you should be able to draw all the structural isomers of a compound, given its molecular formula. In this regard, you should also be able to tell that compounds A, B, and C below are structural isomers of each other, while compounds D, E, and F are not.

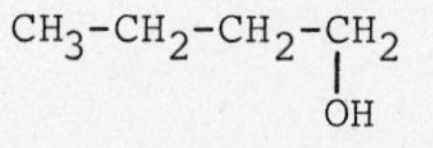

A

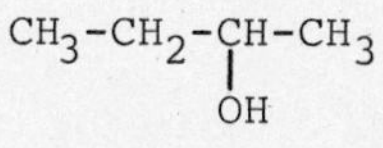

B

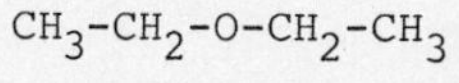

C

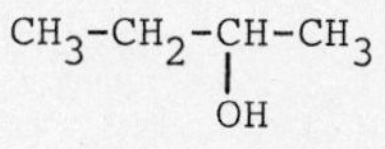

D

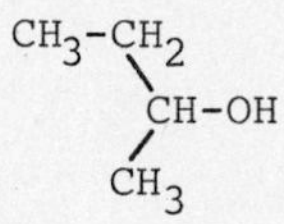

E

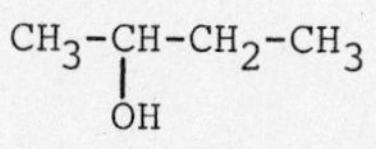

F

Another important concept is the idea of functional groups, subunits of molecular structure which are larger than single atoms. These are important not only in considering structural isomerism, but (as you will discover as the course progresses) also in understanding and predicting the reactions a compounds will undergo.

After discussing the various levels of molecular structure, how this information can be obtained for a compound is presented. In this chapter you should learn how to determine empirical and molecular formulas, and you should understand the concept of functional group tests. The more detailed methods of studying a molecule's structure are presented in the chapters which discuss spectroscopy (Chapters 13 and 15).

In addition to molecular and structural formulas, we also have to have names for compounds, so that we can discuss them verbally, index them, etc. Although nomenclature seems like a sideline to reactions when studying chemistry, it is important to learn it at the outset of the course so you will know what is being discussed the rest of the time. The systematic nomenclature (IUPAC) is the most important; it does become complex (as the molecules to be named become complex), but it is systematic and the step-by-step rules to follow are easily remembered. The simpler aspects of common nomenclature are useful too, just as colloquialisms and contractions are necessary in our everyday language.

Level	Example	
Empirical Formula	$(C_3H_6O)_n$	(this excludes CH_4O, C_3H_8O, etc.)
Molecular Formula	$C_6H_{12}O_2$	(as opposed to C_3H_6O or $C_9H_{18}O_3$, etc.)

Structural Formula

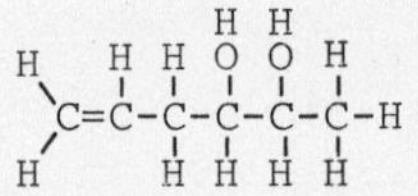

$$CH_2=CHCH_2CHOHCHOHCH_3$$

at this level, one can rule out molecules having the same molecular formula (isomers) but with different topology; i.e., with the atoms connected in a different order, such as

$$CH_3-O-CH_2-CH_2-\underset{|}{\overset{}{CH}}-CH=CH_2 \quad or \quad CH_2=CH-\underset{|}{\overset{}{CH}}-CH_2-\underset{|}{\overset{}{CH}}-CH_3$$
$$\qquad\qquad\qquad OH \qquad\qquad\qquad OH \qquad\quad OH$$

Stereochemical Formula

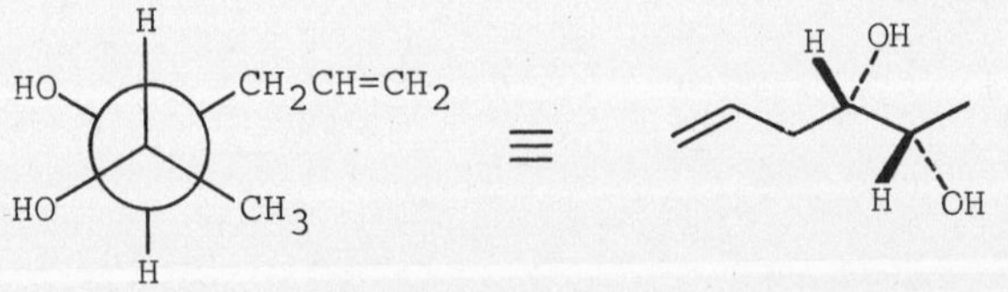

NOTE: *the concept of stereochemistry is not discussed in the text until Chapter 7:*
STEREOISOMERISM

HINTS: BUY A SET OF MODELS! As pointed out in Section 3.2, molecules are three-dimensional and much of organic structure and chemical reactions cannot be understood without thinking in three dimensions. You may not like to admit it, but most people spend their lives on the two-dimensional surface of the earth and have little experience in thinking in three dimensions. Using models is the best way for you to really get an idea of what the two-dimensional illustrations in the text or on the blackboard represent in three dimensions. Other aspects of structure, such as rotation around single bonds (and therefore the floppiness of big molecules), are easily understood using models, too.

Unless the three-dimensional aspects of structure are specifically indicated (for instance, as will be introduced in Chapter 7), structural formulas only show "connectedness", i.e., what atom is bonded to what atom. A common trap that students fall into arises from a misunderstanding of this point. Although the drawings below look different, they **all** represent the same molecule:

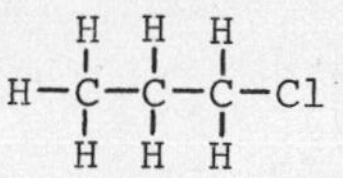

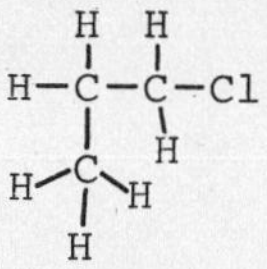

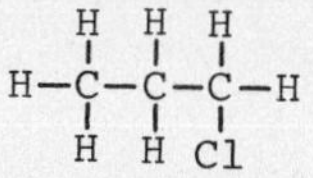

Similarly, the three drawings below represent the same molecule, because of the ability of groups joined by single bonds to rotate relative to each other. The best way to convince yourself of this may be to make models....

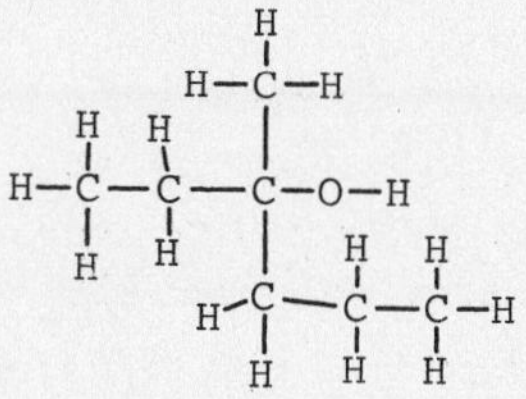

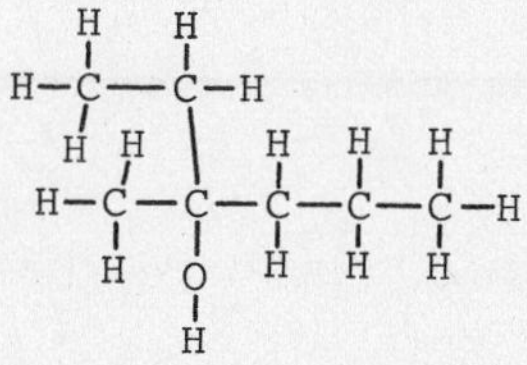

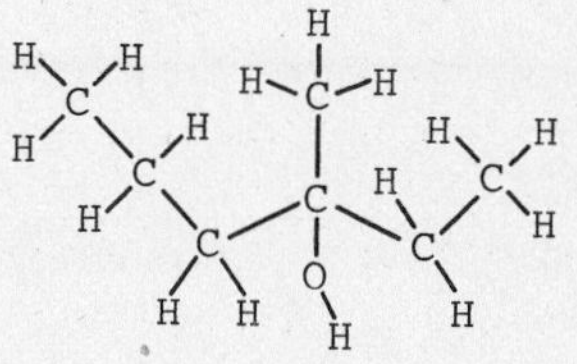

3.D   Answers to Exercises

3.1

C_4H_{10}:   (structure) $\equiv CH_3CH_2CH_2CH_3$;   (structure) $\equiv (CH_3)_3CH$

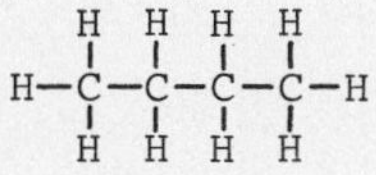

C_5H_{12}:   (structure) $\equiv CH_3CH_2CH_2CH_2CH_3$;

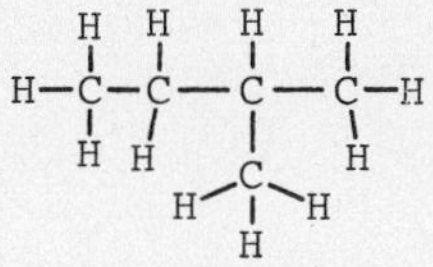

(structure) $\equiv CH_3CH_2CH(CH_3)_2$;   (structure) $\equiv (CH_3)_4C$

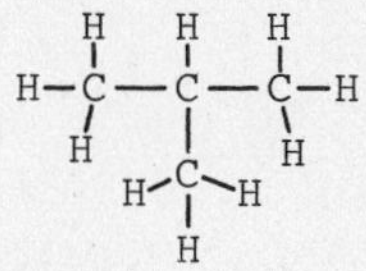

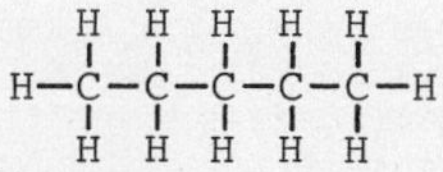

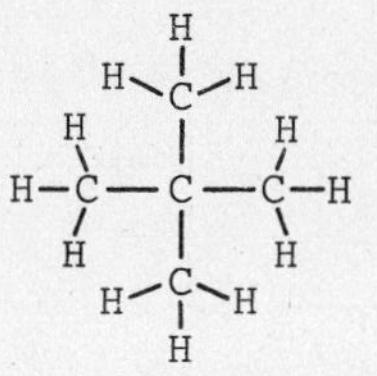

3.2

Structural	Condensed
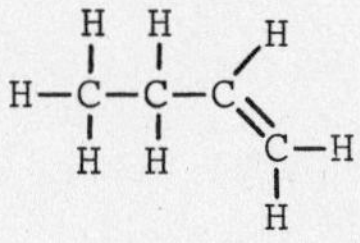 (structure)	$CH_3CH_2CH=CH_2$
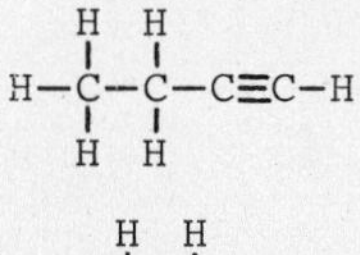 (structure)	$CH_3CH_2C\equiv CH$
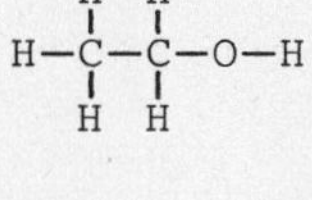 (structure)	CH_3CH_2OH
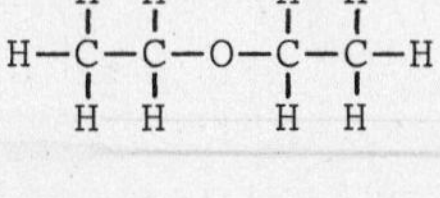 (structure)	$(CH_3CH_2)_2O$

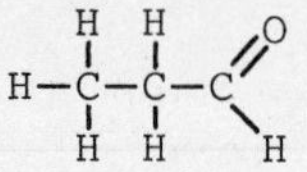

CH_3CH_2CHO

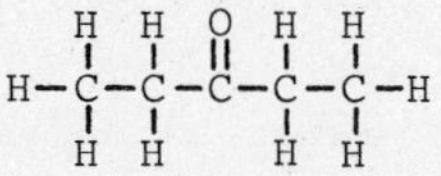

$(CH_3CH_2)_2CO$

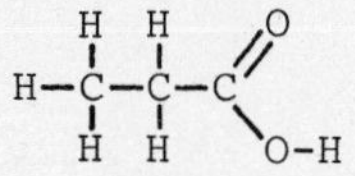

$CH_3CH_2CO_2H$

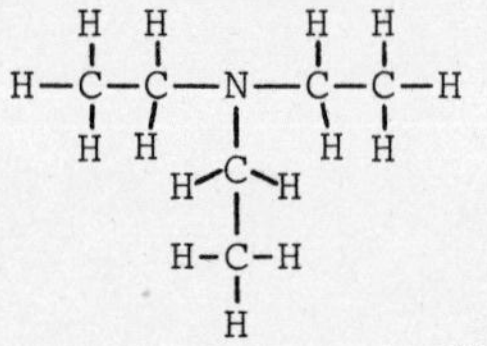

$(CH_3CH_2)_3N$

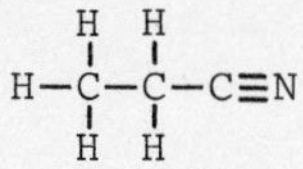

CH_3CH_2N

3.4   Molecular weight of $C_6H_{12}O$: $6 \times 12 = 72$

$12 \times 1 = 12$

$1 \times 16 = \underline{16}$

100

Therefore 3.74 mg $= (3.74 \times 10^{-3}$ g$)/100$ g/mole $= 3.74 \times 10^{-5}$ mole

Overall reaction: $C_6H_{12}O + 8\frac{1}{2} O_2 \longrightarrow 6 CO_2 + 6 H_2O$

3.74×10^{-5} mole of $C_6H_{12}O$ will therefore produce

$6 \times 3.74 \times 10^{-5} = 2.244 \times 10^{-4}$ mole of CO_2 and H_2O

$2.244 \times 10^{-4} \times$ [molecular weight of $CO_2 = 44$] $= 9.87$ mg of CO_2

$2.244 \times 10^{-4} \times$ [molecular weight of $H_2O = 18$] $= 4.04$ mg of H_2O

3.5   0.677 g of CO_2 contains $0.677/44 = 0.0154$ mole of C

0.311 g of H_2O contains $0.311/18 = 0.0173$ mole of $H_2 = 0.0346$ mole of H

Together, this amount of carbon and hydrogen account for:

0.0154 mole $\times$ 12 g/mole $= 0.185$ g of carbon

0.0346 mole $\times$ 1 g/mole $= 0.035$ g of hydrogen

total $= 0.220$ g of the 0.250 g of di-n-butyl ether

The rest must be $0.250 - 0.220 = 0.030$ g $= 0.00188$ mole of oxygen.

0.0154 mole of C ⎫   divide by ⎧ 8.19 C

0.0346 mole of H ⎬   smallest   ⎨ 18.40 H   Therefore di-n-butyl ether is $C_8H_{18}O$,

0.00188 mole of O ⎭   number   ⎩ 1.00 O   or some multiple thereof

[Note: Another way to determine how much C and H the CO_2 and H_2O represent is to realize that:

CO_2 is $12/44 = 27.27\%$ C and H_2O is $2/18 = 11.11\%$ H

0.677 g of CO_2 therefore represents $0.2727 \times 0.677 = 0.185$ g of C, and 0.311 g of H_2O

represents $0.1111 \times 0.311 = 0.035$ g of H, as calculated above.]

3.6 $CH_2=CH-CH_2-OH$ $CH_3-CH=CH-OH$

                (1)   (2)

$$CH_3-CH_2-\overset{\overset{\displaystyle O}{\|}}{CH} \qquad CH_3-\overset{\overset{\displaystyle O}{\|}}{C}-CH_3$$

                                                  (3)   (4)

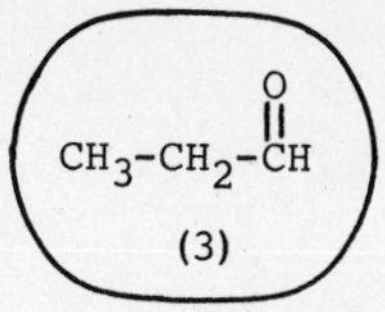

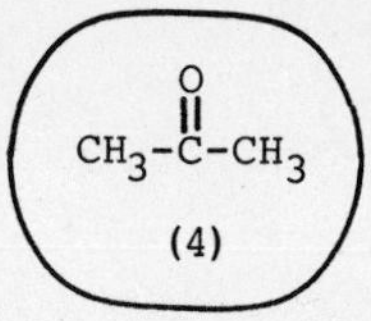

$CH_2=CH-O-CH_3$

                (5)   (6)   (7)   (8)

        (*NOTE*: You will learn in Chapter 14 that (2) is an unstable structure.)

3.7   Pentyl group: $CH_3CH_2CH_2CH_2CH_2$
            Pentyl iodide: $CH_3CH_2CH_2CH_2CH_2I$

3.8

                                    CH_3
                                    CH_2
       3-ethylhexane: $CH_3-CH_2-CH-CH_2-CH_2-CH_3$

                                CH_3
                                CH_2
       "2-ethylhexane": $CH_3-CH-CH_2-CH_2-CH_2-CH_3$
       "2-ethylhexane" is actually 3-methylheptane

3.9 CH_3 CH_3 CH_3 CH_3 CH_3
    $CH_3-CH--CH--CH-CH_2-CH_2-CH_2-CH_3$ $CH_2-CH_2-CH_2-CH_2$
       2,3,4-trimethyloctane   "1,4-dimethylbutane"is simply hexane....

3.10

                        CH_3 CH_3 CH_3
                $CH_3-CH--CH-CH_2-CH-CH_3$

                    2,   3,   5-trimethylhexane (correct name)

    əuɐxǝɥlʎɥʇǝɯᴉɹʇ-ϛ   'ㄣ   'ㄥ   (numbering from wrong end)

                       ⌐ difference is here

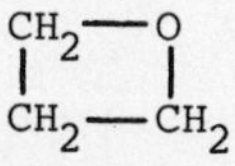

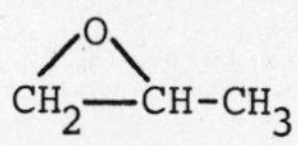

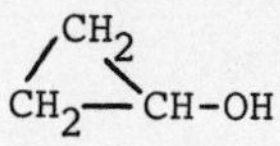

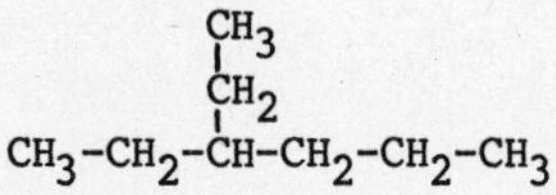

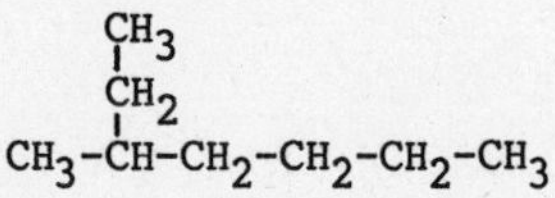

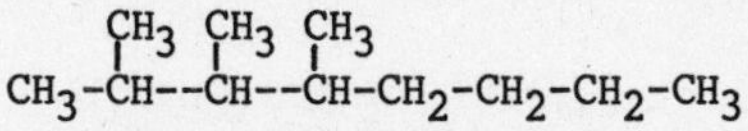

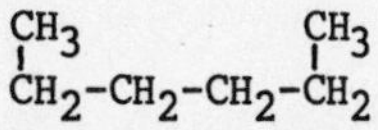

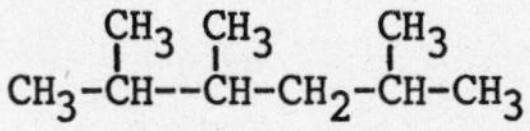

3.11
(a) CH_3
                 CH_3 CH_2
        $CH_3-CH-CH_2-CH-CH_2-CH_2-CH_3$

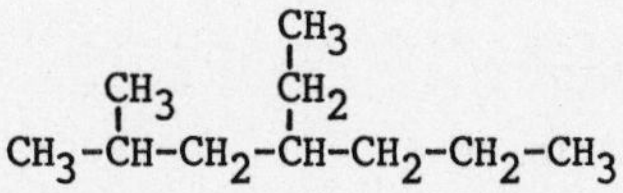

Incorrect name: "2-methyl-4-ethylheptane" ("ethyl" comes before methyl in alphabet)
Correct name: 4-ethyl-2-methylheptane   (note that alphabetization doesn't change numbering scheme)

(b) CH_3
                 CH_3 CH_2
      $CH_3-\underset{\underset{\displaystyle CH_3}{|}}{C}---CH-CH_2-CH_2-CH_3$

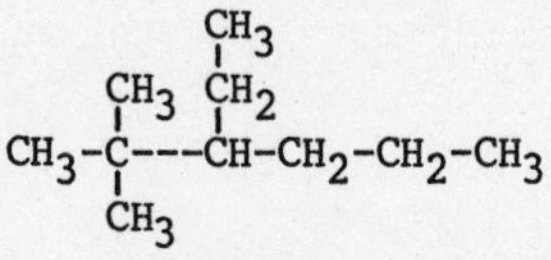

Correct name: 3-ethyl-2,2-dimethylhexane

(c) CH_3 CH_3
                CH
           $CH_3-CH-CH-CH_2-CH_2-CH_3$
                    CH_3

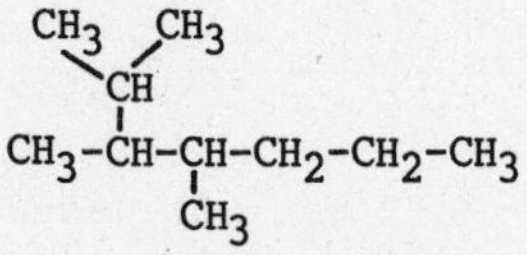

Incorrect: 2-isopropyl-3-methylhexane (longest chain has seven carbons)
   Correct: 2,3,4-trimethylheptane

(d)
$$\begin{matrix} CH_3 & CH_3 \\ | & | \\ CH_2 & CH-CH_3 \\ | & | \\ \end{matrix}$$
$$CH_3-CH_2-CH--CH-CH_2-CH_2-CH_3$$

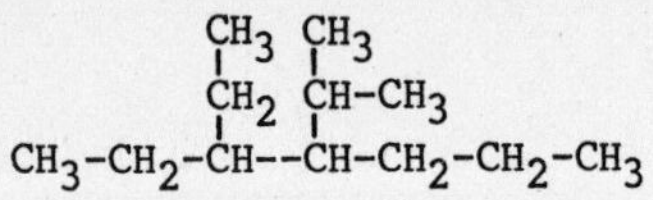

Incorrect: 4-isopropyl-3-ethylhexane (<u>e</u>thyl comes before <u>i</u>sopropyl)

  Correct: 3-ethyl-4-isopropylhexane

3.12
$$\begin{matrix} CH_3 & & Cl \\ | & & | \\ \end{matrix}$$
$$CH_3-CH-CH_2-CH-CH_3$$

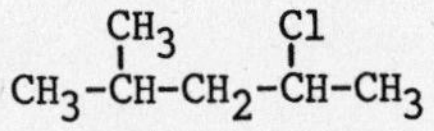

Incorrect: 4-chloro-2-methylpentane (<u>c</u>hloro comes before <u>m</u>ethyl and, other things being equal, should get the lower number)

  Correct: 2-chloro-4-methylpentane

$$\begin{matrix} & CH_3 & \\ & | & \\ X & CH_2 & X \\ | & | & | \\ \end{matrix}$$
$$CH_3-CH-CH_2-CH-CH_2-CH-CH_3$$

  X = Cl: 2,6-dichloro-4-ethylheptane

  X = I: 4-ethyl-2,6-diiodoheptane

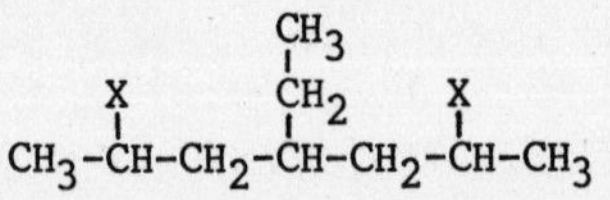

3.E   Answers and Explanations for Problems

1.   (a) 2,2-dimethylhexane (C_8H_{18})

      molecular weight = (8 x 12) + (18 x 1) = 114

      % carbon = (8 x 12)/114 = 84.2%

      % hydrogen = (18 x 1)/114 = 15.8%

    (b) ethyl acetate ($C_4H_8O_2$)

      molecular weight = (4 x 12) + (8 x 1) + (2 x 16) = 88

      % carbon = (4 x 12)/88 = 54.5%

      % hydrogen = (8 x 1)/88 = 9.1%

      % oxygen = (2 x 16)/88 = 36.4%

    (c) nitromethane (CH_3NO_2): 19.7% C, 4.9% H, 23.0% N, 52.5% O

    (d) trinitrotoluene ($C_7H_5N_3O_6$): 37.0% C, 2.2% H, 18.5% N, 42.3% O

2.   (a) 14.3 mg of CO_2 contains 14.3/44 = 3.25 x 10^{-4} mole of C

      5.80 mg of H_2O contains 2 x 5.8/18 = 6.44 x 10^{-4} mole of H

      3.25 x 10^{-4} x 12 = 3.90 mg of C

      6.44 x 10^{-4} x 1 = 0.64 mg of H

    The rest of the sample is assumed to be oxygen:

      5.20 - 3.90 - 0.64 = 0.66 mg = 4.13 x 10^{-5} mole of O

      3.25 x 10^{-4} mole C ⎫ divide by ⎧ 7.87 C

      6.44 x 10^{-4} mole H ⎬ smallest ⎨ 15.6 H   Empirical formula:

      4.13 x 10^{-5} mole O ⎭ number ⎩ 1 O $C_8H_{16}O$

    (b) 12.3 mg of CO_2 = 3.355 mg = 0.280 mmole of C (a mmole is 10^{-3} mole)

      3.90 mg of H_2O = 0.433 mg = 0.433 mmole of H

      3.81 mg of sample - 3.355 mg of C and - 0.433 mg of H = 0.02 mg (≃ 0) unaccounted for

      0.280 mmole C and 0.433 mmole H are compatible with the empirical formulas:

                         C_2H_3, C_4H_6, etc.

    C_2H_3 is excluded by the rules of valence, hence the sample has the empirical formula C_4H_6.

(c)   5.87 mg of CO_2 = 1.60 mg = 0.133 mmole of C

2.40 mg of H_2O = 0.267 mg = 0.267 mmole of H

2.58 - 1.60 - 0.27 = 0.71 mg = 0.0444 mmole of O

$C_{0.133}H_{0.267}O_{0.0444} = C_3H_6O$

(d)   4.54 mg of CO_2 = 1.24 mg = 0.103 mmole of C

1.86 mg of H_2O = 0.207 mg = 0.207 mmole of H

3.10 - 1.24 - 0.21 = 1.65 mg = 0.103 mmole of O

$C_{0.103}H_{0.207}O_{0.103} = CH_2O$

3. (a) "70.4% C, 13.9% H" means: of 100 g of the compound, 70.4 g is carbon, 13.9 g is hydrogen, and the rest (15.7 g) is assumed to be oxygen. A 100-g sample would then contain 70.4/12 = 5.87 moles of carbon, 13.9/1 = 13.9 moles of hydrogen, and 15.7/16 = 0.98 moles of oxygen. This empirical formula of $C_{5.87}H_{13.9}O_{0.98}$ is clearly $C_6H_{14}O$ in integral values. Because this formula represents a fully saturated compound, no multiple of it is possible (see problem #10).

	Weight Ratio	Mole Ratio	Empirical Formula
(b)	92.1% C	92.1/12 = 7.68	$C_{7.68}$
			$\quad\quad = (CH)_n$ (Benzene is C_6H_6)
	7.9% H	7.9/1 = 7.9	$H_{7.9}$
(c)	71.6% C	71.6/12 = 5.97	$C_{5.97}$
	7.5% H	7.5/1 = 7.5	$H_{7.5}$ [divide by the smallest number] → $(C_4H_5N)_n$
	20.9% N	20.9/14 = 1.49	$N_{1.49}$ (Pyrrole is C_4H_5N)
(d)	71.6% C	71.6/12 = 5.97	$C_{5.97}$
	6.7% H	6.7/1 = 6.7	$H_{6.7}$ [divide by the smallest number] → $(C_{17}H_{19}NO_3)_n$
	4.9% N	4.9/14 = 0.35	$N_{0.35}$ (Morphine is $C_{17}H_{19}NO_3$)
	(16.8% O)	16.8/16 = 1.05	$O_{1.05}$ the weight not accounted for is assumed to be oxygen
(e)	74.1% C	74.1/12 = 6.18	$C_{6.18}$
	7.5% H	7.5/1 = 7.5	$H_{7.5}$ [divide by the smallest number] → $(C_{10}H_{12}NO)_n$
	8.6% N	8.6/14 = 0.614	$N_{0.614}$ (Quinine is $C_{20}H_{24}N_2O_2$)
	(9.8% O)	9.8/16 = 0.613	$O_{0.613}$ the weight not accounted for is assumed to be oxygen
(f)	47.4% C	3.95	
	2.6% H	2.6	[divide by the smallest number] → $C_{2.8}H_{1.85}Cl$ → [take multiples until all subscripts are integers] (×5) → $(C_{14}H_9Cl_5)_n$
	50.0% Cl	1.41	
			(DDT is $C_{14}H_9Cl_5$)
(g)	38.4% C	3.2	
	4.9% H	4.9	$(C_2H_3Cl)_n$ (Vinyl chloride is C_2H_3Cl)
	56.7% Cl	1.6	
(h)	23.4% C	1.95	
	1.4% H	1.4	
	65.3% I	65.3/127 = 0.514	$(C_{15}H_{11}I_4NO_4)_n$ (Thyroxine is $C_{15}H_{11}I_4NO_4$)
	1.8% N	0.13	
	(8.1% O)	0.51	

4. (a) 0.0132 g of camphor gives 0.0382 g of CO_2, which is equivalent to
    8.68×10^{-4} mole (0.0382 divided by 44). Therefore 0.0132 g of camphor
    contains 8.68×10^{-4} mole = 0.0104 g of carbon.

    0.0132 g of camphor gives 0.0126 g of H_2O, which is equivalent to
    7.0×10^{-4} mole (0.0126 divided by 18). Therefore 0.0132 g of camphor
    contains 14×10^{-4} mole = 0.0014 g of hydrogen.

    0.0104 g of carbon plus 0.0014 g of hydrogen leaves 0.0014 g which
    is unaccounted for from the 0.0132-g sample of camphor; this is
    assumed to be oxygen (0.0014 divided by 16 = 0.875×10^{-4} mole).

    mole ratio in camphor: $C_{8.68}H_{14}O_{0.875}$ $\xrightarrow[\text{number}]{\text{divide by the smallest}}$ $(C_{10}H_{16}O)_n$

    (Camphor is $C_{10}H_{16}O$)

    (b) <u>1.56 mg of sex attractant</u>:

    3.73 mg = 0.0848 mmole of CO_2
          0.0848 mmole of carbon = 1.018 mg

    1.22 mg = 0.0678 mmole of H_2O
          0.1356 mmole of hydrogen = 0.136 mg
    _____

          1.154 mg accounted for

    The remaining 0.41 mg is assumed
    to be oxygen = 0.0256 mmole

    $C_{0.0848}H_{0.136}O_{0.0256}$ $\xrightarrow[0.0256]{\text{divide by}}$ $C_{3.31}H_{5.31}O$ $\xrightarrow{\times 3}$ $(C_{10}H_{16}O_3)_n$

    (the molecular formula for this compound is $C_{10}H_{16}O_3$)

    (c) <u>2.16 mg of benzo[a]pyrene</u>:

    7.5 mg = 0.17 mmole of CO_2
          0.17 mmole of carbon = 2.05 mg

    0.92 mg = 0.051 mmole of H_2O
          0.102 mmole of hydrogen = 0.10 mg
    _____

          2.15 mg (this accounts for all
                      of the benzo[a]pyrene)

    $C_{0.17}H_{0.102}$ $\xrightarrow[0.102]{\text{divide by}}$ $C_{1.66}H$ $\xrightarrow{\times 3}$ $(C_5H_3)_n$

    (benzo[a]pyrene is $C_{20}H_{12}$)

5. <u>2.03 mg of sample</u>:

    4.44 mg = 0.101 mmole of CO_2
          0.101 mmole of carbon = 1.21 mg = 59.7% C

    0.91 mg = 0.051 mmole of H_2O
          0.102 mmole of hydrogen = 0.10 mg = 5.0% H

    5.31 mg of sample gives X mmole of Cl^- in solution. Because one mmole of
    $AgNO_3$ is required for each mmole of Cl^-, X is equal to 4.80×0.0110 =
    0.0528 mmole of Cl. This is equivalent to 1.87 mg of Cl (0.0528×35.5) in
    5.31 mg of sample = 35.2% Cl.

    59.7% C   59.7/12 = 4.98

     5.0% H   5.0/1 = 5.0 C_5H_5Cl

    35.2% Cl   35.2/35.5 = 0.99

6. $CH_3CH_2CH_2CH_2CH_2Br$ 1-bromopentane

$CH_3CH_2CH_2CHBrCH_3$ 2-bromopentane (this is the same as $CH_3CHBrCH_2CH_2CH_3$; also, 4-bromopentane is just an incorrect name for 2-bromopentane)

$CH_3CH_2CHBrCH_2CH_3$ 3-bromopentane

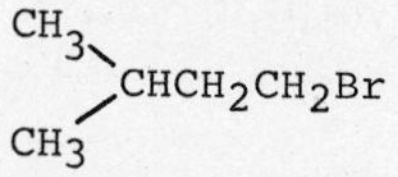

CH_3
$\ $
$CHCH_2CH_2Br$ 1-bromo-3-methylbutane
$/$
CH_3

CH_3
$\ $
$CHCHBrCH_3$ 2-bromo-3-methylbutane
$/$
CH_3

CH_3
$\ $
$CBrCH_2CH_3$ 2-bromo-2-methylbutane
$/$ (note that the direction of numbering has changed;
CH_3 3-bromo-3-methylbutane is an incorrect name)

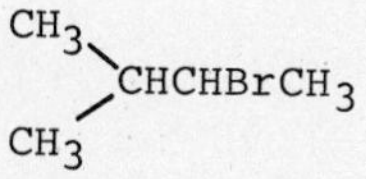

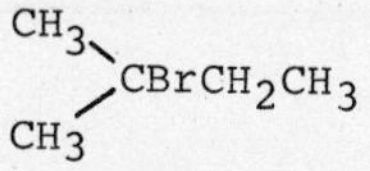

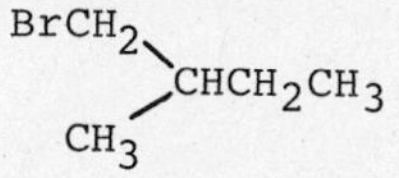

$BrCH_2$
$\ $
$CHCH_2CH_3$ 1-bromo-2-methylbutane CH_3
$/$ (this is the same as $\ $
CH_3 $CHCH_2CH_3$)
                                                    $/$
                                                   $BrCH_2$

CH_3
$|$
CH_3-C-CH_2Br 1-bromo-2,2-dimethylpropane
$|$
CH_3

7. $CH_3CH_2CH_2CH_2OH$ $CH_3OCH_2CH_2CH_3$

$CH_3CH_2CHOHCH_3$ $CH_3OCH(CH_3)_2$

$(CH_3)_2CHCH_2OH$ $CH_3CH_2OCH_2CH_3$

$(CH_3)_3COH$

8. $CH_3CH_2CH_2CH_2CH_2CH_2CH_3$ heptane
$(CH_3)_2CHCH_2CH_2CH_2CH_3$ 2-methylhexane
$CH_3CH_2CH(CH_3)CH_2CH_2CH_3$ 3-methylhexane
$(CH_3)_3CHCH_2CH_2CH_3$ 2,2-dimethylpentane
$(CH_3)_2CHCH(CH_3)CH_2CH_3$ 2,3-dimethylpentane
$(CH_3)_2CHCH_2CH(CH_3)_2$ 2,4-dimethylpentane
$(CH_3CH_2)_3CH$ 3-ethylpentane   (this is the one most people miss!)
$(CH_3)_3CCH(CH_3)_2$ 2,2,3-trimethylbutane

9.   There are **four** monochloro derivatives of heptane (1-chloro-, 2-chloro-, 3-chloro-, and 4-chloroheptane)   4

Six from 2-methylhexane (1-chloro-, 2-chloro-, 3-chloro-, 4-chloro-, 5-chloro-, and 6-chloro-2-methylhexane are all different)   6

Seven   from 3-methylhexane (1-chloro-, 2-chloro-, 3-chloro, 4-chloro-, 5-chloro-, and 6-chloro-3-methylhexane; and 3-chloromethylhexane   7

Four from 2,2-dimethylpentane (1-chloro-,   3-chloro-, 4-chloro-, and 5-chloro-2,2-dimethylpentane)   4

Six from 2,3-dimethylpentane (1-chloro-, 2-chloro-, 3-chloro, 4-chloro-, and 5-chloro-2,3-dimethylpentane, as well as 3-chloromethyl-2-methylpentane)   [Note: You might think that "2-chloromethyl-3-methylpentane" is a 7th isomer, but this is an incorrect name for one of the others. Which one?]   6

Three only from 2,4-dimethylpentane (1-chloro-, 2-chloro-, and 3-chloro-2,4-dimethyl-pentane)   3

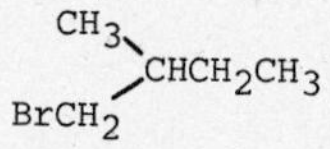

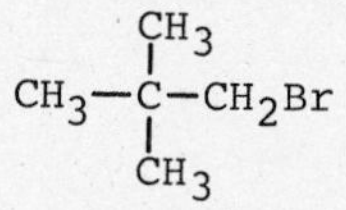

Three from 3-ethylpentane (1-chloro-, 2-chloro-, and 3-chloro-3-ethylpentane)   3

Three from 2,2,3-trimethylbutane (1-chloro-2,2,3-trimethylbutane and 1-chloro- and   3
2-chloro-2,3,3-trimethylbutane; notice how the numbering scheme for the last two
isomers changes from that of the hydrocarbon)

Total is thirty-six structural isomers[*]   36

[*]**NOTE**: You will learn in Chapter 7 that stereoisomers exist for some of these compounds as well.

10. The formula C_5H_{12} represents a fully saturated hydrocarbon; if the molecular formula
were a multiple of this, there would be too many hydrogens to go around.

11. [no answer]

12. (a) alkene   (b) ether   (c) alcohol   (d) alkyl halide   (e) carboxylic acid
    (f) ketone   (g) aldehyde   (h) disulfide   (i) thiol   (j) sulfide   (k) aromatic ring
    (l) primary amine   (m) alkyne   (n) organometallic

13.
(a)
$$CH_3-\underset{\underset{CH_3}{|}}{\overset{\overset{CH_3}{|}}{C}}-CH_3$$

(b)
$$CH_3-\underset{\underset{CH_3}{|}}{\overset{\overset{CH_3}{|}}{CH}}$$

(c)
$$CH_3-\underset{\underset{CH_3}{|}}{\overset{\overset{CH_3}{|}}{C}}-Br \equiv (CH_3)_3CBr$$

(d) $(CH_3)_2CHCH_2I$

(e) $(CH_3)_2CHI$

(f) $CH_3CH_2CHBrCH_3$

14.

(a)
$$\underset{\underset{CH_3}{|}}{\overset{\overset{CH_3}{|}}{HC}}-\underset{\underset{CH_3}{|}}{\overset{\overset{CH_2}{|}\atop\overset{CH_2}{|}\atop\overset{CH_3}{}}{C}}-\underset{\underset{CH_3}{|}}{\overset{\overset{CH_2CH_2CH_3}{}}{CH}}$$

(b)
$$CH_3CH_2CH_2-\underset{\underset{CH_2CH_3}{|}}{\overset{\overset{CH_2CH_3}{|}}{CH}}-F$$

(c)
$$CH_3CH_2CH_2CH_2CH_2\underset{\underset{CH_2}{|}\atop\overset{\overset{CH_2-CH}{}}{|}\atop\overset{\overset{CH_3}{}}{\overset{CH_3}{}}}{CH}CH_2CH_2CH_2CH_3$$

(d)
$$CH_3CH_2CH_2\underset{\underset{CH_3-C-CH_3}{\underset{|}{}}}{CH}CH_2CH_2CH_3$$

(e)
$$\underset{\overset{|}{CH_3}}{\overset{\overset{CH_3}{|}}{CH}}CH_2CH_2CH_2CH_2CH_2CH_2CH_2CH_2CH_2CH_2CH_2CH_2CH_2CH_3 \equiv (CH_3)_2CH(CH_2)_{14}CH_3$$

(f)
$$CH_3CH_2-\underset{\underset{CH_3}{|}}{\overset{\overset{CH_3}{|}}{C}}-\underset{\underset{CH_2CH_2CH_3}{|}}{\overset{\overset{CH-Cl}{|}}{CH}}$$

(g)
$$CH_3-\underset{\underset{CH_3}{|}}{\overset{\overset{CH_3}{|}}{C}}-\underset{\underset{CH_3-C-CH_3}{\underset{|}{}}}{\overset{\overset{CH_3}{|}}{CH}}\atop CHCH_2CH_2CH_2CH_3 \atop CH_2CH_2CH_2CH_2CH_2CH_3$$

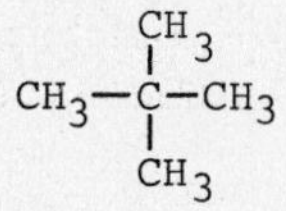

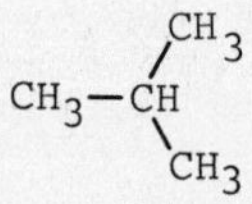

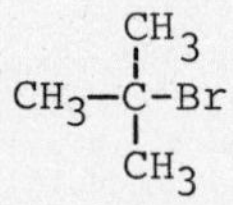

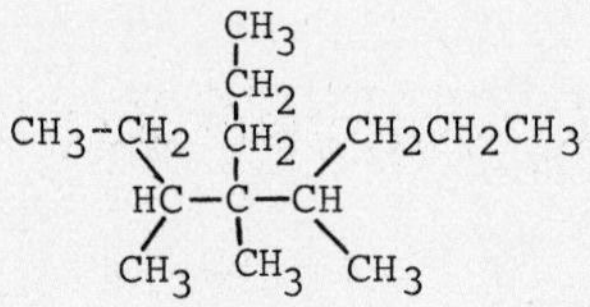

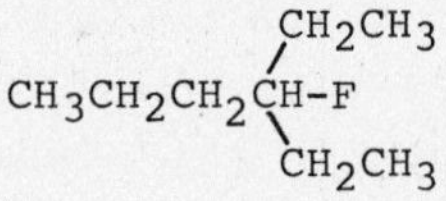

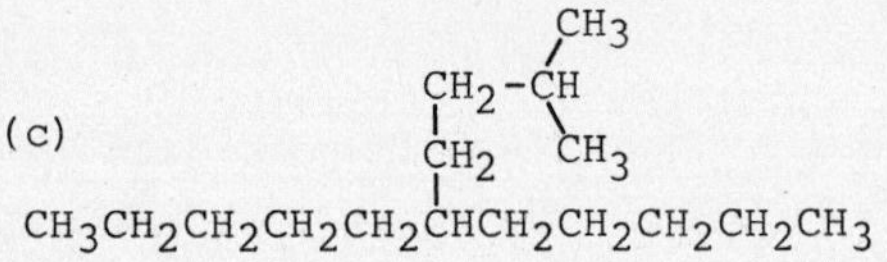

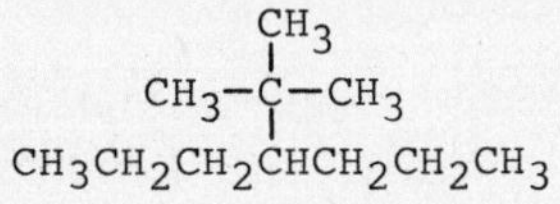

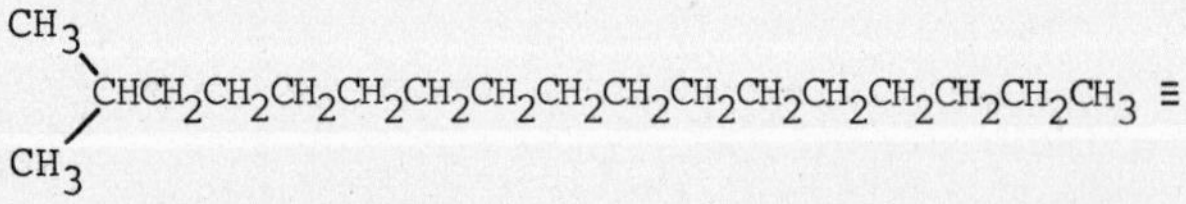

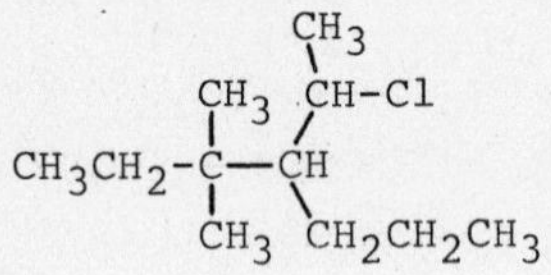

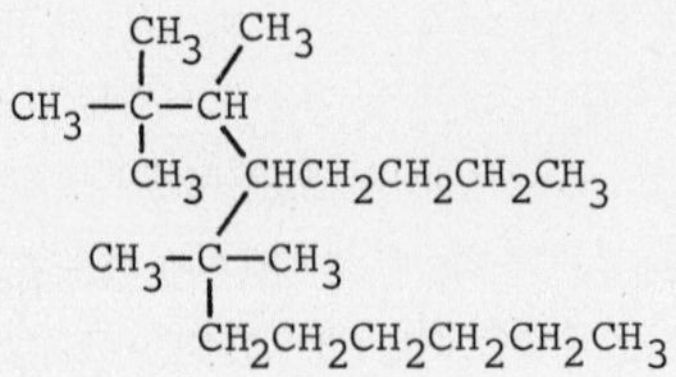

(h) $(CH_3)_2CHCH_2CH_2C(CH_2CH_3)_3$

15. (a) 2,5-dimethylhexane

     (b) 3-ethyl-5,5,7-trimethylnonane

     (c) 4-ethyl-3-methylheptane

     (d) 1-bromo-4-chloro-2-methylpentane

     (e) 5-ethyl-4-iodo-2,2-dimethyloctane

     (f) 3,6-diethyl-2,6-dimethyloctane

     (g) 7-(4,4-dimethylhexyl)-3,3,11,11-tetramethyltridecane

     (h) 3,3-diethylpentane

     (i) 3-ethyl-4-methylhexane

     (j) 4-ethyl-3,3-dimethylhexane

16. (a) Where on the heptane backbone is the methyl attached? This has to be specified in
          a complete name.

     (b) "4-Methylhexane" should be numbered from the other end to give 3-methylhexane.

     (c) The longest chain in "3-propylhexane" has seven carbons; it should be named
          4-ethylheptane.

     (d) When choosing between chains of equal length, the one which has more substituents
          should be chosen: 3-ethyl-2,5,5-trimethyloctane.

     (e) Alkyl and halo substituents should be listed in alphabetical order:
          3-chloro-4-methylhexane.

     (f) The prefix "di-" does not count in alphabetizing: 3-ethyl-2,2-dimethylpentane.

     (g) Numbered from the wrong end: 3,4,5,7-tetramethylnonane.

     (h) A position must be specified for every substituent, even if the position is the
          same: 2,2-dimethylpropane.

3.F   **Supplementary Problems**

   S1. From the analytical values for each compound, derive its empirical
        formula.

        (a) Cecropia moth juvenile hormone: 73.6% C, 10.1% H

        (b) Valium: 67.5% C, 4.6% H, 12.5% Cl, 9.8% N

        (c) Nicotine: 74.0% C, 8.7% H, 17.3% N

        (d) Sarin (a nerve gas): 34.3% C, 7.2% H, 13.6% F, 22.1% P

   S2. The following compounds were shown to contain only carbon, hydrogen,
        oxygen, and (if indicated) nitrogen. Calculate the empirical
        formula for each case.

        (a) Combustion of 5.63 mg of aspirin gave 12.39 mg of CO_2 and
            2.27 mg of H_2O

        (b) Combustion of 1.87 mg of vitamin E gave 5.55 mg of CO_2 and
            1.97 mg of H_2O

        (c) Combustion of 2.79 mg of caffeine gave 5.06 mg of CO_2, 1.30 mg
            of H_2O, and 0.80 mg of N_2

        (d) Combustion of 1.07 mg of epinephrine (adrenaline) gave 2.31 mg
            of CO_2, 0.69 mg of H_2O, and 0.08 mg of N_2

S3. On oxidation of sulfur-containing compounds, the sulfur is oxidized
     to sulfate, which can be determined by conversion to the very insolu-
     ble barium salt $BaSO_4$. Combustion of 3.27 mg of saccharin gave
     5.50 mg of CO_2, 0.81 mg of H_2O, and 0.25 mg of N_2. Oxidation of a
     6.73 mg sample of saccharin and conversion of the sulfate to the
     barium salt gave 8.59 mg of $BaSO_4$. What is the empirical formula
     for saccharin?

S4. (a) What is the percent elemental composition of vitamin C ($C_6H_8O_6$)?

     (b) How much CO_2 and H_2O do you expect to obtain on combustion of a
     3.97 mg sample of vitamin C?

S5. Write out condensed formulas and IUPAC names for all of the isomers
     of each of the following formulas.

     (a) $C_3H_5Cl_3$

     (b) C_6H_{12}

     (c) C_4H_8ClI

S6. Write condensed structural formulas for each of the
     following compounds.

     (a) 2,5,5-trimethylheptane

     (b) 1-bromo-3-ethylpentane

     (c) neopentyl bromide

     (d) 4,4-di(2,2-dimethylpropyl)-2,2,6,6-tetramethylheptane

     (e) 1,2-dichloro-1,1,2,2-tetrafluoroethane ("Freon 114")

     (f) 4-(1,1-dimethylpropyl)-2,2,3-trimethyloctane

S7. Give the IUPAC name for each of the following compounds.

(a)
$$CH_3-CH-\overset{\overset{\displaystyle CH_3}{|}}{\underset{\underset{\displaystyle CH_3}{|}}{\underset{\displaystyle H_3C}{C}}}-CH_3$$

(d) $((CH_3)_3C)_2CHCH_3$

(b) $(CH_3CH_2)_2CHCH_2CH_2CH_2Cl$

(e) $(CH_3)_2CHCH_2\overset{\underset{\displaystyle CH_3}{|}}{C}HCClF_2$

(c)
$$\underset{\displaystyle BrCH_2CH_2CH_2}{\overset{\displaystyle CH_3CH_2CH_2}{CH_3C-CH_2CH_2CH_3}}$$

(f)
$$(CH_3)_2CHCH_2 \diagdown \qquad CH_2CHCH_2CH_3$$
$$CH \qquad CH(CH_3)_2$$
$$|$$
$$CH_2$$
$$|$$
$$(CH_3)_2C$$
$$|$$
$$CH_3CH_2CHCH_2$$
$$|$$
$$CH_3$$

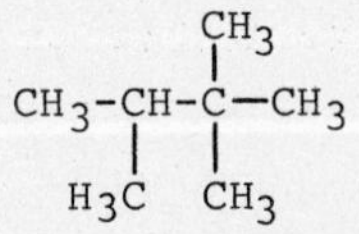

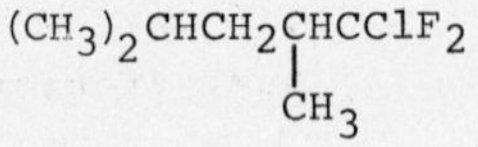

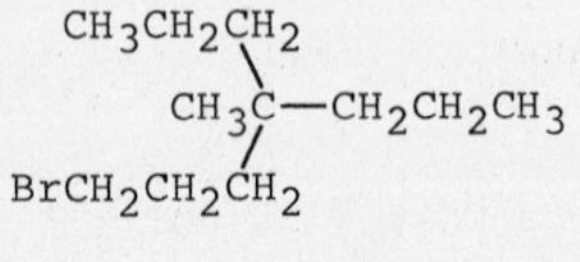

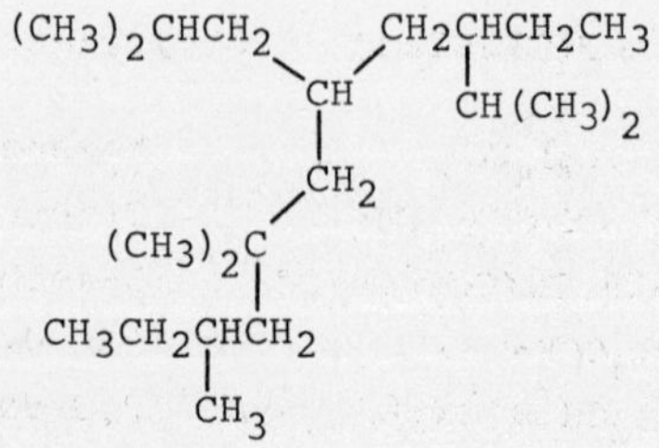

3.G   Answers to Supplementary Problems

S1. (a) $C_{6.13}H_{10.1}O_{1.02} = (C_6H_{10}O)_n$ (Cecropia juvenile hormone is $C_{18}H_{30}O_3$)

(b) $C_{5.63}H_{4.6}Cl_{0.35}N_{0.70}O_{0.35} = (C_{16}H_{13}ClN_2O)_n$ (Valium is $C_{16}H_{13}ClN_2O$)

(c) $C_{6.17}H_{8.7}N_{1.24} = (C_5H_7N)_n$ (Nicotine is $C_{10}H_{14}N_2$)

(d) $C_{2.86}H_{7.2}F_{0.72}O_{1.43}P_{0.71} = (C_4H_{10}FO_2P)_n$ (Sarin is $C_4H_{10}FO_2P$)

S2. (a) $\dfrac{12.39}{44} \times \dfrac{12}{5.63} \times 100 = 60.0\% \ C$ $\dfrac{2.27}{18} \times \dfrac{2}{5.63} \times 100 = 4.5\% \ H$

$100\% - 60.0\% - 4.5\% = 35.5\% \ O$

$C_{60/12}H_{4.5/1}O_{35.5/16} = C_5H_{4.5}O_{2.2} = C_{2.27}H_2O = (C_9H_8O_4)_n$ (Aspirin is $C_9H_8O_4$)

(b) 80.9% C, 11.7% H $100\% - 80.9\% - 11.7\% = 7.4\% \ O$

$C_{6.74}H_{11.7}O_{0.46} = C_{14.6}H_{25.4}O = (C_{25}H_{50}O_2)_n$ (Vitamin E is $C_{25}H_{50}O_2$)

(c) 49.5% C, 5.2% H, 28.7% N $100\% - 49.5\% - 5.2\% - 28.7\% = 16.6\% \ O$

$C_{4.13}H_{5.2}N_{2.05}O_{1.04} = (C_4H_5N_2O)_n$ (Caffeine is $C_8H_{10}N_4O_2$)

(d) 58.9% C, 7.2% H, 7.5% N $100\% - 58.9\% - 7.2\% - 7.5\% = 26.4\% \ O$

$C_{4.9}H_{7.2}N_{0.54}O_{1.65} = C_{9.07}H_{13.33}NO_{3.05} = (C_9H_{13}NO_3)_n$ (Epinephrine is $C_9H_{13}NO_3$)

S3.   45.9% C, 2.75% H, 7.6% N $\dfrac{8.59}{233.3} \times \dfrac{32}{6.73} \times 100 = 17.5\% \ S$

$100\% - 45.9\% - 2.75\% - 7.6\% - 17.5\% = 26.25\% \ O$

$C_{3.8}H_{2.75}N_{0.54}O_{1.64}S_{0.55} = (C_7H_5NO_3S)_n$ (Saccharin is $C_7H_5NO_3S$)

S4. (a)   MW $= (6 \times 12) + (8 \times 1) + (6 \times 16) = 176$

$\dfrac{6 \times 12}{176} \times 100 = 40.9\% \ C$ $\dfrac{8 \times 1}{176} \times 100 = 4.5\% \ H$ $\dfrac{6 \times 16}{176} \times 100 = 54.5\% \ O$

(b) $\dfrac{0.409 \times 3.97}{12} \times 44 = 5.95$ mg of CO_2 $\dfrac{0.045 \times 3.97}{2} \times 18 = 1.61$ mg of H_2O

S5. (a) $CH_3CH_2CCl_3$ 1,1,1-trichloropropane
$CH_3CHClCHCl_2$ 1,1,2-trichloropropane
$CH_2ClCH_2CHCl_2$ 1,1,3-trichloropropane
$CH_3CCl_2CH_2Cl$ 1,2,2-trichloropropane
$CH_2ClCHClCH_2Cl$ 1,2,3-trichloropropane

(NOTE: $CH_2ClCCl_2CH_3$ is 1,2,2-trichloropropane)

(b) $CH_3(CH_2)_4CH_3$ hexane
$(CH_3)_2CH(CH_2)_2CH_3$ 2-methylpentane
$CH_3CH_2CH(CH_3)CH_2CH_3$ 3-methylpentane
$(CH_3)_3CCH_2CH_3$ 2,2-dimethylbutane
$(CH_3)_2CHCH(CH_3)_2$ 2,3-dimethylbutane

(c) $CH_3CH_2CH_2CHClI$ 1-chloro-1-iodobutane

$CH_3CH_2CHClCH_2I$ 2-chloro-1-iodobutane

$CH_3CHClCH_2CH_2I$ 3-chloro-1-iodobutane

$ClCH_2CH_2CH_2CH_2I$ 1-chloro-4-iodobutane

$CH_3CH_2CHICH_2Cl$ 1-chloro-2-iodobutane

$CH_3CHICH_2CH_2Cl$ 1-chloro-3-iodobutane

$CH_3CH_2CClICH_3$ 2-chloro-2-iodobutane

$CH_3CHClCHICH_3$ 2-chloro-3-iodobutane

$(CH_3)_2CHCHClI$ 1-chloro-1-iodo-2-methylpropane

$(CH_3)_2CClCH_2I$ 2-chloro-1-iodo-2-methylpropane

$(CH_3)_2CICH_2Cl$ 1-chloro-2-iodo-2-methylpropane

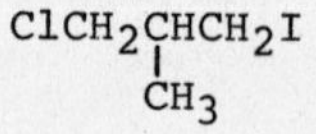

$ClCH_2CHCH_2I$
      | 1-chloro-3-iodo-2-methylpropane
     CH_3

S6. (a) $(CH_3)_2CHCH_2CH_2C(CH_3)_2CH_2CH_3$

                                   (e) $F_2ClCCClF_2$

    (b) $BrCH_2CH_2CH(CH_2CH_3)_2$

    (c) $(CH_3)_2CCH_2Br$

                        CH_3
                         |
                   (f) $(CH_3)_3CCHCH(CH_2)_3CH_3$

          $(CH_3)_3C$
               |
               CH_2 CH_3-C-CH_3
               | |
    (d) $(CH_3)_3CCH_2-C-CH_2C(CH_3)_3$ CH_2CH_3
                   |
           $CH_2C(CH_3)_3$

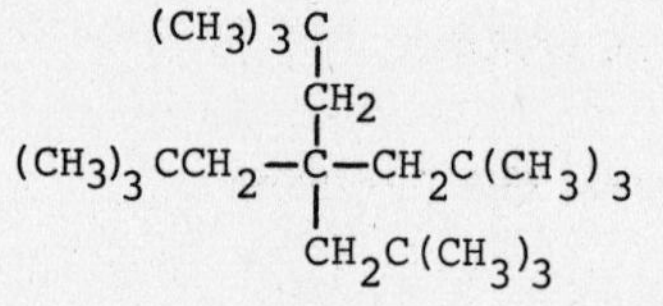

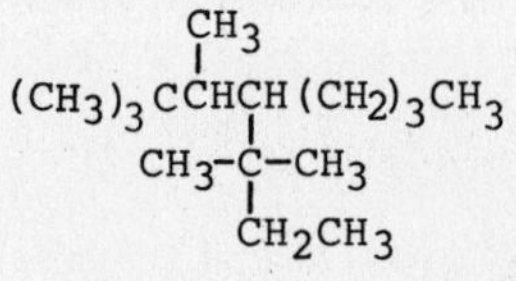

S7. (a) 2,2,3-trimethylbutane

    (b) 1-chloro-4-ethylhexane

    (c) 1-bromo-4-methyl-4-propylheptane

    (d) 2,2,3,4,4-pentamethylpentane

    (e) 1-chloro-1,1-difluoro-2,4-dimethylpentane

    (f) 3-ethyl-2,7,7,9-tetramethyl-5-(2-methylpropyl)undecane

4. ORGANIC REACTIONS

4.C   Important Concepts and Hints

   Whereas Chapters 2 and 3 present the underlying principles of structure, Chapter 4 discusses the principles of reactivity. Two quite separate concepts are those of **equilibrium** (a measure of how completely a reaction proceeds) and **rate** (a measure of how fast a reaction proceeds). Although they are independent, both depend on potential energy differences which organic chemists like to display pictorially with "reaction profile" or "reaction coordinate" diagrams, such as the simple one sketched below. These diagrams are seldom used in a quantitative sense, but they frequently provide a picture of the energy changes associated with a reaction.

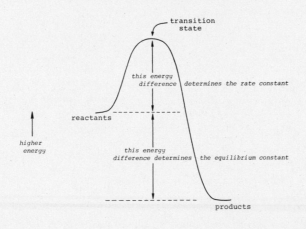

A helpful analogy can be drawn between molecules passing over the energy barrier (through the transition state) leading to product, and water passing over a physical barrier and running downhill. The higher the barrier, the more vigorously the water must be agitated before very much splashes over the edge. This is analogous to raising the temperature of a reaction mixture until enough molecules have the kinetic energy necessary to overcome the activation energy $\Delta G^{\ddagger}$. The energy released as the water runs downhill, on the other hand, depends only on the difference in height between the upper and lower reservoirs, just as the energy released in a reaction depends only on the overall free energy of reaction, ΔG^{O}.

Reaction coordinate diagrams can be useful for an intuitive understanding of the energetics of reaction kinetics and equilibria. However, you should recognize their qualitative nature as well as some pitfalls which you may encounter when using them. Because they really refer only to standard states (approximately 1 M for liquid-phase reactions), they cannot be rigorously applied to reactions in which relative rates and equilibria depend on concentration. For example, see problem #S9 in this Chapter of the Study Guide.

Equilibrium: The equilibrium constant, K = [product(s)]/[reactant(s)], is a measure of how far a reaction will proceed before there is no further change in the concentration of reactants and products. It depends on the potential energy difference between the reactants and products, as expressed by the equation $\Delta G^{O} = -RT \ln K$. This is a useful equation to remember, as it can be applied in many situations. Also useful to remember is a particular consequence of this equation: at normal temperatures (T $\approx$ 300 ^{O}K), every 1.37 kcal mole^{-1} change in ΔG^{O} corresponds to a ten-fold change in the equilibrium constant K (and vice versa).

Rate: The rate of a reaction depends on a constant which is characteristic to each reaction (the rate constant, k), and on the concentration of the reactants. In this regard, be sure you understand the difference between **rate** and **rate constant**, and first- and second-order reactions. The rate constant, k, depends on the activation energy for the reaction, $\Delta G^{\ddagger}$, as shown by the equation:

$$k = constant \times e^{-\Delta G^{\ddagger}/RT}$$

which rearranges to: $\Delta G^{\ddagger} = -RT \ln k + another\ constant.$

This equation is similar to the one which relates the standard free energy of reaction, ΔG^{O}, and the equilibrium constant, K, so the same "1.37 kcal mole^{-1} = a factor of 10" rule-of-thumb applies. Although these equations are similar, don't get $\Delta G^{\ddagger}$ and ΔG^{O} mixed up.

Chapter 4 also discusses acid/base equilibria fairly thoroughly, although you may feel that the topic belongs more to General Chemistry courses. In fact, the fundamental aspects of acid/base equilibria will be referred to repeatedly throughout your course in organic chemistry. These concepts will be useful for explaining why reactions take place, what mechanisms they proceed by, and so on. You should be familiar with the idea that any molecule which donates a proton in the course of a reaction is an "acid", and any molecule which accepts a proton is a "base". All of the equilibria below are acid/base reactions. Note that some molecules can act either as acids or bases, depending on the situation.

Acids		Bases			Bases		Acids
HCl	+	NH_3	$\rightleftharpoons$		Cl^-	+	NH_4^+
HCl	+	H_2O	$\rightleftharpoons$		Cl^-	+	H_3O^+
H_2O	+	CH_3O^-	$\rightleftharpoons$		OH^-	+	CH_3OH
H_2SO_4	+	$O=CH_2$	$\rightleftharpoons$		HSO_4^-	+	$H-\overset{+}{O}=CH_2$
NH_4^+	+	OH^-	$\rightleftharpoons$		NH_3	+	H_2O
NH_3	+	CH_3^-	$\rightleftharpoons$		NH_2^-	+	CH_4

The most useful measure of how easily a compound gives up a proton is its pK_a (frequently called simply "pK"). The easiest way to remember what the numbers mean is the following: in aqueous solution, when the pH equals the pK_a of a compound, it is half-ionized (i.e., half of it is protonated and half of it is unprotonated). Weaker acids have higher pK_a's and therefore require higher pH's before they are half-ionized, and vice versa for stronger acids. Obviously, this relationship is only realistic for pK_a's in the range attainable in water (0-14), but the device is still useful for remembering what pK_a's outside this range mean; for instance, a negative pK_a means that the compound is a very strong acid. On the other hand, a pK_a of 34 means that the compound is a very weak acid, but that the deprotonated form (called the "conjugate base") is a very strong base. Each pK_a unit represents a factor of 10 in equilibrium because it is a logarithmic scale. Remember: a factor of 10 = 1.37 kcal mole^{-1} in energy difference.

NOTE: Later in your course in organic chemistry you may hear: "the pK_a of ammonia is 9". This is a careless statement, although a common one; what is intended is: "the pK_a of the ammonium ion (NH_4^+) is 9". Although we often think of both the acidity of a protonated compound _and_ the basicity of the unprotonated form in terms of pK_a, we should always be aware that pK_a refers to the ability of the protonated species to give up its proton; i.e., for the compound to function as an acid. The pK_a of _ammonia_ ($NH_3 \rightleftharpoons NH_2^- + H^+$) is actually 34.

If the whole concept of pH, and of acids and bases in general, has receded from your memory since you took introductory chemistry, you should definitely go back and review this subject....

4.D   Answers to Exercises

4.1 $\Delta G° = \Delta H° - T\Delta S°$

(a) At 27° C (300° K): $\Delta H° = -10$ kcal mole^{-1} _Don't overlook the difference between cal and kcal!_

$T = 300°$ K

$\Delta S° = -22$ e.u. $= -22$ cal deg^{-1} mole^{-1}

$\therefore \Delta G° = -10,000 - 300 \cdot (-22) = -3400$ cal mole^{-1}
$= -3.4$ kcal mole^{-1}

$\Delta G° = -RT \ln K$
$\Delta G° = -3.4$ kcal mole^{-1} $\therefore \ln K = \dfrac{-3400}{-1.987 \times 300} = 5.70$
$R = 1.987$ cal deg^{-1} mole^{-1}
(cal, not kcal)   and $K = e^{5.7} = 300$ at 300° K
$T = 300°$ K

(b) At 227°C (500° K): $\Delta G° = -10,000 - 500 \cdot (-22) = +1000$ cal mole^{-1}
$= +1.0$ kcal mole^{-1}

$\ln K = \dfrac{1000}{-1.987 \times 500} = -1.01$, and $K = e^{-1.01} = 0.36$

4.2   Rate $= k$ [OH$^-$][CH$_3$Cl]; $k = 6 \times 10^{-6}$ M^{-1} sec^{-1}
Initial reaction rate: (a) $k \times 1.0$ M $\times 0.1$ M $= 6 \times 10^{-7}$ M sec^{-1}
(b) $k \times 0.1$ M $\times 0.1$ M $= 6 \times 10^{-8}$ M sec^{-1}
(c) $k \times 0.01$ M $\times 0.01$ M $= 6 \times 10^{-10}$ M sec^{-1}

After 90% of the methyl chloride has reacted:
(a) $k \times 0.99$ M $\times 0.01$ M $= 5.94 \times 10^{-8}$ M sec^{-1}
(b) $k \times 0.01$ M $\times 0.01$ M $= 6 \times 10^{-10}$ M sec^{-1}
(c) $k \times 0.001$ M $\times 0.001$ M $= 6 \times 10^{-12}$ M sec^{-1}

4.3   Rate-determining step is A $\longrightarrow$ B:

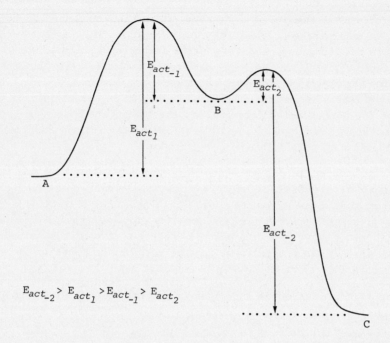

$$E_{act_{-2}} > E_{act_1} > E_{act_{-1}} > E_{act_2}$$

The rate of B → C is the faster one. For a two-step reaction A $\rightleftharpoons$ B → C, in which B is an unstable intermediate (i.e., A → B is endothermic), the rate of A → B can become faster than B → C only if the first transition state is lower than the second (i.e., if $k_{-1} > k_2$).

4.4 $[HA] \rightleftharpoons [H^+] + [A^-]$, $K = \dfrac{[H^+][A^-]}{[HA]}$. $pK_a = -\log K$ and $K = 10^{-pK_a}$

$$[H^+] \cong [A^-] = 1 - [HA] \quad \text{and} \quad K = \frac{(1 - [HA])^2}{[HA]}$$

<u>For HI and HCl</u>:   when K is very large, $[HA] \cong 0$ and $[H^+] \cong 1\,\underline{M}$; pH = 0

<u>For HF</u>: $K = 10^{-3.2} = 6.3 \times 10^{-4}$. In this case, K is small, $[HF] \cong 1\,\underline{M}$ and

$\dfrac{[H^+][F^-]}{1} \cong 6.3 \times 10^{-4}$; $[H^+] = [F^-] = \sqrt{6.3 \times 10^{-4}}$

$$= 2.5 \times 10^{-2}\,\underline{M} \text{ and pH = 1.6}$$

<u>For acetic acid</u>: $K = 10^{-4.76} = 1.74 \times 10^{-5}$. As for HF, very little of HA

dissociates: $[HA] \cong 1\underline{M}$; $\dfrac{[H^+][A^-]}{1} \cong 1.74 \times 10^{-5}$; $[H^+] = \sqrt{1.74 \times 10^{-5}}$

$$= 4.17 \times 10^{-3}\,\underline{M}$$
$$\text{and pH = 2.4}$$

<u>For H$_2$S</u>: $K = 10^{-7}$. Again, very little of H$_2$S

ionizes: $[H_2S] \cong 1\,\underline{M}$ and $[H^+] = [HS^-] = \sqrt{10^{-7}}$

$$= 3.2 \times 10^{-4}\,\underline{M} \text{ and pH = 3.5}$$

4.5 $\dfrac{[H^+][A^-]}{[HA]} = 10^{-pK_a} = 100$; $[H^+] = [A^-] = 1 - [HA]$

$$[H^+] = [A^-] = 0.99\,M; \quad [HA] = 0.01\,M$$

4.6

Acid	Conjugate Base	Strength of Conjugate Base
CH_3CO_2H	$CH_3CO_2^-$	Weak
NH_4^+	$:NH_3$	Moderate
HI, HBr, HCl	I^-, Br^-, Cl^-	Very Weak
HCN	CN^-	Moderate
HF	F^-	Weak
H_2Se	HSe^-	Weak
H_2S	HS^-	Weak-Moderate
CH_3OH	CH_3O^-	Strong
HNO_3	NO_3^-	Very Weak
HNO_2	NO_2^-	Weak
H_3PO_4	$H_2PO_4^-$	Weak
(Second ionization:	$HPO_4^=$	Weak-Moderate)
(Third ionization:	$PO_4^{\equiv}$	Strong)
C_6H_5OH	$C_6H_5O^-$	Moderate
H_2SO_4	HSO_4^-	Very Weak
(Second ionization:	$SO_4^=$	Weak)
H_2O	OH^-	Strong

4.E   Answers and Explanations for Problems

1. (a) $\Delta H° = 7.3$ kcal mole^{-1} ◄─────   *Note difference between*
            $T = 298°$ K   *kcal and cal*
            $\Delta S° = 0.3$ cal deg^{-1} mole^{-1} ◄

   $\Delta G° = \Delta H° - T\Delta S° = 7300 - (298 \times 0.3)$
   $$= 7211 \text{ cal mole}^{-1} = 7.21 \text{ kcal mole}^{-1}$$

   (b) $\Delta G° = 7210$ cal mole^{-1}
            $R = 1.987$ cal deg^{-1} mole^{-1}
                 (cal, not kcal)

            $T = 298°$ K

   $\Delta G° = -RT \ln K$, so that $\ln K = \dfrac{7210}{-1.987 \times 298} = -12.2$

   $$\text{and } K = e^{-12.2} = 5 \times 10^{-6}$$

   (c)   No; the reaction would actually "go to completion" in the opposite
                                                              direction.

2. (a) $\Delta G° = \Delta H° - T\Delta S°$
         $= 22,200 - (298 \times 33.5)$
         $= 12,200$ cal mole^{-1} = 12.2 kcal mole^{-1}

   The equilibrium lies far to the left (a positive $\Delta G°$ indicates an unfavorable
         reaction in the direction written).

   (b) $\Delta G° = \Delta H° - T\Delta S°$
         At 800° K, $\Delta G° = 22,200 - (800 \times 33.5)$
                     $= -4,600$ cal mole^{-1} = -4.6 kcal mole^{-1}

   At this temperature, the equilibrium lies to the right.

(c) The contribution of $\Delta H°$ to $\Delta G°$ is unaffected by temperature, but the contribution of $\Delta S°$ depends directly on temperature because of the $-T\Delta S°$ term. Therefore, at higher temperatures the entropy term $\Delta S°$ becomes more important.

3. (a) At room temperature (300° K), compare $\Delta G°$ for K and for 10K:

$$\Delta G°_A = -RT \ln 10K \qquad \Delta G°_B = -RT \ln K$$

$$\Delta G°_A - \Delta G°_B = -RT(\ln 10K - \ln K) = -RT \ln 10$$
$$= -1.987 \times 300 \times 2.303$$
$$= -1370 \text{ cal mole}^{-1} = -1.37 \text{ kcal mole}^{-1}$$

For a factor of 100, $\Delta G°_A - \Delta G°_B = -RT \ln 100 = -2.75 \text{ kcal mole}^{-1}$

(b) A factor of 10 in K equals a change in $\Delta G°$ of 1.37 kcal mole^{-1} at room temperature. This could arise from a change in $\Delta H°$ of 1.37 kcal mole^{-1} if $\Delta S°$ remained constant, or a change in $\Delta S°$ of $-\dfrac{1370}{298} = -4.6$ e.u., if $\Delta H°$ remained constant.

4. (a) $k = 6 \times 10^{-6} \underline{M}^{-1} \text{ sec}^{-1}$

$[OH^-] = 0.10 \underline{M}$

$[CHCl_3] = 0.05 \underline{M}$

rate $= k[OH^-][CHCl_3]$
$= 6 \times 10^{-6} \underline{M}^{-1} \text{ sec}^{-1} \times 0.10 \underline{M} \times 0.05 \underline{M}$
$= 3.0 \times 10^{-8} \underline{M} \text{ sec}^{-1}$ at the start of reaction

(b) and (c) Each 10% of reaction means a change in $[CHCl_3]$ of 0.005 $\underline{M}$.

% Reaction	k, $\underline{M}^{-1}\text{sec}^{-1}$	$[OH^-]$, $\underline{M}$	$[CHCl_3]$, $\underline{M}$	Rate, $\underline{M}$ sec^{-1}	Time for 10% reaction
0	6×10^{-6}	× 0.10	× 0.050	= 3.0×10^{-8}	
10	6×10^{-6}	× 0.095	× 0.045	= 2.6×10^{-8}	1.67×10^5 sec
20	6×10^{-6}	× 0.090	× 0.040	= 2.2×10^{-8}	1.92×10^5 sec
30	6×10^{-6}	× 0.085	× 0.035	= 1.8×10^{-8}	2.27×10^5 sec
40	6×10^{-6}	× 0.080	× 0.030	= 1.4×10^{-8}	2.78×10^5 sec
50	6×10^{-6}	× 0.075	× 0.025	= 1.1×10^{-8}	3.57×10^5 sec

Total time = 1.22×10^6 sec
= 339 hours

[Using calculus instead of this approximate method, the correct length of time is calculated to be 375 hours. See problem #14 in this Chapter.]

5. (a) The entropy is negative because more order is introduced into the system (less freedom of motion) when two molecules combine to give one.

(b) $\Delta G° = \Delta H° - T\Delta S°$

NOTE!

$= -15.5 \text{ kcal mole}^{-1} - (298 \text{ deg} \times -31.3 \text{ cal deg}^{-1} \text{mole}^{-1})$
$= -6.17 \text{ kcal mole}^{-1}$

(c) $\Delta G° = -RT \ln K$, so that $\ln K = \dfrac{-6170 \text{ cal mole}^{-1}}{-1.987 \text{ cal deg}^{-1} \text{mole}^{-1} \times 298 \text{ deg}} = 10.4$

and $K = e^{10.4} = 3.29 \times 10^4$

$$K = \frac{[C_2H_5Cl]}{[HCl][C_2H_4]} = \frac{P_{C_2H_5Cl}}{P_{HCl} \times P_{C_2H_4}}$$

Because the reaction essentially goes to completion, $P_{C_2H_5Cl}$ at equilibrium = 1 atm (1 atm HCl + 1 atm C_2H_4 ⇌ 1 atm C_2H_5Cl). Furthermore, because $P_{HCl} = P_{C_2H_4}$ at the start of reaction, and one molecule of HCl is consumed for every molecule of C_2H_4, P_{HCl} will always equal $P_{C_2H_4}$.

$$K = \frac{1}{(P_{HCl})^2} = 3.29 \times 10^4 \implies P_{HCl} = P_{C_2H_4} = 5.5 \times 10^{-3} \, \text{atm}$$

(d) For all three components to be present in equal amounts, i.e., at equal pressures of each component: $K = \dfrac{P}{P \cdot P} = \dfrac{1}{P} = 3.29 \times 10^4 \implies P = 3 \times 10^{-5}\,\text{atm}$.

With each component at this pressure, the total pressure will be 9×10^{-5} atm.

6. (a)

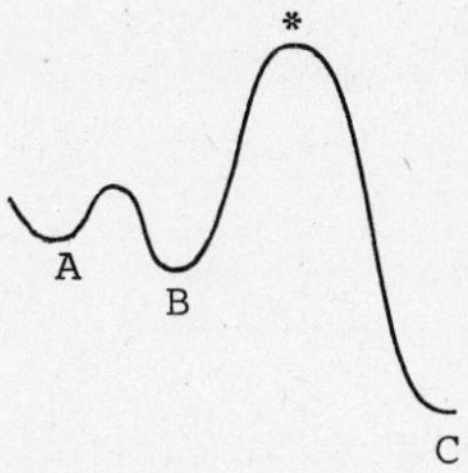

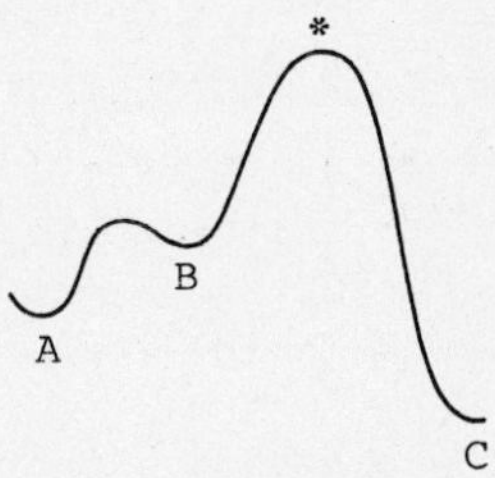

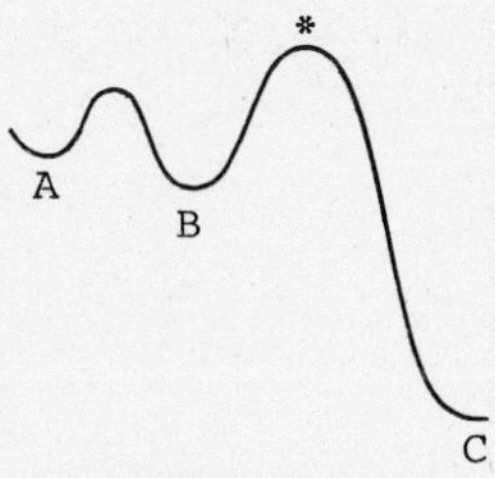

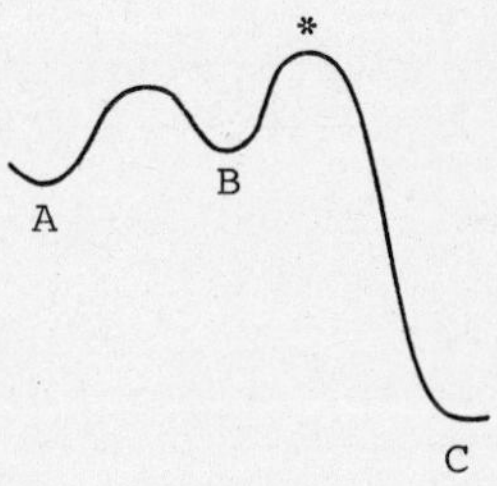

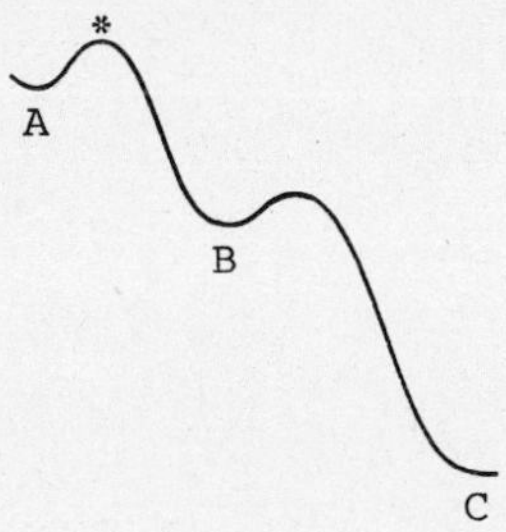

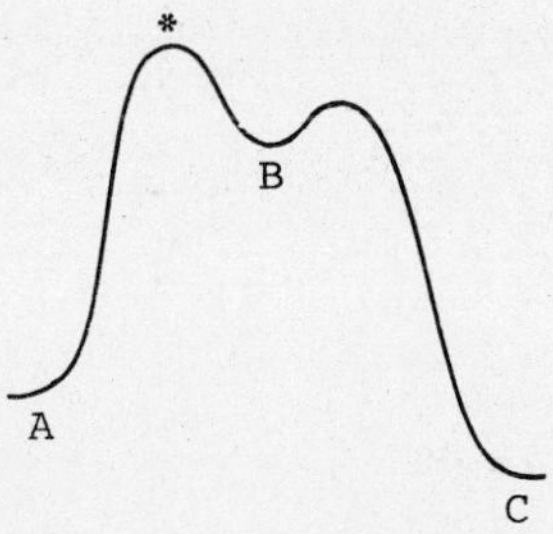

In each case, an asterisk (*) indicates the rate-determining transition state.

7. (a) Endothermic. An "uphill" reaction requires you to put energy <u>in</u>.

(b)

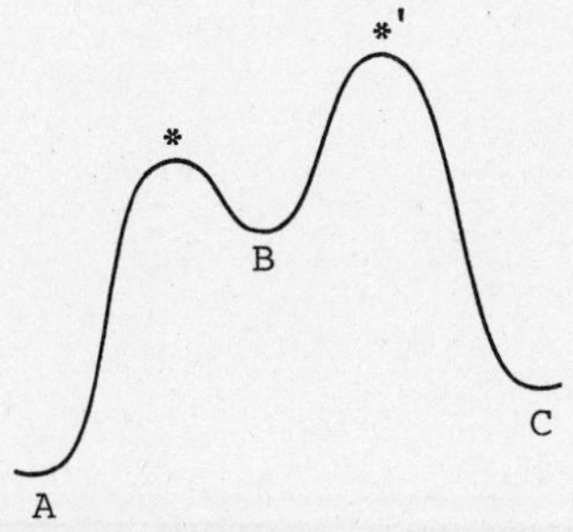

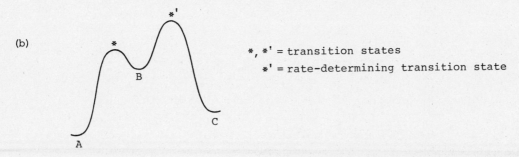

*, *' = transition states
*' = rate-determining transition state

(c) $k_2 > k_3 > k_1 > k_4$ (d) A is most stable   (e) B is least stable

8.

(a)

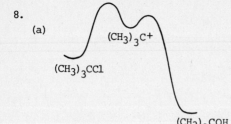

$(CH_3)_3CCl$

$(CH_3)_3C^+$

$(CH_3)_3COH$

(b) endothermic; uphill to the carbocation

(c) exothermic; downhill overall

(d) the first step, because that is the highest barrier to cross

9. Because NH_2^- is such a strong base, the equilibrium with water lies completely to the right: $H_2O + NH_2^- \rightleftharpoons HO^- + NH_3$, and $[OH^-]$ will equal 0.1 M. $[H^+][OH^-] = 10^{-14} \Rightarrow [H^+] = 10^{-13}$ and $pH = 13$.

This result is essentially the same as adding 0.1 M of NaOH itself.

PH_3 is expected to be a stronger acid because the P-H bonds are weaker than N-H bonds (P is below N in the periodic table).

10. Hydrogen is a very, very weak acid (i.e., hydride ion is a very strong base).

11. (a) and (g) The presence of one negative charge makes it more difficult to generate another.

(b), (d), (f), and (h)   The more electronegative oxygen substituents present, the better the negative charge can be stabilized.

(c) The bonds become weaker farther down the periodic table.

(d) Nitrite ion is also stabilized by resonance relative to the hydroxylamine ion.

(e) Because it lies farther to the right in the periodic table, sulfur is more electronegative than phosphorus.

12. At 50% reaction, $[A] = \frac{1}{2}[A]_{initial}$ and $[B] = \frac{1}{2}[B]_{initial}$

$$rate = k \frac{1}{2}[A]_{initial} \times \frac{1}{2}[B]_{initial} = \frac{1}{4}(initial\ rate)$$

13. (a) $[H_2O]$ in water is $\dfrac{1000\ g\ liter^{-1}}{18\ g\ mole^{-1}} = 55\ M$

(b) $k_1[CH_3Cl] = k_2[CH_3Cl][H_2O]$

$k_1 = k_2[H_2O] \Rightarrow k_2 = \dfrac{3 \times 10^{-10}\ sec^{-1}}{55\ M} = 5.45 \times 10^{-12}\ M^{-1}\ sec^{-1}$

The rate constant for the reaction with OH^- is $6 \times 10^{-6}\ M^{-1}\ sec^{-1}$, i.e., much faster.

(c) $\dfrac{0.69}{3 \times 10^{-10}\ sec^{-1}} = 2.3 \times 10^9\ sec = 73\ years$

14. $rate = k[OH^-][CH_3Cl]$ Let $r = [OH^-]_{reacted} = [CH_3Cl]_{reacted}$

At time t, $[OH^-] = 0.10 - r$ and $[CH_3Cl] = 0.05 - r$

$\dfrac{dr}{dt} = k[0.10 - r][0.05 - r]$ so that $\dfrac{dr}{[0.10 - r][0.05 - r]} = kdt$

In a table of integrals, we find:

$$\int \frac{dx}{(a + bx)(c + dx)} = \frac{1}{ad - bc} \ln \frac{c + dx}{a + bx}$$

For our case,   a = 0.10 , c = 0.05 , and b = d = -1

$$\frac{1}{-0.05} \ln\left(\frac{0.05-r}{0.10-r}\right)\Bigg]_{r=0}^{r=0.025} = kt$$

$$8.1 = kt = 6 \times 10^{-6}\, t$$

$$\text{so that } t = 1.35 \times 10^{6} \text{ sec} = 375 \text{ hours}$$

[compare this solution with the approximate one worked out for problem #4]

4.F   Supplementary Problems

S1. (a) At 25 °C, the equilibrium constant K for the addition of water to ethylene
in the gas phase is 23.1 $\underline{M}^{-1}$. Calculate $\Delta G°$ for this reaction at 25 °C.

$$CH_2=CH_2 + H_2O \rightleftharpoons CH_3CH_2OH \qquad K = 23.1\ \underline{M}^{-1} \text{ at } 25\ °C$$

(b) At 400 °K, the equilibrium constant is 0.213 $\underline{M}^{-1}$. Calculate $\Delta H°$ and $\Delta S°$
for the reaction.

(c) Why does the equilibrium constant decrease at higher temperature?

S2. The rate constant k for the reaction: $CH_3CH_2Br + CH_3CH_2O^- \longrightarrow CH_3CH_2OCH_2CH_3$
+ Br^- in ethanol (CH_3CH_2OH) solvent at 25 °C is $7.6 \times 10^{-5}\ \underline{M}^{-1} \text{ sec}^{-1}$,
and the rate equation is: rate = $k[CH_3CH_2Br][CH_3CH_2O^-]$.

(a) If 0.05 mole of CH_3CH_2Br and 0.05 mole of $CH_3CH_2O^-\ Na^+$ are dissolved
in 250 ml of ethanol, to a first approximation how long will it take
before 10% of the CH_3CH_2Br has reacted?

(b) If the same quantities are dissolved in one liter of ethanol?

(c) If 0.05 mole of CH_3CH_2Br is dissolved in one liter of 0.2 $\underline{M}$
$CH_3CH_2O^-\ Na^+$ in ethanol?

S3. The rate constant k' for the reaction
$$(CH_3)_3CBr + CH_3CH_2O^- \longrightarrow (CH_3)_3COCH_2CH_3 + Br^-$$
in ethanol solvent at 25 °C is: $5 \times 10^{-4}\ \underline{M}^{-1} \text{ sec}^{-1}$, and the rate equation
is: rate = $k'[(CH_3)_3CBr]$.

(a) If 0.05 mole of $(CH_3)_3CBr$ and 0.05 mole of $CH_3CH_2O^-\ Na^+$ are dissolved
in 250 ml of ethanol, to a first approximation how long will it take
before 10% of the $(CH_3)_3CBr$ has reacted?

(b) If the same quantities are dissolved in one liter of ethanol?

(c) If 0.05 mole of $(CH_3)_3CBr$ is dissolved in one liter of 0.2 $\underline{M}$
$CH_3CH_2O^-\ Na^+$ in ethanol?

S4. (a) When 0.05 mole of CH_3CH_2I and 0.05 mole of $CH_3CH_2O^-\ Na^+$ are dissolved
in 250 ml of ethanol solvent at 25 °C, it requires 65 minutes before 10%
of the starting material has reacted according to the following equation:

$$CH_3CH_2I + CH_3CH_2O^-\ Na^+ \longrightarrow CH_3CH_2OCH_2CH_3 + Na^+\ I^-$$

What is the approximate rate of the reaction under these conditions?

(b) If the same amounts of starting material are dissolved in 500 ml of the
solvent at 25 °C, 130 minutes are required before 10% reaction has
occurred. What is the rate of reaction this time?

(c) What is the form of the rate equation? Is it a first- or second-order
reaction?

(d) What is the rate constant?

S5. Construct a reaction profile diagram for the following reaction sequence:

(a)

$$A \underset{k_{-1}}{\overset{k_1}{\rightleftharpoons}} B \underset{k_{-2}}{\overset{k_2}{\rightleftharpoons}} C \underset{k_{-3}}{\overset{k_3}{\rightleftharpoons}} D$$

$$k_1 = 3 \times 10^{-3} \text{ sec}^{-1} \qquad k_2 = 10^{-1} \text{ sec}^{-1} \qquad k_3 = 6 \times 10^5 \text{ sec}^{-1}$$
$$k_{-1} = 4 \times 10^3 \text{ sec}^{-1} \qquad k_{-2} = 10^{-3} \text{ sec}^{-1} \qquad k_{-3} = 10^{-5} \text{ sec}^{-1}$$

(b) Which compound has the highest potential energy?

(c) Which compound reacts the fastest?

(d) What is the equilibrium constant $K = \dfrac{[D]}{[A]}$?

(e) What is the rate-limiting step in the conversion of A to D?

(f) Is the conversion of A to B endothermic or exothermic?

(g) What is the most exothermic step?

S6. For each of the following pairs, choose the compound with the higher pK_a.

(a) HCl , H_2S (b) H_2O , HF   (c) $HO-\overset{\overset{O^-}{|}}{\underset{\underset{OH}{|}}{P^+}}-OH$, $HO-\overset{\overset{O^-}{|}}{\underset{\underset{OH}{|}}{P^+}}-O^-$

(d) H_2O , NH_3 (e) H_3O^+ , H_2O (f) H_3O^+ , NH_4^+ (g) HOOH , H_2O

S7. (a) Why can there be no stronger base in water than hydroxide ion?

(b) What is the strongest acid possible in water?

S8. From the pK_a's given below, calculate the pH of a solution obtained when one mole of each substance is dissolved in one liter of water.

(a) $NH_4^+Cl^-$ $pK_a = 9.2$ (b) NH_3 (pK_a of $NH_4^+ = 9.2$)

S9. Consider the following reaction sequence:

$$A \underset{k_{-1}}{\overset{k_1}{\rightleftharpoons}} B , \quad \text{then} \quad B + C \underset{k_{-2}}{\overset{k_2}{\rightleftharpoons}} P$$

$$k_1 = 10^{-5} \text{ sec}^{-1} \qquad k_2 = 2 \times 10^{-2} \text{ M}^{-1} \text{ sec}^{-1}$$
$$k_{-1} = 10^{-3} \text{ sec}^{-1} \qquad k_{-2} = 10^{-8} \text{ sec}^{-1}$$

(a) Draw a reaction coordinate diagram for the overall process $A + C \rightleftharpoons P$.

(b) The rate equation for formation of P is: $\text{rate} = \dfrac{d[P]}{dt} = \dfrac{k_1 k_2 [A][C]}{k_{-1} + k_2 [C]}$ Under standard state conditions ([A] = [C] = 1 $\underline{M}$), $k_{-1} + k_2[C]$ is approx. equal to $k_2[C]$, and the expression reduces to: $\dfrac{d[P]}{dt} \cong \dfrac{k_1 k_2 [A][C]}{k_2 [C]} = k_1[A]$.

What is the rate-limiting step under these conditions?

(c) What is the approximate form of the rate equation if [A] = [C] = 0.001 $\underline{M}$? What is now the rate-limiting step? What does this suggest about the limitations of reaction coordinate diagrams?

S10.   Consider the following reaction sequence:

$$A \underset{k_{-1}}{\overset{k_1}{\rightleftharpoons}} B + C \ , \quad \text{then} \quad B + D \underset{k_{-2}}{\overset{k_2}{\rightleftharpoons}} P$$

$$k_1 = 2 \times 10^{-5} \ \text{sec}^{-1} \qquad\qquad k_2 = 3 \times 10^{-2} \ \underline{M}^{-1} \text{sec}^{-1}$$

$$k_{-1} = 10^{-2} \ \underline{M}^{-1} \text{sec}^{-1}. \qquad\qquad k_{-2} = 10^{-8} \ \text{sec}^{-1}$$

(a) Draw a reaction coordinate diagram for the overall process $A + D \rightleftharpoons C + P$

(b) The complete rate equation for this reaction is:

$$\text{rate} = \frac{d[P]}{dt}$$

If $[A] = [D] = 0.1 \ \underline{M}$ and $[C] = 0$ at the start of the reaction, what is the approximate form of the rate equation and what is the rate-determining step?

$$= \frac{k_1 k_2 [A][D]}{k_{-1}[C] + k_2[D]}$$

(c) What is the approximate form of the rate equation if $[C] = 2 \ \underline{M}$? What is now the rate-determining step?

4.G   Answers to Supplementary Problems

S1. (a) $\Delta G° = -RT \ln K$; $\Delta G°_{298} = -1.86$ kcal mole^{-1}

    (b)   To calculate $\Delta H°$ and $\Delta S°$, you need $\Delta G°$ at two different temperatures: $\Delta G° = \Delta H° - T\Delta S°$.   If $K = 0.213$ at 400° K, $\Delta G°_{400} = +1.23$ kcal mole^{-1}.

$$\Delta G°_{298} = \Delta H° - (298 \times \Delta S°) = -1.86$$
$$\Delta G°_{400} = \Delta H° - (400 \times \Delta S°) = +1.23$$

$$\Delta G°_{298} - \Delta G°_{400} = (-298 + 400)\Delta S° = -3.09 \text{ kcal mole}^{-1};$$
$$\Delta S° = -30.3 \text{ cal deg}^{-1} \text{ mole}^{-1} \text{ (e.u.)}$$

$$\Delta H° = \Delta G° + T\Delta S° = -10.9 \text{ kcal mole}^{-1}$$

    (c)   The equilibrium constant decreases at higher temperatures because the unfavorable entropy term ($T\Delta S°$) becomes more important. The entropy for this reaction is unfavorable (negative) because two molecules are combining to form one.

S2.   rate (moles liter^{-1} sec^{-1}) $\times$ time (sec) = amount (moles liter^{-1})

$$k[CH_3CH_2Br][CH_3CH_2O^-]t = [CH_3CH_2OCH_2CH_3]$$

(Note that this approximation is valid only for very short reaction times. As soon as $[CH_3CH_2Br]$ and $[CH_3CH_2O^-]$ change, the rate changes too.)

For 10% reaction, $[CH_3CH_2OCH_2CH_3] = 0.1 \times [CH_3CH_2Br]$

and the equation reduces to: $k[CH_3CH_2Br][CH_3CH_2O^-]t \cong 0.1 \times [CH_3CH_2Br]$

For 10% reaction, $t \cong \dfrac{0.1}{k[CH_3CH_2O^-]}$; $k = 7.6\times10^{-5}$ M^{-1} sec^{-1}

  (a) $[CH_3CH_2O^-] = \dfrac{0.05 \text{ mole}}{0.25 \text{ liter}} = 0.2$ M $\Rightarrow t = \dfrac{0.1}{7.6\times10^{-5}\times0.2} = 6580$ sec $= 1.83$ hr

  (b) $[CH_3CH_2O^-] = \dfrac{0.05 \text{ mole}}{1.0 \text{ liter}} = 0.05$ M $\Rightarrow t = \dfrac{0.1}{7.6\times10^{-5}\times0.05} = 26{,}300$ sec $= 7.31$ hr

  (c) $[CH_3CH_2O^-] = 0.2$ M $\Rightarrow t = 1.83$ hr   (as in part (a))

S3. $k'[(CH_3)_3CBr]t = [(CH_3)_3COCH_2CH_3]$

For 10% reaction, $[(CH_3)_3COCH_2CH_3] = 0.1 \times [(CH_3)_3CCBr]$

and the equation above reduces to: $k'[(CH_3)_3CBr]t \cong 0.1 \times [(CH_3)_3CBr]$

For 10% reaction, $t \cong \dfrac{0.1}{k'} = \dfrac{0.1}{5\times10^{-4} \text{ sec}^{-1}} = 200$ sec $= 3.3$ min

Because the rate of the reaction is *independent* of $[CH_3CH_2O^-]$ (a first-order reaction), the length of time for 10% reaction is the same for all three cases ((a), (b), and (c)). As far as each molecule of $(CH_3)_3CBr$ is concerned, the presence or absence of a nearby $CH_3CH_2O^-$ molecule is unimportant in determining how fast it is going to react.

S4.   (a)   10% reaction = $\dfrac{0.005 \text{ mole}}{0.25 \text{ liter}}$ = 0.02 $\underline{M}$ (change in [CH$_3$CH$_2$I])

rate = $\dfrac{0.02\,\underline{M}}{65}$ = 3.08×10^{-4} $\underline{M}$ min^{-1} (5.13×10^{-6} $\underline{M}$ sec^{-1})

(b)   10% reaction = $\dfrac{0.005 \text{ mole}}{0.5 \text{ liter}}$ = 0.01 $\underline{M}$ (change in [CH$_3$CH$_2$I])

rate = $\dfrac{0.01\,\underline{M}}{130}$ = 7.69×10^{-5} $\underline{M}$ min^{-1} (1.28×10^{-6} $\underline{M}$ sec^{-1})

(c) The two likely possibilities are:

rate = k [CH$_3$CH$_2$I][CH$_3$CH$_2$O$^-$]   <u>OR</u>   rate = k'[CH$_3$CH$_2$I]

Try the first-order equation: case (a) rate = 5.13×10^{-6} $\underline{M}$ sec^{-1} = k'[CH$_3$CH$_2$I]

so that k' = $\dfrac{5.13 \times 10^{-6}}{0.2}$ = 2.57×10^{-5} sec^{-1}

INCONSISTENT

case (b) rate = 1.28×10^{-6} $\underline{M}$ sec^{-1} = k'[CH$_3$CH$_2$I]

so that k' = $\dfrac{1.28 \times 10^{-6}}{0.1}$ = 1.28×10^{-5} sec^{-1}

Next, try the second-order equation:

case (a)   rate = 5.13×10^{-6} $\underline{M}$ sec^{-1} = k[CH$_3$CH$_2$I][CH$_3$CH$_2$O$^-$]

so that   k = $\dfrac{5.13 \times 10^{-6}}{0.2 \times 0.2}$ = 1.28×10^{-4} $\underline{M}^{-1}$ sec^{-1}

CONSISTENT

case (b)   rate = 1.28×10^{-6} $\underline{M}$ sec^{-1} = k [CH$_3$CH$_2$I][CH$_3$CH$_2$O$^-$]

so that   k = $\dfrac{1.28 \times 10^{-6}}{0.1 \times 0.1}$ = 1.28×10^{-4} $\underline{M}^{-1}$ sec^{-1}

Therefore, this is a second-order reaction, and the rate equation is:

rate = k [CH$_3$CH$_2$I][CH$_3$CH$_2$O$^-$]

(d) As calculated in (c),   k = 1.28×10^{-4} $\underline{M}^{-1}$ sec^{-1}

S5. (a)

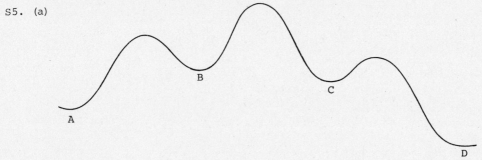

(b)   B

(c) C (to go to D), because it has the lowest activation energy and thus
the fastest rate constant of any of the reactions.

(d)   K = $\dfrac{[D]}{[A]}$ = $\dfrac{k_1 \times k_2 \times k_3}{k_{-1} \times k_{-2} \times k_{-3}}$ = 4.5×10^6

(e) B to C   (f) endothermic   (g) C to D

S6. (a) H_2S is less basic (= higher pK_a) because S lies to the left of Cl in the periodic table (it is less electronegative).

(b) H_2O (same reason as for (a))

(c) $H_2PO_4^-$, because one negative charge destabilizes a second.

(d) NH_3 (same reason as for (a))

(e) H_2O, because loss of a proton from a cationic molecule is easier than from a neutral one, other factors being equal.

(f) NH_4^+ (same reason as for (a))

(g) H_2O, because in HOOH, one oxygen acts as an electronegative substituent on the other.

S7.. (a) The equilibrium: $Base^- + H_2O \rightleftharpoons Base-H + OH^-$
will always take place. A base stronger than OH^- (pK_a of Base-H > 14) will simply react with water to give OH^-.

(b) For a similar reason, H_3O^+ is the strongest acid possible in water.

S8. (a)
$$\frac{[NH_3][H^+]}{[NH_4^+]} \cong \frac{[NH_3][H^+]}{1} = 10^{-9.2}$$

so that $[H^+] = \sqrt{10^{-9.2}} = 2.51 \times 10^{-5}$

and pH = 4.6

(compare with Exercise at the end of Section 4.5)

(b) $NH_3 + H_2O \rightleftharpoons NH_4^+ + OH^-$ $[NH_3] = 1 - [NH_4^+] = 1 - [OH^-]$

$$[NH_4^+] = \frac{10^{-14}}{[H^+]} \quad \text{so that} \quad \frac{[NH_3][H^+]}{[NH_4^+]} = \frac{\left(1 - \frac{10^{-14}}{[H^+]}\right)[H^+]}{\frac{10^{-14}}{[H^+]}}$$

$$10^{14} \times [H^+]^2 - [H^+] - K = 0$$

$$[H^+] = 2.5 \times 10^{-12} \quad \text{and pH = 11.6}$$

S9.   (a)

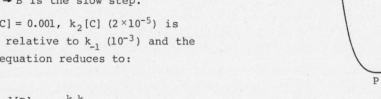

(b) Under standard state conditions, the conversion of A → B is the slow step.

(c) If [C] = 0.001, $k_2[C]$ (2×10^{-5}) is small relative to k_{-1} (10^{-3}) and the rate equation reduces to:

$$\frac{d[P]}{dt} = \frac{k_1 k_2}{k_{-1}}[A][C]$$

The reaction is now second-order and B + C → P is the rate-determining step. Notice how the rate-determining step can change with concentration. The reaction coordinate diagram does not provide a valid picture for concentrations other than standard state, unless all the transformations involved are first-order.

S10.   (a)

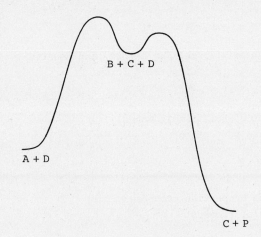

(b) $k_{-1}[C] = 0$ during the early part of the reaction, and

$$\frac{d[P]}{dt} = \frac{k_1 k_2 [A][D]}{k_2 [D]} = k_1 [A]$$

The first step is rate-limiting.

(c)   If $[C] = 2$, then $k_{-1}[C] + k[D] = (10^{-2} \times 2) + (3 \times 10^{-2}) \times 0.1$

$$= 2.3 \times 10^{-2} \cong k_{-1}[C]$$

so that $\dfrac{d[P]}{dt} = \dfrac{k_1 k_2 [A][D]}{k_{-1}[C]}$

The second step is now rate-determining.

5. ALKANES

5.C   Important Concepts and Hints

Chapter 5 presents the structural and physical properties of a specific class of organic compounds, the saturated hydrocarbons. Although there are only a few chemical reactions to be discussed for the alkanes (Chapter 6), carbon chains form the backbone of all other organic molecules, and it is therefore important to know what their shapes are, how their conformations differ in three dimensions, and how much more stable one isomer is compared to another. In this connection, the following terms are used over and over, and you should know what they mean: **anti** and **gauche**, **eclipsed** and **staggered**, **ring strain**, **chair conformation**, and **axial** and **equatorial**. Be sure you also understand the concept of **heat of formation** as an indication of relative thermodynamic stability.

By now you should be completely familiar with the relationship between free energy differences and relative amounts ($\Delta G^o = -\ RT \ln K$), and also quite convinced of the value of your molecular model kit.

HINTS: In problems which ask you to calculate energy differences (ΔH^o or ΔG^o), the best way to figure out what to subtract from what is:

(1) Write the equation for the reaction, with the products on the right;

(2) Write the thermodynamic value you are interested in comparing under the formula
     or name of each component, keeping the signs straight;

(3) ADD the values for the products and SUBTRACT the values for the starting materials,
     again paying attention to the signs.

As an example, calculate ΔH^O for the following reaction:

(1) $CH_2=CH_2$ + HBr CH_3CH_2Br

(2) ΔH^O_f =   12.5   -8.7   -15.2

(3) ΔH^O = +(-15.2) - (12.5-8.7) = -19 kcal mole^{-1}

This will give you the thermodynamic value for the overall transformation, with the correct sign
for the direction in which you have written the equation. If you write the reaction backward, you
change the sign of the value that you calculate.

If you like to remember things visually, the following scheme can also help you keep track of
when to add and when to subtract.

(1) Across the page, draw a line representing zero energy.

(2) To determine the energy content of the reactants, go **UP** for positive values
    and **DOWN** for negative values, moving sequentially. For instance,
    "$CH_2=CH_2$ (ΔH^O_f = +12.5) + HBr (ΔH^O_f = -8.7)" would result in:

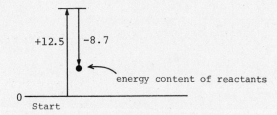

(3) Determine the energy content of the products the same way:

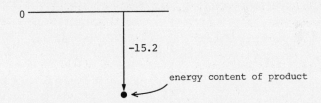

(4) Visually, then it is easy to see whether going from reactants to products is
    uphill (endothermic, $\Delta H^O > 0$) or downhill (exothermic, $\Delta H^O < 0$):

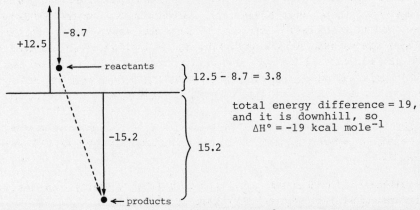

Also, remember that ΔH and ΔG are usually presented as "kcal mole^{-1}", whereas ΔS and the gas
constant R are given as "cal deg^{-1} mole^{-1}" (the same as an entropy unit, e.u.). A kcal is 1000
cal.

5.D   Answers to Exercises

5.1 The distance between eclipsed hydrogens in ethane is about 2.3 Å, as indicated by molecular models (trigonometry with r(C-H) = 1.10 Å, r(C-C) = 1.54 Å, and tetrahedral angles gives 2.27 Å). The distance between staggered hydrogens in ethane is about 2.5 Å. By contrast, in gauche-butane one pair of 1,4-hydrogens is only 2.0 Å apart. It is this close approach of these two hydrogens that probably accounts for most of the relative instability of the gauche conformation.

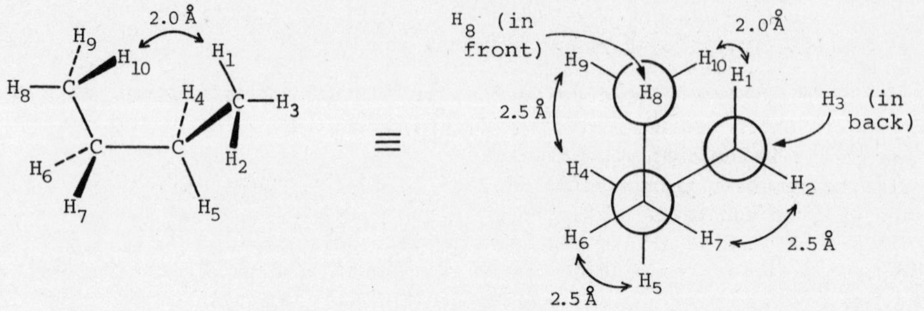

5.2

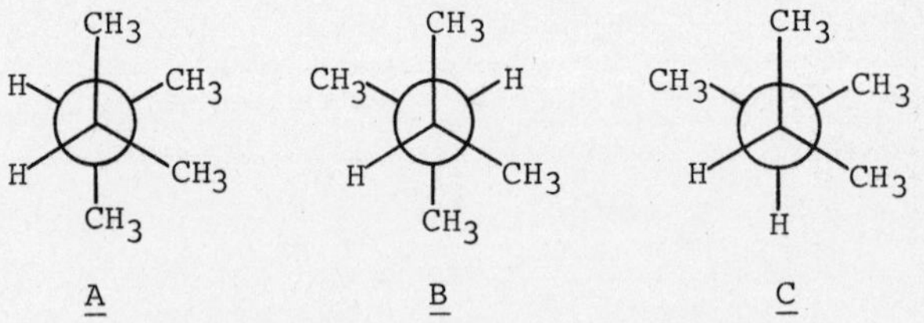

A and C are equivalent and have equal energy

5.3   2,3-Dimethylbutane: Conformation D, with two gauche interactions, is of lower energy than the other two minima, B and F, which have three gauche interactions each. Of the three energy maxima, C and E each have two CH_3-H interactions and one CH_3-CH_3 interaction. Eclipsed conformation A has two CH_3-CH_3 interactions and one H-H eclipsed interaction.

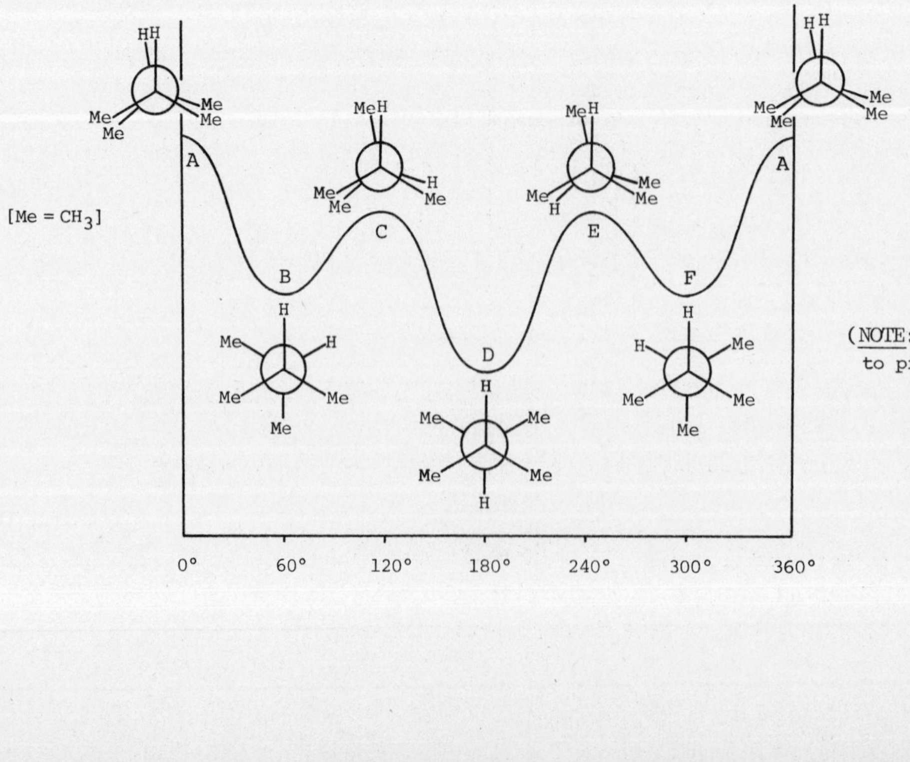

[Me = CH_3]

(NOTE: see answer to problem #5, too)

5.4

(a)

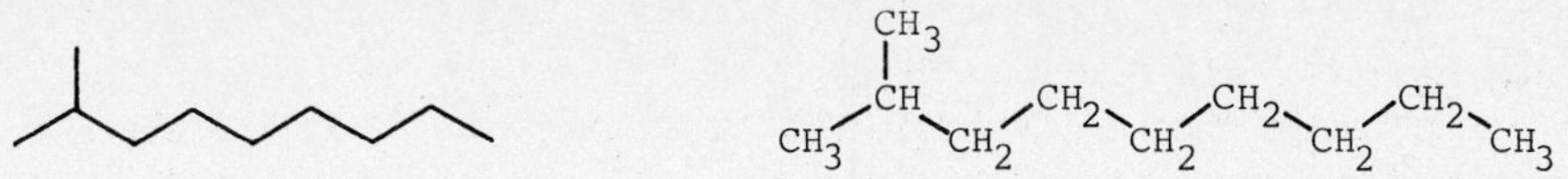

CH$_3$
|
CH
/ \
CH$_3$ CH$_2$—CH$_2$—CH$_2$—CH$_2$—CH$_2$—CH$_3$

(b)

CH$_3$
|
CH   CH$_2$—CH$_3$
/ \   /
CH$_3$ C
/ \
H$_3$C CH$_3$

(c)

CH$_3$
|
CH
/ \
CH$_3$—CH$_2$—CH   CH$_2$—CH$_2$—CH$_2$—CH$_3$
|
CH$_2$
|
CH$_3$

(d)

CH$_2$—CH$_3$ CH$_2$—CH$_2$—CH$_3$
\   /
CH$_3$—C
/ \
CH$_2$ CH$_3$
|
Cl

5.5

(a)

CH$_3$ CH$_3$
\   /
C
/   \
CH$_2$ CH$_2$
| |
CH$_2$ CH
\   /   \
CH$_2$ CH$_3$

(b)

CH$_2$—CH   CH$_2$—CH$_3$
/   \
CH$_3$ CH$_3$
|
CH
/ \
CH$_2$ CH$_2$
\   /
CH$_2$—CH$_2$

(c)

Cl
|
CH
/ \
CH$_2$ CH$_2$
| |
CH$_2$ CH$_2$
\   /
CH
|
CH$_2$—Cl

(d)

CH$_3$ CH$_3$
\   /
C—C
/   \
CH$_3$ CH$_2$ CH$_3$

5.6

Standard states
(graphite + H$_2$)

ΔH°_f -35.1   -36.9   -40.3   kcal mole^{-1}

n-pentane

$\Delta H^{\circ} = 1.8$

2-methylbutane

$\Delta H^{\circ} = 3.4$

2,2-dimethylpropane

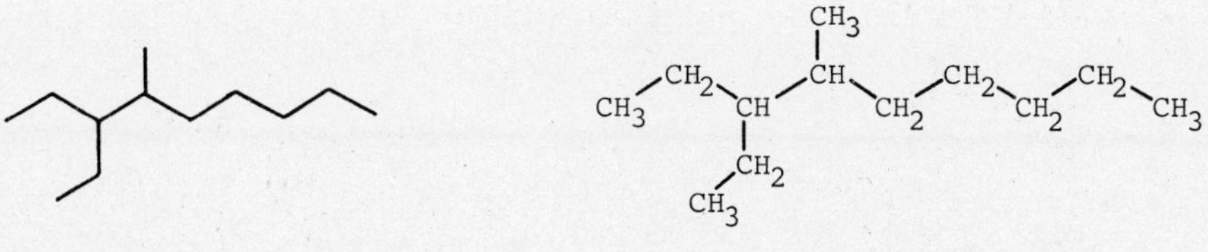

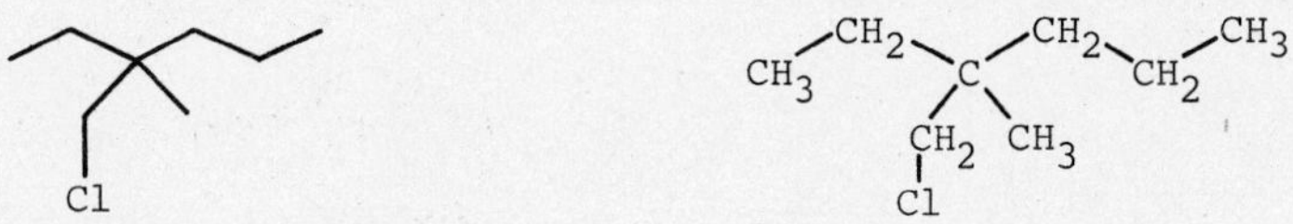

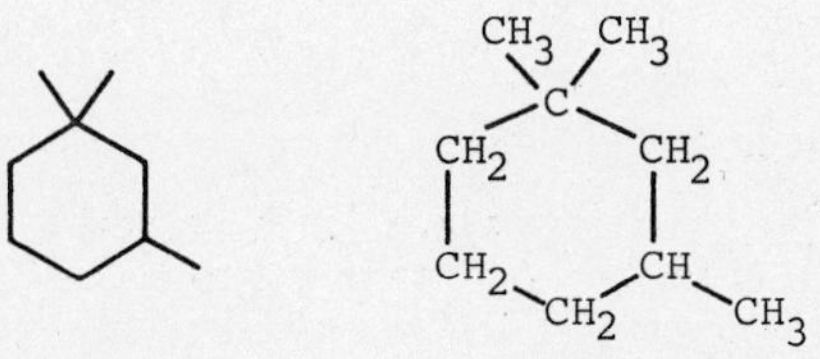

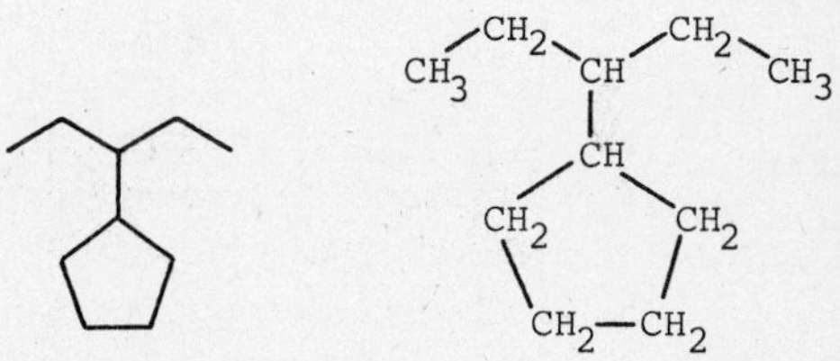

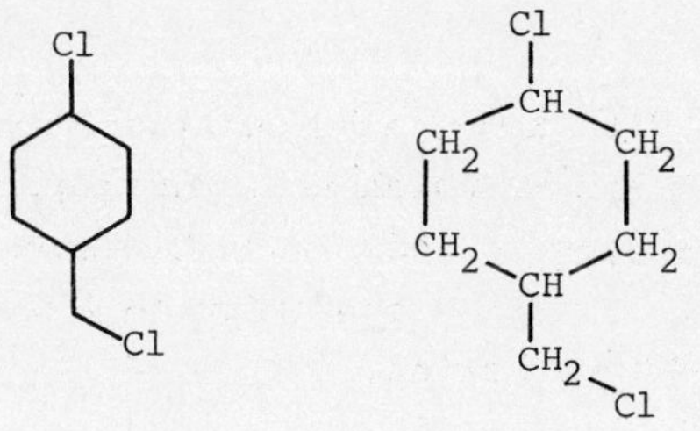

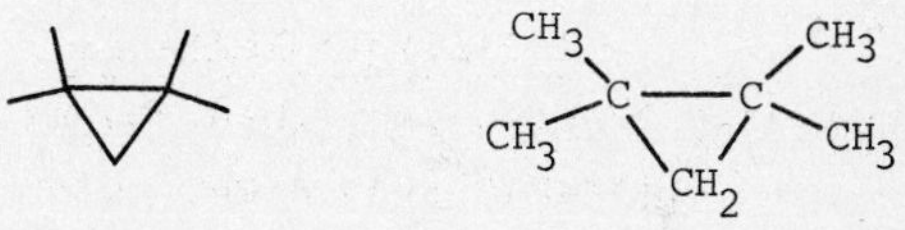

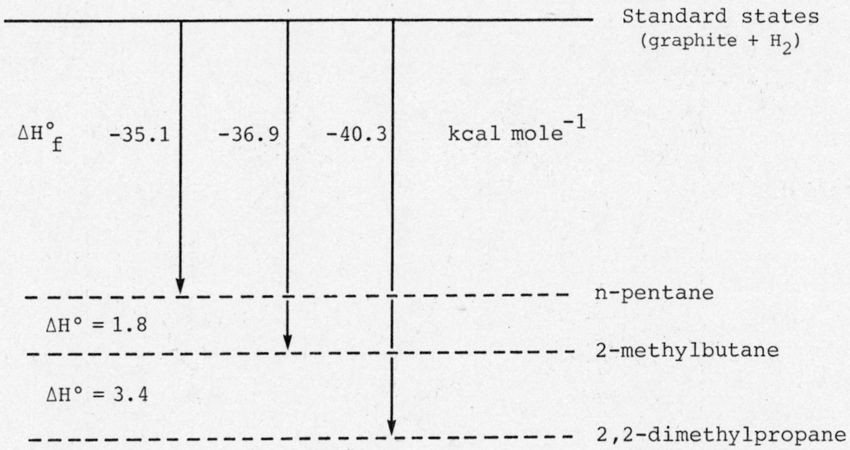

5.7 $(CH_3)_2CHCH_2CH_3 + H_2 \longrightarrow CH_3CH_3 + CH_3CH_2CH_3$

$\Delta H^{\circ}_f = $ -36.9   0   -20.2   -24.8

$\Delta H^{\circ} = -(-36.9 + 0) + (-20.2 - 24.8) = -8.1$ kcal mole^{-1}

5.8   Cyclohexane is strain-free, and its heat of formation per CH_2 group ($\Delta H^o{}_f/6 = -4.92$ kcal mole^{-1}) is taken as the standard. If cyclooctane were also strain-free, it would have $\Delta H^o{}_f = -4.92 \times 8 = -39.36$ kcal mole^{-1}. The actual $\Delta H^o{}_f$ of -29.7 kcal mole^{-1} indicates that the strain energy of cyclooctane is $-29.7 - (-39.4) = 9.7$ kcal mole^{-1}.

5.10   Although you may think that we're trying to teach you art in part (b), consider this point: many exam answers are marked wrong because the structures drawn are incomprehensible to the grader....

5.11

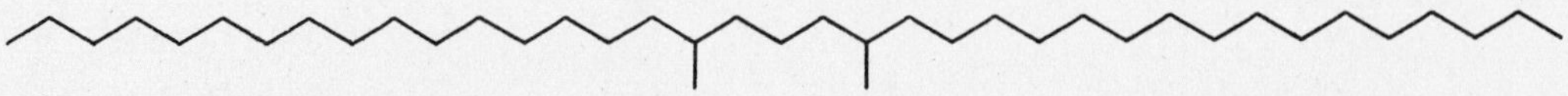

17,21-dimethylheptatriacontane

5.E   Answers and Explanations for Problems

1.   (a) 1-ethyl-1-methylcyclohexane
     (b) 1-isopropyl-3-methylcyclohexane   or
          1-methyl-3-(1-methylethyl)cyclohexane
     (c) t-butylcyclodecane   or   (1,1-dimethylethyl)cyclodecane
     (d) 1,1-dimethylcyclopropane
     (e) isobutylcyclopentane   or   (2-methylpropyl)cyclopentane
     (f) 1-cyclobutyl-3-methylpentane
     (g) 1-bromo-3-methylcyclohexane
     (h) 1-ethyl-2-iodocyclopentane

2.

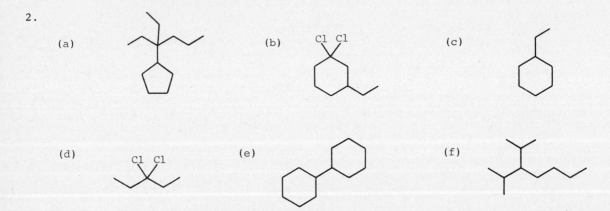

(a)   (b)   (c)

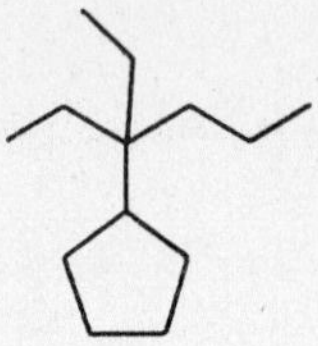

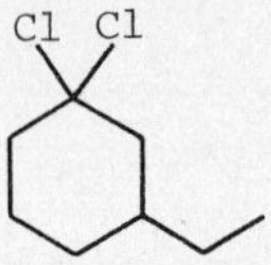

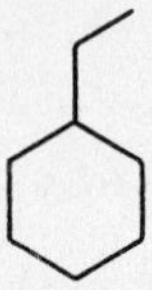

(d)   (e)   (f)

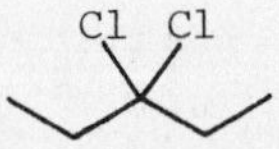

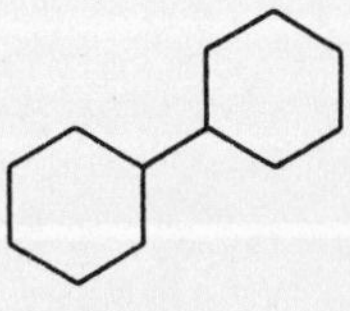

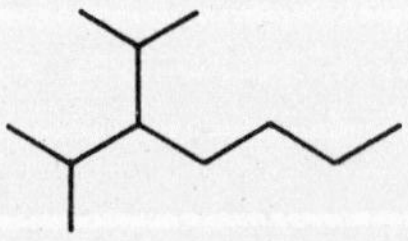

3.   The extra CH_2 group in heptane relative to hexane raises the b.p. by $98.4 - 68.7 = 30°$. To estimate the b.p.'s of the heptane isomers, add 30° to the most similar branched hexane:

Name	Line Structure	Estimated b.p.
heptane		(98.4 °C)
2-methylhexane		90
3-methylhexane		93

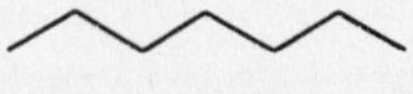

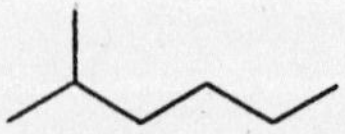

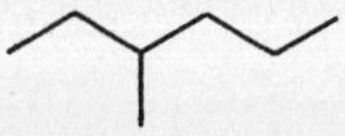

Name	Line Structure	Estimated b.p.
2,2-dimethylpentane		80
2,3-dimethylpentane		88
2,4-dimethylpentane		82

The structural difference between hexane and 2-methylpentane (-8.4 °C in b.p.) is the same as that between 2-methylhexane and 2,4-dimethylpentane. This explains the estimate of 90 - 8 = 82 °C for the b.p. of the latter compound.

3,3-dimethylpentane		80
3-ethylpentane		90
2,2,3-trimethylbutane		80

The b.p. for 2,2,3-trimethylbutane was estimated by adding a methyl to 2,2-dimethylbutane rather than 2,3-dimethylbutane.

4. C_2-C_3 anti C_2-C_3 gauche

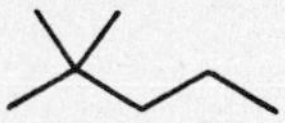

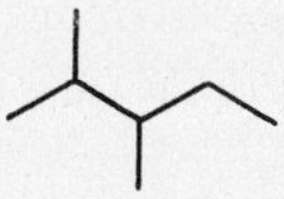

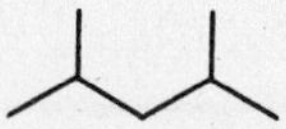

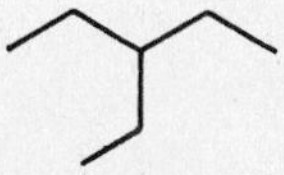

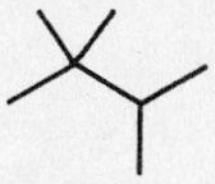

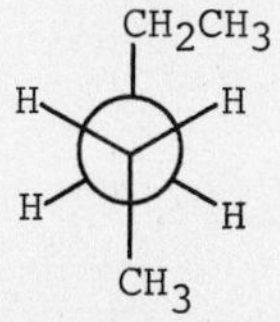

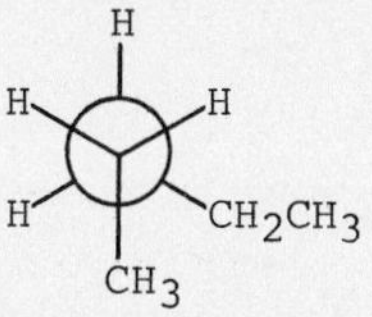

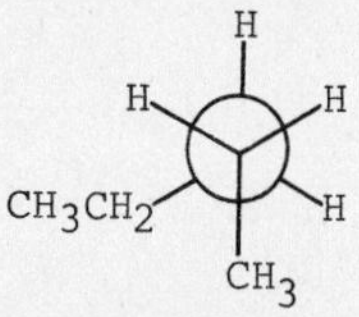

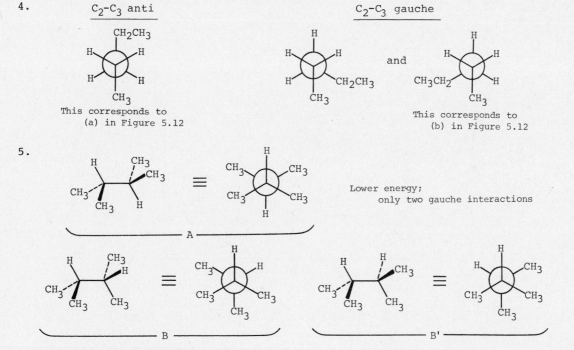

This corresponds to   This corresponds to
(a) in Figure 5.12   (b) in Figure 5.12

5.

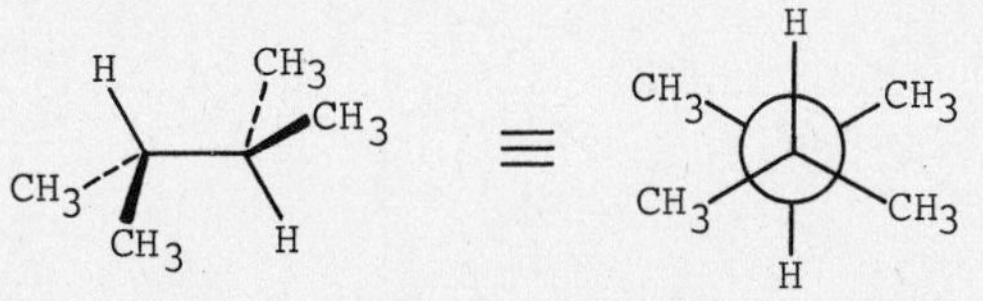

Lower energy;
only two gauche interactions

Both B and B' have three gauche interactions, and so are expected to be 0.9 kcal mole^{-1} less stable than A.

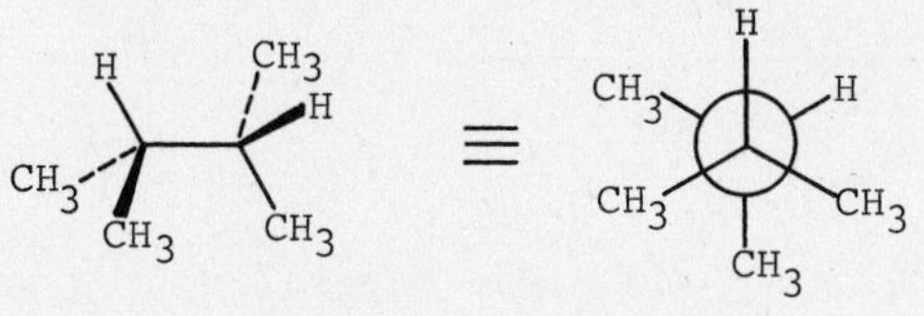

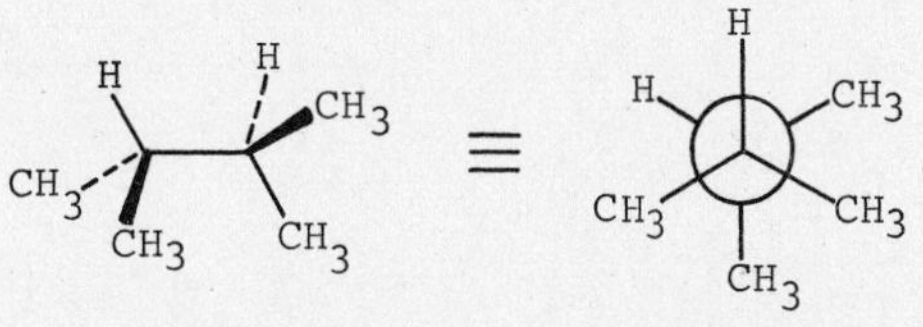

$$K = \frac{[A]}{[B]} = \frac{[A]}{[B']} \qquad \text{and} \qquad \Delta G^\circ = -RT \ln K$$

$$-0.9 \, \text{kcal mole}^{-1} = -1.987 \, \text{cal deg}^{-1} \text{mole}^{-1} \times 298 \, \text{deg} \times \ln K$$

Based on this prediction, the mixture would consist of 4.5 parts A / 1 part B / 1 part B'
= 69% A, 31% B + B'

The situation is actually more complicated than this:
The geminal methyls undergo steric hindrance as well, and the
angle between them is more than 109°. This leads to greater interaction between the vicinal methyls in the anti conformation than
predicted above, and a much smaller difference in energy between
the two staggered conformations of 2,3-dimethylbutane.

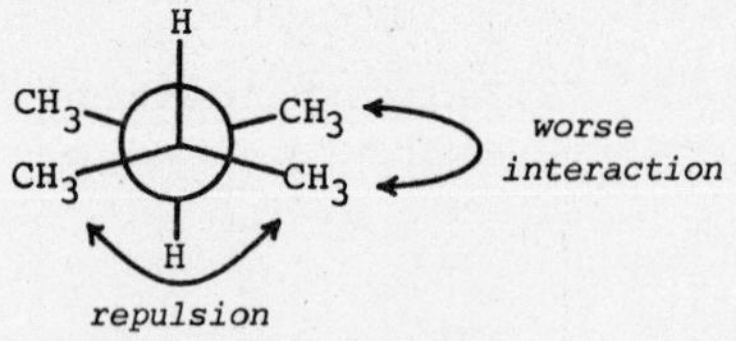

6. Adamantane is $C_{10}H_{16}$ (mw = 136) and is very symmetrical -- almost spherical.
    For comparison, 2,2,3,3-tetramethylbutane (C_8H_{18}; mw = 114) has bp 106 °C and
    mp 100 °C. Adamantane would be expected to have a similar bp (it is even
    more symmetrical than tetramethylbutane, but a little larger). The symme-
    trical structure would suggest a high mp. In fact, adamantane melts at 270
    °C (in a sealed tube). At atmospheric pressure, adamantane sublimes instead
    of melting; that is, it goes directly from the solid to the vapor state.

7.

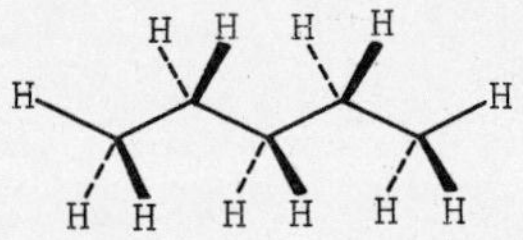

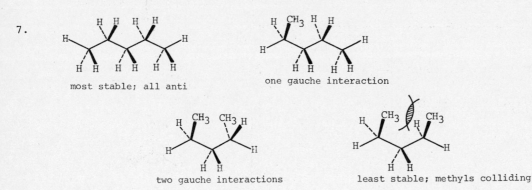

8. 2-Methylbutane:

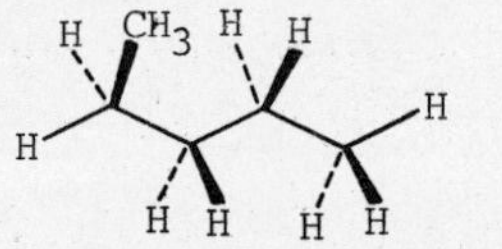

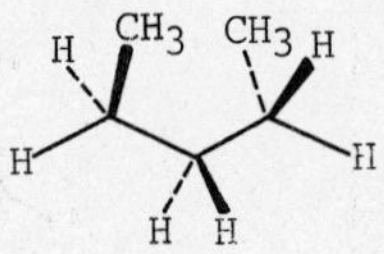

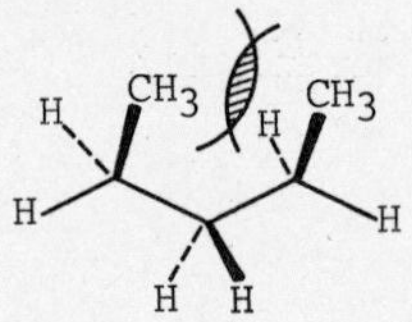

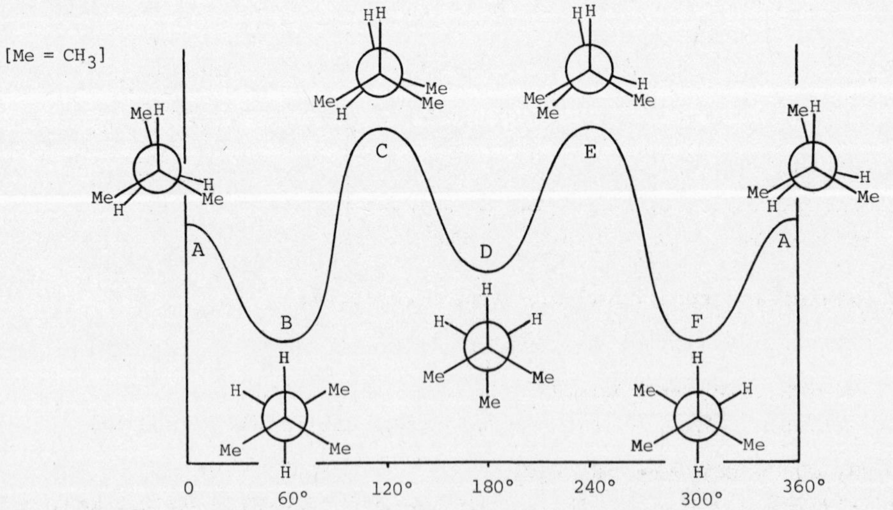

The three energy minima are B, D, and F. Conformations B and F are equivalent
and equal in energy; they both have one gauche interaction. Conformation D,
with two gauche interactions, is less stable. In rotating about the C_2-C_3
bond from B to F, the molecule passes through an eclipsed conformation (energy

maximum) in which there are three CH_3-H interactions. In passing from B to D and also from D back to F, the molecule passes through another type of eclipsed conformation. In these conformations (C and E), there is one CH_3-CH_3 interaction, one CH_3-H interaction, and one H-H interaction. Conformations C and E are equivalent and are of higher energy than conformation A.

2,2-Dimethylbutane:

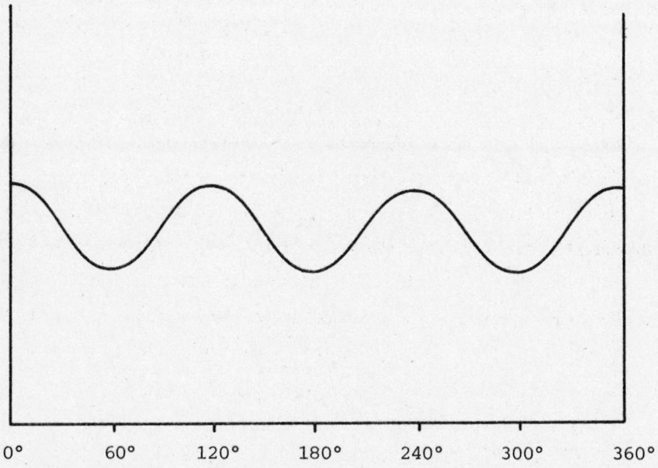

Maxima:

Minima:

All minima are equal, and all maxima are equal.

2,2,3,3-Tetramethylbutane:

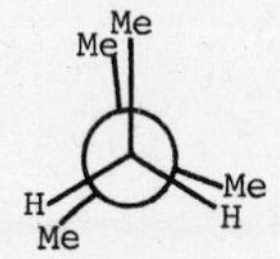

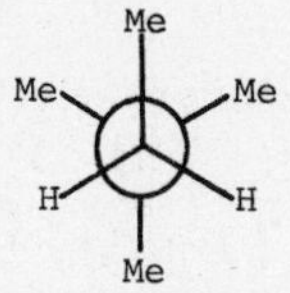

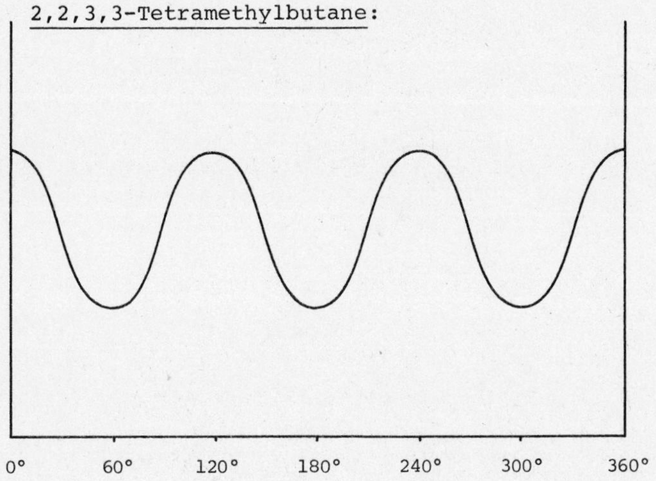

Maxima:

Minima:

All minima are equal, and all maxima are equal.

9. (a) $CH_2=CH_2$ + H_2 $\longrightarrow$ CH_3CH_3

ΔH°_f =   +12.5   (0)   -20.2 ΔH° = -20.2 - 12.5 = -32.7 kcal mole^{-1}

(b) $CH_2=CH_2$ + HCl $\longrightarrow$ CH_3CH_2Cl

ΔH°_f =   +12.5   -22.1   -26.1 ΔH° = -26.1 - (12.5 - 22.1) = -16.5 kcal mole^{-1}

(c) $CH_2=CH_2$ + H_2O $\longrightarrow$ CH_3CH_2OH

ΔH°_f =   +12.5   -57.8   -56.2 ΔH° = -56.2 - (12.5 - 57.8) = -10.9 kcal mole^{-1}

These calculations indicate that the enthalpy term (ΔH°) of the free energy change ΔG° is favorable (negative), but without knowing the entropy term (ΔS°)

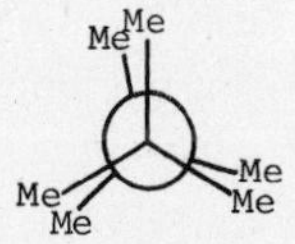

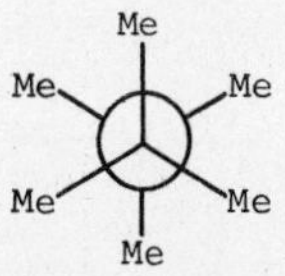

you can't say very much about the equilibrium constant. See, for example, Supplementary Problem #S1 in Chapter 4, which is concerned with the change in the position of equilibrium (c) above with temperature. However, you could predict that the entropy change for each of these reactions would be about the same (two molecules ⟶ one molecule), and because of the enthalpy differences between (a), (b), and (c), the equilibrium constant for reaction (a) would be greater than that for (b), and (b) greater than (c).

The enthalpy change of the overall reaction bears no particular relationship to the energy of activation, which is what governs the **rate** of reaction.

10.

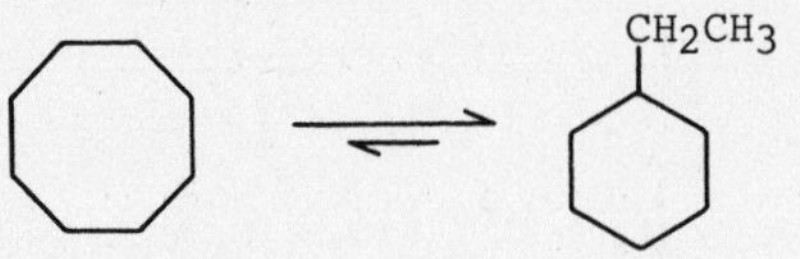

$$K = \frac{[\text{ethylcyclohexane}]}{[\text{cyclooctane}]}$$

$\Delta H^\circ_f =$ −29.7   −41.0 $\Delta H^\circ = -11.3 \text{ kcal mole}^{-1}$

If $\Delta H^\circ = \Delta G^\circ = -RT \ln K$,   then $K = 1.9 \times 10^8$

The fact that the equilibrium is even more in favor of ethylcyclohexane results from the favorable contribution from entropy to the free energy of this isomerization ($\Delta G^\circ = \Delta H^\circ - T\Delta S^\circ$). There is more freedom of motion in ethylcyclohexane than in cyclooctane (the ethyl group can spin relative to the cyclohexane ring, for instance); this results in a positive ΔS° and therefore a negative contribution to ΔG°.

11.

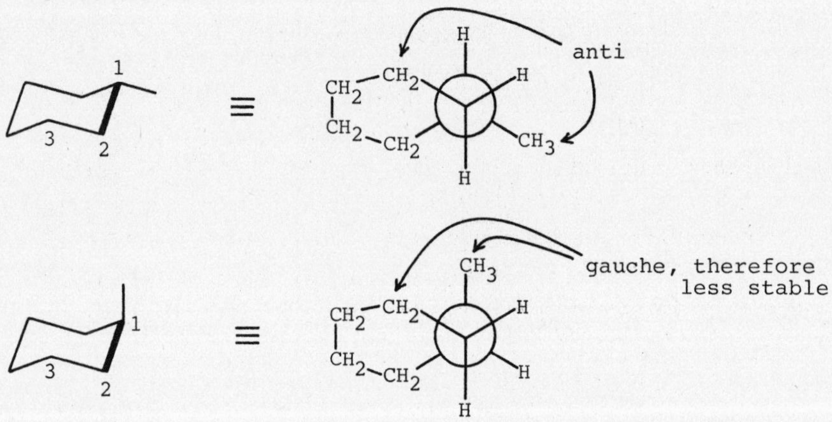

12. $\Delta G^\circ = \Delta H^\circ - T\Delta S^\circ$

$-0.89 = -2.05 - (298 \times \Delta S^\circ)$, so that $\Delta S^\circ = -3.89 \text{ cal deg}^{-1} \text{mole}^{-1}$

A negative entropy change indicates more "restriction of freedom". In this instance, it arises because there are fewer different conformations possible for isobutane than for butane.

$\Delta G^\circ = -RT \ln K = -0.89 \text{ kcal mole}^{-1}$; therefore $K = 4.5$

13.   pentane $\rightleftharpoons$ isopentane
$\Delta G^\circ = -1.54 \text{ kcal mole}^{-1}$ and $K_1 = \dfrac{[\text{isopentane}]}{[\text{pentane}]} = 13.5$

isopentane $\rightleftharpoons$ neopentane
$\Delta G^\circ = -0.10 \text{ kcal mole}^{-1}$ and $K_2 = \dfrac{[\text{neopentane}]}{[\text{isopentane}]} = 1.2$

Ratio of pentane/isopentane/neopentane = $1 : 13.5 : (13.5 \times 1.2)$, which is equivalent to 3%/44%/53%.

14.   Compare: ethane   propane   butane   pentane
$\Delta H^\circ_f =$ −20.2   −24.8   −30.4   −35.1
difference: −4.6   −5.6   −4.7

average = −5.0 kcal mole⁻¹ per −CH₂− group

ethane: two CH$_3$- ; ΔH°_f = -20.2, which is equivalent to -10.1 per CH$_3$-

propane: two CH$_3$- + one -CH$_2$-
                              (-5.0) ΔH°_f = -24.8 $\Longrightarrow$ -9.9 per CH$_3$-

butane: two CH$_3$- + two -CH$_2$-
                             (-10.0) ΔH°_f = -30.4 $\Longrightarrow$ -10.2 per CH$_3$-

pentane: two CH$_3$- + three -CH$_2$-
                               (-15.0) ΔH°_f = -35.1 $\Longrightarrow$ -10.1 per CH$_3$-

average = -10.1 kcal mole^{-1} per CH$_3$- group

isobutane: three CH$_3$- + one -CH-
                   (-30.3) ΔH°_f = -32.4 $\Longrightarrow$ -2.1 per -CH-

isopentane: three CH$_3$- + one -CH$_2$- + one -CH-
               (-30.3)   (-5.0) ΔH°_f = -36.9 $\Longrightarrow$ -1.6 per -CH-

average = -1.9 kcal mole^{-1} per -CH-

neopentane: four CH$_3$- + one -C-
                (-40.4) ΔH°_f = -40.3 $\Longrightarrow$ +0.1 per -C-

ΔH°_f (kcal mole^{-1})

PREDICTIONS

	Estimated	Found
hexane: two CH$_3$- + four -CH$_2$- (-20.2) (-20.0)	-40.2	-39.9
2-methylpentane: three CH$_3$- + two -CH$_2$- + one -CH-	-42.2	-41.8
3-methylpentane: (-30.3) (-10.0) (-1.9)		-41.1
2,2-dimethylbutane: four CH$_3$- + one -CH$_2$- + one -C- (-40.4) (-5.0) (+0.1)	-45.3	-44.3
2,3-dimethylbutane: four CH$_3$- + two -CH- (-40.4) (-3.8)	-44.2	-42.6
nonane: two CH$_3$- + seven -CH$_2$- (-20.2) (-35.0)	-55.2	-54.7
2,2,4,4-tetramethylpentane: six CH$_3$- + one -CH$_2$- + two -C- (-60.6) (-5.0) (+0.2)	-65.4	-57.8

The steric strain of makes it difficult to put the molecule together; i.e., less energy than estimated is released on forming this compound from its elements.

NOTE: from a more extensive comparison of hydrocarbon heats of formation, the ΔH°_f incremental values below have been calculated:

CH$_3$-   -10.12 kcal mole^{-1}
-CH$_2$-   -4.93
-CH-   -1.09
-C-   +0.80

15. Boiling points and melting points have nothing to do with relative thermodynamic stability. M.p. and b.p. are only indications of the stability of the solid vs. liquid vs. gaseous states of a molecule, whereas thermodynamic stability is in relation to possible reactions or decompositions. For example, hexahydro-1,3,5-trinitro-1,3,5-triazine (cyclonite or RDX) is a high-melting solid (m.p. 204 $^\circ$C) which on decomposition releases over 300 kcal mole^{-1}. (This substance is used as a high explosive.)

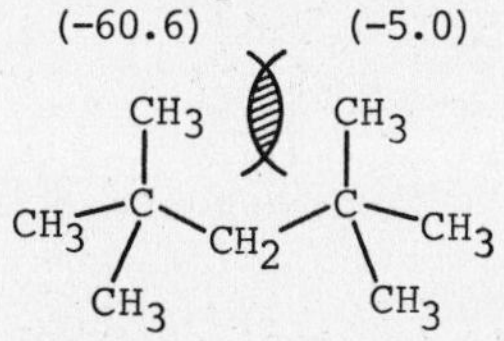

5.F Supplementary Problems

S1. Write the structures for all of the isomers of C_5H_{10} which have only C-C single bonds, and provide IUPAC names for each structure.

S2. Write line structures for each of the following compounds:

(a) 1-ethyl-2-propylcyclopentane
(b) 1,1,4-tribromocyclohexane
(c) 3-chloro-1,1-dicyclopropylcycloheptane
(d) 1-(3-chloropropyl)-4-t-butylcyclohexane
(e) cyclotetradecane

S3. Using the heats of formation given in Appendix I, calculate or estimate ΔH° for the following reactions:

(a)  + H_2 ⟶ $CH_3CH_2CH_3$

(b)  + H_2 ⟶ $CH_3CH_2CH_2CH_3$

(c) 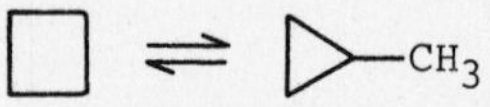

(estimate)

(d) CH_3CH_3 + HCl ⟶ CH_4 + CH_3Cl

(e)  + HCl ⟶ $CH_3CH_2CH_2Cl$

(f) 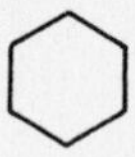 + HCl ⟶ $CH_3(CH_2)_4CH_2Cl$ *(estimate)*

S4. From the data provided in Appendix I, calculate ΔH° for the following isomerizations:

$CH_3CH_2CH_2CH_2CH_3$ ⇌ $CH_3CH_2CH(CH_3)_2$

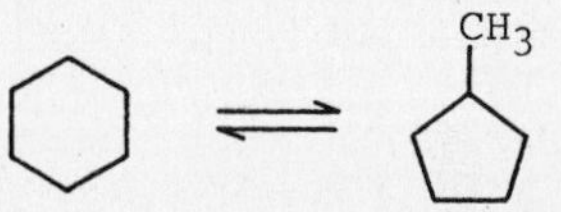

How do you account for the fact that increased branching is favorable in one case and not the other?

S5. Make a model of t-butylcyclobutane. Which conformation do you expect would be the most stable? Do the same for t-butylcyclopentane.

S6. Which of the following pairs represent structural isomers? Which are conformational isomers? Which are not isomers at all?

(a) 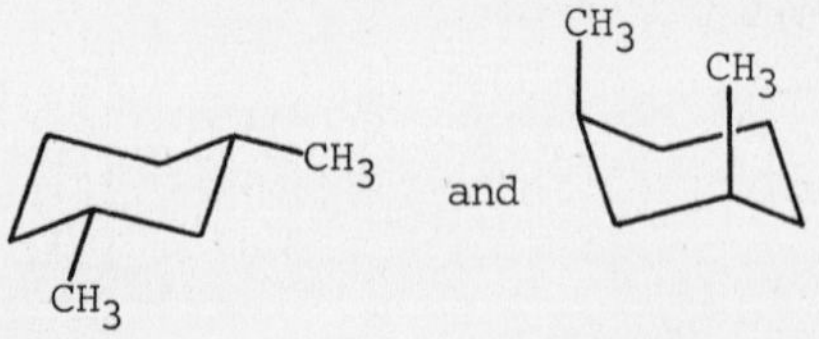

(b) 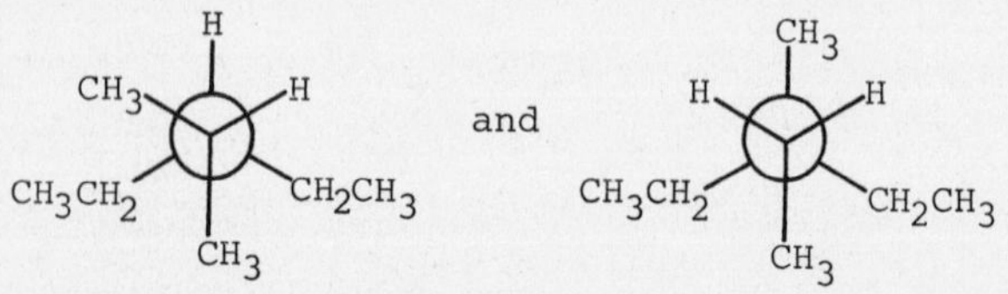

(c) 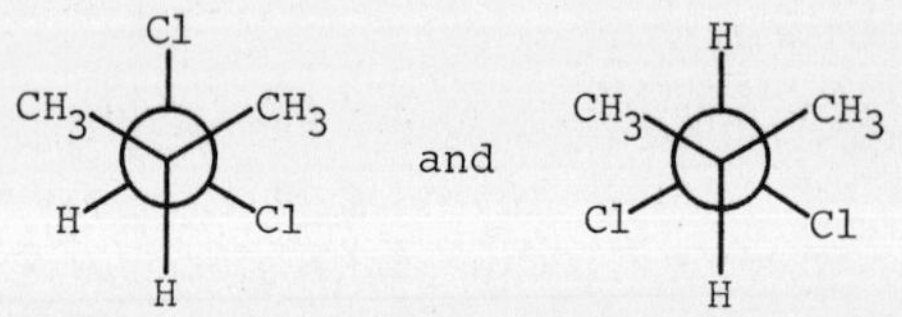

(d) 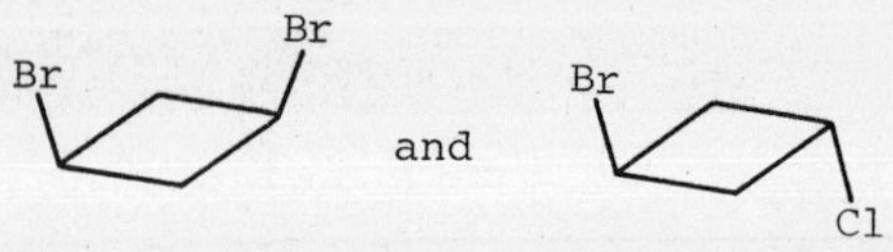

(e)

and

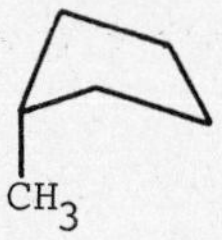

(f)

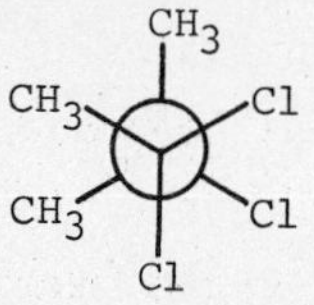

and

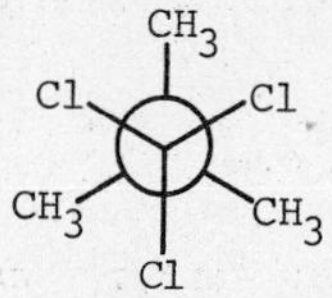

5.G   Answers to Supplementary Problems

S1.

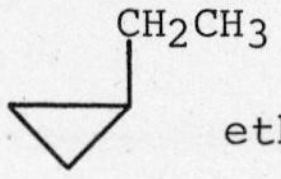

ethylcyclopropane

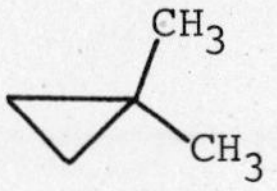

1,1-dimethyl-cyclopropane

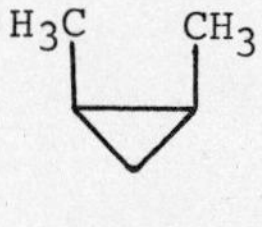

cis-1,2-dimethyl-cyclopropane

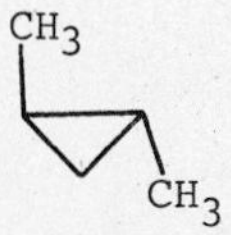

trans-1,2-dimethyl-cyclopropane

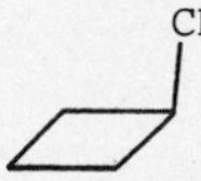

methylcyclobutane

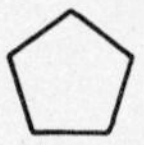

cyclopentane

S2.   (a)

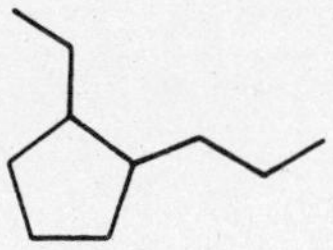

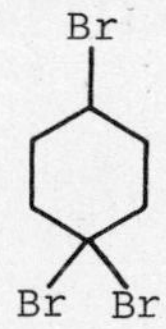

(c)

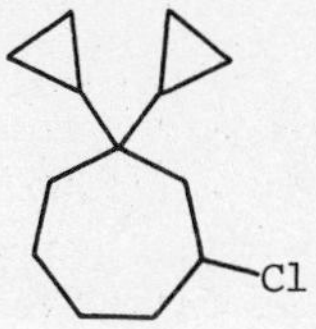

(d)

(b)

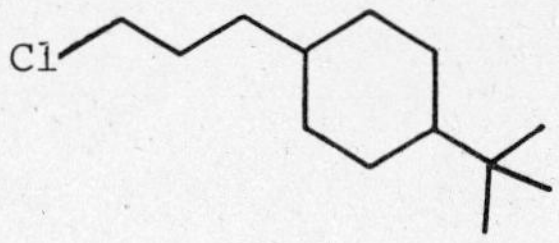

(e)

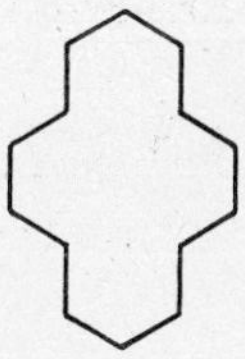

S3. ΔH°_f (products) $-$ ΔH°_f (starting materials) = ΔH° of the reaction

$\underline{NOTE}$: ΔH°_f for H_2 = 0

(a) $-24.8 - 12.7 = -37.5$ kcal mole^{-1}

(b) $-30.4 - 6.8 = -37.2$ kcal mole^{-1}

(c)   To calculate the change in ΔH°_f caused by the addition of a methyl group:

ΔH°_f(isobutane) $- \Delta H^{\circ}_f$(propane) = -7.6 kcal mole^{-1}

ΔH°_f(methylcyclopentane) $- \Delta H^{\circ}_f$ (cyclopentane) = -6.9 kcal mole^{-1} } Average is -7.3

ΔH°_f(methylcyclohexane) $- \Delta H^{\circ}_f$ (cyclohexane) = -7.5 kcal mole^{-1}

Using this calculated average, the estimated ΔH°_f(methylcyclopropane) is $12.7 - 7.3 = 5.4$ kcal mole^{-1}, and ΔH° for the conversion cyclobutane $\longrightarrow$ methylcyclopropane is $5.4 - 6.8 = -1.4$ kcal mole^{-1}.

(d) $-17.9 - 20.6 - (-20.2) - (-22.1) = +3.8$ kcal mole^{-1} (an endothermic reaction)

(e) $-31.0 - 12.7 - (-22.1) = -21.6$ kcal mole^{-1}

(f)   Estimate that ΔH°_f (CH$_3$(CH$_2$)$_4$CH$_2$Cl) is approx. ΔH°_f(CH$_3$CH$_2$CH$_2$Cl) + 3 ΔH°_f(-CH$_2$-):

= -46.0 kcal mole^{-1} (see problem #16 in this Chapter)

ΔH° for the reaction = $-46.0 - (-29.5) - (-22.1) = +5.6$ kcal mole^{-1}

S4.   pentane   2-methylbutane
           $\Delta H° = -36.9 - (-35.1) = -1.8$ kcal mole^{-1}

           cyclohexane   methylcyclopentane
           $\Delta H° = -25.3 - (-29.5) = +4.2$ kcal mole^{-1}

There is some strain in cyclopentane (6 kcal mole^{-1}, in fact), and none in cyclohexane, and this overcomes the small difference in $\Delta H°_f$ which is attributed to branching.

S5.

        "equatorial" better than "axial"   when t-butyl is attached to the "flap"
                                                            of the "envelope", it is in the least
                                                            crowded position

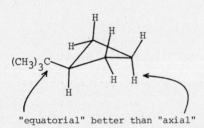

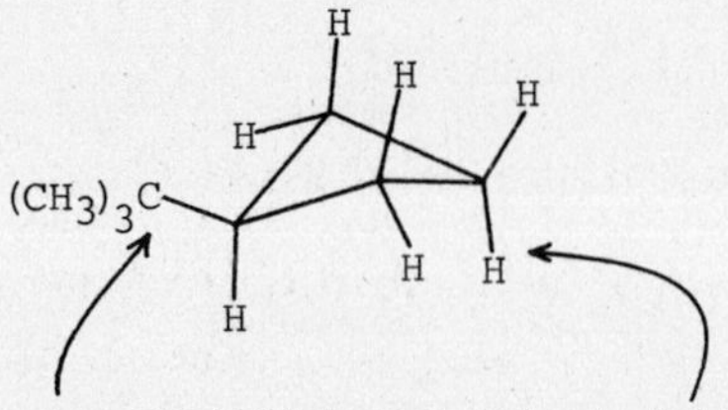

S6.   Structural isomers: (b), (f)
       Conformational isomers: (a), (c), (e)
       Not isomers: (d)

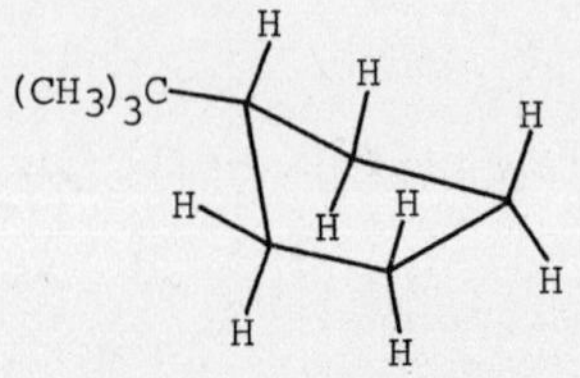

6. REACTIONS OF ALKANES

6.A   Chapter Outline and Important Terms Introduced

6.1   Bond Dissociation Energies (what it takes to break a bond)

vibrational energy levels   free radicals

zero point energy   stability of radicals: tertiary >
                                                  secondary > primary > methyl

6.2   Pyrolysis of Alkanes: Cracking (reactions of alkanes at high temperatures)
disproportionation:

$$CH_3CH_2CH_2CH_2CH_3 \xrightarrow{\Delta} CH_3CH_3 + CH_2{=}CHCH_3$$

6.3   Halogenation of Alkanes (the first thorough analysis of a reaction mechanism)
   Chlorination

$$RH + Cl_2 \longrightarrow RCl + HCl \quad \text{(can use } SO_2Cl_2, \text{ too)}$$

   homolysis vs. heterolysis   principle of microscopic reversibility

   chain reaction   relative reactivity

   initiation, propagation,   statistical factor
     and termination steps

Halogenation with Other Halogens
   selectivity of bromination

6.4   Combustion of Alkanes (how to **determine** relative stabilities)
heat of combustion
alkylperoxy radical

6.5   Average Bond Energies (to generalize between compounds)
heat of atomization

6.B   Important Reactions Introduced

NOTE: Starting with this chapter of the Study Guide, we will present an outline of the
           important reactions introduced in each chapter in the text, indicating some of the
           key aspects that you should remember.

Free radical halogenation (6.3)

Equation: $R_3C{-}H + X_2 \longrightarrow R_3C{-}X + HX$

Generality: R = alkyl or H
                 X = F (seldom used)
                     Cl (poor selectivity)
                     Br (very selective for tertiary C–H)

Key features: $3^\circ > 2^\circ > 1^\circ$ C–H bond selectivity
                 (Cl: 5:4:1; Br: $3^\circ \ggg 2^\circ \gg 1^\circ$)
                 Useful reaction for functionalizing alkanes

6.C   Important Concepts

   In Chapter 6 you are introduced for the first time to a detailed description of a reaction:
free-radical halogenation. Although many industrial processes and other important reactions
involve free-radical chemistry, such reactions usually receive less attention in introductory
organic courses than do reactions which proceed by ionic mechanisms (involving charged intermediates).
Nevertheless, free-radical halogenation provides you with the opportunity to analyze closely the
various aspects of chemical reactivity.

   Many students approach each new reaction as another group of facts to be memorized. As we
said in the introduction, memory is important, but it is not enough by itself. You should approach

each new reaction with a series of questions, such as: "What sort of functional group transformation does it accomplish? What is the mechanism? What is the generality of the reaction? What are the stereochemical features to keep in mind? What limitations does it have?" These are general questions which will help you to understand the chemistry involved and fit the reaction into your chemical knowledge. Only after you have asked these questions should you ask: "What is unusual or unique about the reaction?" During the process of answering the first questions, you will probably have found the answer to the last one.

One of the essential facts to keep in mind is that all of organic chemistry makes logical sense. For free-radical halogenation, the details of each step are discussed thoroughly, and it is pointed out how the mechanism makes sense in light of the basic principles discussed in previous chapters. Many of the subsequent reactions presented in the text will be discussed in as much detail as this one, many more in less detail, but they are all sensible. Don't pretend that organic reactions are magic; ask yourself questions about the reactions you see, and if you can't make sense of them, ask your teachers.

6.D Answers to Exercises

6.1 $CH_4 \longrightarrow CH_3\cdot + H\cdot$ ΔH^O (kcal mole^{-1})

$\Delta H^O{}_f = $ −17.9   +35   +52 $35 + 52 - (-17.9) = 105$

> *Note*: be aware of significant figures. A sum cannot be more accurate than the least accurate of the numbers that go into it. $\Delta H^\circ{}_f$ for the radicals are known less precisely than for methane. The overall enthalpy change cannot be determined more precisely than $\Delta H^\circ{}_f$ for the radicals: $35 + 52 - (-17.9) = 104.9$ is therefore not a correct answer.

$CH_3CH_3 \longrightarrow 2\ \cdot CH_3$

$\Delta H^O{}_f = $ −20.2   2 x 35   90

$CH_3CH_3 \longrightarrow CH_3CH_2\cdot + H\cdot$

−20.2   26   52   98

$CH_3CH_2CH_3 \longrightarrow (CH_3)_2CH\cdot + H\cdot$

−24.8   18   52   95

$(CH_3)_3CH \longrightarrow (CH_3)_3C\cdot + H\cdot$

−32.4   9   52   93

$(CH_3)_4C \longrightarrow (CH_3)_3C\cdot + \cdot CH_3$

−40.3   9   35   84

$(CH_3)_3CH \longrightarrow (CH_3)_2CHCH_2\cdot + H\cdot$

−32.4   14   52   98

6.2

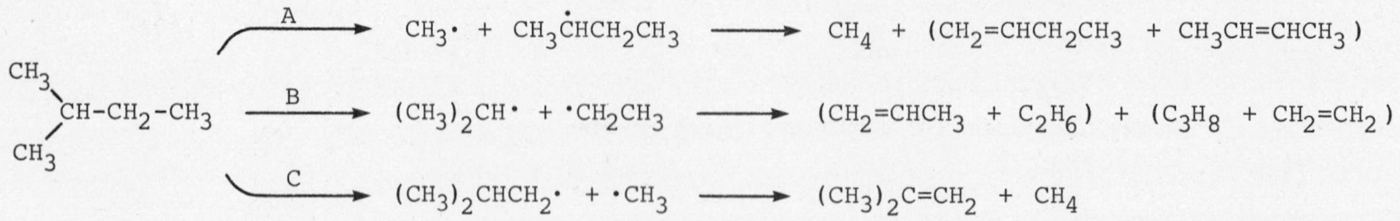

$$\begin{array}{l}
\xrightarrow{\ A\ } CH_3\cdot + CH_3\dot{C}HCH_2CH_3 \longrightarrow CH_4 + (CH_2{=}CHCH_2CH_3 + CH_3CH{=}CHCH_3) \\[4pt]
\underset{CH_3}{\overset{CH_3}{>}}CH{-}CH_2{-}CH_3 \xrightarrow{\ B\ } (CH_3)_2CH\cdot + \cdot CH_2CH_3 \longrightarrow (CH_2{=}CHCH_3 + C_2H_6) + (C_3H_8 + CH_2{=}CH_2) \\[4pt]
\xrightarrow{\ C\ } (CH_3)_2CHCH_2\cdot + \cdot CH_3 \longrightarrow (CH_3)_2C{=}CH_2 + CH_4
\end{array}$$

Path A: ΔH^O (kcal mole^{-1})

$(CH_3)_2CHCH_2CH_3 \longrightarrow CH_3\cdot + CH_3\dot{C}HCH_2CH_3$

$\Delta H^O{}_f = $ −36.9   +35   +13   85

Path B:

$(CH_3)_2CHCH_2CH_3 \longrightarrow (CH_3)_2CH\cdot + \cdot CH_2CH_3$

$\Delta H^O{}_f = $ −36.9   +18   +26   81

Path C:

$$(CH_3)_2CHCH_2CH_3 \longrightarrow (CH_3)_2CHCH_2 \cdot + \cdot CH_3$$

$\Delta H^o_f =$ -36.9 $+14$ $+35$ 86

The easiest fragmentation is that depicted in Path B. Therefore the major products are expected to be ethane, propane, ethene, and propene.

6.3   *Initiation:* $Cl_2 \longrightarrow 2\ Cl\cdot$ 58

Propagation:

$$Cl\cdot + CH_3CH_3 \longrightarrow HCl + CH_3CH_2\cdot$$

$\Delta H^o_f =$ 29 -20.2 -22.1 26 -5

$$CH_3CH_2\cdot + Cl_2 \longrightarrow CH_3CH_2Cl + Cl\cdot$$

       26   0 -26.1 29 -23

Termination:

$$2\ CH_3CH_2\cdot \longrightarrow CH_3CH_2CH_2CH_3$$

$\Delta H^o_f =$ 2×26 -30.4 -82

$$2\ Cl\cdot \longrightarrow Cl_2$$ -58

$$CH_3CH_2\cdot + Cl\cdot \longrightarrow CH_3CH_2Cl$$

       26   29 -26.1 -81

ΔH^o for the overall reaction:

$$CH_3CH_3 + Cl_2 \longrightarrow CH_3CH_2Cl + HCl$$

$\Delta H^o_f =$ -20.2 0 -26.1 -22.1 $\Delta H^o = -28.0$ kcal mole^{-1}

Note that the initiation and termination steps are not part of the overall reaction.

6.4
       CH$_3$ ——these three hydrogens are different
              from the other primary ones
       CH$-$CH$_2-$CH$_3$
       CH$_3$

these six hydrogens are equivalent

Product						
ClCH$_2$⟍CHCH$_2$CH$_3$ / CH$_3$	6	×	1	=	6	6/22 = 27%
$(CH_3)_2CClCH_2CH_3$	1	×	5	=	5	5/22 = 23%
$(CH_3)_2CHCHClCH_3$	2	×	4	=	8	8/22 = 36%
$(CH_3)_2CHCH_2CH_2Cl$	3	×	1	=	3	3/22 = 14%
					22	100%

6.5

(a)   CH$_3$ CH$_3$
    CH$_3-$C$-$C$-$CH$_3$ (b) cyclooctane
       CH$_3$ CH$_3$

(c)

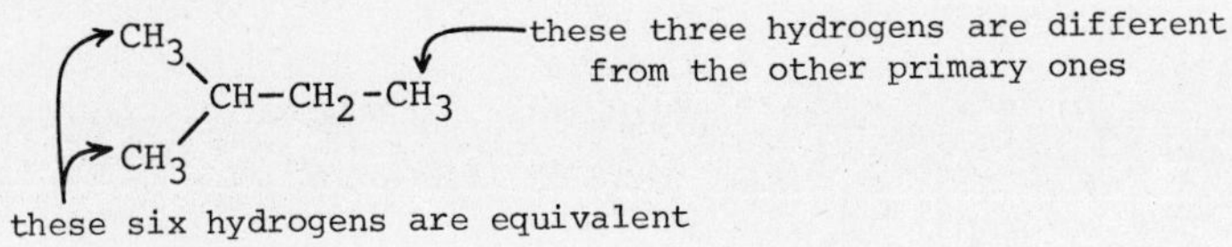

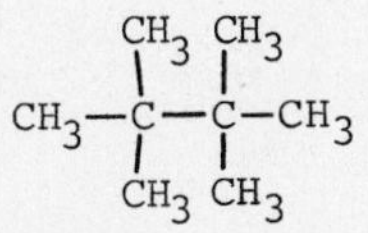

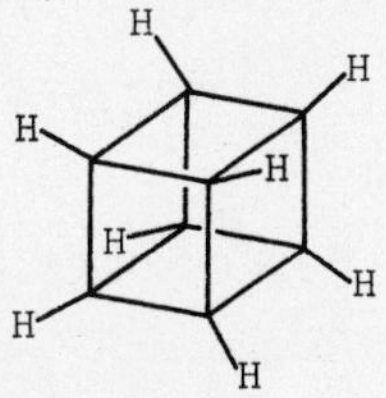

"Cubane"

6.6 $\Delta\Delta G^{\ddagger} = -RT \ln(\Delta k)$ ——difference in reaction rate
        —— difference in activation energy

$$-3000\ (\text{cal mole}^{-1}) = --1.987\ (\text{cal deg}^{-1}) \times 600\ (\text{deg K}) \times \ln(\Delta k)$$

$$\ln(\Delta k) = 2.5 \qquad \Delta k = 12.2$$

6.7 $\Delta H^{\circ}_f (\underline{t}\text{-}C_4H_9\cdot) + \Delta H^{\circ}_f (X\cdot) - DH^{\circ} (\underline{t}\text{-}C_4H_9\text{-}X) = \Delta H^{\circ}_f (\underline{t}\text{-}C_4H_9X)$

X = F	9	+	18.9	-	108	=	-80
X = Cl	9	+	28.9	-	79	=	-41
X = Br	9	+	26.7	-	65	=	-29
X = I	9	+	25.5	-	50	=	-16

$$(CH_3)_3CH + X_2 \longrightarrow (CH_3)_3CX + HX \qquad \Delta H^{\circ} \text{ (kcal mole}^{-1})$$

ΔH°_f, X = F	-32.4	0	-80	-65.0		-113
ΔH°_f, X = Cl	-32.4	0	-41	-22.1		-31
ΔH°_f, X = Br	-32.4	7.4	-29	-8.7		-13
ΔH°_f, X = I	-32.4	14.9	-16	+6.3		+8

NOTE: ΔH°_f for Br_2 and I_2 in the gas phase are not zero because the standard states of
these elements are the liquid and solid phases, respectively. It takes energy to
transfer them to the gas phase where the comparison between reactants and products
is made.

6.8   butane: $C_4H_{10} + 6\frac{1}{2} O_2 \longrightarrow 4 CO_2 + 5 H_2O \qquad \Delta H^{\circ}_{comb.} = -634.82$ kcal mole^{-1}

isobutane: $C_4H_{10} + 6\frac{1}{2} O_2 \longrightarrow 4 CO_2 + 5 H_2O \qquad \Delta H^{\circ}_{comb.} = -632.77$ kcal mole^{-1}

graphite
and hydrogen: $4 C + 5 H_2 + 6\frac{1}{2} O_2 \longrightarrow 4 CO_2 + 5 H_2O$

$\Delta H^{\circ}_f =$ 0   0   0 $4 \times (-94.05) + 5 \times (-57.80) = -665.20$ kcal mole^{-1}

Therefore, for butane, $\Delta H^{\circ}_f = -665.20 - (-634.82) = -30.38$ kcal mole^{-1}

isobutane, $\Delta H^{\circ}_f = -665.20 - (-632.77) = -32.43$ kcal mole^{-1}

6.9   Pentane: $\Delta H^O = \Delta H_{combustion}$ (kcal mole^{-1})

$CH_3CH_2CH_2CH_2CH_3 + 8 O_2 \longrightarrow 5 CO_2 + 6 H_2O$

$\Delta H^O_f =$ -35.1   0 $5x(-94.1) + 6x(-57.8)$ -782.2

2-Methylbutane:

$(CH_3)_2CHCH_2CH_3 + 8 O_2 \longrightarrow 5 CO_2 + 6 H_2O$

$\Delta H^O_f =$ -36.9   0 $5x(-94.1) + 6x(-57.8)$ -780.4

2,2-Dimethylpropane:

$(CH_3)_4C + 8 O_2 \longrightarrow 5 CO_2 + 6 H_2O$

$\Delta H^O_f =$ -40.3   0 $5x(-94.1) + 6x(-57.8)$ -777.0

6.10   <u>Using average bond energies:</u> $CH_3\text{—}H + Cl\text{—}Cl \longrightarrow CH_3\text{—}Cl + H\text{—}Cl$

Bond energies: 99   58   81   103

Bonds gained - bonds broken: -(99 + 58)   +(81 + 103) = 27 kcal mole^{-1}

<u>Using heats of formation:</u>

$\Delta H^O_f =$ -17.9   0   -20.6   -22.1   -24.8 kcal mole^{-1}

6.11   Butane: $CH_3CH_2CH_2CH_3 \longrightarrow$ 4 C atoms + 10 H atoms

<u>Using heats of formation:</u> $\Delta H_{atomization}$

$\Delta H^O_f =$ -30.4 $4 \times (170.9)$ $10 \times (52.1)$ 1235 kcal mole^{-1}

<u>Using average bond energies:</u>

Bonds broken: 10 C—H bonds   10 x 99

3 C—C bonds   3 x 83   1239 kcal mole^{-1}

2-Methylpropane:　$(CH_3)_3CH \longrightarrow$ 4 C atoms + 10 H atoms

Using heats of formation:

$$\Delta H^o_f = \qquad -32.4 \qquad 4 \times (170.9) \quad 10 \times (52.1) \qquad 1237 \text{ kcal mole}^{-1}$$

Using average bond energies, you get the same answer as for butane:

Bonds broken: 10 C—H bonds　10 × 99　　　　　　　1239 kcal mole^{-1}

3 C—C bonds　　3 × 83

6.E　Answers and Explanations for Problems

1.　(a)　$CH_3CH_2CH_2CH_2CH_3 \xrightarrow{\Delta} CH_4 + CH_3CH_3 + CH_2{=}CH_2 + CH_3CH_2CH_3 +$

$CH_3CH{=}CH_2 + CH_3CH_2CH_2CH_3 + CH_3CH_2CH{=}CH_2$

(b)　$CH_3CH_2CH_2CH_2CH_3 \xrightarrow{\Delta} CH_3CH_2CH_2CH_2{\cdot} + CH_3{\cdot}$

$\longrightarrow CH_3CH_2CH_2{\cdot} + {\cdot}CH_2CH_3$

$2\,CH_3{\cdot} \longrightarrow CH_3CH_3$

$CH_3{\cdot} + CH_3CH_2{\cdot} \longrightarrow CH_3CH_2CH_3$

$\longrightarrow CH_4 + CH_2{=}CH_2$

$2\,CH_3CH_2{\cdot} \longrightarrow CH_3CH_2CH_2CH_3$

$\longrightarrow CH_3CH_3 + CH_2{=}CH_2$

$CH_3{\cdot} + CH_3CH_2CH_2{\cdot} \longrightarrow CH_3CH_2CH_2CH_3$

$\longrightarrow CH_4 + CH_3CH{=}CH_2$

$CH_3CH_2{\cdot} + CH_3CH_2CH_2{\cdot} \longrightarrow CH_3(CH_2)_3CH_3$

$\longrightarrow CH_2{=}CH_2 + CH_3CH_2CH_3$

$\longrightarrow CH_3CH_3 + CH_3CH{=}CH_2$

$CH_3{\cdot} + CH_3CH_2CH_2CH_2{\cdot} \longrightarrow CH_3(CH_2)_3CH_3$

$\longrightarrow CH_4 + CH_3CH_2CH{=}CH_2$

Note that longer alkanes can also be produced by recombination of $CH_3CH_2CH_2{\cdot}$ and $CH_3CH_2CH_2CH_2{\cdot}$ radicals.

ΔH^o, kcal mole^{-1}

(c)

		ΔH^o, kcal mole^{-1}
$CH_3CH_2CH_2CH_2CH_3 \longrightarrow$	$CH_3CH_2CH_2CH_2{\cdot} + CH_3{\cdot}$	+86
$\longrightarrow$	$CH_3CH_2CH_2{\cdot} + CH_3CH_2{\cdot}$	+82
$CH_3{\cdot} + CH_3{\cdot} \longrightarrow$	CH_3CH_3	−90
$CH_3{\cdot} + CH_3CH_2{\cdot} \longrightarrow$	$CH_3CH_2CH_3$	−86
$\longrightarrow$	$CH_4 + CH_2{=}CH_2$	−66
$CH_3CH_2{\cdot} + CH_3CH_2{\cdot} \longrightarrow$	$CH_3CH_3 + CH_2{=}CH_2$	−60
$CH_3{\cdot} + CH_3CH_2CH_2{\cdot} \longrightarrow$	$CH_3CH_2CH_2CH_3$	−86
$\longrightarrow$	$CH_4 + CH_3CH{=}CH_2$	−69
$CH_3CH_2{\cdot} + CH_3CH_2CH_2{\cdot} \longrightarrow$	$CH_2{=}CH_2 + CH_3CH_2CH_3$	−59
$\longrightarrow$	$CH_3CH_3 + CH_3CH{=}CH_2$	−62
$CH_3{\cdot} + CH_3CH_2CH_2CH_2{\cdot} \longrightarrow$	$CH_4 + CH_3CH_2CH{=}CH_2$	−69

OVERALL REACTIONS:

$$\begin{array}{ll} & \underline{\Delta H^\circ, \text{ kcal mole}^{-1}} \\ CH_4 + CH_3CH_2CH=CH_2 & \\ -17.9 \quad\quad -0.2 & +17.0 \\ \\ CH_3CH_2CH_2CH_2CH_3 \longrightarrow \quad CH_3CH_3 + CH_3CH=CH_2 & \\ \Delta H^\circ_f = -35.1 \quad\quad\quad -20.2 \quad\quad 4.9 & +19.8 \\ \\ CH_3CH_2CH_3 + CH_2=CH_2 & \\ -24.8 \quad\quad\quad 12.5 & +22.8 \end{array}$$

2.(a) 1) $Br_2 \longrightarrow 2\, Br\cdot$ $\Delta H^\circ = DH^\circ = 2\, \Delta H^\circ_f(Br\cdot) - \Delta H^\circ_f(Br_2)$
                                                 $= 46 \text{ kcal mole}^{-1}$

2) $CH_3CH_3 + Br\cdot \longrightarrow CH_3CH_2\cdot + HBr$

To use DH° values, you must break this step into two reactions:

$$\begin{array}{lll} CH_3CH_3 \longrightarrow CH_3CH_2\cdot + H\cdot & \quad DH^\circ = 98 \\ H\cdot + Br\cdot \longrightarrow HBr & \quad -DH^\circ = -87.5 \end{array}$$

$CH_3CH_3 + \cancel{H\cdot} + Br\cdot \longrightarrow CH_3CH_2\cdot + \cancel{H\cdot} + HBr$, and $\Delta H^\circ = 11 \text{ kcal mole}^{-1}$

The use of heats of formation (Appendix I) gives a similar answer:

$$\begin{array}{llll} CH_3CH_3 + Br\cdot \longrightarrow CH_3CH_2\cdot + HBr \\ \Delta H^\circ_f = \quad -20.2 \quad 26.7 \quad\quad\quad 26 \quad\quad -8.7 \quad\quad H^\circ = +11 \text{ kcal mole}^{-1} \end{array}$$

3) $CH_3CH_2\cdot + Br_2 \longrightarrow CH_3CH_2Br + Br\cdot$
      $\Delta H^\circ = DH^\circ(Br-Br) - DH^\circ(CH_3CH_2-Br)$
              $= 46 - 68 = -22 \text{ kcal mole}^{-1}$

(b)   (2) + (3) = ΔH° for the overall reaction
              $= 11 + (-22) = -11 \text{ kcal mole}^{-1}$

(c)   To check: $Br_2 + CH_3CH_3 \longrightarrow CH_3CH_2Br + HBr$
            $\Delta H^\circ_f = \quad 7.4 \quad -20.2 \quad\quad\quad -15.2 \quad\quad -8.7 \quad\quad \Delta H^\circ = -11.1 \text{ kcal mole}^{-1}$

The values are the same, except for precision. ΔH°_f for radicals are not known as accurately as for normal compounds *(see explanatory Note accompanying answer to Exercise 6.1)*

3. The reaction of $Br\cdot$ with ethane is an endothermic reaction, and therefore is likely to be slow, because the activation energy $\Delta H^\ddagger$ is $\geq \Delta H^\circ = +11 \text{ kcal mole}^{-1}$. In contrast, the reaction of ethyl radical with Br_2 is very exothermic ($\Delta H^\circ = -22 \text{ kcal mole}^{-1}$). Because radical hydrogen abstraction has a relatively low $\Delta H^\ddagger$ for exothermic reactions, the reaction of $C_2H_5\cdot$ with Br_2 is expected to be fast. Therefore $[Br\cdot] > [C_2H_5\cdot]$.

A good analogy is the scene on a ski slope. On the average, there are as many people coming down the mountain as are going up, but there are more waiting in line at the bottom than waiting at the top.

4. (a) All of the hydrogens in spiropentane are equivalent. Thus, there is only one possible monochlorospiropentane. Furthermore, the dichloro compounds have higher boiling points and can be separated by distillation.

(b) Mechanism:
                    $Cl_2 \longrightarrow 2\,Cl\cdot$ (initiation)

                                                                (propagation)

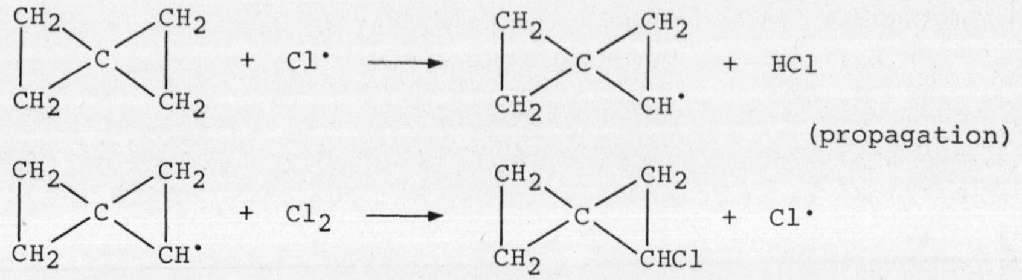

$$2 \ R\cdot \longrightarrow R\text{-}R \quad (R\cdot = \bowtie . \text{ or } Cl\cdot) \quad \text{(termination)}$$

5. In Section 6.3 , we found the relative reactivities of primary (1°), secondary (2°), and tertiary (3°) hydrogens to be $1:4.0:5$ in chlorination reactions.

(a)

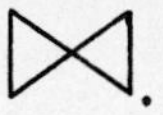

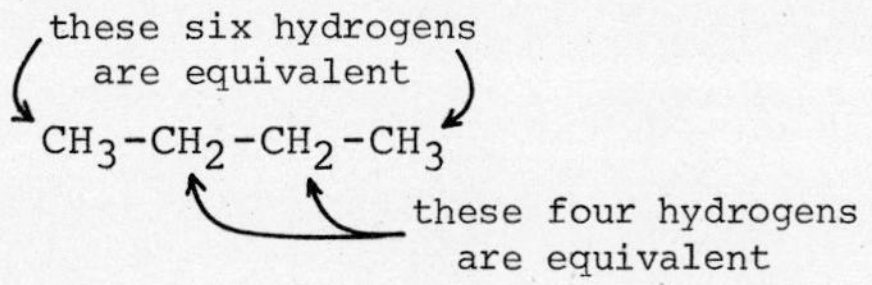

these six hydrogens
are equivalent

$CH_3\text{-}CH_2\text{-}CH_2\text{-}CH_3$

these four hydrogens
are equivalent

Product	Statistical Factor		Relative Reactivity		Relative Amount	Percent of Mixture
$CH_3CH_2CH_2CH_2Cl$	6	×	1	=	6	6/22 = 27%
$CH_3CH_2CHClCH_3$	4	×	4	=	16	16/22 = 73%
					22	100%

(b)

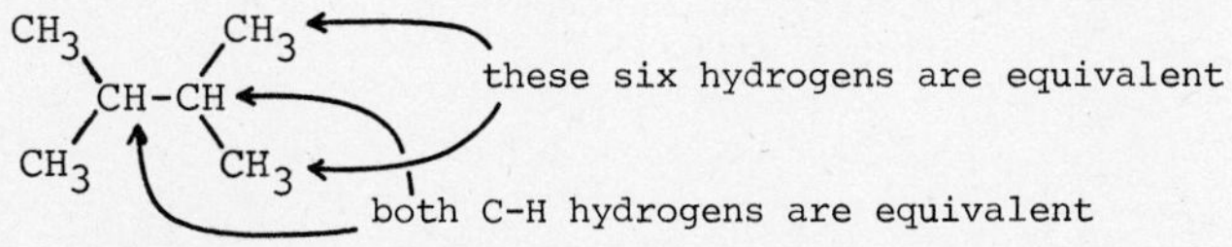

$\begin{array}{cc} CH_3 & CH_3 \\ & CH\text{-}CH \\ CH_3 & CH_3 \end{array}$

these six hydrogens are equivalent

both C-H hydrogens are equivalent

Product						
$\begin{array}{cc} ClCH_2 & CH_3 \\ & CH\text{-}CH \\ CH_3 & CH_3 \end{array}$	12	×	1	=	12	12/22 = 55%
$\begin{array}{cc} CH_3 & CH_3 \\ & CCl\text{-}CH \\ CH_3 & CH_3 \end{array}$	2	×	5	=	10	10/22 = 45%
					22	100%

(c)

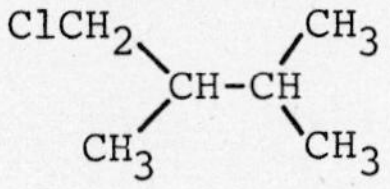

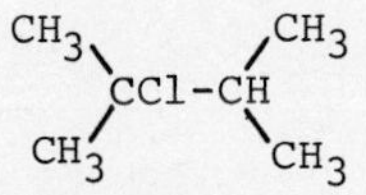

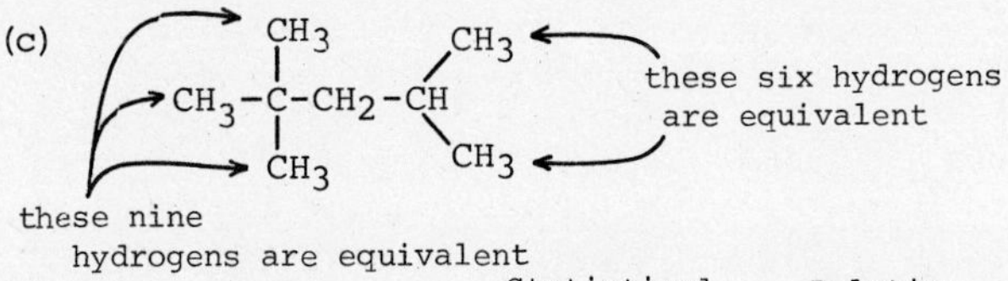

these nine
hydrogens are equivalent

$\begin{array}{ccc} & CH_3 & CH_3 \\ CH_3\text{-}C\text{-}CH_2\text{-}CH & \\ & CH_3 & CH_3 \end{array}$

these six hydrogens
are equivalent

Product	Statistical Factor		Relative Reactivity		Relative Amount	Percent of Mixture
$ClCH_2\text{-}\overset{\displaystyle CH_3}{\underset{\displaystyle CH_3}{C}}\text{-}CH_2CH(CH_3)_2$	9	×	1	=	9	9/28 = 32%
$(CH_3)_3CCHClCH(CH_3)_2$	2	· ×	4	=	8	8/28 = 29%
$(CH_3)_3CCH_2CCl(CH_3)_2$	1	×	5	=	5	5/28 = 18%
$(CH_3)_3CCH_2\overset{\displaystyle CH_2Cl}{\underset{\displaystyle CH_3}{CH}}$	6	×	1	=	6	6/28 = 21%
					28	100%

(d) $(CH_3)_3CCH(CH_3)_2$

Product						
$ClCH_2\text{-}\overset{\displaystyle CH_3}{\underset{\displaystyle CH_3}{C}}\text{-}CH(CH_3)_2$	9	×	1	=	9	9/20 = 45%
$(CH_3)_3CC(CH_3)_2Cl$	1	×	5	=	5	5/20 = 25%

[cont'd on next page]

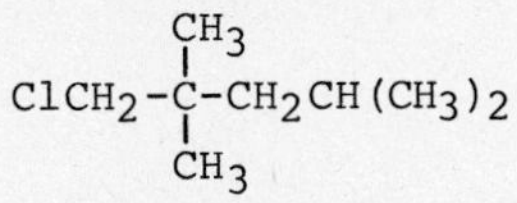

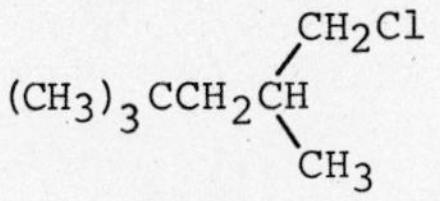

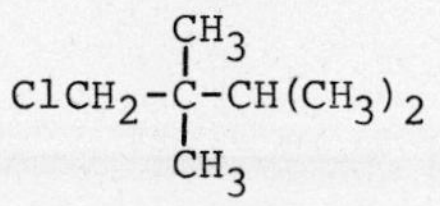

$$(CH_3)_3CCH \begin{matrix} CH_2Cl \\ \\ CH_3 \end{matrix}$$ 6 × 1 = $\underline{6}$ 6/20 = 30%

20 100%

(e) $CH_3CH_2CH_2CH_2CH_3$ these four hydrogens are different from these two hydrogens

Product

$CH_3CH_2CH_2CH_2CH_2Cl$	6	×	1	= 6	6/30 = 20%
$CH_3CH_2CH_2CHClCH_3$	4	×	4	= 16	16/30 = 53%
$CH_3CH_2CHClCH_2CH_3$	2	×	4	= 8	8/30 = 27%

30   100%

Note how chlorination is generally impractical as a synthetic method when the molecule contains non-equivalent hydrogens.

6. (a) $BrCH_2CH_2CH_2CH_3$ 6 × 1 =   6   6/886 = 0.7%

$CH_3CHBrCH_2CH_3$ 4 × 220 = 880   880/886 = 99.3%

886   100 %

(b) $BrCH_2\overset{\overset{\textstyle CH_3}{|}}{C}HCH_2CH_3$ 6 × 1 =   6   6/19449 = 0.03%

$(CH_3)_2CBrCH_2CH_3$ 1 × 19000 = 19000   19000/19449 = 97.7%

$(CH_3)_2CHCHBrCH_3$ 2 × 220 = 440   440/19449 = 2.3%

3 × 1 =   3   3/19449 = 0.02%

19449

(c) $BrCH_2\overset{\overset{\textstyle CH_3}{|}}{\underset{\underset{\textstyle CH_3}{|}}{C}}CH_2CH(CH_3)_2$ 9 × 1 =   9   9/19455 = 0.05%

$(CH_3)_3CCH_2CBr(CH_3)_2$ 1 × 19000 = 19000   19000/19455 = 97.7%

$(CH_3)_3C\overset{\overset{\textstyle Br}{|}}{C}HCH(CH_3)_2$ 2 × 220   440   440/19455 = 2.3%

$(CH_3)_3CCH_2\overset{\overset{\textstyle CH_3}{|}}{C}HCH_2Br$ 6 × 1 =   6   6/19455 = 0.03%

19455

(d) $BrCH_2\overset{\overset{\textstyle CH_3}{|}}{\underset{\underset{\textstyle CH_3}{|}}{C}}CH(CH_3)_2$ 9 × 1 =   9   9/19015 = 0.05%

$(CH_3)_3C\overset{\overset{\textstyle Br}{|}}{C}C(CH_3)_3$ 1 × 19000 = 19000   19000/19015 = 99.9%

$(CH_3)_3C\overset{\overset{\textstyle CH_3}{|}}{C}HCH_2Br$ 6 × 2 =   12   12/19015 = 0.03%

19015

(e) $CH_3CH_2CH_2CH_2CH_2Br$ 6 × 1 =   6   6/1326 = 0.5%

$CH_3CH_2CH_2CHBrCH_3$ 4 × 220 = 880   880/1326 = 66.4%

$CH_3CH_2CHBrCH_2CH_3$ 2 × 220 = 440   440/1326 = 33.2%

1326

$$\Delta H° \ (kcal \ mole^{-1})$$

7. (a)

$$CH_3CH_2Cl + HCl$$
$$-26.1 \quad -22.1 \qquad\qquad -28.0$$

$$C_2H_6 + Cl_2$$
$$\Delta H°_f = \ -20.2 \quad\ 0$$

$$2 \ CH_3Cl \qquad\qquad\qquad -21.0$$
$$2 \times (-20.6)$$

(b) $$C_2H_6 + Cl\cdot \longrightarrow CH_3Cl + CH_3\cdot$$
$$\Delta H°_f = \ -20.2 \quad 26.7 \qquad -20.6 \qquad 35 \qquad\qquad +8$$

$$CH_3\cdot + Cl_2 \longrightarrow CH_3Cl + Cl\cdot$$
$$\Delta H°_f = \quad 35 \qquad 0 \qquad\quad -20.6 \quad 26.7 \qquad\qquad -29$$

(c) Although there is no thermodynamic difficulty with either step, the reaction of ethane with the chlorine atom to give ethyl radical and HCl is so much more favorable ($\Delta H° = -5$ kcal mole^{-1}; see Exercise 6.3) than the reaction to give $CH_3\cdot$ and CH_3Cl that the latter is not observed.

8. Cyclopropane:

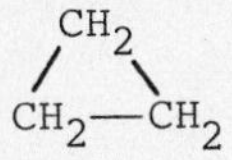

$$\begin{array}{c} CH_2 \\ / \ \ \backslash \\ CH_2 \!\!-\!\! CH_2 \end{array} \longrightarrow \text{3 C atoms and 6 H atoms}$$

<u>Using average bond energies:</u>

   3 C—C bonds (3×83) and 6 C—H bonds (6×99) = 843 kcal mole^{-1}

<u>Using heats of formation:</u>

   $-\Delta H°_f$ (cyclopropane) + $3 \times \Delta H°_f$ (C atom) + $6 \times \Delta H°_f$ (H atom)
   $$-12.7 \qquad\quad + \ 3 \times 170.9 \quad\ + \ 6 \times 52.1 = 812.6 \text{ kcal mole}^{-1}$$

The calculation using the average bond energies overestimates the heat of atomization by 30 kcal mole^{-1} because it does not take the ring strain into account. This difference is in fact a good approximation of the ring strain (see Table 5.5 in the text).

Cubane:

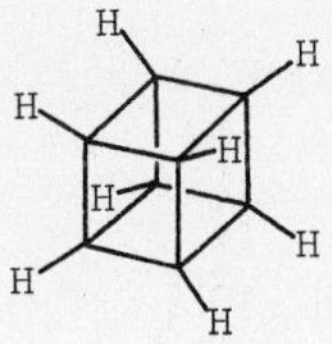

$$\longrightarrow \text{8 C atoms and 8 H atoms}$$

<u>Using average bond energies:</u>

   12 C—C bonds (12×83) and 8 C—H bonds (8×99) = 1788 kcal mole^{-1}

<u>Using heats of formation:</u>

   $-\Delta H°_f$ (cubane) + $8 \times \Delta H°_f$ (C atom) + $8 \times \Delta H°_f$ (H atom)
   $$-148.7 + 8 \times 170.9 \quad + \ 8 \times 52.1 \quad = \ 1635.3 \text{ kcal mole}^{-1}$$

   strain energy $\approx$ 153 kcal mole^{-1}

9. $\triangle$ $+ \ 4\tfrac{1}{2} \ O_2 \longrightarrow 3 \ CO_2 + \ 3 \ H_2O$
$$\Delta H°_f = 12.7 \qquad 0 \qquad\quad 3 \times (-94.05) \ \ 3 \times (-57.80) \qquad \Delta H° = \Delta H°_{combustion} = -468.25 \text{ kcal mole}^{-1}$$

   $\bigcirc$ $+ \ 9 \ O_2 \longrightarrow 6 \ CO_2 + \ 6 \ H_2O$
$$\Delta H°_f = \qquad\quad 0 \qquad\quad 6 \times (-94.05) \ \ 6 \times (-57.80) \qquad \Delta H° = -881.6 \text{ kcal mole}^{-1}$$
$$-29.5$$

Since the molecular weight of cyclohexane is twice that of cyclopropane, on a weight basis cyclopropane releases $(2 \times 468)/882 = 1.06$ times as much energy on combustion as cyclohexane does. If the two fuels cost the same, cyclopropane would be the more economical.

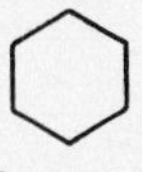

10. (a) ΔH°_f (CH$_3\cdot$) + ΔH°_f (F$\cdot$) - DH$^\circ$ (CH$_3$-F) = ΔH°_f (CH$_3$F)

$$35 + 19 - 110 = -56 \text{ kcal mole}^{-1}$$

$$\begin{array}{c} \text{CH}_3\text{Cl} + \text{HF} \\ -20.6 \quad -65 \end{array} \qquad \Delta H^\circ = -55 \text{ kcal mole}^{-1}$$

CH$_4$ + ClF

ΔH°_f = -18   -12.2

$$\begin{array}{c} \text{CH}_3\text{F} + \text{HCl} \\ -56 \quad -22.1 \end{array} \qquad \Delta H^\circ = -48 \text{ kcal mole}^{-1}$$

(b) CH$_3$Cl and HF, because their formation releases the greatest amount of energy.

(c)

$$\begin{array}{c} \text{CH}_3\text{Cl} + \text{F}\cdot \\ -20.6 \quad 18.9 \end{array} \qquad \Delta H^\circ = -25 \text{ kcal mole}^{-1}$$

CH$_3\cdot$ + ClF

ΔH°_f = 35   -12.2

$$\begin{array}{c} \text{CH}_3\text{F} + \text{Cl}\cdot \\ -56 \quad 26.7 \end{array} \qquad \Delta H^\circ = -52 \text{ kcal mole}^{-1}$$

One would predict from this comparison that CH$_3$F would be formed faster.

This case provides a good illustration of a situation which is frequently encountered: the product which is formed more quickly (called the product of "kinetic control") is not always the most stable one (which is called the product of "thermodynamic control"). This sort of situation results from the independence of the activation energy ($\Delta G^{\ddagger}$) and the overall energy change (ΔG°) in a reaction.

11.

$$\underline{\Delta H^\circ \text{ (kcal mole}^{-1})}$$

CH$_4$ + HNO$_3$ $\longrightarrow$ CH$_3$NO$_2$ + H$_2$O

ΔH°_f = -17.9   -32.1   -17.9   -57.8   -25.7

CH$_4$ + $\cdot$NO$_2$ $\longrightarrow$ CH$_3\cdot$ + HNO$_2$

-17.9   7.9   35   -18.4   +27   this step is highly endothermic and is therefore slow; it requires high temperature

HNO$_2$ + HNO$_3$ $\longrightarrow$ 2 NO$_2\cdot$ + H$_2$O

-18.4   -32.1   2 × 7.9   -57.8   + 8.5

CH$_3\cdot$ + $\cdot$NO$_2$ $\longrightarrow$ CH$_3$NO$_2$

35   7.9   -17.9   -61

Possible alternatives for CH$_3\cdot$:

$$\begin{array}{c} \text{CH}_3\text{OH} + \cdot\text{NO}_2 \\ -48.1 \quad 7.9 \end{array} \qquad -43$$

CH$_3\cdot$ + HNO$_3$

35   -32.1

$$\begin{array}{c} \text{CH}_3\text{NO}_2 + \text{HO}\cdot \\ -17.9 \quad 9.3 \end{array} \qquad -12$$

Resonance structures for NO$_2\cdot$:

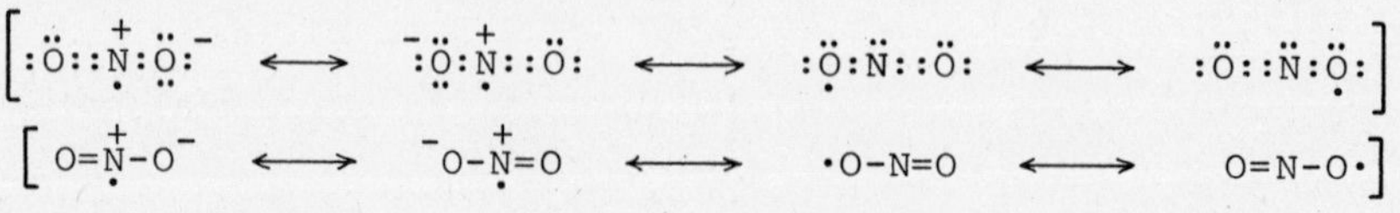

$$\begin{array}{c} \text{CH}_3\text{ONO} \\ -15.8 \end{array} \qquad \Delta H^\circ = -59 \text{ kcal mole}^{-1}$$

CH$_3\cdot$ + NO$_2\cdot$

35   7.9

$$\begin{array}{c} \text{CH}_3\text{NO}_2 \\ -17.9 \end{array} \qquad \Delta H^\circ = -61 \text{ kcal mole}^{-1}$$

12. At high concentrations of CH_4 and low concentrations of Cl_2, the rate at which chlorine atoms find and react with CH_4 molecules will become faster than the rate at which methyl radicals find and react with Cl_2. At equal concentrations of CH_4 and Cl_2, the reaction of chlorine atoms with CH_4 will be rate-determining. The chlorine atoms will be present at higher concentration (see problem #3). The relative rates of the propagation steps determine which radical is in excess, which in turn determines which termination process is faster. Termination processes involving Cl· will predominate if Cl· + CH_4 is the slow step.

13.

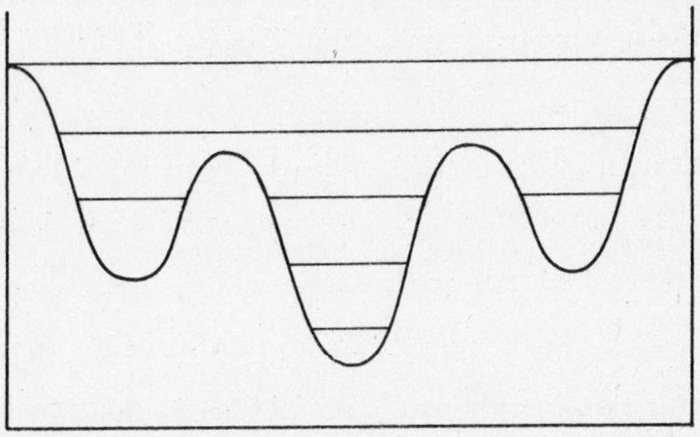

Free rotation at the 5th or 6th quantum level.

6.F Supplementary Problems

S1. Cracking propane to give a mixture of methane and ethylene is an endothermic process (compare with problem #1 in this chapter). However, from the point of view of entropy, splitting one molecule into two is a favorable process, as reflected by the standard entropy change, $\Delta S°$, for the reaction in question:

$$CH_3CH_2CH_3 \longrightarrow CH_4 + CH_2=CH_2 \qquad \Delta S° = +33 \text{ e.u.}$$

(a) Using this number and Appendix I, calculate the temperature at which equilibrium favors the smaller molecules; i.e., $K > 1$.

(b) In a more efficient cracking process, called hydrocracking, hydrogen is mixed with the hydrocarbons to be cracked. What products would you expect from the cracking of propane in the presence of hydrogen?

(c) Calculate $\Delta H°$ for the reaction you have written for part (b).

S2. From the data below and in Table 6.2 and Appendix I, calculate or predict $DH°$ for the weakest bond in each of the compounds listed below.

(a)

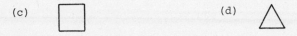

(b) $CH_3-\underset{\underset{CH_3}{|}}{\overset{\overset{CH_3}{|}}{C}}-\underset{\underset{CH_3}{|}}{\overset{\overset{CH_3}{|}}{C}}-CH_3$ $\qquad (\Delta H°_f = -54.0 \text{ kcal mole}^{-1})$

(c) ☐

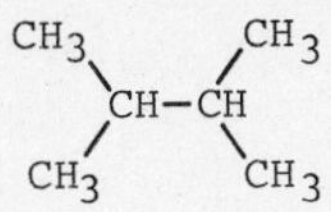

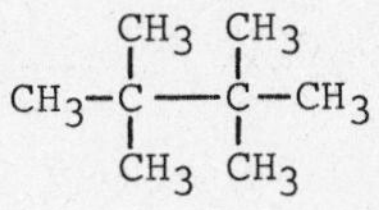

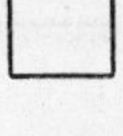

(d) △

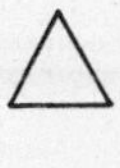

S3. Free radical halogenation can also be accomplished using sulfuryl chloride

$(Cl-\overset{\overset{O}{\|}}{\underset{\underset{O}{\|}}{S}}-Cl)$ via the following propagation steps:

$$R\cdot \ + \ ClSO_2Cl \ \longrightarrow \ RCl \ + \ \cdot SO_2Cl$$
$$\cdot SO_2Cl \ + \ RH \ \longrightarrow \ R\cdot \ + \ HSO_2Cl$$
$\left.\right\}$ *Propagation*

$$(HSO_2Cl \ \xrightarrow{\ fast\ } \ SO_2 \ + \ HCl)$$

(a) From the product compositions below, calculate the selectivity of the
$\cdot SO_2Cl$ radical for primary, secondary, and tertiary hydrogens.

$$\underset{CH_3}{\overset{CH_3}{}}CH-CH_3 \ + \ ClSO_2Cl \ \xrightarrow{\ h\nu\ } \ (CH_3)_3CCl \ + \ (CH_3)_2CHCH_2Cl$$
$$ 31\% 69\%$$

$$CH_3CH_2CH_2CH_2CH_3 \ + \ ClSO_2Cl \ \xrightarrow{\ h\nu\ } \ CH_3CH_2CH_2CH_2ClCH_3 \ + \ CH_3CH_2CH_2CH_2CH_2Cl \ + \ CH_3CH_2CHClCH_2CH_3$$
$$ 48\% 28\% 24\%$$

(b) Predict the relative amounts of monochlorinated products obtained
from this reaction with 2,4-dimethylpentane.

S4. On heating with HI, alkyl iodides react to give alkanes and I_2.
   (a) Using $CH_3I \ + \ HI \ \longrightarrow \ CH_4 \ + \ I_2$ as an example, calculate $\Delta H°$ for
       the reaction.
   (b) Propose a mechanism for this reaction and justify the steps involved
       by calculating $\Delta H°$ for each one. (*HINT:* take advantage of the principle of
       microscopic reversibility.)

S5. One of the mechanisms by which HBr can add to alkenes is illustrated
    below for ethylene:

$$Br\cdot \quad CH_2 = CH_2 \ \longrightarrow \ Br-CH_2-CH_2\cdot$$

$$BrCH_2CH_2\cdot \quad H-Br \ \longrightarrow \ BrCH_2CH_3 \ + \ Br\cdot$$

   (a) Using the data in Table 6.2 and in Appendices I and II, estimate $\Delta H°$
       for each of the steps above and for the overall reaction.
   (b) Do the same calculations for the reaction of HCl by the same mech-
       anism. What do you conclude about the relative rates of the two
       reactions?

   (c) Two isomeric products are possible for the addition of HBr to 2-
       methylpropene. Write out the steps involved in the formation of each
       one and estimate $\Delta H°$ for each of them. Which isomer is more stable?
       Which one will be the major product (formed faster)?

S6. (a) Calculate the average bond dissociation energy for CCl_4 using the
        data from Appendix I.
   (b) Calculate the C-H bond dissociation energy for $CHCl_3$ (chloroform).
   (c) Is the reaction $CH_4 \ + \ CCl_4 \ \longrightarrow \ CH_3Cl \ + \ CHCl_3$ likely to take
        place on thermodynamic grounds?
   (d) Is the reaction likely to take place on kinetic grounds? In other words,
        are any of the steps in the mechanism you wrote very endothermic?

6.G   Answers to Supplementary Problems

S1. (a) $C_3H_8 \longrightarrow CH_4 + C_2H_4$ $\Delta H° = +19.4$ kcal mole^{-1}

   $\Delta S° = +33$ e.u.

   K is greater than 1 when $\Delta G°$ is less than zero;

   since $\Delta G° = \Delta H° - T\Delta S°$, $19,400 - T \times 33 < 0$, so that $T > 588°K$

   (b) $C_3H_8 + H_2 \longrightarrow CH_4 + C_2H_6$

   (c) $\Delta H°_f$: -24.8 0 -17.9 -20.2 $\Delta H° = -13.3$ kcal mole^{-1}

S2. (a) $(CH_3)_2CH-CH(CH_3)_2 \longrightarrow 2\ (CH_3)_2CH\cdot$

   $\Delta H°_f$: -42.6 2×18 $\Delta H° = DH° = 79$ kcal mole^{-1}

   (b) $(CH_3)_3C-C(CH_3)_3 \longrightarrow 2\ (CH_3)_3C\cdot$

   $\Delta H°_f$: -54.0 2×9 $\Delta H° = DH° = 72$ kcal mole^{-1}

   (c) To calculate DH° for $\square \longrightarrow \cdot CH_2CH_2CH_2CH_2\cdot$, follow the sequence below:

   (1) $H_2 + \square \longrightarrow CH_3CH_2CH_2CH_3$ $\Delta H° = -37.2$ kcal mole^{-1}

   (2) $CH_3CH_2CH_2CH_3 \longrightarrow 2\,H\cdot + \cdot CH_2CH_2CH_2CH_2\cdot$ $\Delta H° = 2\ DH°$(primary C-H) = $+196$ kcal mole^{-1}

   (3) $2\,H\cdot \longrightarrow H_2$ $\Delta H° = -DH°\,(H_2) = -104$ kcal mole^{-1}

   DH° for the ring opening of cyclobutane is the sum of *(1)*, *(2)* and *(3)*:

   DH° = $-37.2 + 196 + (-104) = 55$ kcal mole^{-1}

   (d) The same sequence may be applied to $\triangle \longrightarrow \cdot CH_2CH_2CH_2\cdot$; only for step *(1)* is the value for $\Delta H°$ different:

   (1)' $H_2 + \triangle \longrightarrow CH_3CH_2CH_3$ $\Delta H° = -37.5$ kcal mole^{-1}

   DH° for the ring opening of cyclopropane is calculated to be $+55$ kcal mole^{-1} also. For your interest, compare this figure with the values you calculate for the cleavage of the cyclopentane and cyclohexane rings.

S3. (a) Reaction of $(CH_3)_2CH$ results in 31% tertiary and 69% primary chlorination.

Relative Amount		Statistical Factor		Relative Reactivity
31%	=	1	×	3° reactivity
69%	=	9	×	1° reactivity

   Rel. reactivity: $3°/1° = \dfrac{31}{69/9} = 4$

   Reaction of $CH_3CH_2CH_2CH_2CH_3$ results in 48% 2-chloro isomer, 24% 3-chloro isomer, and 28% 1-chloro isomer.

48%	=	4	×	2° reactivity
24%	=	2	×	2° reactivity
28%	=	6	×	1° reactivity

   Rel. reactivity: $2°/1° = \dfrac{24/2}{28/6} = 2.6$

   Therefore, the ratio of 3° reactivity : 2° reactivity : 1° reactivity =

   $4 : 2.6 : 1$

(b)

$$(CH_3)_2CHCH_2CH(CH_3)_2 \longrightarrow \underset{ClCH_2}{\overset{CH_3}{CHCH_2CH(CH_3)_2}} + \underset{}{\overset{Cl}{(CH_3)_2CCH_2CH(CH_3)_2}} + \underset{}{\overset{Cl}{(CH_3)_2CHCHCH(CH_3)_2}}$$

Statistical factor:	12	2	2
Relative reactivity:	1	4	2.6
Relative amounts:	12 (= 12×1)	8 (= 2×4)	5.2 (= 2×2.6)
Percent of mixture:	48%	32%	20%

S4. (a)

$$CH_3I + HI \longrightarrow CH_4 + I_2$$

ΔH°_f: 3.4   6.3   -17.9   0 $\Delta H^\circ = -27.6$ kcal mole^{-1}

(b)

$$CH_3-I \longrightarrow CH_3{}^\bullet + I^\bullet \qquad DH^\circ = 56 \text{ kcal mole}^{-1}$$

but many other initiation steps are possible; for example, from traces of peroxide, light, etc.

propagation $\begin{cases} \\ \\ \\ \\ \end{cases}$

$$I^\bullet + CH_3I \longrightarrow CH_3{}^\bullet + I_2$$

ΔH°_f: 25.5   3.4   35   0 $\Delta H^\circ = +6$ kcal mole^{-1}

$$CH_3{}^\bullet + HI \longrightarrow CH_4 + I^\bullet$$

ΔH°_f: 35   6.3   -17.9   25.5 $\Delta H^\circ = -34$ kcal mole^{-1}

S5. (a)

$$Br^\bullet + CH_2{=}CH_2 \longrightarrow BrCH_2CH_2{}^\bullet$$

Calculate from the sequence:

ΔH° (kcal mole^{-1})

(1) $H^\bullet + Br^\bullet \longrightarrow HBr$ $\Delta H^\circ = -DH^\circ$(HBr):   -87.5

(2) $HBr + CH_2{=}CH_2 \longrightarrow CH_3CH_2Br$ -19.0

(3) $CH_3CH_2Br \longrightarrow H^\bullet + {}^\bullet CH_2CH_2Br$ $\Delta H^\circ = DH^\circ$(primary C-H):   98

The sum of (1), (2), and (3) = ΔH° for the first step: -8.5

$${}^\bullet CH_2CH_2Br + HBr \longrightarrow CH_3CH_2Br + Br$$

Calculate from the sequence:

(4) $HBr \longrightarrow H^\bullet + Br^\bullet$ $\Delta H^\circ = DH^\circ$ (HBr):   +87.5

(5) ${}^\bullet CH_2CH_2Br + H^\bullet \longrightarrow CH_3CH_2Br$ $\Delta H^\circ = -DH^\circ$(primary C-H):   -98

The sum of (4) and (5) = ΔH° for the second step: -10.5

ΔH° for the overall reaction was calculated as eq. (2) above.

(b) For HCl addition, the following changes in the sequence of equations are made:

ΔH° (kcal mole^{-1})

(1)' $\Delta H^\circ = -DH^\circ$ (HCl)   -103.2

(2)' $\Delta H^\circ = \Delta H^\circ_f$ (C$_2$H$_5$Cl) $- \Delta H^\circ_f$ (HCl) $- \Delta H^\circ_f$ (C$_2$H$_4$)   -16.5

(3)'   remains approximately the same   +98

The sum of (1)', (2)', and (3)' = ΔH° for the first step

(Cl$^\bullet$ + CH$_2$=CH$_2$ $\longrightarrow$ $^\bullet$CH$_2$CH$_2$Cl):   -21.7

(4)' $\Delta H^\circ = DH^\circ$ (HCl)   +103.2

(5)'   remains approximately the same   -98

The sum of $(4)'$ and $(5)' = \Delta H°$ for the second step

$$(\cdot CH_2CH_2Cl + HCl \longrightarrow CH_3CH_2Cl + Cl\cdot)$$
$$= +5.2 \text{ kcal mole}^{-1}$$

Again, the overall reaction is eq. (2) above: $\Delta H° = -16.5 \text{ kcal mole}^{-1}$

Because the second step in the chain reaction involving HCl is endothermic ($\Delta H° = +5.2$ kcal mole^{-1}), this reaction proceeds much more slowly than the HBr addition.

(c)

$$(CH_3)_2CBrCH_2\cdot \xleftarrow[Path\ A]{Br\cdot} (CH_3)_2C=CH_2 \xrightarrow[Path\ B]{Br\cdot} (CH_3)_2\overset{\cdot}{C}CH_2Br$$

$$\downarrow HBr \qquad\qquad\qquad\qquad\qquad\qquad\qquad \downarrow HBr$$

$$(CH_3)_2CBrCH_3 + Br \qquad\qquad\qquad\qquad (CH_3)_2CHCH_2Br + Br\cdot$$

for Path A:

$$\Delta H°_f((CH_3)_3CBr) = \Delta H°_f(Br\cdot) + \Delta H°_f((CH_3)_3C\cdot) - DH°((CH_3)_3C\text{-}Br)$$
$$= \boxed{-31} \text{ kcal mole}^{-1}$$

$\Delta H° \text{ (kcal mole}^{-1})$

(6) $H\cdot + Br\cdot \longrightarrow HBr$ $\Delta H° = -DH°(HBr)$: -87.5

(7) $(CH_3)_2C=CH_2 + HBr \longrightarrow (CH_3)_3CBr$

$\Delta H°_f$: -4.3 -8.7 $\boxed{-31}$ *(from above)* -18

(8) $(CH_3)_3CBr \longrightarrow (CH_3)_2CBrCH_2\cdot + H\cdot$ $\Delta H° = DH°(\text{primary C-H})$: $+98$

The sum of (6), (7), and (8) = $\Delta H°$ for the first step

$(Br\cdot + (CH_3)_2C=CH_2 \longrightarrow (CH_3)_2CBrCH_2\cdot)$: -7.5

$$(CH_3)_2CBrCH_2\cdot + HBr \longrightarrow (CH_3)_3CBr + Br\cdot$$

$\Delta H° = -DH°(\text{primary C-H}) + DH°(HBr)$: -10.5

for Path B:

$$\Delta H°_f((CH_3)_2CHCH_2Br) = \Delta H°_f(Br\cdot) + \Delta H°_f((CH_3)_2CHCH_2\cdot) - DH°(\text{primary C-Br})$$
$$= \boxed{-27} \text{ kcal mole}^{-1}$$

$\Delta H° \text{ (kcal mole}^{-1})$

(6) same as for Path A -87.5

(9) $(CH_3)_2C=CH_2 + HBr \longrightarrow (CH_3)_2CHCH_2Br$

$\Delta H°_f$: -4.3 -8.7 $\boxed{-27}$ *(from above)* -14

(10) $(CH_3)_2CHCH_2Br \longrightarrow (CH_3)_2\overset{\cdot}{C}CH_2Br + H\cdot$ $\Delta H° = DH°(\text{tertiary C-H})$: $+93$

The sum of (6), (9), and (10) = $\Delta H°$ for the first step

$((CH_3)_2C=CH_2 + Br\cdot \longrightarrow (CH_3)_2\overset{\cdot}{C}CH_2Br)$: -8.5

$$(CH_3)_2\overset{\cdot}{C}CH_2Br + HBr \longrightarrow (CH_3)_2CHCH_2Br + Br\cdot$$

$\Delta H°$ for the second step $= -DH°(\text{tertiary C-H}) + DH°(HBr)$: -5.5

t-Butyl bromide ($\Delta H°_f = -31$ kcal mole^{-1}) is more stable than isobutyl bromide ($\Delta H°_f = -27$ kcal mole^{-1}). However, the isobutyl isomer will be formed predominantly because the most favorable reaction of Br$\cdot$ with 2-methylpropene is the one which leads to the tertiary radical ($\Delta H° = -8.5$ kcal mole^{-1}; *Path B*) rather than to the primary radical ($\Delta H° = -7.5$ kcal mole^{-1}; *Path A*).

This is another example of a reaction in which the less stable product is formed more rapidly than the more stable product.

S6. (a) $CCl_4 \longrightarrow \cdot \overset{\cdot}{\underset{\cdot}{C}} \cdot + 4\,Cl\cdot$

ΔH°_f: -25.2   170.9   4 × 28.9 ΔH° = 311.7 kcal mole^{-1};

average per C–Cl bond = 78 kcal mole^{-1}

(b) $CHCl_3 \longrightarrow H\cdot + \cdot CCl_3$

Calculate from the sequence: ΔH° (kcal mole^{-1})

   (1) $CHCl_3 + Cl\cdot \longrightarrow CCl_4 + H\cdot$

ΔH°_f: -24.6   28.9   -25.2   52.1   22.6

   (2) $CCl_4 \longrightarrow \cdot CCl_3 + Cl\cdot$ ΔH° = DH°(C–Cl):   78

(from (a) above)

The sum of *(1)* and *(2)* = ΔH° for the overall reaction :   101

(c) $CH_4 + CCl_4 \longrightarrow CH_3Cl + CHCl_3$

ΔH°_f: -17.9   -25.2   -20.6   -24.6 ΔH° = -2.1 kcal mole^{-1}

On the basis of a negative overall enthalpy, one would assume
that the reaction could take place.

(d) Assuming that an initiation step can occur, the most reasonable propa-
     gation steps are:

   (I) $\cdot CCl_3 + CH_4 \longrightarrow CHCl_3 + \cdot CH_3$

ΔH°_f: 23.9   -17.9   -24.6   35 ΔH° = +4 kcal mole

   ($\Delta H^\circ_f(\cdot CCl_3) = \Delta H^\circ_f(CHCl_3) + DH°(Cl_3C\text{–}H) - \Delta H^\circ_f(H\cdot)$

use value calculated for (b) above

= 23.9 kcal mole^{-1})

   (II) $\cdot CH_3 + CCl_4 \longrightarrow CH_3Cl + \cdot CCl_3$

ΔH°_f: 35   -25.2   -20.6   23.9 ΔH° = -6.5 kcal mole^{-1}

Neither of these steps is unacceptably exothermic.

7. STEREOISOMERISM

7.A   Chapter Outline and Important Terms Introduced

7.1   Chirality and Enantiomers (mirror images which are different)

    chirality   enantiomers

    chiral and achiral   stereoisomers

    non-superimposable   stereocenter

7.2   Physical Properties of Enantiomers: Optical Activity
                                     (the only physical difference between enantiomers)

    plane polarized light   specific rotation, $[\alpha]$

    dextrorotatory and levorotatory   polarimeter

7.3   Nomenclature of Enantiomers: the R-S Convention
                                 (describing three dimensions using one dimension)

    absolute configuration   higher atomic number

    sequence rule   first point of difference

7.4   Racemates (chiral molecules, optically inactive mixtures)

    racemate   racemic compound

    racemic mixture   racemization

7.5   Compounds Containing More than One Stereocenter, Diastereomers
                                (stereoisomers with **different** physical properties)

    n stereocenters $\implies$ 2^n stereoisomers (but look out for meso compounds)

7.6   Stereoisomeric Relationships in Cyclic Compounds (looking for planes and points of symmetry)

    symmetry plane

7.7   Conformations of Substituted Cyclohexanes (chair conformations revisited)

    equilibria between two possible chair conformations

    boat   skew-boat

7.8   Chemical Reactions and Stereoisomerism (what happens when a stereocenter is involved)

    inversion of absolute configuration

    enantiomeric transition states

7.B   Important Reactions Introduced: none

7.C   Important Concepts and Hints

    Stereoisomerism can be the most exciting aspect of organic chemistry. If you can take a molecule off a two-dimensional page and see it in three dimensions with your mind's eye, you will have a lot of fun studying Chapter 7 and discovering the details of stereochemistry throughout the course. Stereoisomerism can also be a very difficult and challenging subject, simply because you have to be able to imagine three-dimensional objects when confronted with two-dimensional pictures. This takes practice, which very few individuals have had (remember, most people have been stuck on the two-dimensional surface of the earth all their lives....). However, it is easy for you to have this practice: **USE YOUR MODELS!** As you go through the chapter, make models of the structures and compounds described, so you can see a three-dimensional representation alongside the two-dimensional representation in the text. For instance, make a model of the four 2-chloro-3-iodobutane stereoisomers and match them up with the structures depicted in Figure 7.9. Work the exercises and problems with models until you are confident of your understanding. Then, go through them again without models so that you can practice and develop your ability to make the mental transition between two and three dimensions.

The most important concepts in Chapter 7 are those of **chirality** and **optical activity**, and how they differ (see the discussion under **Chiral** in the Glossary); how to describe **absolute configurations** using the **R-S convention**; how to draw molecules so as to depict their absolute configuration (**Wedged** and **Dashed** bonds; **Newman projections**) and how to manipulate these pictures in your mind and on paper; and the relationships between **enantiomers**, **diastereomers**, and **meso** compounds.

7.D Answers to Exercises

7.1 Items c, d, e, f, g, h, j, k, and l are clearly chiral; a, b, i, and m are not chiral, unless one takes into account the printing on them. A portrait (n) is probably chiral, unless it is perfectly symmetrical; i.e., a face-on view, hair parted in the middle, arms <u>not</u> folded, etc.

7.2 _, b, and c

7.4 $\alpha = [\alpha] \times \ell \times d \quad V = \pi r^2 \ell, \quad \ell = \frac{V}{\pi r^2} = \frac{300\ \text{cm}^3}{\pi \times 6.25\ \text{cm}^2} = 15.3\ \text{cm}$

$[\alpha] = 66°, \quad \ell = 15.3\ \text{cm} = 1.53\ \text{dc}, \quad d = 60/300 = 0.2\ \text{g mL}^{-1}$

therefore $\alpha = +20.2°$

7.5 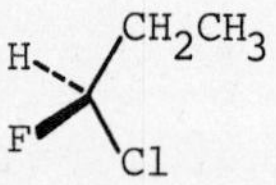

or

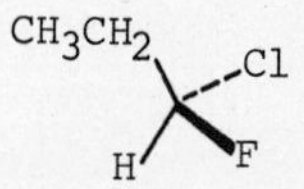

Be sure to note that there are other ways you can draw this compound

7.6 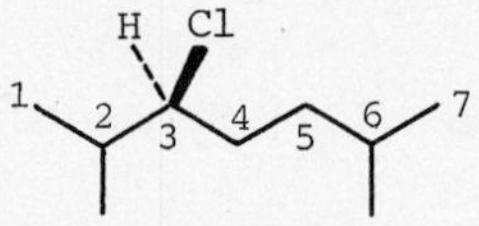

(S)-3-chloro-2,6-dimethylheptane

7.7 (a) 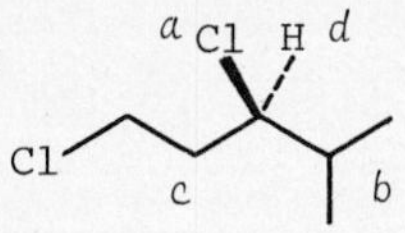

$(CH_3)_2CH$- has higher rank than $Cl\text{-}CH_2\text{-}CH_2$ because the <u>first difference</u> in going out the chain is two carbons (two methyls) vs. one carbon ($Cl\text{-}CH_2$); the fact that there is a chlorine farther out doesn't matter.

Lowest priority <u>in back</u>: 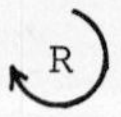

(b) 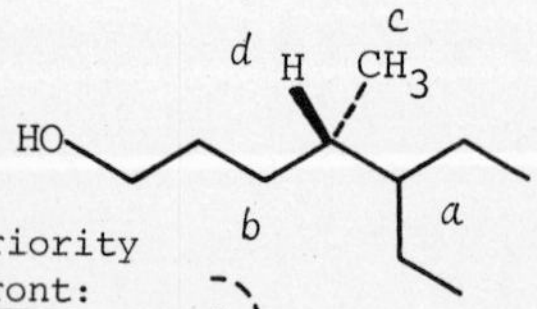

In this drawing, the lowest priority (d) is in front so when you go from a → c [↺] you have to reverse the assignment: S

Lowest priority <u>in front</u>: 

7.8 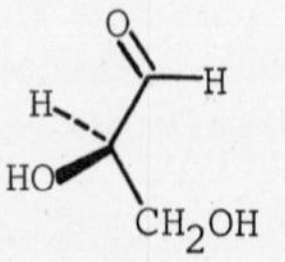

=

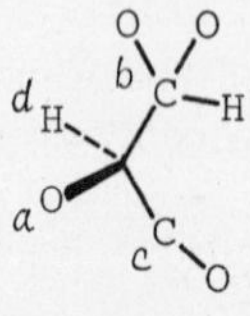

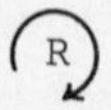

7.9

(a) 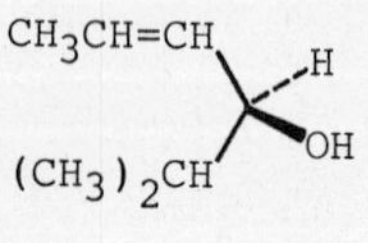

=

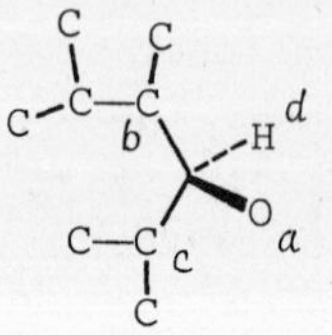

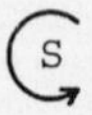

(b) 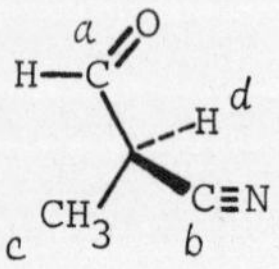

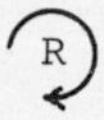

7.10

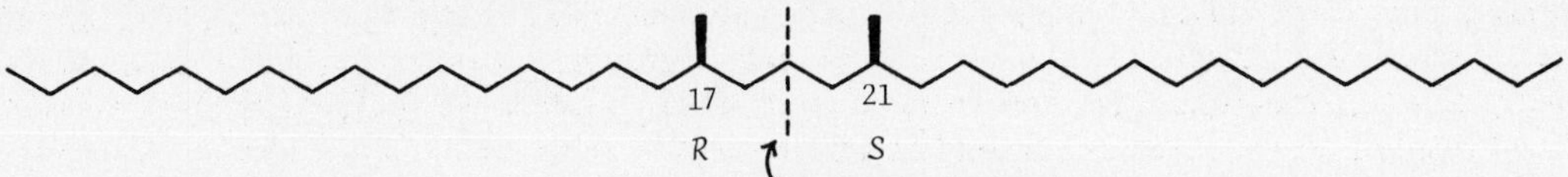

17 21
R   S

plane of symmetry; compound is meso

7.11

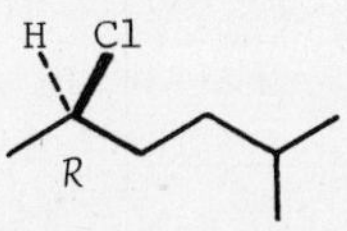

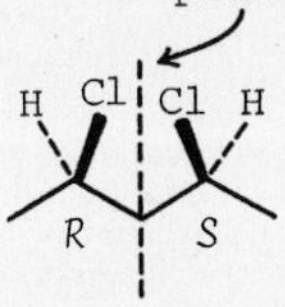

2-(R)-chloro-5-methylhexane   2(R),4(S)-2,4-dichloropentane

7.15

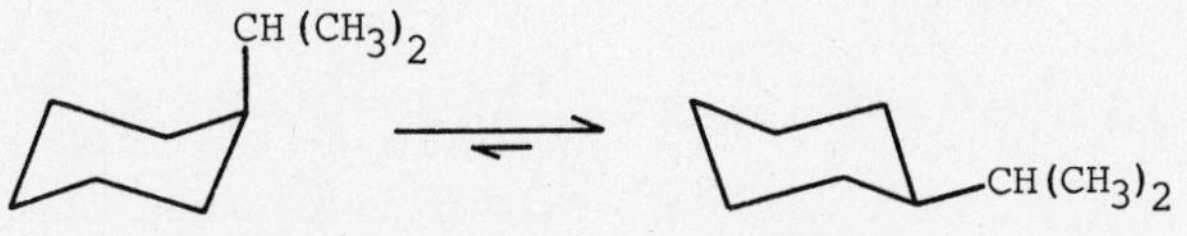

$\Delta G^\circ = -RT \ln K$ (ΔG° values are listed in Table 7.1)

$-2.1 \text{ kcal mole}^{-1} = -2100 \text{ cal mole}^{-1} = -(1.987 \text{ cal deg}^{-1} \text{mole}^{-1})(298 \text{ deg}) \ln K$

$K = 35$

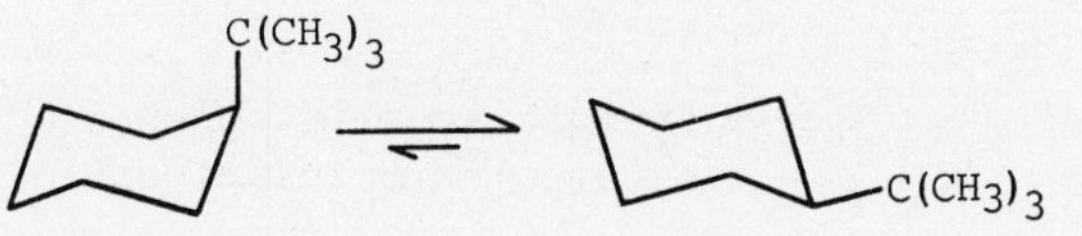

$(-5000 \text{ to } -6000) = = 1.987 \times 298 \times \ln K$

$K \approx 4600 \text{ to } 25,000$

7.16

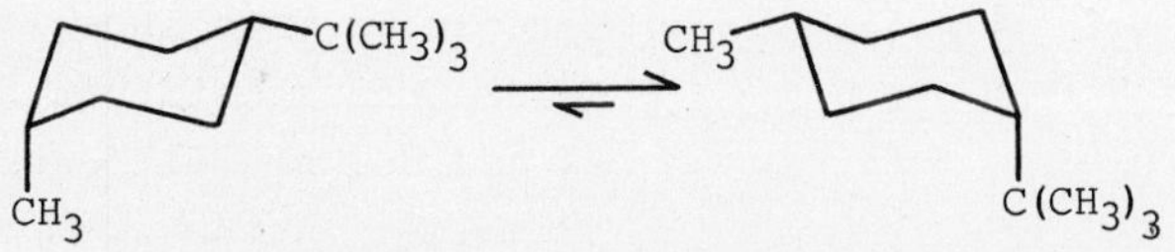

axial $CH_3 \longrightarrow$ equatorial CH_3: $\Delta G^\circ = -1.7 \text{ kcal mole}^{-1}$

equatorial $C(CH_3)_3 \longrightarrow$ axial $C(CH_3)_3$: $\Delta G^\circ \approx 5\text{-}6 \text{ kcal mole}^{-1}$ *(choose 5)*

Sum : $\Delta G^\circ \approx +3.3 \text{ kcal mole}^{-1}$

$\Delta G^\circ = -RT \ln K = +3,300 = -(1.987)(298) \ln K$

$K = 0.0038$ *(i.e., conformation on the left is strongly favored)*

7.E   Answers and Explanations for Problems

1. (a) $1 \underline{M} \ C_5H_{11}Cl = 106.5 \text{ g liter}^{-1} = 0.1065 \text{ g ml}^{-1} = c$

$l = 10 \text{ cm} = 1 \text{ dc}$

$\alpha = +3.64^\circ; \quad [\alpha]_D = \dfrac{\alpha}{l \times c} = \dfrac{3.64}{1 \times 0.1065} = +34.2^\circ$

(b) $c = 0.096 \text{ g ml}^{-1}, \quad l = 0.5 \text{ dc}, \quad \alpha = -1.80^\circ;$

therefore, $[\alpha]_D = -37.5^\circ$

2.   (a), three: RR, SS, and meso (RS)

(b) and (c), four: RR, SS, RS, and SR

(d) and (e), eight: RRR, RRS, RSR, SRR, RSS, SRS, SSR, and SSS

When no possibility of meso compounds exists, as in these cases, the number of possible stereoisomers is equal to 2^n, where n = the number of stereocenters in the molecule.

(f) is achiral.

3. (a)

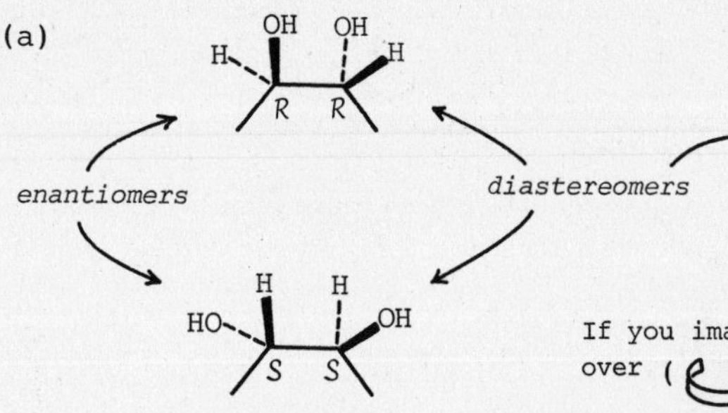

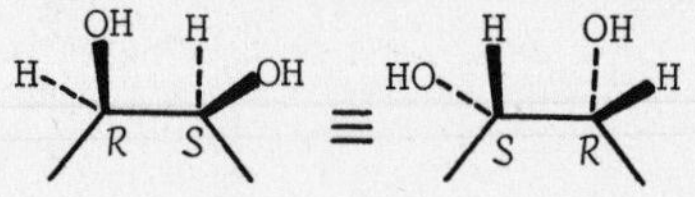

enantiomers   *diasteromers*   (meso)

If you imagine turning one of the pictures of the meso compound
over (   ),   you can see that they represent the same structure.
180°

(b)

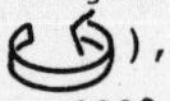

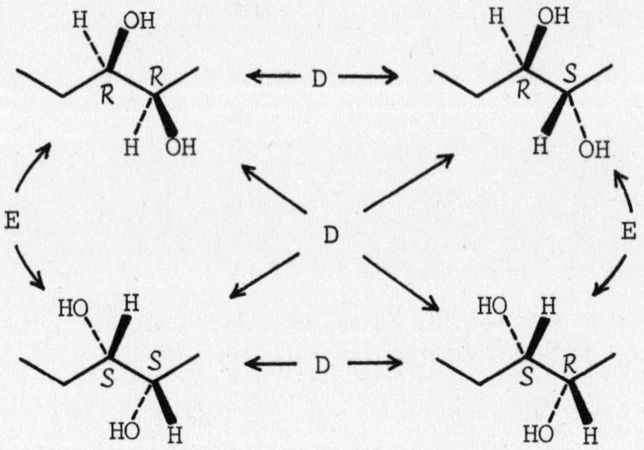

There is no meso isomer in
this case because the two
ends of the molecules are
different.

E = enantiomeric relationship
D = diastereomeric relationship

(c)

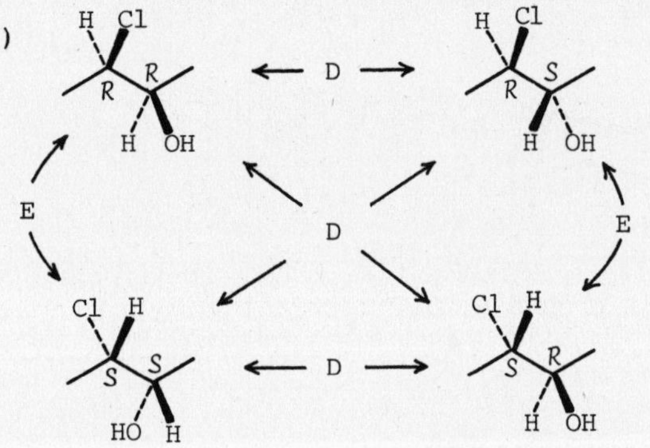

There is no meso isomer
because the substituents at
C-2 and C-3 are different.

(d)

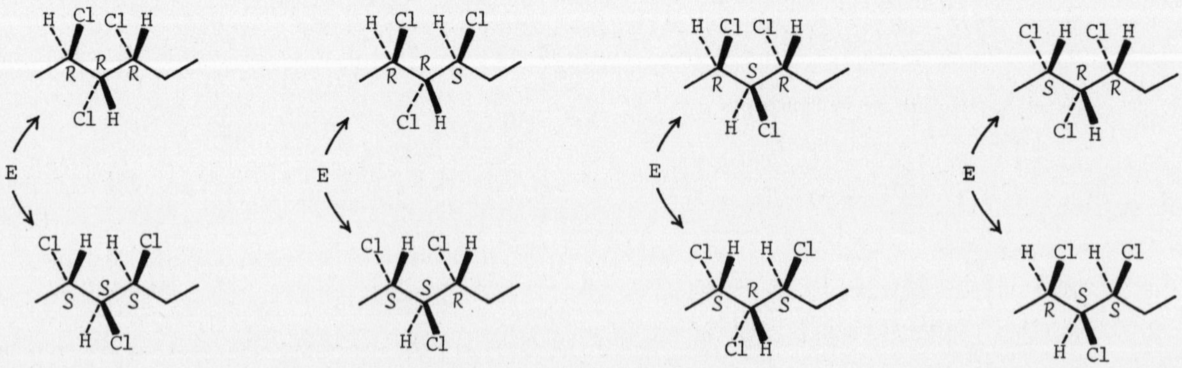

All pairs not indicated to be enantiomers are diastereomers.

(e)

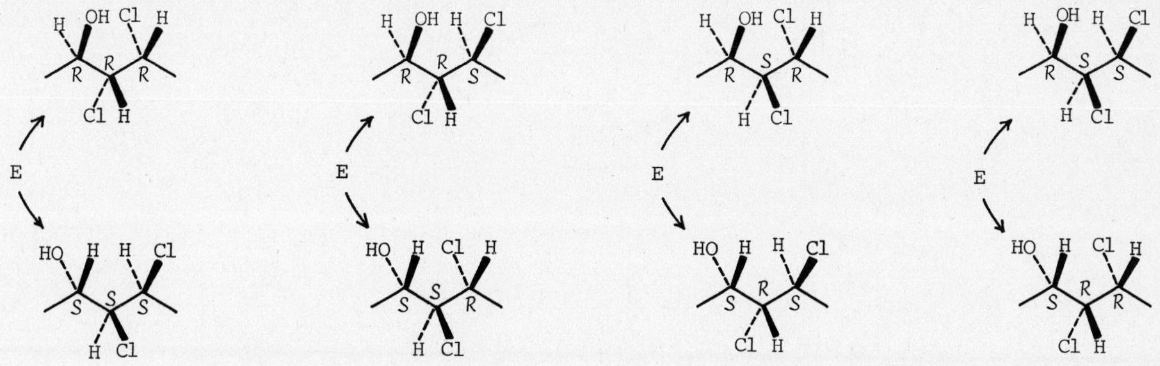

All pairs not indicated to be enantiomers are diastereomers.

4.

(a) 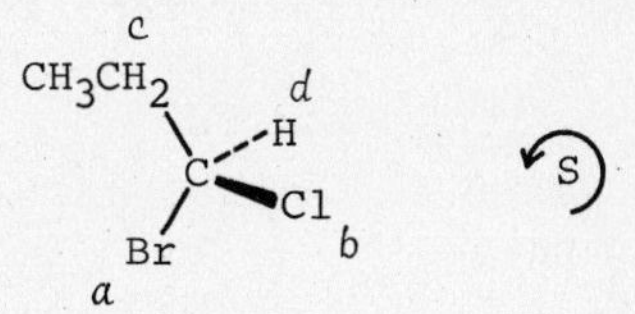 CH₃CH₂ ... C ... H, Cl, Br   S   lowest priority in back

(b) 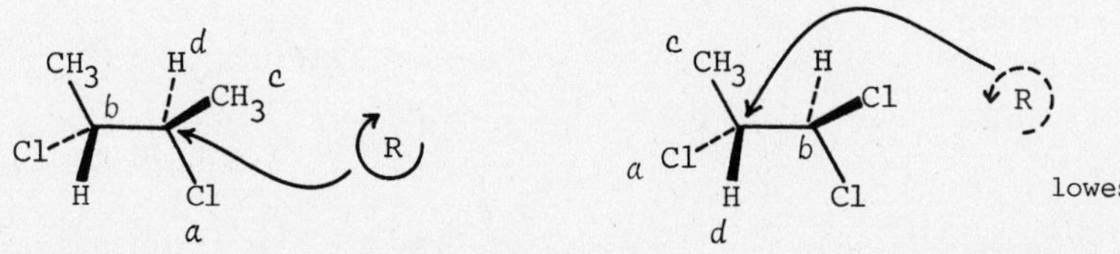 This is the R,R-diastereomer

(c) 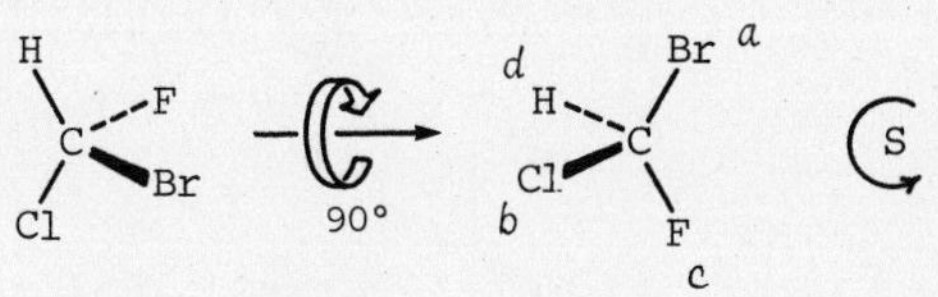 90°   S   (d) 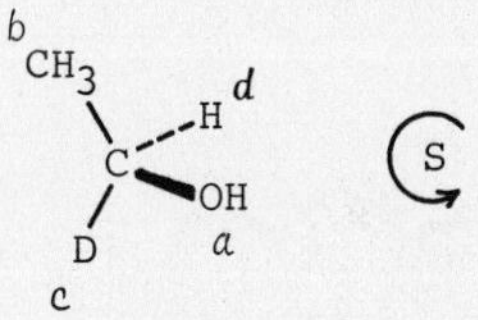   S

(e) 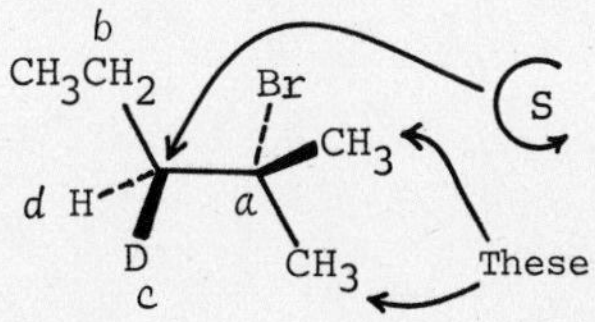 These groups are the same, so the bromine-containing carbon is not a stereocenter

(f) 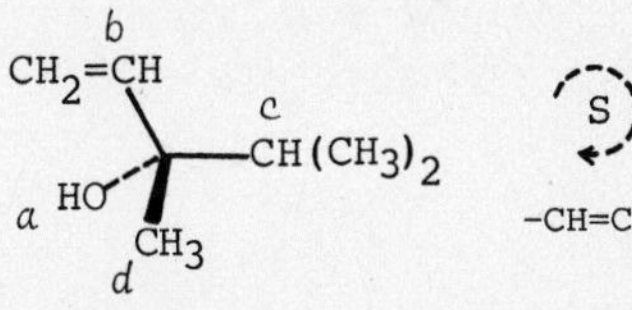 -CH=CH₂ counts as 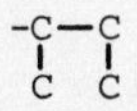 and therefore has priority over

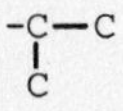

(g) 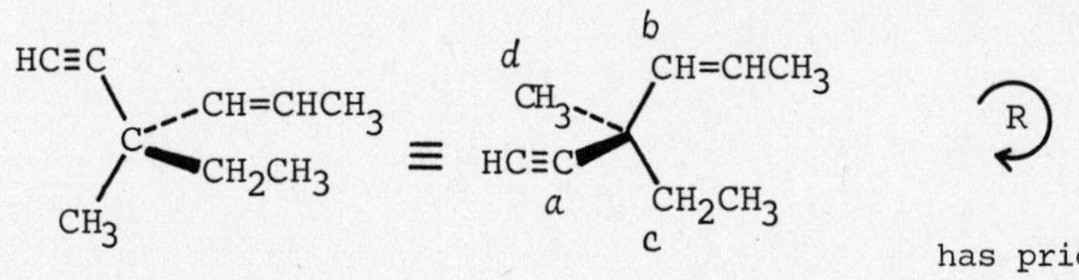 -C≡CH counts as 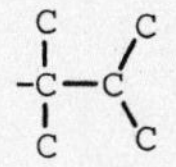 and has priority over -CH=CHCH₃ (which is equivalent to 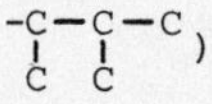)

(h) 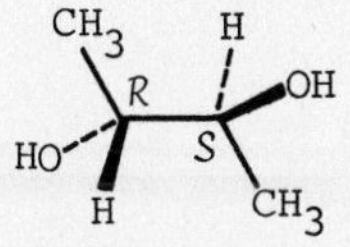 (meso)

5. (a)

≡

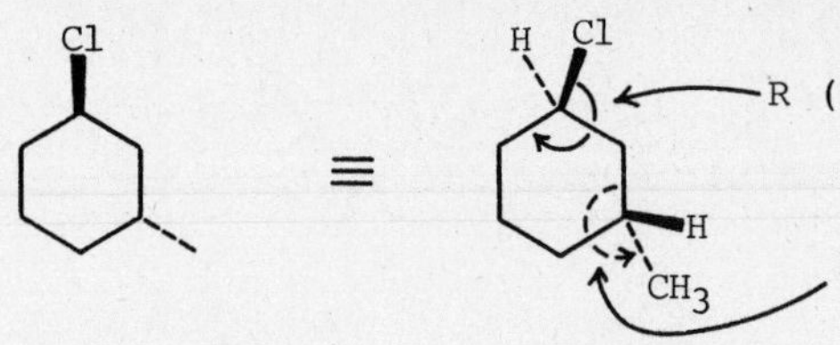

R (hydrogen is in back)

R (hydrogen is in front)

(b)

R (hydrogen is in front)

(c)

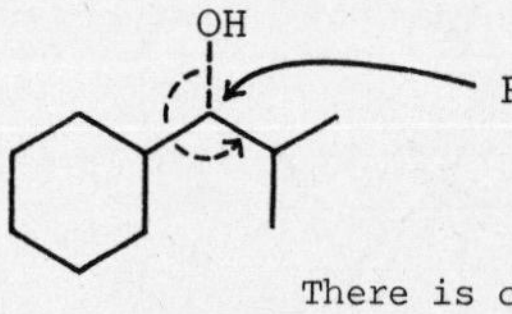

There is only one stereocenter in this molecule.

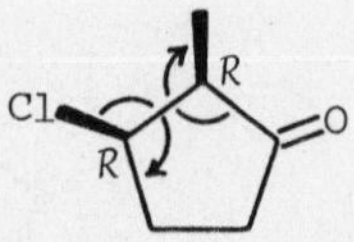

(d) Determining the stereochemistry at C-6 is straightforward:

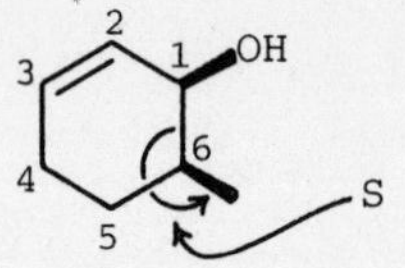

It is harder for C-1. Write the two paths along the ring in terms of the equivalent carbon chains:

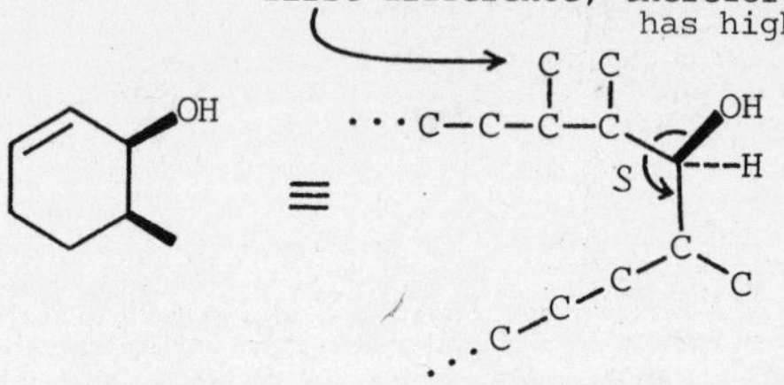

first difference, therefore this direction has higher priority

≡

6. (a)

(b)

(c)

≡

(d)

≡

7.

these are the same molecule

enantiomers

180°

180°

these are the same molecule

meso

meso

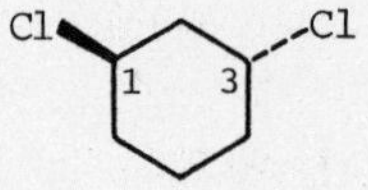

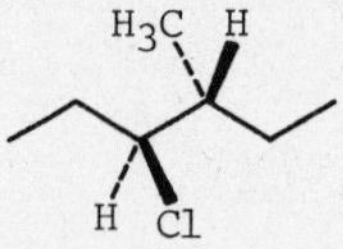

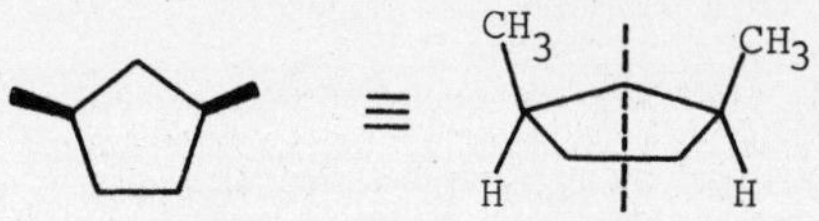

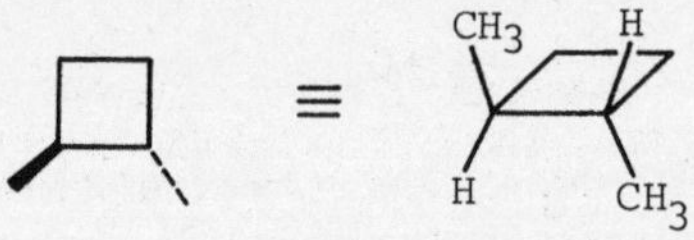

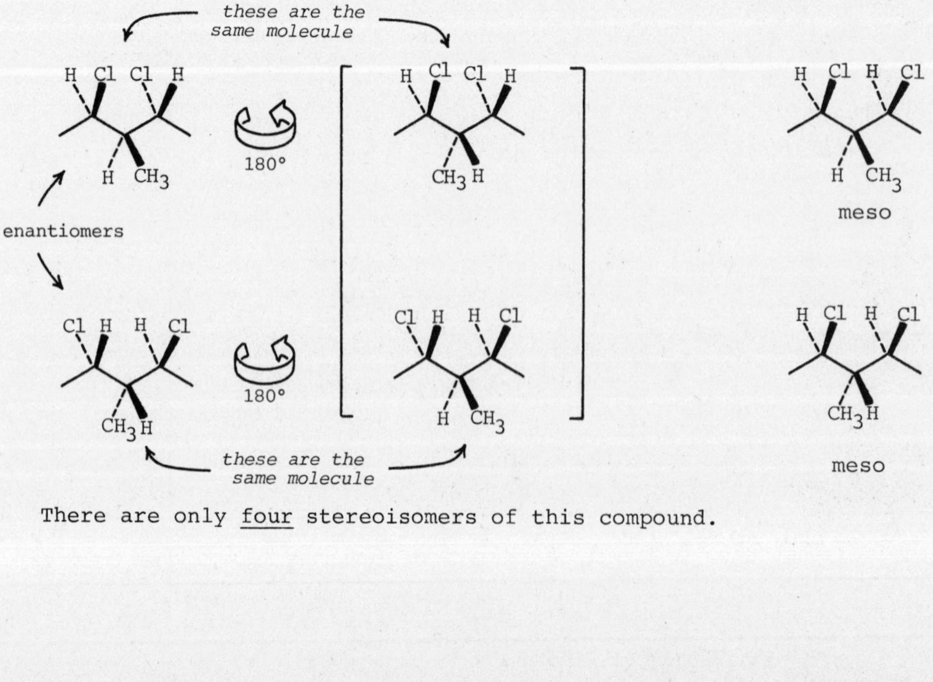

There are only <u>four</u> stereoisomers of this compound.

8.

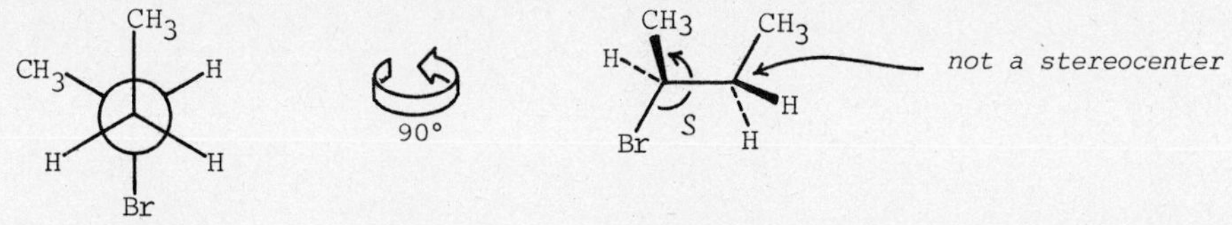

not a stereocenter

(a)

the same

(b)

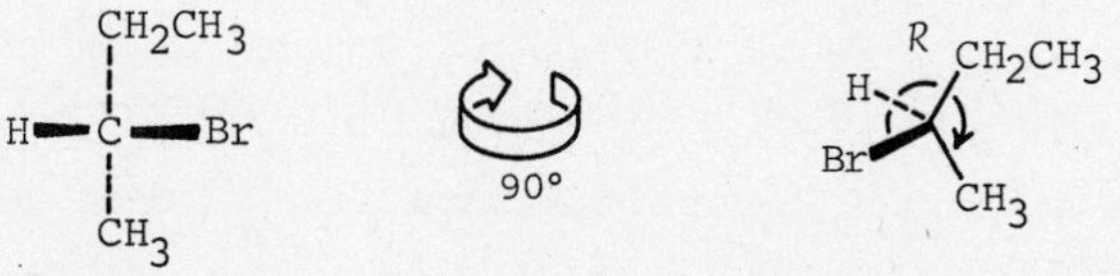

Enantiomer

(c)

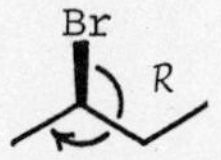

Enantiomer

(d)

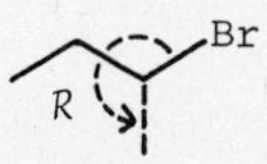

Enantiomer

9.

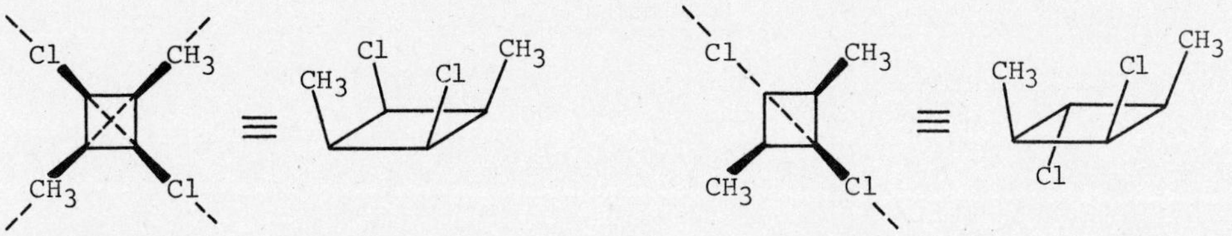

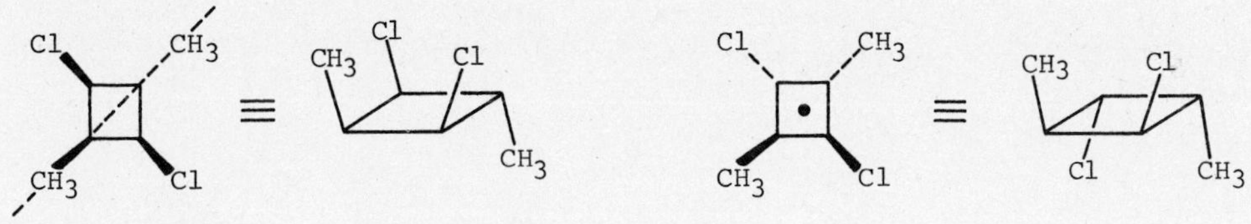

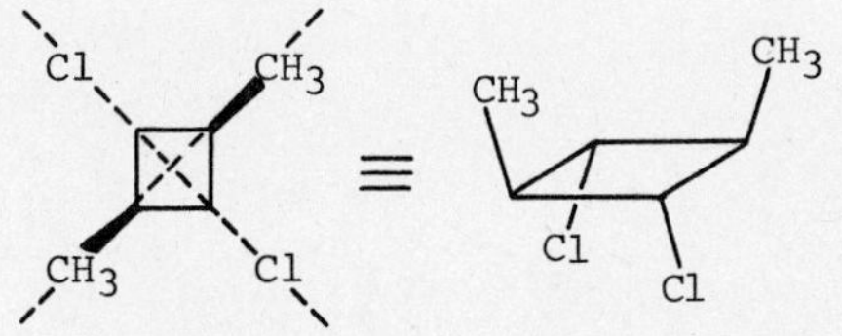

------ = plane of symmetry

• = center of symmetry

None of these stereoisomers is chiral.

10.

(a)

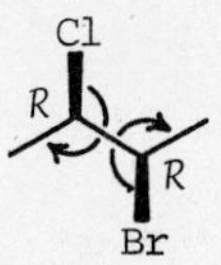

(b)

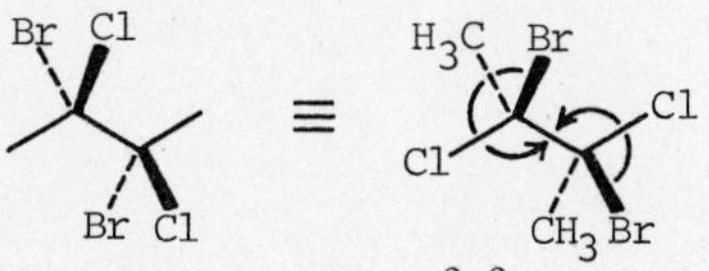

S,S

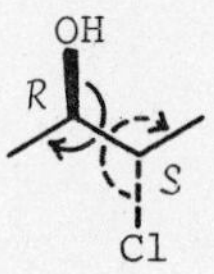

This is a good one to make a model for

(c)

(d)

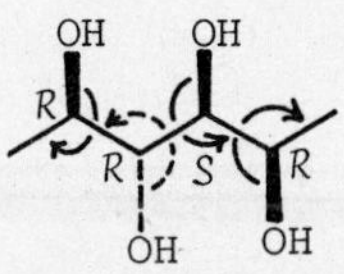

(e)

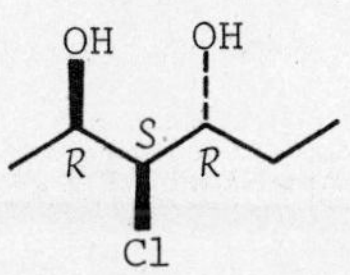

(f)

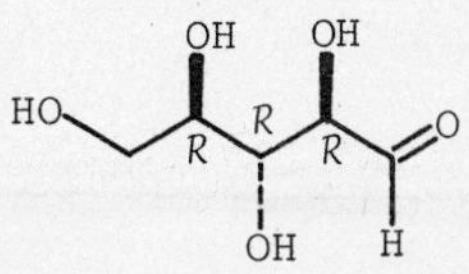

11. (a) [structure] (b) [structure] (c) [structure]

this is not a stereocenter: the two carbon
substituents are identical! [See problem #7.]

12. [structures] ≡ [structure] $\xrightarrow[\text{other chair}]{\text{flip to}}$ [structure]

These are mirror images of each other.

That is, the two conformations are enantiomeric. The two enantiomers of
cis-1,2-dimethylcyclohexane are simply different conformations of the same
molecule. Because the chair ⇌ chair interconversion is fast at ordinary
temperatures, *cis*-1,2-dimethylcyclohexane behaves, on the time-average,
as an achiral, meso compound.

13. $\Delta G° = -RT \ln K$

		$\Delta G°$ (kcal mole^{-1})	$\ln K$	K	Percent Equatorial
(a)	[structure]	-1.0	1.69	5.42	84.4
(b)	[structure]	-0.2	0.338	1.40	58.3
(c)	[structure]	-0.25	0.422	1.53	60.5

14.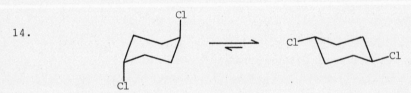

$\Delta G° \cong 2 \times \Delta G°$ for axial ⟶ equatorial chlorocyclohexane
        $= 2 \times 0.5 = 1.0$ kcal mole^{-1}

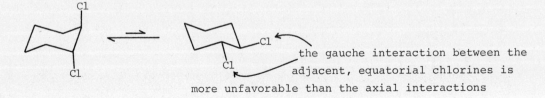

the gauche interaction between the
adjacent, equatorial chlorines is
more unfavorable than the axial interactions

15.

Cis   C-1—C-2   C-1—C-6   C-2—C-3   Sum of gauche interactions

3

Trans

1

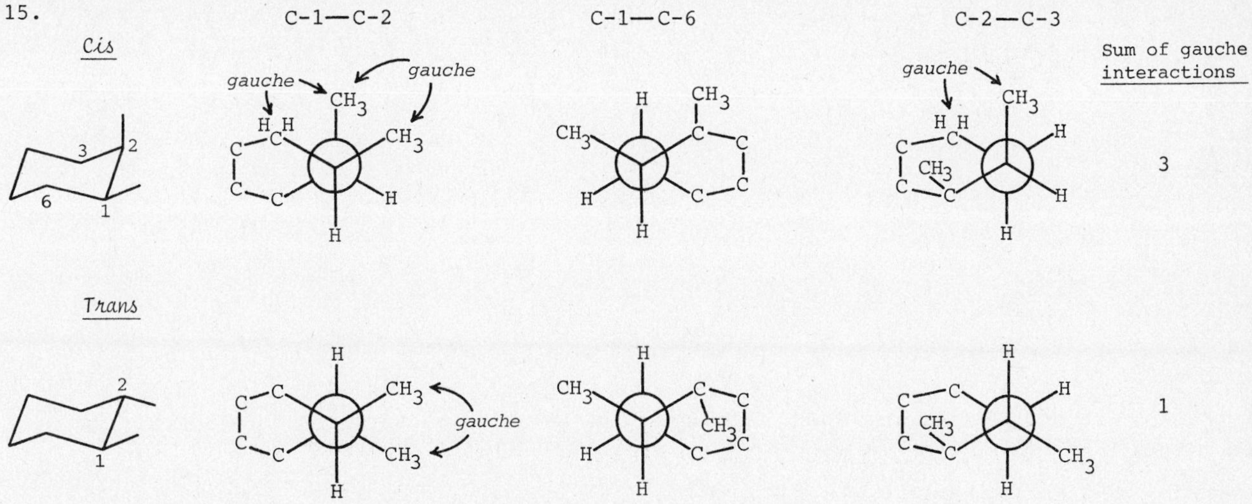

The <u>cis</u> isomer has two more gauche interactions than the <u>trans</u>: $2 \times 0.9 = 1.8$ kcal mole^{-1}

From Appendix I: ΔH°_f(cis) $- \Delta H^\circ_f$(trans) $= -41.3 - (-43.0) = 1.7$ kcal mole^{-1}

16.

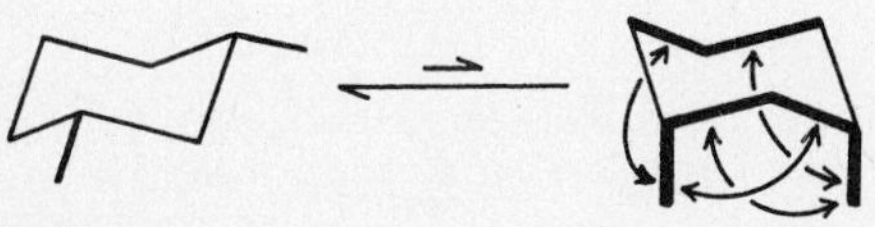

no gauche   four gauche interactions, which suggest $4 \times 0.9 = 3.6$ kcal mole^{-1} less stable
interactions

The diaxial conformation of <u>cis</u>-1,3-dimethylcyclohexane is even
more unstable because the two methyl groups are so close that
they are actually trying to occupy the same space:

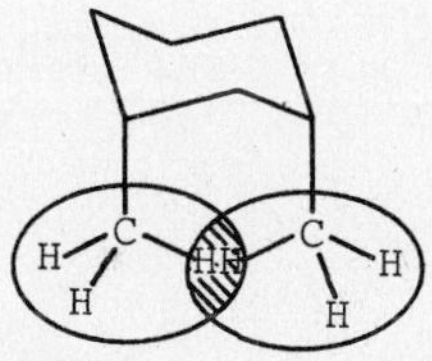

17. (a)

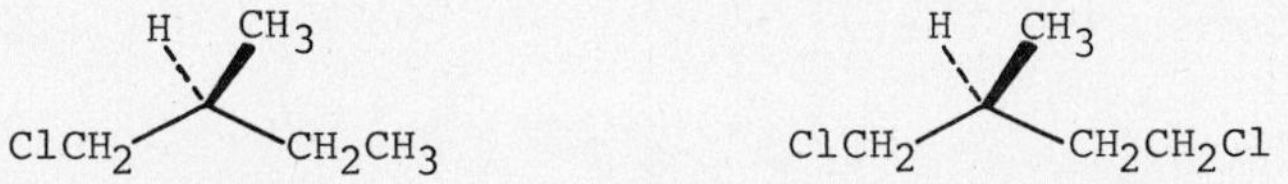

$ClCH_2$ CH_2CH_3 $ClCH_2$ CH_2CH_2Cl stereocenter is unaffected by
                                                              reaction at the 4-position

This demonstrates that there is no *a priori* relationship between sign of
rotation ((+) or (−)) and configuration (R or S).

(b) $ClCH_2\overset{CH_3}{\underset{Cl}{C}}CH_2CH_3$ is produced *via* the $ClCH_2\overset{CH_3}{\underset{\cdot}{C}}CH_2CH_3$ free radical intermediate.
Since the product from this intermediate is racemic, the
intermediate itself is probably achiral, either because it is achiral by
symmetry (planar radical), or (if the radical is pyramidal) because it
inverts much faster than it reacts. Other evidence is required to distinguish between these two alternatives.

$ClCH_2—\overset{\cdot}{C}\overset{CH_3}{\underset{CH_2CH_3}{}}$ $ClCH_2\overset{\cdot}{\underset{CH_2CH_3}{C}}CH_3$ $\xrightarrow{\text{fast}}$ $ClCH_2\overset{CH_2CH_3}{\underset{\cdot}{C}}CH_3$

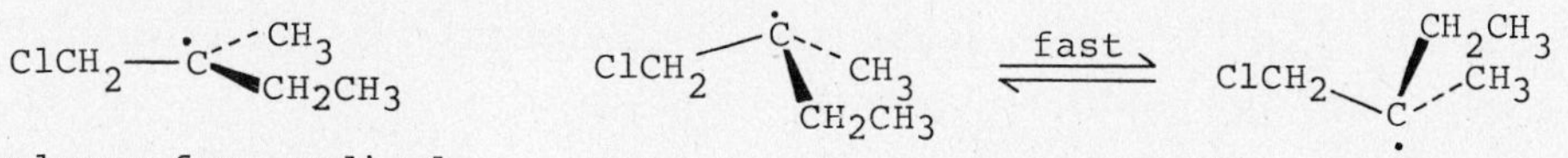

planar free radical   rapidly equilibrating pyramidal free radicals
(achiral)   (effectively achiral)

18.

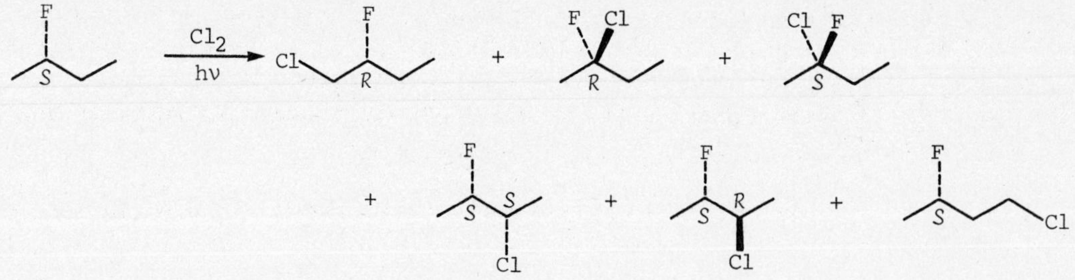

(a)

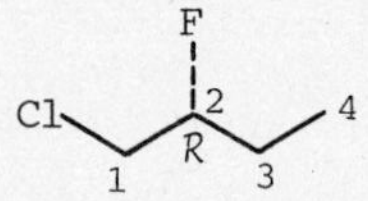

(b)

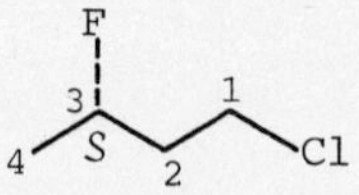

The stereocenter has been unaffected in formation of these two products. The 1-chloro-2-fluoro isomer is "R" only because of a change in the priority of the substituents.

(c)

Equal amounts formed via the achiral intermediate radical:

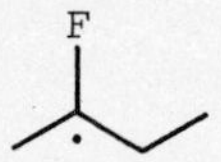

(see problem #17(b))

(d)

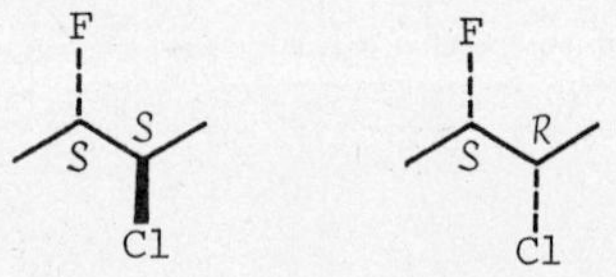

16% 24%

The radical intermediate leading to these isomers is still chiral:

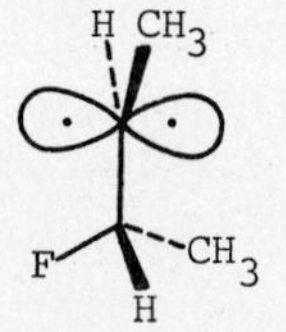

The transition states leading to the two products are therefore <u>diastereomeric</u>:

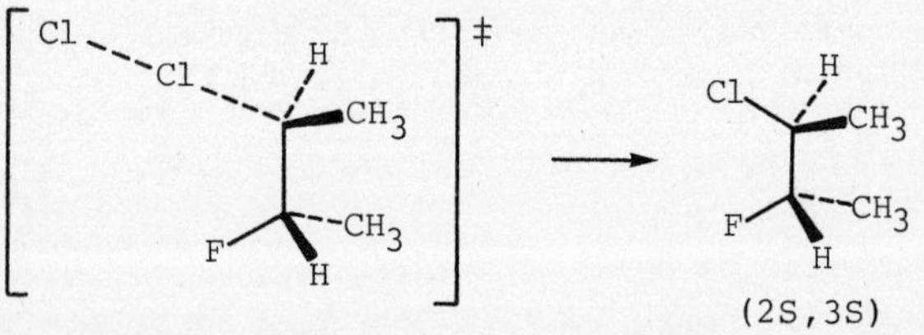

(2S,3S)

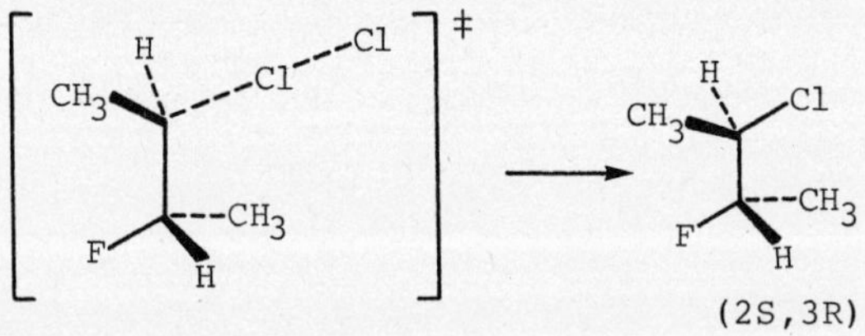

(2S,3R)

Since the transition states are diastereomeric, they will have different physical properties, including different free energies of formation. Since the two competing reactions start at the same place and pass through transition states of different energies, the two activation energies are different. Therefore one diastereomer will be formed in greater amount than the other.

7.F Supplementary Problems

S1. Calculate $[\alpha]_D$ for each of the following compounds:

(a) A 0.13 <u>M</u> solution of strychnine (mw = 334.4) in ethanol in a 10-cm cell gives an observed rotation of -2.26°.

(b) A solution of 3.2 g of common sugar (sucrose, mw = 342.3) in 15 ml of water in a 5-cm cell gives an observed rotation of +7.1°.

S2. Predict the observed rotation (α) for the following solutions. Assume a cell length of 10 cm for each case.

(a) 3 g of morphine hydrate (mw = 303.3, $[\alpha]_D$ = -132°) in 50 ml of methanol.

(b) Pure (-)-2-chlorobutane (d = 0.87, $[\alpha]_D$ = -8.48°).

S3. (a) Pure (−)-α-pinene has a specific rotation, $[\alpha]_D^{20} = -51.3°$. What is the optical purity of a sample of α-pinene which shows a specific rotation of −35.9° (i.e., how much of each enantiomer is present)?

(b) Predict the specific rotation of a mixture of 30% of (−)-2-bromobutane (d = 1.254, $[\alpha]_D^{20} = -23.13°$) and 70% of the (+)-enantiomer.

S4. For each of the following compounds, make a model and label each stereocenter R or S as appropriate.

(a)

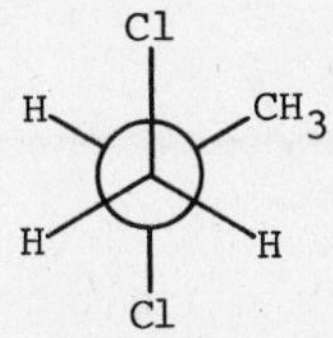

(b)

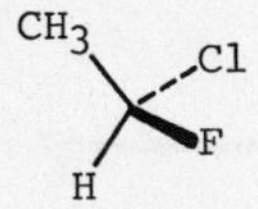

(c)

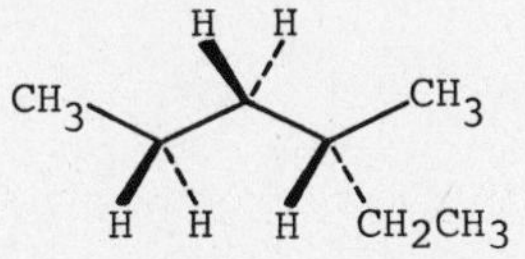

(d)

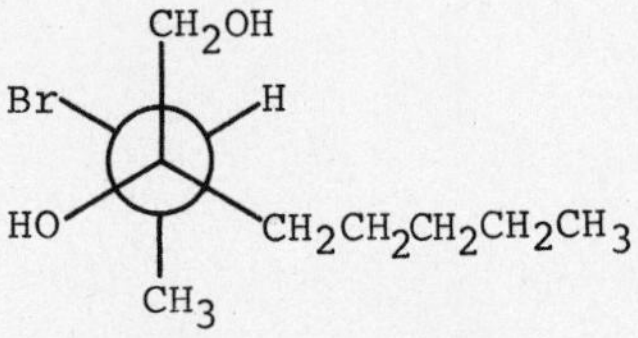

S5. What is the relationship between the molecules of each of the following pairs (i.e., are they the same, enantiomers, diastereomers, structural isomers, etc.)? For each stereocenter in these molecules, assign R or S as appropriate.

(a)

(b)

(c)

(d)

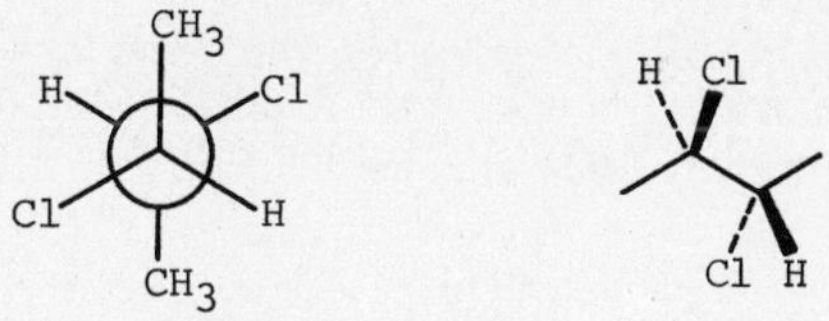

(e)

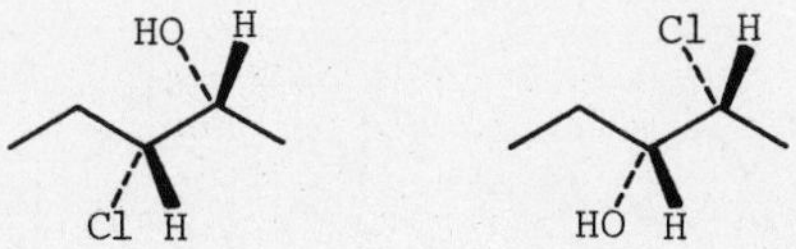

(f)

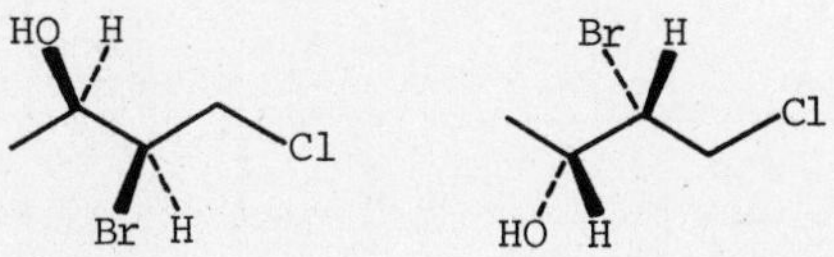

(g)

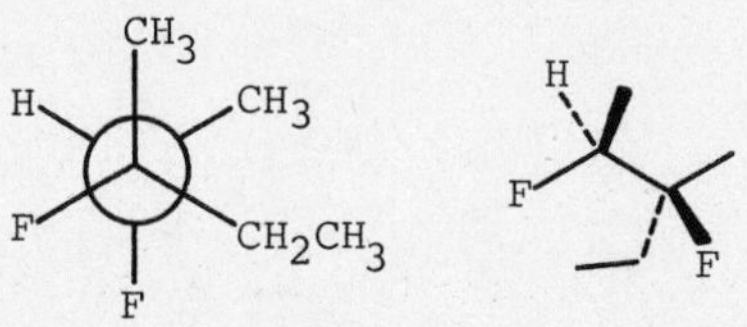

(h)

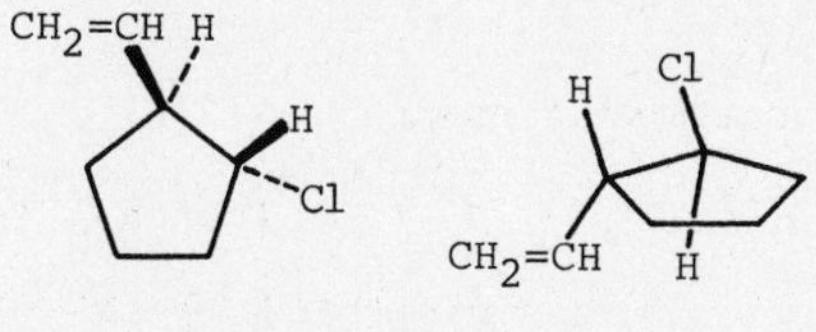

S6. For each of the compounds illustrated below, draw: (1) the enantiomer (2) a diastereomer (3) a Newman projection (for (a)) or a line drawing (for (b)).

(a)

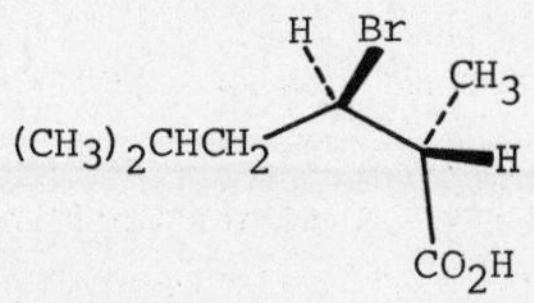

(b)

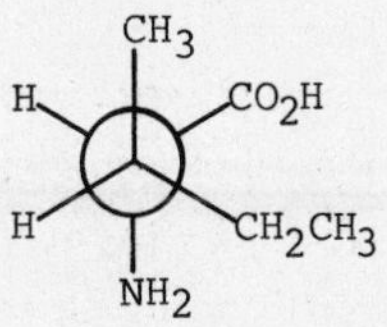

S7. Write structures for all of the isomers of trimethylcyclopentane.
Which ones are chiral and which ones are achiral?

S8. Consider the free-radical chlorination of 1,1,4,4-tetramethylcyclohexane with Cl_2.

    (a) Write the structures of all of the possible monochloro isomers.

    (b) Assign the configuration of each stereocenter as you have drawn it.

    (c) Predict the relative amounts of each isomer.

7.G   Answers to Supplementary Problems

S1. (a) $\dfrac{0.13 \times 334.4}{1000} = 0.0435$ g ml^{-1}; $[\alpha]_D = \dfrac{-2.26}{1 \times 0.0435} = -52.0°$

(b) $[\alpha]_D = \dfrac{+7.1}{0.5 \times 3.2/15} = +66.6°$

S2. (a) $\alpha = [\alpha]_D \times \ell \times c$
$= -132 \times 1 \times 3/50 = -7.92°$

(b) $\alpha = -8.48 \times 1 \times 0.87 = -7.38°$

S3. (a)   -35.9° is 35.9/51.3 = 70% of the rotation expected for the pure enantiomer. There-fore "30%" of the mixture is racemic and "70%" of it is the pure (-)-enantiomer. For the whole mixture, then, 70% + 15% = 85% of it is the (-)-enantiomer and 15% of of it is the (+)-enantiomer. The optical purity is 70%; this is frequently also referred to as the "enantiomeric excess".

(b)   Consider this mixture to be 60% racemic and 40% (+)-enantiomer:

(-)-enantiomer ⟶   ⟵ (+)-enantiomer
30% + 30% + 40% = 100%
racemic mixture   ↖ "(+)-enantiomer"

Because the racemic portion shows no rotation, the observed rotation will be 40% of that expected for the pure (+)-enantiomer: 0.4 × (-23.13) = -9.25°.

S4. (a) ≡ (structure)   R   (b) R   (c) R   (d) (structure)

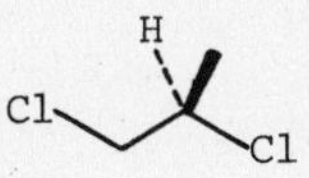

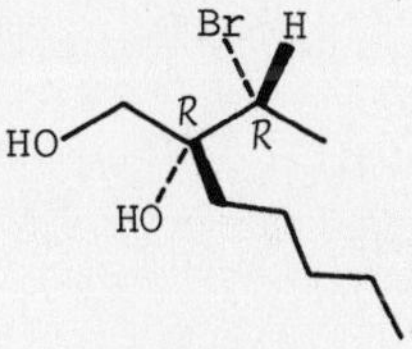

S5. (a) identical; R   (b) diastereomers: (structures)

(c) enantiomers (structure)

(d) identical: (structure)   *meso isomer*

(e) structural isomers: (structures)

(f) identical: (structure)

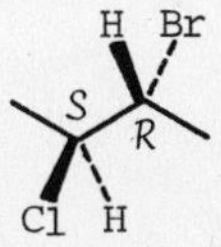

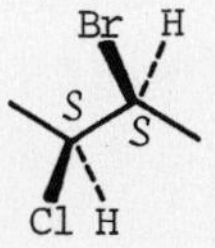

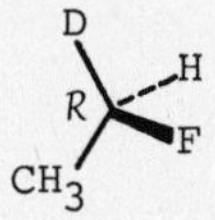

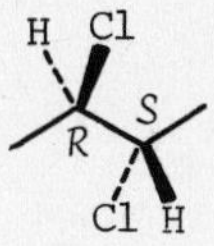

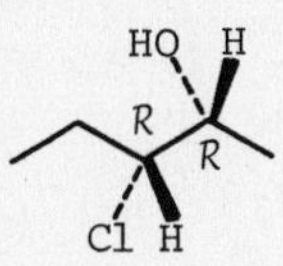

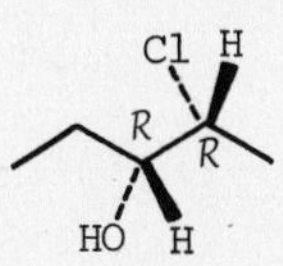

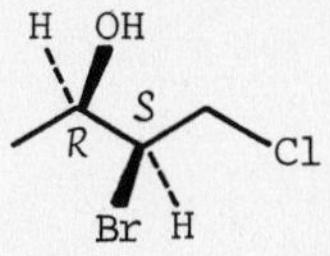

(g) Diastereomers:

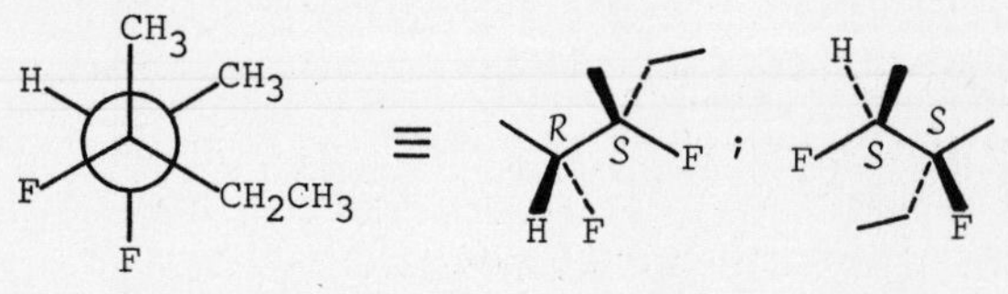

(h) Enantiomers:

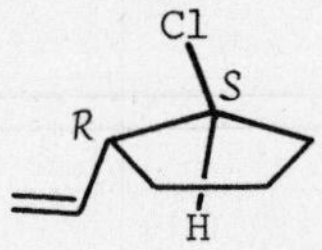

S6. (a)

(1)

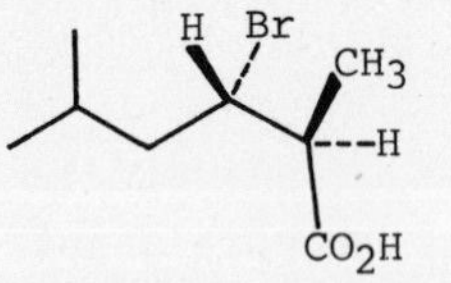

(2)

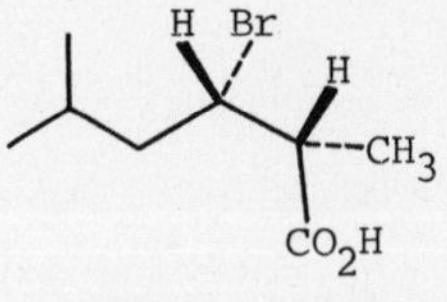

or

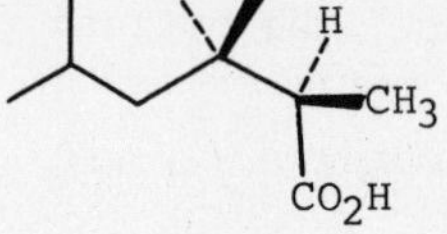

(3)

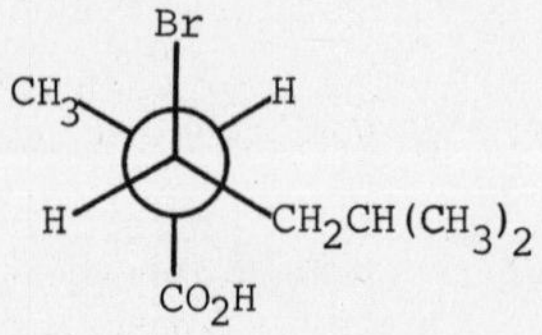

(b)

(1)

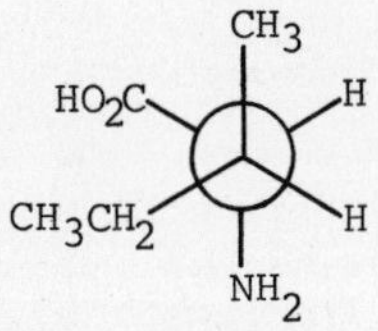

(2)

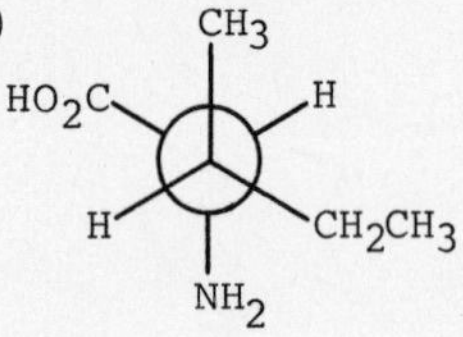

or

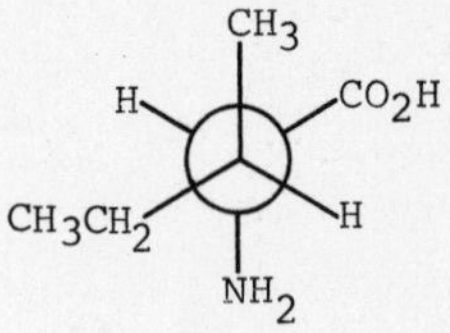

(3)

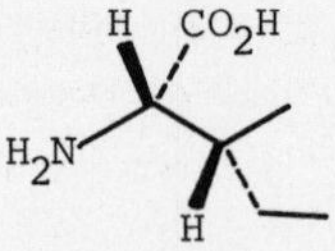

S7. <u>Chiral:</u>

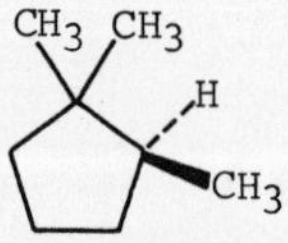

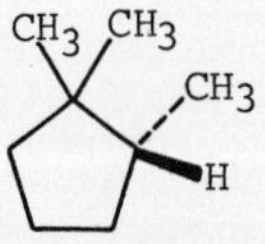

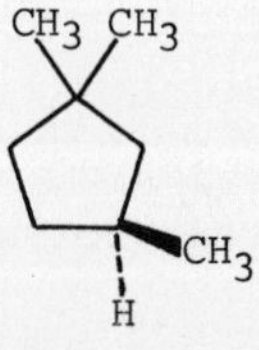

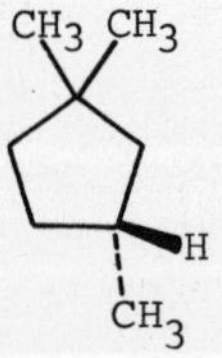

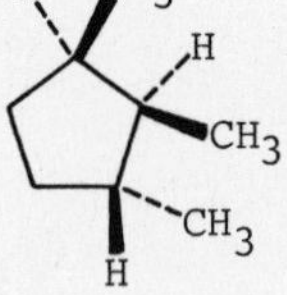

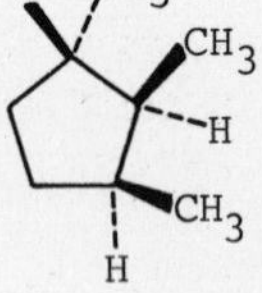

<u>Achiral:</u>

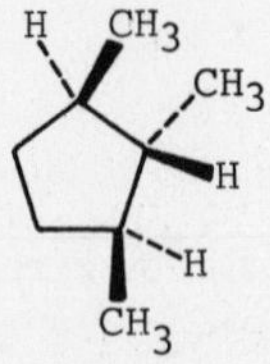

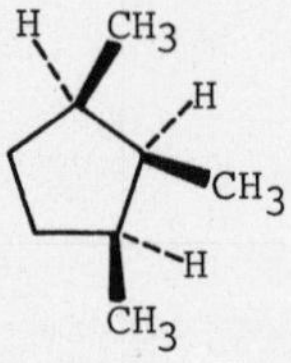

S8.

(a),(b)

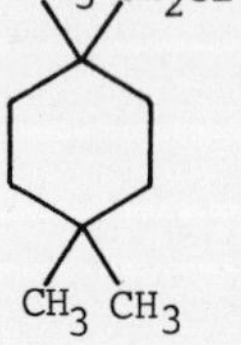

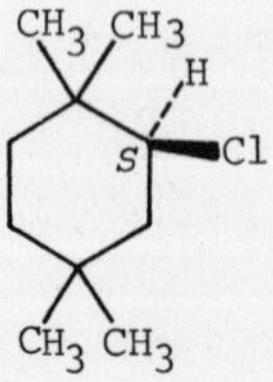

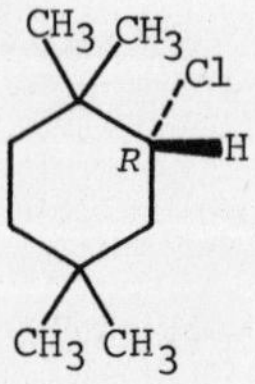

(c)   12 × 1 = 12; 27%   4 × 4 = 16; 36%   4 × 4 = 16; 36%

8. ALKYL HALIDES; NUCLEOPHILIC SUBSTITUTION AND ELIMINATION

8.A   Chapter Outline and Important Terms Introduced

8.1   <u>Structure of Alkyl Halides</u> (size of halogens, bond lengths)

dipole moment   Van der Waals radius

8.2   <u>Physical Properties of Alkyl Halides</u> (boiling points, melting points)
polarizability

8.3   <u>Conformations of Alkyl Halides</u>
barriers to rotation

8.4   <u>Some Uses of Halogenated Hydrocarbons</u> (from dry cleaning to DDT)

8.5   <u>Nomenclature of Organometallic Compounds</u>
e.g. butyllithium, ethylmagnesium chloride (without a space between the organic prefix
and the name of the metal)

8.6   <u>Structures of Organometallic Compounds</u>

electropositive   three-center, two-electron bond
carbanion   Grignard reagent

8.7   <u>Physical Properties of Organometallic Compounds</u> (sensitive to water and air)

8.8   <u>Preparation of Organometallic Compounds</u>
   A.   Reaction of an Alkyl Halide with a Metal
        Grignard reaction   formation of alkyllithium
   B.   Reaction of Organometallic Compounds with Salts
        electropositivity

8.9   <u>Reactions of Organometallic Compounds</u>
   A.   Hydrolysis: specific deuteration
   B.   Reaction with Halogens
   C.   Reaction with Oxygen

8.B   Important Reactions Introduced

<u>Formation of organometallic compounds from alkyl halides</u> (8.8.A)

Equation: $R-X + 2 M \longrightarrow R-M + MX$ (M = monovalent metal, such as Li or Na)
                 $R-X + Mg \longrightarrow R-Mg-X$ (formation of Grignard reagent)

Generality: R = alkyl or aryl
              M = highly electropositive metal (such as Li, Na, K, Mg)
              X = Cl, Br, I (F not usually reactive enough)
              an ether is the usual solvent

Key features: important way to prepare **anionic** carbon derivatives

<u>Reaction of organometallic compounds with salts</u> <u>(8.8.B)</u>

Equation: $n\ R-M + M'X_n \longrightarrow R_nM' + n\ MX$

Generality: equilibrium process
              M' must be less electropositive (= more electronegative) than M

Key features: important way to prepare organometallic compounds with metals which are not electro-
               positive enough to react directly with R-X

<u>Reactions</u> <u>of</u> <u>organometallic</u> <u>compounds</u> <u>with</u> <u>water</u>   (8.9.A)

Equation: $R-M$ + H_2O ——> $R-H$ + $M-OH$

Generality: M = Li, Na, K, Mg, other metals with electronegativities less than 1.7

Key features: Useful for preparing specifically deuterated or tritiated compounds

8.C   Important Concepts and Hints

In this chapter two important classes of organic compounds are introduced: alkyl halides and organometallic compounds. They are discussed primarily from the point of view of structure and physical properties, as well as the fact that alkyl halides are the most important precursors to organometallic compounds.

One of the important concepts to realize from this chapter is the difference in the electronic character between these two classes of compounds. In the alkyl halides, the halogen is **more electronegative** than carbon, and the bond between the two elements is polarized toward the halogen. That is, the electrons that occupy the bonding orbital between the two atoms are pulled toward the halogen atom, leaving the carbon atom with a partial positive charge. The situation is exactly reversed in the organometallic compounds: metals are **more electropositive** (= less electronegative) than carbon, with the result that there is partial negative charge on carbon.

As you might expect, and as you will see more dramatically in Chapter 9, where the major reactions of alkyl halides are presented, the fact that alkyl halides and organometallic compounds have opposite electronic characteristics means that they have the opposite behavior when it comes to the types of reactions that they undergo. Because the carbon atom in organometallic compounds is partially negative, it comes as no surprise that these compounds react with molecules that are positively charged. The simplest case is the reaction with a proton, as described in the section on hydrolysis of organometallic species. Other examples are the equilibrium reactions between organometallic compounds and metal salts. In contrast, alkyl halides react with negatively charged molecules, or those which can at least furnish a pair of electrons for the new bond, as described in Chapter 9.

8.D   Answers to Exercises

8.1

$$H_3C \overset{\delta+}{-} \overset{\delta-}{X} \qquad \mu = q \cdot d$$

charge, distance, dipole moment

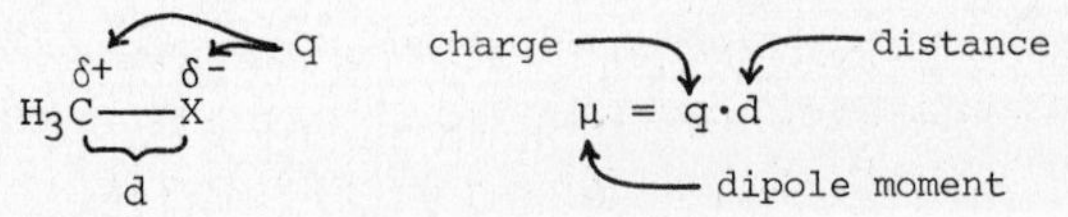

For X = F: $q = \dfrac{\mu}{d} = \dfrac{1.82 \times 10^{-18} \text{ esu} \cdot \text{cm}}{1.39 \times 10^{-8} \text{ cm}} = 1.3 \times 10^{-10}$ esu

One electronic charge is 4.8×10^{-10} esu, so 1.3×10^{-10} esu corresponds to
1.3/4.8 = 0.27 of an electronic charge.

X	μ (D = 10^{-18} esu·cm)	d (Å = 10^{-8} cm)	q (esu)	Fractional charge (q/4.8 × 10^{-10} esu)
F	1.82	1.39	1.3×10^{-10}	0.27
Cl	1.94	1.78	1.1×10^{-10}	0.23
Br	1.79	1.93	0.93×10^{-10}	0.19
I	1.64	2.14	0.77×10^{-10}	0.16

8.2   (a) <u>t</u>-Butyl bromide has a higher melting point than <u>n</u>-butyl bromide. Little internal freedom of motion needs to be lost on incorporation of the <u>t</u>-butyl bromide molecule into the crystal, whereas the <u>n</u>-butyl bromide molecule loses its freedom to rotate about the C_1-C_2 and C_2-C_3 bonds. Therefore entropy makes it more difficult for <u>n</u>-butyl bromide to crystallize (see Section 5.3).

(b) To estimate bp of [structure with Cl] :

Compare [structure] bp 36 °C

with [structure] bp 63 °C   +27

From [structure with Cl] bp 108 °C   +27

estimate [structure with Cl] (est. bp 135 °C)

To estimate bp of [structure with Cl] :

compare [structure] bp 36 °C

with [structure with Cl] bp 108 °C   +72

also [structure] bp 36 °C

with [structure] bp 63 °C   +27

From [structure] bp 69 °C   +27

estimate [structure] (est. bp 96 °C)   +72

and [structure with Cl] (est. bp 168 °C)

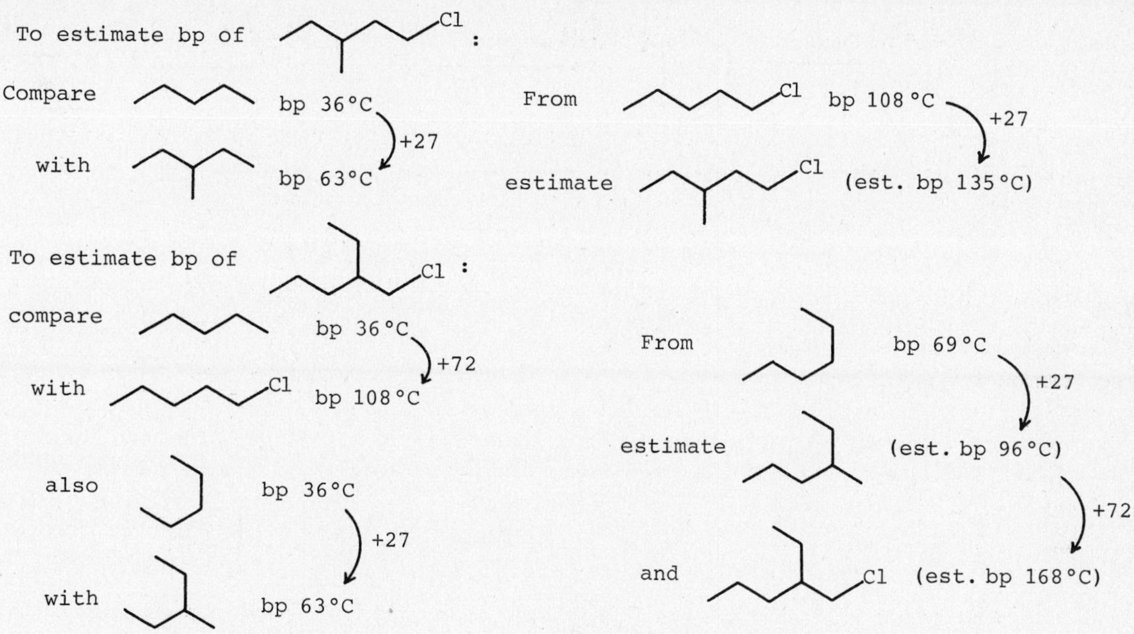

8.3   (a) isopropylmagnesium chloride   (d) tetramethyllead

      (b) tetramethylsilane   (e) diethyldimethylstannane

      (c) butyllithium

8.4   Lewis Structure   Dative Bonds

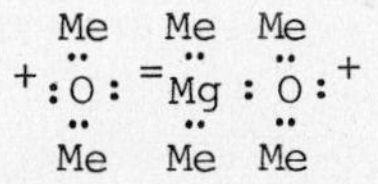

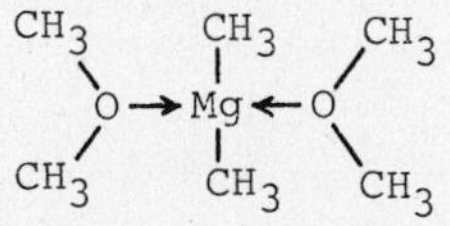

$$+ \overset{Me}{\underset{Me}{:\ddot{O}:}} \ = \overset{Me}{\underset{Me}{\ddot{Mg}}} \ \overset{Me}{\underset{Me}{:\ddot{O}:}} +$$

[structure: CH$_3$ / O → Mg ← O with CH$_3$ groups]

[*NOTE*: each "Me:" = H:$\overset{H}{\underset{H}{\ddot{C}}}$:]

According to the Lewis structure, each oxygen has one formal positive charge
(2 + ½ of 6 shared = 5, one less than in element) and the magnesium is -2
(½ of 8 shared = 4, two more than in element).

8.5 CH_3MgI methylmagnesium iodide CH_3Li methyllithium

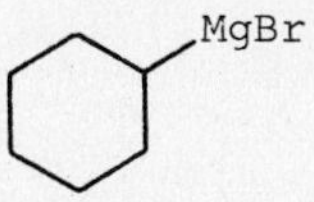

[cyclohexyl-MgBr structure] cyclohexylmagnesium bromide

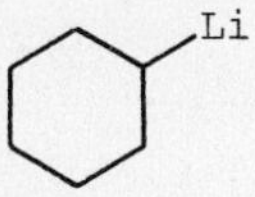

[cyclohexyl-Li structure] cyclohexyllithium

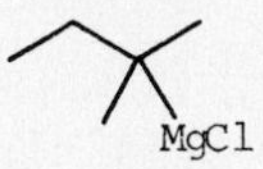

[structure MgCl] 2,2-dimethylpropylmagnesium chloride

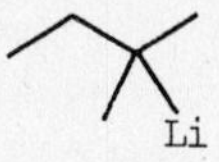

[structure Li] 2,2-dimethylpropyllithium

8.6

                                                            Electronegativity

(a) $2 (CH_3)_3Al + 3 ZnCl_2 \rightleftharpoons 3 (CH_3)_2Zn + 2 AlCl_3$ Al < Zn
                                                            (1.5)   (1.6)

(b) $2 (CH_3)_2Hg + SiCl_4 \rightleftharpoons (CH_3)_4Si + 2 HgCl_2$ Hg > Si
                                                            (1.9)   (1.7)

(c) $(CH_3)_2Mg + CaBr_2 \rightleftharpoons (CH_3)_2Ca + MgBr_2$ Mg > Ca
                                                            (1.2)   (1.0)

8.7 (a) 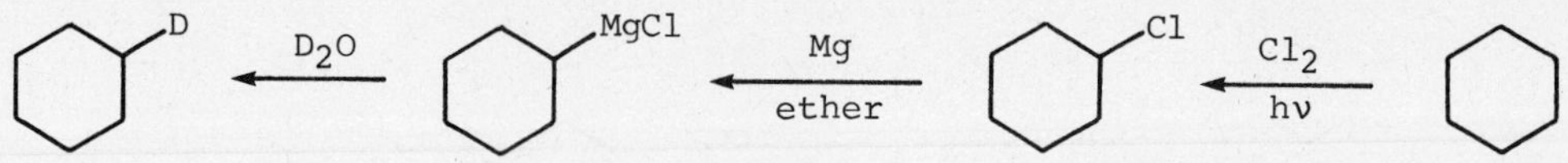

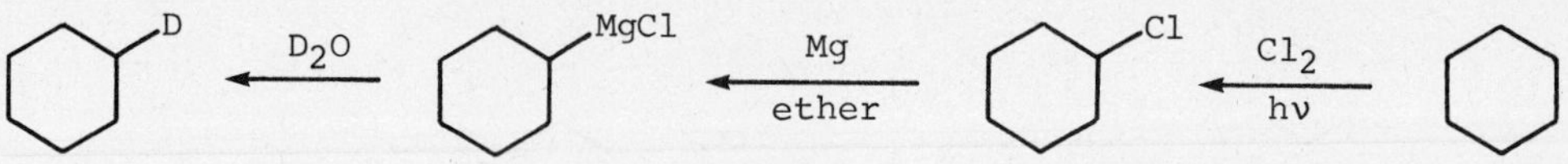

(b) $(CH_3)_3C\text{-}D \xleftarrow{D_2O} (CH_3)_3C\text{-}MgBr \xleftarrow[\text{ether}]{Mg} (CH_3)_3C\text{-}Br \xleftarrow[h\nu]{Br_2} (CH_3)_3CH$

(c) $(CH_3)_3C\text{-}CH_2\text{-}D \xleftarrow{D_2O} (CH_3)_3C\text{-}CH_2\text{-}Li \xleftarrow[\text{ether}]{Li} (CH_3)_3C\text{-}CH_2\text{-}Cl \xleftarrow[h\nu]{Cl_2} CH_3\text{-}C(CH_3)_2\text{-}CH_3$

8.E Answers and Explanations for Problems

1. (a) 

(b) 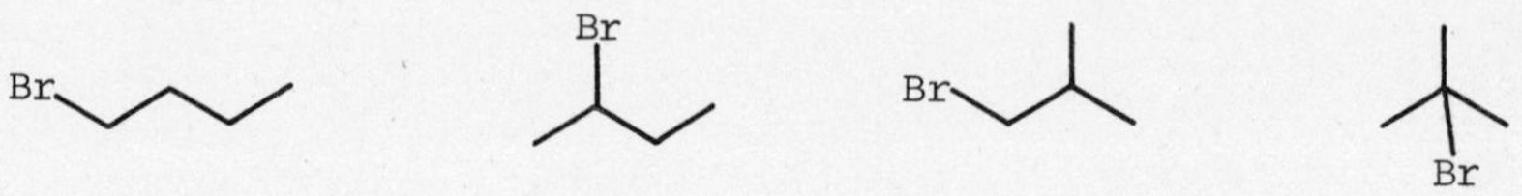

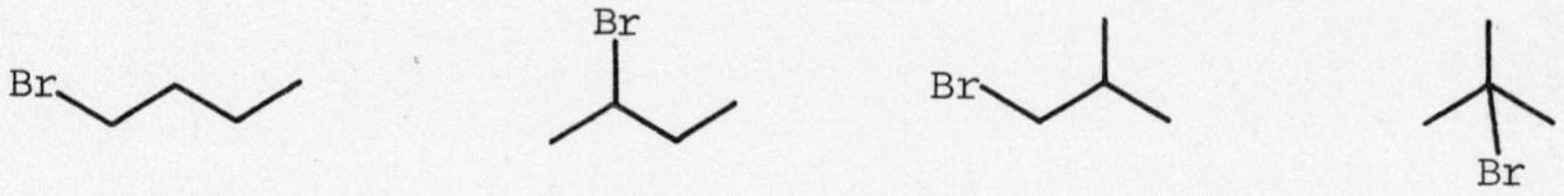

(c) 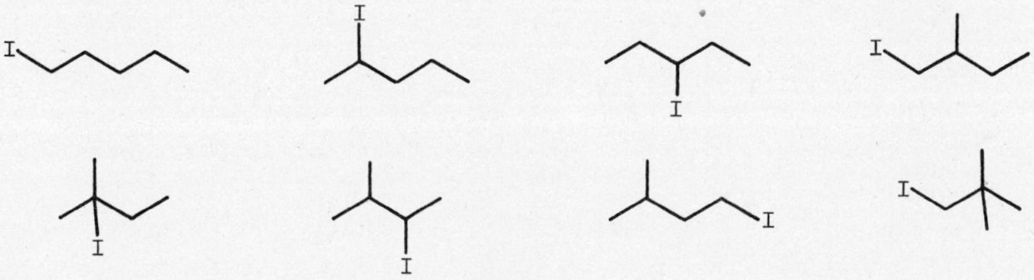

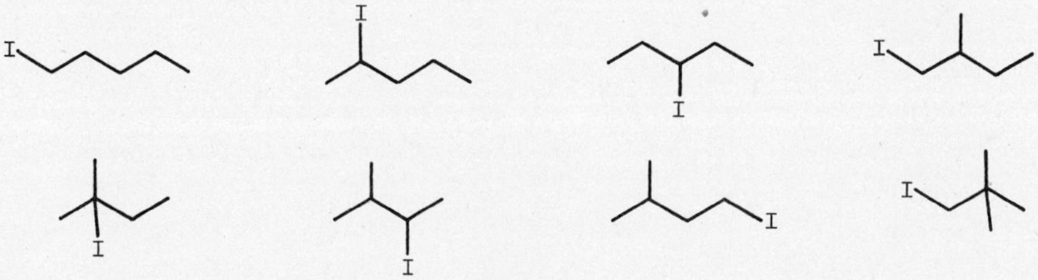

(d) 1: 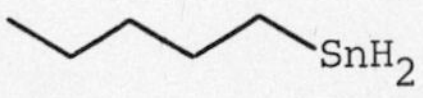 2: 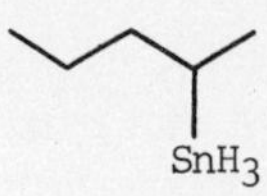 3: 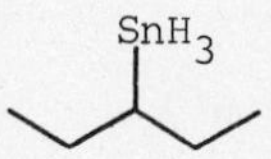 4: 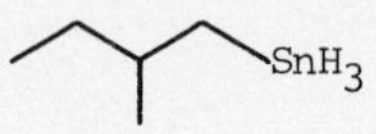

5: 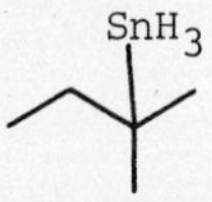 6: 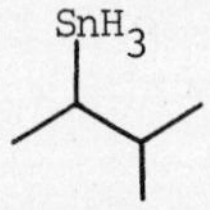 7: 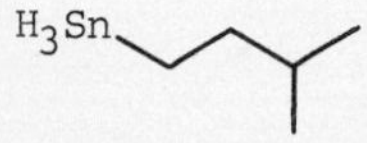 8: 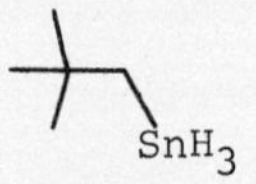 9: 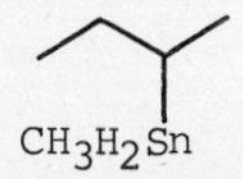

10: 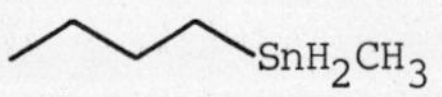 11: 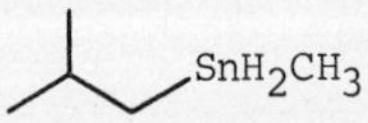 12: 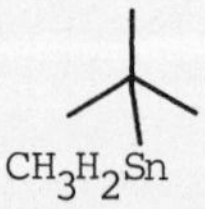 13: 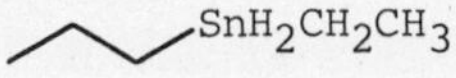

14: 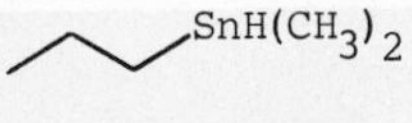 15: 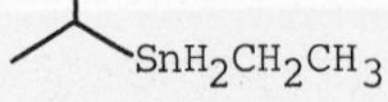 16: 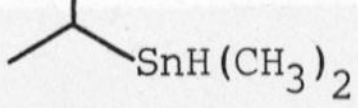

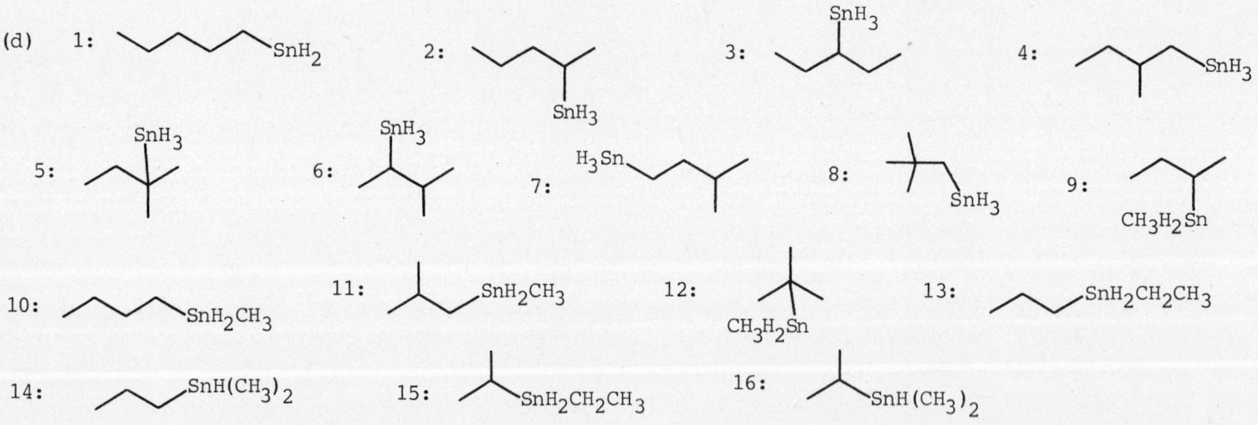

Another way to systematically determine these isomers is to recognize that tin has the same valence as carbon: write the skeletons of all the six-carbon isomers, and look for the unique positions where a C can be replaced with an Sn:

17: $(CH_3CH_2)_2SnHCH_3$ 18: $CH_3CH_2Sn(CH_3)_3$

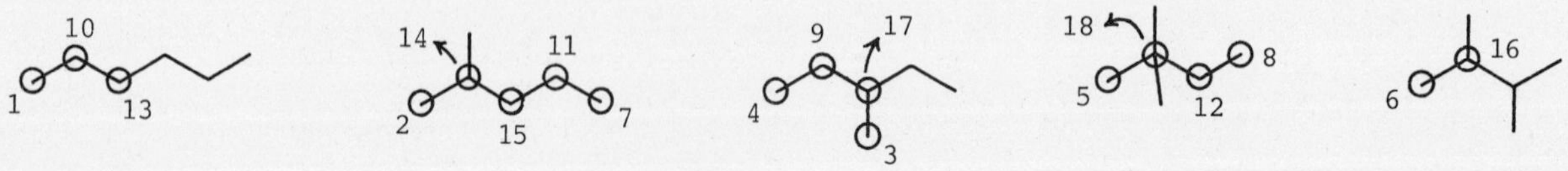

(e) 

 $(CH_3CH_2)_2Mg$

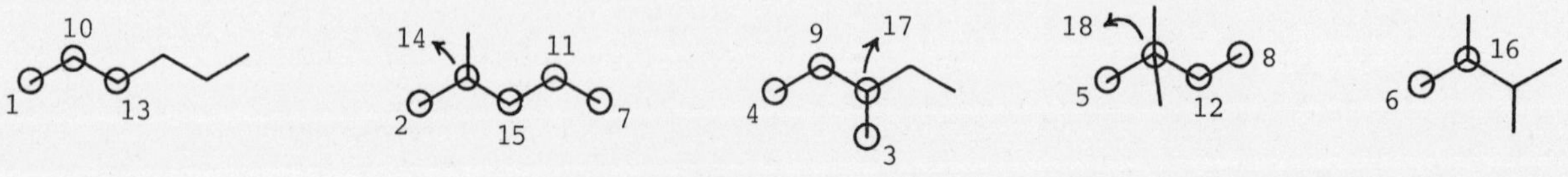

(f)

2.

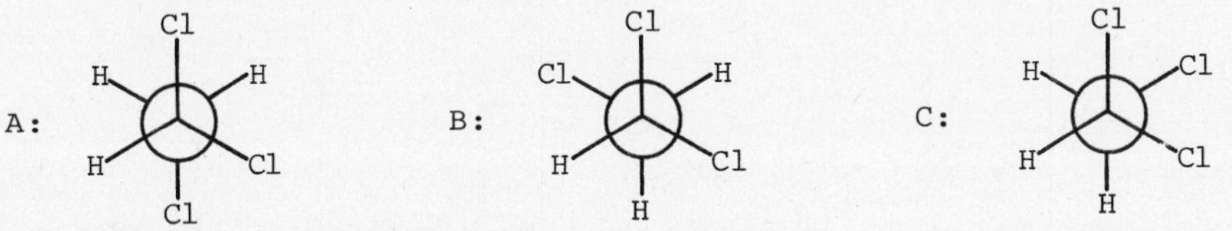

A: B: C:

A and B are equivalent and equal in energy, and are more stable than C. A and B have one gauche and one anti interaction; C has two gauche interactions. Anti is more stable in the gas phase where dipole-dipole interactions are more important. Such interactions are less important in the liquid phase because they are masked by the dielectric effect of the liquid, and other interactions can dominate. Interconversion of A and B is accomplished through the eclipsed conformation D, in which there are three H-Cl interactions. Conversion to C goes through E, in which there is a Cl-Cl interaction.

D: E:

3. (a)

$(CH_3)_3C-CD(CH_3)_2 \xleftarrow{D_2O} (CH_3)_3C-C(CH_3)_2 \text{ (MgBr)} \xleftarrow[\text{ether}]{Mg} (CH_3)_3C-C(CH_3)_2 \text{ (Br)} \xleftarrow[h\nu]{Br_2} (CH_3)_3CCH(CH_3)_2$

*Why is bromination and not
chlorination used here?*

(b)

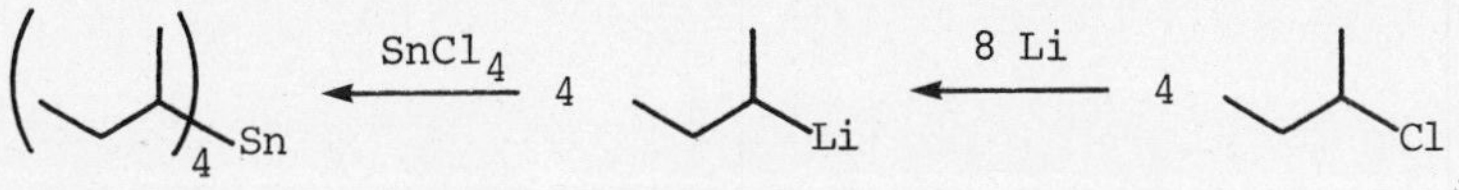

$\left(\right)_4 Sn \xleftarrow{SnCl_4} 4 \quad \xleftarrow{8 Li} 4 \quad$

(c) $(CH_3)_3CCH_2Br \xleftarrow{Br_2} (CH_3)_3CCH_2MgCl \xleftarrow{Mg} (CH_3)_3CCH_2Cl$

(d) $(CH_3CH_2)_2Cd \xleftarrow{CdCl_2} 2 \ CH_3CH_2MgCl \xleftarrow{2 Mg} 2 \ CH_3CH_2Cl$

(e) $[(CH_3)_3C]_2Hg \xleftarrow{HgBr_2} 2 \ (CH_3)_3CMgCl \xleftarrow{2 Mg} 2 \ (CH_3)_3CCl$

4. This problem, like Exercise 8.6, can be answered by comparing the ionization potentials of the metals (Table 8.6). The _more_ electropositive (= less electronegative) element prefers to exist as the cation in an inorganic salt rather than bound to carbon with some covalent bonding.

Electronegativity

(a)   Al (1.5) < Ca (1.7)   K > 1
(b)   Hg (1.9) > Zn (1.6)   K < 1
(c)   Mg (1.2) < Si (1.7)   K > 1
(d)   Li (1.0) < H (2.2)   K >> 1
(e)   Zn (1.6) > Li (1.0)   K < 1

5.

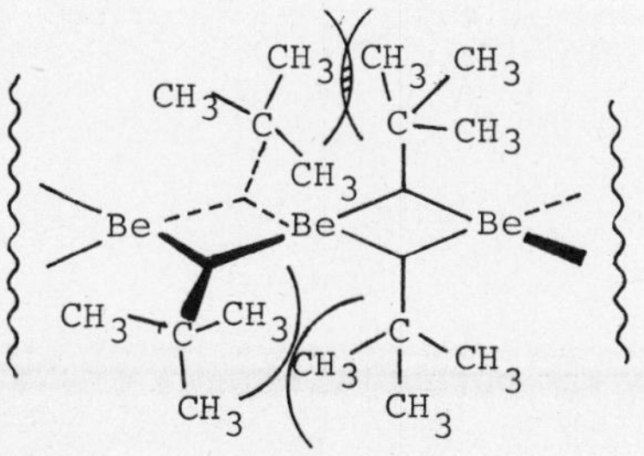

$(CH_3)_3C - Be - C(CH_3)_3$ $\xrightarrow{180°}$

(a) For di-<u>t</u>-butylberyllium, the <u>t</u>-butyl group is too bulky to permit the polymeric structure; instead, it exists as a monomer with sp hybridization (see drawing).

(b) The molecule is linear about Hg: CH_3—Hg—CH_3. The bonding is C_{sp3}-Hg$_{sp}$. Mercury has two valence electrons; hence, bonds use sp hybrids, much as in beryllium.

6. $(CH_3)_3B + CH_3Li$ $(CH_3)_4B^- Li^+$

The compound is tetrahedral about boron; that is, C_{sp3}-B_{sp3}.

7.

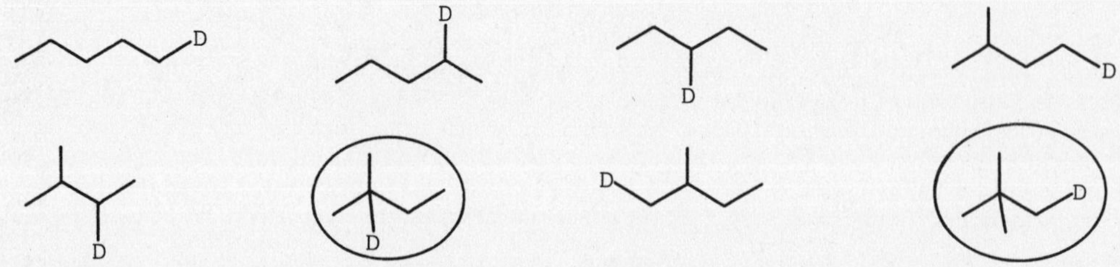

Only the circled isomers can reasonably be prepared by the route:

$$R-H \xrightarrow[h\nu]{Br_2} R-Br \xrightarrow{Mg} R-MgBr \xrightarrow{D_2O} R-D$$
(alkane)

The halides which would lead to the other isomers cannot be prepared <u>selectively</u> by free radical halogenation of the alkanes.

8. Dimerization and disproportionation are typical reactions which occur between two alkyl radicals (see Section 6.2 of the text). Free radical intermediates are involved in the formation of Grignard reagents (see Section 8.8.A).

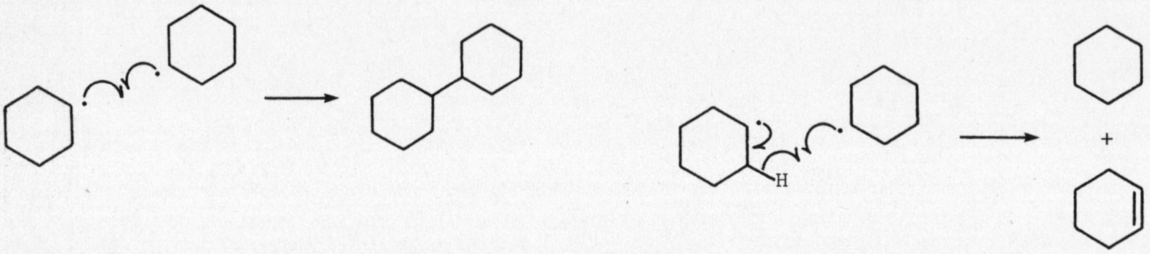

8.F   Supplementary Problems

S1. Write Lewis structures for the trimethylaluminum dimer (Figure 8.3 in the Text) and trimethylantimony.

S2. The reaction between trimethylaluminum and trimethylantimony leads to the formation of a compound with the formula $C_6H_{18}AlSb$. Propose a structure for this material and write a Lewis structure to account for the bonding scheme.

S3. 1-Bromo-6-methoxyhexane can be converted to the Grignard reagent, whereas the corresponding alcohol cannot. Explain.

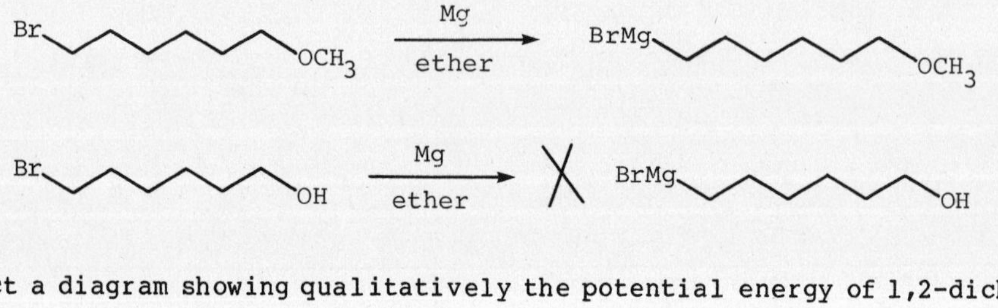

S4. Construct a diagram showing qualitatively the potential energy of 1,2-dichloroethane as a function of rotation about the C–C bond.

8.G   Answers to Supplementary Problems

S1.   Trimethylaluminum dimer: Trimethylantimony:

$$
\begin{array}{ccc}
 & H_3 & \\
H_3C. & \overset{..}{C} & .CH_3 \\
 & Al :: Al & \\
H_3C^{..} & \overset{}{C} & ^{..}CH_3 \\
 & H_3 &
\end{array}
$$

$$
\begin{array}{c}
H_3C:Sb:CH_3 \\
\overset{..}{} \\
CH_3
\end{array}
$$

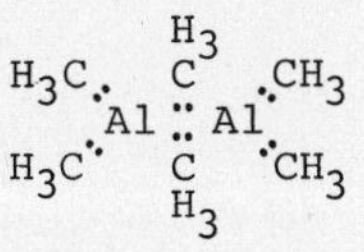

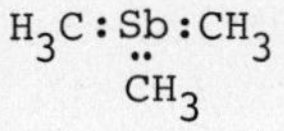

Each electron pair in the center is shared
by two aluminums and one carbon.

S2.
$$
\begin{array}{c}
\quad\; \text{Me}\;\; \text{Me} \\
\overset{-}{} \quad \overset{..}{}\;\; \overset{}{} \quad + \\
\text{Me}: \text{Al}: \text{Sb}: \text{Me} \\
\quad \overset{..}{}\;\; \overset{..}{} \\
\quad\; \text{Me}\;\; \text{Me}
\end{array}
\qquad
\text{Me} = CH_3
$$

S3.   The alcohol function reacts with the Grignard reagent as soon as it is formed:

S4.

0°   60°   120°   180°   240°   300°   360°

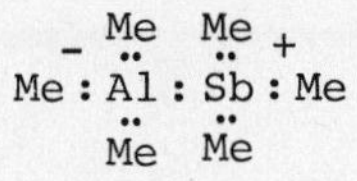

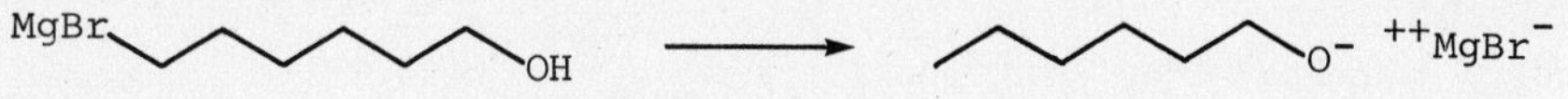

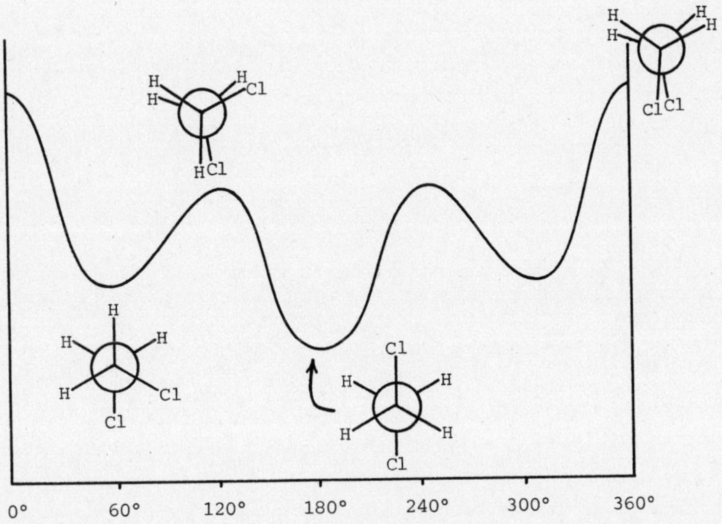

9. NUCLEOPHILIC SUBSTITUTION

9.A   Chapter Outline and Important Terms Introduced

9.1   The Displacement Reaction (the first "ionic" reaction discussed in detail)

nucleophile

9.2   Mechanism of the Displacement Reaction (how the bonds are made and broken, and the stereochemistry of reaction)

reaction kinetics	second-order kinetics
stereochemistry	bimolecular mechanism
inversion of configuration	S_N2 = $\underline{S}$ubstitution$_{\underline{N}ucleophilic}$bimolecular(**2**)

9.3   Effect of Alkyl Structure on Displacement Reactions

steric hindrance	β-branching
α-branching	"neopentyl-type" systems

9.4   Nucleophilicity and Solvent Effects (factors affecting the nucleophile)

A. Solvent Properties
       dielectric constant   nucleophilicity
B. Polar Aprotic Solvents
C. Hydroxylic Solvents
       hydrogen-bonding
D. Ambident Nucleophiles

9.5   Leaving Groups

not limited to halides   leaving group ability vs. basicity

9.6   Elimination Reactions (a competing reaction)

bimolecular elimination   E2 = $\underline{E}$limination-bimolecular (**2**)
steric hindrance

9.7 S_N1 Reactions: Carbocations

solvolysis reaction	relative stability of carbocations:
unimolecular,	tertiary > secondary > primary > methyl
first-order kinetics	hyperconjugation
carbocation	S_N1 = $\underline{S}$ubstitution$_{\underline{N}ucleophilic}$unimolecular(**1**)

9.8   Ring Systems (special aspects in cyclic molecules)

bond angle strain   intramolecular vs. intermolecular

9.B   Important Reactions Introduced

Displacement reactions (9.1, 9.2)

Equation: $Nu:^- + R{-}X \longrightarrow Nu{-}R + X^-$

Generality: X^- = good leaving group (= HX is strong acid)
                  for S_N2: R = unhindered alkyl (methyl > 1° > 2° >> 3°)
                            $Nu:^-$ = good nucleophile
                  for S_N1: R = substituted alkyl (3° > 2° >> 1° or methyl)
                            X = good leaving group

Key features: S_N2 proceeds with inversion of configuration and involves bimolecular process
                  S_N1 proceeds through planar carbocation and involves unimolecular process
                  E2 (elimination) reactions interfere if $Nu:^-$ is strong base
                     and R is sterically hindered
                  Influence of solvent (dielectric constant and hydrogen bonding) on reaction rate

9.C   Important Concepts and Hints

This chapter is your introduction to a detailed analysis of an organic reaction which proceeds via an ionic (heterolytic) mechanism instead of by a free-radical (homolytic) mechanism. The displacement reaction is the primary reaction of interest for alkyl halides and a reaction of major importance in organic chemistry. It is analyzed in detail in Chapter 9 because it provides an opportunity to examine all of the factors which are generally important in understanding any reaction.

In Section 6.C of this Study Guide, we suggested that you approach each new reaction with a series of questions to help you organize your thinking. As an example, the sort of questions you should ask and the sort of answers you should give yourself are illustrated below for displacement reactions.

(1) **Qu:** What functional group transformation does the reaction accomplish?
     ANS: In general terms, $Nu^- + R\text{-}X \longrightarrow R\text{-}Nu + X^-$
          where Nu = nucleophile, R = alkyl group, and X = leaving group.

(2) **Qu:** What is the mechanism of the reaction?
     ANS: For some combination of reactants, the bimolecular S_N2 mechanism is involved, with simultaneous attack of Nu and departure of X from opposite sides of the carbon atom; for other combinations of reactants, the stepwise S_N1 mechanism is involved, with initial loss of X to give a carbocationic intermediate (slow) and subsequent attack by Nu to give product (fast).

(3) **Qu:** What is the generality of the reaction? That is, what characteristics must the reactants have?
     ANS: **Nu**, the nucleophile, must have a lone pair of electrons (i.e., must be a Lewis base) in order to form a bond to the carbon. **Nucleophilicity** increases with basicity (to the left in the Periodic Table, other factors being equal) and with **polarizability** (down in the Periodic Table, other factors being equal), and helps to determine whether the reaction will proceed via the S_N2 or S_N1 mechanism. Stronger nucleophiles favor S_N2 reactions (other factors being equal).
     R, the alkyl group, plays the major role in determining the mechanism (S_N1 or S_N2) and rate of the reaction. Displacement reactions at tertiary carbon occur by the S_N1 mechanism and at primary carbon by the S_N2 mechanism. Both situations reflect the combined influences of steric hindrance and carbocation stability. Substitution at secondary carbon is the gray area, and whether these reactions proceed by the S_N1 or S_N2 mechanism, or both simultaneously, depends on other factors. Steric effects are not limited to substitution on the carbon undergoing reaction (α**-branching**), but are seen at more remote positions as well (β**-branching**, effects of cyclic systems).
     X, the leaving group, must be stable when it departs with two electrons (usually as an anion). This is most easily evaluated by considering the pK_a of HX: a low pK_a indicates that HX is a strong acid, which means that X^- is a weak base, which in turns says that X^- is stable and a good leaving group. Under most circumstances, the pK_a of HX should be less than 2 or 3 for the reaction to occur at a reasonable rate. ($R'O^-$ [R'=alkyl or H] is essentially **never** a leaving group in an S_N1 or S_N2 reaction.) The "better" the leaving group is (i.e., the more stable X^- is), the faster the displacement reaction occurs, but the influence is greater on S_N1 reactivity than on S_N2 reactivity.
     Solvent plays a role in the way it stabilizes the reactants in comparison to intermediates and transition states. For instance, if a polar, hydroxylic solvent (such as methanol) can form hydrogen bonds to the nucleophile (such as chloride ion) more strongly than it can to the transition state, the S_N2 reaction will be slowed; if a neutral alkyl halide (such as <u>t</u>-butyl bromide) must ionize in order to react (by the S_N1 mechanism), then a polar solvent will speed up the reaction.

(4) **Qu:** What are the stereochemical features to keep in mind?
     ANS: S_N2 Backside attack and **inversion** of configuration at the carbon undergoing substitution.
          S_N1 Planar, carbocation intermediate which the nucleophile can approach from either side. Leads to racemic products if that carbon is the only stereocenter in the molecule.

(5) **Qu:** What are the limitations; that is, what possible side reactions should be kept in mind?

ANS: Elimination reactions (E2) compete with substitution when the nucleophile is fairly basic (RO^- [R = alkyl or H], CN^-, RS^-, NH_2^-, etc.) and S_N2 displacement is slowed because of steric hindrance. Elimination competes when the nucleophile is impatient for reaction (basic; i.e., unstable as its anion Nu^-) and doesn't want to wait around for S_N1-type ionization to occur. This is always an important point to keep in mind: very basic nucleophiles give mostly elimination products, except with unhindered primary alkyl halides.

This Question-and-Answer outline for displacement reactions is quite lengthy and detailed for two reasons: first, because it covers a complex topic, and second, because we want to provide you with a comprehensive example. A good exercise for you would be to make a similar outline for free-radical halogenation (Chapter 6). A more skeletal outline of the questions and answers above, using key words to trigger your memory, would be:

(1) <u>Functional Group Transformation</u>

$$Nu^- + R-X \longrightarrow R-Nu + X^-$$

(2) <u>Mechanism</u>

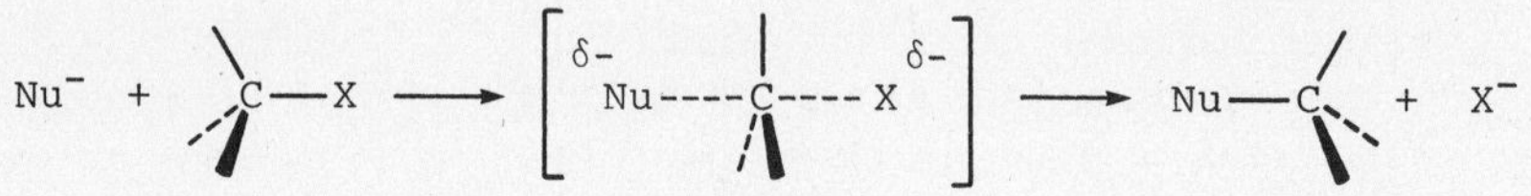

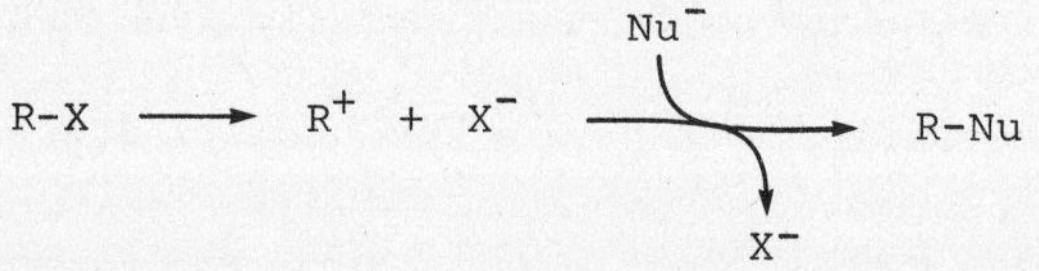

(3) <u>Generalizations</u>

Nu: Lewis base; more basic, more polarizable $\Rightarrow$ better nucleophile

R: **S_N2** methyl > $1°$ > $2°$ > $3°$; β-branching slows reaction, too

S_N1 $3°$ > $2°$ > $1°$ >> methyl ; decision hard only for $2°$

X: X^- less basic $\Rightarrow$ better leaving group

Solvent: dipolar solvents speed reactions

H-bonding slows S_N2 by tying up Nu^-

(4) <u>Stereochemistry</u>

S_N2: inversion

S_N1: loss of configuration via planar carbocation

(5) <u>Side Reactions</u>

Elimination (E2) if Nu is basic and/or R-X is sterically hindered.

HINTS: Organic chemists love to show what is going where in a reaction mechanism by drawing arrows, and writing these mechanisms often involves a lot of "arrow-pushing". A brief catalog of arrows which you will encounter in organic chemistry follows, as well as a description of those used when writing mechanisms.

A single-headed arrow written in an equation (for example, A + B $\longrightarrow$ C) is used by organic chemists instead of the = sign common to general chemistry equations (for example, $P_4 + 3\ OH^- + 3\ H_2O = PH_3 + 3\ H_2PO_2^-$). Reversible reactions are written with two single-headed arrows pointing in opposite direction. Often, an idea of the position of equilibrium is given by the relative length of the arrows:

$$HCN + OH^- \rightleftharpoons CN^- + H_2O$$

These double arrows often connect different conformations of the same molecule, for example:

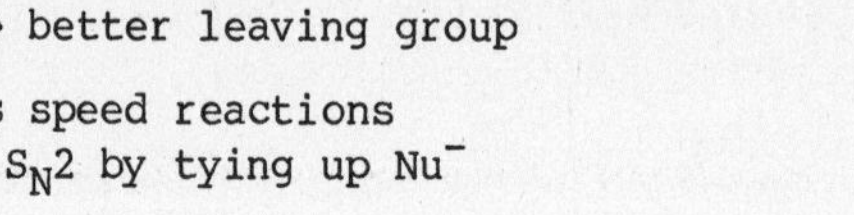

A double-headed arrow is distinct from the equilibration idea of $\rightleftharpoons$, and is specifically used between resonance structures, for example:

$$\left[\ ^-:\ddot{O}-C\equiv N: \ \longleftrightarrow \ :\ddot{O}=C=N:^- \right] \quad or \quad \left[\ \longleftrightarrow \ \longleftrightarrow \ \right]$$

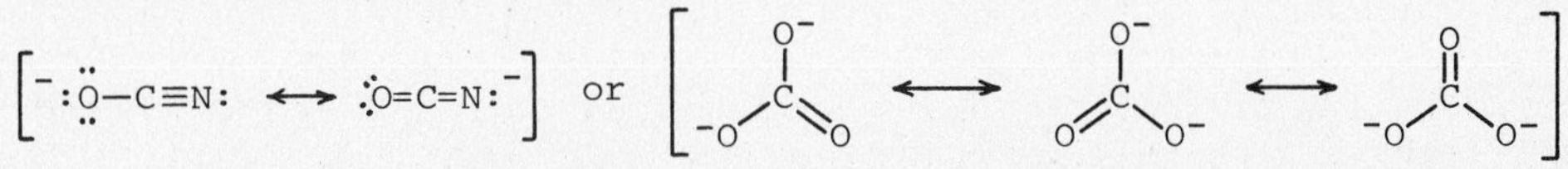

The curved arrows that you see leading molecules around in describing reaction mechanisms represent a pair of electrons. The vast majority of reactions which you will encounter involve heterolytic cleavage of bonds (and their formation) and in essentially every instance the electrons travel in pairs. For instance, in a displacement reaction, the leaving group (X) always departs with the two electrons in the C-X bond, and the two electrons in the C-Nu bond come in with the nucleophile Nu:

$$H:\ddot{O}:^- \quad + \quad \longrightarrow \quad H:\ddot{O}:C \quad + \quad :\overset{\circ\circ}{\underset{\circ\circ}{Cl}}:^-$$

$$HO^- \ \curvearrowright CH_3 \overset{\frown}{-} Cl \quad \longrightarrow \quad HO-CH_3 \ + \ Cl^-$$

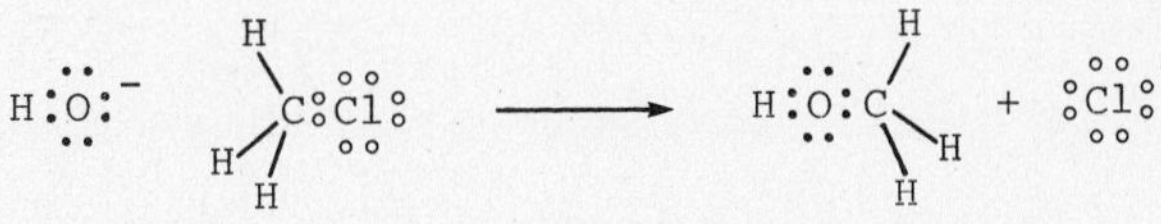

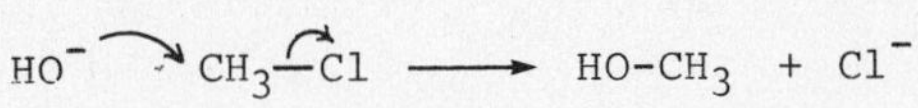

The situation is more complicated for an E2 elimination reaction, because more bonds are being formed and broken, but the arrows help to keep everything organized:

$$CH_3O^- \quad \longrightarrow \quad CH_3O^-$$

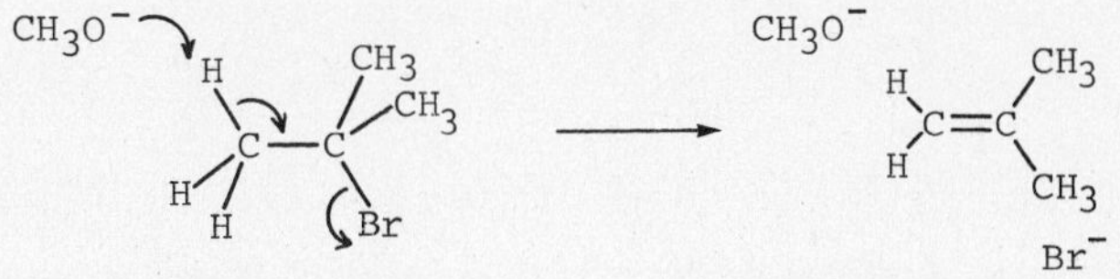

Pushing arrows is valuable because it helps you to keep track of electrons and charges and often prevents you from writing absurd mechanisms. Always bear in mind that an arrow represents the movement of a pair of electrons.

Sometimes, when describing free-radical reactions in which odd electron species are reacting, it is useful to show the movement of a <u>single</u> electron. Organic chemists often use "fish hook" or single-headed arrows to represent this:

$$Cl \cdot \ \curvearrowright \ H \overset{\frown}{-} CH_3 \quad \longrightarrow \quad Cl-H \ + \ \cdot CH_3$$

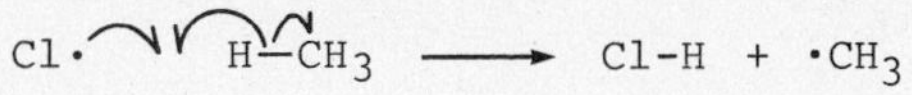

9.D　Answers to Exercises

9.1　Displacement reactions with methyl iodide:

Attacking Reagent		Product	
Name	Structure	Structure	Name
hydroxide ion	$H:\ddot{O}:^-$	$H:\ddot{O}:CH_3$	methanol
ethoxide ion	$CH_3CH_2:\ddot{O}:^-$	$CH_3CH_2:\ddot{O}:CH_3$	ethyl methyl ether
hydrosulfide ion	$H:\ddot{S}:^-$	$H:\ddot{S}:CH_3$	methanethiol
thiocyanate ion	$^-:\ddot{N}::C::\ddot{S}: \longleftrightarrow :N:::C:\ddot{S}:^-$	$:N:::C:\ddot{S}:CH_3$	methyl thiocyanate
cyanide ion	$:N:::C:^-$	$:N:::C:CH_3$	(methyl cyanide) acetonitrile
azide ion	$^-:\ddot{N}::\overset{+}{N}::\ddot{N}:^-$	$^-:\ddot{N}::\overset{+}{N}::\ddot{N}:CH_3$	methyl azide
ammonia	$H:\overset{\displaystyle H}{\underset{\displaystyle H}{\ddot{N}}}$	$H:\overset{\displaystyle H}{\underset{\displaystyle H}{\overset{+}{N}}}:CH_3 \ I^-$	methylammonium iodide
water	$H:\ddot{O}:H$	$H:\overset{\displaystyle H}{\ddot{O}}:\!^+CH_3 \ I^-$	methyloxonium iodide

Attacking Reagent		*Product*	
Name	Structure	Structure	Name

acetate ion** $CH_3:C\overset{\cdots}{\underset{\cdots}{O}}:\overset{..\!\!\overset{\cdots}{O}:}{}-$ $CH_3:C\overset{\cdots}{\underset{CH_3}{O}}:$ methyl acetate

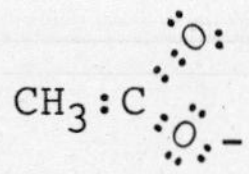

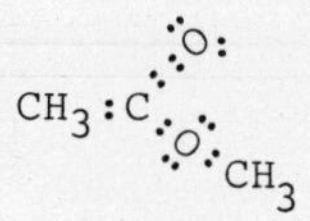

nitrate ion** $:\overset{..}{O}::\overset{+}{N}\overset{:\overset{\cdots}{O}:}{\underset{\overset{\cdots}{O}:}{}}-$ $:\overset{..}{O}::\overset{+}{N}\overset{:\overset{\cdots}{O}:}{\underset{O:CH_3}{}}-$ methyl nitrate

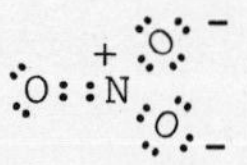

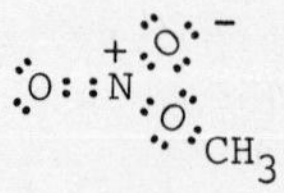

trimethyl-
phosphine $CH_3:\overset{\overset{CH_3}{|}}{\underset{\underset{CH_3}{|}}{P}}:$ $CH_3:\overset{\overset{CH_3}{|}+}{\underset{\underset{CH_3}{|}}{P}}:CH_3 \quad I^-$ tetramethylphosphonium
iodide

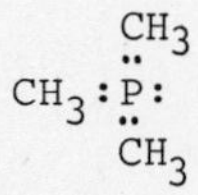

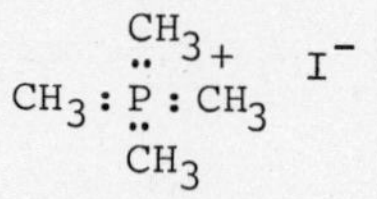

triethylamine $Et:\overset{\overset{Et}{|}}{\underset{\underset{Et}{|}}{N}}:$ $Et = CH_2CH_3$ $Et:\overset{\overset{Et}{|}+}{\underset{\underset{Et}{|}}{N}}CH_3 \quad I^-$ trimethylammonium
iodide

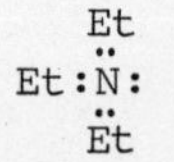

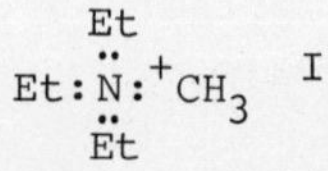

diethyl sulfide $Et:\overset{..}{\underset{..}{S}}:Et$ $Et:\overset{..}{\underset{\underset{CH_3}{|}}{S}}:Et \quad I^-$ diethylmethylsulfonium
iodide

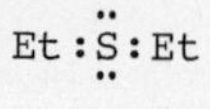

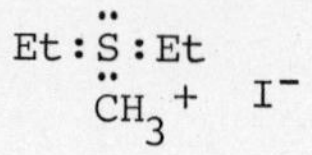

**NOTE: *only one resonance structure is shown*

9.2, 9.3

(a)

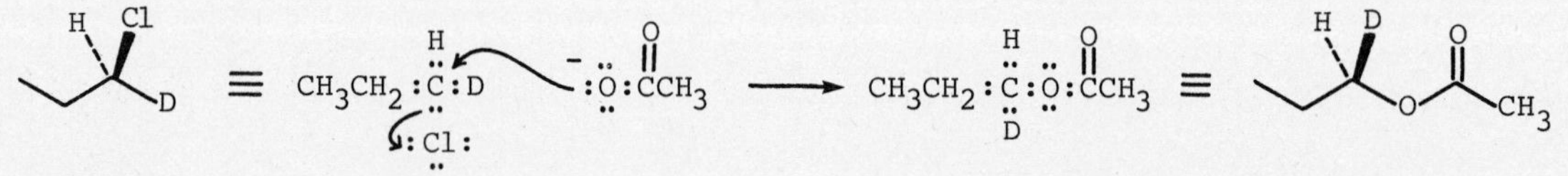

(b)

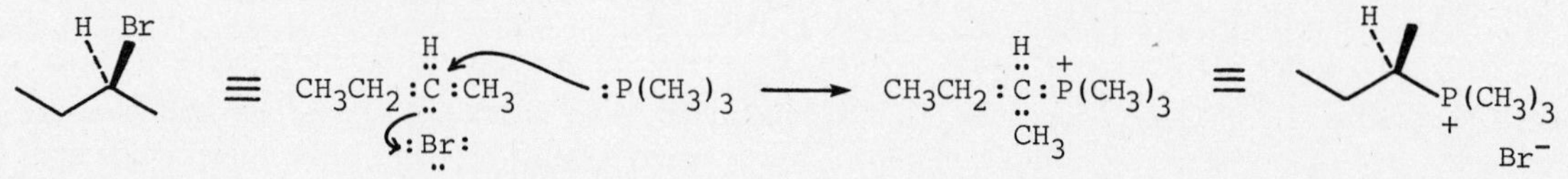

(c)

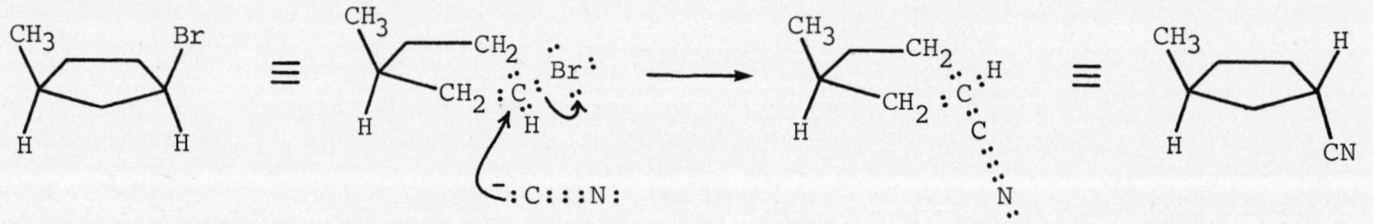

9.4

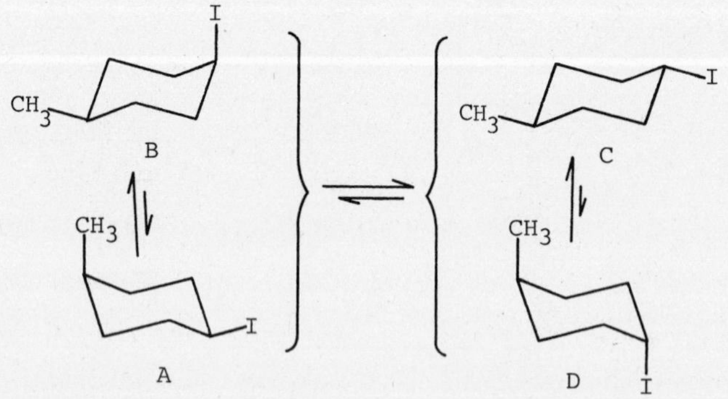

ΔG°_f differences for isomers: A- axial methyl: +1.7 kcal mole^{-1}

                                      B- axial iodine: +0.45 kcal mole^{-1}

                                      C- no axial substituents

$A:B:C:D = \underline{0.06 : 0.47} : \underline{1 : 0.03}$ D- axial methyl and axial iodine:

                cis   *trans*   +2.15 kcal mole^{-1}

                34%   66%

9.5 (a) Imagine starting with 2-iodobutane.

Addition of a methyl to C-1, to give
3-iodopentane:

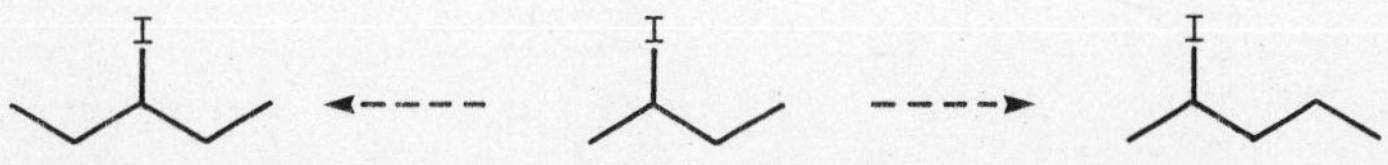

results in more steric ← —— *less reactive than* ——→
hindrance (β-branching) at
C-2 than addition of a methyl at C-4, to give 2-iodopentane:

(b)

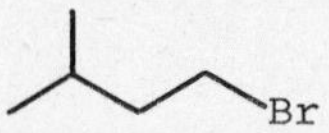

more reactive than 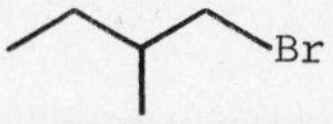 (β-branching)

(c)

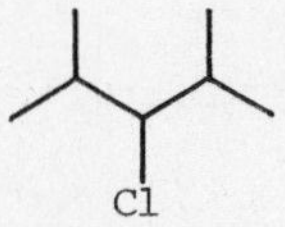

> 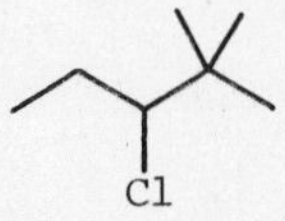 this is a "neopentyl-like" compound

(d)

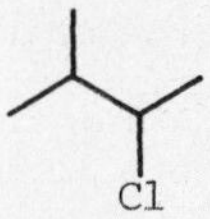

>  tertiary halide << secondary halide
in S_N2 reaction   (α-branching)

9.6 $I^- > {}^-CN > {}^-SCN > NO_2^- > N_3^- = Br^- > (CH_3)_2S > Cl^- > CH_3CO_2^-$

9.7 rate = $k_2[CH_3I][Nu]$; 99.9% reaction means $[CH_3I]$ goes from 0.1 $\underline{M}$ to 0.0001 $\underline{M}$ and $[Nu]$ goes from 1.0 $\underline{M}$ to 0.9 $\underline{M}$. To simplify the calculation, you can treat $[Nu]$ as a constant because it changes by only 10% over the course of the reaction (pseudo-first-order conditions); choose $[Nu]$ = 0.95 $\underline{M}$.

$$-\frac{d[CH_3I]}{dt} = k_2[CH_3I][Nu] \qquad -\int_{0.10}^{0.0001}\frac{d[CH_3I]}{[CH_3I]} = k_2[Nu]\int_0^t dt$$

$$-\ln[CH_3I]\Big]_{0.1}^{0.0001} = k_2[Nu]\,t\Big]_0^t$$

$$-(-2.303 - (-9.21)) = 10^{-2} \times 0.95(0-t)$$
$$t = 7.3 \times 10^2 \text{ sec} = 12 \text{ min}$$

9.8

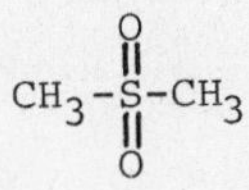

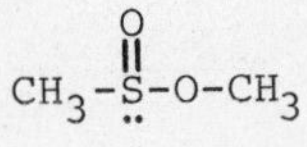

9.9

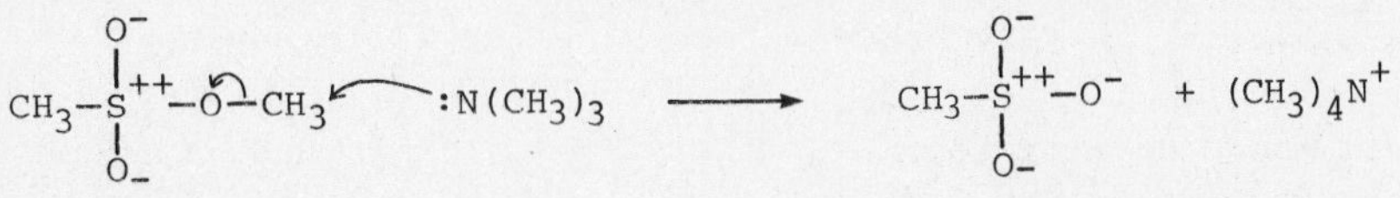

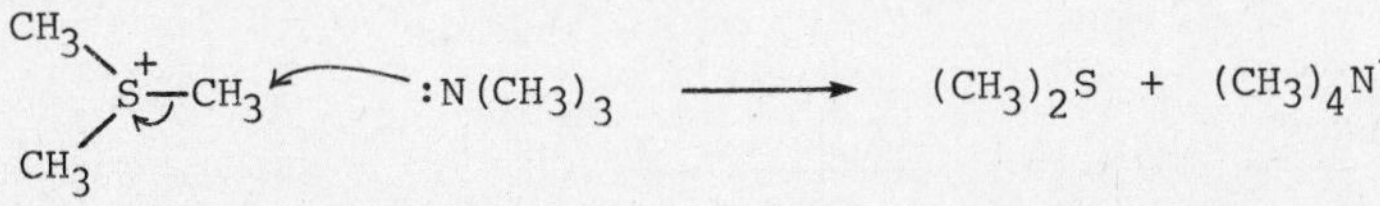

9.10 (a)

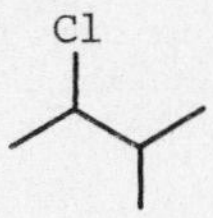

(β-branching slows S_N2 reaction, therefore E2 reaction
occurs more frequently)

(b) $CH_3CH_2O^-$ (stronger base than $CH_3CO_2^-$)

(c)   Cl   (secondary halide slower S_N2 and faster E2 than primary)

(d)   Cl   (tertiary halide much slower S_N2 than secondary)

9.11

1:   Cl ⬡   + NaSCN $\xrightarrow[\Delta]{CH_3OH}$ SCN ⬡   + NaCl   mostly

2: CH_3 Cl ⬡   + NaSCN $\xrightarrow[\Delta]{CH_3OH}$ CH_3 OCH_3 ⬡   + HSCN + NaCl

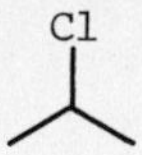

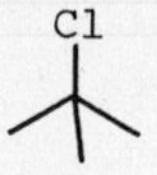

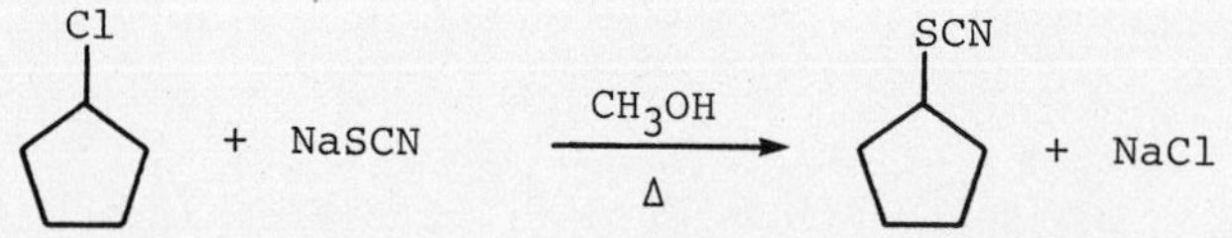

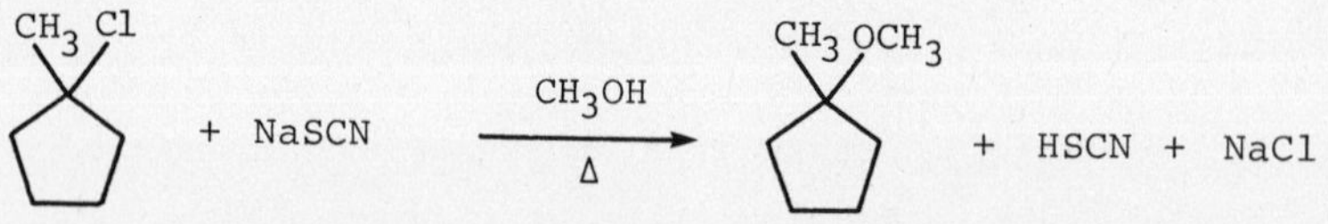

Reaction **1**, with secondary halide and good nucleophile, occurs mostly by S_N2 mechanism: $^-$SCN is a better nucleophile than solvent methanol, so cyclopentyl thiocyanate is the major product.

Reaction **2**, with tertiary halide, occurs mostly by S_N1 mechanism: the carbocation intermediate reacts at similar rates with thiocyanate ion and methanol so that, because there is much more methanol (solvent) than thiocyanate, the product is the ether.

9.12   (a)   cyclopentyl bromide > cyclobutyl bromide   *(see Table 9.9)*

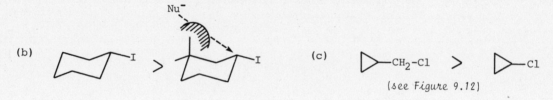

(b)   ⬡—I   >   ⬡—I   (c)   ▷—CH_2—Cl   >   ▷—Cl

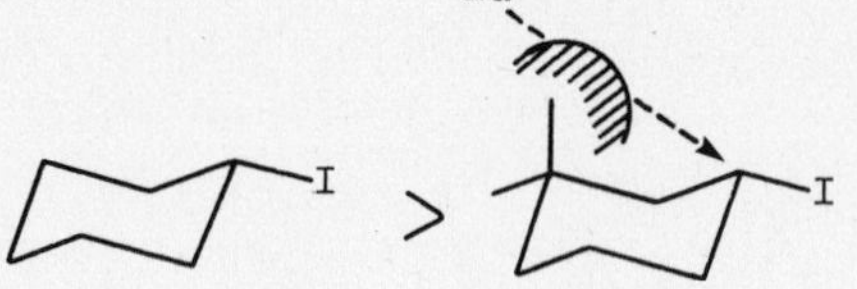

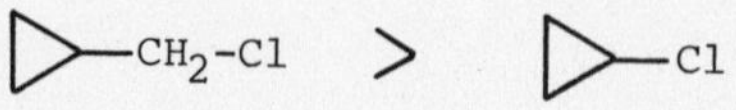

(see Figure 9.12)

9.E   **Answers and Explanations for Problems**

1.   (a)   ⬠—I   secondary halide, good nucleophile (S_N2)   (b)   ⬠—I   tertiary halide, nucleophile is weak base (S_N1)

(c) CH_3SCN $^-$SCN is ambident nucleophile: reaction in hydrogen bonding solvent occurs at more polarizable sulfur end (S_N2)

(d) $(CH_3CH_2)_2C{=}CHCH_3$ Strong base, tertiary halide (Elimination)

(e)   CN   secondary halide, good nucleophile (S_N2)   (f) N^+ Br^- Intramolecular S_N2 reaction

(g) $(CH_3)_3CCl$ + 2 Na $\xrightarrow{\text{ether}}$ $(CH_3)_3CNa$ $\xrightarrow{(CH_3)_3CCl}$ $(CH_3)_3CH$ + $CH_2{=}C(CH_3)_2$ + NaCl
                                   strong base

The t-butylsodium formed in the organometallic reaction is such a strong base that it reacts with the halide starting material as soon as it is formed, by an elimination reaction.

(h) $(CH_3)_2CCH_2CH_2O_2CCH_3$ primary halide (S_N2)

(i) $CH_3CH_2CH_2O{-}N{=}O$ NO_2^- is ambident nucleophile: reaction in dipolar, aprotic solvent occurs at atom bearing most of negative charge
                                           (O instead of N)

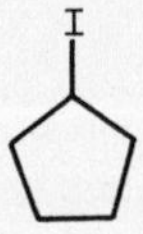

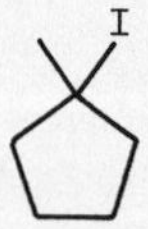

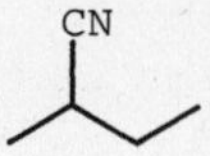

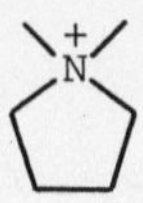

(j) $(CH_3)_2CHCH_2N_3$ primary halide, excellent nucleophile (S_N2)

2. Because the C-O bond is not affected in the first step, the intermediate mesylate ($\underline{s}$-butyl-$^{18}OSO_2CH_3$) still has the R configuration. The departure of the ^{18}O with the mesylate group shows that the substitution proceeds with cleavage of the C-O bond and by either an S_N2 or S_N1 mechanism (as opposed to cleavage of the S-O bond). Because OH⁻ is a strong nucleophile and the alkyl group is not tertiary, the reaction is expected to go by an S_N2 mechanism and inversion of configuration. Therefore the product is (S)-2-butanol.

$\underline{Note}$: there is probably a lot of elimination taking place as a side reaction in this example, but the question only concerns the stereochemistry of the 2-butanol that $\underline{is}$ formed.

3.
$$(CH_3)_2CXCH_2CH_3 \xrightarrow{k_x} X^- + (CH_3)_2\overset{+}{C}CH_2CH_3$$

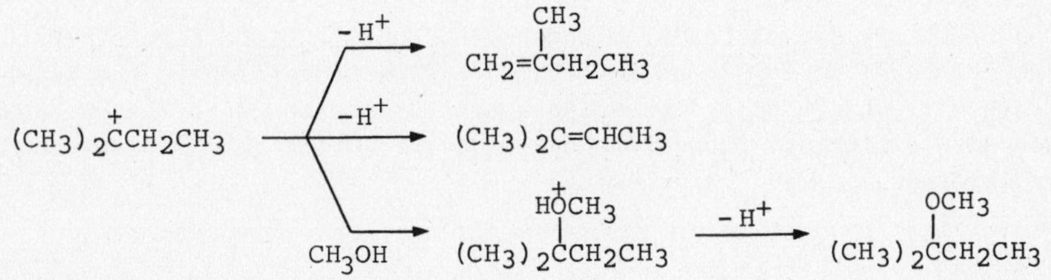

The k_x step is rate-determining and is different in rate for X = Cl, Br, I. The same carbocation is produced from each halide, and gives the same mixture of products.

4. (a) A tertiary halide is sterically hindered and leads to a relatively stable carbocation; water is a weak nucleophile. Both imply an S_N1 substitution mechanism, by way of a planar, $\underline{achiral}$ carbocation:

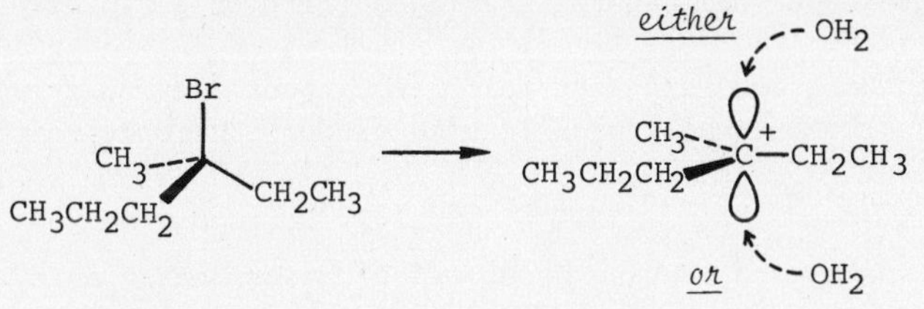

reaction is equally likely on both sides of the molecule, resulting in racemic product

(b) In this case, the chiral center is not involved in the reaction and is therefore unchanged:

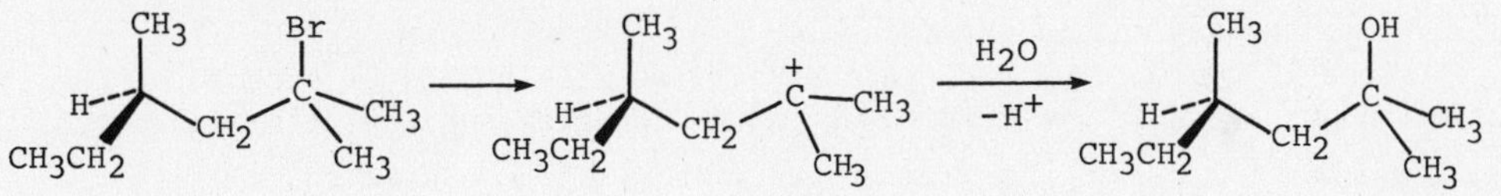

5. (a) In general, the more stable the leaving group is as the free Lewis base, the faster the S_N2 reaction. This is conveniently estimated by considering how basic the leaving group is (or how acidic the protonated compound (the conjugate acid) would be). The leaving group acquires additional electron density in the S_N2 transition state, and its basicity is a good indication of how easily it can accommodate (stabilize) this increased negative charge. For instance in this case, I⁻ is a weaker base than Cl⁻ (HI is a stronger acid than HCl; see Appendix IV), and alkyl iodides are generally more reactive in displacement reactions than alkyl chlorides.

(b) Water is a weak nucleophile, therefore the S_N1 mechanism is the most probable; $\underline{t}$-butyl bromide reacts faster by an S_N1 mechanism than isopropyl bromide does because the tertiary carbocation is more easily formed than a secondary one.

(c) The methyl branch slows down the S_N2 reaction by steric hindrance; the straight-chain halide reacts faster.

(d) ^-CN is stabilized by hydrogen-bonding solvation to methanol and its reactivity is reduced; ^-CN reacts faster in dimethylformamide because this polar aprotic solvent does not form hydrogen bonds to anions.

(e) Reaction with $:NH_3$ is an S_N2 reaction which is faster with the unbranched, less sterically hindered, primary halide.

(f) Hydroxide is more basic than acetate ion, hence it is a better nucleophile.

(g) Phosphorus is more nucleophilic than nitrogen. In general, 3rd-period atoms are more nucleophilic than their 2nd-period counterparts; hence, trimethylphosphine is more reactive toward methyl bromide than trimethylamine.

(h) The reaction giving CH_3CH_2SCN is faster. SCN^- is an ambident anion and may react on sulfur or nitrogen. Sulfur is the more nucleophilic end, and the faster reaction occurs there (see answer to Problem #1(c)).

(i) Even though the anions are about equal in basicity, sulfur is more nucleophilic because of its greater polarizability.

(j) In a displacement reaction, the carbon atom undergoing substitution changes hybridization from sp^3 (bond angles 109°) to sp^2 (bond angles 120°) when proceeding to the transition state. Ring strain will oppose this "spreading apart" of the bonds to the carbon and will make the reaction more difficult. Therefore cyclobutyl chloride reacts much more slowly than cyclopentyl chloride.

(k) The three-membered and four-membered rings have about the same amount strain (see Table 5.5). The likelihood that the ends of the chain will find each other to make a three-membered ring is higher than for the ends of a chain which forms a four-membered ring. Therefore △O (oxirane, ethylene oxide) is formed faster than ☐O (oxetane).

6. (a) No; ^-CN is a poor leaving group. HCN is a relatively weak acid; recall that there is a good correlation between the acidity of H-Y and the leaving ability of Y^- in displacement reactions.

(b) Slow; F^- is a relatively strong base (HF is a weak acid) and a poor leaving group.

(c) No; ^-OH is a strong base and an exceptionally poor leaving group. The only reaction observed is an acid-base reaction:

$$(CH_3)_3COH + NH_2^- \rightleftharpoons (CH_3)_3CO^- + NH_3$$

(d) Okay; $CH_3OSO_3^-$ is a weak base and a good leaving group. The corresponding acid, CH_3OSO_2OH, is a strong acid, comparable to H_2SO_4.

(e) No; $^-NH_2$ is a very strong base and a perfectly miserable leaving group. NH_3 is a very weak acid.

(f) Okay; I^- is a perfectly good leaving group.

(g) No; ^-OH is a strong base and an exceptionally poor leaving group.

(h) No; S_N reactions in cyclopropyl and cyclobutyl rings will not occur because of the large increase in ring strain that would build up in the transition state (see Figure 9.12).

7. (a)
$$N_3^- + CH_3Cl \xrightarrow{\text{(slower)}} CH_3N_3 + Cl^- \quad \text{more basic}$$
$$N_3^- + CH_3I \xrightarrow{\text{(faster)}} CH_3N_3 + I^- \quad \text{less basic}$$

Many other examples could have been cited, for this is the most common situation. If HX is more acidic than HY, X^- is less basic than Y^-, and RX is more reactive than RY.

(b)
$$CH_3Br + SCN^- \longrightarrow CH_3SCN + CH_3NCS$$
$$\text{(major)} \quad \text{(minor)}$$

(c)
$$(CH_3)_3CCl \xrightarrow[\text{acetone}]{H_2O} (CH_3)_3COH \quad \text{(faster)}$$
$$(CH_3)_2CHCl \xrightarrow[\text{acetone}]{H_2O} (CH_3)_2CHOH \quad \text{(slower)}$$

(d)
$$CH_3CH_2CH_2I + CH_3S^- \longrightarrow CH_3CH_2CH_2SCH_3 \quad \text{(faster)}$$
$$(CH_3)_2CHI + CH_3S^- \longrightarrow (CH_3)_2CHSCH_3 \quad \text{(slower)}$$

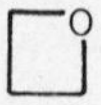

Other examples could be chosen among primary halides with branching in the β-position. Recall that relative rates are: $CH_3CH_2CH_2-$ > $(CH_3)_2CHCH_2-$ > $(CH_3)_3CCH_2-$, entirely because of steric hindrance effects.

(e) CH_3CH_2Cl + SH^- $\xrightarrow{C_2H_5OH}$ CH_3CH_2SH *(slower)*

CH_3CH_2Cl + SH^- $\xrightarrow{DMF}$ CH_3CH_2SH *(faster)*

In general, anions are less reactive in S_N2 reactions in hydroxylic solvents (such as alcohol) than in polar aprotic solvents (such as DMF, HMPT, and DMSO). In hydroxylic solvents, hydrogen bonds to the anion need to be broken in order to form the S_N2 transition state.

8. (b) (assuming that the carbon atom undergoing the substitution is the only stereocenter in the molecule) ;   (d), (e), (g), (h)

9. (a), (c), (f), (h)   Note that (h) is true for both S_N1 and S_N2 reactions.

10.   (a) SCN^- (b) I^- (c) $P(CH_3)_3$ (d) CH_3S^-

In each case, the nucleophile giving the larger substitution/elimination ratio contains an atom further down the Periodic Table, and is therefore more polarizable. Greater polarizability enhances nucleophilicity more than basicity; that is, polarizability is relatively more important in S_N2 reactions at carbon and is relatively less important in E2 reactions at hydrogen.

11.

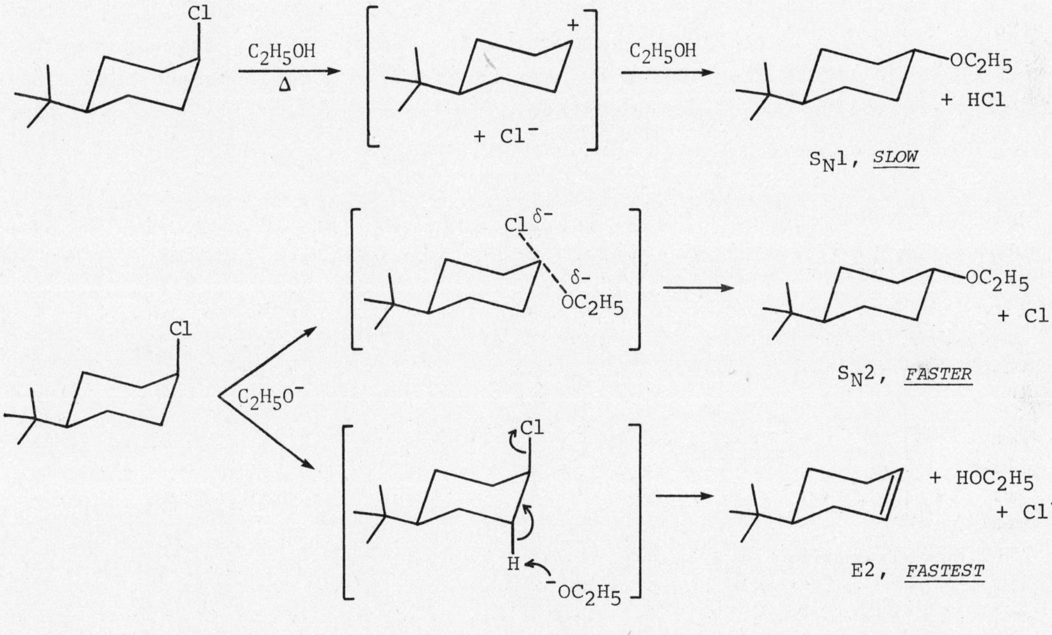

12. Nu^- + CH_3I $\longrightarrow$ $Nu-CH_3$ + I^-

Nu^-	$-\Delta H^\circ_f(Nu^-)$	$-\Delta H^\circ_f(CH_3I)$	$+\Delta H^\circ_f(Nu-CH_3)$	$+\Delta H^\circ_f(I^-)$	$= \Delta H^\circ$ (kcal mole^{-1})
CN^-	– 16	– 3.4	+ 17.6	–45.1	–47
$CH_3CO_2^-$	–(–120.5) –	3.4	+ –97.9	–45.1	–25.9
NO_2^-	– (–27.1) –	3.4	+ –17.9	–45.1	–39.3
Cl^-	– (–54.5) –	3.4	+ –20.6	–45.1	–14.6
Br^-	– (–50.9) –	3.4	+ – 9.1	–45.1	– 6.7
I^-	– (–45.1) –	3.4	+ 3.4	–45.1	0

13. For the cyclization reaction, both reactants are part of the same molecule, and the reaction can only have first-order kinetics. The reaction of the amino group of one molecule with the alkyl bromide of another (the *inter*molecular displacement rather than the *intra*molecular or cyclization reaction) has second-order kinetics; hence, the rate of this reaction is reduced much more than the other by reducing the concentration:

$$\frac{inter}{intra} = \frac{k_{inter}\left[H_2N(CH_2)_4Br\right]^2}{k_{intra}\left[H_2N(CH_2)_4Br\right]} = \frac{k_{inter}}{k_{intra}}\left[H_2N(CH_2)_4Br\right]$$

The ratio of the two is concentration-dependent, and the cyclization reaction is favored by "high dilution" methods.

14. In the equilibrium between carboxylate anion (RCO_2^-) and carboxylic acid (RCO_2H), in which a full negative charge is lost, the chloroacetate ion is $10^{1.9}$ = 79 times less reactive than acetate ion:

$$RCO_2^- + H^+ \overset{1/K_a}{\rightleftharpoons} RCO_2H \qquad 1/K_a = 10^{(pK_a)}$$

In going to the transition state for the S_N2 reaction in methanol, the difference in reactivity is only 10, a reduction by a factor of 8. This suggests that only one-eighth of a charge is lost in going from the hydrogen-bonded carboxylate ion to the transition state:

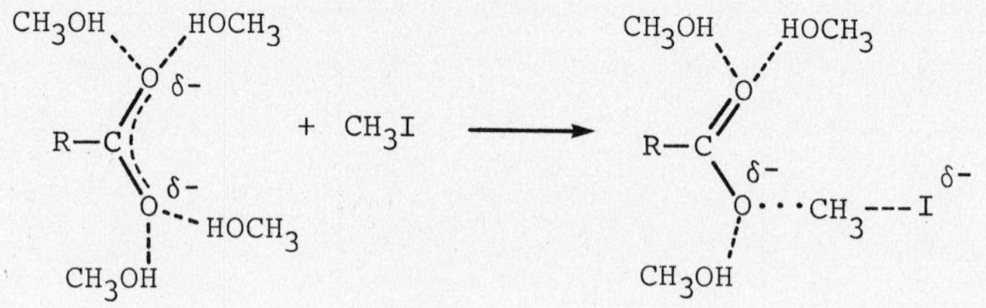

15.

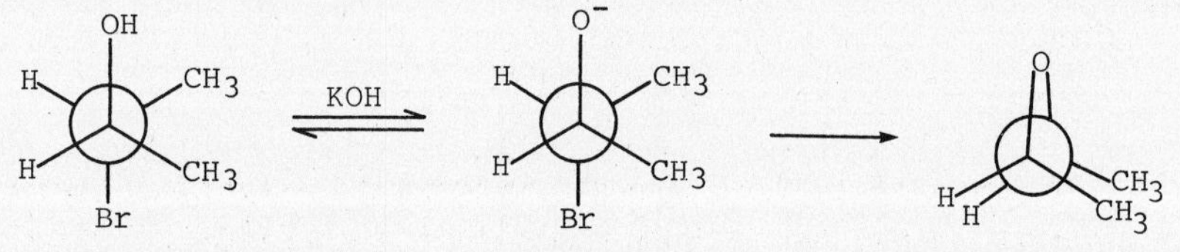

(or the enantiomer)

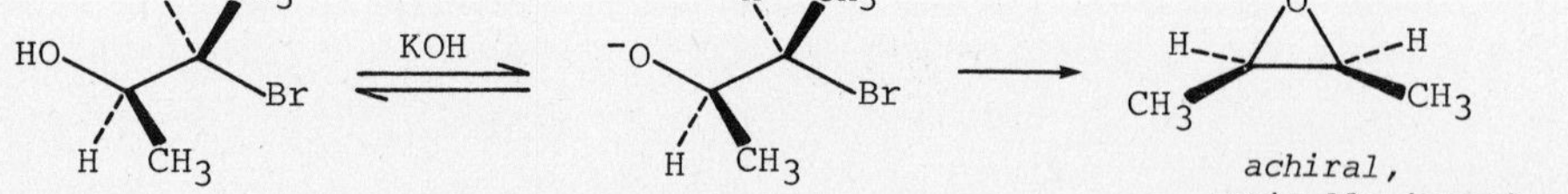

achiral, optically inactive

Although the cyclization reaction is unimolecular, it still proceeds by the "S_N2" mechanism involving backside attack and inversion of configuration.

Work out the sterochemistry of this reaction with the other *enantiomer* of the starting material and demonstrate that it gives the same product. Then do it for a *diastereomer*, and show that it gives a chiral product.

16. (a) $CH_3CH_2CH_2Br + NaSH \xrightarrow{C_2H_5OH} CH_3CH_2CH_2SH + NaBr$

(b) $(CH_3)_2CHCH_2CH_2Cl + KCN \xrightarrow{C_2H_5OH} (CH_3)_2CHCH_2CH_2CN + KCl$

(c) $CH_3CH_2CH_2I + Na^+ {}^-OCH_3 \xrightarrow{CH_3OH} CH_3CH_2CH_2OCH_3 + NaI$

_or_ $CH_3CH_2CH_2O^- {}^+Na + CH_3I \xrightarrow{CH_3CH_2CH_2OH} CH_3CH_2CH_2OCH_3 + NaI$

(d) $CH_3CH_2CH_2Br$ + NaOH $\xrightarrow{H_2O}$ $CH_3CH_2CH_2OH$ + NaBr

(e) $NaNO_3$ + CH_3I $\xrightarrow{CH_3OH}$ CH_3ONO_2 + NaI

(f) $CH_3CH_2CH_2CH_2Cl$ + NaN_3 $\xrightarrow{CH_3OH}$ $CH_3CH_2CH_2CH_2N_3$ + NaCl

17.   (a)   Look at models or pictures of chair structures:

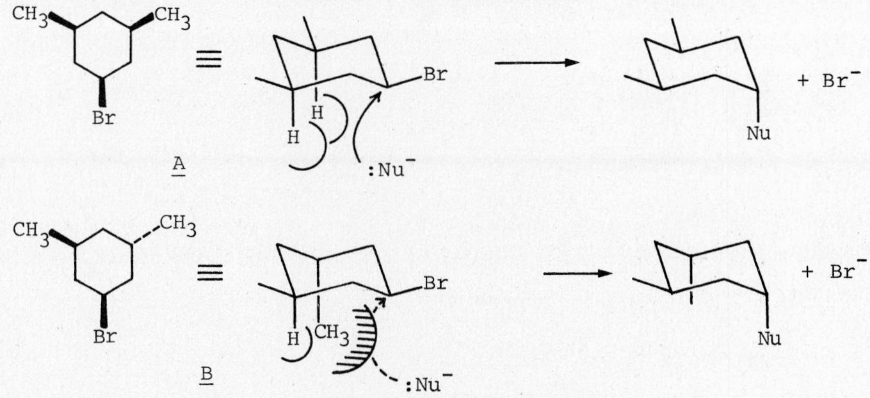

Axial attack is hindered even more by an axial methyl.

(b)

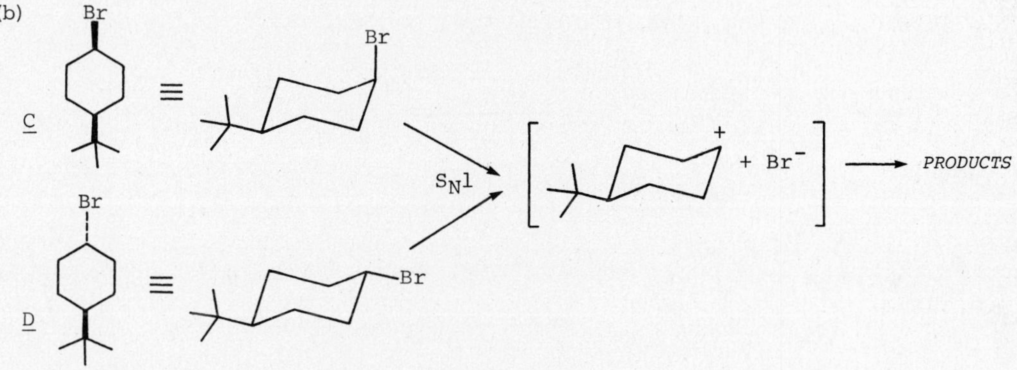

Both $\underline{C}$ and $\underline{D}$ lead to the same carbocation intermediate in an S_N1 reaction. However, $\underline{C}$ is less stable than $\underline{D}$ to begin with because the bromine is in the axial position ($\underline{t}$-butyl is *always* equatorial), so that it doesn't have to go as far "uphill" in order to react. This can be depicted in a reaction profile diagram:

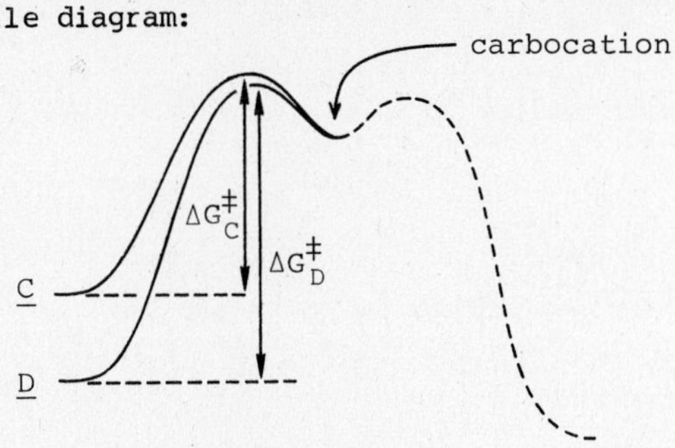

$$\Delta G_C^{\ddagger} < \Delta G_D^{\ddagger}$$

(c) $\underline{t}$-Butyl chloride reacts via the S_N1 mechanism involving the intermediate $\underline{t}$-butyl cation. The higher the dielectric constant of a solvent, the more it can mask the attraction of a negative charge (the departing Cl^- ion) for a positive charge (the $\underline{t}$-butyl cation), and the easier it is for the $\underline{t}$-butyl chloride molecule to ionize. The dielectric constant of methanol is higher than that of ethanol, therefore S_N1 reactions proceed faster in methanol.

9.F Supplementary Problems

S1. Predict the major product and mechanism of each of the following reactions:

(a) $(CH_3)_2CHCH_2Cl + NaN_3 \xrightarrow{CH_3OH}$

(b) 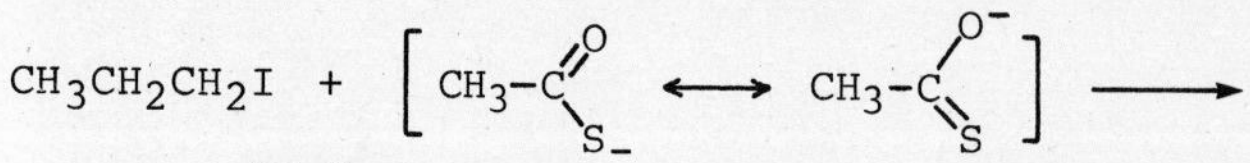 $CH_3CH_2CH_2I + \left[CH_3-\overset{O}{\underset{S_-}{C}} \longleftrightarrow CH_3-\overset{O^-}{\underset{S}{C}} \right] \longrightarrow$

(c) $NaCN + $ $\longrightarrow$

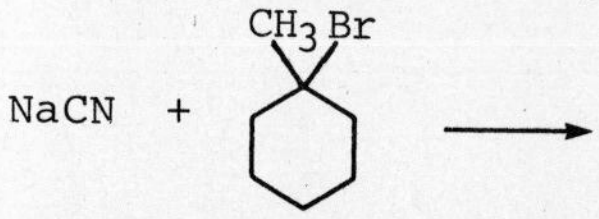

(d) $(CH_3)_3CBr + NaCl \xrightarrow{CH_3OH}$

(e) $(CH_3)_2\underset{OH}{\overset{|}{C}}CH_2CH_2CH_2Br + NaNH_2 \longrightarrow$

(f) $CH_3CH_2CH_2Cl + :N(CH_3)_3 \longrightarrow$

(g) $CH_3CH_2-\overset{CH_3}{\underset{CH_3}{\overset{|}{\underset{|}{C}}}}-CHClCH_3 + NaOH \longrightarrow$

(h) 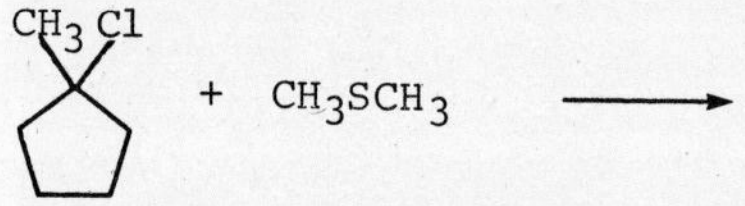 $+ CH_3SCH_3 \longrightarrow$

(i) $BrCH_2CH_2CH_2-\overset{\cdot\cdot}{\underset{CH_3}{\overset{|}{N}}}-CH_2CH_2CH_2CH_2Br \xrightarrow{acetone}$

S2. What are the absolute configurations of the products of the following reaction sequences?

(a)

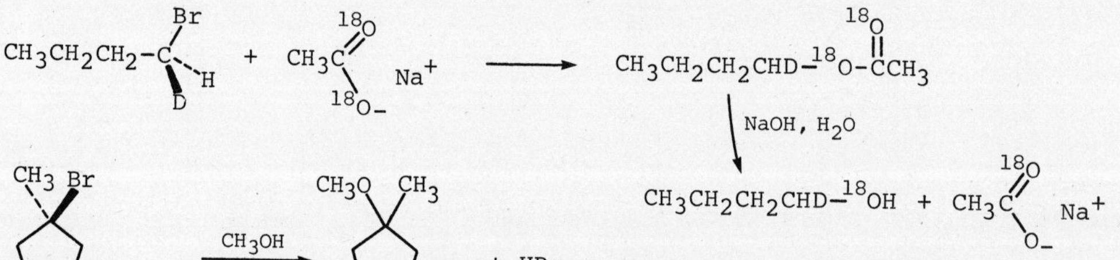

(b)

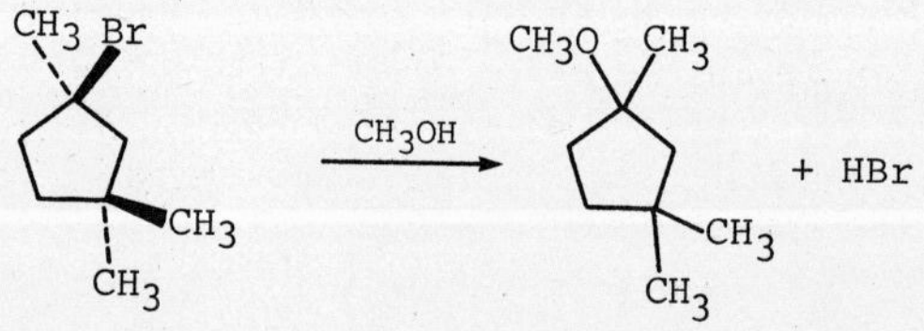

(c)

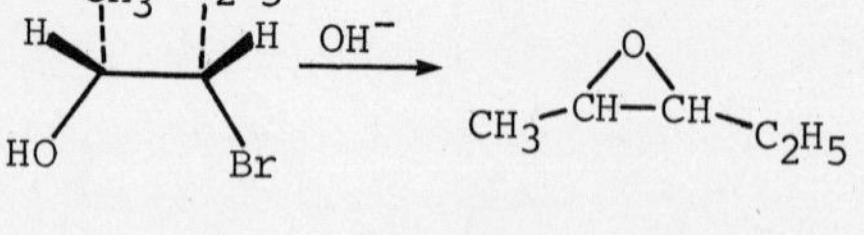

(d)

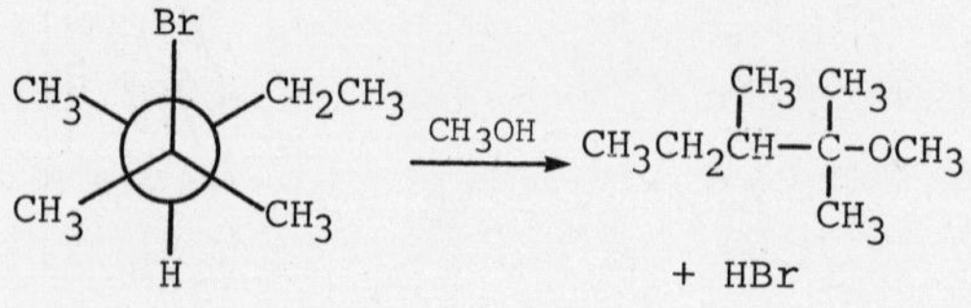

(e)

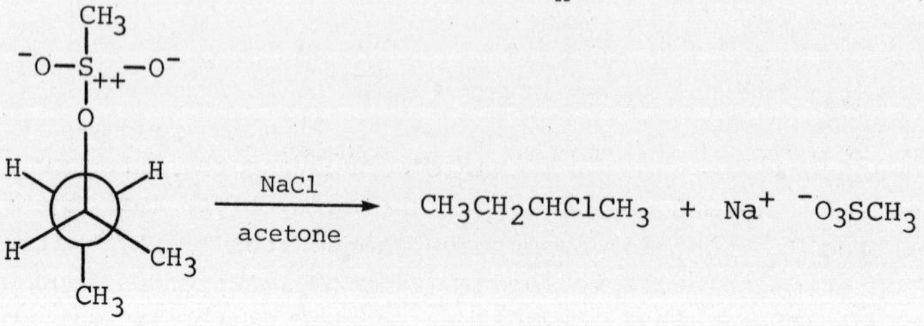

S3. Rank the following nucleophiles in order of their rate of reaction with methyl sulfate in methanol:

$$Cl^-, \ OH^-, \ F^-, \ SH^-, \ H_2O$$

S4. Rank the following compounds in order of their rate of reaction with sodium azide in methanol:

$$CH_3Br, \ (CH_3)_3CCH_2Cl, \ CH_3CH_2CHClCH_3, \ CH_3CH_2CHBrCH_3, \ (CH_3)_2CHCH_2CH_2Br$$

S5. Rank the following compounds in order of their rate of reaction in refluxing (boiling) methanol:

$$CH_3CH_2CHBrCH_3, \ CH_3CH_2CHClCH_3, \ (CH_3)_3CCH_2Br,$$

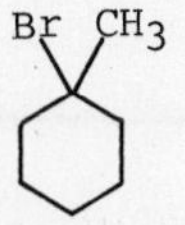

S6. For each of the sets of reactions and conditions below, choose that corresponding to the <u>faster</u> process. Indicate which explanations in the list of statements following are the most pertinent ones for each case. Note that more than one explanation may apply to each set of reactions.

(a) $CH_3CH_2CH_2Br \ + \ Y^- \ \xrightarrow{CH_3OH} \ CH_3CH_2CH_2Y \ + \ Br^-$

$\qquad\qquad Y^- = CH_3O^- \ or \ CH_3CO_2^-$

(b) $(CH_3)_3CCl \ + \ CH_3O^- \ \xrightarrow{CH_3OH} \ A \ + \ Cl^-$

$\qquad\qquad A = (CH_3)_3COCH_3 \ or \ (CH_3)_2C{=}CH_2 + CH_3OH$

(c) $R{-}Br \ + \ HS^- \ \longrightarrow \ R{-}SH \ + \ Br^-$

$\qquad R = (CH_3)_2CHCH_2CH_2Br \ or \ CH_3CH_2CHCH_2Br$
$\qquad\qquad\qquad\qquad\qquad\qquad\qquad\quad |$
$\qquad\qquad\qquad\qquad\qquad\qquad\qquad CH_3$

(d) $Cl^- \ + \ CH_3CH_2OSO_2CH_3 \ \xrightarrow{solvent} \ CH_3CH_2Cl \ + \ CH_3SO_3^-$

$\qquad\qquad\qquad\qquad\qquad\qquad\qquad\quad\ \ O$
$\qquad\qquad\qquad\qquad\qquad\qquad\qquad\quad\ \ ||$
$\qquad\qquad solvent = CH_3CCH_3 \ or \ CH_3CH_2OH$

(e) $CH_3CH_2CHICH_3 \ + \ (CH_3)_3Z \ \longrightarrow \ CH_3CH_2CHCH_3 \ + \ I^-$
$\qquad\qquad\qquad\qquad\qquad\qquad\qquad\qquad\qquad\qquad\quad |$
$\qquad\qquad\qquad Z = N \ or \ P \qquad\qquad\qquad\qquad\ \ {}_+^{\ \ Z}(CH_3)_3$

(f) $\qquad\quad\ \ CH_3$
$\qquad\qquad\ \ |$
$CH_3CH_2{-}C{-}CHBrCH_3 \ + \ CH_3O^- \ \xrightarrow{CH_3OH} \ D \ + \ Br^-$
$\qquad\qquad\ \ |$
$\qquad\qquad\ \ CH_3$

$\qquad\qquad D = CH_3CH_2C(CH_3)_2CHCH_3 \ or \ CH_3CH_2C(CH_3)_2C{=}CH_2 + CH_3OH$
$\qquad\qquad\qquad\qquad\qquad\qquad\qquad\ |$
$\qquad\qquad\qquad\qquad\qquad\qquad OCH_3$

(g) $+ \ CH_3Y \ \longrightarrow$ $+ \ Y^-$

$\qquad\qquad Y^- = F^- \ or \ Br^-$

(h) $R{-}Br \ + \ CH_3OH \ \longrightarrow \ R{-}OCH_3 \ + \ HBr$

$\qquad R{-}Br =$ or

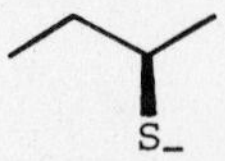

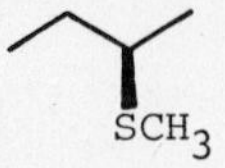

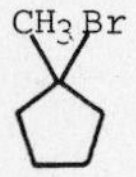

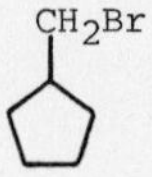

(i) $CH_3CH_2CHBrCH_3 \ + \ Y^- \ \longrightarrow \ CH_3CH_2CHYCH_3 \ + \ Br^-$

$\qquad\qquad Y^- = N_3^- \ or \ NH_2^-$

EXPLANATIONS

(A) Steric hindrance from α-branching results in slower S_N2 reactions.

(B) Steric hindrance from α-branching has little effect on S_N2 reactions.

(C) Steric hindrance from β-branching results in slower S_N2 reactions.

(D) Steric hindrance from β-branching has little effect on S_N2 reactions.

(E) The order of stability of carbocations is 3° > 2° > 1°.

(F) The order of stability of carbocations is 3° < 2° < 1°.

(G) E2 reactions are generally poor for tertiary systems.

(H) Stronger bases make poorer leaving groups.

(I) The reactivity of anions in protic solvents is diminished by hydrogen bonding.

(J) The reactivity of cations in polar solvents is diminished by interaction with the solvent lone pair electrons.

(K) Very strong bases favor elimination over substitution.

(L) Other factors being equal, stronger bases are generally better nucleophiles.

(M) Other factors being equal, the more polarizable reagent is the better nucleophile.

(N) Reagents with no lone pair electrons are relatively poor nucleophiles.

(O) Chiral molecules are generally more effective nucleophiles.

(P) Neopentyl-type systems are exceptionally slow in S_N2 reactions because of steric hindrance.

9.G   Answers to Supplementary Problems

S1. (a) $(CH_3)_2CHCH_2N_3$; S_N2

(b) $CH_3CH_2CH_2S-\overset{\overset{O}{\parallel}}{C}CH_3$; S_N2

(c) 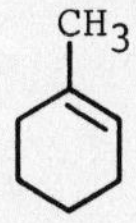   + HCN ; E2   (d) $(CH_3)_3COCH_3$ + HBr ; S_N1

(don't forget that the solvent can react!)

(e)

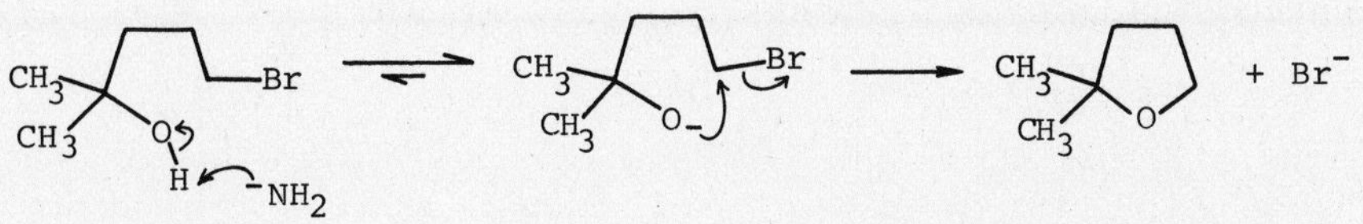

(f) $CH_3CH_2CH_2\overset{+}{N}(CH_3)_3\ Cl^-$; S_N2 (g) $CH_3CH_2C(CH_3)_2CH=CH_2$; E2

(too hindered for S_N2, and strong base)

(h) 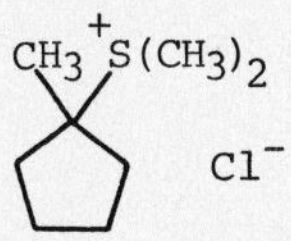 Cl^- ; S_N1

(i)

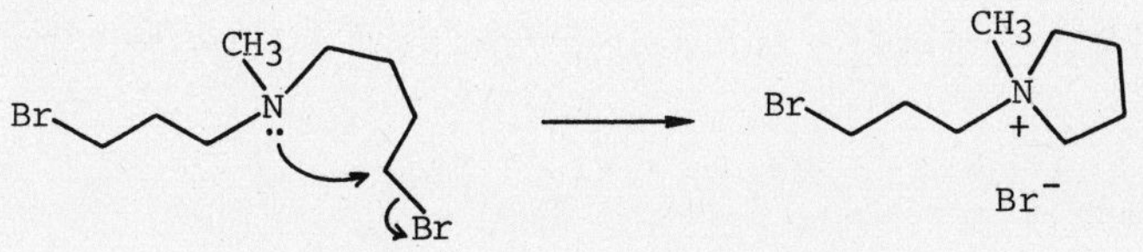

S2. (a) 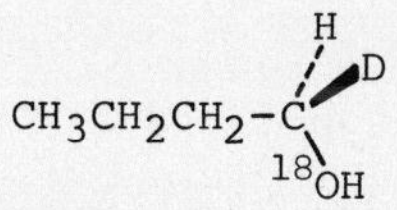   (R) ;   the first step is S_N2 with inversion; the
second step does not affect the CHD-O bond.

(b) 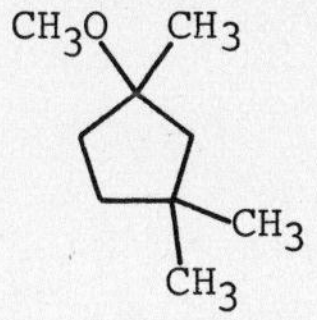   racemic;   reaction proceeds via achiral carbocation
                                    (S_N1)

(c)

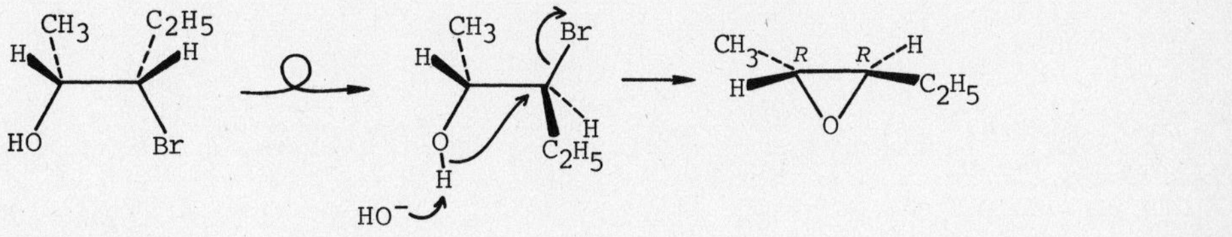

(d) The reaction is S_N1, but
     does not involve the stereocenter: 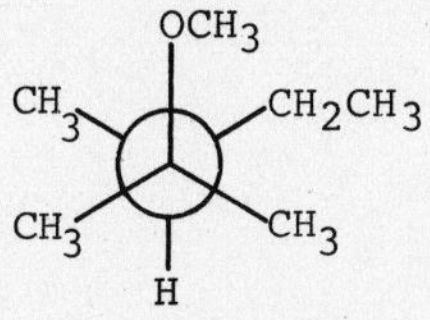   (S)

(e) A mixture of S_N2 and S_N1 reactions,
     resulting in partial inversion,
     partial racemization.
                Major enantiomer: 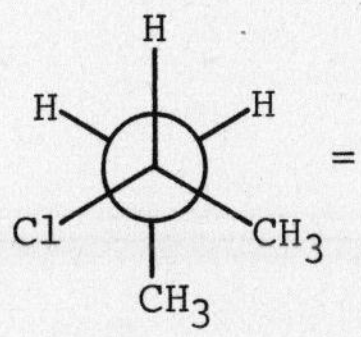   = (S)-2-chlorobutane

S3. $SH^- > OH^- > Cl^- > F^- > H_2O$

S4. $\underline{S_N2}$: $CH_3Br > (CH_3)_2CHCH_2CH_2Br > CH_3CH_2CHBrCH_3 > CH_3CH_2CHClCH_3 > (CH_3)_3CCH_2Cl$

S5. $\underline{S_N1}$:

$> CH_3CH_2CHBrCH_3 > CH_3CH_2CHClCH_3 > (CH_3)_3CCH_2Br$

S6.   (a) $Y^- = CH_3O^-$;   L

      (b) $A = (CH_3)_2C=CH_2 + CH_3OH$;   A (K)

      (c) $R = (CH_3)_2CHCH_2CH_2Br$;   C

      (d)   solvent = $CH_3\overset{O}{\overset{\|}{C}}CH_3$;   I

      (e) $Z = P$;   M

      (f) $D = CH_3CH_2C(CH_3)_2CH=CH_2 + CH_3OH$;   P

      (g) $Y^- = Br^-$;   H

      (h) $RBr =$

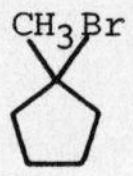

;   E

      (i) $Y^- = N_3^-$;   K

      $\underline{NOTE}$: "Explanations" B, D, F, and O are $\underline{false}$ statements.

10. ALCOHOLS AND ETHERS

10.A   Chapter Outline and Important Terms Introduced

10.1   Introduction: Structures
    sp^3-hybridization   alcohols and ethers as functional groups

10.2   Nomenclature of Alcohols
    alkyl alcohol system   hydroxyalkyl substituents
    alkanols (IUPAC system)

10.3   Physical Properties (solubility, boiling point, etc.)
    dipole moment   dielectric constant
    hydrogen bonding

10.4   Acidity of Alcohols: Inductive Effects
      $ROH \rightleftharpoons RO^- + H^+$
      $ROH + B^-$ (strong base) $\rightleftharpoons RO^- + HB$

    reactions with strong bases   inductive effects
    effects of electron-withdrawing groups   ion pair

10.5   Preparation of Alcohols (functional group interconversions)
    hydrolysis of alkyl halides   acetate displacement

10.6   Reactions of Alcohols

    A.   Reactions of Alcohols with Alkyl Halides
    B.   Conversion of Alcohols into Alkyl Halides
        alkyloxonium salts   inorganic esters:
                                                  chlorosulfite, phosphite, sulfonate
    C.   Carbocation Rearrangements
        outline of best ways for ROH $\longrightarrow$ RX
    D.   Dehydration of Alcohols: Formation of Ethers and Alkenes
        alkylsulfuric acid
    E.   Oxidation of Alcohols (loss of two protons and two electrons)
        chromic acid   chromate ester
        pyridinium chlorochromate (PCC)   catalytic oxidation
        nitric acid   [balancing oxidation/reduction reactions]

10.7   Nomenclature of Ethers
    $alkyl_1$ $alkyl_2$ ether   alkoxyalkane

10.8   Physical Properties of Ethers
    THF

10.9   Preparation of Ethers
    Williamson ether synthesis   reaction of alcohols with sulfuric acid

10.10   Reactions of Ethers
    reactions with acids   autoxidation to peroxides

10.11   Cyclic Ethers
    A.   Epoxides: Oxiranes
        heteroatom   glycols, glymes
    B.   Higher Cyclic Ethers
        THF   crown ethers

10.12   Multistep Synthesis (how to design a sequence of reactions)
    avoid isomers   work backwards

10.B   Important Reactions Discussed

A number of reactions are discussed which have been presented before in a more general context. The reactions of alkyl halides with water (hydrolysis) or another alcohol (ether formation) are simply nucleophilic substitution reactions, and proceed by either the S_N1 or S_N2 mechanisms as discussed in Chapter 9.

Conversion of alcohols to alkyl halides   (10.5)

Acid-catalyzed:

Equation: $ROH \ + \ HX \ \xrightarrow{\ H^+\ } \ RX \ + \ H_2O$

Generality: easiest for 3° ROH; 1^O and 2^O okay if carbocation rearrangements can be avoided

Key features: mechanism involves oxonium ions (ROH_2^+); (X^- will **not** displace OH^-)
                    1^O ROH react via S_N2; 2^O and 3° ROH via S_N1
                    carbocation rearrangements common

Via inorganic esters:

Equation: $ROH \ + \ SOCl_2 \ \longrightarrow \ RCl \ + \ SO_2 \ + \ HCl$
                    $3 \ ROH \ + \ PX_3 \ \longrightarrow \ 3 \ RX \ + \ H_3PO_3$

Generality: good for 1^O, 2^O, and 3° ROH
                    $SOCl_2$ for RCl
                    PCl_3, PBr_3, or $P + I_2$ ($\rightarrow PI_3$) for RCl, RBr, and RI

Key features: milder conditions than HX
              can be run with pyridine (non-basic conditions) to minimize carbocation rearrangements

Note: The table at the end of Section 10.6.C in the Text is a very useful summary of the best conditions to use to convert ROH to RX.

Dehydration of alcohols to ethers   (10.6.D)

Equation:

$$2 \ ROH \ \xrightarrow{\ H_2SO_4\ } \ ROR \ + \ H_2O$$

Generality: For formation of 1^O, symmetrical ethers only

Key features: limited utility, strong acid conditions
                    dehydration occurs with 2^O or 3° ROH

Oxidation of alcohols to ketones and aldehydes   (10.6.E)

Equation:
$$3 \ \overset{\overset{\textstyle OH}{|}}{R-CH-R'} \ + \ 2 \ Cr^{VI} \ reagent \ \longrightarrow \ 3 \ \overset{\overset{\textstyle O}{||}}{R-C-R'} \ + \ Cr^{III}$$

Generality: 1^O and 2^O alcohols, to give ketones and aldehydes, respectively
                    3° not oxidized under normal conditions

Key features: for 2^O alcohol to ketone: $K_2Cr_2O_7$ in aqueous H_2SO_4 ("Jones reagent")
                    with 1^O alcohol, aq. Cr^{VI} reagents give overoxidation to carboxylic acid
                    for 1^O alcohol to aldehyde: pyridinium chlorochromate ("PCC") in CH_2Cl_2

Williamson ether synthesis   (10.9)

Equation: $RX \ + \ R'O^- \ \longrightarrow \ ROR' \ + \ X^-$

Generality: best with CH_3X, 1^O RX
                    3° RX give only elimination (E2)
                    $R'O^-$ can be 1^O, 2^O, or 3°

Key features: S_N2 mechanism
                    $R'O^-$ is strong base, so E2 is frequent side reaction
                    intramolecular reaction gives cyclic ethers

Reactions of epoxides (10.11.A)

Equation: for reactions with basic nucleophiles (base-catalyzed mechanism):

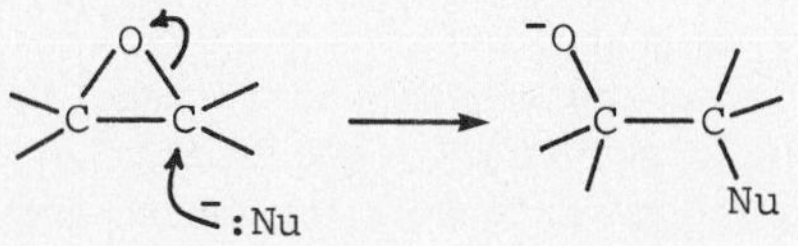

for reactions under acidic conditions (acid-catalyzed mechanism):

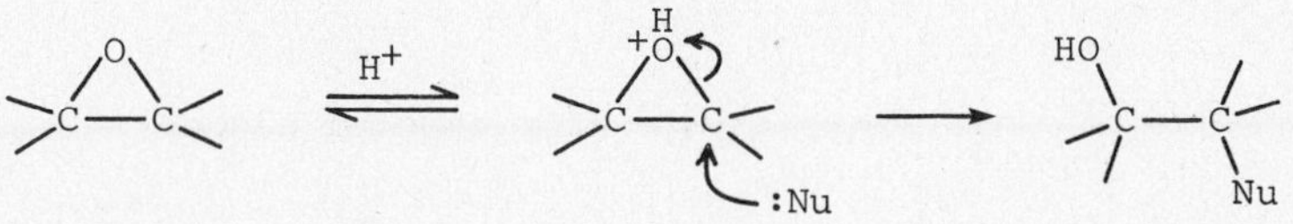

Generality: useful nucleophiles are H_2O (OH^-) (to give glycols)
                    or Grignard reagents (to form C–C bonds)
                    acid catalysis leads to reaction at more substituted end (S_N1-like mechanism)
                    basic reactions occur at less substituted end (S_N2-like)

Key features: reactivity is due to ring strain of three-membered ring

10.C   Important Concepts and Hints

Chapter 10 outlines the chemistry of alcohols and ethers in the way that other functional groups will be discussed throughout the text. First, the nomenclature, physical properties, and spectroscopic properties of molecules that contain the hydroxy group or the ether linkage are presented. Although these topics were introduced in preceding chapters, they must be expanded upon to show how they apply to each additional functional group.

The bulk of the chapter is devoted to the functional group interconversions in which alcohols and ethers take part. In other words, the ways you can make alcohols and ethers (preparation) and what you can make from them (reactions) are presented. As the course progresses, you will realize that a **lot** of organic reactions are being discussed (along with a lot of mechanisms). If you learn each reaction by itself, you will soon be overwhelmed by details, at the expense of understanding. You will always need to learn specific facts, but you should try to get an overview and an understanding of the relationship between these facts. As an example, consider the following reactions:

$$(CH_3)_2CHCH_2CH_2OH \xrightarrow{\ PBr_3\ } (CH_3)_2CHCH_2CH_2Br$$

$$(CH_3)_2CHCH_2CH_2Br \xrightarrow{\ NaOH\ } (CH_3)_2CHCH_2CH_2OH$$

If you approach organic chemistry as a collection of unrelated reactions, you will learn the first reaction twice -- first, as a way to prepare alkyl bromides and second, as a reaction of alcohols. Similarly, you will learn the second reaction twice -- both as a way to prepare alcohols and as a reaction of alkyl bromides. On the other hand, if you try to get an overview, you will think of the reactions above as **one** interconversion of functional groups: alcohol ⇌ alkyl halide. At this point you will have learned the most important aspect of these two reactions -- that they exist. Your thinking of functional group interconversions should grow to resemble the diagram below, with the connecting arrows representing ways to interconvert the indicated functional groups. With this as a framework, organizing the specific details in your mind becomes easier. At first you will know just a few reactions which interconvert alcohols and alkyl halides; as your knowledge grows you will learn more of them, their limitations and exceptions and side reactions, and so on.

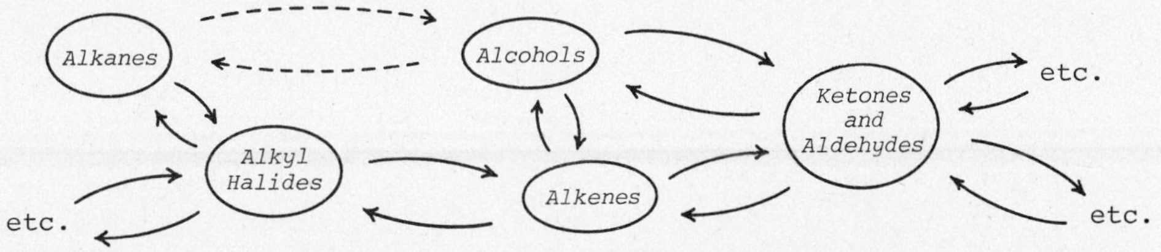

Although an understanding of the framework outlined above is a starting point, you must still know the specific reactions involved. After all, a singer has to know some songs. Think of the functional group interconversions as music and the specific reactions as your repertoire. In this regard, Appendix II in this Study Guide is useful. It is a list of reactions, organized on the basis of functional group preparations and carbon-carbon bond forming reactions. You can try to memorize it if you want to, but it would be wiser to learn a little at a time, referring to it frequently to refresh your memory, using it in the framework suggested above.

10.D   Answers to Exercises

10.1   (a)   neopentyl alcohol

(b)   β-bromopropyl alcohol

(c)   ω-chloropentyl alcohol

10.2   (a)   (b)   (c)

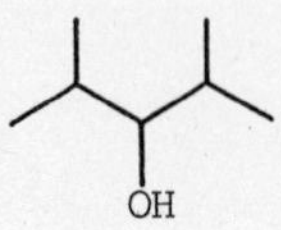

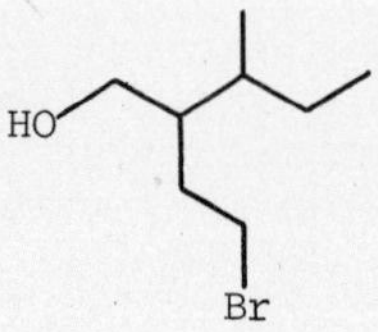

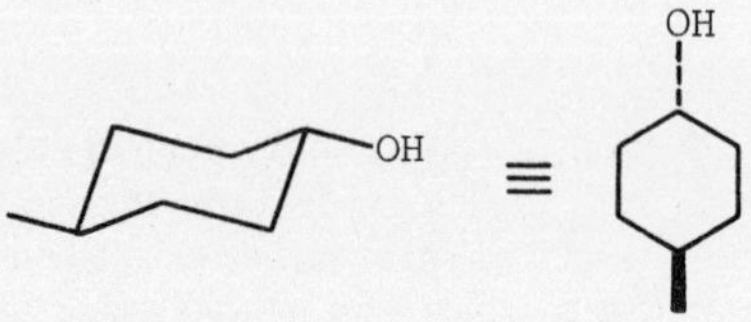

10.3   (a)   "2-Isopropyl-1-butanol" should be named 2-ethyl-3-methyl-1-butanol (choose the carbon chain that has more, smaller substituents).

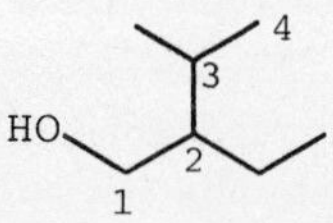

(b)   The name "2-ethyl-4-butanol" does not include the longest carbon chain in the root: 3-methyl-1-pentanol.

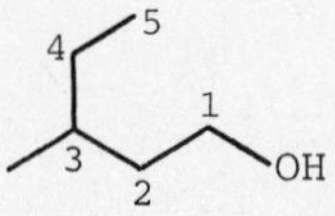

(c)   "2,2-Dichloro-5-hydroxymethylheptane" should be named as an alkanol: 5,5-dichloro-2-ethyl-1-hexanol.

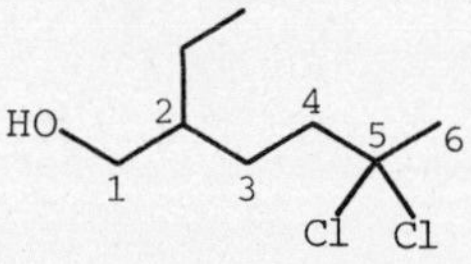

10.4   (a)   2,4,7-trimethyl-4-octanol   (c)   5-chloro-2-methyl-3-hexanol

(b)   2,3,3-trimethyl-2-butanol   (d)   trans-3-chlorocyclobutanol

10.5   (a) $CH_3CHClCH_2OH$ is more acidic because the electronegative substituent is closer to the hydroxy group.

(b) $CH_3OCH_2CH_2OH$ is more acidic because CH_3O is more electron-withdrawing than ethyl.

(c)   The dichloro compound is more acidic because it has more electron-withdrawing groups than the monochloro compound.

(d)   cis-3-Chlorocyclohexanol is more acidic than trans-4-chlorocyclohexanol for the same reason given in (a) above.

10.6   (a)

(b)   (c)

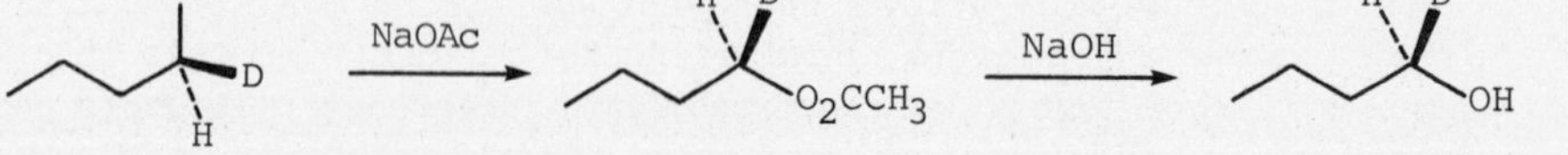

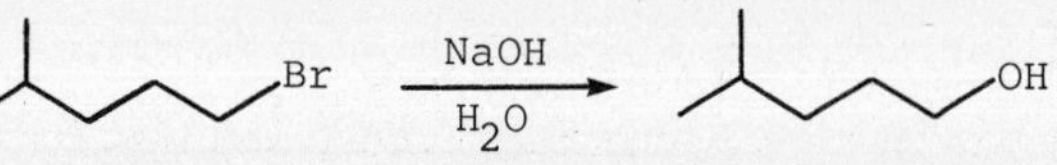

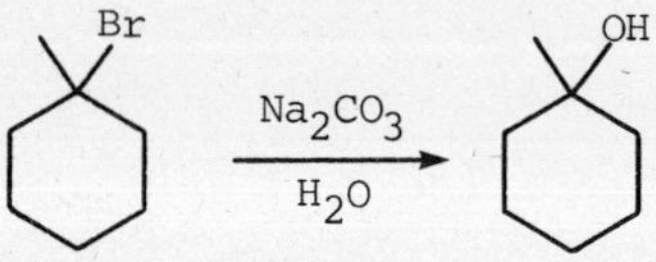

10.7   All of them can:

(a)

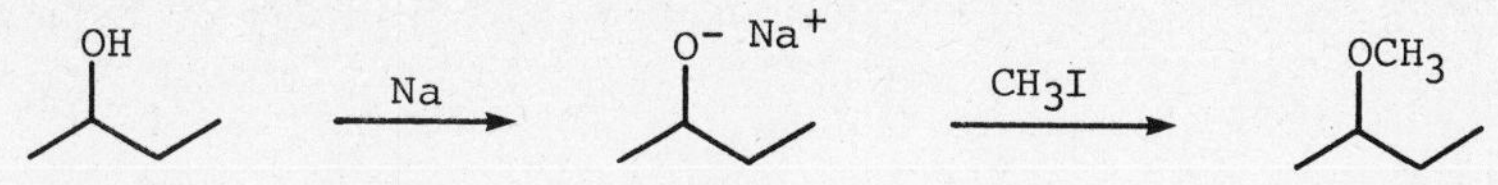

The alternative ($CH_3O^- Na^+$ + 2-bromobutane) leads to a lot of elimination.

(b) $(CH_3)_3CBr$ + $HOCH(CH_3)_2$ $\xrightarrow{\text{solvent}}$ $(CH_3)_3COCH(CH_3)_2$ [S_N1]

The reaction works because the halide is tertiary and can react via an S_N1 mechanism. A reaction between an <u>alkoxide</u> and an alkyl halide could not lead to <u>t</u>-butyl isopropyl ether; elimination would occur instead.

(c) CH_3CH_2Br + $Na^+ \ ^-OCH_2C(CH_3)_3$ $\longrightarrow$ $CH_3CH_2OCH_2C(CH_3)_3$ [S_N2]

The alternative ($CH_3CH_2O^- Na^+$ + $BrCH_2C(CH_3)_3$) will not work because of steric hindrance.

10.8

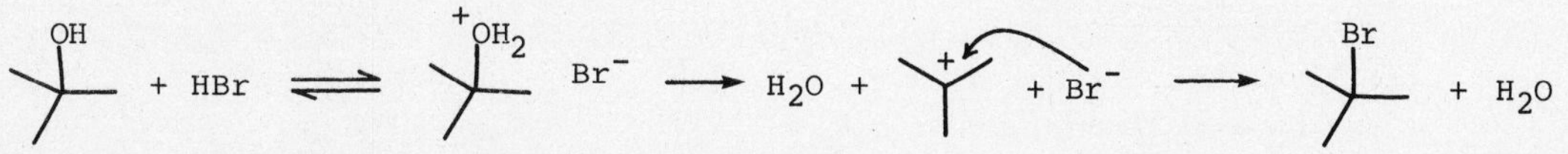

10.9   The reaction between the alcohol and $SOCl_2$ leads first to the chlorosulfite ester and HCl. In the absence of water or a base, HCl is only slightly dissociated and there is only a low concentration of Cl^- ion to carry out the second step. As a mild base, pyridine converts the HCl to pyridinium ion and chloride ion, greatly increasing the concentration of the latter and thereby the rate of reaction.

10.10   (a) $CH_2CH_2OCH_2CH_2OH$ + PBr_3 $\longrightarrow$ $CH_3CH_2OCH_2CH_2O-PBr_2$ + H^+ + Br^-

$CH_3CH_2OCH_2CH_2Br$ + $^-OPBr_2$ + H^+

HOPBr$_2$ can react with two more alcohol molecules in the same way.

(b)

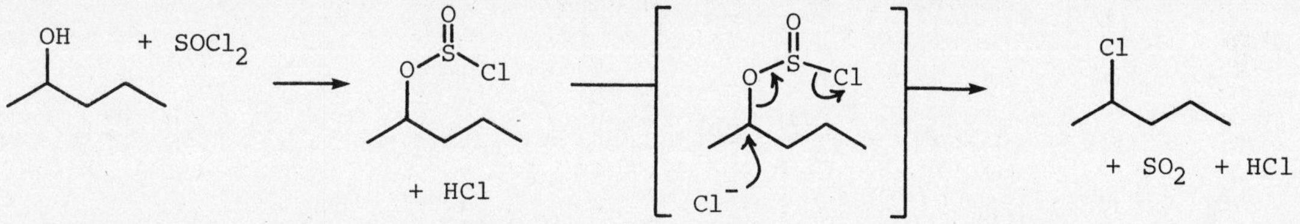

(c) $CH_3CH_2CH_2CH_2-OH$ + PI_3 $\longleftarrow$ $1/2 \ (2\,P + 3\,I_2)$

$CH_3CH_2CH_2CH_2-OPI_2$ + H^+ + I^- $\longrightarrow$ $CH_3CH_2CH_2CH_2-I$ + $HOPI_3$

10.11   (a)   (<u>R</u>)-2-bromobutane   (b)   <u>trans</u>-1-bromo-4-methylcyclohexane

10.12   Rearrangement of the secondary cation from ionization of 2-pentanol could at best only lead to another secondary cation. On the other hand, migration of the hydrogen from the 3-position on ionization of 3-methyl-2-butanol leads to a tertiary cation, which is more stable. Since there is some positive charge on both carbons in the transition state for rearrangement, the transition state that leads to the tertiary cation is of lower energy and that rearrangement occurs faster.

10.14   (a) 3° alcohol with no fear of rearrangement: HCl at 0 ^{O}C

(b) 1^O alcohol: $SOCl_2$ in pyridine

(c) 1^O alcohol, small chance of rearrangement: PBr_3, < 0 ^{O}C

(d) 2^O alcohol, complete inversion of configuration desired:
         <u>p</u>-toluenesulfonyl chloride to give tosylate, then NaBr

(e) 2^O alcohol, complete inversion of configuration desired: $SOCl_2$ and pyridine

10.15 The conditions necessary for the acid-catalyzed dehydration of a primary alcohol such as 1-butanol are so vigorous that the product will isomerize to a mixture of 1- and 2-butenes during the reaction.

10.16 Equation:

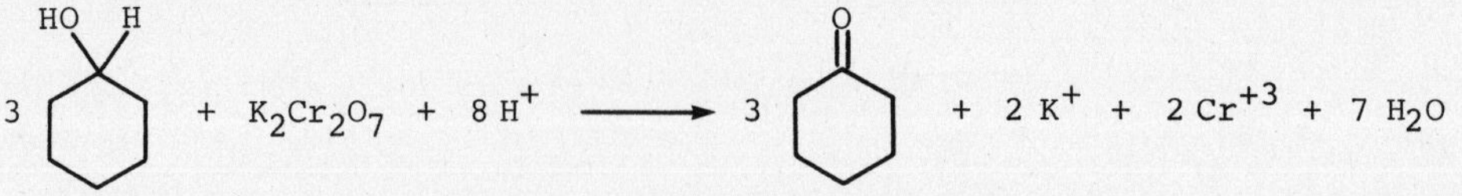

$$3 \quad \text{[cyclohexanol]} + K_2Cr_2O_7 + 8\,H^+ \longrightarrow 3 \quad \text{[cyclohexanone]} + 2\,K^+ + 2\,Cr^{+3} + 7\,H_2O$$

(2 moles of Cr^{+6} = 1 mole of dichromate are required for every 3 moles of alcohol)

70 g (0.70 mole) of cyclohexanol requires $\dfrac{2 \times (0.7)}{3}$ = 0.47 mole

= 137.3 g of $K_2Cr_2O_7$

10.17

	Common	IUPAC
(a)	cyclohexyl ethyl ether	ethoxycyclohexane
(b)	sec-butyl ethyl ether or 1-methylpropyl ethyl ether	2-ethoxybutane
(c)	isobutyl isopropyl ether	2-methyl-1-(1-methylethoxy)propane

10.18 $(CH_3)_3CCH_2O^- \, Na^+ \quad CH_3O_3SC_6H_5 \longrightarrow (CH_3)_3CCH_2OCH_3 + Na^+ \, {}^-O_3SC_6H_5$

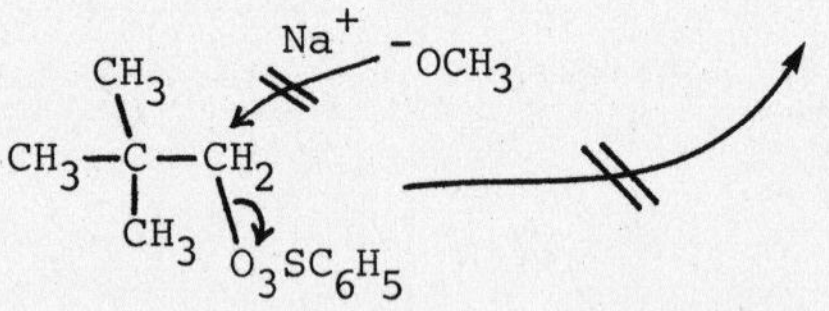

$$CH_3-\overset{\overset{\displaystyle CH_3}{|}}{\underset{\underset{\displaystyle CH_3}{|}}{C}}-CH_2 \quad \overset{Na^+ \, ^-OCH_3}{\nparallel} \quad O_3SC_6H_5$$

Steric hindrance (β-branching) blocks backside attack of methoxide ion on neopentyl benzene-sulfonate

10.19

(a) [bromocyclohexane with methyl] + CH₃OH *(solvent)* ⟶ [methoxycyclohexane with methyl] + HBr   [S_N1]

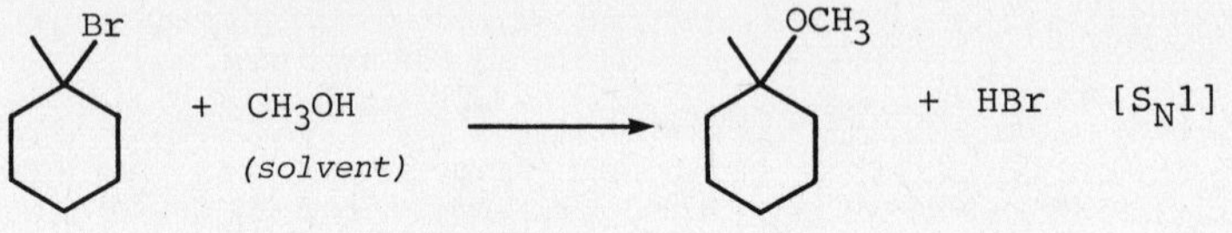

(b) $2\ CH_3CH_2CH_2CH_2OH \xrightarrow[\Delta]{H_2SO_4} (CH_3CH_2CH_2CH_2)_2O$

10.20 $CH_3OCH_2C(CH_3)_3 + HBr \longrightarrow CH_3Br + HOCH_2C(CH_3)_3$

10.21

Cis:

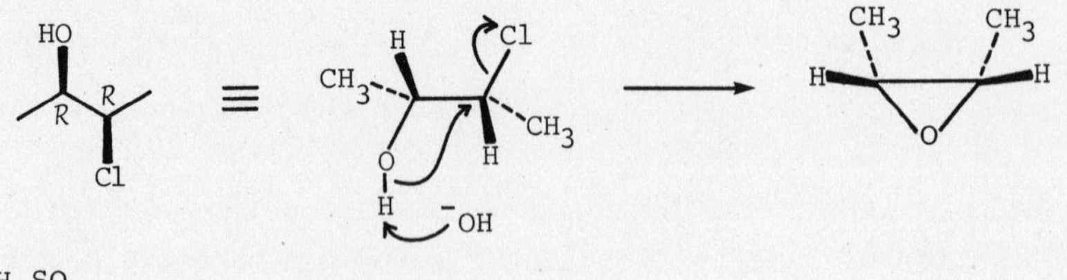

10.22

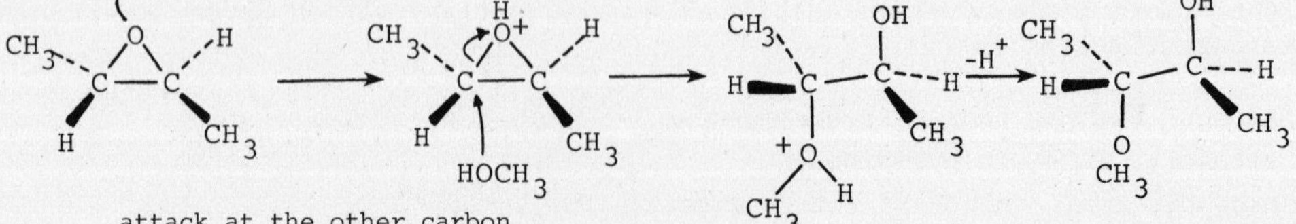

attack at the other carbon leads to the same compound

(2S,3R)-3-methoxy-2-butanol

The enantiomeric epoxide leads to the (2R,3S) product.

10.23

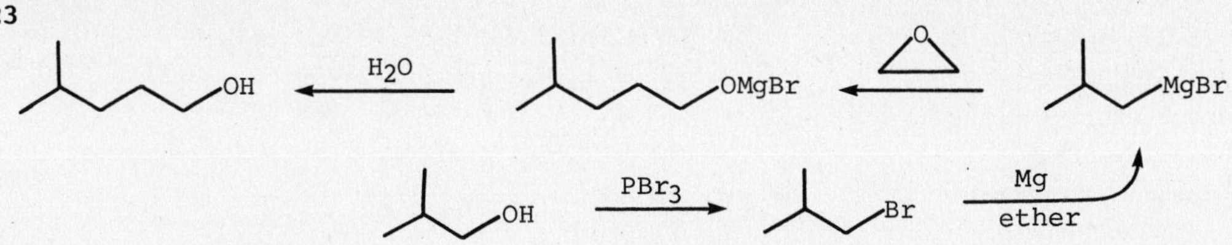

10.24

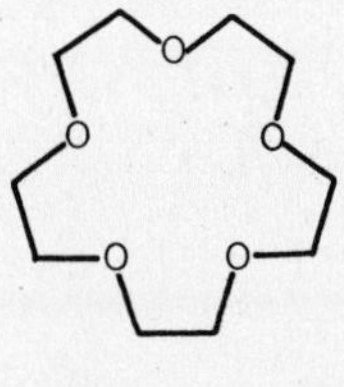

10.25

(a)

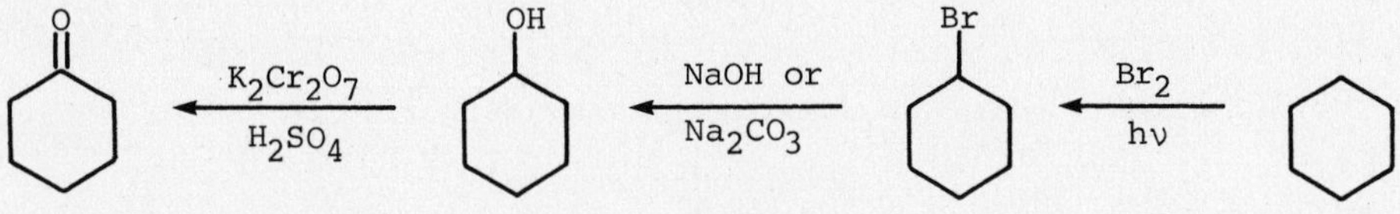

(b) $CH_3CH_2CN \xleftarrow{\text{NaCN}} CH_3CH_2Br \xleftarrow[\text{h}\nu]{\text{Br}_2} CH_3CH_3$

(c)

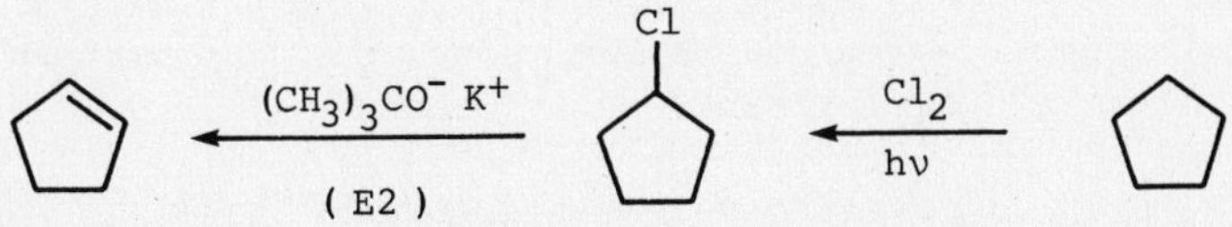

$\underline{NOTE}$: For each of these examples, either bromination or chlorination will work equally well.

10.E   Answers and Explanations for Problems

1.   (a) $CH_3OCH_2CH(CH_3)_2$

     (b) $(CH_3)_3CCH_2OH$

     (c)

     (d)

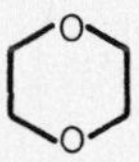

     (e)

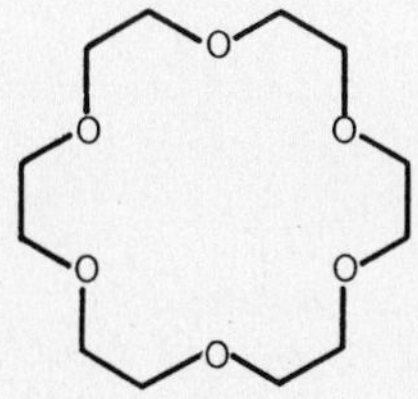

     (f)
           $CH_3CHCH_2OCH_2CHCH_3$

     (g) $CH_3CH_2CHCH_3$
           $\qquad\quad\;\; OH$

     (h) $(CH_3)_2CHCH_2OH$

2.   (a)

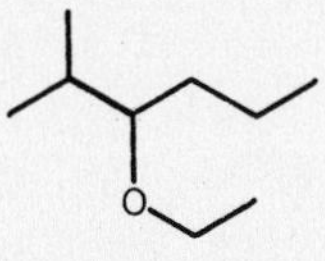

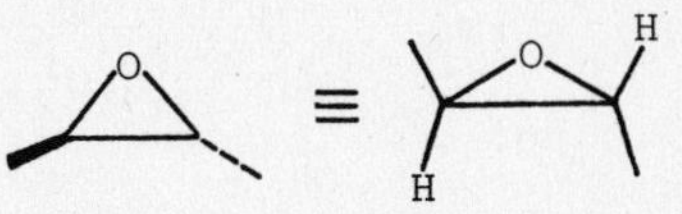

     (b)

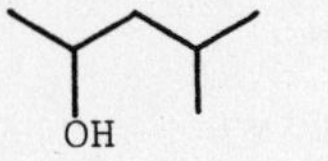

     (c)

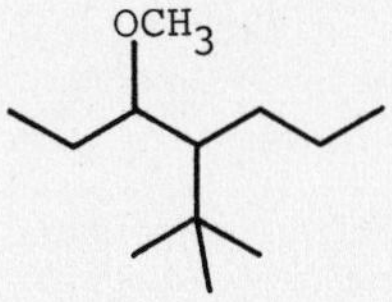

     (d)

     (e)

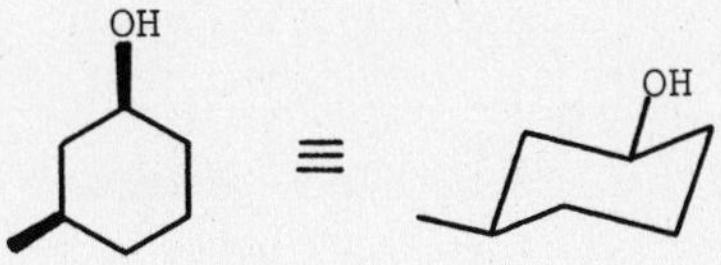

     (f)

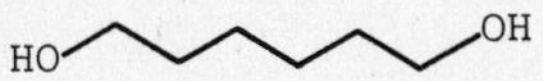

3. (a) 3-methyl-2-propyloxirane   (f) 2,3,5-trimethyl-3-hexanol

(b) 2-ethyl-3-methyl-1-pentanol   (g) (2R,4S)-heptane-2,4-diol
                                                      or   (2R,4S)-2,4-heptanediol

(c) 6-chloro-2-ethyl-4-methyl-1-hexanol

(d) 3-methoxy-2-pentanol   (h) (2S,5R)-6-chloro-5-methoxy-2-hexanol

(e) 3,3-dimethylcyclopentanol *(NOTE: the position of the alcohol doesn't have
                         to be specified in a cycloalkanol, since carbon #1 is automatically the one with the OH.)*

4. (a) "4-hexanol" is numbered from the wrong end;
           correct name: 3-hexanol

(b) "2-hydroxy-3-methylhexane" should be named as an alkanol;
           correct name: 3-methyl-2-hexanol

(c) "3-(hydroxymethyl)-1-hexanol" should be named as a diol;
           correct name: 2-propyl-1,4-butanediol

(d) "2-isopropyl-1-butanol" should be named 2-ethyl-3-methyl-1-butanol.

5. 1) $CH_3OCH_2CH_2CH_2CH_3$ ⎰ 1-methoxybutane
                                       ⎱ n-butyl methyl ether

    2) OCH_3
           |
       $CH_3CHCH_2CH_3$ *   ⎰ 2-methoxybutane*
                                       ⎱ sec-butyl methyl ether

    3) $CH_3CH_2OCH_2CH_2CH_3$ ⎰ 1-ethoxypropane
                                      ⎱ ethyl propyl ether

    4) $CH_3CH_2OCH(CH_3)_2$ ⎰ 2-ethoxypropane
                                     ⎱ ethyl isopropyl ether

    5) $CH_3OCH_2CH(CH_3)_2$ ⎰ 1-methoxy-2-methylpropane
                                     ⎱ isobutyl methyl ether

    6) $CH_3OC(CH_3)_3$ ⎰ 2-methoxy-2-methylpropane
                                     ⎱ t-butyl methyl ether

     * chiral; this is the only isomer
           capable of optical activity:

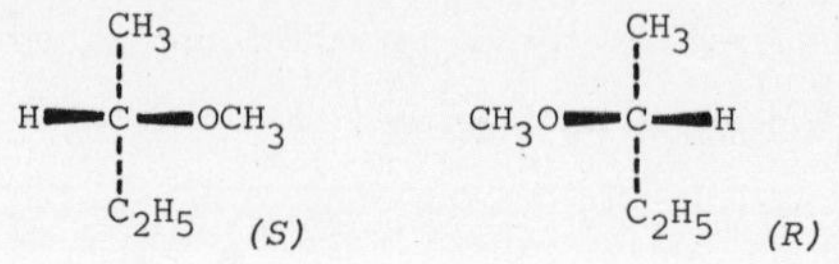

6.

1)	$CH_3CH_2CH_2CH_2CH_2CH_2OH$	1-hexanol	1°
2)	$CH_3CH_2CH_2CH_2\overset{OH}{C}HCH_3$	2-hexanol	2°
3)	$CH_3CH_2CH_2\overset{OH}{C}HCH_2CH_3$	3-hexanol	2°
4)	$(CH_3)_2CHCH_2CH_2CH_2OH$	4-methyl-1-pentanol	1°
5)	$(CH_3)_2CHCH_2\overset{OH}{C}HCH_3$	4-methyl-2-pentanol	2°
6)	$(CH_3)_2CH\overset{OH}{C}HCH_2CH_3$	2-methyl-3-pentanol	2°
7)	$(CH_3)_2\overset{OH}{C}CH_2CH_2CH_3$	2-methyl-2-pentanol	3°
8)	$HOCH_2\overset{CH_3}{C}HCH_2CH_2CH_3$	2-methyl-1-pentanol	1°
9)	$CH_3CH_2\overset{CH_3}{C}HCH_2CH_2OH$	3-methyl-1-pentanol	1°
10)	$CH_3CH_2\overset{H_3C\ OH}{CH-CHCH_3}$	3-methyl-2-pentanol	2°

11) $CH_3CH_2\overset{\overset{\displaystyle CH_3}{|}}{\underset{\underset{\displaystyle OH}{|}}{C}}CH_2CH_3$ 3-methyl-3-pentanol   3

12) $CH_3\overset{\overset{\displaystyle H_3C}{|}}{CH}-\overset{\overset{\displaystyle CH_3}{|}}{CH}CH_2OH$ 2,3-dimethyl-1-butanol   1

13) $CH_3\overset{\overset{\displaystyle H_3C}{|}}{CH}-\overset{\overset{\displaystyle CH_3}{|}}{\underset{\underset{\displaystyle OH}{|}}{C}}CH_3$ 2,3-dimethyl-2-butanol   3

14) $CH_3CH_2\overset{\overset{\displaystyle CH_2OH}{|}}{CH}CH_2CH_3$ 2-ethyl-1-butanol   1

15) $CH_3\overset{\overset{\displaystyle CH_3}{|}}{\underset{\underset{\displaystyle CH_3}{|}}{C}}CH_2CH_2OH$ 3,3-dimethyl-1-butanol   1

16) $CH_3\overset{\overset{\displaystyle H_3C}{|}}{\underset{\underset{\displaystyle CH_3}{|}}{C}}-\overset{\overset{\displaystyle OH}{|}}{CH}CH_3$ 3,3-dimethyl-2-butanol   2

17) $HOCH_2\overset{\overset{\displaystyle CH_3}{|}}{\underset{\underset{\displaystyle CH_3}{|}}{C}}CH_2CH_3$ 2,2-dimethyl-1-butanol   1

7.   (a)   The name is incorrect since it mixes common and systematic nomenclature.

          <u>Correct</u>   IUPAC: 2-methoxy-2-methylbutane

                     Common: methyl <u>t</u>-pentyl ether, or <u>t</u>-amyl methyl ether

Amyl is an older common name for pentyl;   e.g., <u>n</u>-amyl, isoamyl, <u>tert</u>-amyl.   In modern usage, amyl is being replaced increasingly by pentyl, but the name is common in the older literature.

8.   (a) $CH_3CH_2CH_2OCH_2CH_2CH_3$ *sulfuric acid-catalyzed ether formation*

     (b) $CH_3CH_2CH_2OH \;+\; CH_2=C(CH_3)_2$ *E2 elimination (remember: 3° halide and strong base)*

     (c) $(CH_3)_3COCH_2CH_2CH_3$ *Williamson ether synthesis*

     (d) CH_3CH_2CHO *Volatile aldehydes can be isolated under these conditions*

     (e)   *Standard chromic acid ("Jones") oxidation*

     (f) $CH_3CH_2CH_2I \;+\; Na^{+-}O_3S$—⬡—$CH_3$ *S_N2 displacement, sodium tosylate precipitates*

     (g) $CH_3CH_2CH_2Br$ *Acid-catalyzed formation of alkyl halide.*

     (h) $(CH_3CH_2)_2\overset{\overset{\displaystyle Br}{|}}{C}CH_2CH_2CH_3$ *Reaction proceeds with rearrangement to give the tertiary carbocation as an intermediate*

     (i) $(R)-CH_3CHClCH_2CH_3$ *Alkyl chloride formation with inversion of configuration*

     (j) $(CH_3CH_2)_2CHO^-K^+ \;+\; H_2\uparrow$ *Potassium hydride is a strong base*

     (k)   2 $CH_3CH_2CH_2I$

     (l) $CH_3CH_2CHBrCH_2CH_3 \;+\; CH_3Br$ *Acid-catalyzed formation of alkyl halide*

9.   (a) and (b)   Primary alcohols are best converted to primary alkyl chlorides with $SOCl_2$ in pyridine.

     (c)   In this case, rearrangement is desired, so a reagent favoring carbocation intermediates should be chosen: $ZnCl_2 + HCl$.

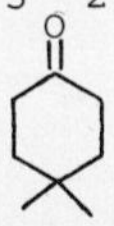

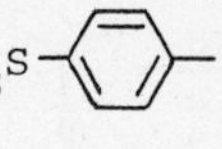

(d) The best way to make alkyl iodides from alcohols is to carry out a displacement on a sulfonate ester intermediate:

$$CH_3CH_2CH_2\overset{\overset{\displaystyle OH}{|}}{C}HCH_3 \ + \ C_6H_5SO_2Cl \ \longrightarrow \ CH_3CH_2CH_2\overset{\overset{\displaystyle OSO_2C_6H_5}{|}}{C}HCH_3 \ \xrightarrow[\text{acetone}]{NaI} \ CH_3CH_2CH_2\overset{\overset{\displaystyle I}{|}}{C}HCH_3$$

(e) Rearrangement must be avoided: PBr_3 at 0 $^\circ$C.

(f) Tertiary chloride from the alcohol, with no fear of rearrangement: HCl at 0 $^\circ$C.

10. (a) Rearrangement is desired: $ZnCl_2$ + HCl

(b) $(CH_3)_2CH\overset{\overset{\displaystyle OH}{|}}{C}HCH_3 \ + \ PBr_3 \ \xrightarrow{\text{low temp.}} \ (CH_3)_2CH\overset{\overset{\displaystyle Br}{|}}{C}HCH_3$

(c) $(CH_3CH_2)_3C\!-\!OH \ + \ H_2SO_4 \ \xrightarrow{\Delta} \ CH_3CH\!=\!C\overset{\displaystyle CH_2CH_3}{\underset{\displaystyle CH_2CH_3}{\big\langle}}$

A drop of sulfuric acid or a small amount of sulfonic acid is sufficient. Alternatively, the alcohol can be passed over hot Al_2O_3.

(d) $CH_3CH_2CH_2CH_2OH \ + \ SOCl_2 \ \longrightarrow CH_3CH_2CH_2CH_2Cl \ \xrightarrow{CN^-} \ CH_3CH_2CH_2CH_2CN$

(e) $(CH_3)_3CCl \ + \ H_2O \ \xrightarrow{\Delta} (CH_3)_3COH \ \xrightarrow{K} (CH_3)_3CO^-K^+ \ \xrightarrow[\Delta]{CH_3I} (CH_3)_3C\!-\!OCH_3$

Note that the reverse procedure of treating $(CH_3)_3CCl$ with $CH_3O^-K^+$ will not work, because the halide is tertiary and E2 elimination would dominate.

(f) $(CH_3)_2CHCH_2OH \ \xrightarrow[H_2SO_4, \ \Delta]{HBr} \ (CH_3)_2CHCH_2Br \ \xrightarrow{CH_3S^-\ Na^+} \ (CH_3)_2CHCH_2SCH_3$

(g) $(CH_3)_3COH + HBr \ \longrightarrow \ (CH_3)_3CBr \ \xrightarrow{Mg} \ (CH_3)_3CMgBr \ \xrightarrow[\text{2. } H_2O]{\text{1. } \triangle\!\!\!\!O} \ (CH_3)_3CCH_2CH_2OH$

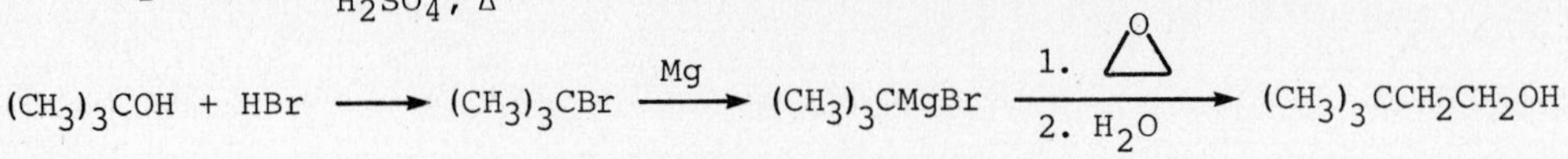

11. (a) $CH_4 + Br_2 \ \xrightarrow{h\nu} \ CH_3Br \ \xrightarrow{NaOH} \ CH_3OH$

(b)

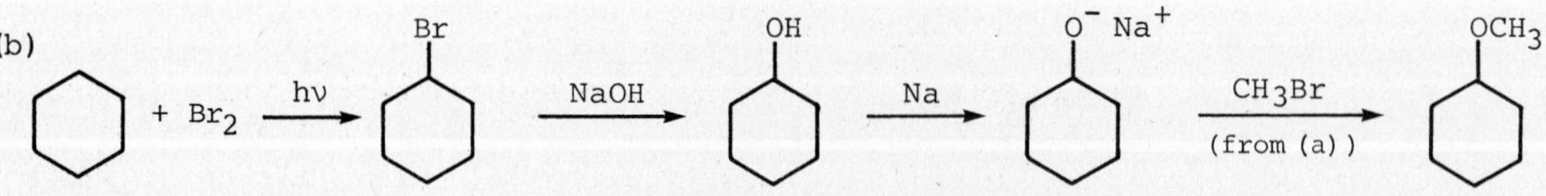

(c) $CH_3CH_2CH_3 \ + \ Br_2 \ \xrightarrow{h\nu} \ CH_3CHBrCH_3 \ \xrightarrow{(CH_3)_3CO^-\ K^+} \ CH_3CH\!=\!CH_2$ [E2]

(d) $CH_3CH_3 \ + \ Br_2 \ \xrightarrow{h\nu} \ CH_3CH_2Br \ \xrightarrow{NaSH} \ CH_3CH_2SH$

12.

$$CH_3CH_2\overset{\overset{\displaystyle OH}{|}}{C}DCH_3 \ + \ H^+ \ \rightleftharpoons \ CH_3CH_2\overset{\overset{\displaystyle {}^+OH_2}{|}}{C}DCH_3 \ \rightleftharpoons \ CH_3CH_2\overset{\overset{\displaystyle +}{|}}{C}DCH_3 \ \xrightarrow{Br^-} \ CH_3CH_2\overset{\overset{\displaystyle Br}{|}}{C}DCH_3$$

$$CH_3\overset{\overset{\displaystyle +}{|}}{C}HCHDCH_3 \ \xrightarrow{Br^-} \ CH_3\overset{\overset{\displaystyle Br}{|}}{C}HCHDCH_3$$

Equilibration of secondary carbocations has occurred.

13.

product observed

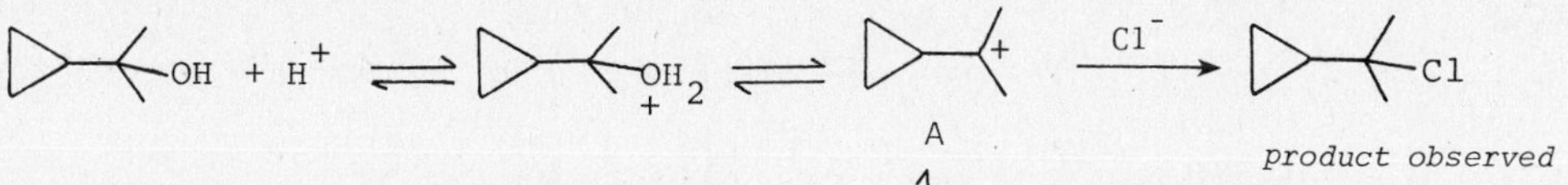

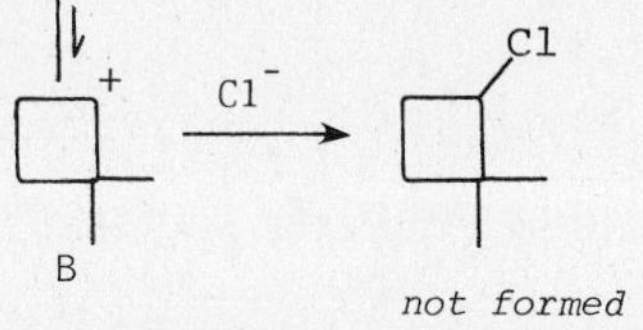

The possible rearrangement, A → B, is not observed.
The ring strain of a cyclobutane ring is as high as
that of a cyclopropane ring (see Table 5.5 in text), so
that the isomerization A → B would involve conversion of
a tertiary to a secondary carbocation with no relief of
ring strain.

not formed

14. (a) $3 (CH_3)_2CHOH + 2 KMnO_4 + 2 H^+ \longrightarrow 3 (CH_3)_2C=O + 2 MnO_2 + 2 K^+ + 4 H_2O$

(b) $ClCH_2CH_2CH_2OH + 4 HNO_3 \longrightarrow ClCH_2CH_2CO_2H + 4 NO_2 + 3 H_2O$

(c)

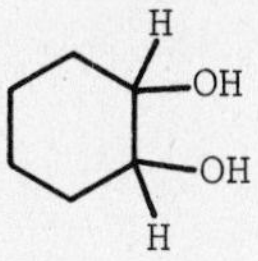

$+ K_2Cr_2O_7 + 8 H^+ \longrightarrow HO_2C(CH_2)_4CO_2H + 2 K^+ + Cr^{+3} + 5 H_2O$

15. (a) The rearrangement requires a carbocation intermediate. The formation of
the high-energy primary carbocation cannot compete with S_N2 displacement on
the oxonium ion.

$$(CH_3)_2CHCH_2OH + H^+ \rightleftharpoons (CH_3)_2CHCH_2\overset{+}{O}H_2 \xrightarrow{Br^-} (CH_3)_2CHCH_2Br + OH_2$$

$$\cancel{\longrightarrow} (CH_3)_3CHCH_2{}^+ \longrightarrow (CH_3)_3C^+$$

The secondary carbocation forms far more readily:

$$(CH_3)_2CH\overset{\overset{+OH_2}{|}}{C}HCH_3 \longrightarrow (CH_3)_2CH\overset{+}{C}HCH_3 \longrightarrow (CH_3)_2\overset{+}{C}CH_2CH_3 \xrightarrow{Br^-} (CH_3)_2CBrCH_2CH_3$$

(b) Mixtures of ethers generally result:

$$R'CH_2OH + R''CH_2OH \xrightarrow{H_2SO_4} R'CH_2OCH_2R' + R'CH_2OCH_2R'' + R''CH_2OCH_2R''$$

Either alcohol forms $R CH_2\overset{+}{O}H_2$ and can be displaced by either alcohol.
However, t-butyl alcohol readily forms a carbocation,

$$(CH_3)_3COH + H^+ \rightleftharpoons (CH_3)_3C\overset{+}{O}H_2 \longrightarrow (CH_3)_3C^+$$

which reacts more readily with methanol than with the bulkier t-butyl alcohol:

$$(CH_3)_3C^+ + CH_3OH \longrightarrow (CH_3)_3C\overset{\overset{+}{O}CH}{\underset{H}{}} \rightleftharpoons (CH_3)_3COCH_3 + H^+$$

(c) $C_2H_5OC_2H_5 + HI \rightleftharpoons CH_3CH_2\overset{+}{\underset{H}{O}}CH_2CH_3 + I^-$

$$\overset{I^-}{\underset{CH_3}{}}\overset{\overset{H}{|}}{C}H_2\overset{+}{O}CH_2CH_3 \longrightarrow CH_3CH_2I + CH_3CH_2OH$$

$$CH_3CH_2OH + HI \rightleftharpoons CH_3CH_2\overset{+}{O}H_2 + I^- \longrightarrow CH_3CH_2I + OH_2$$

16.

$$CH_3CH_2OCH_2CH_2CH_2CH_3 + HBr \rightleftharpoons CH_3CH_2\overset{\overset{H}{|+}}{O}CH_2CH_2CH_2CH_3 + Br^-$$

$$CH_3CH_2\overset{\overset{H}{|+}}{O}CH_2CH_2CH_2CH_3 + Br^- \begin{cases} CH_3CH_2Br + HOCH_2CH_2CH_3 \\ \\ CH_3CH_2OH + BrCH_2CH_2CH_3 \end{cases}$$

$$(CH_3)_3COCH_2CH_3 \; + \; HBr \rightleftharpoons (CH_3)_3\overset{H}{\underset{+}{C}}OCH_2CH_3 \; + \; Br^-$$

$$(CH_3)_3\overset{H}{\underset{+}{C}}OCH_2CH_3 \rightleftharpoons (CH_3)_3C+ \; + \; HOCH_2CH_3$$

$$(CH_3)_3C+ \; + \; Br^- \rightleftharpoons (CH_3)_3CBr$$

In the first case, product is formed by S$_N$2 attack on the protonated ether. Attack can occur at either primary carbon at comparable rates, so both ethyl and n-butyl bromide are produced. In the second case, the ether cleaves by an S$_N$1 process to give the t-butyl cation, and thus t-butyl bromide is the main product. The tertiary carbocation is sufficiently stable that it is produced readily by concentrated acid, even in the cold. Recall that tertiary alcohols rapidly give the halide with cold concentrated HCl or HBr.

17.

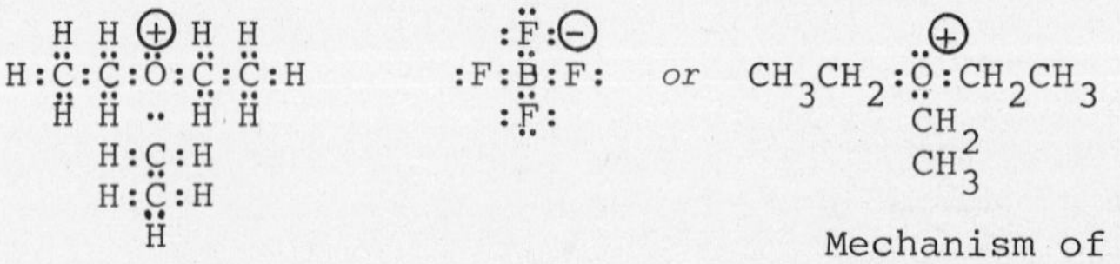

Mechanism of Ethylation

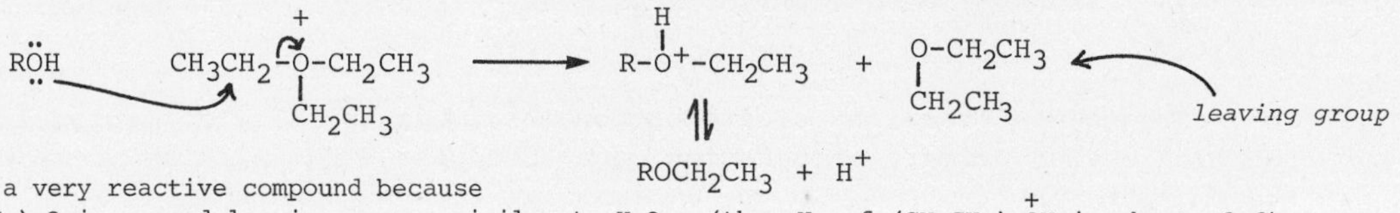

It is a very reactive compound because $(CH_3CH_2)_2O$ is a good leaving group, similar to H_2O. (the pK_a of $(CH_3CH_2)_2\overset{+}{O}H$ is about -3.6)

18.

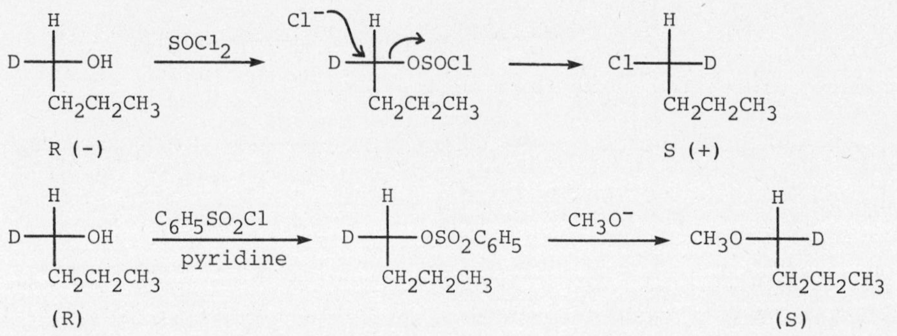

19.

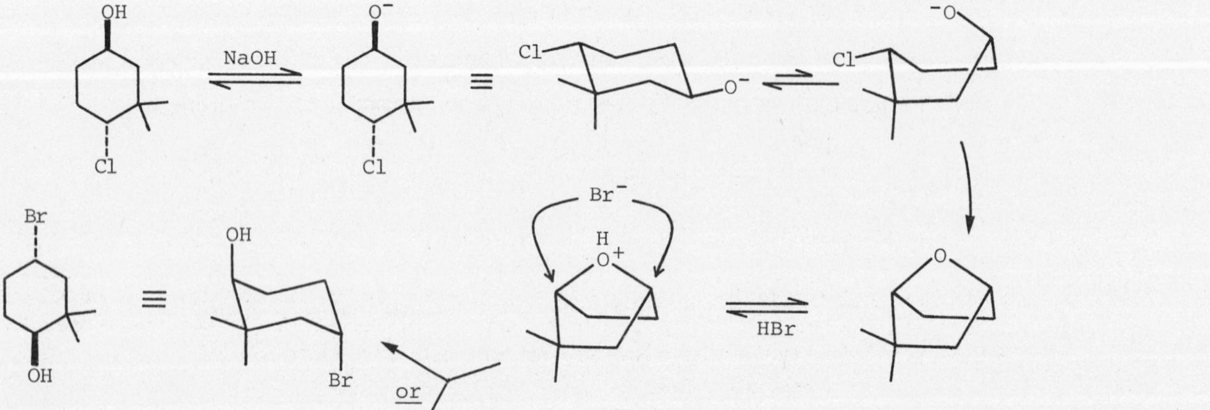

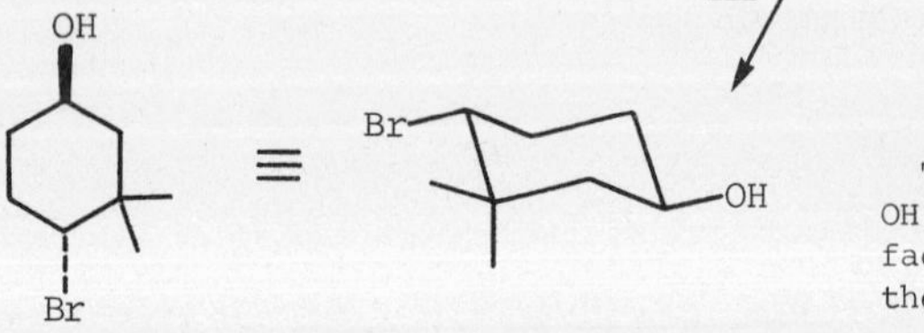

The clues here are the *trans* relationship of the OH and Br in both isomers of the product, and the fact that the bromine can end up at either end of the molecule.

20.

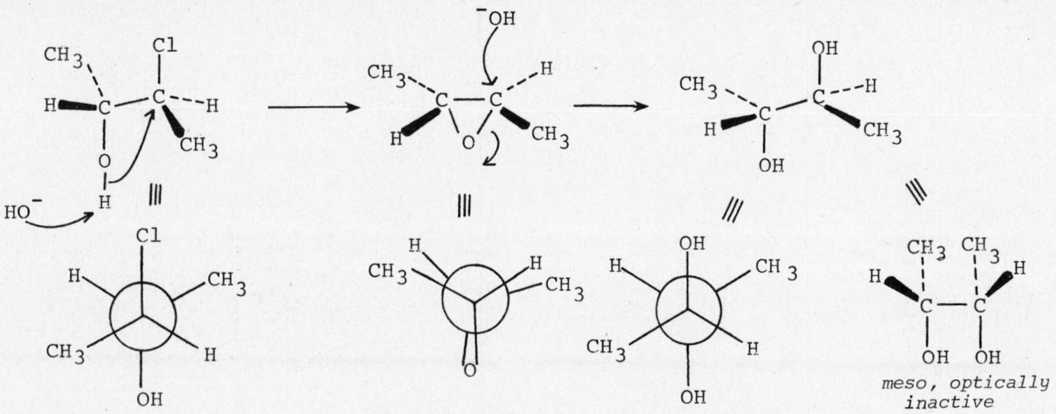

(You will find that you get the same result regardless of which end of the epoxide is attacked in the hydrolysis step)

21.

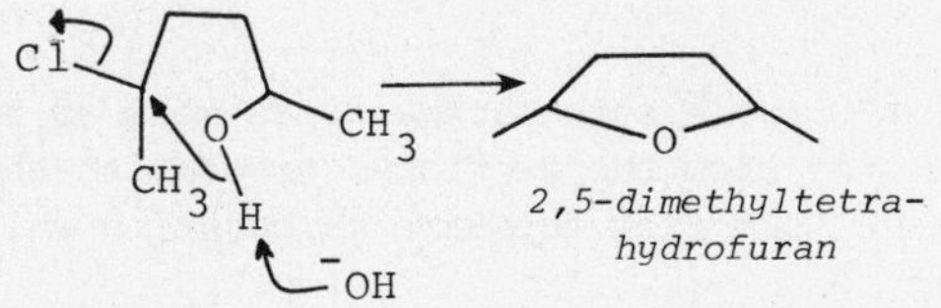

2,5-dimethyltetra-
hydrofuran

The product could
exist as an achiral,
cis isomer:

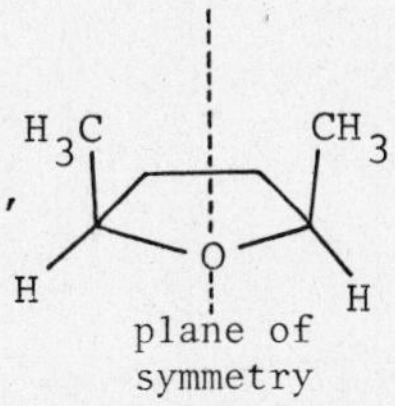

plane of
symmetry

or as a chiral,
trans, isomer:

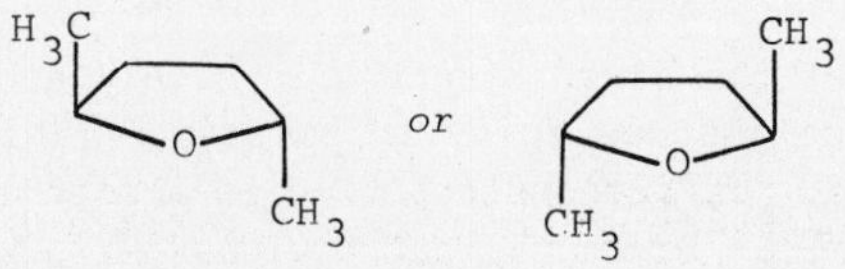

The starting material was **not** racemic (it was optically active), so if the <u>trans</u> isomer had been formed, it would not have been racemic. However, the product obtained is optically **inactive**, suggesting that the product is the achiral, **meso** isomer: the <u>cis</u> compound. This means that the starting material was either (2R,5R)-5-chloro-2-hexanol or the (2S,5S) isomer, and **not** the (2R,5S) or (2S,5R) isomers:

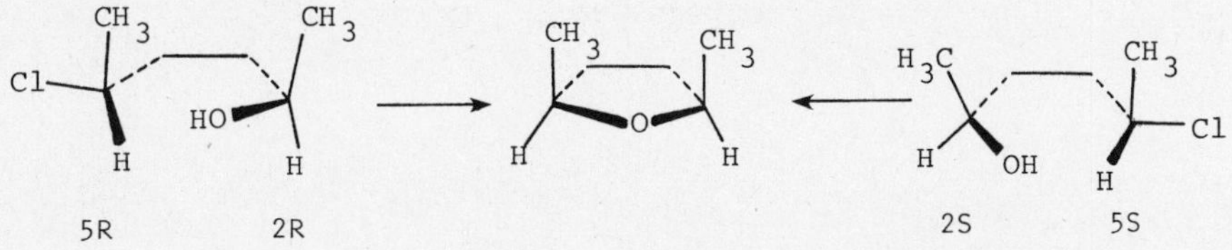

22. The cavity inside 18-crown-6 is just the right size for K^+ to fit in (diameter of K^+ = 2.66 Å) Na^+ is smaller (diameter = 1.96 Å) and it is not coordinated so tightly. Therefore, 18-crown-6 solubilizes potassium salts much more effectively than sodium salts.

23.

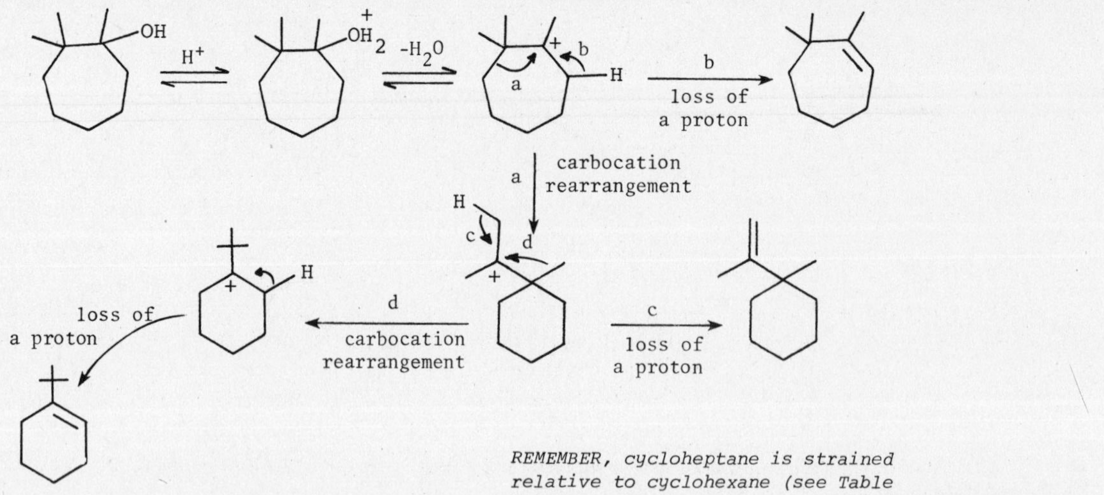

REMEMBER, *cycloheptane is strained relative to cyclohexane (see Table 5.5 in text).*

(One of the ways to solve mechanism problems is to work both backwards as well as forwards. For instance, 1-t-butylcyclohexene must have come from the tertiary carbocation shown above it in the scheme; that in turn must have come from the same carbocation which led to 1-isopropenyl-1-methylcyclohexane, etc.)

24.

$$CH_3CH_2OH \ + \ Br^- \ \rightleftharpoons \ CH_3CH_2Br \ + \ OH^-$$

ΔH_f°:   -56.2   -50.8   -15.2   -32.9 $\Delta H^\circ = +58.9$ kcal mole^{-1}

$$CH_3CH_2OH \ + \ HBr \ \rightleftharpoons \ CH_3CH_2Br \ + \ H_2O$$

ΔH_f°:   -56.2   -8.7   -15.2   -57.8 $\Delta H^\circ = -8.1$ kcal mole^{-1}

Note that the first reaction is highly endothermic; OH$^-$ is a much stronger base than Br$^-$ in the gas phase just as it is in solution. This reaction is also endothermic in solution and is not observed. The second reaction is almost thermoneutral in contrast, and is actually slightly exothermic. Since the entropy change is close to zero (two molecules give two molecules), the equilibrium lies on the right.

The difference between the two reactions can be seen from the following comparison: the O-H bond strength is much greater than the Br-H bond strength, and this **difference** is greater than for the C-O and C-Br bond strengths (see Appendix III).

25.

Charge-dipole:

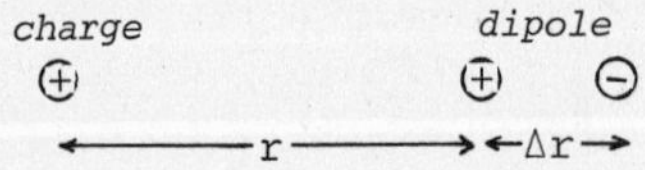

$$E = \frac{1}{r} - \frac{1}{(r + \Delta r)}$$

$$\frac{(r + \Delta r) - r}{r(r + \Delta r)} = \frac{\Delta r}{r(r + \Delta r)} \cong \frac{\Delta r}{r^2}$$

since Δr is much less than r

Dipole-dipole:

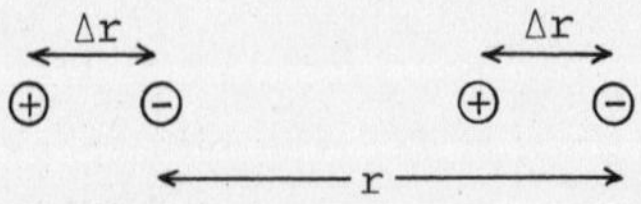

$$E = \frac{1}{r} + \frac{1}{r} - \frac{1}{r + \Delta r} - \frac{1}{r - \Delta r}$$

$$= \frac{2(r+\Delta r)(r-\Delta r) - r(r+\Delta r) - r(r-\Delta r)}{r(r+\Delta r)(r-\Delta r)}$$

$$= \frac{2r^2 - 2\Delta r^2 - r^2 + r\Delta r - r^2 - r\Delta r}{r^3 - r\Delta r^2}$$

$$= \frac{-2\Delta r^2}{r^3 - r\Delta r^2} \cong \frac{-2\Delta r^2}{r^3} \qquad \text{(for } \Delta r \ll r)$$

26. (a) The best method is to first convert all temperatures into °K and take the reciprocals. A plot of ln P $\underline{\text{vs.}}$ 1/T gives a good straight line with a slope of -5.08×10^3. The corresponding slope using log P is -2.21×10^3.

Thus, $\Delta H_v = -(-5.08 \times 10^3)(R = 1.986 \text{ cal deg}^{-1} \text{ mole}^{-1})$
$= 10.1 \text{ kcal mole}^{-1}$

Compared to propane, we see that hydrogen bonding increases the heat of vaporization by about 5.6 kcal mole^{-1}.

(b) $\mu = q \cdot d$ 1.7×10^{-18} esu-cm $= q \times 0.96 \times 10^{-8}$ cm

$q = 1.78 \times 10^{-10}$ esu

Since the electronic charge is 4.8×10^{-10} esu, q corresponds to 0.37 electronic charges. That is, the dipole moment corresponds to

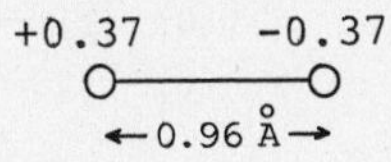

The net electrostatic attraction between two such dipoles is:

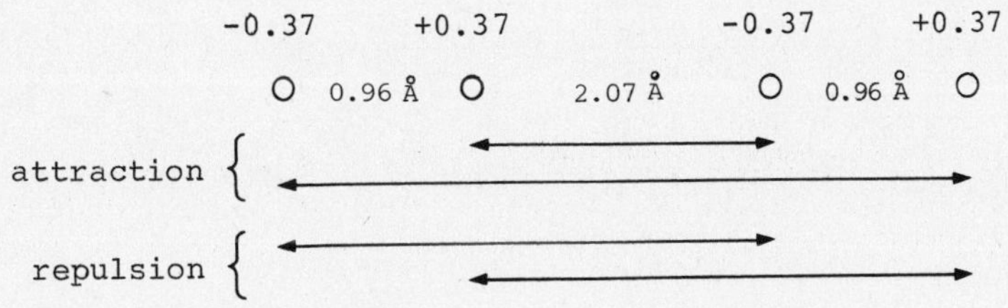

The net attraction is given by:

$$(0.37)^2 \left[-\frac{1}{2.07} - \frac{1}{3.99} + 2 \times \frac{1}{3.03} \right] (332) = -3.3 \text{ kcal mole}^{-1}$$

We see that even this crude model gives a result which has the correct order of magnitude.

27.

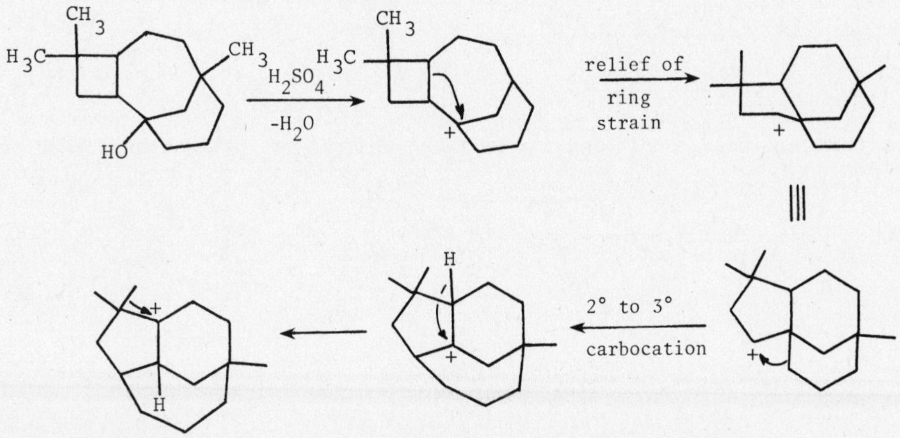

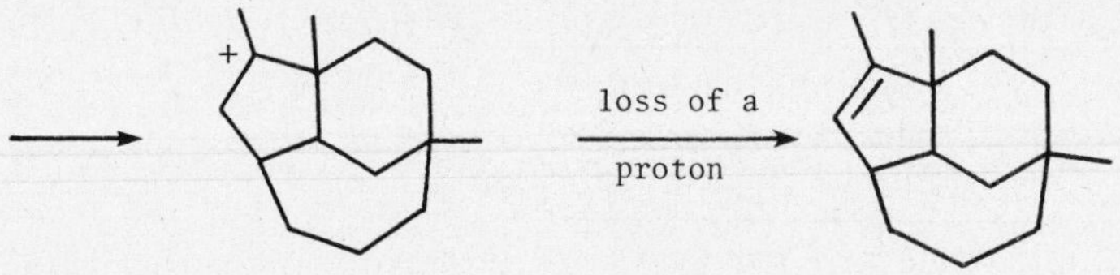

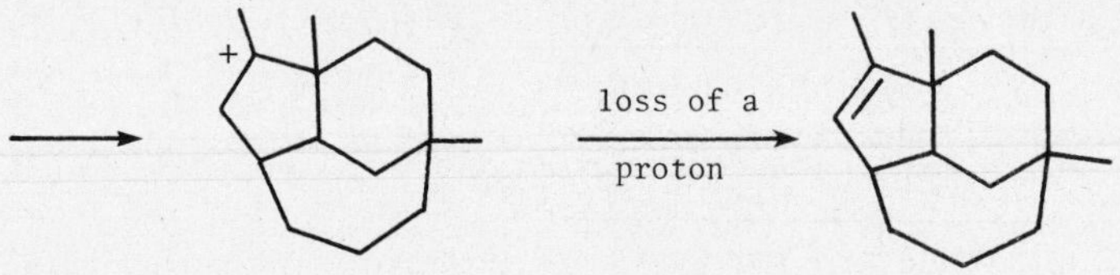

The last two rearrangements take place to relieve strain in the tricyclic structure, which is hard to see without knowing the stereostructure of the molecule. In a question like this, the problem-solving approach of working backwards, as pointed out in the answer to Problem #23, is very useful. For instance, the final product must have resulted from the last carbocation depicted, which must have arisen from the methyl migration shown, etc.

10.F Supplementary Problems

S1. Provide the structure and IUPAC name for each of the following compounds:

(a) α-chloroethyl ethyl ether
(b) γ-chloropropyl alcohol
(c) di(neopentyl) ether
(d) ω-chloroheptyl alcohol

S2. All of the names below are incorrect. Provide a correct name, either common or IUPAC, for each:

(a) isopropanol
(b) 2,2-dimethyl-5-hexanol
(c) β,β-dichloropropanol
(d) 2,3-dihydroxybutane

S3. Give the principal product(s) from each of the following reactions:

(a)

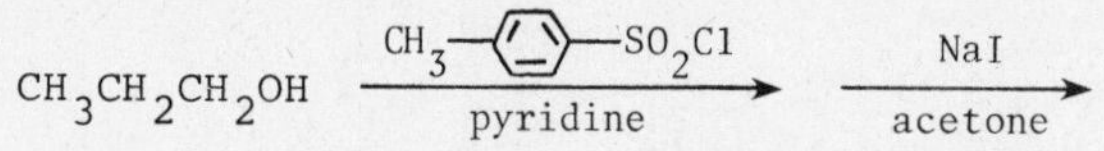

(b) $ICH_2CH_2CH_2CH_2I \xrightarrow{NaOH}$

(c) $(CH_3)_2CHOCH_3 \xrightarrow[\text{light}]{O_2}$

(d)

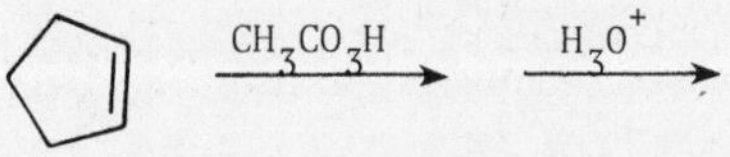

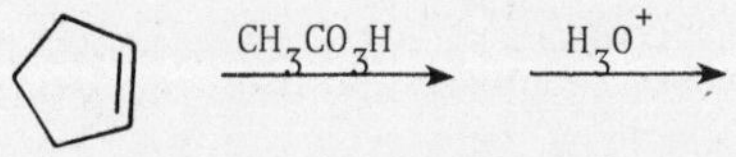

(e) $(CH_3)_3COC(CH_3)_3 \xrightarrow[\Delta\ (\text{heat})]{H_2SO_4}$

(f)

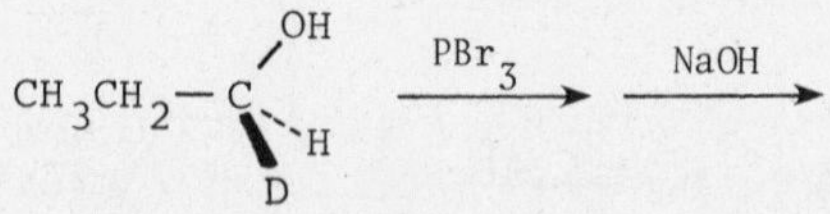

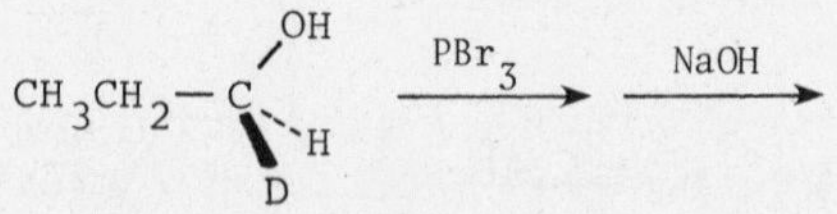

S4. Give the reagents and best conditions for carrying out the following transformations:

(a) $CH_3-CH_2-C(CH_3)_2-Br \longrightarrow CH_3-CH_2-C(CH_3)_2-OH$

(b) $CH_3-CH_2-CH{=}CH_2 \longrightarrow CH_3-CH_2-CHOH-CH_2OH$

(c)

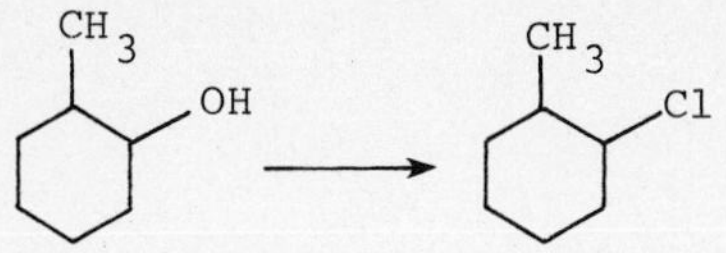

(d)

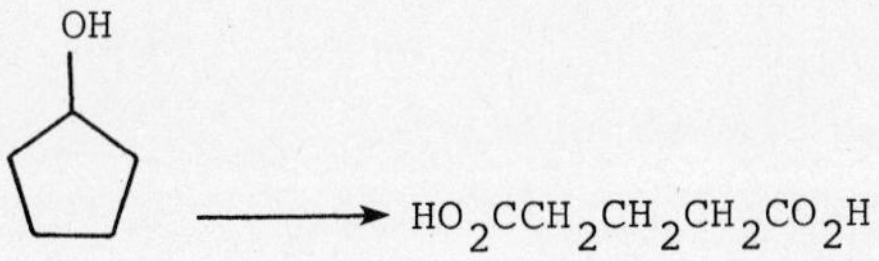

$\longrightarrow$ $HO_2CCH_2CH_2CH_2CO_2H$

S5. Rank the following compounds in order of decreasing acidity.

(a) CH_3CH_2OH (c) $ClCH_2CH_2OH$

(b) $CH_3-\overset{\overset{\displaystyle CH_3}{|}}{\underset{\underset{\displaystyle CH_3}{|}}{C}}-OH$ (d) $ClCH_2CH_2CO_2H$

(e) CF_3CH_2OH

(f) CF_3OCH_3

S6. Which of the following reactions give(s) optically active products?   Justify your answers.

(a)

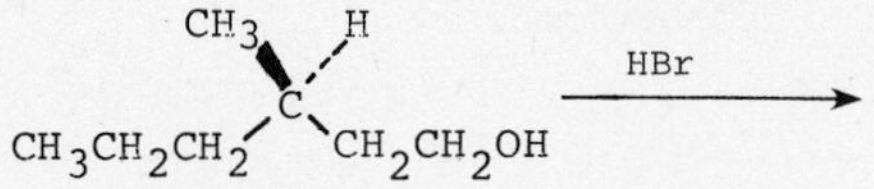

$\xrightarrow{\text{HBr}}$

(b)

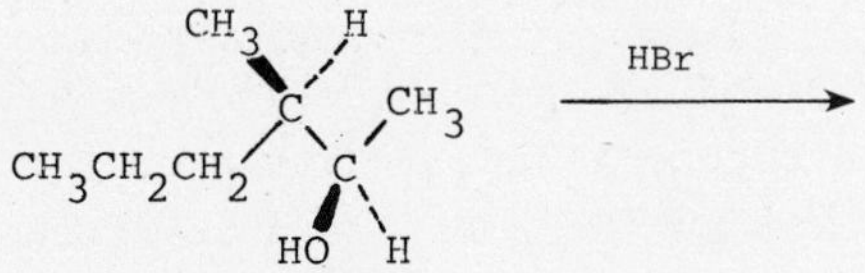

$\xrightarrow{\text{HBr}}$

(c)

$\xrightarrow{\text{HBr}}$

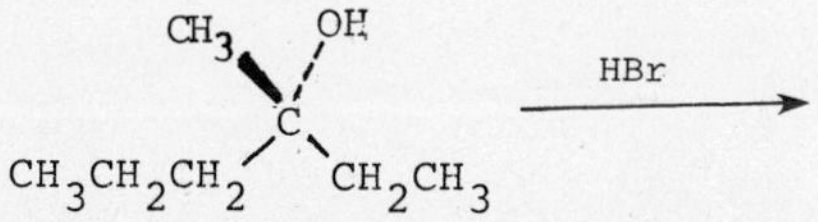

S7. (S)-1-Bromo-2-methylbutan-2-ol is converted to an optically active epoxide with dilute sodium hydroxide, as depicted below. The epoxide ring can be cleaved either in strong base or in acid to give diol products. What is the difference (if any) between the products formed by the acidic and basic hydrolysis conditions? Write a step-by-step mechanism to explain any differences you expect to see.

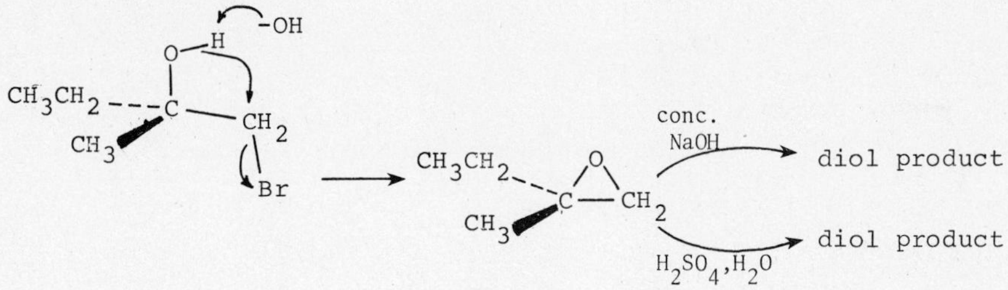

10.G   Answers to Supplementary Problems

S1.

(a) 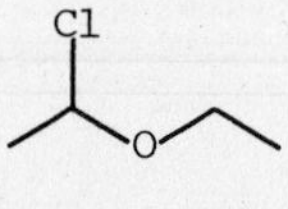   1-chloro-1-ethoxyethane

(c) 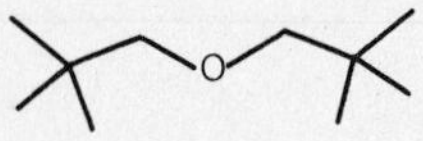   2,2-dimethyl-1-
      (2,2-dimethylpropoxy)propane

(b)   3-chloropropanol

(d)    7-chloroheptanol

S2.   (a) Mixture of common and IUPAC usage: isopropyl alcohol and 2-propanol are correct.
      (b) As an "alkanol", the chain should be numbered to give the lowest number to the hydroxyl
           group: 5,5-dimethyl-2-hexanol.
      (c) Mixture of common and IUPAC usage: β,β-dichloropropyl alcohol or 2,2-dichloro-1-
           propanol.
      (d) Should be named as an alkanediol: 2,3-butanediol.

S3.   (a) $CH_3CH_2CH_2I$

      (b) 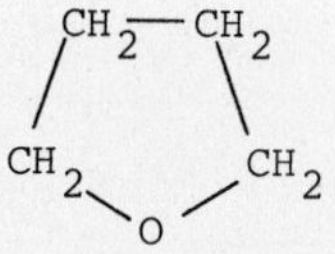 After substitution of one of the iodides with
           hydroxyl, the second iodide is attacked faster
           <u>intra</u>molecularly by the alkoxide anion than it
           is displaced <u>inter</u>molecularly by hydroxide:

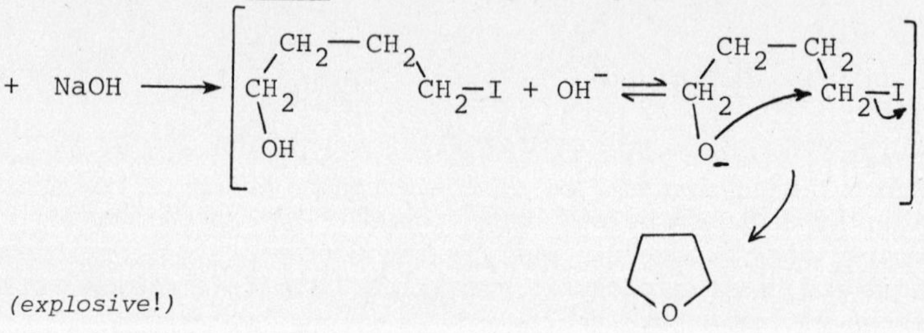

           $ICH_2CH_2CH_2CH_2I$ + NaOH ⟶

      (c) 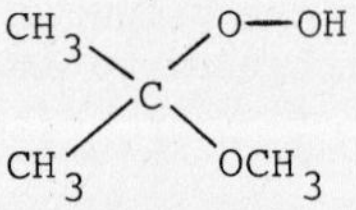 (explosive!)

      (d)

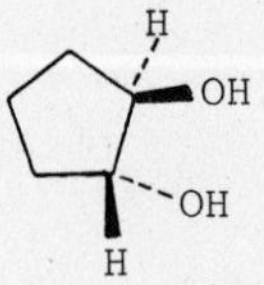

      (e) 2 $(CH_3)_2C{=}CH_2$

      (f) 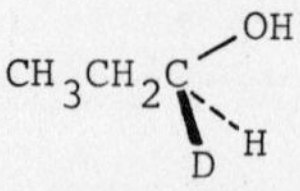 (Two inversions give the same product back again)

S4.   (a)

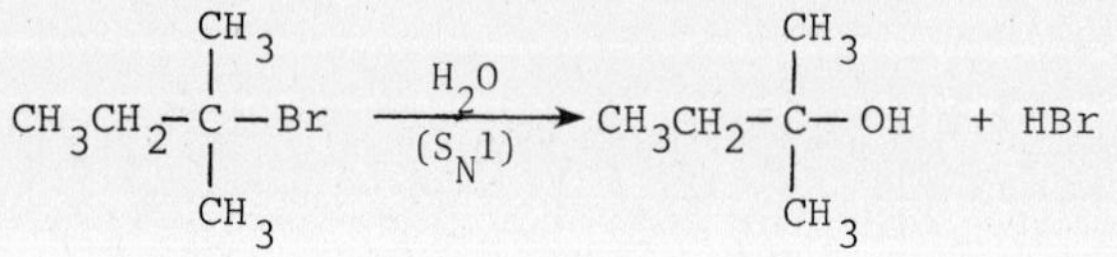

           $CH_3CH_2{-}\underset{\underset{CH_3}{|}}{\overset{\overset{CH_3}{|}}{C}}{-}Br$ $\xrightarrow[(S_N1)]{H_2O}$ $CH_3CH_2{-}\underset{\underset{CH_3}{|}}{\overset{\overset{CH_3}{|}}{C}}{-}OH$ + HBr

(b) $CH_3 - CH_2 - CH = CH_2$ + CH_3CO_3H $\longrightarrow$ $CH_3 - CH_2 - CH - CH_2$ $\xrightarrow{H_3O^+}$

$CH_3CH_2CHOHCH_2OH$

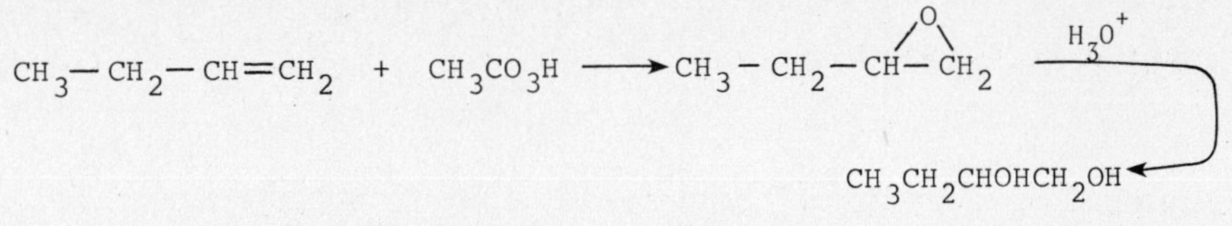

(c)

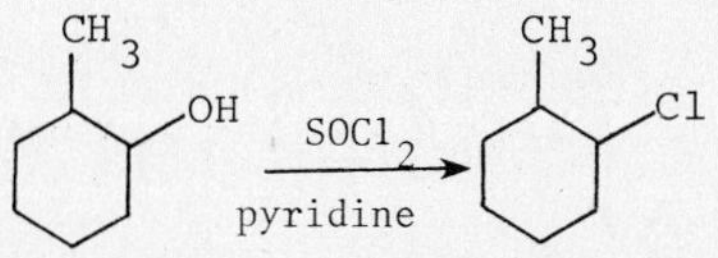

$\xrightarrow[\text{pyridine}]{SOCl_2}$

(Carbocation rearrangement must be avoided)

(d)

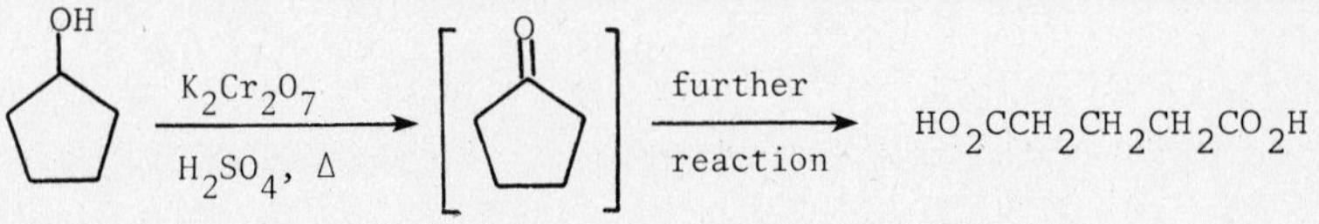

$\xrightarrow[H_2SO_4, \ \Delta]{K_2Cr_2O_7}$ $\left[\right]$ $\xrightarrow[\text{reaction}]{\text{further}}$ $HO_2CCH_2CH_2CH_2CO_2H$

S5.   Most acidic: $ClCH_2CH_2CO_2H$ *(it's a carboxylic acid)*

CF_3CH_2OH

$ClCH_2CH_2OH$

CH_3CH_2OH

$(CH_3)_3COH$

Least acidic: CF_3OCH_3 *(there's no hydrogen which can dissociate)*

S6.   (a)

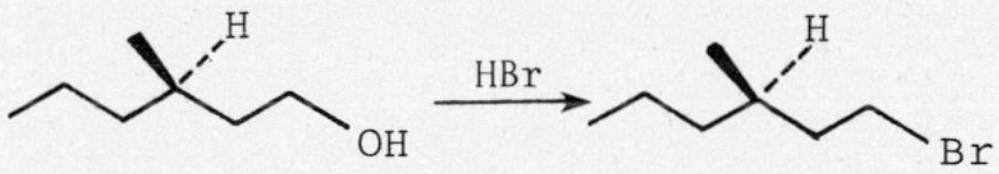

The stereocenter is not involved in the reaction so the product is optically active.

(b)

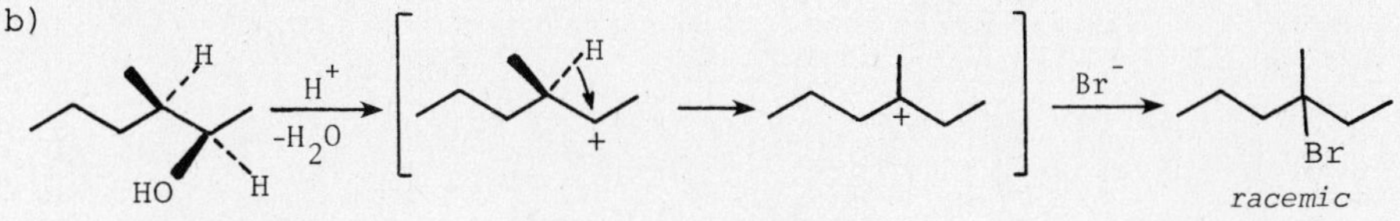

The reaction involves a rearrangement to give a planar, achiral carbocation intermediate and therefore a racemic product.

(c)

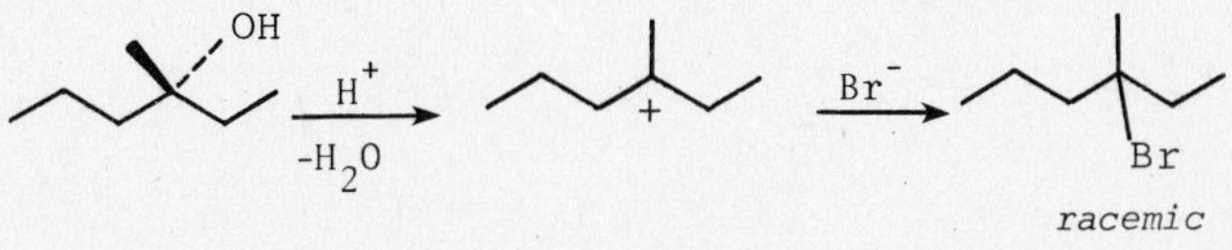

This reaction involves the same achiral intermediate.

S7.   Acidic hydrolysis:

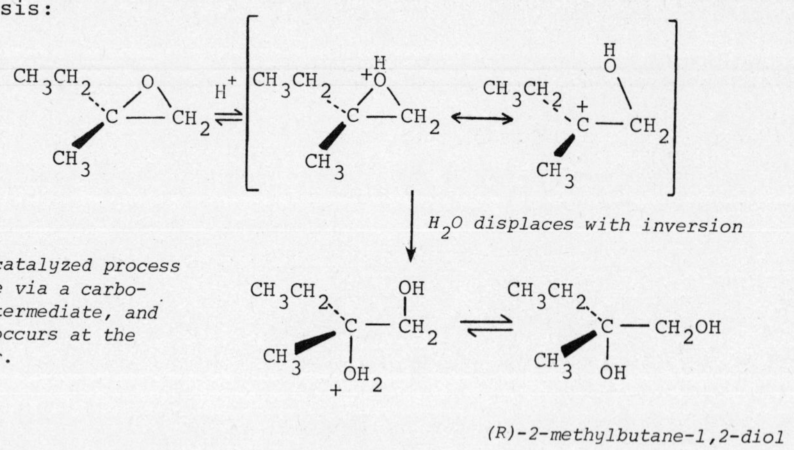

The acid-catalyzed process favors cleavage via a carbo-cation-like intermediate, and the inversion occurs at the tertiary center.

H_2O displaces with inversion

(R)-2-methylbutane-1,2-diol

Basic hydrolysis:

(S)-2-methylbutane-1,2-diol

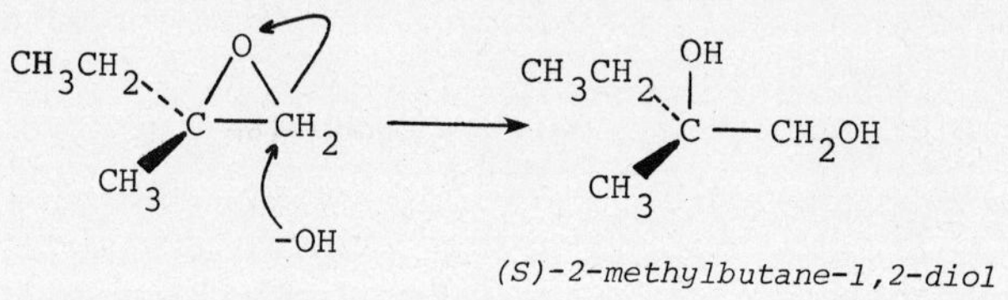

The mechanism of the basic hydrolysis is like the S_N2 mechanism, and attack and inversion at the less sterically hindered, primary carbon occurs, leading to the enantiomer of the product obtained in acid.

11. ALKENES

11.A Chapter Outline and Important Terms Introduced

11.1 <u>Electronic Structure</u>

- σ- and π-bonds
- configurational vs. conformational isomers

11.2 <u>Nomenclature of Alkenes</u>

- olefin
- alkylenes
- vinyl group
- <u>cis</u> and <u>trans</u>
- **Z** (zusammen) and **E** (entgegen)

11.3 <u>Physical Properties of Alkenes</u>

11.4 <u>Relative Stabilities of Alkenes: Heats of Formation</u>

- steric hindrance
- effects of substitution

11.5 <u>Preparation of Alkenes</u>

A. Dehydrohalogenation of Alkyl Halides (and sulfonates)
- rate depends on [RX] and [Base]
- isotope effects
- stereospecificity
- E2 mechanism
- rate depends on leaving group
- <u>anti</u> elimination stereochemistry

B. Dehydration of Alcohols
- acid-catalyzed
- alumina at 350-400 °C
- alkene isomerization

C. Industrial Preparation of Alkenes
- cracking:

$$RCH_2CH_2R' \xrightarrow{700\text{-}900\ ^{\circ}C} RH + CH_2{=}CHR'$$

11.6 <u>Reactions of Alkenes</u>

A. Catalytic Hydrogenation
- <u>syn</u> addition stereochemistry

B. Addition of Halogens
- cyclic halonium ion
- vicinal dihalides
- <u>anti</u> addition stereochemistry

C. Addition of HX and Water
- Markovnikov's Rule
- addition of mercuric acetate
- hydration

D. Hydroboration
- organoboranes
- "anti-Markovnikov" hydration

E. Oxidation
- glycol formation
- <u>syn</u> addition of hydroxyls
- oxidative cleavage with ozone
- epoxidation with a peracid (<u>syn</u> addition)

F. Addition of Carbenes and Carbenoids: Preparation of Cyclopropanes
- <u>syn</u> addition

G. Free Radical Additions
- addition of HBr (not HCl or HI)
- addition of CX_4
- anti-Markovnikov orientation

11.B   Important Reactions Introduced

<u>Dehydrohalogenation</u> <u>of</u> <u>alkyl</u> <u>halides</u> <u>(and</u> <u>sulfonates)</u>   (11.5.A)

Equation:

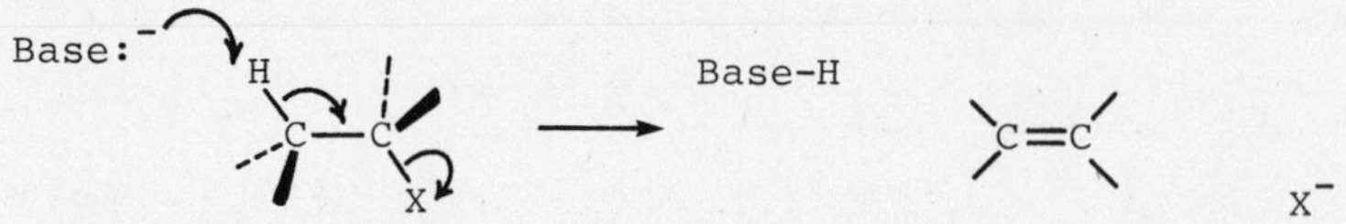

Generality: Base = $^-$OH or $^-$OR, $^-$NH$_2$, or in some cases a 3° amine (R$_3$N:)

X = good leaving group, such as Cl$^-$, Br$^-$, I$^-$, or sulfonate ester ($^-$O$_3$SR')
(**not** $^-$OH or $^-$OR)

Key features: concerted, bimolecular mechanism (E2)

faster if X is a better leaving group

<u>anti</u> relationship between C—H and C—X bonds that are broken

more stable isomer (more substituted > less substituted; <u>trans</u> > <u>cis</u>) usually
favored, but bulky base (e.g. (CH$_3$)$_3$CO$^-$) forms less substituted isomer

<u>Dehydration</u> <u>of</u> <u>alcohols</u>   (11.5.B)

Equation:

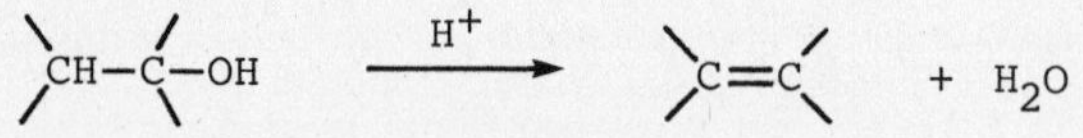

Generality: ease of reaction: 3° > 2° > 1° alcohol

H$^+$ usually H$_2$SO$_4$; also Al$_2$O$_3$, heat

Key features: more stable olefin favored

mechanism involves carbocation intermediates (El mechanism)

possibility of carbocation rearrangements

<u>Hydrogenation</u> <u>of</u> <u>alkenes</u>   (11.6.A)

Equation:

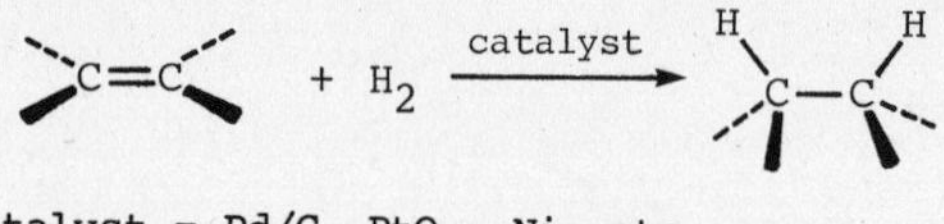

Generality: catalyst = Pd/C, PtO$_2$, Ni, etc.

sometimes requires high pressure of H$_2$ gas (for hindered or very stable double bond)

Key features: <u>syn</u> addition stereochemistry

sometimes double bond rearrangement observed before H$_2$ addition

<u>Electrophilic</u> <u>addition</u> <u>to</u> <u>alkenes</u>   (11.6.B)

Equation:

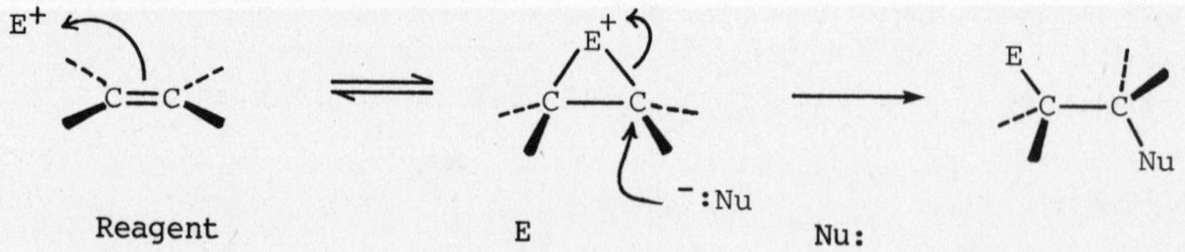

Reagent	E	Nu:
X$_2$/CCl$_4$ solvent	X	X	[X = Cl, Br, I]
X$_2$/ROH solvent	X	OR	[X = Cl, Br, I; R = H or alkyl]
Hg(OAc)$_2$/ROH	Hg(OAc)	OR	[R = H, alkyl, or acetyl]

Generality:

Key features: <u>anti</u> addition stereochemistry as result of cyclic halonium ion (or "mercurinium" ion)

Markovnikov orientation (Nu becomes attached to carbon that is best able
to stabilize positive charge)

Addition of HX and water to alkenes (11.6.C)

Equation:

$$\text{C}=\text{C} \ + \ \text{H-Nu} \ \overset{\text{H}^+}{\rightleftharpoons} \ \text{CH-C}^+ \ \overset{:\text{Nu}}{\longleftarrow} \ \longrightarrow \ \text{CH-C-Nu}$$

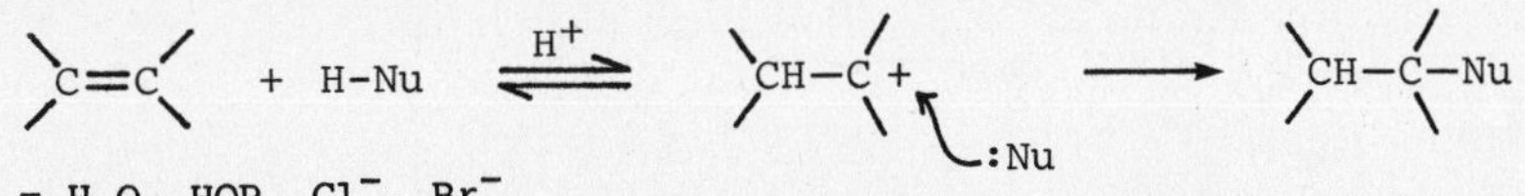

Generality: Nu = H_2O, HOR, Cl^-, Br^-

Key features: acid-catalyzed, via carbocation intermediate (therefore rearrangements possible)

Markovnikov orientation (Nu becomes attached to carbon that is best able to stabilize positive charge)

no specificity for syn or anti stereochemistry of addition

Note: HBr can add via a free radical mechanism (see below)

Hydroboration (11.6.D)

Equation:

$$\text{H-BR}_2 \quad\quad \text{C}=\text{C} \ \longrightarrow \ \overset{\text{H}}{\underset{}{\text{C}}}-\overset{\text{BR}_2}{\underset{}{\text{C}}} \ \overset{H_2O_2}{\underset{OH^-}{\longrightarrow}} \ \overset{\text{H}}{\underset{}{\text{C}}}-\overset{\text{OH}}{\underset{}{\text{C}}}$$

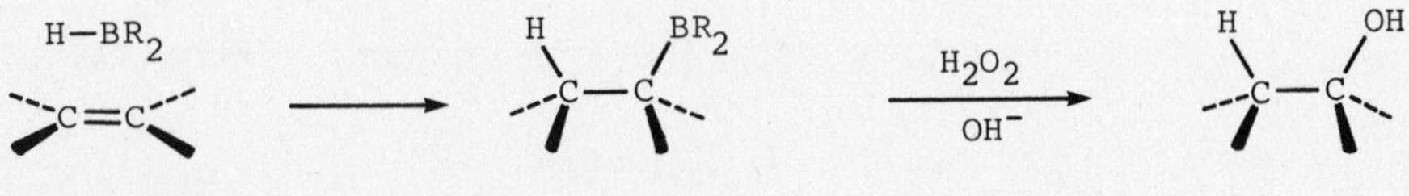

Generality: normal alkenes

hydroboration reagent: R = H ($B_2H_6 \rightleftharpoons 2 \ BH_3$) or alkyl

Key features: syn addition of H and B

retention of configuration in oxidation of C—B to C—O bond

boron becomes bonded to less-substituted (= less hindered) carbon, therefore overall process is syn, anti-Markovnikov hydration of alkene

Oxidation of alkenes to vicinal diols (11.6.E)

Equation:

$$\text{C}=\text{C} \ \overset{MO_4}{\longrightarrow} \ \begin{matrix} \text{O} \quad \text{O} \\ \text{M} \\ \text{O} \quad\quad \text{O} \\ \text{C}-\text{C} \end{matrix} \ \overset{H_2O}{\longrightarrow} \ \overset{\text{HO} \quad\quad \text{OH}}{\text{C}-\text{C}}$$

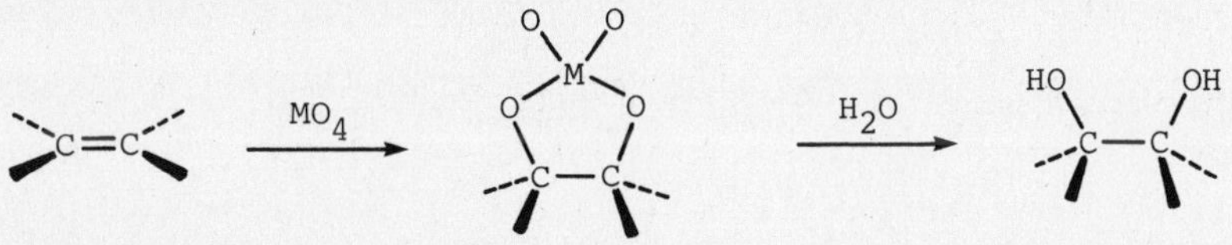

Generality: MO_4 = OsO_4 or MnO_4^-

Key features: syn addition of hydroxyl groups

OsO_4 is toxic and expensive, but can be used catalytically with H_2O_2

aq. MnO_4^- ($KMnO_4$, dilute, cold) is cheap, but reaction often goes in low yield

Oxidative cleavage of alkenes (11.6.E)

Equation:

$$\text{C}=\text{C} \ \overset{O_3}{\longrightarrow} \ \overset{\text{reduction}}{\longrightarrow} \ \text{C}=\text{O} \quad \text{O}=\text{C}$$

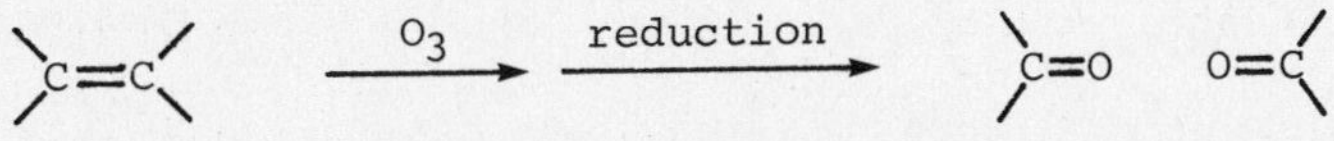

Generality: very general; almost all types of alkenes undergo this reaction

Key features: mechanism involves cyclic peroxide intermediates (molozonides and ozonides: explosive)

work-up involves reduction of ozonide: Zn/H_2O to give ketones and aldehydes, or $NaBH_4$ to give alcohol products

Epoxidation of alkenes (11.6.E)

Equation:

$$\text{C}=\text{C} \ + \ \text{RCO}_3\text{H} \ \longrightarrow \ \overset{\text{O}}{\overset{\triangle}{\text{C}-\text{C}}} \ + \ \text{RCO}_2\text{H}$$

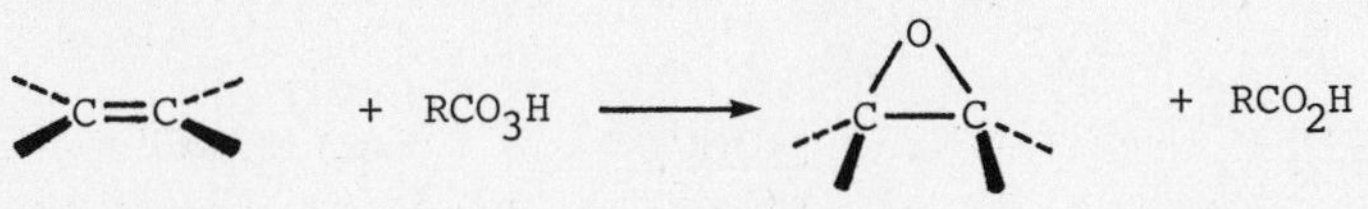

Generality: RCO_3H usually CH_3CO_3H or [benzene ring with Cl and CO_3H substituents]

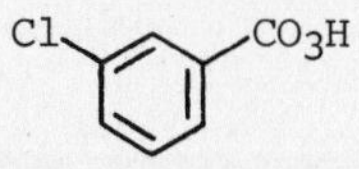

Key features: more substituted double bonds react faster

stereospecific syn addition

Carbene addition to alkenes (11.6.F)

Equation:

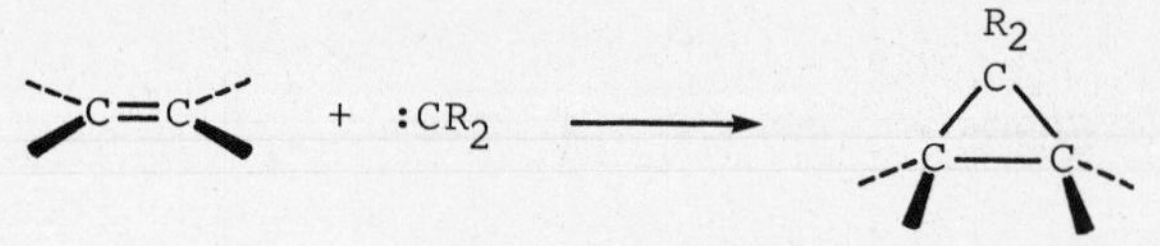

Generality: $:CR_2$ = $:CCl_2$ or $:CBr_2$ from HCX_3 + strong base

= $:CH_2$ from $CH_2N_2 \xrightarrow{h\nu}$ $:CH_2$ + N_2

or = ":CH_2" from CH_2I_2 + Zn $\longrightarrow$ $IZnCH_2I$

Key features: stereospecific syn addition

Free radical addition to alkenes (11.6.G)

Equation:

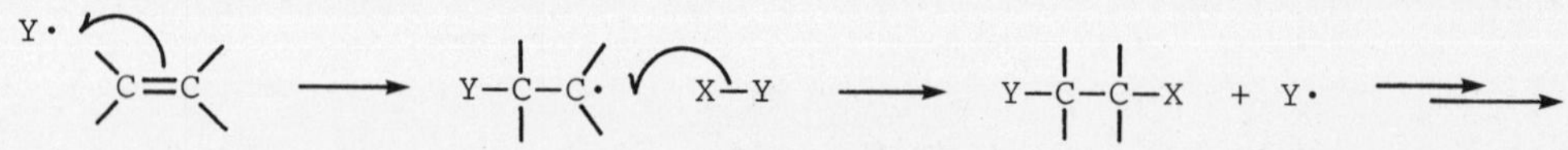

Generality: X—Y = H—Br (not HCl, HI, or HOR), X—CX_3, and H—SR

Key features: "anti-Markovnikov" orientation (Y becomes bonded to **least** substituted carbon)
lack of stereoselectivity

11.C Important Concepts and Hints

The two general methods for formation of carbon-carbon double bonds, E2 elimination of alkyl halides and acid-catalyzed dehydration of alcohols and ethers, have been presented briefly before (sections 9.6 and 10.6.D). In this chapter they are discussed in greater detail.

The major reactions of alkenes involve addition of a reagent to the two ends of the double bond. This results in rehybridization of the carbons involved, from sp^2 to sp^3, and conversion of the π-bond to two σ-bonds as shown schematically below:

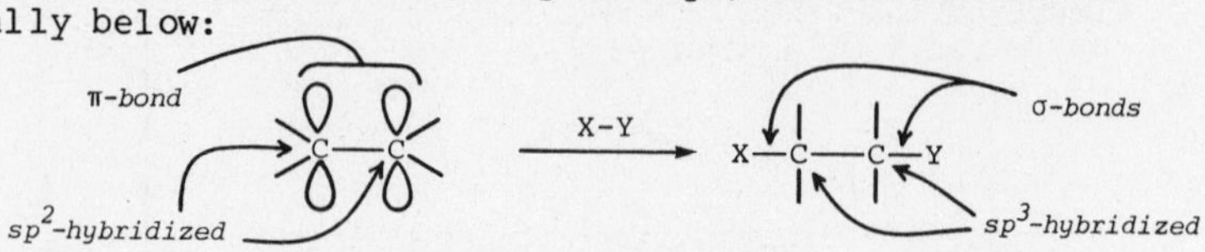

A wide variety of reagents, X-Y, and products are possible, and a number of different mechanisms are observed. The discussion of addition reactions in the text is organized by type of reaction and product. To provide you with a different perspective, we have outlined them below according to the type of **mechanism**, with examples, an indication of the reagents each applies to, and the section in the text where it is discussed.

ONE-STEP ADDITIONS

1.	Hydrogenation	11.6.A	4.	Ozonide formation	11.6.E
2.	Hydroboration	11.6.D	5.	Epoxidation	11.6.E
3.	Glycol formation with $KMnO_4$ or OsO_4/H_2O_2	11.6.E	6.	Carbene addition	11.6.F

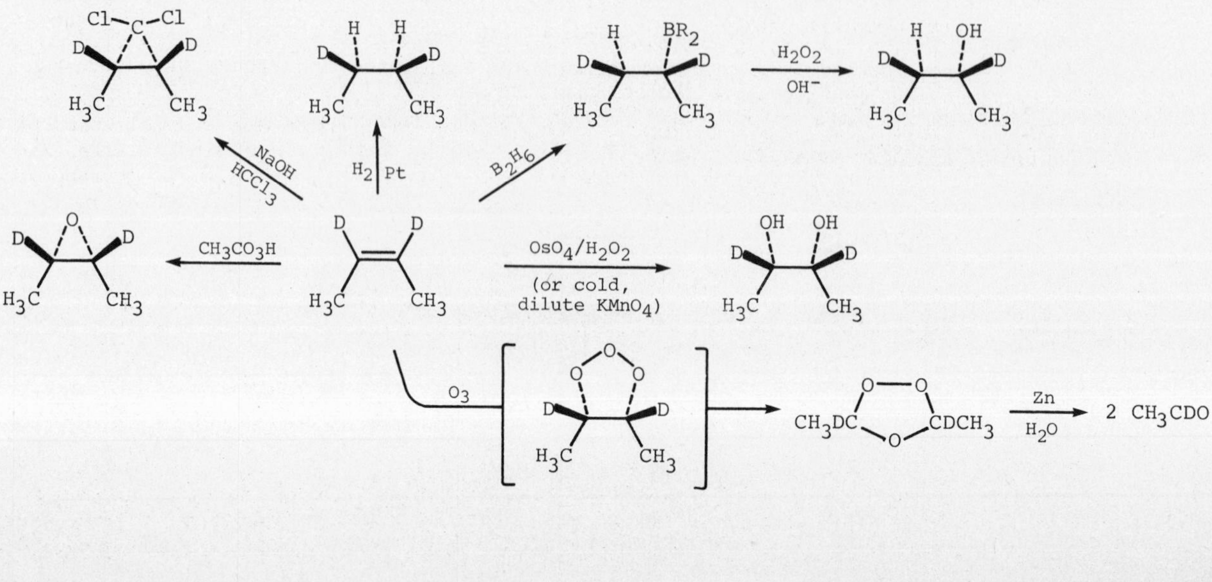

Because they are all one-step additions, the two new σ-bonds are formed with the syn relation-ship, that is, from the same face of the double bond. (You may hear this referred to as "cis" addition, but the terms cis and trans should strictly speaking be applied only to cyclic systems or to those in which double bond stereochemistry remains in the product.)

Hydroboration is the only case above in which an unsymmetrical addition takes place (i.e., X ≠ Y). The boron group becomes attached to the sterically less congested end of the double bond, usually the less substituted end. Note also that the stereochemistry at that carbon is retained on replacing the C-B bond with C-OH.

TWO-STEP ADDITIONS

A. Radical Chain Reactions (11.6.G)

$$CH_3-CH=CH_2 \quad + \quad Y\cdot \quad \longrightarrow \quad CH_3-\overset{\cdot}{C}H-CH_2Y$$

$$CH_3-\overset{\cdot}{C}H-CH_2Y \quad + \quad X-Y \quad \longrightarrow \quad CH_3-\underset{X}{\overset{|}{C}H}-CH_2Y \quad + \quad Y\cdot$$

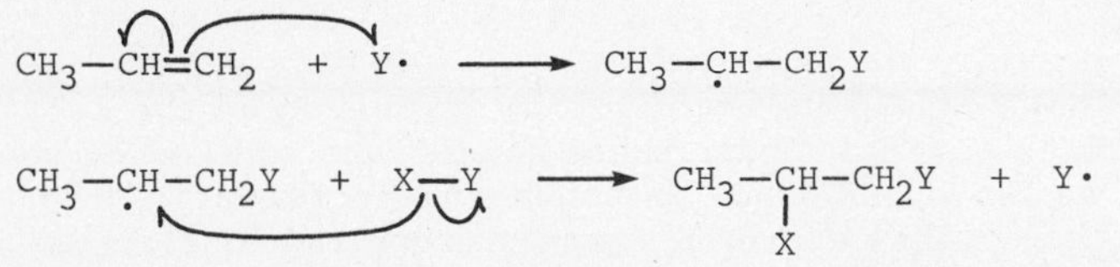

X-Y = H-Br (not HCl, HI); X-CX_3 (X = Cl, Br); H-SR (R = H, alkyl, etc.);   or $\overset{\diagup}{\underset{\diagdown}{C}}=\overset{\diagup}{\underset{\diagdown}{C}}$ (polymerization)

The first propagation step is addition of a free radical to one end of the π-bond to generate an alkyl radical. Note that the radical is **at the other end** of the original double bond. This reaction occurs in such a way as to generate the more stable free radical (tertiary > secondary > primary), so the Y· attacks the least substituted end of the double bond. There is no stereo-chemical preference in the second step, so mixtures of diastereomers are possible. For example:

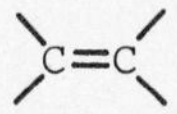

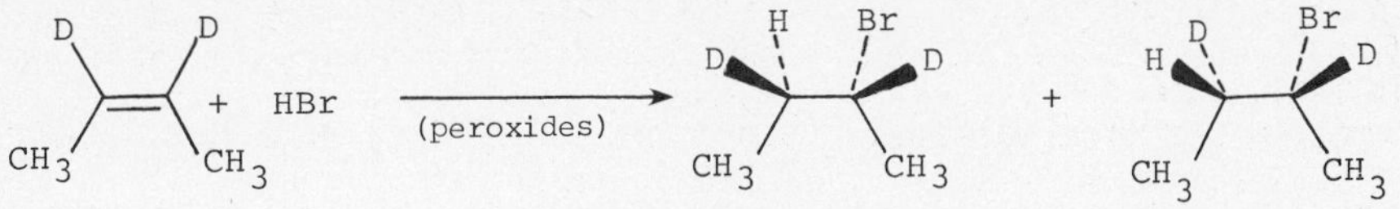

(each of these is produced in racemic form; that is, an equal amount of the enantiomer of each of the above is also produced)

B. Electrophilic Additions

1. Acid-catalyzed additions: HX and H_2O (11.6.C)

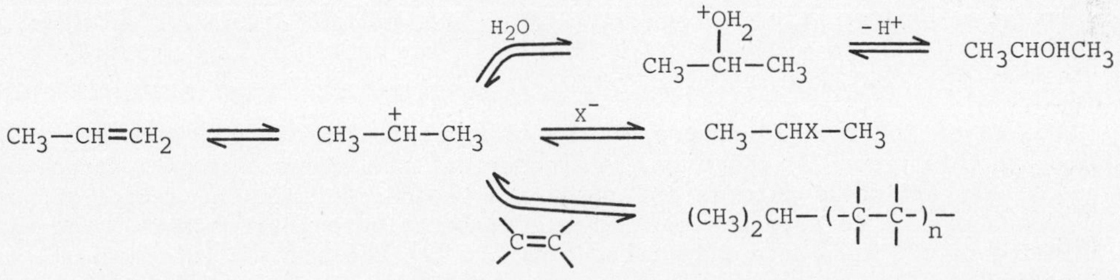

So-called electrophilic additions involve the attack of both an electrophile and a nucleo-phile, but the electrophile attacks first. An isolated double bond is itself weakly nucleophilic, so its preference for reaction with the electrophile is understandable. In acid-catalyzed addi-tions, the first species to attack the double bond is a proton. It forms a C-H bond, using the two electrons that were in the π-bond and generating a carbocation at the other end. Because of the greater stability of $3^O > 2^O > 1^O$ carbocations, the proton is attached to the less substituted end of the double bond. This generality is the original formulation of Markovnikov's rule. Two other generalities result from the intermediacy of the carbocation: 1) carbocation rearrangements are possible, obviously; and 2) stereochemical preference is usually not seen on attack by the nucleo-phile. For instance:

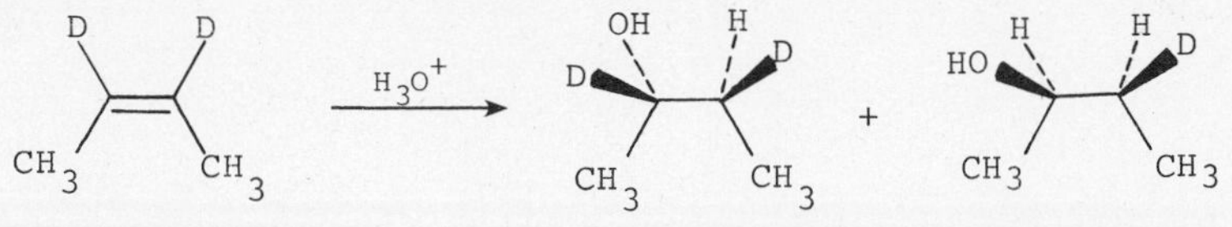

(as racemic mixtures)

   Confusion can arise over the use of acid (typically H_2SO_4) to cause **both** the addition of water to a double bond to make an alcohol, and removal of water from an alcohol to make an alkene. Students often ask: how can the same reagent carry out opposing reactions? The situation is easily understood when you realize that there are not two reactions, only one -- the equilibration of an alcohol with an alkene plus water -- and that the acid is only a catalyst. It is not consumed or formed during the course of the reaction, and it will speed up the reaction in either direction.

$$CH_3\text{--}\overset{\displaystyle OH}{\underset{|}{CH}}\text{--}CH_3 + H^+ \rightleftharpoons CH_3\text{--}\overset{\displaystyle {}^+OH_2}{\underset{|}{CH}}\text{--}CH_3 \rightleftharpoons H_2O + CH_3\text{--}\overset{+}{CH}\text{--}CH_3 \rightleftharpoons CH_3\text{--}CH\text{=}CH_2 + H^+ + H_2O$$

   The factors which control the direction that the reaction proceeds are the conditions: in dilute aqueous acid (a **lot** of water around), the equilibrium is driven to the left (as written above), and alcohol is formed from an alkene. Under these conditions an alcohol would not form appreciable amounts of alkene. On the other hand, in concentrated sulfuric acid (60% to 95%, depending on ease of dehydration), especially at higher temperatures, the equilibrium is driven to the right by distillation of the alkene from the reaction mixture and by protonation of the water formed (e.g., $H_2O + H_2SO_4 \rightleftharpoons H_3O^+ + H_2SO_4^-$).

2. Via bridged, cationic intermediates: X_2 (11.6.B)

                                   $Hg(OAc)_2$ (11.6.C)

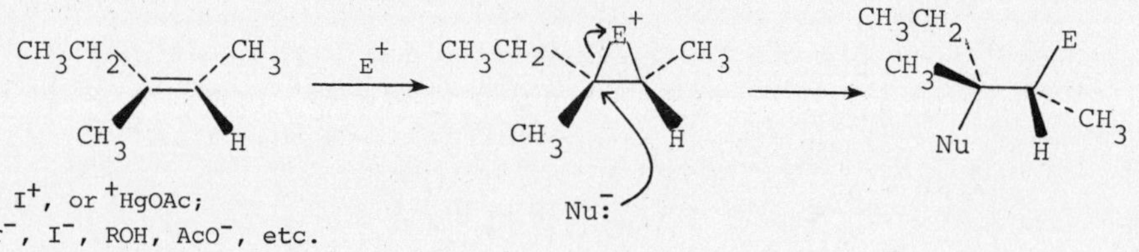

$E^+ = Cl^+, Br^+, I^+, $ or $ {}^+HgOAc;$
$Nu:^- = Cl^-, Br^-, I^-, ROH, AcO^-, $ etc.

Related reaction: hydrolysis of epoxides (10.11.A)

   Because of the bridged nature of the cationic intermediate, there are two generalities for reactions of this type: 1) there is a sterochemical preference for **anti** attack by the nucleophile; and 2) Markovnikov's rule is followed in a broader definition: attack of an electrophile occurs in such a way as to form the more stable carbocationic intermediate. You can rationalize this by thinking of the resonance structures possible for the bridged intermediate: the one with a tertiary carbocation is more important than the secondary carbocation, and nucleophilic attack occurs faster at that position.

                                                                least important

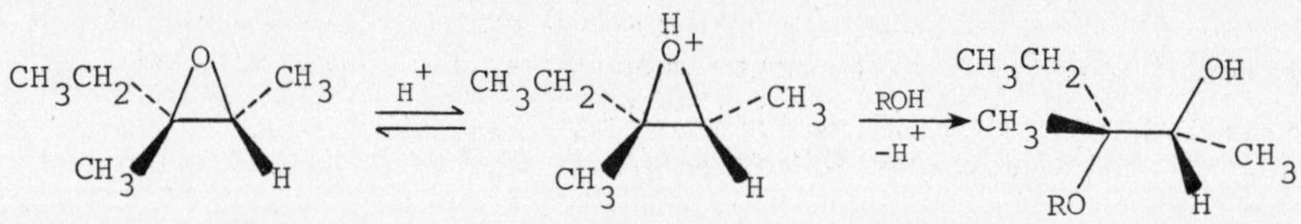

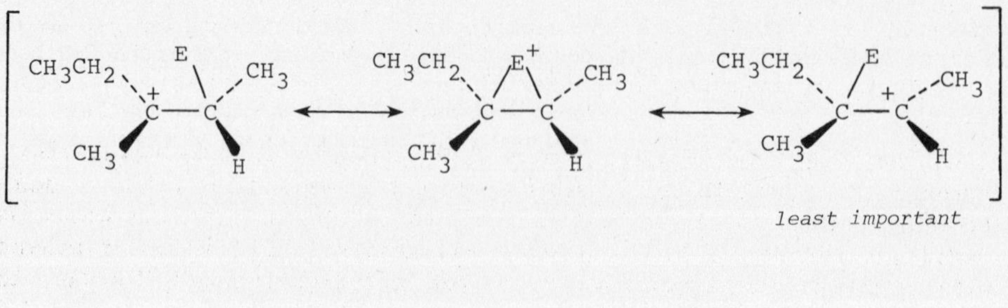

11.D   Answers to Exercises

11.1   (a) Three:

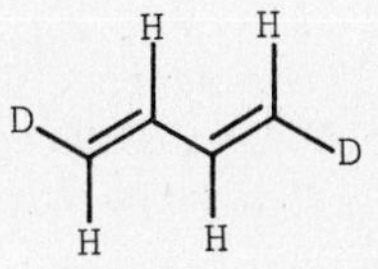

trans, trans   trans, cis   cis, cis

(b) Two:

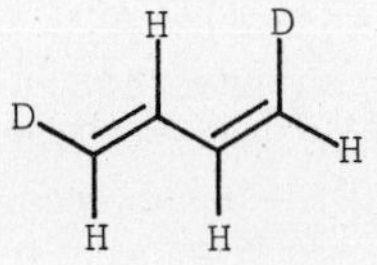

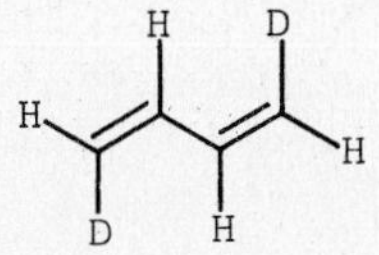

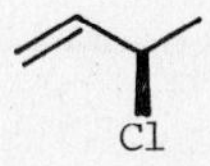

(R)-3-chloro-1-butene   (S)-3-chloro-1-butene

11.2   (a) trans-4-octene   (c) trans-2,5-dimethyl-3-heptene
        (b) 1-hexene   (d) 5-chloro-2-methyl-2-pentene

11.3   (a) (Z)-2-chloro-2-hexene   (c) (E)-3,4-dimethyl-3-hexene
        (b) (Z)-3-(1-chloroethyl)-3-hexen-2-ol (d) (E)-1-chloropropene

11.4   (a) "2-(chloromethyl)-2-pentene" is incorrect because a five-
             carbon backbone can be chosen which includes the halogen.
             Correct name: 1-chloro-2-methyl-2-pentene.

        (b) Both of the substituents on one end of the double bond are
             the same, so the E specification does not apply.
             Correct name: 2-methyl-2-hexene.

        (c) In choosing which direction to number the carbon backbone, an
             alcohol functional group takes precedence over a double bond,
             so "trans-pent-2-en-4-ol" is numbered from the wrong end.
             Correct name: trans-pent-3-en-2-ol.

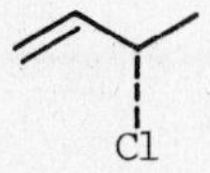

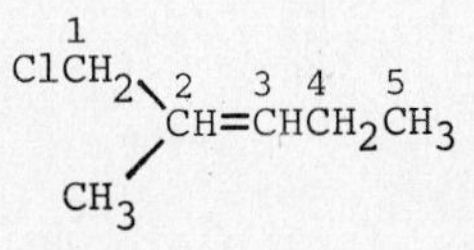

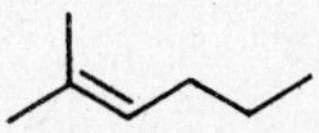

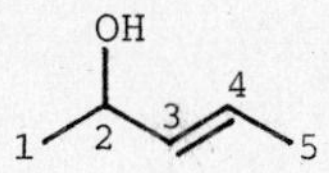

11.5   cis-2-pentene $\rightleftharpoons$ trans-2-pentene
        $\Delta H^\circ_f = $ -7.0   -7.9 $\Delta H^\circ = -0.9$ kcal mole^{-1}

        Assuming that ΔS° is ~0, so that $\Delta G^\circ \approx \Delta H^\circ$:

            at 25 °C = 298 °K: $\Delta G^\circ = -RT \ln K$ $-900/(-1.987 \times 298) = \ln K$;   K = 4.6
            at 300 °C = 573 °K: $-900/(-1.987 \times 573) = \ln K$;   K = 2.2

11.6   trans-cyclooctene $\rightleftharpoons$ cis-cyclooctene $\Delta G^\circ = -9.1$ kcal mole^{-1}

        $\Delta G^\circ = -RT \ln K$: $-9100/(-1.987 \times 298) = \ln K$; $K = 4.72 \times 10^6$

        % trans at equilibrium = 2.1×10^{-5}

11.7   If H_2O and C_2H_5OH have equal dissociation constants in C_2H_5OH solution, then the ratio of
        hydroxide (OH^-) to ethoxide ($C_2H_5O^-$) will be the same as the ratio of (water + hydroxide) to
        (ethanol + ethoxide). In one liter of ethanol solution, there are about 1000 mL x 0.789 g/mL
        (density of ethanol) = 789 g = 789 g/(46 g/mole) = 17.2 moles of ethanol. The amount of
        (water + hydroxide) is equal to the amount of hydroxide added (1 mole), therefore the ratio
        of hydroxide to ethoxide is about 1/17.

11.8   For a primary alkyl halide, the mechanism of a substitution reaction is S_N2, and the rate
        will be directly dependent on the concentration of the base. The mechanism for the elimina-

tion reaction is E2, hence this rate is also directly dependent on the concentration of base. Therefore to a first approximation, the **ratio** of substitution to elimination will be independent of base concentration.

11.9 The substitution reaction will be unaffected by the presence or absence of deuterium on the β-carbon and will therefore occur at the same rate for the two substrates. The elimination reaction will be slower for the deutero compound, however, since the carbon-deuterium bond is partially broken in the transition state. The ratio of substitution/elimination will therefore be higher for the deuterated substrate.

11.11

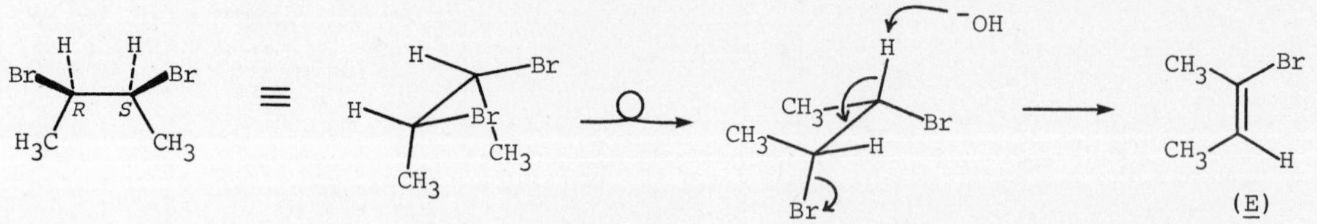

11.12 Hot sulfuric acid would <u>not</u> be a good method in this case, since double bond isomerization and loss of the deuteriums would occur:

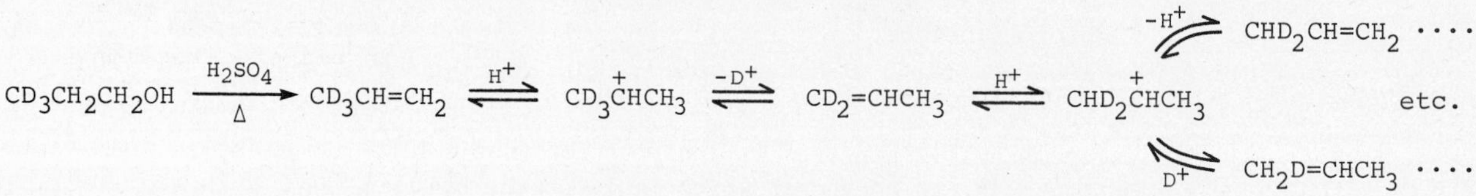

11.13 1-Methylcyclohexene, via cationic rearrangement to the more stable tertiary cation and loss of a proton:

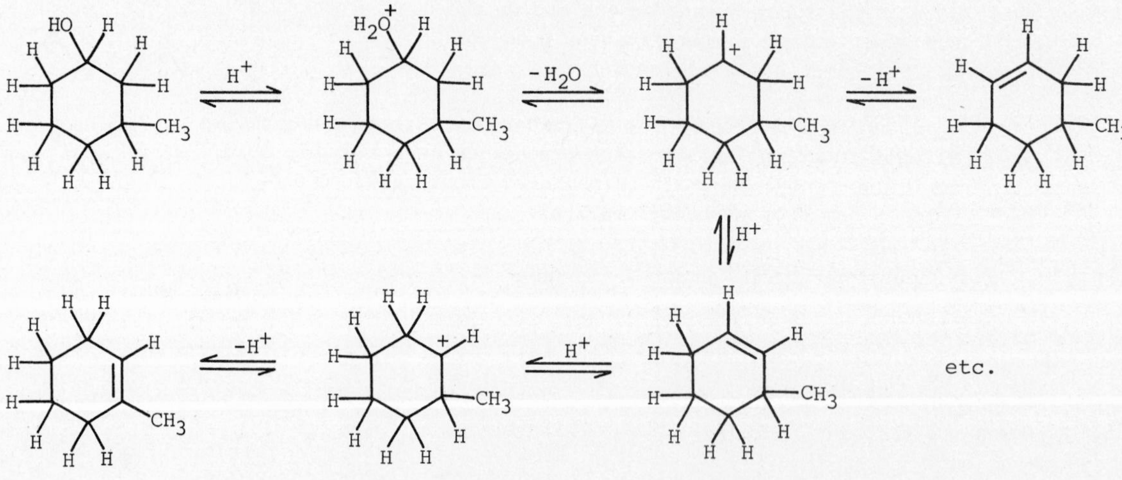

most stable

NOTE: **Many** equilibria between various alkenes and carbocations are possible in this system. _All_ of them can take place (for example, as depicted for the formation of 4-methylcyclohexene), but only the important ones, leading to the most stable product (1-methylcyclohexene), are shown.

11.14

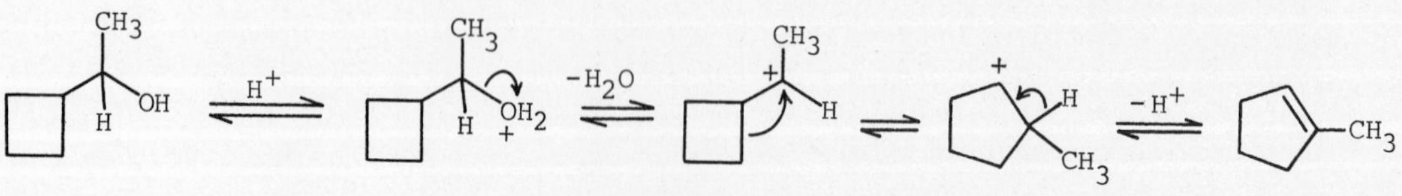

11.15 Using palladium as catalyst results in isomerization and loss of chirality before hydrogenation occurs:

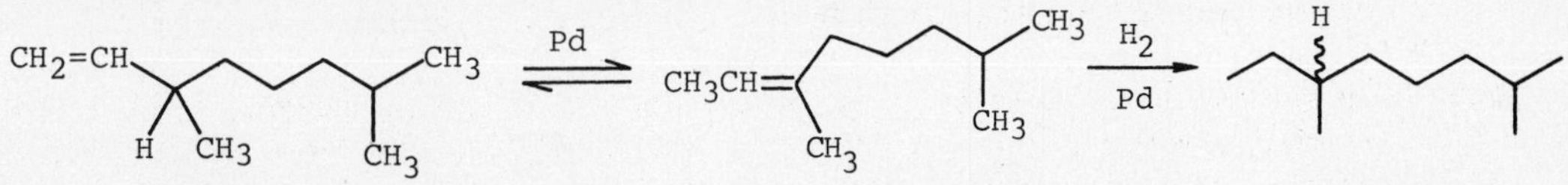

optically active   *achiral*   *racemic*

11.16

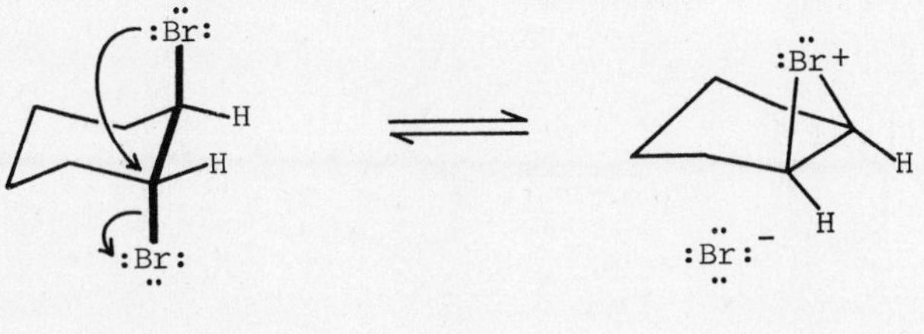

This path can be followed in either direction.

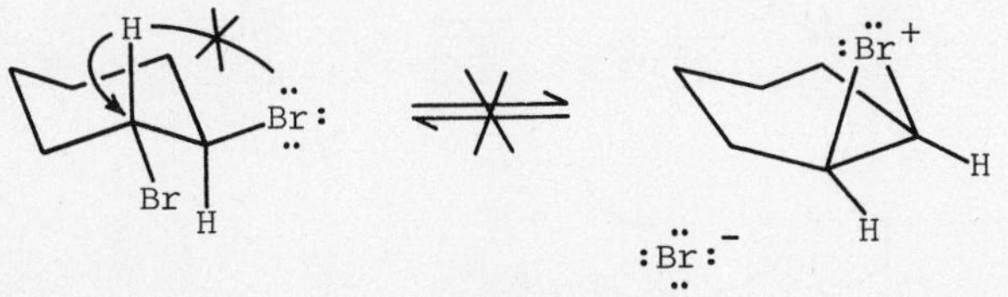

This path can**not** be followed, in either direction.

11.17

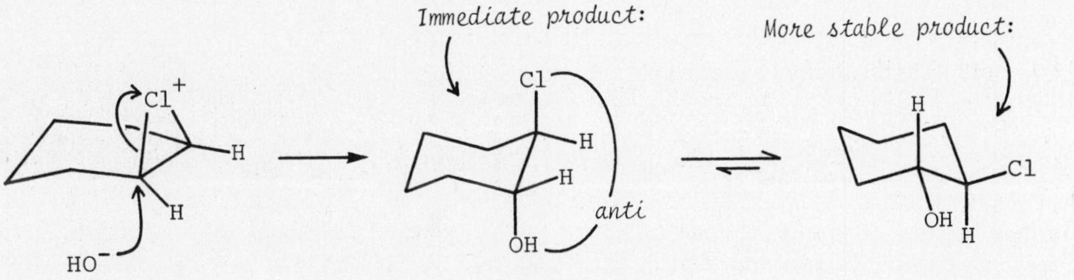

Immediate product: *More stable product:*

anti

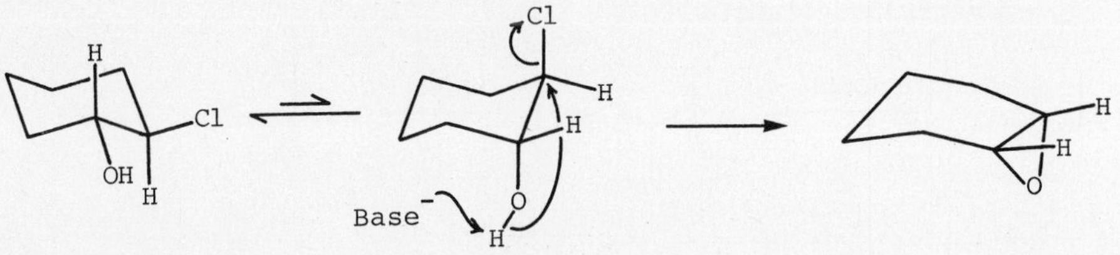

Base⁻

11.18   (a) <u>trans</u>-1,2-dibromo-1-methylcyclohexane

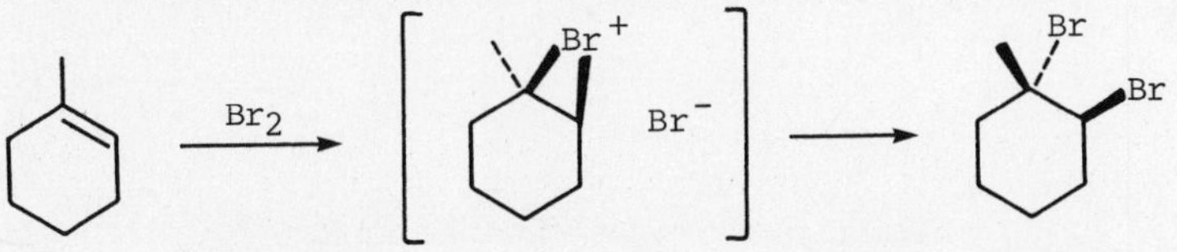

(b) (2<u>S</u>,3<u>S</u>)-3-chloro-2-butanol (and its enantiomer)

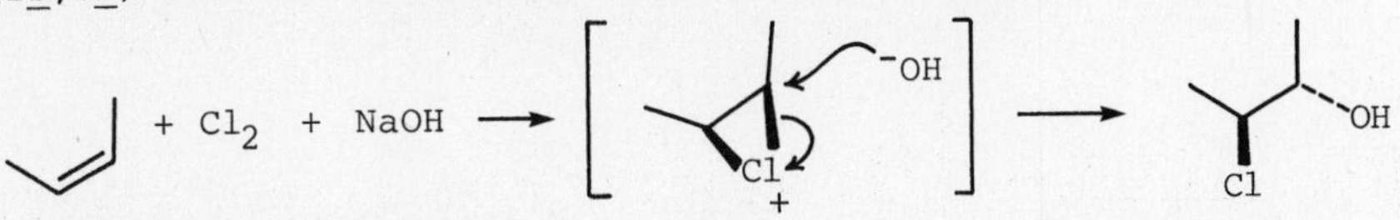

(c) (2<u>R</u>,3<u>R</u>)-2,3-butanediol (and its enantiomer)

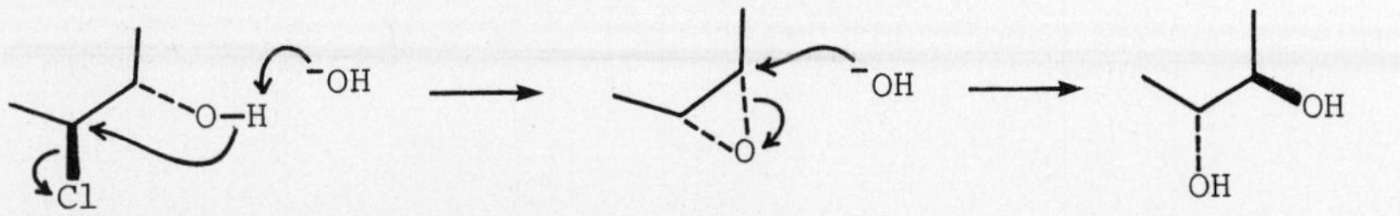

11.19

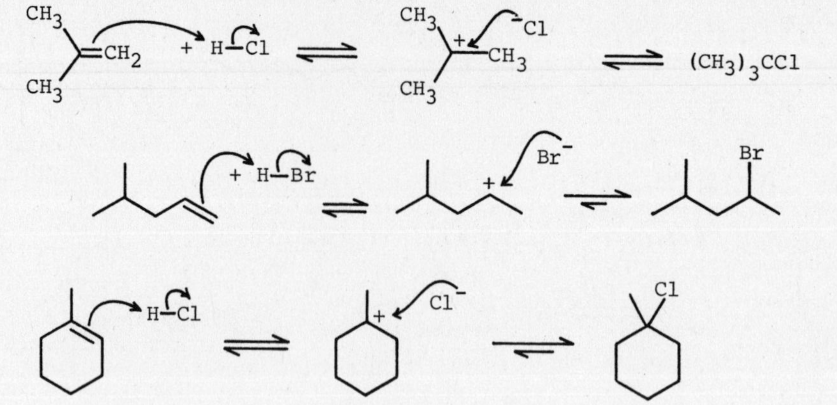

$$CH_2=C(CH_3)_2 + H\!-\!Cl \rightleftharpoons \overset{+}{C}(CH_3)_3 \quad Cl \rightleftharpoons (CH_3)_3CCl$$

(secondary/tertiary carbocation mechanism with H–Br and Br^- giving 2-bromo-4-methylpentane)

(methylcyclohexene + H–Cl → tertiary carbocation + Cl^- → 1-chloro-1-methylcyclohexane)

11.20

$$CH_3-CH=CH-CH_3 \xrightarrow{H^+} CH_3-\overset{+}{C}H-CH_2-CH_3 \xrightarrow{Br^-} CH_3-CHBr-CH_2-CH_3$$

or

$$\xrightarrow{H^+} \text{(carbocation)} \xrightarrow{Br^-}$$

similar stability

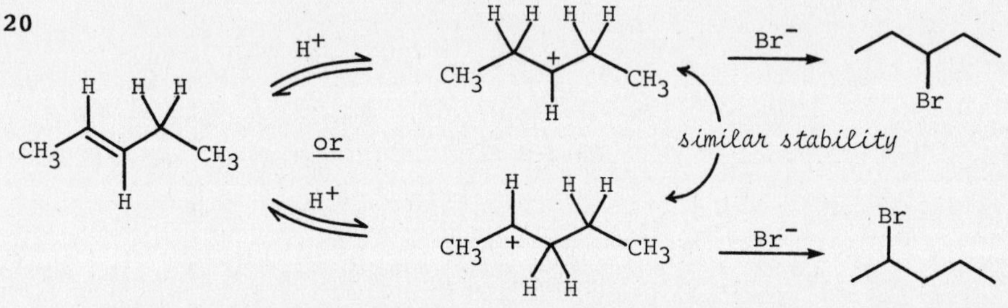

11.21   (a)   1-methylcyclohexyl acetate:

$$\text{(1-methylcyclohexene)} \xrightarrow{Hg(OAc)_2} \text{(OAc, HgOAc adduct)} \xrightarrow{NaBH_4} \text{(1-methylcyclohexyl acetate)}$$

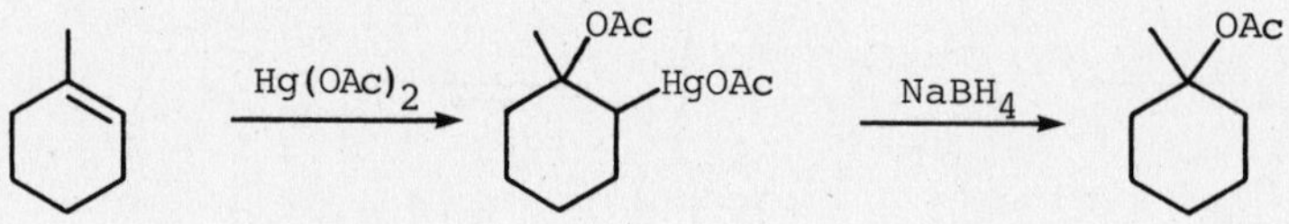

     (b)   1,1-dimethylbutyl acetate:

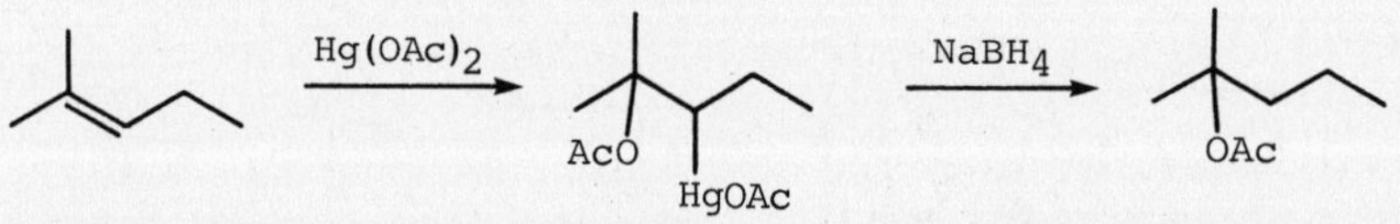

$$\text{(2-methyl-2-pentene)} \xrightarrow{Hg(OAc)_2} \text{(AcO, HgOAc adduct)} \xrightarrow{NaBH_4} \text{(1,1-dimethylbutyl acetate, OAc)}$$

11.22

$$CH_3O\!-\!\underset{OCH_3}{\overset{OCH_3}{B}} \xrightarrow{\ ^-OH} \quad CH_3O\!-\!\overset{-}{\underset{OCH_3}{B}}\!-\!OCH_3 \ \rightleftharpoons \ CH_3O^- + \ CH_3O\!-\!\underset{OCH_3}{\overset{OH}{B}} \xleftarrow{\ ^-OH}$$

$$HO\!-\!\underset{OH}{\overset{OH}{B}} \xleftarrow{-CH_3O^-} HO\!-\!\overset{-}{\underset{OCH_3}{B}}\!-\!OH \xleftarrow{OH^-} HO\!-\!\underset{OCH_3}{\overset{OH}{B}} \xleftarrow{-CH_3O^-} CH_3O\!-\!\overset{-}{\underset{OCH_3}{B}}\!-\!OH$$

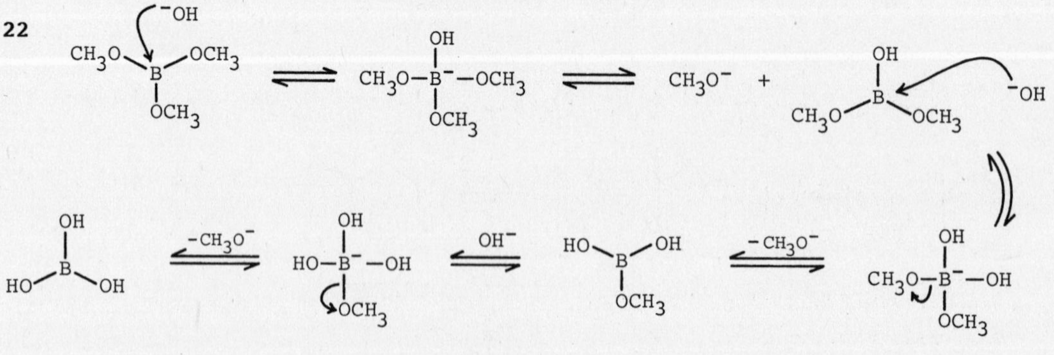

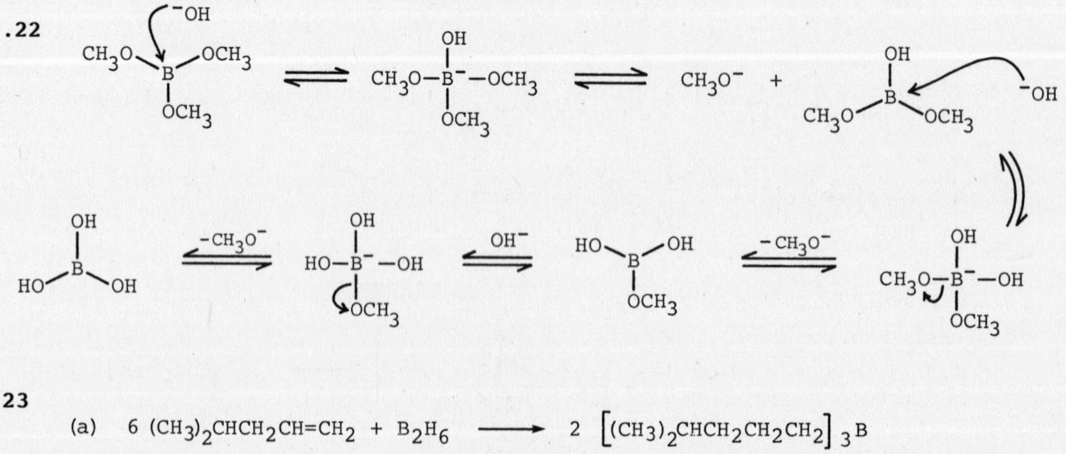

11.23   (a) $6\ (CH_3)_2CHCH_2CH=CH_2 + B_2H_6 \longrightarrow 2\ [(CH_3)_2CHCH_2CH_2CH_2]_3B$

$$\downarrow H_2O_2\ |\ OH^-$$

$$(CH_3)_2CHCH_2CH_2CH_2OH + \text{borate salts}$$

(b)

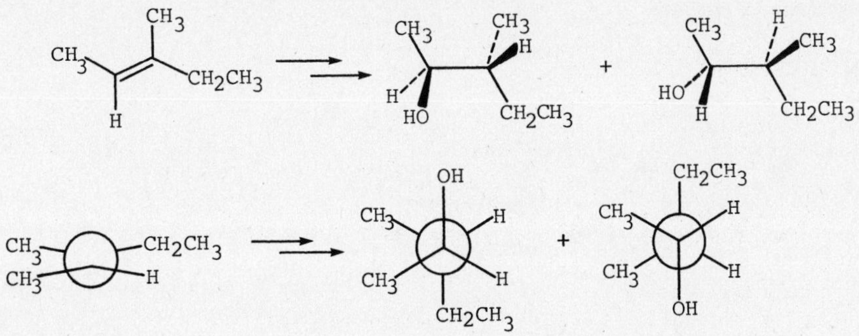

(racemic mixture)

(c)

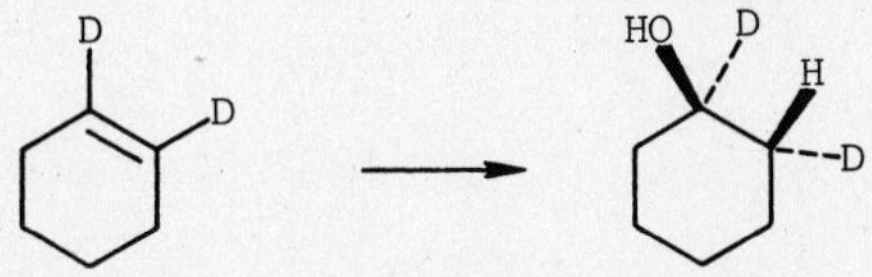

(racemic)

11.24

(a)

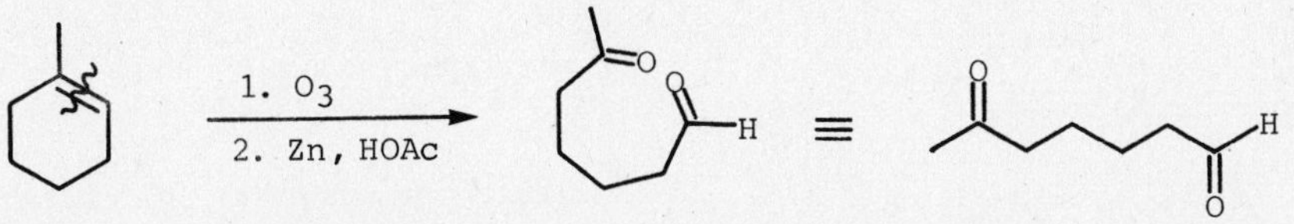

$$\xrightarrow{\text{1. O}_3 \quad \text{2. Zn, HOAc}}$$

(b)

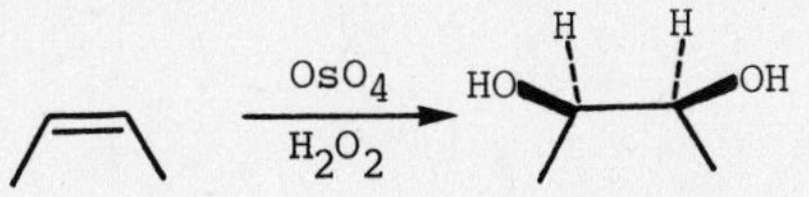

$$\xrightarrow[\text{H}_2\text{O}_2]{\text{OsO}_4}$$

(meso)

(c)

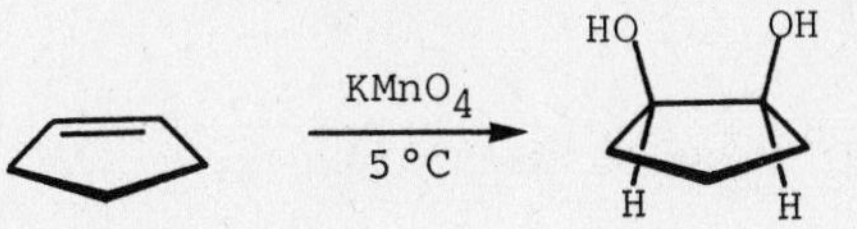

$$\xrightarrow[\text{5 °C}]{\text{KMnO}_4}$$

(cis)

11.25

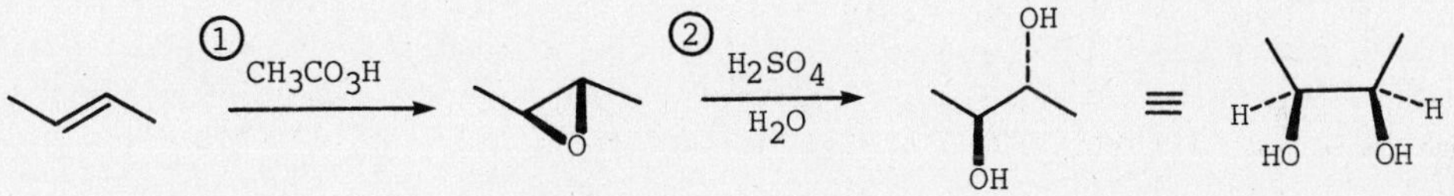

$$\xrightarrow[\text{CH}_3\text{CO}_3\text{H}]{①} \qquad \xrightarrow[\text{H}_2\text{O}]{② \quad \text{H}_2\text{SO}_4}$$

(meso)

11.26

(a)

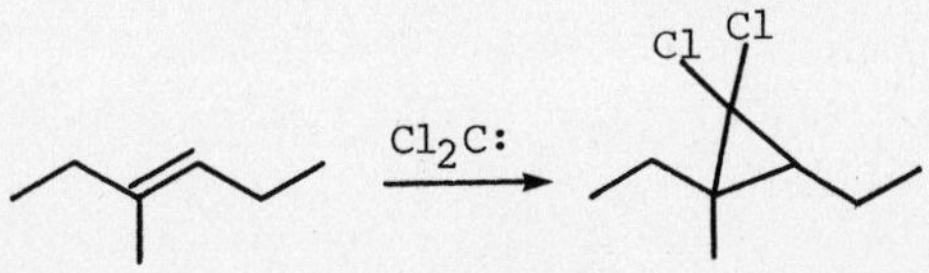

$$\xrightarrow{\text{Cl}_2\text{C:}}$$

(b)

$$\xrightarrow[\text{Zn (Cu)}]{\text{CH}_2\text{I}_2}$$

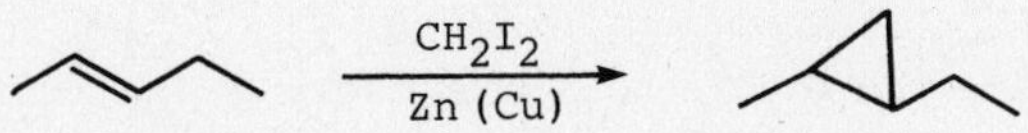

11.27

$$CH_3S\cdot \ + \ CH_2=CH_2 \ \longrightarrow \ CH_3SCH_2CH_2\cdot$$

Bonds formed:	C–S	-65 kcal mole^{-1}
	C–C	-83
Bonds broken:	C=C	$+150$
Overall change:		$+\ 2$ kcal mole^{-1}

$$CH_3SCH_2CH_2\cdot \ + \ CH_3SH \ \longrightarrow \ CH_3SCH_2CH_3 \ + \ CH_3S\cdot$$

Bonds formed:	C–H	-104 kcal mole^{-1}
Bonds broken:	S–H	$+\ 83$
Overall change:		$-\ 21$ kcal mole^{-1}

11.E   Answers and Explanations for Problems

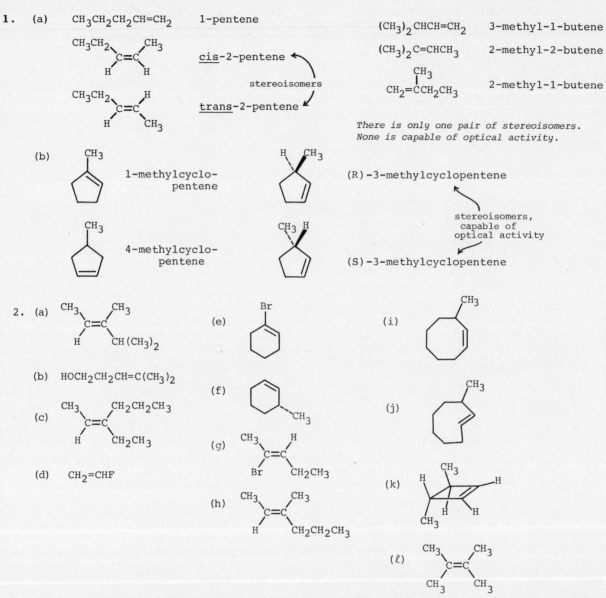

1.   (a)   CH₃CH₂CH₂CH=CH₂   1-pentene

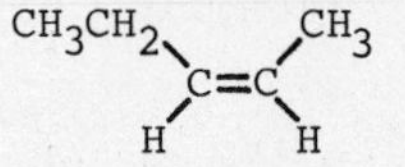

cis-2-pentene

stereoisomers

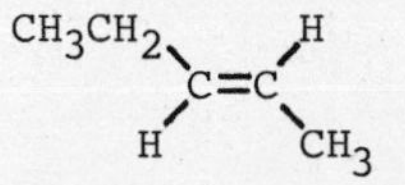

trans-2-pentene

$(CH_3)_2CHCH=CH_2$ 3-methyl-1-butene

$(CH_3)_2C=CHCH_3$ 2-methyl-2-butene

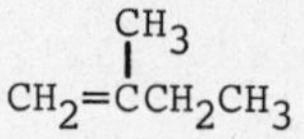

$CH_2=CCH_2CH_3$ (with CH₃ branch)   2-methyl-1-butene

*There is only one pair of stereoisomers.
None is capable of optical activity.*

(b)   1-methylcyclo-
pentene

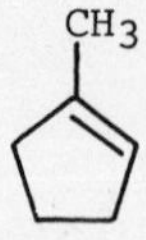

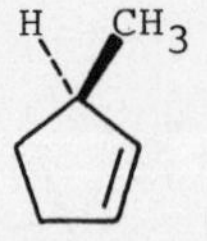

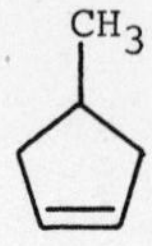

4-methylcyclo-
pentene

(R)-3-methylcyclopentene

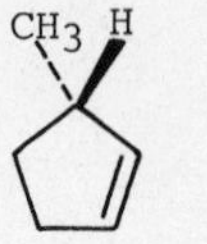

(S)-3-methylcyclopentene

stereoisomers,
capable of
optical activity

2.   (a), (b), (c), (d), (e), (f), (g), (h), (i), (j), (k), (ℓ)

(b)   HOCH₂CH₂CH=C(CH₃)₂

(d)   CH₂=CHF

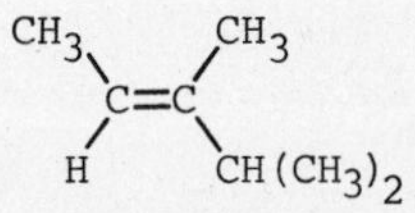

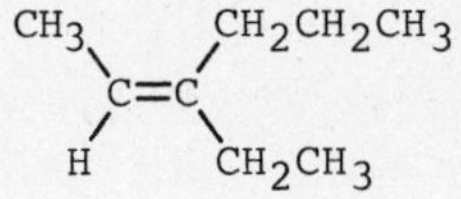

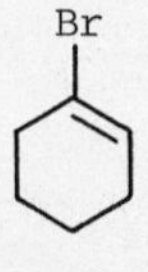

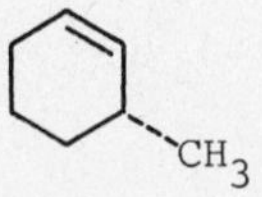

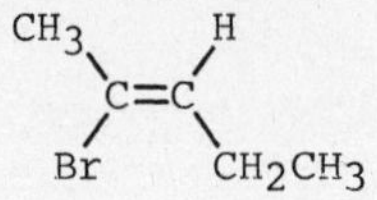

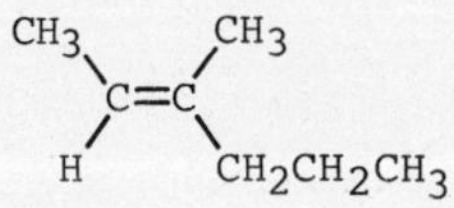

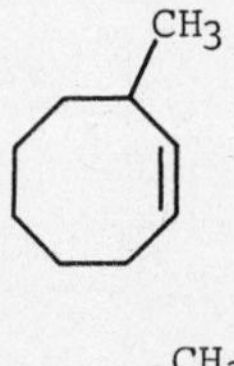

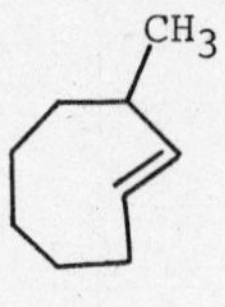

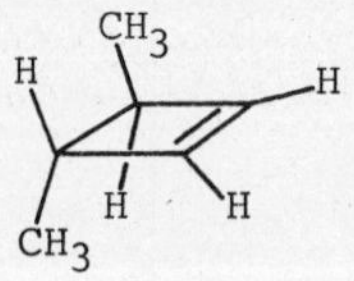

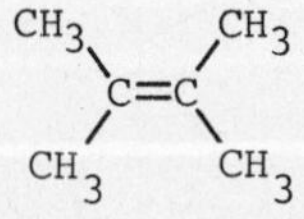

3.   (a)   "2-methylcyclopentene" is numbering the double bond from the wrong direction: correct name
is 1-methylcyclopentene

(b)   The double bond takes precedence in numbering the carbon chain:
correct name is 4-methyl-cis-2-pentene

(c)   There is no stereochemistry for unsubstituted 1-butene: correct name is simply 1-butene

(d)   Common and systematic nomenclature should not be mixed: correct name is 1-bromo-2-
methylpropene

(e)   same error as in (a):   correct name is 4-chlorocyclohexene

(f)   One end of the double bond has two identical substituents, therefore there is no stereochemistry to specify (see (c) above); also, "3-ethyl-3-pentene" is numbered from the
wrong end: correct name is 3-ethyl-2-pentene

(g)   The hydroxyl group takes precedence over the double bond in numbering: correct name is
trans-3-penten-2-ol

(h)   In case of two chains of identical length, the one with more, smaller substituents should
be chosen: correct name is (Z)-3-ethyl-2-methyl-3-heptene

4. (a) (R)-3-methyl-1-hexene

(b) 1-methylcyclohexene

(c) (E)-3,4-dimethyl-3-heptene

(d) (Z)-4-isopropyl-3-methyl-3-heptene

(e) (Z)-1-bromo-1-chloro-2-fluoro-
2-iodoethene

(f) 4-chloro-1-butene

(g) 4-chloro-2-ethyl-1-butene

(h) 2-(2-chloroethyl)-1-pentene

(i) (Z)-1-chloro-3-heptene

(j) 4-penten-1-ol

(k) (S,E)-hex-4-en-3-ol or
(S,E)-4-hexen-3-ol

(l) (R)-2-ethyl-4-methyl-1-hexene

5. (a) $(CH_3CH_2)_3CH$

3-ethylpentane

(b) 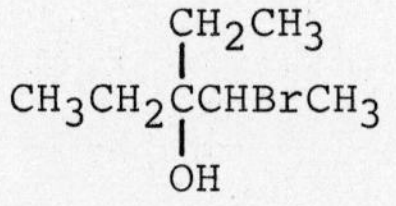
CH_2CH_3
$CH_3CH_2CCHBrCH_3$
OH

2-bromo-3-ethyl-3-pentanol

(c) 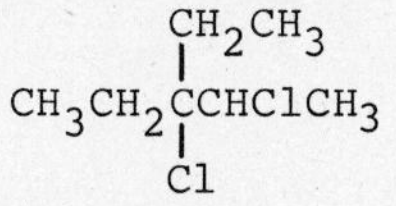
CH_2CH_3
$CH_3CH_2CCHClCH_3$
Cl

2,3-dichloro-3-ethylpentane

(d) 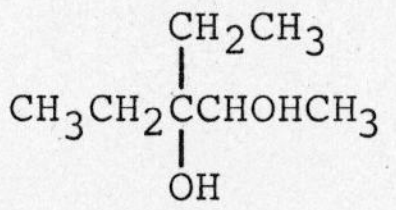
CH_2CH_3
$CH_3CH_2CCHOHCH_3$
OH

3-ethylpentane-2,3-diol

(e) 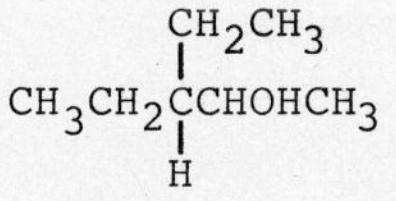
CH_2CH_3
$CH_3CH_2CCHOHCH_3$
H

3-ethyl-2-pentanol

(ℓ)
CH_2CH_3
$CH_3CH_2C-CHCH_3$
C
Br Br

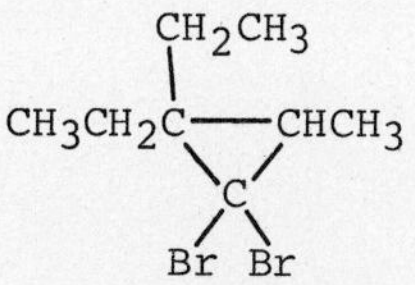

1,1-dibromo-2,2-diethyl-3-methylcyclopropane

(m)
CH_2CH_3
$CH_3CH_2C-CHCH_3$
CH_2

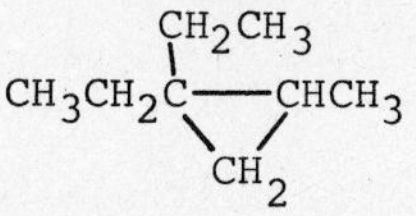

1,1-diethyl-2-methylcyclopropane

(f) $(CH_3CH_2)_3COH$

3-ethyl-3-pentanol

(g) $CH_3CH_2COCH_2CH_3$ + CH_3CHO

diethyl ketone   acetaldehyde
or 3-pentanone

(h) $(CH_3CH_2)_3CBr$

3-bromo-3-ethylpentane

(i) 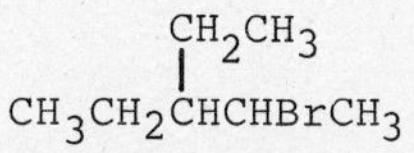
CH_2CH_3
$CH_3CH_2CHCHBrCH_3$

2-bromo-3-ethylpentane

(j) 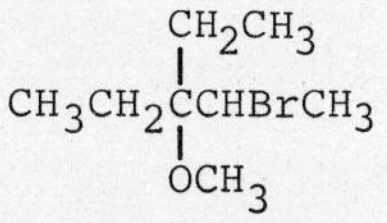
CH_2CH_3
$CH_3CH_2CCHBrCH_3$
OCH_3

2-bromo-3-ethyl-3-methoxypentane

(k) 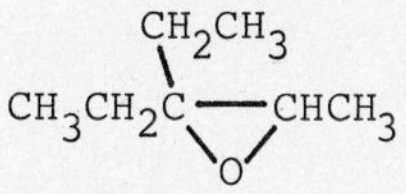
CH_2CH_3
$CH_3CH_2C-CHCH_3$
O

2,2-diethyl-3-methyloxirane

6. Same products from

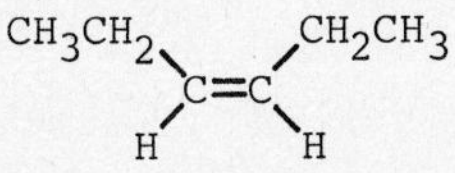

CH_3CH_2 CH_2CH_3
C=C
H H

and

CH_3CH_2 H
C=C
H CH_2CH_3

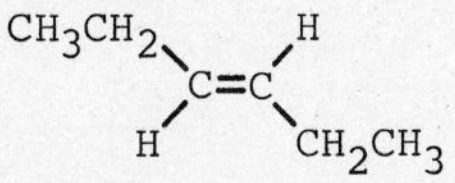

(a) hexane

(e,f) 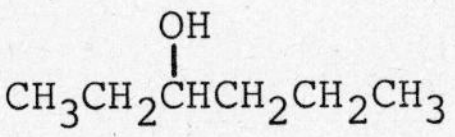
OH
$CH_3CH_2CHCH_2CH_2CH_3$ 3-hexanol

(g) CH_3CH_2CHO propionaldehyde

(h,i)
Br
$CH_3CH_2CHCH_2CH_2CH_3$ 3-bromohexane

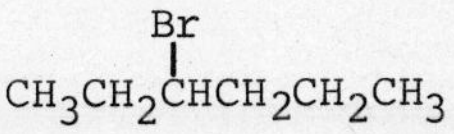

Different products:

(b)

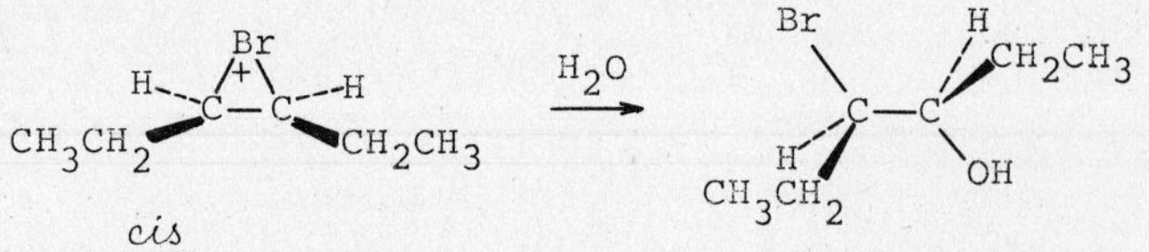

CH_3CH_2—C—C—CH_2CH_3 (with H, Br, H, H substituents)

$\underline{cis}$

$\xrightarrow{H_2O}$

(3R,4R)-4-bromo-3-hexanol
plus an equal amount of the (3S,4S)
                                  enantiomer

To indicate that this diastereomer is present as a racemic
mixture, the designation (3RS,4RS) may be used.

$\textit{trans}$-3-hexene gives

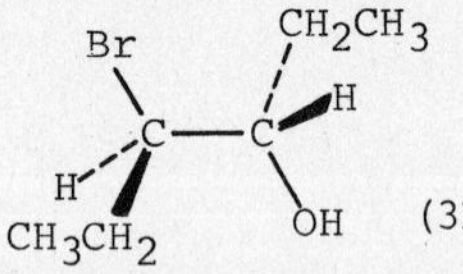

(3RS,4SR)-4-bromo-3-hexanol

(c) $\textit{cis}$ gives (±) (or dl) 3,4-dichlorohexane
     $\textit{trans}$ gives meso-3,4-dichlorohexane

(d) $\textit{cis}$ gives meso-3,4-hexanediol
     $\textit{trans}$ gives (±)-3,4-hexanediol

(j) Same as (b), except for CH_3O instead of OH:
     $\textit{cis}$ gives (3RS,4RS)-3-bromo-4-methoxyhexane
     $\textit{trans}$ gives (3RS,4SR)-3-bromo-4-methoxyhexane

(k) $\textit{cis}$ gives $\textit{cis}$-2,3-diethyloxirane

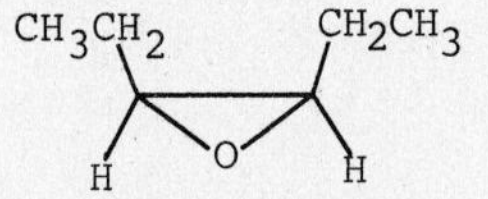

     $\textit{trans}$ gives $\textit{trans}$-2,3-diethyloxirane

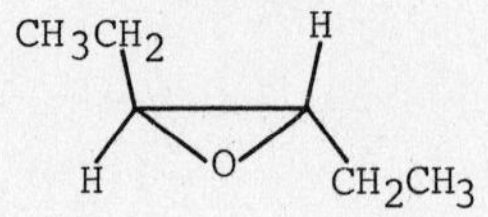

(ℓ) $\textit{cis}$ gives $\textit{cis}$-1,1-dibromo-2,3-diethylcyclopropane

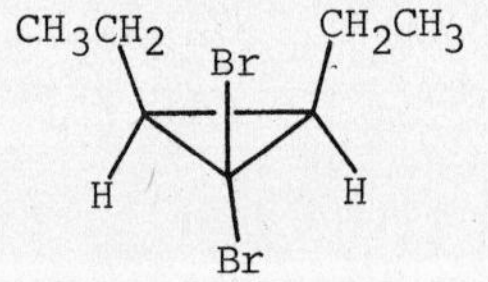

     $\textit{trans}$ gives $\textit{trans}$-1,1-dibromo-2,3-diethylcyclopropane

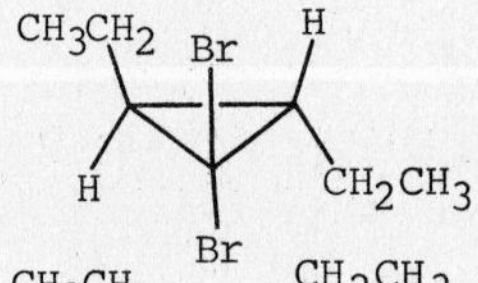

(m) $\textit{cis}$ gives $\textit{cis}$-1,2-diethylcyclopropane

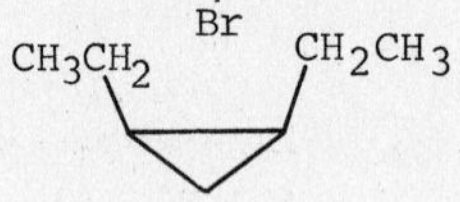

     $\textit{trans}$ gives $\textit{trans}$-1,2-diethylcyclopropane

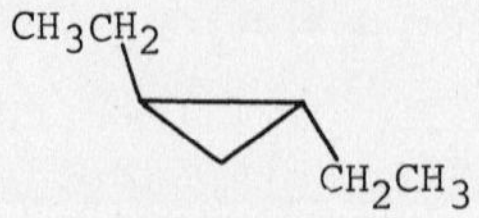

7. (a) [structure] cyclohexane

(h, i) [structure with Br] bromocyclohexane

(b) [structure with Br, OH] (±)-*trans*-2-bromo-cyclohexanol

(j) [structure with Br, OCH$_3$] (±)-*trans*-1-bromo-2-methoxycyclohexane

(c) [structure with Cl, Cl] (±)-*trans*-1,2-dichloro-cyclohexane

(k) [epoxide structure with O] epoxycyclohexane

(d) [structure with OH, OH] *cis*-1,2-cyclo-hexanediol

(ℓ) [bicyclic structure with Br, Br] 7,7-dibromo-bicyclo[4.1.0]heptane

(e, f) [structure with OH] cyclohexanol

(m) [bicyclic structure] bicyclo[4.1.0]heptane

(g) [structure] $\overset{O}{\overset{\|}{C}}(CH_2)_4\overset{O}{\overset{\|}{C}}$ with H's hexanedial

8. (a) $CH_3CH_2CH_2CH=CH_2$

(b) [cyclopentane structure with H, CH$_2$OH]

(c) [structure] $CH_3CH_2\overset{Cl}{\underset{H}{C}}-\overset{CH_3}{\underset{Cl}{C}}H$ + enantiomer

(d) [cyclopentane with OH, OH]

(e) $\overset{H}{\underset{CH_3}{C}}=\overset{CD_2CH_3}{\underset{H}{C}}$

(f) $\overset{H}{\underset{(CH_3)_3C}{C}}=\overset{CH_3}{\underset{CH_2CH_3}{C}}$

(g) [cyclopentane epoxide with O]

(h) $CH_3\overset{O}{\overset{\|}{C}}CH_2-\overset{CH_3}{\underset{CH_3}{C}}-CH_2\overset{O}{\overset{\|}{C}}H$

(i) [cyclohexane structure with Br, C(CH$_3$)$_3$, H, Br] (*t*-butyl is always equatorial)

product from *anti*, diaxial addition

9. (a) $CH_3CHBrCH_3 \xrightarrow[\substack{or \\ t\text{-}C_4H_9OK/t\text{-}C_4H_9OH \\ \Delta}]{C_2H_5OK/C_2H_5OH} CH_3CH=CH_2 \xrightarrow[peroxides]{HBr} CH_3CH_2CH_2Br$

(b) $CH_3CHOHCH_3 \xrightarrow[\substack{or \\ H_2SO_4,\Delta}]{Al_2O_3,\Delta} CH_3CH=CH_2 \xrightarrow[]{B_2H_6} \xrightarrow[OH^-]{H_2O_2} CH_3CH_2CH_2OH$

(c) [cyclohexane] $\xrightarrow[h\nu]{Cl_2}$ [cyclohexyl-Cl] $\xrightarrow[\Delta]{\substack{C_2H_5ONa, \\ C_2H_5OH}}$ [cyclohexene] $\xrightarrow[\substack{or \\ H_2O_2/OsO_4}]{cold\ dil.\ KMnO_4}$ [cyclohexane with H, OH, OH, H]

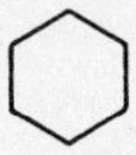

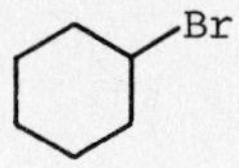

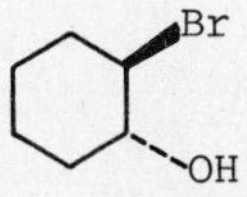

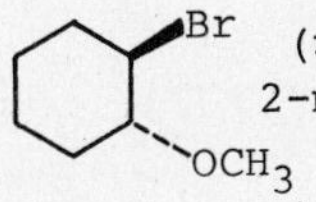

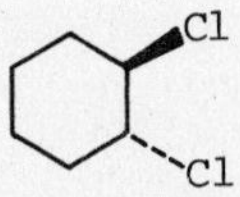

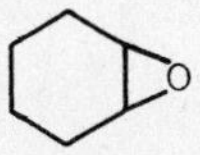

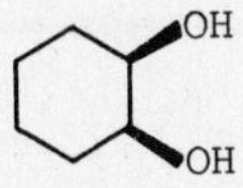

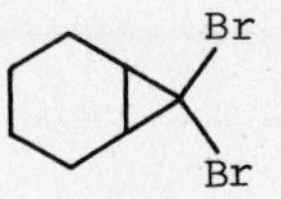

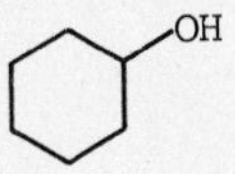

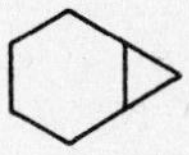

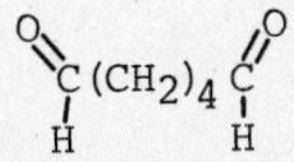

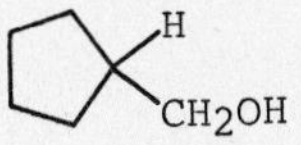

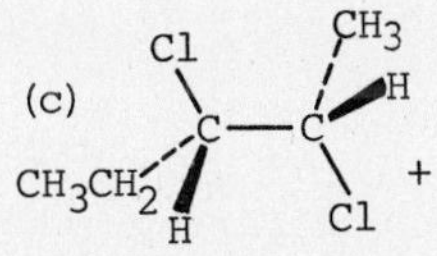

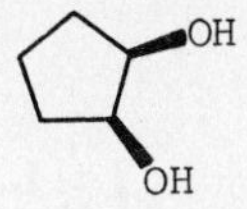

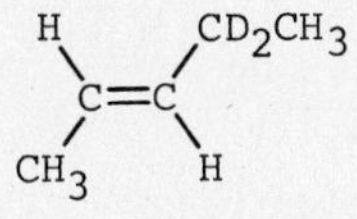

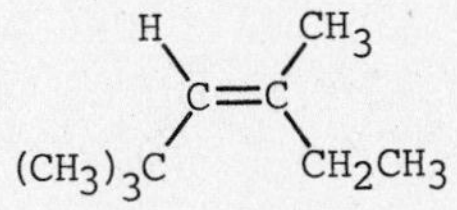

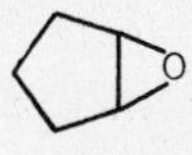

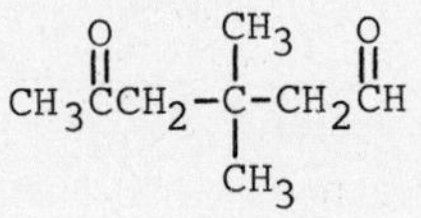

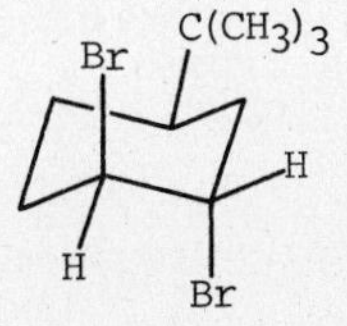

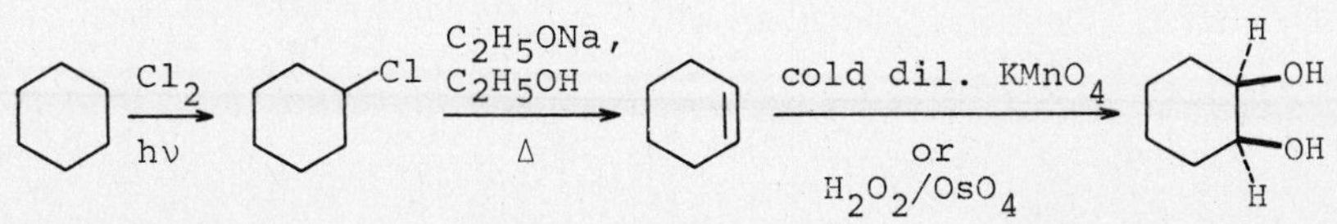

(d) [cyclohexene] $\xrightarrow{CH_3CO_3H}$ [cyclohexene oxide] $\xrightarrow[H_2O]{H_2SO_4}$ [trans-1,2-cyclohexanediol, OH, OH]

(e)
$$CH_3CH_2\underset{CH_3}{C}=CH_2 \xrightarrow[CH_3OH]{Hg(OAc)_2} CH_3CH_2\underset{\underset{OCH_3}{|}}{\overset{\overset{CH_3}{|}}{C}}-CH_2HgOAc \xrightarrow[NaOH]{NaBH_4} CH_3CH_2\underset{\underset{OCH_3}{|}}{\overset{\overset{CH_3}{|}}{C}}-CH_3$$

$$\searrow \underset{\text{or HBr/inhibitors}}{\overset{\text{or HCl}}{\longrightarrow}} CH_3CH_2\underset{\underset{X}{|}}{\overset{\overset{CH_3}{|}}{C}}-CH_3 \xrightarrow[(S_N1 \; reaction)]{CH_3OH} CH_3CH_2\underset{\underset{OCH_3}{|}}{\overset{\overset{CH_3}{|}}{C}}-CH_3$$

(f)
$$CH_3CH_2\underset{CH_3}{C}=CH_2 \xrightarrow{B_2H_6} \xrightarrow[OH^-]{H_2O_2} CH_3CH_2\underset{CH_3}{CH}CH_2OH \xrightarrow{K} \xrightarrow{CH_3I} CH_3CH_2\underset{CH_3}{CH}CH_2OCH_3$$

(g) [methylenecyclopentane, CH_2] $\xrightarrow{O_3} \xrightarrow[AcOH]{H_2O \; or}$ [cyclopentanone, O]

10. (a) [bromomethylcyclopentane, Br] $\xrightarrow[HOC(CH_3)_3]{KOC(CH_3)_3}$ [methylenecyclopentane] $\xrightarrow[2.\; NaBH_4,\; CH_3OH]{1.\; O_3,\; CH_2Cl_2}$ [cyclopentanol, OH]

(b) [bromocyclopentane, Br] $\xrightarrow{alc.\; KOH}$ [cyclopentene] $\xrightarrow{HOBr}$ [trans-2-bromocyclopentanol, Br, OH]

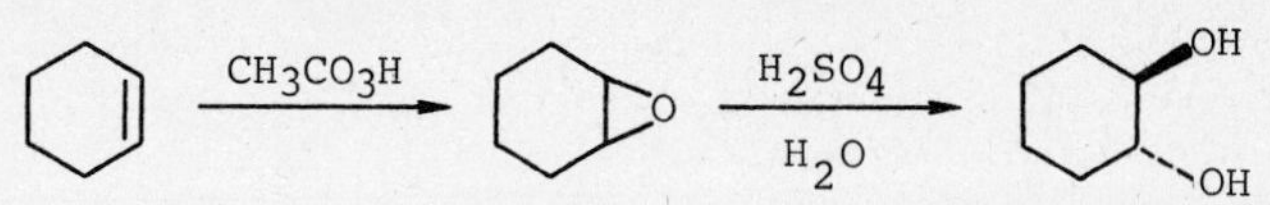

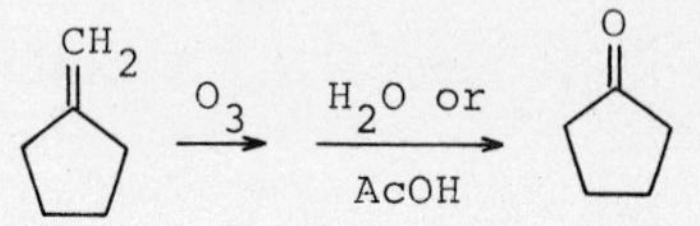

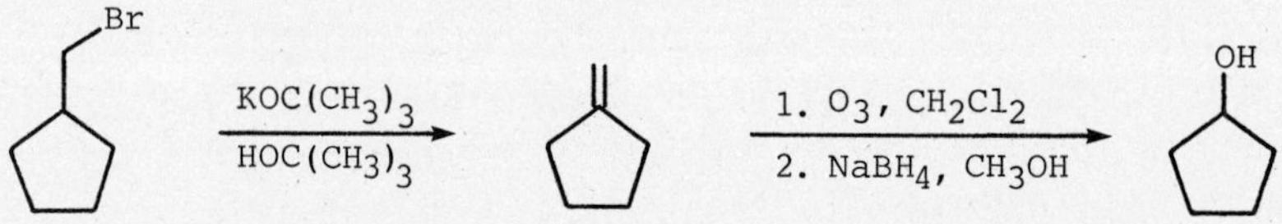

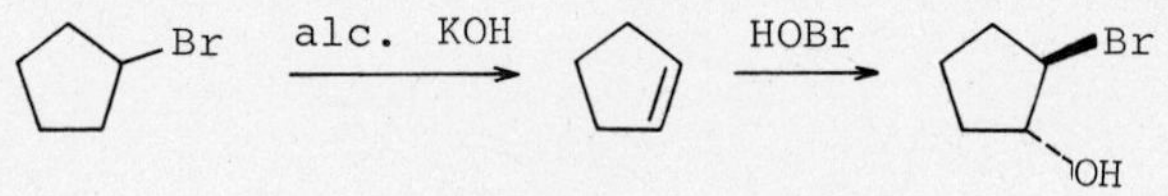

(c)
$$CH_3CH_2CH_2CH_2CH_2OH \xrightarrow[H_2SO_4]{HBr} CH_3CH_2CH_2CH_2CH_2Br \xrightarrow{t-BuO^-}$$

$$\downarrow Al_2O_3, \; \Delta$$

$$CH_3CH_2CH_2CH=CH_2 \xrightarrow[\substack{inhibitors \\ (ionic)}]{HBr} CH_3CH_2CH_2\underset{Br}{CH}CH_3$$

(d)
$$CH_3CH_2\underset{\underset{D}{|}}{\overset{\overset{CH_3}{|}}{C}}CH_2OH \xrightarrow[\Delta]{Al_2O_3} CH_3CH_2\underset{CH_3}{C}=CH_2 \xrightarrow[cat.]{H_2} CH_3CH_2CH(CH_3)_2$$

(e)
$$CH_3CH_2CH_2CH(CH_3)_2 \xrightarrow[h\nu]{Br_2} CH_3CH_2CH_2\underset{\underset{}{}}{\overset{\overset{Br}{|}}{C}}(CH_3)_2 \xrightarrow{t-BuO^-}$$

$$CH_3CH_2CH_2\underset{CH_3}{C}=CH_2 \xrightarrow{B_2H_6} \xrightarrow[OH^-]{H_2O_2} CH_3CH_2CH_2\underset{CH_3}{CH}CH_2OH$$

(f) [cyclohexane] $\xrightarrow[h\nu]{Cl_2}$ $\xrightarrow[HOC_2H_5]{NaOC_2H_5}$ $\xrightarrow[Zn(Cu)]{CH_2I_2}$ [bicyclo[4.1.0]heptane]

(g)
$$CH_3CH_2-\underset{\underset{Br}{|}}{C}(CH_3)_2 \xrightarrow[HOC(CH_3)_3]{KOC(CH_3)_3} CH_3CH_2-\underset{\underset{CH_2}{\|}}{C}{-CH_3} \xrightarrow[CHCl_3]{KOH} [CH_3CH_2, CH_3, Cl, Cl \; cyclopropane]$$

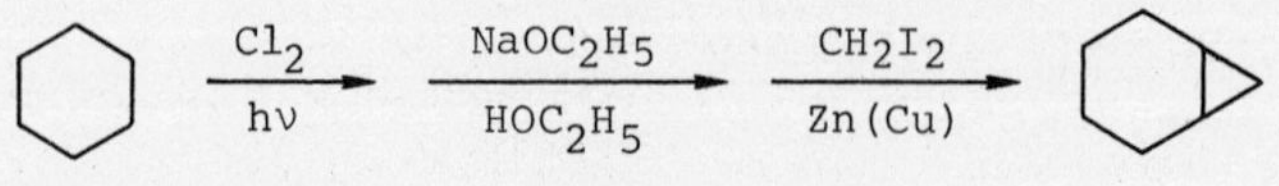

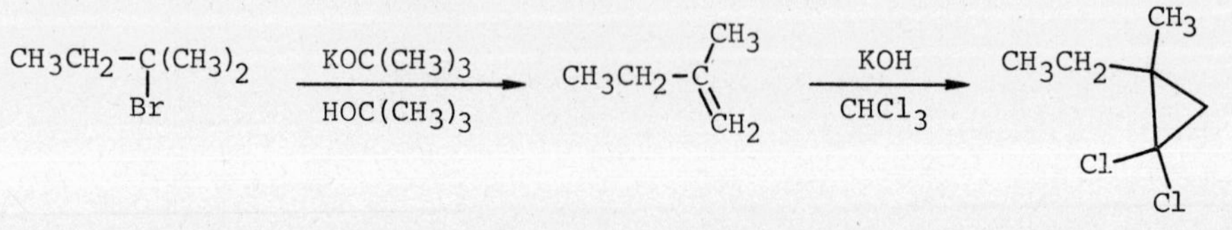

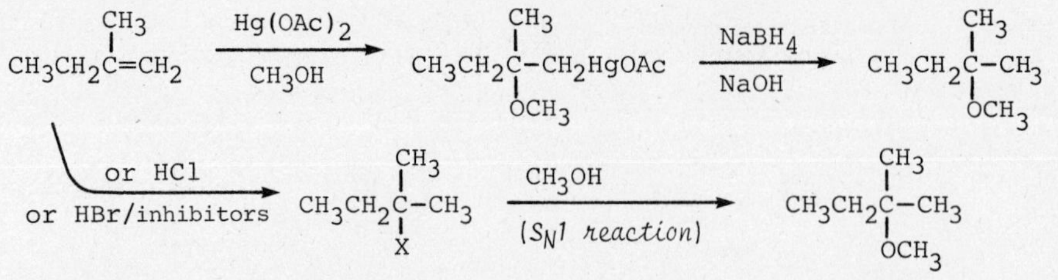

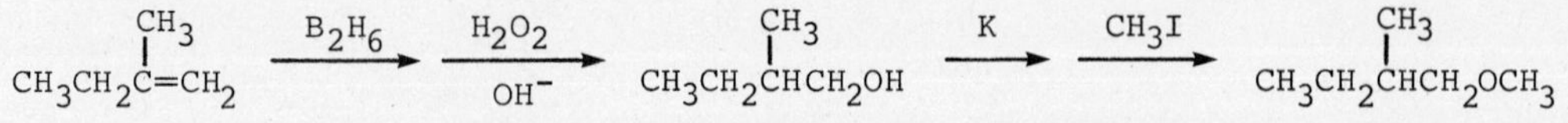

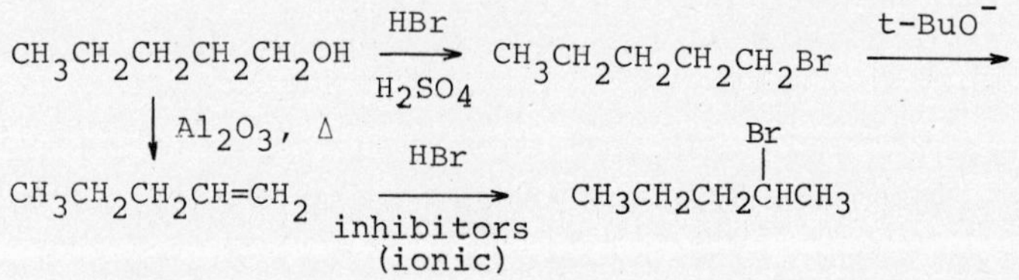

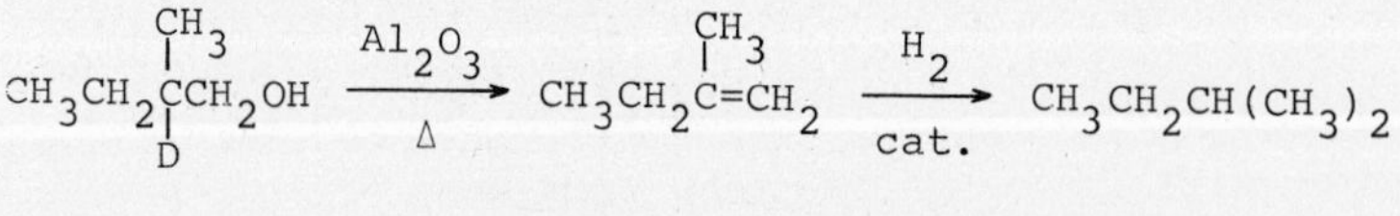

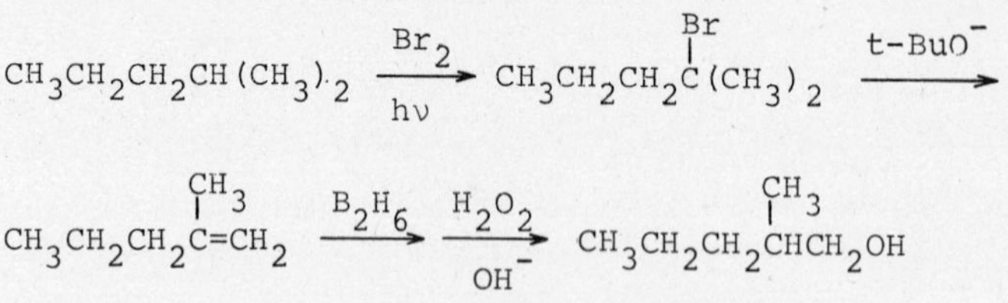

11. (a)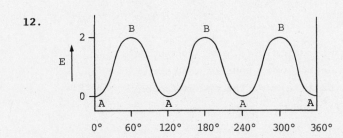

(b)

$$\underset{\text{Br}}{\overset{\text{Br}}{\bigcirc}} \xleftarrow[\text{CCl}_4]{\text{Br}_2} \bigcirc \xleftarrow[\Delta]{\text{H}_2\text{SO}_4} \overset{\text{OH}}{\bigcirc}$$

(c)

$$\text{HO}\diagdown\diagup\diagdown\diagup\text{OH} \xleftarrow[\text{2. NaBH}_4]{\text{1. O}_3}$$

(d)

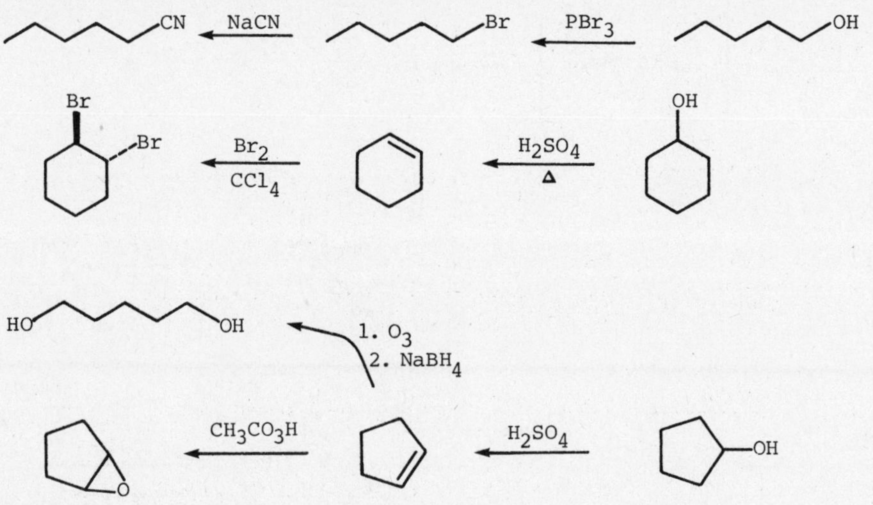

$$\overset{\triangle}{\underset{O}{\bigcirc}} \xleftarrow{\text{CH}_3\text{CO}_3\text{H}} \bigcirc \xleftarrow{\text{H}_2\text{SO}_4} \bigcirc\text{-OH}$$

12.

E ↑ (graph with peaks labeled B at ~60°, 180°, 300° and valleys labeled A at 0°, 120°, 240°, 360°, E axis marked 0 and 2)

0° 60° 120° 180° 240° 300° 360°

The angle plotted is the dihedral angle between the plane of the double bond and the $C-C_{methyl}-H$ plane.

13.   The structure of 4,4-dimethyl-2-pentene is:

cis   trans

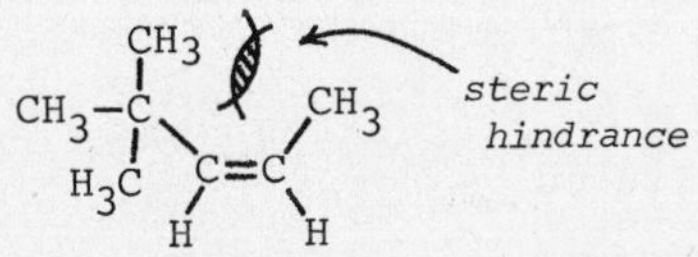

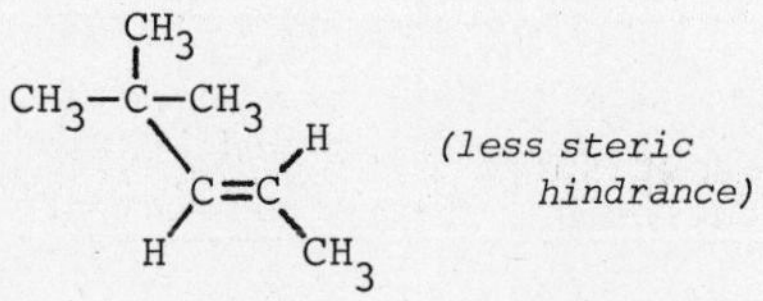

$$\underset{\text{H}_3\text{C}}{\overset{\text{CH}_3}{\text{CH}_3-\text{C}}}\underset{\text{H}}{\overset{\text{CH}_3}{\diagup}}\text{C}=\text{C}\underset{\text{H}}{\diagdown}$$ steric hindrance

$$\text{CH}_3-\overset{\text{CH}_3}{\underset{}{\text{C}}}-\text{CH}_3 \quad \overset{\text{H}}{\underset{\text{CH}_3}{\text{C}=\text{C}}}\overset{}{\underset{}{}}$$ (less steric hindrance)

In the cis isomer, the terminal methyl groups are close in space, and the electron clouds interact and repel each other (steric hindrance).

14.

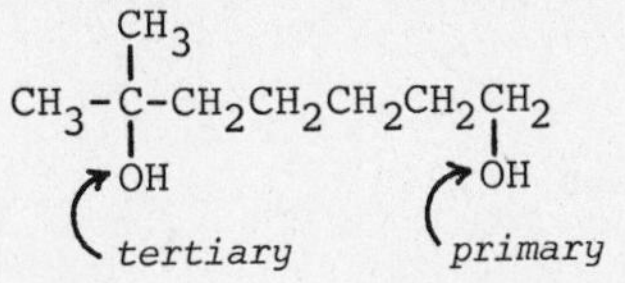

$$\text{CH}_3-\overset{\text{CH}_3}{\underset{\text{OH}}{\text{C}}}-\text{CH}_2\text{CH}_2\text{CH}_2\text{CH}_2\text{CH}_2$$
$$\overset{}{\underset{\text{OH}}{}}$$
tertiary   primary

The tertiary hydroxyl groups dehydrate readily under acid conditions via the relatively stable tert-carbocations. Primary hydroxyl groups dehydrate much less readily.

$$(\text{CH}_3)_2\underset{\text{OH}}{\overset{}{\text{C}}}(\text{CH}_2)_5\text{OH} + \text{H}^+ \longrightarrow (\text{CH}_3)_2\overset{+}{\text{C}}(\text{CH}_2)_5\text{OH} \longrightarrow (\text{CH}_3)_2\text{C}=\text{CH}(\text{CH}_2)_4\text{OH} + \text{some} \quad \overset{\text{CH}_3}{\underset{}{\text{CH}_2=\text{C}(\text{CH}_2)_5\text{OH}}}$$

15.   Both isomers are produced via the carbocation, $\overset{\text{CH}_3}{\underset{\text{CH}_3}{\overset{}{\text{C}}}}\overset{+}{-}\text{CH}_2\text{C}(\text{CH}_3)_3$.

Loss of a primary hydrogen gives

$$\overset{\text{CH}_3}{\underset{}{\text{CH}_2=\text{CCH}_2\text{C}(\text{CH}_3)_3}}$$, a disubstituted alkene with little steric hindrance. Loss of a sec-H gives a trisubstituted alkene with much steric hindrance between the adjacent methyl and t-butyl. Look at models!

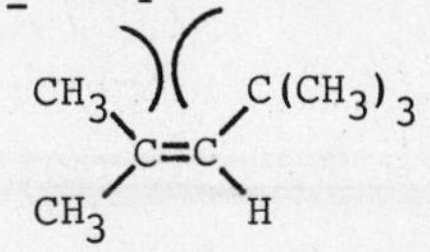

$$\underset{\text{CH}_3}{\overset{\text{CH}_3}{\text{C}=\text{C}}}\underset{\text{H}}{\overset{\text{C}(\text{CH}_3)_3}{}}$$

16.

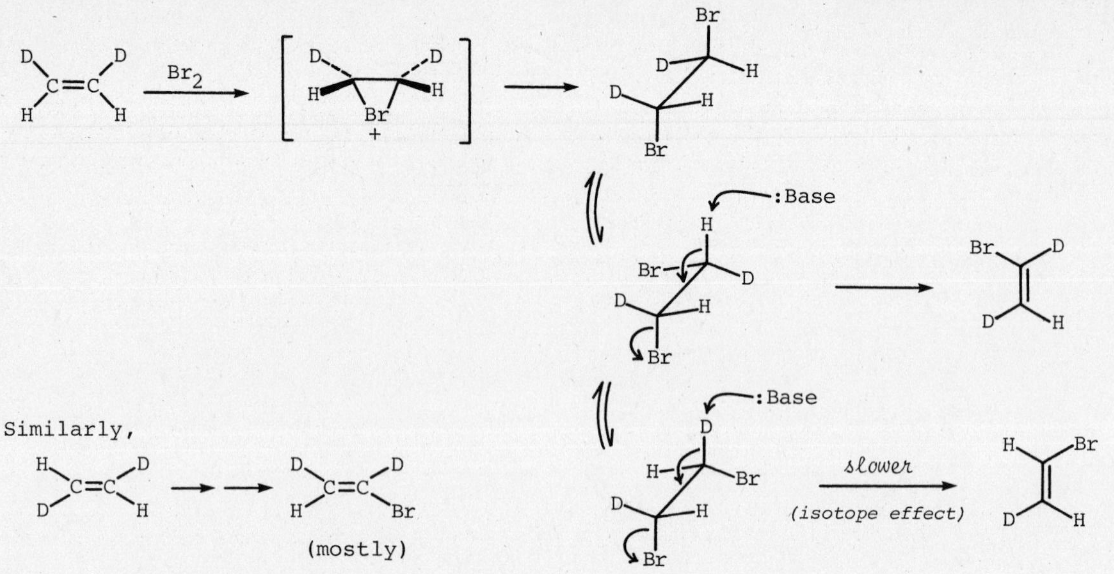

Similarly,

the reaction gives (mostly) the product shown.

17.

$CH_3CHBrCH_3$ reacts by two pathways:

S_N2 → $CH_3\overset{OC_2H_5}{\underset{|}{C}HCH_3}$

$E2$ → $CH_3CH=CH_2$

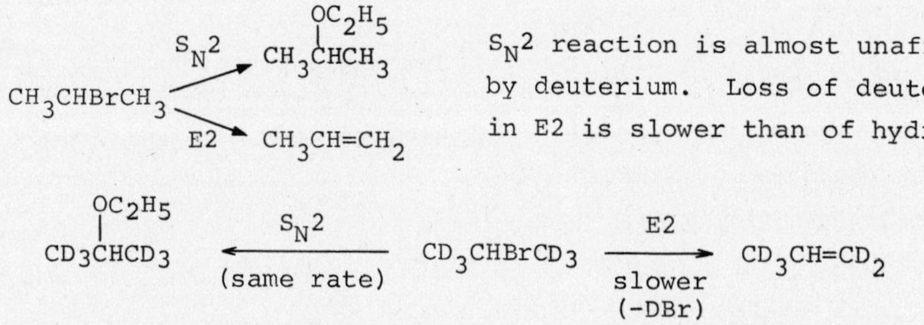

S_N2 reaction is almost unaffected by deuterium. Loss of deuterium in E2 is slower than of hydrogen.

$CD_3\overset{OC_2H_5}{\underset{|}{C}HCD_3}$ $\xleftarrow[\text{(same rate)}]{S_N2}$ $CD_3CHBrCD_3$ $\xrightarrow[\substack{\text{slower}\\(-DBr)}]{E2}$ $CD_3CH=CD_2$

The deuterium isotope effect, k_D/k_H (E2), $= \dfrac{1/2}{3/1} = 1/6$

18.

Monosubstituted ethylenes	$-\Delta H^\circ_{hydrog}$	Disubstituted ethylenes	$-\Delta H^\circ_{hydrog}$
propene	29.7	cis-2-butene	28.5
1-butene	30.2	cis-2-pentene	28.1
1-pentene	29.8	trans-2-butene	27.4
		trans-2-pentene	27.2
		2-methylpropene	28.1
		2-methyl-1-butene	28.3

Alkyl substitution on a double bond has a stabilizing effect (see Section 11.4), therefore less energy is released on hydrogenation of the alkylethylenes than for ethylene itself. Similarly, trans-alkenes are more stable than cis-alkenes, and they have less negative ΔH°_{hydrog}.

19.

$CH_3CH_2\overset{+}{C}HCH_3$
$+ Cl^-$

$CH_3CH_2CH=CH_2 + HCl$ (less stable)

$CH_3CH=CHCH_3 + HCl$ (more stable)

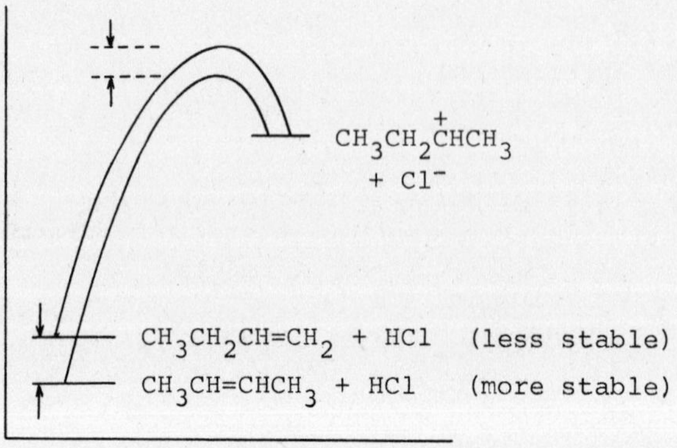

The difference in energies of the two transition states is probably less than the difference in energies of the two reactants. Thus, $\Delta H^{\ddagger}$ for 1-butene is smaller than $\Delta H^{\ddagger}$ for 2-butene, and 1-butene reacts more rapidly. On this basis, cis-2-butene should be more reactive than trans-2-butene. In general, when two isomers give the same intermediate or product via comparable transition states, the **less** stable isomer reacts **faster**, because it has a smaller energy barrier to overcome.

20.

$$CH_3CH_2CH_2\overset{\overset{\text{Br}}{|}}{C}HCH(CH_3)_2 \xrightarrow{\text{base}} CH_3CH_2CH_2CH=C\overset{CH_3}{\underset{CH_3}{\diagdown}} + CH_3CH_2CH=CHCH(CH_3)_2$$

$$C \qquad\qquad\qquad D + E, \; \underline{cis} + \underline{trans}$$

$$D + E \longrightarrow F + CH_3CH_2\overset{\overset{\text{OH}}{|}}{C}HCH_2CH(CH_3)_2 \qquad\qquad CH_3CH_2CH_2\overset{\overset{\text{OH}}{|}}{C}HCH(CH_3)_2$$

$$F$$

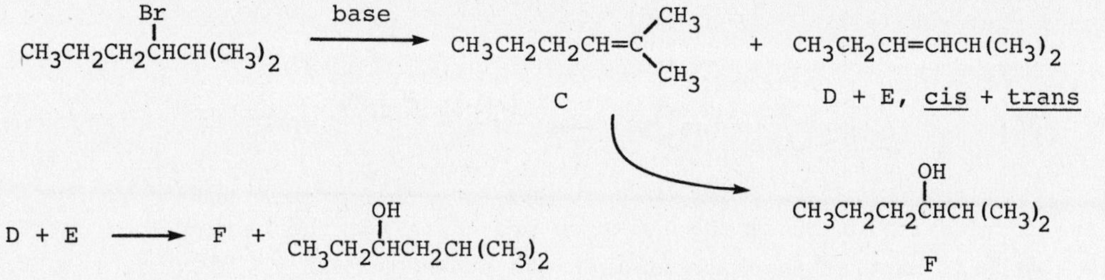

From the data given, we cannot determine whether D is cis or trans.

When working this type of "roadmap" problem, it helps to summarize the data in the following manner:

$$C_7H_{15}Br \xrightarrow{\text{base}} \underset{(C_7H_{14})}{C + D + E} \xrightarrow{H_2/\text{catalyst}} CH_3\overset{\overset{CH_3}{|}}{C}HCH_2CH_2CH_2CH_3$$

$$C \xrightarrow[]{B_2H_6} \xrightarrow[OH^-]{H_2O_2} F \quad (alcohol)$$

$$D + E \xrightarrow[]{B_2H_6} \xrightarrow[OH^-]{H_2O_2} F + G \quad (isomeric\ alcohol)$$
$$\text{about equal amounts}$$

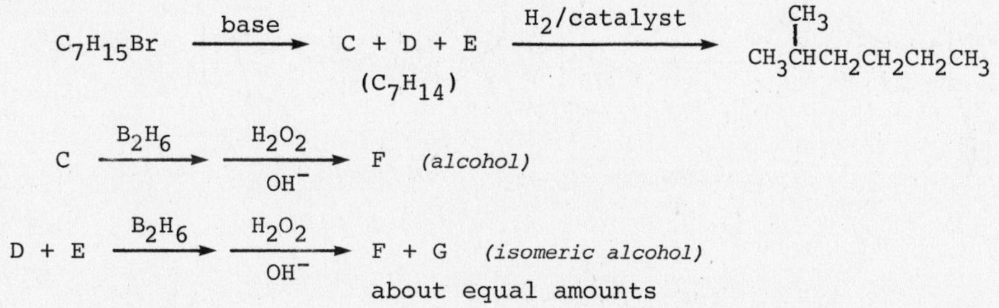

We can rule out 1-Br and 6-Br (E2 would give a single alkene), 2-Br, (E2 would give two alkenes), 4-Br (E2 would give four alkenes, two cis-trans pairs). For 5-Br,

$$(CH_3)_2CHCH_2CH_2\underset{\underset{\text{Br}}{|}}{C}HCH_3 \longrightarrow (CH_3)_2CHCH_2CH=CHCH_3 + (CH_3)_2CHCH_2CH_2CH=CH_2$$
$$cis \text{ and } trans$$

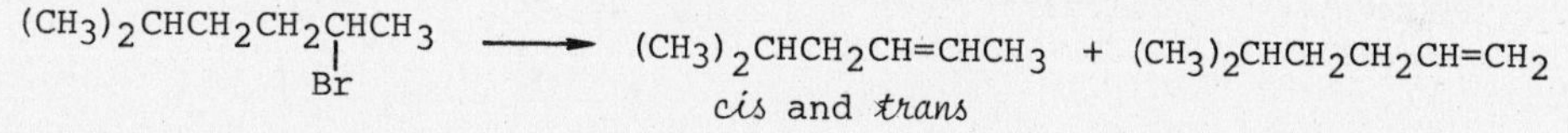

but with B_2H_6 and H_2O_2/OH^-, 5-methyl-1-hexene would give mainly 5-methyl-1-hexanol, and the 5-methyl-2-hexenes cannot give this alcohol. This leaves only $(CH_3)_2CH\underset{\underset{\text{Br}}{|}}{C}HCH_2CH_2CH_3$, which reacts as shown above.

21. (a)

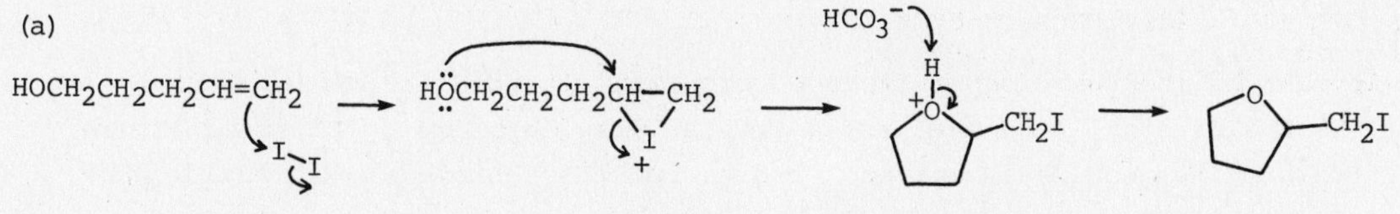

(b)

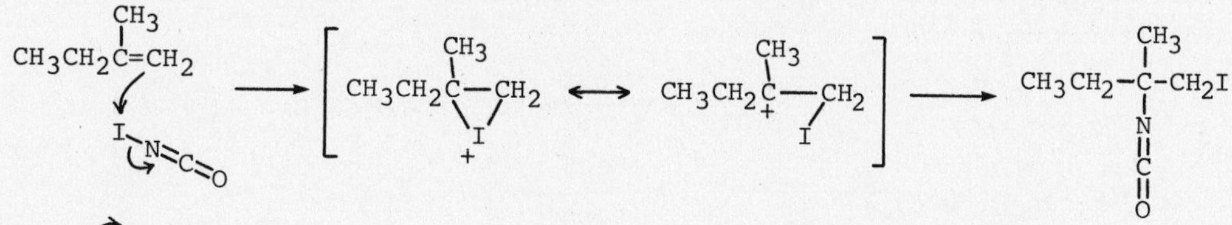

(c)

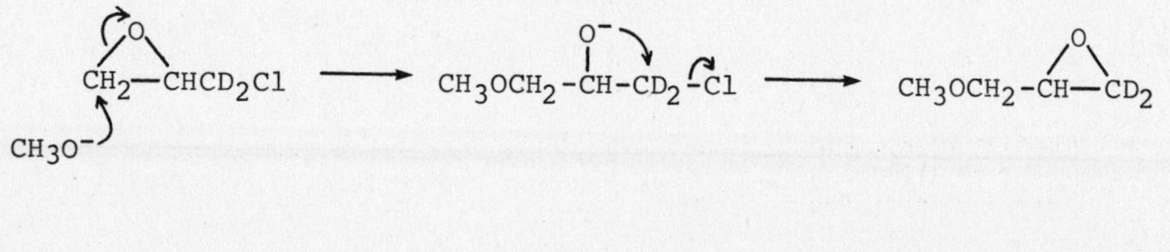

22. Attack from the top side of the molecule (as
shown at the right) is sterically hindered, so
the incoming reagent approaches from the bottom.
With m-chloroperbenzoic acid, the incoming
reagent is the peracid and the indicated epoxide
is formed preferentially:

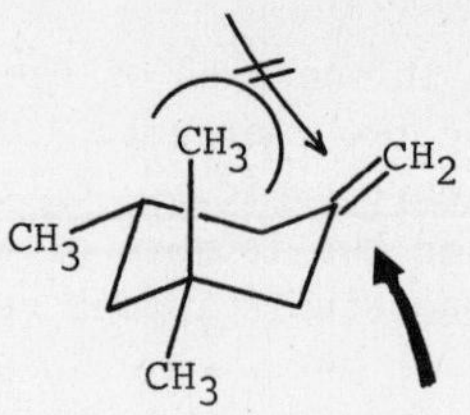

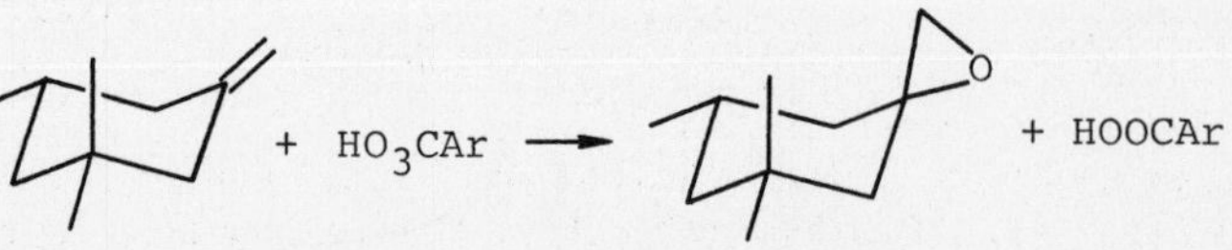

$$+ \ HO_3CAr \ \longrightarrow \ + \ HOOCAr$$

When the epoxide is formed in the two-step procedure via the bromohydrin, it
is the attack of bromine which determines the stereochemistry. Because
addition of water is *anti* to this, the final epoxide has the opposite
configuration:

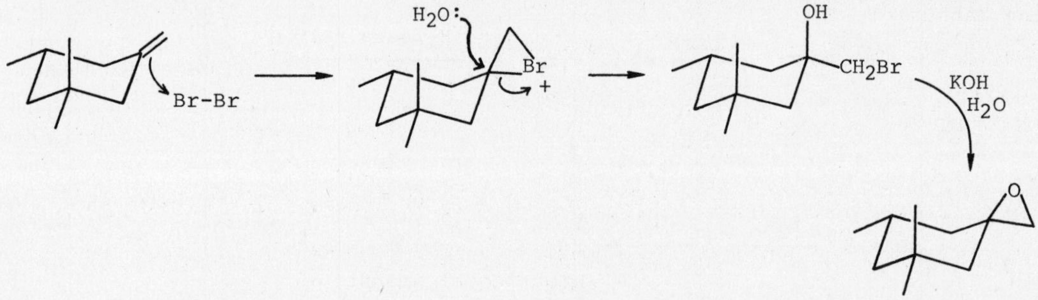

23.

$$\underset{C_{11}H_{24}O}{\underline{H}} \ \xrightarrow{PBr_3} \ \underset{C_{11}H_{23}Br}{\underline{I}} \ \xrightarrow[HOC_2H_5]{KOC_2H_5} \ \underset{C_{11}H_{22}}{\underline{J} \ (major)} \ + \ \underset{C_{11}H_{22}}{\underline{K} \ (minor)}$$

1. O_3
2. $NaBH_4$

The sequence:

1. O_3 2. $NaBH_4$ cleaves double
bonds and reduces the products
to alcohols, therefore $\underline{J}$ and $\underline{K}$
must be

$(CH_3)_2CHCH_2CH=CHCH_2CH_2CH(CH_3)_2$.

$(CH_3)_2CHCH_2OH$ $(CH_3)_2CHCH_2CH_2OH$

$\underline{J}$ must be the *trans* isomer (formed more easily) and $\underline{K}$ the *cis* isomer.
The 2,8-dimethyl-4-nonenes arose from an alkyl bromide by E2 elimination.
Two bromides could have given $\underline{J}$ and $\underline{K}$, but the 4-bromo isomer would have
given 2,8-dimethyl-3-nonene as well. Therefore $\underline{I}$ must be 5-bromo-2,8-
dimethylnonane and $\underline{H}$ must be the corresponding alcohol.

$$\underset{Br}{(CH_3)_2 CHCH_2 \overset{|}{C}HCH_2CH_2CH_2CH(CH_3)_2} \ \xrightarrow[HOC_2H_5]{KOC_2H_5} \ (CH_3)_2CHCH=CHCH_2CH_2CH_2CH(CH_3)_2$$

$+ \ \underline{J} \ \text{and} \ \underline{K}$

$$\underset{Br}{(CH_3)_2 CHCH_2CH_2\overset{|}{C}HCH_2CH_2CH(CH_3)_2} \ \xrightarrow[HOC_2H_5]{KOC_2H_5} \ \underline{J} \ \text{and} \ \underline{K} \ \text{only}$$

$\underline{I}$

$$\underset{OH}{(CH_3)_2CHCH_2CH_2\overset{|}{C}HCH_2CH_2CH(CH_3)_2}$$

$\underline{H}$

24.

optically active

achiral,
∴ optically inactive
isomer

chiral, ∴
optically active isomer

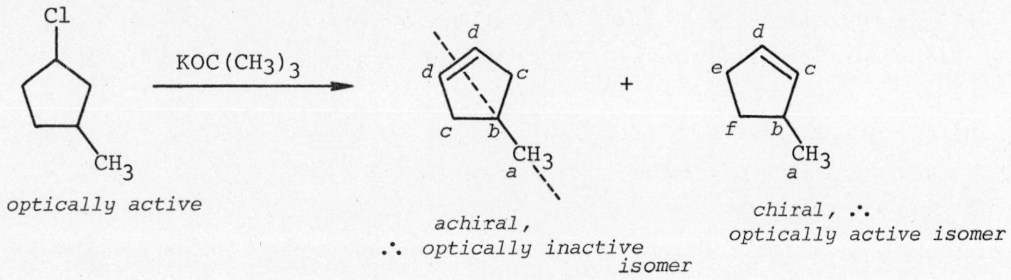

25. <u>Both</u> reactions must have ΔH^O that is not too positive; otherwise, $E^{\ddagger}$ is too high and reaction will be slow. For Y = Br, HS, $(CH_3)_3C$, both ΔH^O's are negative (exothermic), and both steps should be facile. For Y = I, the first step (a) has ΔH^O = +5 kcal mole^{-1}; the activation energy is at least this high, but this reaction could still be possible. For the other compounds, one step or the other is no good; that is, one ΔH^O is so positive that the reaction has a high activation energy and is slow.

26. $\Delta H^{\circ}_f (CH_3CH{=}CH_2)$ = 4.9 kcal mole^{-1} *(Appendix I)*

$\Delta H^{\circ}_f (\cdot CN)$ = 99 kcal mole^{-1} *(Appendix II)*

$\Delta H^{\circ}_f (HCN)$ = $\Delta H^{\circ}_f (H\cdot) + \Delta H^{\circ}_f (\cdot CN) - DH^{\circ}(H{-}CN)$
          = 52 + 104 - 125 = 31 kcal mole^{-1} *(also given in Appendix I)*

$\Delta H^{\circ}_f (CH_3CH_2CH_2CN)$ = $\Delta H^{\circ}_f (CH_3CH_2CN) + \Delta H^{\circ}_f (-CH_2-)$
              = 12.1 - 5.0 = 7.1 kcal mole^{-1} *(see problem #16, Chapter 5)*

$\Delta H^{\circ}_f (CH_3\overset{\bullet}{C}HCH_2CN)$ = $\Delta H^{\circ}_f (CH_3CH_2CH_2CN) + DH^{\circ}(CH_3\underset{H}{C}HCH_2CN) - \Delta H^{\circ}_f (H\cdot)$
              = 7 + 95 - 52 = 50 kcal mole^{-1}

(a) $CH_3-CH{=}CH_2$ + HCN $\longrightarrow$ $CH_3CH_2CH_2CN$
     ΔH°_f =   4.9   31   7 ΔH°_f = -29 kcal mole^{-1}

(b) *STEP 1:* $CH_3CH{=}CH_2$ + $\cdot CN$ $\longrightarrow$ $CH_3\overset{\bullet}{C}HCH_2CN$
          ΔH°_f =   4.9   104   50 ΔH°_f = -59 kcal mole^{-1}

 STEP 2: $CH_3\overset{\bullet}{C}HCH_2CN$ + HCN $\longrightarrow$ $CH_3CH_2CH_2CN$ + $\cdot CN$
          ΔH°_f =   50   31   7   104 ΔH° = +30 kcal mole^{-1}

(c) The overall reaction is exothermic, but the second step is far too endothermic. The intermediate $CH_3\overset{\bullet}{C}HCH_2CN$ radicals would dimerize rather than abstract H from HCN.

11.F Supplementary Problems

S1. Write structures for the following compounds:

    (a) <u>cis</u>-3-methyl-2-heptene   (e) (<u>Z</u>)-3-bromo-3-hexene

    (b) (<u>R</u>)-5-methylhex-4-en-2-ol   (f) 1-chloro-6-methylcyclohexene

    (c) (<u>Z</u>)-4-methyl-2-pentene   (g) (<u>E</u>)-cyclododecene

    (d) (<u>E</u>)-5-chloro-3-isopropyl-5-methyl-2-hexene

S2. Show how to accomplish the following transformations in a practical manner (more than one step is necessary in each case).

    (a) $CH_3CH_2CH_2CH_2OH$ $\longrightarrow$ $CH_3CH_2\underset{OH}{\overset{}{C}}HCH_3$ (b)

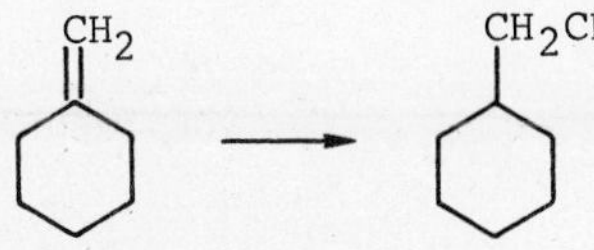

(c) $CH_3CH=CH_2 \longrightarrow$

(f)

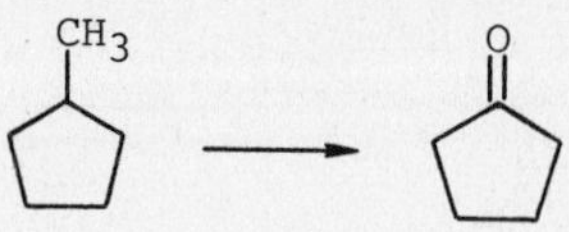

(d)

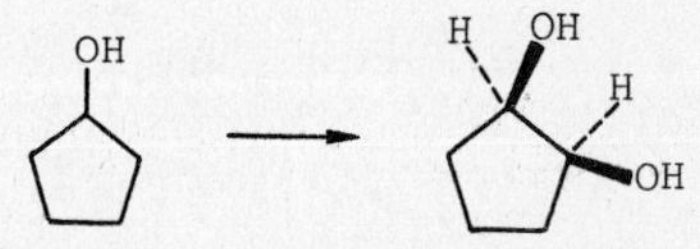

(g)

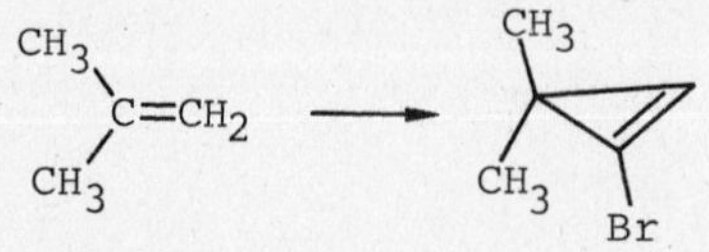

(e)

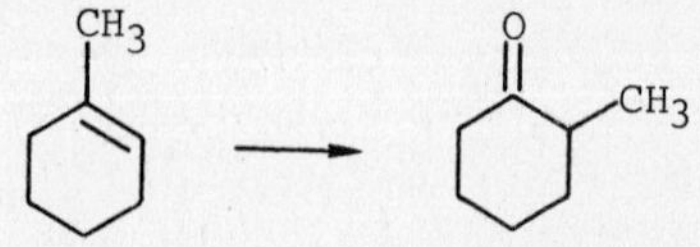

(h)

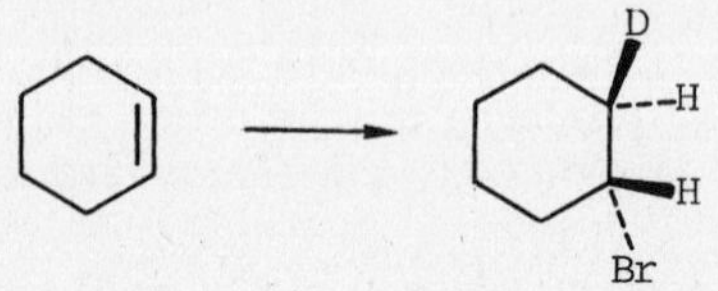

*(without any of
the cis isomer)*

S3. Predict the product from the reaction of iodinemonochloride (ICl) with
     1-methylcyclohexene, and justify your choice by writing a step-by-step
     mechanism for its formation.

S4. Predict the major products from the following reaction sequences.

(a) 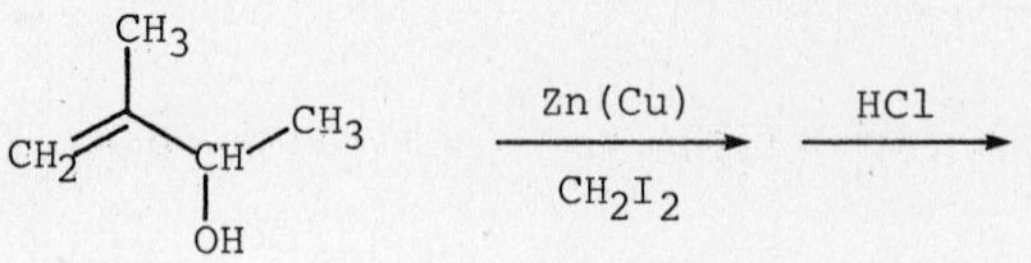
$$\xrightarrow[CH_2I_2]{Zn(Cu)} \xrightarrow{HCl}$$

(b) 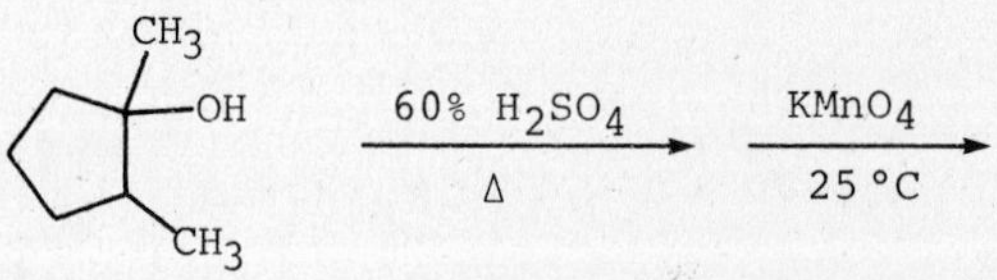
$$\xrightarrow[\Delta]{60\% \ H_2SO_4} \xrightarrow[25\,°C]{KMnO_4}$$

(c) $CH_3CH_2CH=CHC(CH_3)_3 \xrightarrow[HOC_2H_5]{Hg(OAc)_2} \xrightarrow{NaBH_4}$

(d) $(CH_3)_2C=CHCH_3 \xrightarrow[CH_3OH]{Br_2} \xrightarrow[HOC_2H_5]{KOC_2H_5} \xrightarrow[Pt]{D_2}$

S5. A hydrocarbon (**A**) of formula C_7H_{12} was treated successively with diborane and alkaline hydrogen
     peroxide to provide compound **B** ($C_7H_{14}O$) as the only product. Reaction of **B** with p-toluene-
     sulfonyl chloride and pyridine, and then with potassium t-butoxide in t-butyl alcohol gave an
     isomeric hydrocarbon **C** (C_7H_{12}). Finally, treatment of **C** with ozone in methanol, followed by
     work-up using sodium borohydride, afforded 2-methyl-1,6-hexanediol.
     Write complete structures for **A**, **B**, and **C** which are consistent with this information.

S6. Write a reasonable mechanism for the following transformation:

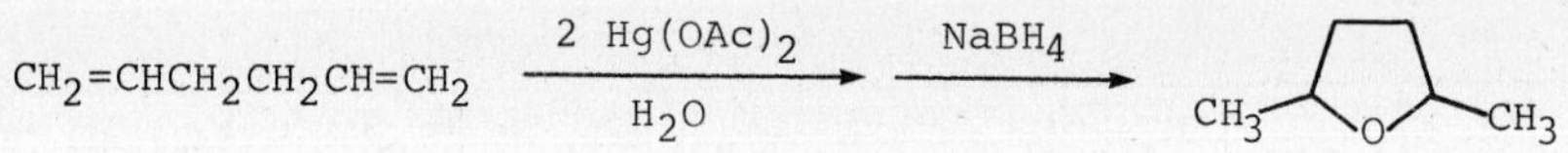

$$CH_2=CHCH_2CH_2CH=CH_2 \xrightarrow[H_2O]{2 \ Hg(OAc)_2} \xrightarrow{NaBH_4}$$

S7. The bond dissociation energy for H–SH is 90 kcal mole^{-1}. Using this value and Appendices I and II, determine H^O for each step in the free radical addition of H_2S to ethylene. Is the proposed reaction feasible by this mechanism?

S8. Using Appendices I and II, determine whether the free radical addition of water to ethylene to give ethanol is feasible thermodynamically.

11.G   Answers to Supplementary Problems

S1. (a)

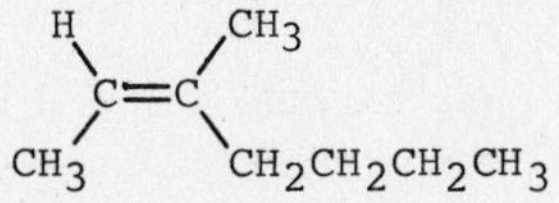

(b)

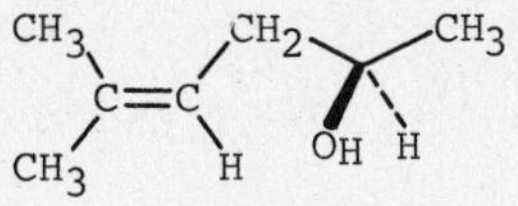

(c)

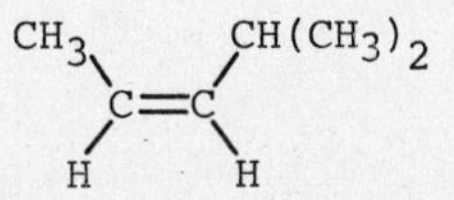

(d)

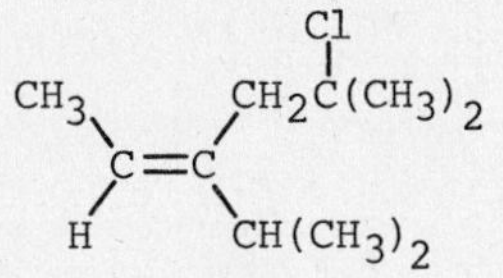

(e)

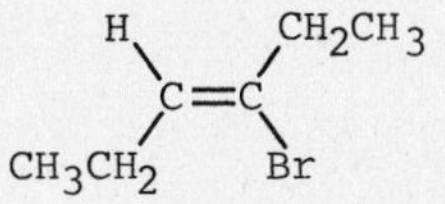

(f)

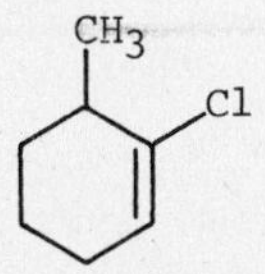

(g)

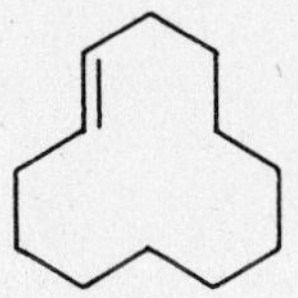

S2. (a) $CH_3CH_2CH_2CH_2OH \xrightarrow[400°]{Al_2O_3} CH_3CH_2CH=CH_2 \xrightarrow[H_2O]{H_2SO_4} CH_3CH_2\underset{\underset{OH}{|}}{C}HCH_3$

(b)

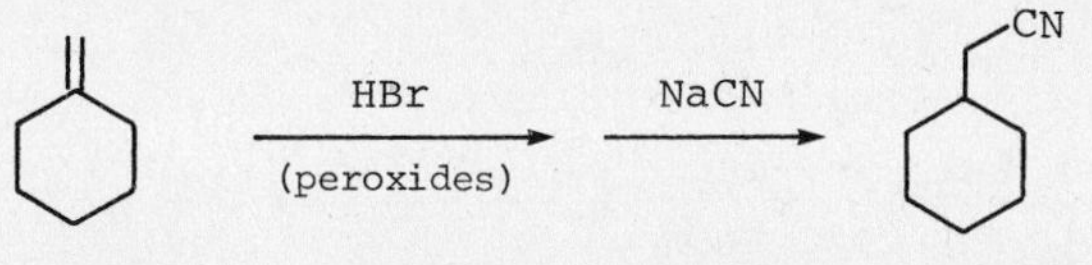

(c) $CH_3CH=CH_2 \xrightarrow[2.\ NaSH]{1.\ HCl} CH_3\underset{\overset{|}{SH}}{C}HCH_3 \xrightarrow[\substack{100° \\ [O_2]}]{CH_3CH=CH_2} (CH_3)_2CH-S-CH_2CH_2CH_3$

(d)

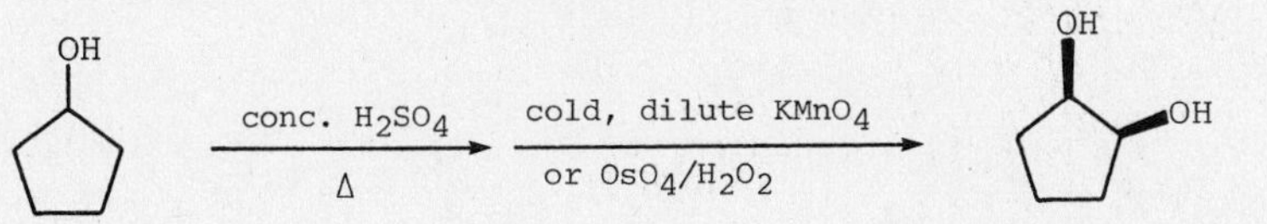

(e)

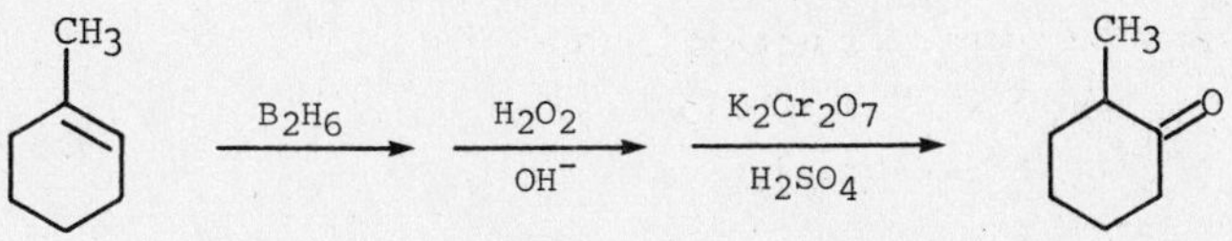

(f)

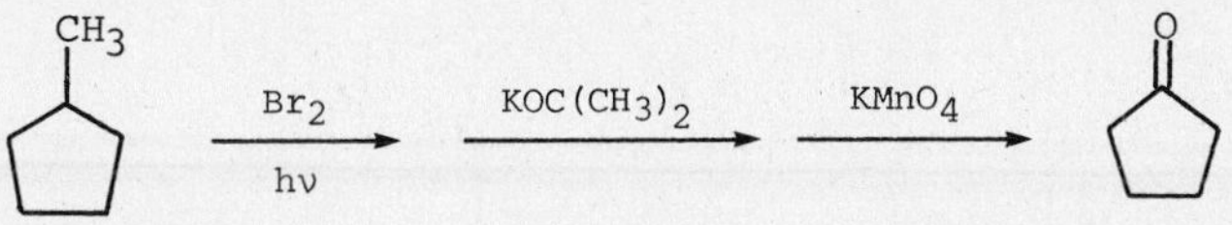

(g) 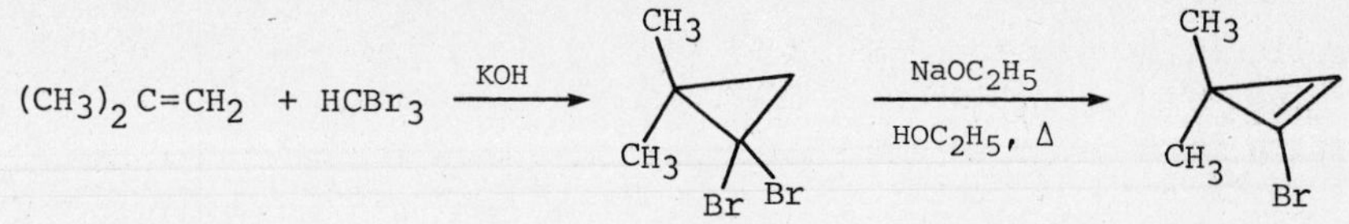 $(CH_3)_2C=CH_2$ + $HCBr_3$ $\xrightarrow{KOH}$ $\xrightarrow[HOC_2H_5, \Delta]{NaOC_2H_5}$

(h) 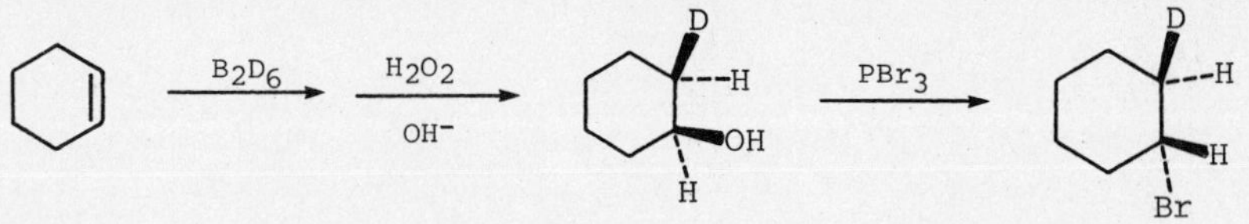 $\xrightarrow{B_2D_6}$ $\xrightarrow[OH^-]{H_2O_2}$ $\xrightarrow{PBr_3}$

S3.

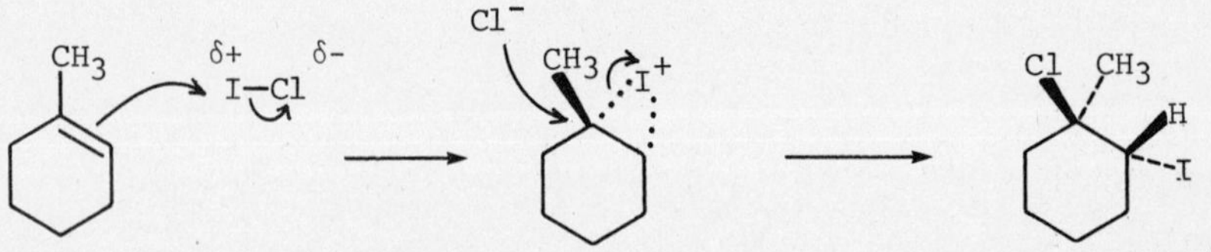

Anti addition,
Markovnikov
orientation

S4. (a)

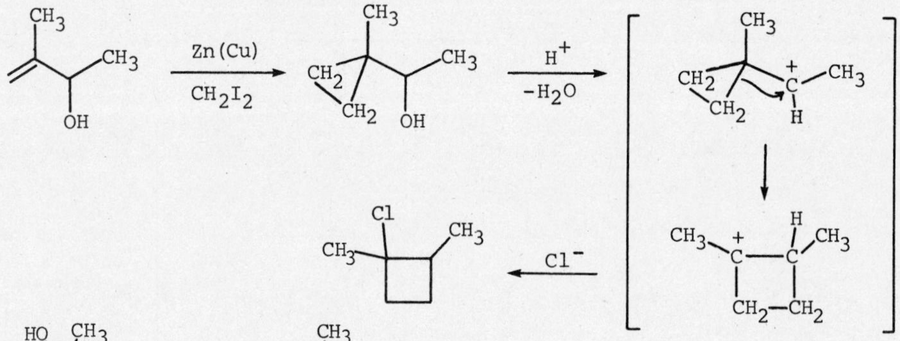

(b)

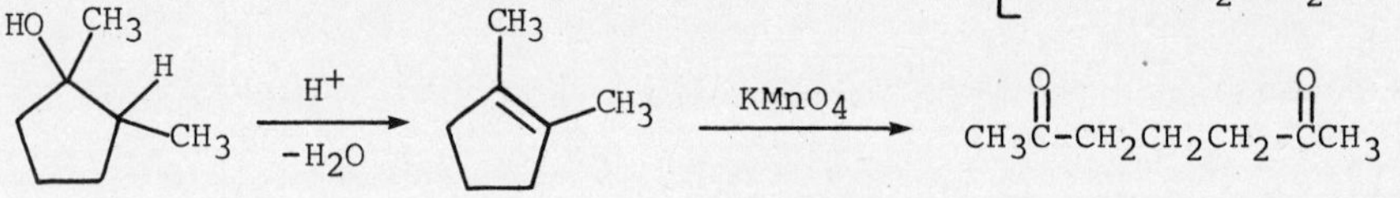

(c) 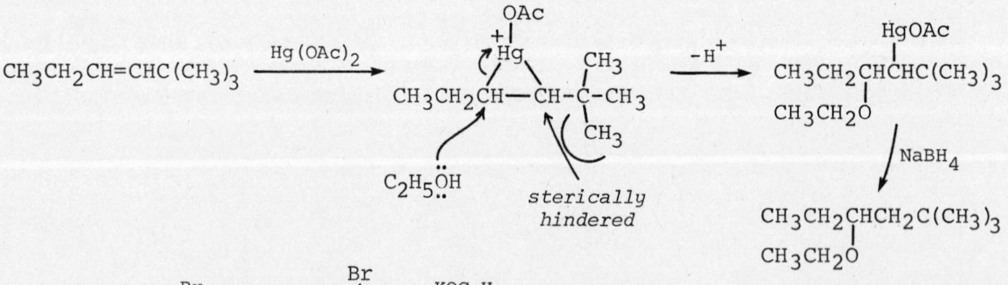 $CH_3CH_2CH=CHC(CH_3)_3$ $\xrightarrow{Hg(OAc)_2}$ $\xrightarrow{-H^+}$ $\xrightarrow{NaBH_4}$

(d) 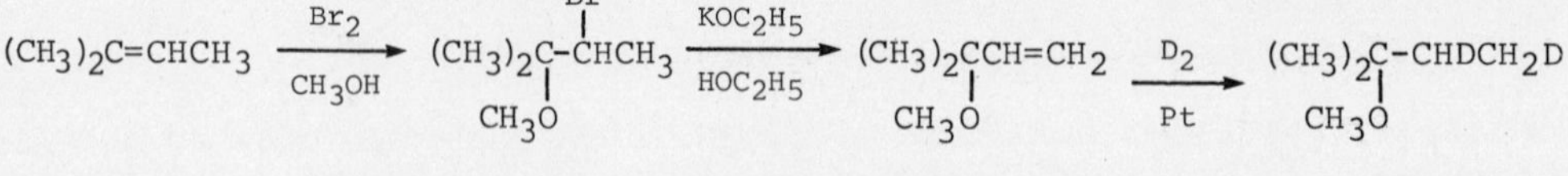 $(CH_3)_2C=CHCH_3$ $\xrightarrow{Br_2}{CH_3OH}$ $\xrightarrow[HOC_2H_5]{KOC_2H_5}$ $\xrightarrow{D_2}{Pt}$

S5.

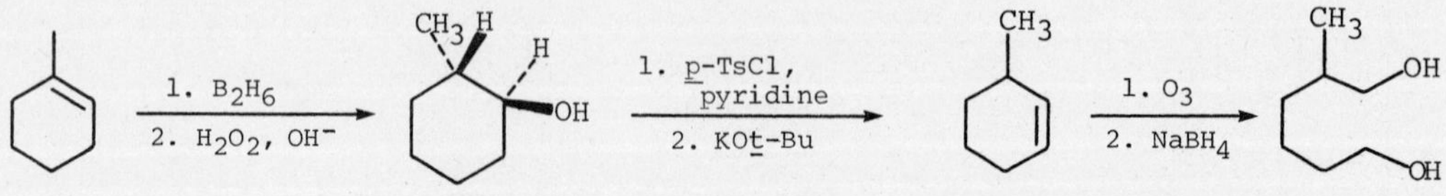

S6.

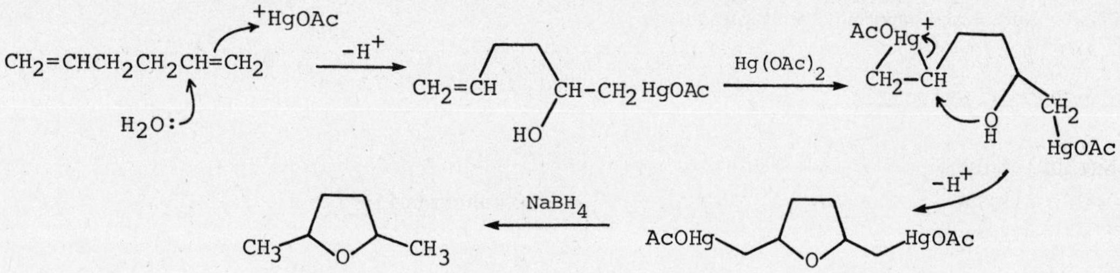

S7. $\Delta H^\circ_f (\cdot CH_2CH_2SH) = \Delta H^\circ_f (CH_3CH_2SH) + DH^\circ (\text{primary C-H}) - \Delta H^\circ_f (H\cdot)$
$$= -11 + 98 - 52 = 35 \text{ kcal mole}^{-1}$$

$$CH_2=CH_2 + \cdot SH \longrightarrow \cdot CH_2CH_2SH$$
$\Delta H^\circ_f = \quad\; 12.5 \qquad 34 \qquad\qquad 35 \qquad\qquad \Delta H^\circ = -12 \text{ kcal mole}^{-1}$

$$\cdot CH_2CH_2SH + H_2S \longrightarrow CH_3CH_2SH + HS\cdot$$
$\Delta H^\circ_f = \quad 35 \qquad\quad -4.8 \qquad\qquad -11 \qquad\; 34 \qquad \Delta H^\circ = -7 \text{ kcal mole}^{-1}$

The proposed reaction is clearly feasible, because each step is exothermic.

S8. $\Delta H^\circ_f (\cdot CH_2CH_2OH) \cong \Delta H^\circ_f (CH_3CH_2OH) + DH^\circ (\text{primary C-H}) - \Delta H^\circ_f (H\cdot)$
$$= -56 + 98 - 52 = -10 \text{ kcal mole}^{-1}$$

$$CH_2=CH_2 + \cdot OH \longrightarrow \cdot CH_2CH_2OH$$
$\Delta H^\circ_f = \quad\; 12.5 \qquad 9.4 \qquad\qquad -10 \qquad\qquad \Delta H^\circ = -32 \text{ kcal mole}^{-1}$

$$\cdot CH_2CH_2OH + H_2O \longrightarrow CH_3CH_2OH + \cdot OH$$
$\Delta H^\circ_f = \quad\;\; -10 \qquad\;\; -57.8 \qquad\qquad -56.2 \qquad 9.4 \qquad \Delta H^\circ = +21 \text{ kcal mole}^{-1}$

The second step is too endothermic for this mechanism of hydration to be feasible.

12. ALKYNES AND NITRILES

Alkylation of acetylide and cyanide anions (12.5.B)

Equation:

$$R-C\equiv C-H + M^+Base^- \longrightarrow Base-H + R-C\equiv C{:}^-M^+ \xrightarrow{\;R'X\;} R-C\equiv C-R' + MX$$
$$N\equiv C{:}^-M^+ \xrightarrow{\quad''\quad} N\equiv C-R' + MX$$

Generality: R = H, alkyl, aryl
                M^+Base^- = $NaNH_2$, butyllithium, $R''MgX$
                for acetylene alkylation: R'X = 1^0 alkyl halide or sulfonate (otherwise E2)
                for cyanide alkylation: R'X = 1^0 or 2^0 alkyl halide or sulfonate
                    (E2 with R = 3^0 alkyl)

Key features: important carbon-carbon bond-forming process

Synthesis and isomerization of alkynes via elimination (12.5.C)
Equation:

$$\left.\begin{array}{c} R-CHX-CHX-R' \\ or \\ R-CX_2-CH_2-R' \end{array}\right\} \xrightarrow[\text{base}]{\text{strong}} R-CX=CH-R' \xrightarrow[\text{base}]{\text{strong}} R-C\equiv C-R'$$

Generality: R = H, alkyl, or aryl; X = Cl, Br, I
                strong base = very hot KOH or KOR, or $NaNH_2$

Key features: reaction can be stopped after first elimination
triple bond isomerization often occurs:

$$R-C\equiv C-CH_3 \underset{KOH, \Delta}{\overset{1.\ NaNH_2\ or\ KAPA,\ 2.\ H_2O}{\rightleftharpoons}} R-CH_2-C\equiv CH$$

Partial hydrogenation of alkynes: cis (12.6.A)

Equation:

$$R-C\equiv C-R' \xrightarrow{H_2/catalyst} \underset{H}{\overset{R}{\diagdown}}C=C\underset{H}{\overset{R'}{\diagup}}$$

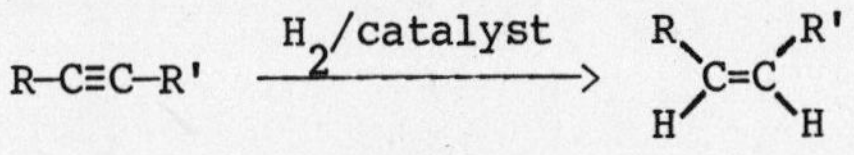

Generality: R = H, alkyl, or aryl
catalyst = Pd/BaSO$_4$ + poison (= quinoline) or Ni-B

Key features: syn addition of hydrogens gives cis stereochemistry

Partial reduction of alkynes: trans (12.6.A)

Equation:

$$R-C\equiv C-R' \xrightarrow{[H]} \underset{H}{\overset{R}{\diagdown}}C=C\underset{R'}{\overset{H}{\diagup}}$$

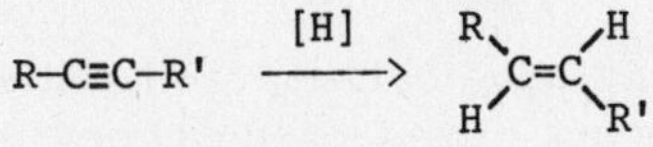

Generality: R = H or alkyl
[H] = Na or Li in liquid NH$_3$, or LiAlH$_4$

Key features: trans stereospecificity

Reduction of nitriles (12.6.A)

Equation: $R-C\equiv N \longrightarrow R-CH_2-NH_2$

Generality: R = alkyl or aryl
[H] = H$_2$/Pt, H$_2$/Ni, or LiAlH$_4$

Hydration of alkynes: mercuric ion catalyzed addition of H$_2$O (12.6.B)

Equation:

$$R-C\equiv C-R' + H_2O \xrightarrow[H_2SO_4]{Hg^{+2}} R-\overset{O}{\overset{\|}{C}}-CH_2-R'$$

Generality: R = alkyl or aryl; R' = H, alkyl, or aryl

Key features: Markovnikov orientation
works best if R' = H or same as R (otherwise gives mixture of isomers)
mechanism involves enol (vinyl alcohol) intermediate

Hydration of alkynes via hydroboration (12.6.D)

Equation:

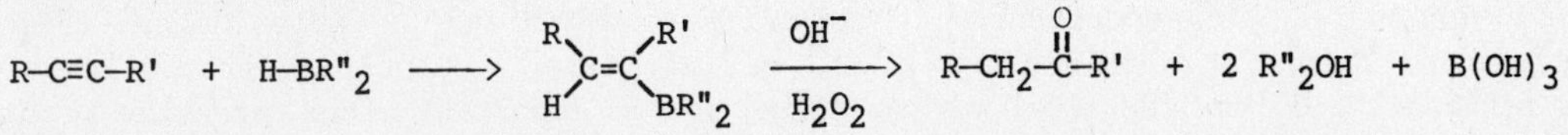

$$R-C\equiv C-R' + H-BR''_2 \longrightarrow \underset{H}{\overset{R}{\diagdown}}C=C\underset{BR''_2}{\overset{R'}{\diagup}} \xrightarrow[H_2O_2]{OH^-} R-CH_2-\overset{O}{\overset{\|}{C}}-R' + 2\ R''_2OH + B(OH)_3$$

Generality: R = alkyl or aryl, R' = H, alkyl, or aryl
R" = H (B$_2$H$_6$ $\rightleftharpoons$ 2 BH$_3$) or alkyl or other alkenyl groups

Key features: "anti-Markovnikov" orientation
works best if R' = H or same as R (otherwise gives mixture of isomers)
mechanism involves enol (vinyl alcohol) intermediate

Addition of HX to alkynes (12.6.B)

Equation:

$$R-C\equiv C-R' + HX \longrightarrow R-CX=CH-R' \xrightarrow{HX} R-CX_2-CH_2-R'$$

Generality: R, R' = H, alkyl, or aryl
X = Cl, Br

Key features: Markovnikov orientation

can be stopped after one addition step

<u>Hydration</u> <u>of</u> <u>nitriles</u>   (12.6.C)

Equation:

$$R-C\equiv N \xrightarrow{\;H_2O\;} R-\overset{\overset{\displaystyle O}{\|}}{C}-NH_2$$

Generality: requires either acid (e.g. aq. H_2SO_4) or base (e.g. aq. NaOH) catalysis

12.C   Important Concepts and Hints

<u>Chemistry</u> <u>of</u> <u>Alkynes</u>.   Because the chemistry of alkynes is so similar to that of alkenes, it is useful to focus on the contrasts. Look particularly at reduction methods: you can hydrogenate alkynes with <u>syn</u> delivery of H_2, just as you can in alkene chemistry. However, with alkynes there is the added complication of stopping after the first addition or not, depending on the catalyst you use. Sodium in ammonia reduces alkynes (to <u>trans</u> alkenes), but does not reduce ordinary alkenes.

Electrophilic addition to alkynes is subject to the same orientation and stereochemical effects as alkenes (Markovnikov or anti-Markovnikov, <u>syn</u> or <u>anti</u> or neither). There are two complications: with alkynes the addition can occur **twice**, and the hydration reactions (Markovnikov-oriented with Hg^{++}, dil. H_2SO_4, or anti-Markovnikov with B_2H_6/H_2O_2, OH^-) do not lead to alcohols but to ketones or aldehydes instead.

$NaNH_2$ vs. Na, NH_3.   Much of the chemistry of alkynes involves either sodium amide or sodium in ammonia as reagents, and students get confused over the difference between them. Sodium amide is a salt, comprised of the sodium cation (Na^+) and amide anion (NH_2^-), and it is often used when a very strong base is required ($NH_3 \rightleftharpoons NH_2^- + H^+$; $pK_a = 34$). Benzene, or liquid ammonia itself, is frequently employed as solvent for reactions involving $NaNH_2$.

When sodium <u>metal</u> (Na^o) is dissolved in liquid ammonia, it ionizes to give a dark blue solution of sodium cations (Na^+) and solvated electrons (e^-). The solvated electron is a powerful reducing agent; it is for this purpose that "sodium in ammonia" (Na,NH_3) is used.

<u>Organic</u> <u>Synthesis</u>.   In the chapter on alkynes, you encounter the first reaction that is useful for formation of carbon-carbon bonds: alkylation of acetylide anions with alkyl halides. Reactions such as this are important because they allow you to build larger molecules, instead of just interchanging functional groups. There are limitations to be sure -- the alkyl halide must be primary and unhindered, and there cannot be functional groups elsewhere which are sensitive to strong base in the molecule.

Now that you know a way to build large molecules from small ones, you will encounter a very important learning device -- synthetic problems. These questions ask you to devise a way to make the target compound starting from simpler materials. From the beginning of alchemy to the present day, finding ways to turn simpler (or cheaper) compounds into more complicated (or expensive) ones has been a major pursuit of chemists. When you have learned a greater variety of carbon-carbon bond forming reactions and functional group interconversions, a whole chapter in the text will be devoted to Organic Synthesis (Chapter 16). At this time, it is still worthwhile to get you started on synthesis problems the right way by giving you an important hint: work the problems **backwards**.

When you want to go somewhere you've never been before, you find your destination on a map and work your way backward to where you are, before you actually set out. You don't just climb on the first bus that goes by your house, or drive down the first freeway you see, and <u>then</u> determine whether it's going to your destination. The same is true for synthesis problems -- don't take the starting materials and see what you can turn them into, hoping eventually to bump into the target. You should look at the target and think what its immediate precursor could be. Look for appropriate places for carbon-carbon bond-forming reactions, and work your way backwards to simpler compounds until you get to the starting materials (a lot more will be said on this subject when you reach Chapter 16).

<u>Road-Map</u> <u>Problems</u>.   You will also encounter problems which give you an idea of how to figure out the structure of a compound by chemical methods. These are called road-map problems (sometimes they seem more like road-block problems....), and are actually just puzzles that need to be solved

logically from the clues given. The best way to approach them is to be organized: write down schematically all the information presented in words in the problem. Then, look for the compound about which the most is known relative to the possibilities for it. If the structure of this key compound is actually provided, or if you can figure out what it is, work your way outward from that point as logically as you can. The best advice is to be systematic. Problem #16 and its answer are a good example of this approach.

Degrees of Unsaturation. In solving road-map problems, one particular point is important -- using the formula to deduce "degrees of unsaturation". A degree of unsaturation can be a ring or a π-bond. Both C=C and C=O double bonds are unsaturations; a C≡C triple bond is **two** unsaturations. For hydrocarbons and oxygen-containing compounds, the formula tells you directly the number of degrees of unsaturation: for every two hydrogens less than (2 x number of carbons + 2) there is one unsaturation. For instance, $C_7H_{10}O_2$ has three degrees of unsaturation, and it could be represented by the following possibilities (as well as many others):

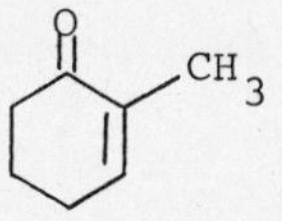

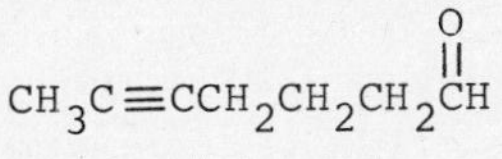

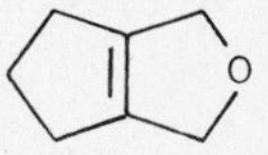

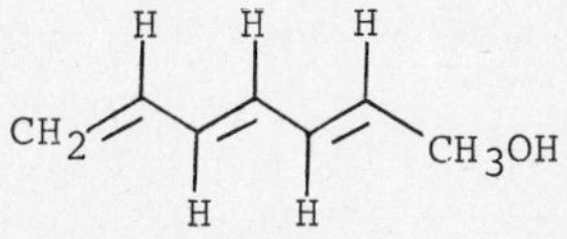

When halogens are present in the molecule, simply count them as hydrogens; e.g., $C_3H_5Br_2Cl$ is saturated ($CH_3-CHCl-CHBr_2$ is one possibility). When nitrogens are present, ignore them but also subtract one hydrogen for each nitrogen; $C_5H_{11}N$: and $CH_3CH_2CH_2CH_2CH=NH$ each have one unsaturation.

You can't distinguish the different types of unsaturation (π-bond or ring) from the formula, but there are often clues given from reactions that a compound undergoes. For example, hydrogenation usually removes only C=C or C≡C unsaturation, not rings or C=O. (We say usually because cyclopropane rings and ketones and aldehydes can be reduced under vigorous hydrogenation conditions.)

12.D   Answers to Exercises

12.1 $HC≡CCH_2CH_2CH_2OH$
      4-pentyn-1-ol

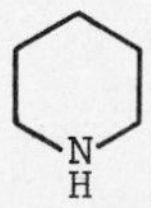

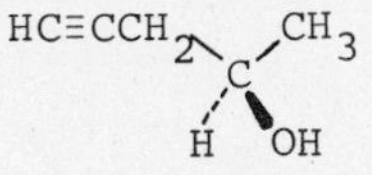

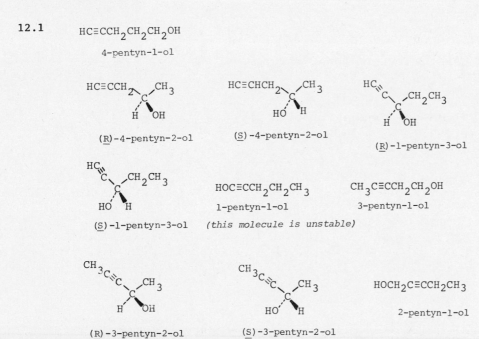

(R)-4-pentyn-2-ol   (S)-4-pentyn-2-ol   (R)-1-pentyn-3-ol

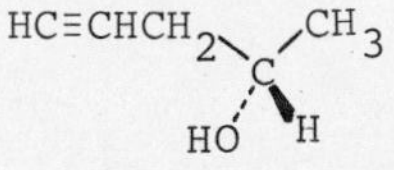

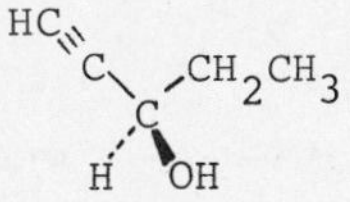

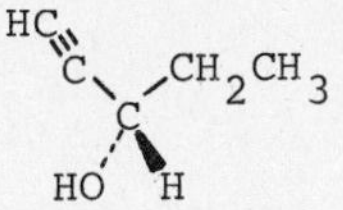

(S)-1-pentyn-3-ol $HOC≡CCH_2CH_2CH_3$ $CH_3C≡CCH_2CH_2OH$
               1-pentyn-1-ol   3-pentyn-1-ol
          (this molecule is unstable)

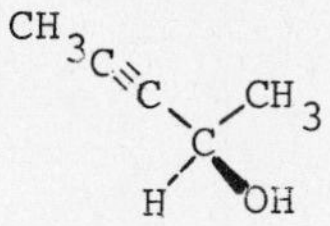

(R)-3-pentyn-2-ol   (S)-3-pentyn-2-ol $HOCH_2C≡CCH_2CH_3$
                                 2-pentyn-1-ol

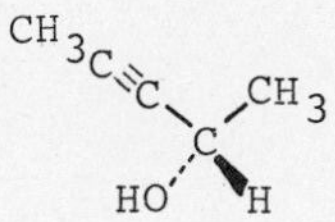

12.2 (a) $CH_3\text{-}C\equiv C\text{-}CH_3$ (b) 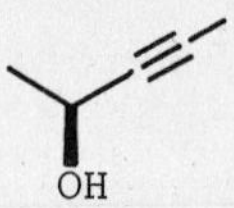 (c) 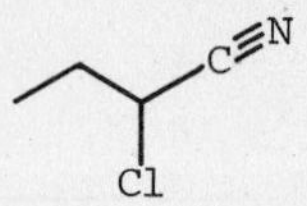

12.3 The equilibrium constant K for the equilibrium: $R\text{-}H \rightleftharpoons R^- + H^+$ is 10^{-pK_a} (see Section 4.5).

The equilibrium constant for the acid-base reaction:

$$R\text{-}H + R'^- \rightleftharpoons R^- + R'\text{-}H$$

can be calculated by dissecting the reaction into two components:

$$R\text{-}H \rightleftharpoons R^- + H^+ \qquad K = 10^{-pK_a}$$

$$+ \quad R'^- + H^+ \rightleftharpoons R'\text{-}H \qquad K = 1/10^{-pK_a} = 10^{pK_a'}$$

Sum: $$R\text{-}H + R'^- \rightleftharpoons R^- + R'\text{-}H \qquad K = 10^{(pK_a' - pK_a)}$$

For $HC\equiv CH + NH_2^- \rightleftharpoons HC\equiv C^- + NH_3$:
$pK_a' - pK_a = 34 - 25 = 9$; therefore $K_{eq} = 10^9$

For $H_2C{=}CH_2 + NH_2^- \rightleftharpoons H_2C{=}CH^- + NH_3$:
$pK_a' - pK_a = 34 - 44 = -10$; therefore $K_{eq} = 10^{-10}$

For $CH_4 + NH_2^- \rightleftharpoons CH_3^- + NH_3$:
$pK_a' - pK_a = 34 - 50 = -16$; therefore $K_{eq} = 10^{-16}$

12.4 pK_a (HCN) = 9.2; pK_a (H_2O) = 15.7

For $HCN + OH^- \rightleftharpoons CN^- + H_2O$ $\quad K_{eq} = 10^{(15.7-9.2)} = 10^{6.5} = 3.16 \times 10^6$

12.5 1-pentyne will form a precipitate with $AgNO_3$, whereas 2-pentyne will not.

12.6 Cyanide ion (pK_a of HCN = 9.2) is much less basic than an acetylide ion (pK_a of $HC\equiv CH$ = 25), therefore it is less likely to cause elimination reactions.

12.7 (a) 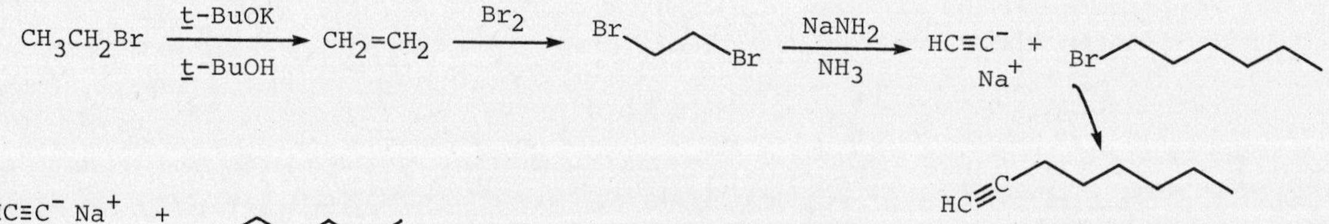

(b) 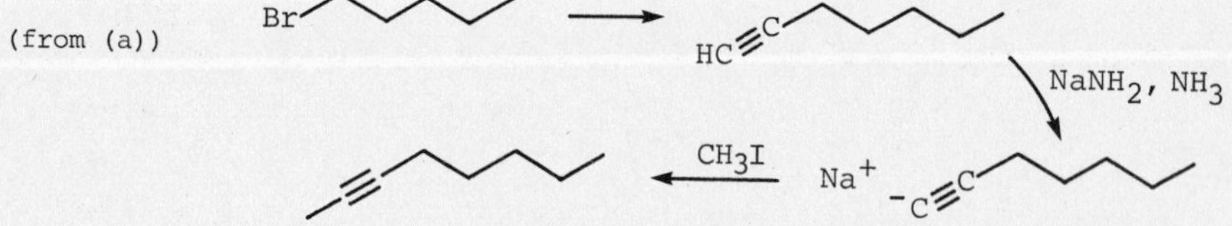

(c) 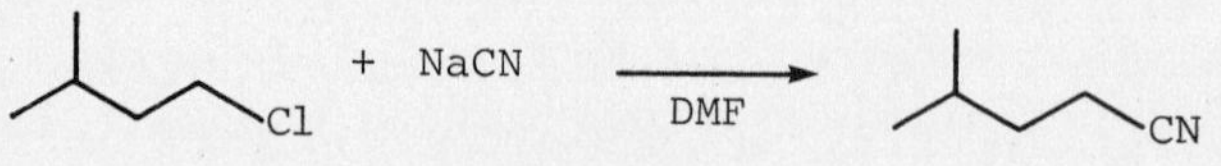

12.8 $CH_3CH_2C\equiv CH \rightleftharpoons CH_3C\equiv CCH_3$

$\Delta H^\circ_f =$ 39.5   34.7 $\qquad \Delta H^\circ = 34.7 - 39.5 = -4.8$ kcal $mole^{-1}$

12.9

$$CH_3CH_2CH{=}CHCH_3 + Br_2 \xrightarrow{CCl_4} CH_3CH_2CHBrCHBrCH_3$$

$$\downarrow KOH \quad C_2H_5OH, \Delta$$

$$CH_3CH_2CH_2C\equiv CH \xleftarrow[150°C]{NaNH_2} CH_3CH_2C\equiv CCH_3 + 2\ KBr$$

Isomerization of an internal alkyne to the terminal isomer involves the following steps:

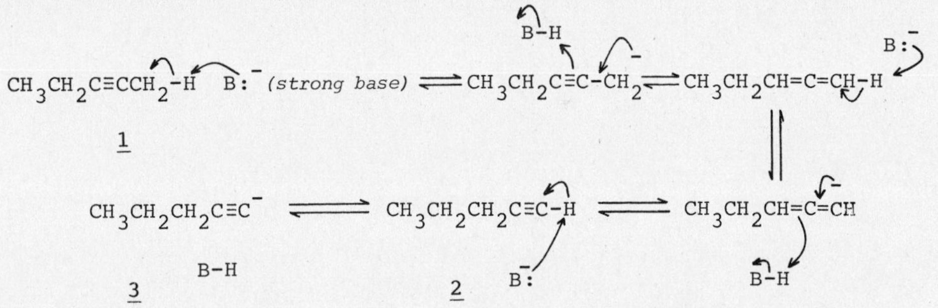

When hydroxide is used as the base (KOH in ethanol, for example), the equlibrium **2** ⇌ **3** favors **2**; that is, hydroxide is a _weaker_ base than the acetylide ion. Therefore, the equilibration that takes place is between the internal alkyne **1** and the terminal alkyne **2**, and the former predominates because it is more stable.

When amide ion is the base (NaNH$_2$, for example), the equilibrium **2** ⇌ **3** favors **3**; that is, amide ion is a _stronger_ base than the acetylide ion. Therefore, the equilibration that takes place favors **3**, and when the reaction is worked up the terminal alkyne is obtained.

The ability to obtain either the internal or the terminal alkyne by choosing the appropriate base is a useful aspect of alkyne chemistry.

12.10 (a)

(b)

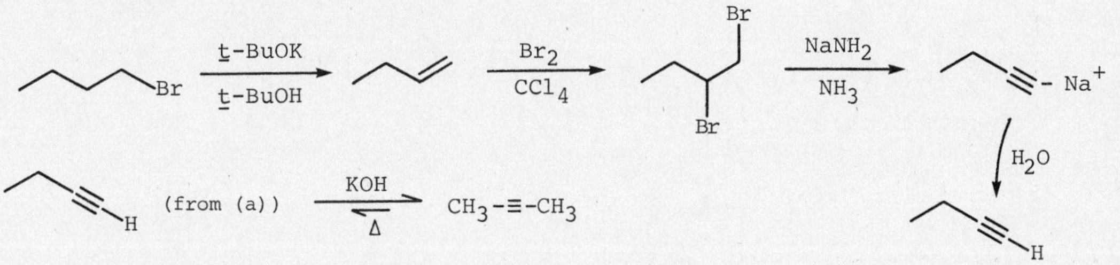

(c)

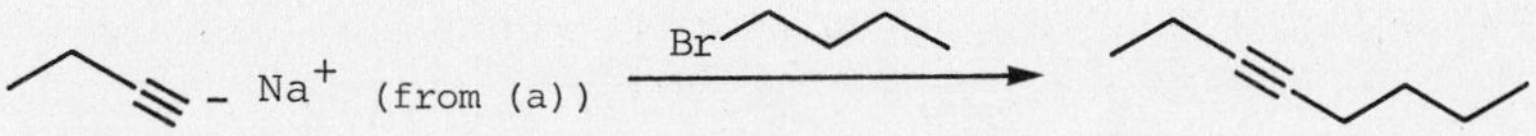

(d)

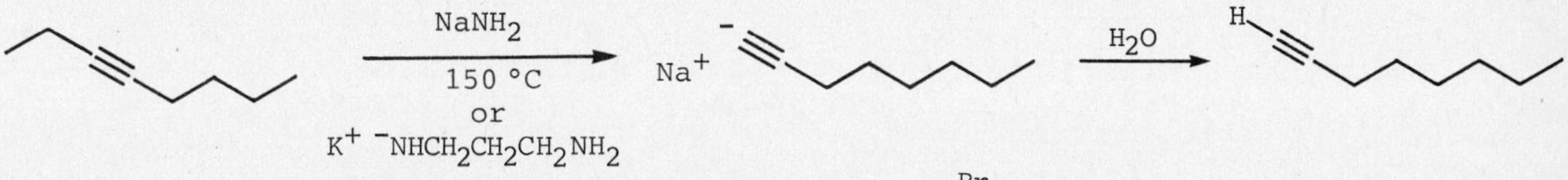

12.11 (a)

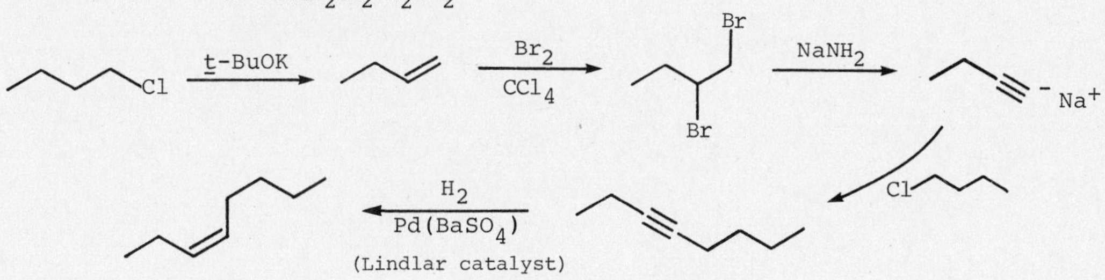

(b) 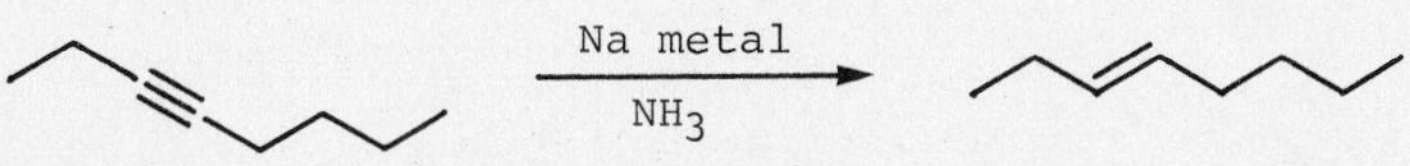 (from (a))

(c) (from (a))

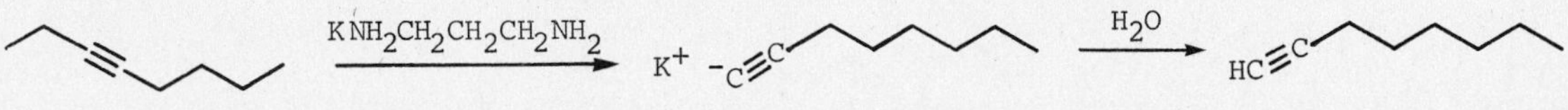

12.12

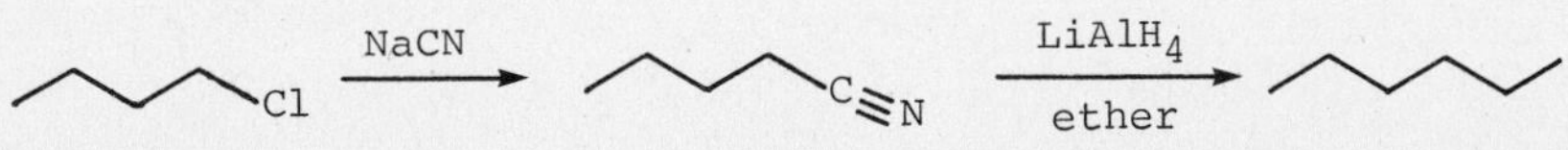

12.13

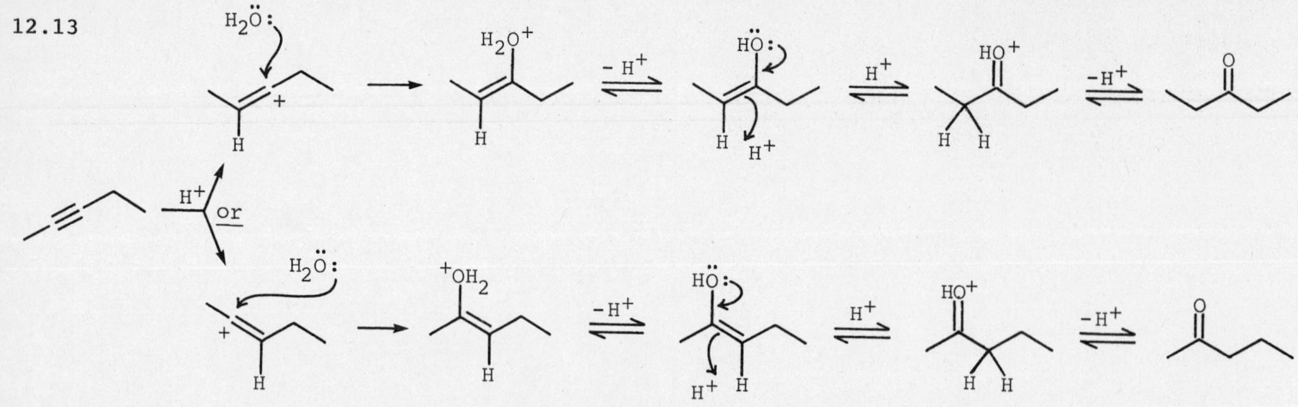

The two cations differ only in substitution with ethyl versus methyl, which is a very minor difference. They will therefore be very similar in stability and both products will be formed in similar amounts.

12.14

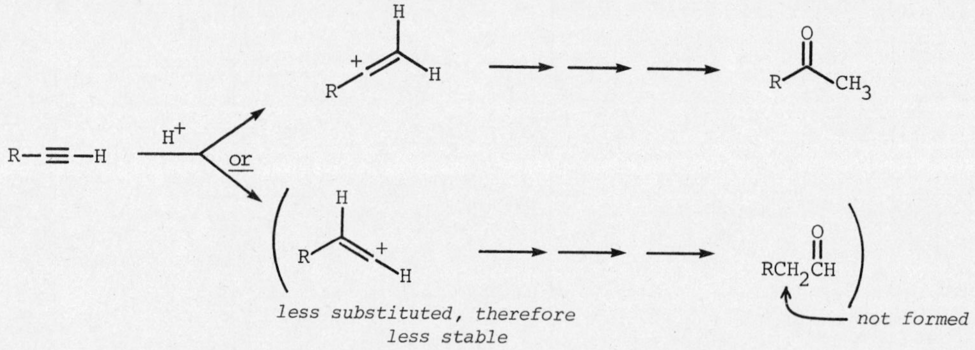

less substituted, therefore less stable

not formed

In the case of a terminal alkyne, the two possible cations do differ substantially in terms of alkyl substitution. The more substituted cation will be formed more easily, and the methyl ketone will be the major product.

12.15

(a)

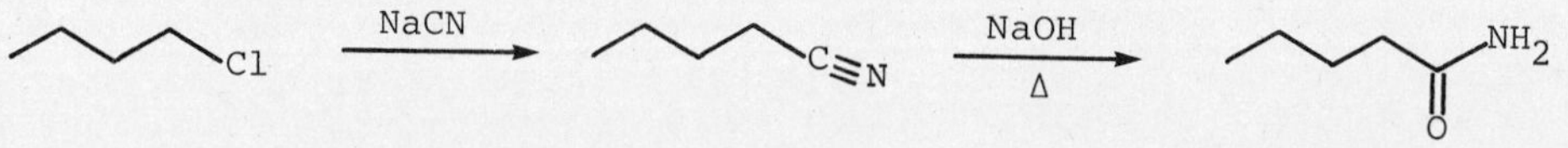

(b)

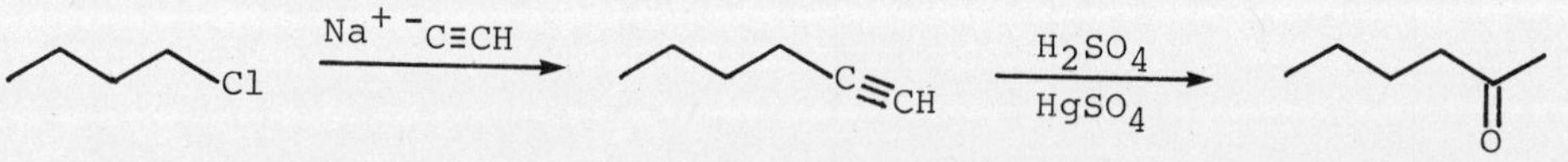

12.16

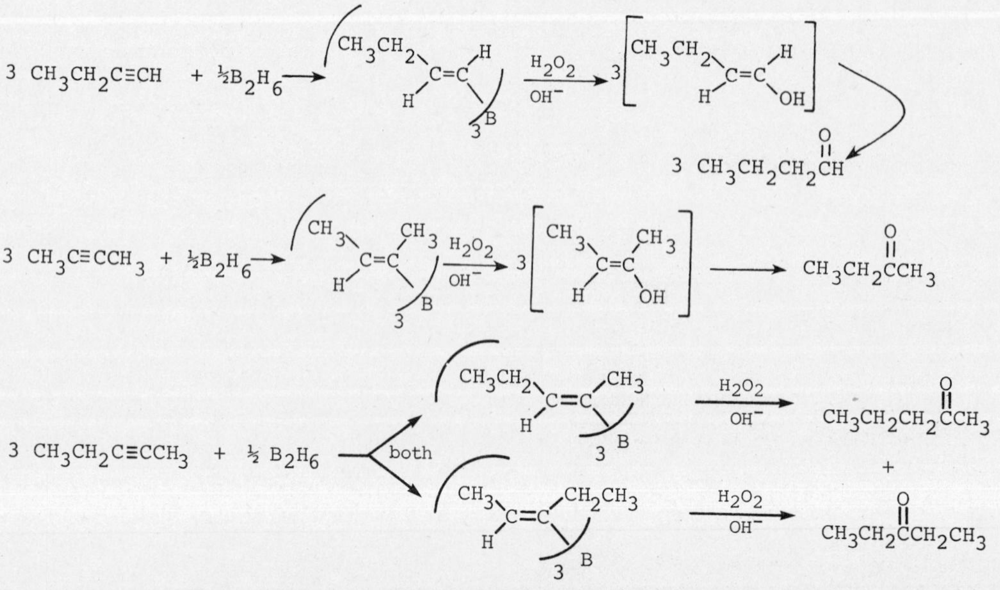

12.17

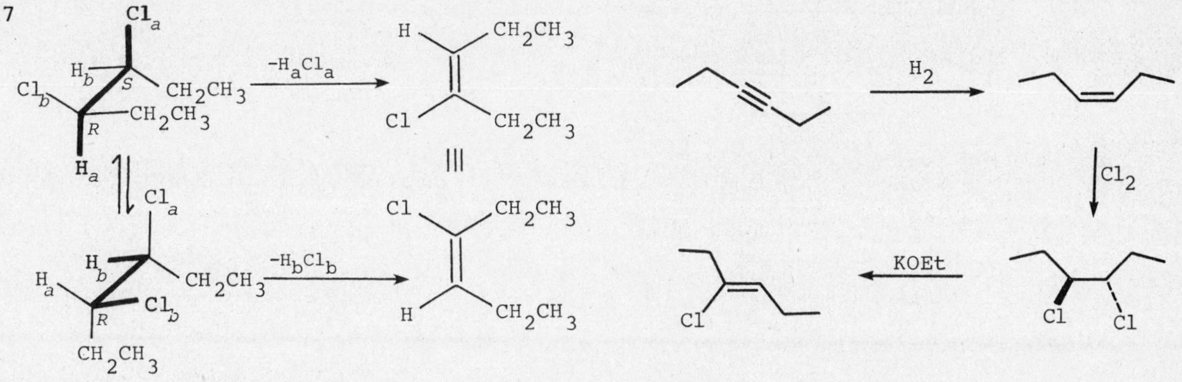

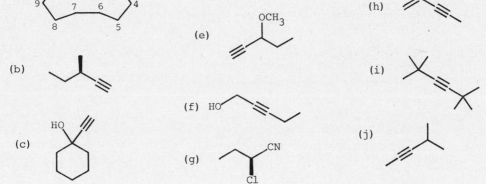

12.E   **Answers and Explanations for Problems**

1.   (a) $—C≡C—CH(CH_3)_2$ (c) [structure]   (e) [structure] Br   (g) $CH_3—O—C≡CH$

(b) $CH_3C≡N$ (d) $(CH_3)_3C—C≡C—C(CH_3)_3$

(f) [structure]

2.   (a) [10-membered ring with positions labeled 1,2,3,4,5,6,7,8,9,10]

(d) $CH_3OC≡CH$

(e) [structure] OCH$_3$

(h) [structure]

(b) [structure]

(i) [structure]

(c) HO [structure with ≡CH]

(f) HO [structure]

(g) [structure] CN / Cl

(j) [structure]

3.   (a) 6-bromo-1-hexyne   (e) (R)-pent-1-en-4-yn-3-ol
(b) 2,2-dimethyl-3-hexyne   (f) 2-butyn-1,4-diol
(c) propanenitrile   (g) hex-1-en-5-yne
(d) cyclopropylacetylene, or   (h) (Z)-2-chloro-2-butene
    ethynylcyclopropane

4.   (a) $CH_3CH_2C≡C^- Li^+$ (d) No reaction   (g) $CH_3CH_2COCH_3$

(b) $CH_3CH_2CH_2CH_3$ (e) $CH_3CH_2C≡CAg$

(c) [structure]   (f) $CH_3CH_2CH_2CHO$

(h) CH_3CH_2 \ /H C=C / \ H   H

5.   (a) No reaction   (d) No reaction   (g) $CH_3CH_2COCH_3$

(b) $CH_3CH_2CH_2CH_3$ (e) No reaction

(c) [structure]   (f) $CH_3CH_2COCH_3$

(h) CH_3 \ /CH_3 C=C / \ H   H

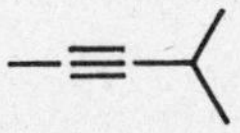

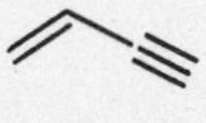

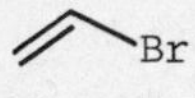

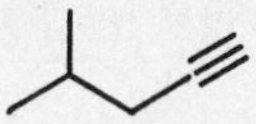

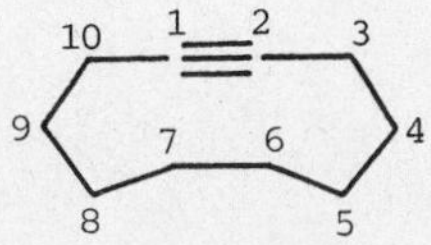

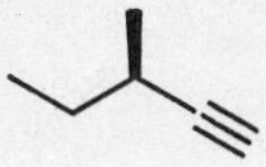

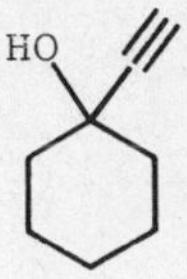

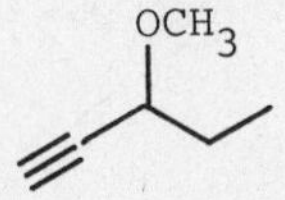

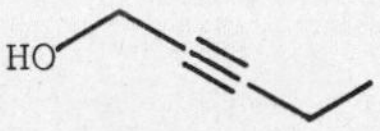

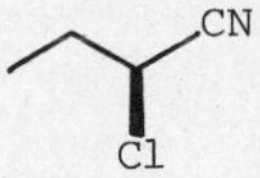

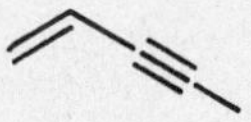

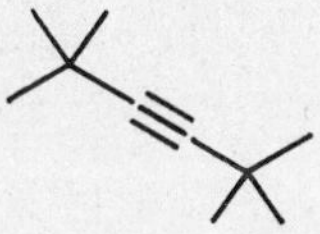

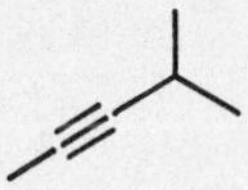

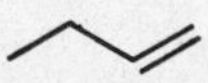

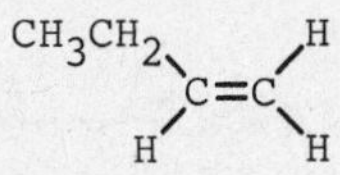

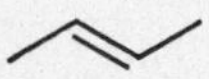

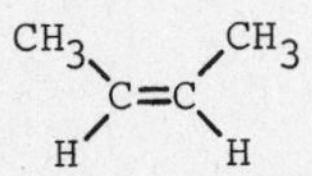

6.   (a) $CH_3CH_2CH_2CH_2NH_2$ (as HCl salt)

(d) $CH_3CH_2CH_2CH_2NH_2$

(b) and (c) [structure] O‖C / NH$_2$

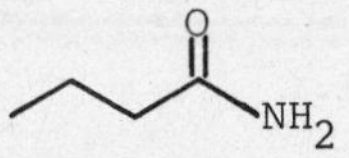

7.

(a) $(CH_3)_2CHBr$ $\xleftarrow[\text{(radical inhibitors)}]{\text{HBr}}$ $CH_2=CHCH_3$ $\xleftarrow[\text{poisoned Pd catalyst}]{H_2}$ $HC\equiv CCH_3$

(b) CH_3COCH_3 $\xleftarrow[\text{HgSO}_4]{\text{H}_2\text{SO}_4}$ $HC\equiv CCH_3$

(c) $CH_3CH_2CH=O$ $\xleftarrow[\text{2. H}_2\text{O}_2,\ \text{OH}^-]{\text{1. B}_2\text{H}_6}$ $CH_3C\equiv CH$

(d) $CH_3CH_2CH_2CH_2CH_2CH_3$ $\xleftarrow[\text{Pt}]{H_2}$ $CH_3CH_2CH_2C\equiv CCH_3$ $\longleftarrow$ $Na^+ {}^-C\equiv CCH_3$ $\xleftarrow{\text{NaNH}_2}$ $HC\equiv CCH_3$

$CH_3CH_2CH_2Br$ $\xleftarrow[\text{peroxides}]{\text{HBr}}$ $CH_3CH=CH_2$ (from (a))

(e)
$\begin{array}{c} CH_3CH_2CH_2 \\ \end{array} \underset{H}{\overset{}{C}}=\underset{CH_3}{\overset{H}{C}}$ $\xleftarrow[\text{liquid NH}_3]{\text{Na}}$ $CH_3CH_2CH_2C\equiv CCH_3$ (from (d))

(f) $CH_3CCl=CH_2$ $\xleftarrow{\text{HCl (one mole)}}$ $CH_3C\equiv CH$

(g) $CH_3CH_2CH_2CN$ $\xleftarrow[\text{DMF}]{\text{NaCN}}$ $CH_3CH_2CH_2Br$ (from (d)

(h) $CH_3CH_2CH_2CH_2NH_2$ $\xleftarrow[\text{ether}]{\text{LiAlH}_4}$ $CH_3CH_2CH_2CN$ (from (g))

8.

a) $CH_3CH_2CH_2CH_3$ $\xrightarrow{\text{Cl}_2 \\ h\nu}$ $CH_3CH_2\underset{Cl}{\overset{}{C}}HCH_3 + CH_3CH_2CH_2CH_2Cl$

$\downarrow$ alc KOH

$CH_3CH=CHCH_3 + CH_3CH_2CH=CH_2$

$\downarrow$ HCl

$CH_3CH_2\underset{Cl}{\overset{}{C}}HCH_3$

b) $CH_3CH_2CH_2CH=CH_2$ $\xrightarrow{\text{Cl}_2}$ $CH_3CH_2CH_2CHClCH_2Cl$ $\xrightarrow[\text{NH}_3]{\text{NaNH}_2}$ $CH_3CH_2CH_2C\equiv C^-Na^+$

$\xrightarrow{H_3O^+}$ $CH_3CH_2CH_2C\equiv CH$

c) $CH_3CH_2CH_2Br$ $\xrightarrow[\text{t-BuOH}]{\text{t-BuO}^-}$ $CH_3CH=CH_2$ $\xrightarrow{\text{Br}_2}$ $CH_3\underset{Br}{\overset{Br}{C}}HCH_2Br$ $\xrightarrow[\Delta]{\text{KOH}}$

$CH_3C\equiv CH$ $\xrightarrow[]{\text{NaNH}_2}$ $\xrightarrow{CH_3CH_2CH_2Br}$ $CH_3CH_2CH_2C\equiv CCH_3$

d) $HC\equiv CH$ $\xrightarrow[\text{Lindlar catalyst}]{H_2}$ $CH_2=CH_2$ $\xrightarrow{\text{HBr}}$ CH_3CH_2Br $\xrightarrow{\text{NaC}\equiv\text{CH}}$ $CH_3CH_2C\equiv CH$

or $\xrightarrow[\text{2. CH}_3\text{COOH}]{\text{1. B}_2\text{H}_6}$

$CH_3CH_2CH_2CH_2OH$ $\xleftarrow[\text{OH}^-]{\text{H}_2\text{O}_2}$ $\xleftarrow{\text{B}_2\text{H}_6}$ $CH_3CH_2CH=CH_2$ $\xleftarrow[\substack{\text{Lindlar} \\ \text{catalyst} \\ (\text{Pd/BaSO}_4, \\ \text{quinoline})}]{H_2}$

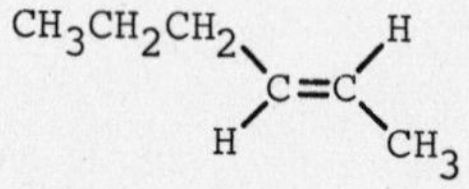

(e) $CH_3CH_2C\equiv CH$ $\xrightarrow[\text{2. } C_2H_5Br]{\text{1. NaNH}_2}$ $CH_3CH_2C\equiv CCH_2CH_3$ $\xrightarrow[\substack{\text{2. Hg(OAc)}_2, \\ \text{CH}_3\text{OH} \\ \text{3. NaBH}_4}]{\text{1. H}_2/\text{Lindlar}}$ $CH_3CH_2\underset{\underset{OCH_3}{|}}{CH}CH_2CH_2CH_3$

     (from (d))

(f) $(CH_3)_3C$ $\underset{H}{\overset{H}{>}}C=C\underset{C(CH_3)_3}{\overset{}{<}}$ $\xrightarrow{Br_2}$ $\xrightarrow{\text{2 NaNH}_2}$ $(CH_3)_3CC\equiv C(CH_3)_3$ $\xrightarrow[\text{Lindlar}]{H_2}$ $(CH_3)_3C\underset{H}{\overset{}{>}}C=C\underset{H}{\overset{C(CH_3)_3}{<}}$

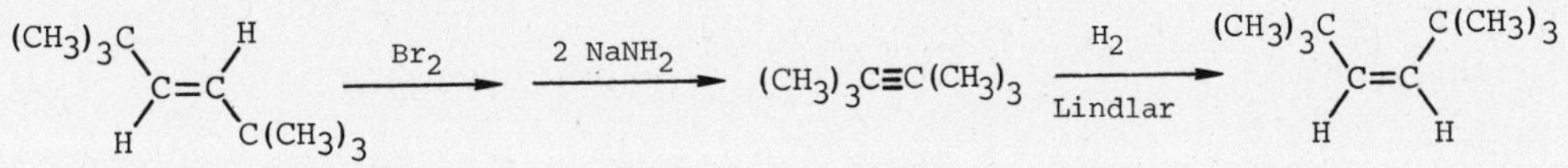

(g) $CH_3CH_2CH_2OH$ $\xrightarrow[\Delta]{H_2SO_4}$ $CH_3CH=CH_2$ $\xrightarrow[\text{2. 2 NaNH}_2]{\text{1. Br}_2}$ $CH_3C\equiv CH$ $\xrightarrow[Hg^{++}]{H_2SO_4}$ $CH_3\overset{O}{\overset{||}{C}}CH_3$

(h) $CH_3CH_2C\equiv CH$ $\xrightarrow{\text{n-BuLi}}$ $CH_3CH_2C\equiv CLi$ $\xrightarrow{D_2O}$ $CH_3CH_2C\equiv CD$ $\xrightarrow[\text{2. CH}_3\text{COOH}]{\text{1. B}_2\text{H}_6}$

$$CH_3CH_2\underset{H}{\overset{}{>}}C=C\underset{H}{\overset{D}{<}}$$

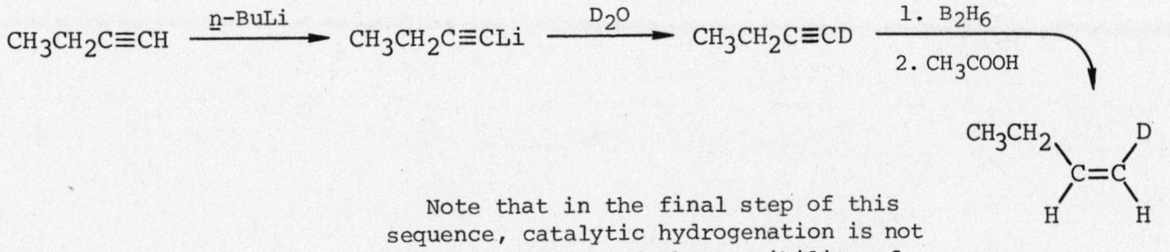

Note that in the final step of this
sequence, catalytic hydrogenation is not
recommended because of the possibility of
some H–D exchange.

(i) $2\ HC\equiv CH$ $\xrightarrow[\substack{\text{pyridine} \\ 60\,°C}]{CuCl_2}$ $HC\equiv C-C\equiv CH$ $\xrightarrow{H_2/Pt}$ $CH_3CH_2CH_2CH_3$

9. (a)

(b)

(c) CH_3CH_2I $\xrightarrow[\text{t-BuOH}]{\text{t-BuOK}}$ $CH_2=CH_2$ $\xrightarrow{Br_2}$ Br—⌐—Br $\xrightarrow{\text{3 NaNH}_2}$ $Na^+\ ^-C\equiv CH$

(d)   (from (c))

10. (a)

(b) $CH_3OCH_2CH_2CH_2CH_2CN$ $\xleftarrow{\text{NaCN}}$ $CH_3OCH_2CH_2CH_2CH_2Br$ $\xleftarrow[\text{peroxides}]{\text{HBr}}$ $CH_3OCH_2CH_2CH=CH_2$

$$CH_3OCH_2CH_2C\equiv CH \xrightarrow[\substack{\text{poisoned-Pd} \\ \text{catalyst or Ni-B}}]{H_2}$$

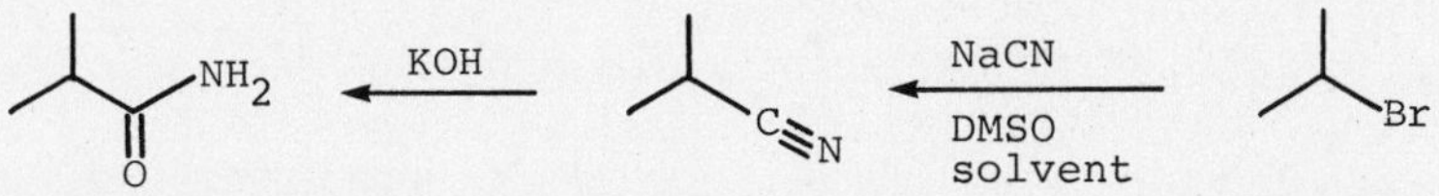

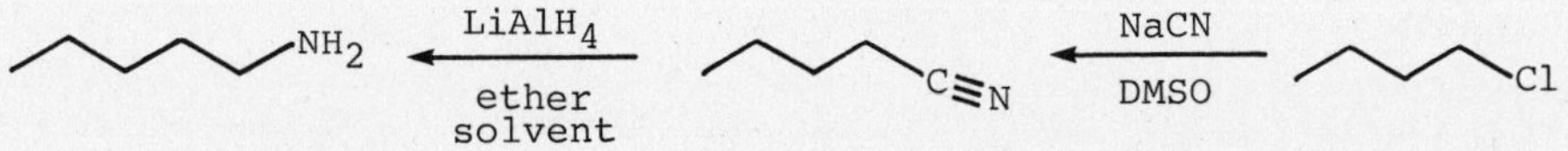

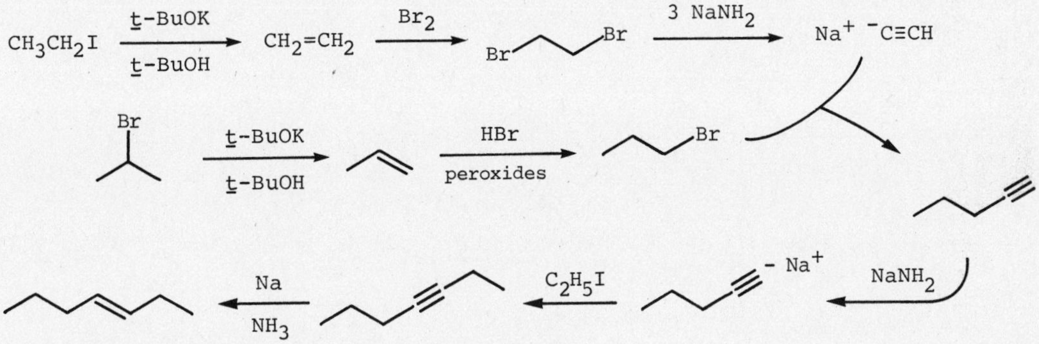

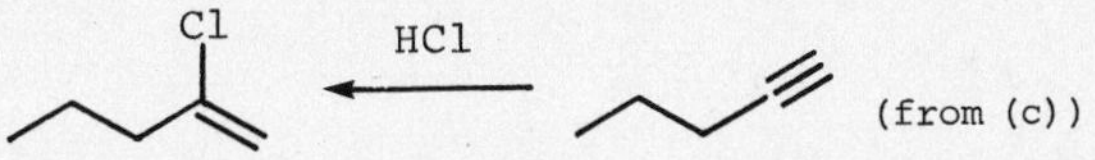

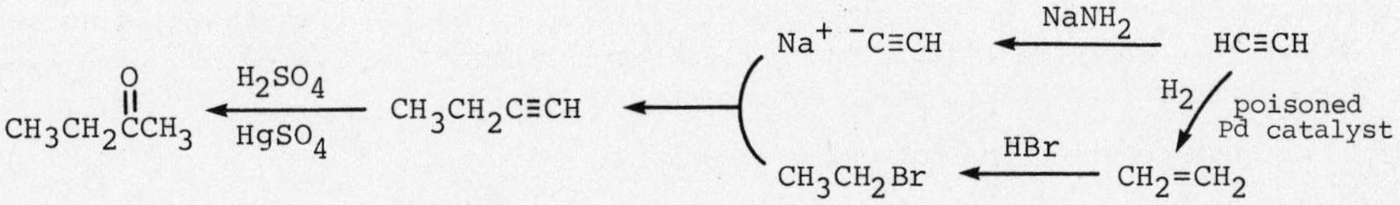

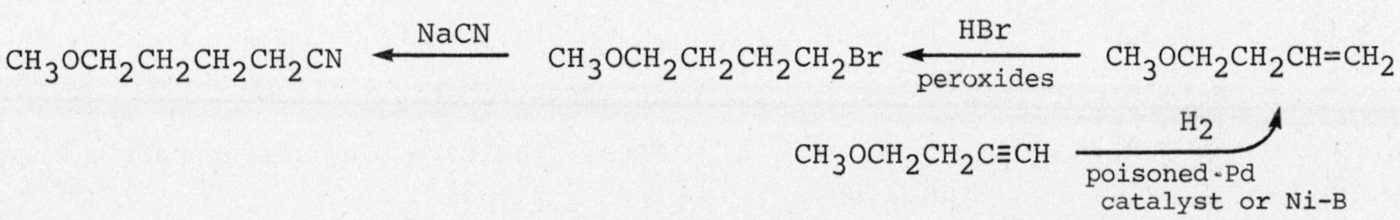

(c) $HC \equiv CH + NaNH_2 \longrightarrow HC \equiv CNa \xrightarrow{C_2H_5I} CH_3CH_2C \equiv CH \xrightarrow{NaNH_2} CH_3CH_2C \equiv CNa$

$$\downarrow CH_3CH_2CH_2I$$

$$CH_3CH_2C \equiv CCH_2CH_2CH_3$$

(d) $(CH_3)_2\overset{\overset{\displaystyle OH}{|}}{C}CH_2CH_3 \xrightarrow[\Delta]{H_2SO_4} (CH_3)_2C = CHCH_3 \xrightarrow[\text{peroxide}]{HBr} (CH_3)_2CHCHBrCH_3$

$$\downarrow t\text{-BuO}^-$$

$CH_3I \overbrace{}^{(CH_3)_2CHC \equiv CNa} \xleftarrow{NaNH_2} (CH_3)_2CHCHBrCH_2Br \xleftarrow{Br_2} (CH_3)_2CHCH = CH_2$

$$(CH_3)_2CHC \equiv CCH_3$$

11. $(CH_3)_2CHCH_2CH_2OH \xrightarrow[\substack{\text{or} \\ PBr_3}]{HBr/H_2SO_4} (CH_3)_2CHCH_2CH_2Br$

$CH_3(CH_2)_9CH_2OH \xrightarrow[\substack{\text{or} \\ PBr_3}]{HBr/H_2SO_4} CH_3(CH_2)_9CH_2Br$

$HC \equiv CH \xrightarrow[\text{liq. } NH_3]{NaNH_2} HC \equiv C^- Na^+ \xrightarrow{(CH_3)_2CHCH_2CH_2Br} (CH_3)_2CHCH_2CH_2C \equiv CH$

$$\downarrow NaNH_2$$

$(CH_3)_2CHCH_2CH_2C \equiv C(CH_2)_{10}CH_3 \xleftarrow{CH_3(CH_2)_9CH_2Br} (CH_3)_2CHCH_2CH_2C \equiv C^-$

$$H_2/Pt \downarrow$$

$$(CH_3)_2CH(CH_2)_{14}CH_3$$

12. $CH_3(CH_2)_xCH_2OH \xrightarrow[\substack{\text{or} \\ PBr_3}]{HBr/H_2SO_4} CH_3(CH_2)_xCH_2Br$

$HC \equiv CH \xrightarrow[\text{liq. } NH_3]{NaNH_2} HC \equiv C^- \xrightarrow{CH_3(CH_2)_6CH_2Br} CH_3(CH_2)_6CH_2C \equiv CH \xrightarrow{NaNH_2}$

$\xrightarrow{CH_3(CH_2)_{11}CH_2Br} CH_3(CH_2)_6CH_2C \equiv CCH_2(CH_2)_{11}CH_3 \xrightarrow[\substack{\text{or } 1. B_2H_6 \\ 2. CH_3COOH}]{Pd/BaSO_4/H_2 \atop \text{quinoline}}$

$CH_3(CH_2)_6CH_2 \underset{H}{\overset{}{\diagdown}} C = C \underset{H}{\overset{(CH_2)_{12}CH_3}{\diagup}}$

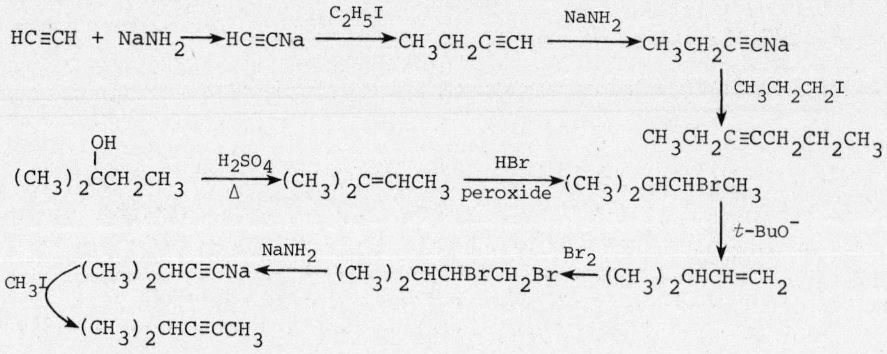

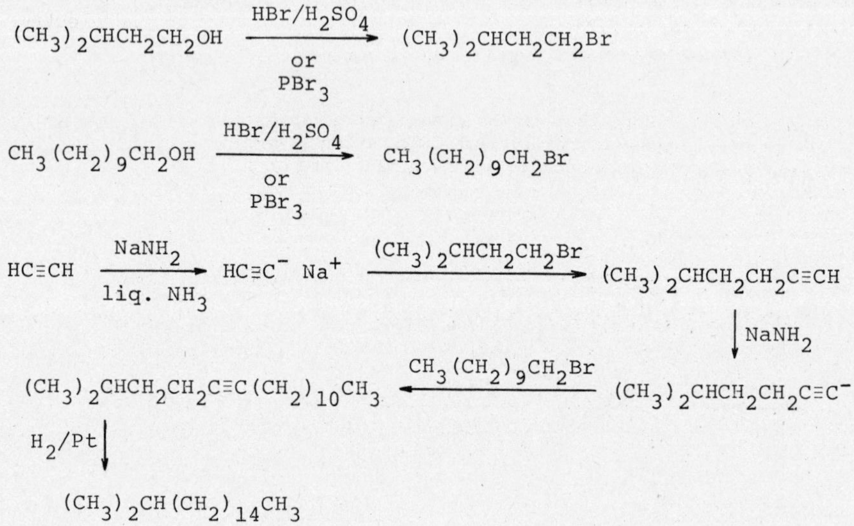

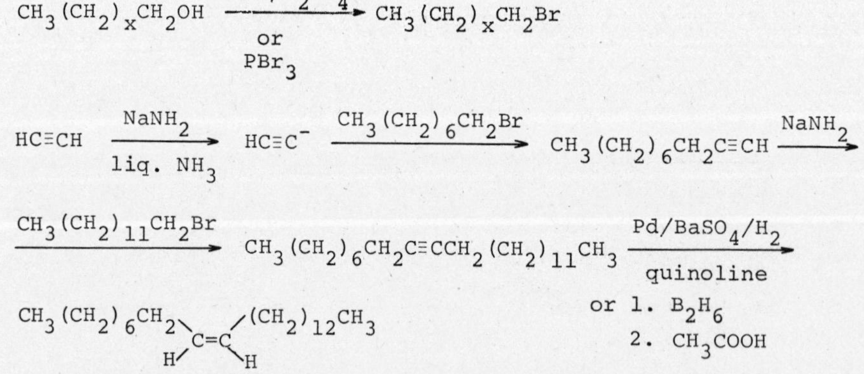

cis-9-tricosene

13.   (a)   Solutions of C_2H_6 in $NH_3/NaNH_2$ have so little carbanion that there is no reaction with CH_3I (see exercise 12.3). $NaNH_2$ will react instead to give CH_3NH_2. C_2H_2 is converted completely into $HC \equiv C^-$, which can react with CH_3I.

(b)   We must consider the following equations:

$$RH = R\cdot + H \qquad \Delta H° = DH°$$

$$H\cdot = H^+ + e \qquad \Delta H° = \text{ionization potential of } H\cdot, \text{ constant for all } RH$$

$$\underline{R\cdot + e = R^- \qquad \Delta H° = -(\text{electron affinity of } R\cdot)}$$

$$RH = H^+ + R^- \qquad = -E.A. \text{ (\textbf{Note}: positive E.A. corresponds to negative } \Delta H)$$

$$\Delta H° = DH° + I.P.(H\cdot) - E.A.(R\cdot)$$

The difference in enthalpy, $\Delta H_2° - \Delta H_1° \equiv \Delta\Delta H°$, for two different hydrocarbons, R_2H and R_1H, is therefore given by:

$$\Delta\Delta H° = [DH_2° - DH_1°] - [E.A.(R_2\cdot) - E.A.(R_1\cdot)]$$

For $R_2H \equiv HC\equiv CH$ and $R_1H \equiv CH_3CH_3$ the negative $\Delta\Delta H°$ despite the positive $(DH_2° - DH_1°)$ means that

$$[E.A.(HC\equiv C\cdot) - E.A.(CH_3CH_2\cdot)] > [DH°(HC\equiv C-H) - DH°(C_2H_5-H)].$$

The E.A. of $HC\equiv C\cdot$ corresponds to putting an electron in an sp hybrid orbital, whereas the E.A. of $C_2H_5\cdot$ involves putting an electron in an sp^3 hybrid orbital. The greater s-character of the sp-hybrid gives ethynyl radical a high electron affinity. The experimental values of these electron affinities are not known accurately, but the available data give $[E.A.(HC\equiv C\cdot) - E.A.(C_2H_5\cdot)] = 50$ kcal mole^{-1}, a value substantially higher than the difference in bond dissociation energies.

In short, although increasing s-character in an orbital increases the stability of a bond involving the orbital, it increases the stability of a lone pair still more. An electron pair in a bond involves two orbitals, whereas a lone pair involves a single orbital.

14.   a)   Overall retention of configuration shows that the vinyl anion is not linear and that protonation of vinyl anion by NH_3 is faster than inversion of the carbanion carbon:

    b)

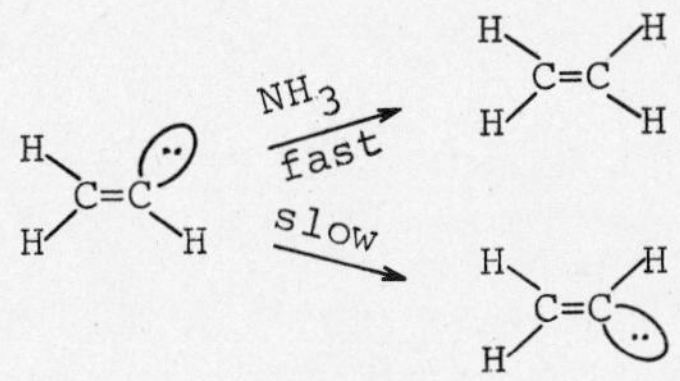

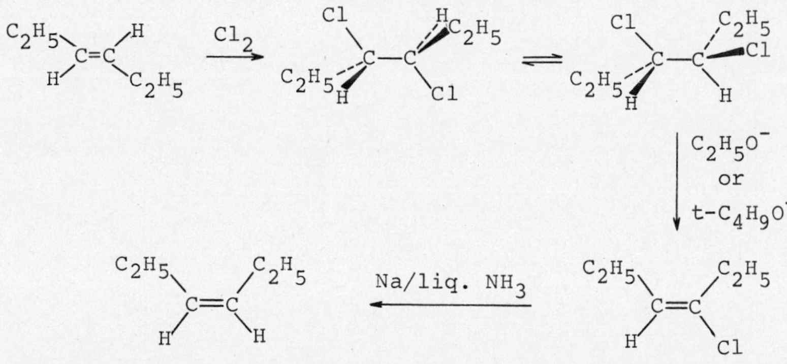

15.

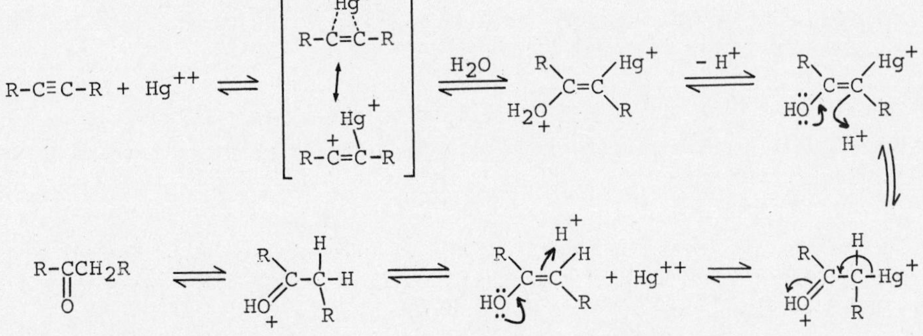

The interconversions of   will be discussed in greater detail in Chapter 14.

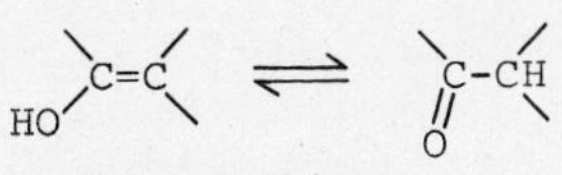

16. The information in this roadmap problem is summarized as follows:

$$\underset{\substack{C_8H_{14}\\ \text{optically active}}}{\underline{C}} \xleftarrow{H_2/\text{Lindlar}} \underset{\substack{C_8H_{12}\\ \text{optically active}}}{\underline{A}} \xrightarrow{Na/NH_3} \underset{\substack{C_8H_{14}\\ \text{optically inactive}}}{\underline{D}}$$

$$\underline{A} \xrightarrow{H_2/Pt} \underline{B}\ \ C_8H_{18}$$

B, C_8H_{18}, corresponds to C_nH_{2n+2} and must be a saturated hydrocarbon. Thus **A** has three units of unsaturation (3 C=C or 1 C=C + 1 C≡C). The reactions **A → C** and **A → D** show that **A** has a triple bond. Our part structure is (C=C)(C≡C)C_4H_{12}. From these reductions, **C** has a cis double bond and **D** has a trans, yet this difference is sufficient to render one optically inactive. The only rational solution is:

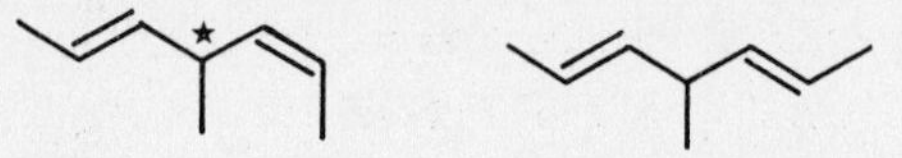

optically active $\underline{C}$ optically inactive $\underline{D}$

Therefore:

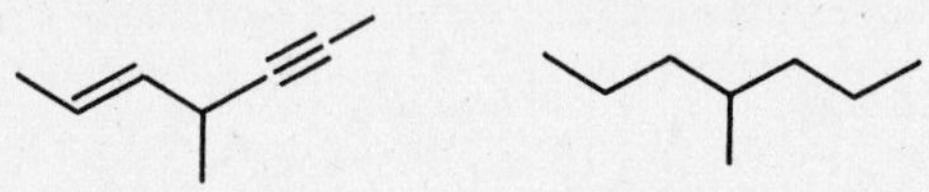

$\underline{A}$ $\underline{B}$

17.

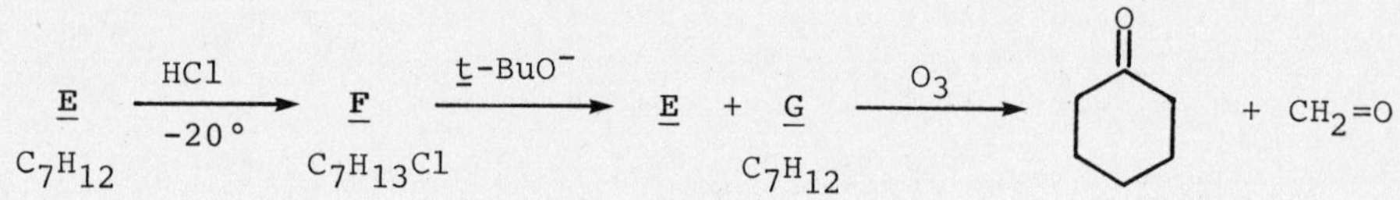

From the last reaction, G must be 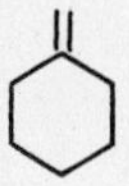. Then F must be 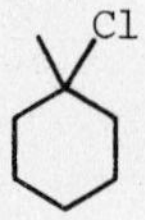 and E is 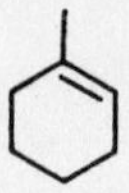.

F cannot be 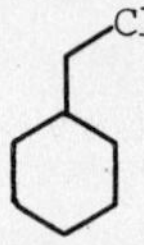 because this chloride cannot be formed by addition of HCl to an alkene.

18.

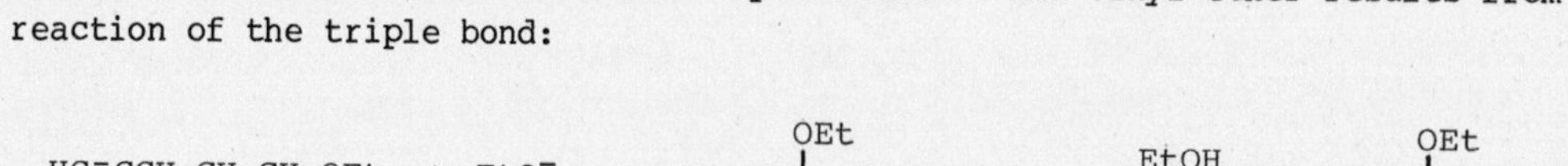

+ HC≡CCH$_2$CH$_2$CH$_2$OEt

but no EtOCH=CHCH$_2$CH$_2$CH$_2$OEt

The terminal -CH$_2$OEt comes from a normal S_N2 reaction on the primary bromide. The terminal HC≡C- group results from E2 elimination of the vinyl bromide. The vinyl ether results from a subsequent reaction of the triple bond:

$$HC{\equiv}CCH_2CH_2CH_2OEt + EtO^- \longrightarrow H\bar{C}{=}\underset{}{\overset{OEt}{C}}CH_2CH_2CH_2OEt \xrightarrow{EtOH} H_2C{=}\overset{OEt}{C}CH_2CH_2CH_2OEt$$

Ethoxide ion adds to the triple bond to give the primary carbanion, H$\bar{C}$=, rather than the less stable secondary carbanion, =$\bar{C}$-C. This latter mode of addition, if it occurred, would give rise to EtOCH=CHCH$_2$CH$_2$CH$_2$OEt, but cannot compete with the alternative mode of addition.

19.

	DH°		
CH_3CH_2-F	107	$CH_2=CH-F$	?
CH_3CH_2-Cl	81	$CH_2=CH-Cl$	88
CH_3CH_2-Br	68	$CH_2=CH-Br$	76
CH_3CH_2-I	53	$CH_2=CH-I$	?

For the chloride and bromide, DH° for the vinyl compound is 7-8 kcal mole^{-1} higher than for the
ethyl compound. Rough estimates for $CH_2=CHF$ and CH_2CHI are 115 and 61 kcal mole^{-1}, respectively.
The vinyl-halide bond is stronger in part because of increased s character and in part because
of delocalization of a halide lone pair electron with the double bond.

$$C_2H_5-X \quad \overset{\curvearrowleft}{} {}^{C_{sp^3}-X} \qquad C_2H_3-X \quad \overset{\curvearrowleft}{} {}^{C_{sp^2}-X} \qquad \left[\, CH_2=CH-\ddot{X} \quad \longleftrightarrow \quad {}^-\ddot{C}H_2-CH=X^+ \,\right]$$

this structure contributes a
small but significant amount

12.F   Supplementary Problems

S1. Write out the structure corresponding to each of the following names:

    (a) neopentylacetylene   (d) 1,5,9-cyclododecatriyne

    (b) 1,3,3-tribromopropyne   (e) 2,2,7,7-tetramethyl-3,5-octadiyne

    (c) sodium acetylide   (f) ethyne

S2. Give the IUPAC name for each of the following compounds:

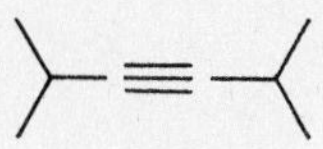

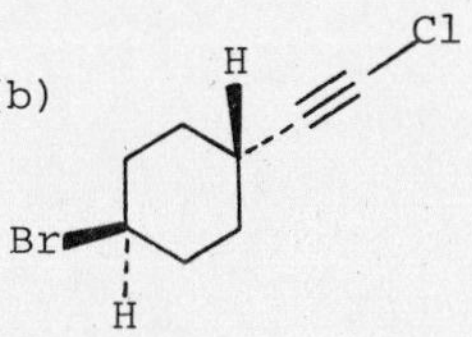

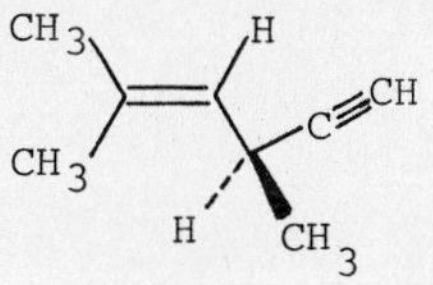

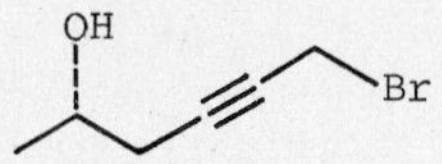

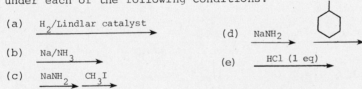

S3. Give the principal product of reaction of compound (c), problem #S2,
under each of the following conditions:

    (a) $\xrightarrow{\text{H}_2/\text{Lindlar catalyst}}$

    (b) $\xrightarrow{\text{Na/NH}_3}$

    (c) $\xrightarrow{\text{NaNH}_2 \quad \text{CH}_3\text{I}}$

    (d) $\xrightarrow{\text{NaNH}_2}$ (bromocyclohexane) $\rightarrow$

    (e) $\xrightarrow{\text{HCl (1 eq)}}$

S4. Show how each of the following conversions can be accomplished in
good yield. You may use other organic compounds if necessary.

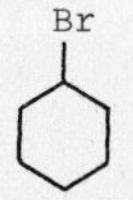

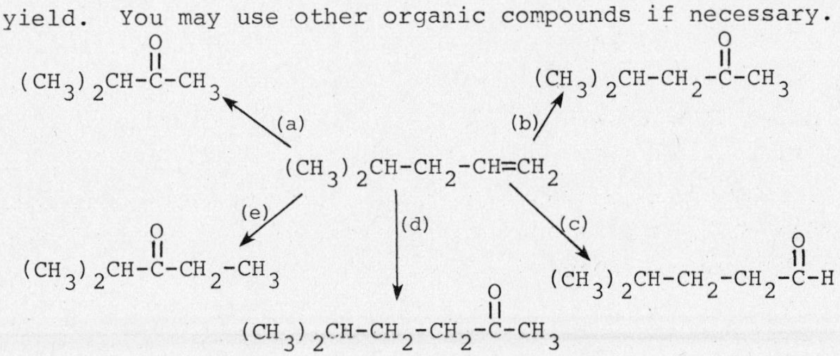

Do you anticipate any problems with the route you would most likely select for conversion (e)?

S5. The sex attractant of the galechiid moth *Bryotopha similis* is a derivative of <u>trans</u>-9-tetra-decen-1-ol, and one of the components of the sex attractant of the butterfly *Lycorea ceresceres* is a derivative of <u>cis</u>-11-octadecen-1-ol. Show how to synthesize these two alcohols from 8-bromo-1-octanol and any other compound of four carbons or less. (*HINT*: protect the hydroxy group during your synthesis by forming the <u>t</u>-butyl ether; see end of Section 10.9 in the Text.)

S6. (a) Using Appendix I, calculate the heat of hydrogenation, $\Delta H^{\circ}_{hydrog.}$ for each step in the hydrogenation of 2-butyne to butane.

(b) Do you expect this to be a good model for calculating $\Delta H^{\circ}_{hydrog.}$ of cyclodecyne? If not, in which step(s) do you think the biggest difference will be seen?

S7. Show how to synthesize both <u>cis</u>- and <u>trans</u>-1,2-dichlorocyclododecane stereospecifically from cyclododecane.

S8. Treatment of <u>cis</u>-3-hexene with bromine and then KOH in ethanol gives the vinyl halide, <u>Z</u>-bromo-3-hexene. However, when the same sequence of reactions is applied to cyclohexene, no vinyl halide (1-bromocyclohexene) is produced. Instead, 1,3-cyclohexadiene is obtained. Provide an explanation for the difference in behavior of these two alkenes.

12.G   Answers to Supplementary Problems

S1.

(a) $CH_3-\underset{\underset{CH_3}{|}}{\overset{\overset{CH_3}{|}}{C}}-CH_2-C{\equiv}C-CH_2-\underset{\underset{CH_3}{|}}{\overset{\overset{CH_3}{|}}{C}}-CH_3$

(b) $Br-C{\equiv}C-CHBr_2$

(c) $HC{\equiv}CNa$

(d)

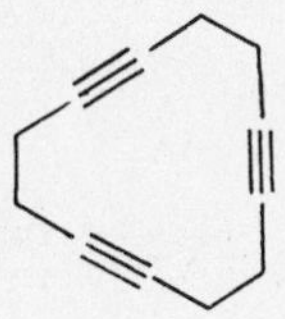

(e) $(CH_3)_3CC{\equiv}C-C{\equiv}CC(CH_3)_3$

(f) $HC{\equiv}CH$

S2. (a) 2,5-dimethyl-3-hexyne

(b) <u>trans</u>-1-(2-chloroethynyl)-4-bromocyclohexane

(c) (<u>S</u>)-2,4-dimethylhex-2-en-5-yne

(d) (<u>S</u>)-6-bromo-4-hexyn-2-ol

S3. (a) and (b) $(CH_3)_2C{=}CHCH\underset{\underset{CH_3}{|}}{CH}{=}CH_2$

(c) $(CH_3)_2C{=}CHCH\underset{\underset{CH_3}{|}}{C}{\equiv}CCH_3$

(d) $(CH_3)_2C{=}CHCH\underset{\underset{CH_3}{|}}{C}{\equiv}CH$ + + NaBr
(2° RX undergoes E2)

(e) $(CH_3)_2CClCH_2CH\underset{\underset{CH_3}{|}}{C}{\equiv}CH$

(electrophilic addition to alkenes is faster than to alkynes)

S4. (a) $(CH_3)_2CHCH_2CH{=}CH_2 \xrightarrow[\text{2) } NaBH_4]{\text{1) } O_3} (CH_3)_2CHCH_2CH_2OH \xrightarrow[\Delta]{Al_2O_3} (CH_3)_2CHCH{=}CH_2$

$\downarrow Br_2$

$(CH_3)_2CH\overset{\overset{O}{\|}}{C}CH_3 \xleftarrow[H_2SO_4]{Hg^{++}} (CH_3)_2CHC{\equiv}CH \xleftarrow{NaNH_2} (CH_3)_2CHCHBrCH_2Br$

(b) $(CH_3)_2CHCH_2CH{=}CH_2 \xrightarrow[\text{2) } NaNH_2]{\text{1) } Br_2} (CH_3)_2CHCH_2C{\equiv}CH \xrightarrow[H_2SO_4]{Hg^{++}} (CH_3)_2CHCH_2\overset{\overset{O}{\|}}{C}CH_3$

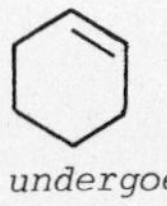

(c) $(CH_3)_2CHCH_2C\equiv CH$ *(from (b))* $\xrightarrow{B_2H_6}$ $\left[(CH_3)_2CHCH_2CH=CH\right]_3B \xrightarrow[OH^-]{H_2O_2}$

$$(CH_3)_2CHCH_2CH_2\overset{O}{\overset{\|}{C}}H$$

(d) $(CH_3)_2CHCH_2C\equiv CH$ *(from (b))* $\xrightarrow{NaNH_2}(CH_3)_2CHCH_2C\equiv CNa \xrightarrow{CH_3I}(CH_3)_2CHCH_2C\equiv CCH_3$

$\downarrow NaNH_2, 150°C$

$(CH_3)_2CHCH_2CH_2\overset{O}{\overset{\|}{C}}CH_3 \xleftarrow[H_2SO_4]{Hg^{++} \quad H_2O} (CH_3)_2CHCH_2CH_2C\equiv CNa$

(e) $(CH_3)_2CHCH_2C\equiv CH$ *(from (b))*$\xrightarrow[C_2H_5OH]{KOH}(CH_3)_2CHC\equiv CCH_3 \xrightarrow[H_2SO_4]{Hg^{++}} (CH_3)_2CH\overset{O}{\overset{\|}{C}}CH_2CH_3$

$+ \quad (CH_3)_2CHCH_2\overset{O}{\overset{\|}{C}}CH_3$

The trouble with route (e) is that it will produce a lot of the isomeric ketone as well.

S5.

$BrCH_2(CH_2)_6CH_2OH \xrightarrow[H^+]{(CH_3)_2C=CH} BrCH_2(CH_2)_6CH_2OC(CH_3)_3 \xrightarrow{HC\equiv CNa} HC\equiv C(CH_2)_8OC(CH_3)_3$

$\xrightarrow[\text{2. H}^+]{\text{1. Na/NH}_3} CH_3(CH_2)_3C\equiv C(CH_2)_8OC(CH_3)_3 \xleftarrow[\underline{n}\text{-BuBr}]{NaNH_2}$ $\xrightarrow[\text{quinoline}]{H_2 \quad Pd/BaSO_4/}$

$CH_2=CH(CH_2)_8OC(CH_3)_3$

$$\underset{\text{H}}{\overset{\text{H}}{\underset{\diagdown}{\overset{\diagup}{C}}}}=\underset{(CH_2)_8OH}{\overset{CH_3(CH_2)_3}{C}}$$ *trans-9-tetradecen-1-ol*

$\downarrow HBr \\ h\nu$

$Br(CH_2)_{10}OC(CH_3)_3$

$\underline{n}\text{-BuBr} + NaC\equiv CC_2H_5 \longrightarrow CH_3(CH_2)_3C\equiv CCH_2CH_3 \xrightarrow[150°C]{NaNH_2} CH_3(CH_2)_5C\equiv CNa$

$(CH_3)_2C=CH_2 \quad +$

$$\underset{H}{\overset{CH_3(CH_2)_5}{\underset{\diagup}{\overset{\diagdown}{C}}}}=\underset{H}{\overset{(CH_2)_{10}OH}{C}}$$

cis-11-octadecen-1-ol

$\xleftarrow[\text{2. H}^+]{\text{1. H}_2, \text{ Lindlar} \\ \text{catalyst}} CH_3(CH_2)_5C\equiv C(CH_2)_{10}OC(CH_3)_3$

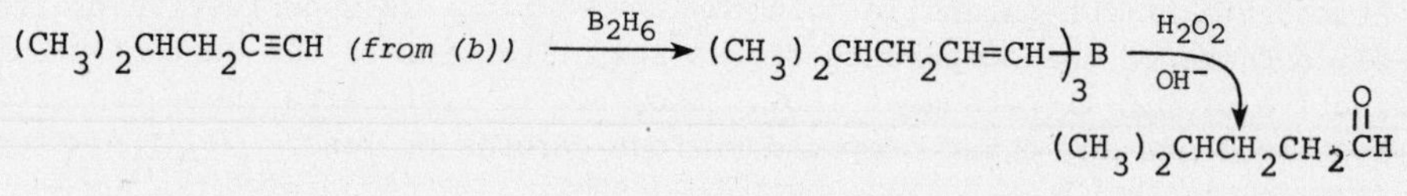

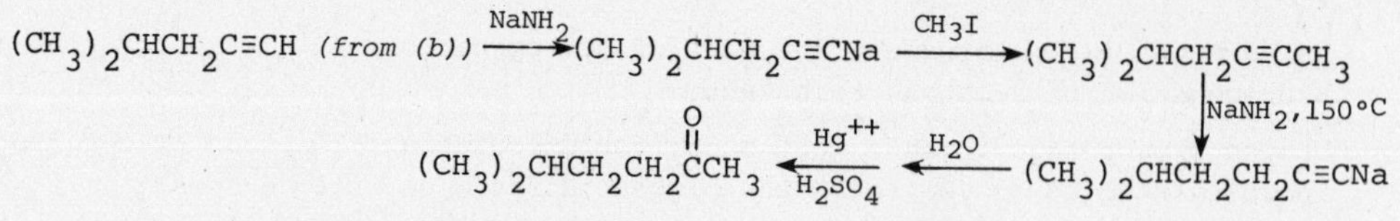

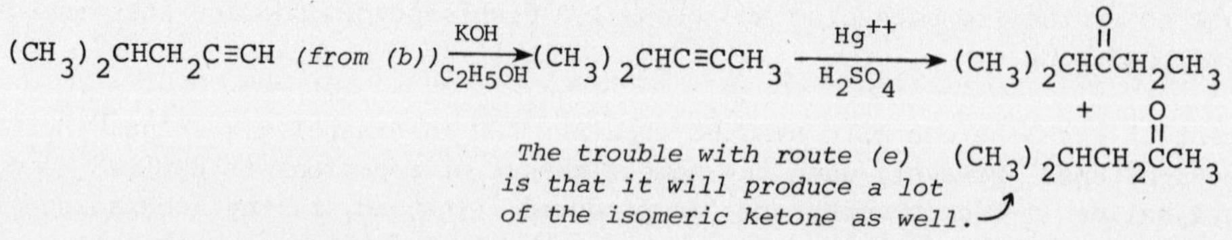

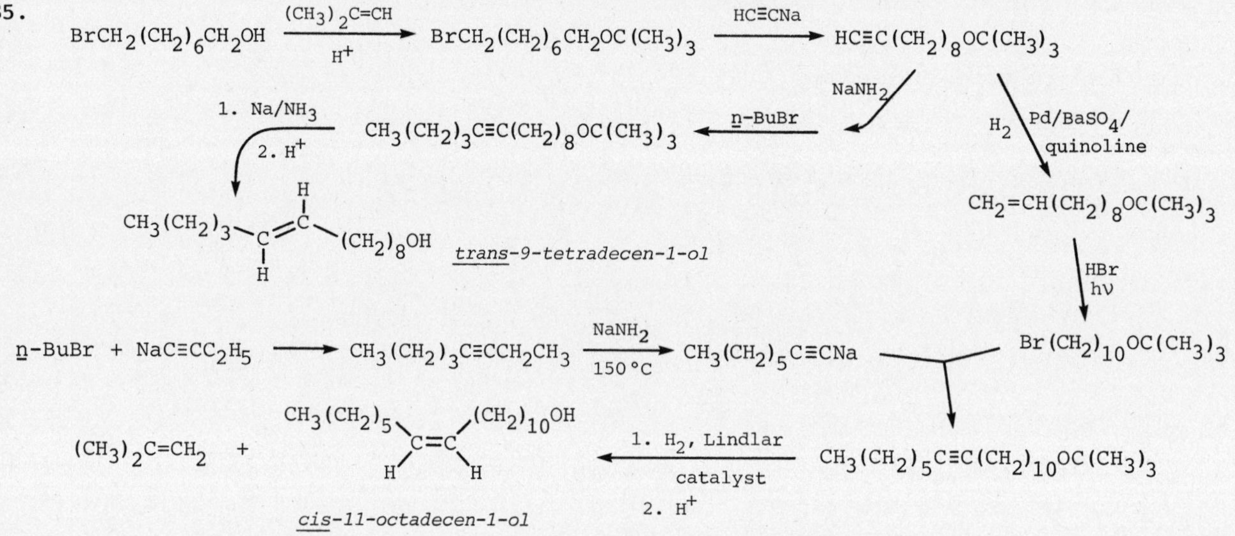

S6.

(a) $CH_3C\equiv CCH_3 \quad + \quad H_2 \quad \longrightarrow \quad cis\text{-}CH_3CH=CHCH_3$

ΔH_f°:   34.7   0   -1.9 $\Delta H^\circ_{hydrog(1)} = -36.6$ kcal mole^{-1}

   $cis\text{-}CH_3CH=CHCH_3 + H_2 \longrightarrow CH_3CH_2CH_2CH_3$

ΔH_f°:   -1.9   0   -30.4 $\Delta H^\circ_{hydrog(2)} = -28.5$ kcal mole^{-1}

(b)   In cyclodecyne there is a lot of strain because the $C\text{-}C\equiv C\text{-}C$ group
      of atoms must bend to fit into the ring structure. This strain
      will be released in going from cyclodecyne to *cis*-cyclodecene, so
      $\Delta H^\circ_{hydrog(1)}$ will be more negative than predicted in (a). The
      second step should be similar to the acyclic model.

S7.

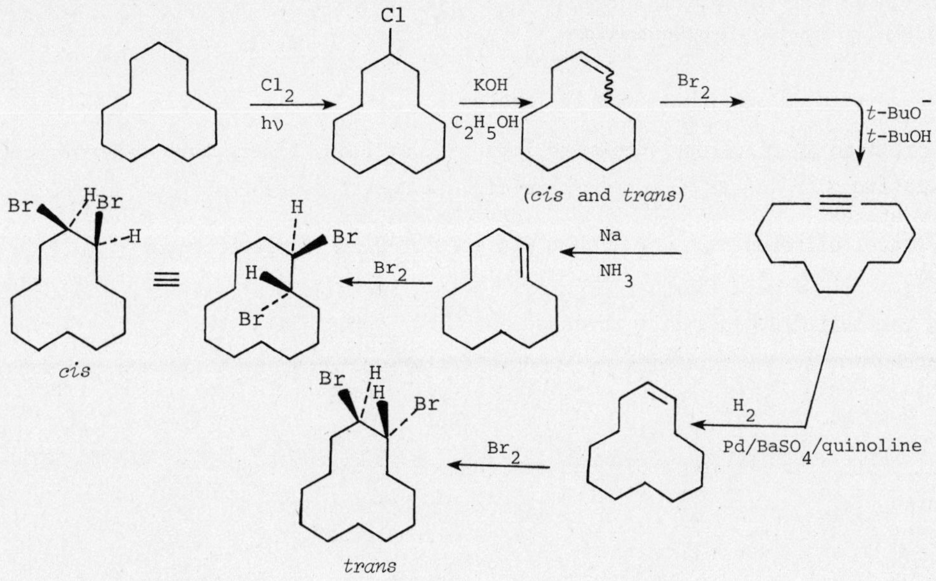

(cis and trans)

cis

trans

S8.

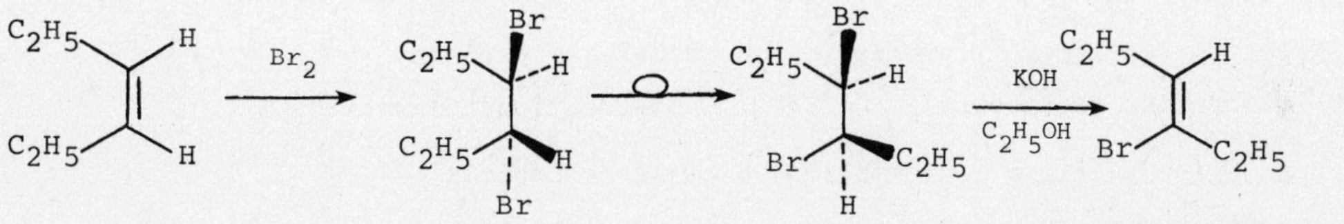

via *anti* elimination

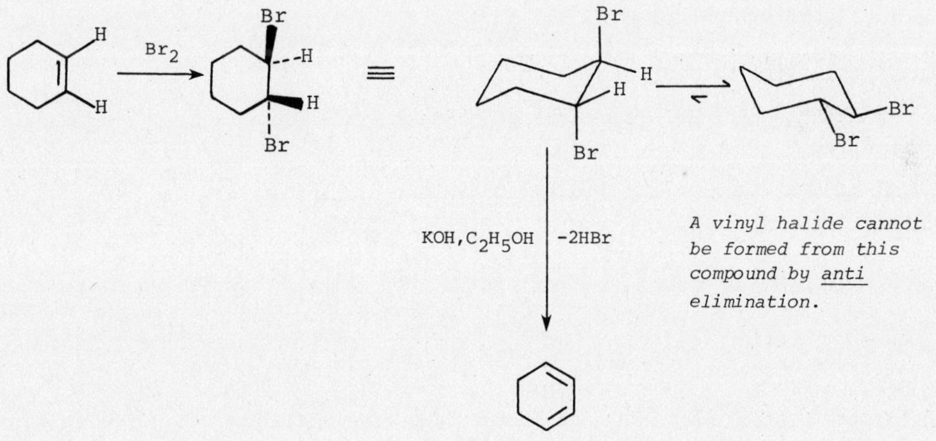

A vinyl halide cannot be formed from this compound by anti *elimination.*

KOH,C₂H₅OH | -2HBr

13. NUCLEAR MAGNETIC RESONANCE SPECTROSCOPY

13.A   Chapter Outline and Important Terms Introduced

13.1   Structure Determination (what does it involve?)

13.2   Introduction to Spectroscopy (the most important methods of structure determination)

quantization   microwave spectroscopy
quantum states   infrared spectroscopy
energy level differences   ultraviolet-visible spectroscopy
$\Delta E = h\nu$

13.3   Nuclear Magnetic Resonance (the physics behind the technique)

nuclear spin   spin "flipping"
magnetic moment   magnetogyric ratio
α- and β-spins $\nu = \gamma H/2\pi$

13.4   Chemical Shift (information about the environment of the proton)

shielding   tetramethylsilane (TMS)
diamagnetic shielding   parts per million (ppm)
resonance δ scale
upfield-downfield

13.5   Relative Peak Areas (information on numbers of protons)

integration of spectra   saturation/relaxation

13.6   Spin-Spin Splitting (information on adjacent protons)

magnetic non-equivalence   coupling constant, J
applied vs. effective field   binomial pattern
(singlet), doublet, triplet,
        (quartet, multiplet, etc.)

13.7   More Complex Splitting (the real world....)

"first-order" vs. non-first order spectra
$J_{ab} \neq J_{ac}$ overlap of patterns

13.8   Effect of Conformation on Coupling Constants

dihedral angle dependence   Karplus curve

13.9   Remote Shielding by Multiple Bonds: Magnetic Anisotropy (why alkenes are downfield
                                                    and alkynes upfield)

induced magnetic field   upfield shift of acetylenic hydrogens
π-electron circulation   long range coupling

13.10   Dynamical Systems (slow or fast on the "NMR time scale")

Heisenberg Uncertainty Principle   chair-chair interconversion
NMR time scale   variable temperature NMR
magnetic equivalence

13.11   Chemical Exchange of Hydrogens Bonded to Oxygen (why the coupling sometimes disappears)

13.12   Carbon NMR Spectroscopy (cmr)

natural abundance   proton decoupling and
Fourier transform instrumentation   off-resonance decoupling
chemical shift prediction α-, β-, and γ-effects
symmetry   stereochemical effects

13.13   Solving Spectral Problems (useful generalizations and hints)

13.B   Important Reactions Introduced: none in this chapter

13.C   Important Concepts and Hints

NMR spectroscopy has become the most important method available to organic chemists for determining the structure of a compound.   Chapter 13 presents the physical principles that underly the technique, and describes the spectra observed for alkanes, alkenes, alkynes, and alkyl halides. As other functional groups are introduced in subsequent chapters, their characteristic NMR resonances will be discussed. The facts that make up the topic of NMR form a logical framework and are as intuitively understandable as the rest of organic chemistry. Nevertheless, a common tendency for many students when presented by tables of numbers is to <u>memorize</u>. A certain amount of instant recall will help you in solving NMR problems, although as the Text points out, it is really important to know only the general regions in the NMR spectrum where various types of hydrogens or carbons appear, rather than memorizing exact resonance positions. The following outline is a general guide to the things that you should definitely "know" about NMR:

I.   "To the right" in an NMR spectrum is:

    A. more "shielded"

    B. "upfield" (= higher field strength for a given resonance frequency)

    C. "lower frequency" (to reach resonance for a given magnetic field)
       [and vice versa: "to the left" = "deshielded" = "downfield" = "higher frequency"]

II. For proton spectra (<u>not</u> CMR), **area** is proportional to **number of protons**

III. Chemical shift depends on substituents:

    A. For proton spectra, the following generalizations are very useful:
      1. Alkyl hydrogens have δ ~ 1 ppm
      2. δ (tertiary C-H) > δ (secondary C-H) > δ (primary C-H)
      3. A halogen atom on the same carbon causes a downfield shift by 2-3 ppm
      4. A halogen on the next carbon still has an effect of about 0.5 ppm
        It is useful to learn the NMR characteristics of each functional group as they are introduced in subsequent chapters.

    B. For carbon spectra:
      1. Learn some basic shifts (e.g., methane-butane)
      2. Learn the substituent effects (α-, β-, γ-effects)
        When it comes to solving spectral problems, it helps to know right away what chemical shift corresponds to what possibilities.

IV. As a basic rule, **n** adjacent protons leads to a splitting of **n+1** peaks.
    This can easily become more complicated, however.
    J for neighboring hydrogens on an alkane chain is usually 4-10 Hz.

V.   You should also be aware of complications in splitting patterns which arise from:
    A. non-first order spectra
    B. non-equivalent coupling constants
    C. dihedral angle dependence

NMR spectral problems are usually one of two types: given the structure of the compound, predict the spectrum it would give; or, given the spectral data, deduce the structure of the compound. Solving the first type of question is fairly straightforward.

    FIRST: Pick out the non-equivalent nuclei (nuclei can be equivalent either through symmetry alone, or through conformational interconversions and symmetry);

    SECOND: Predict the chemical shift for each group;

    THIRD: For proton spectra, (a) assign relative area (number of nuclei) in each group; (b) calculate splitting patterns.
       For carbon spectra, sometimes you are asked to predict the multiplicity of the off-resonance decoupled spectrum.

    FOURTH: Look for complications....

Solving the second type of problem is like solving a puzzle. It can be fun and there is a system. It is most complex for proton spectra, where there are the added complications of splitting patterns and relative areas to deal with, so we will point out a systematic way to approach this kind of question. Take the following example:

    formula = $C_6H_{12}Br_2$

    NMR spectrum, δ, ppm: 0.9 (t, 3H), 1.4 (s, 6H), 1.8 (m, 2H), 4.6 (t, 1H)

1. Write out, **underlined**, groups that correspond to the relative areas of each resonance (starting with the most probable combinations), including enough unprotonated carbons and other substituents to satisfy the formula:

   "3H" is usually a methyl: $\underline{CH_3}-$

   "6H" is usually two methyls: $\underline{CH_3}-$, $\underline{CH_3}-$ (but it could be 3 x $-\underline{CH_2}-$)

   "2H" is usually a CH_2: $-\underline{CH_2}-$

   "1H" is, of course: $-\underline{CH}-$

   other: $-\underline{C}-$, 2 $\underline{Br}-$ to satisfy $C_6H_{12}Br_2$

   Make sure the number of protons you have written adds up to the number in the molecule; if it doesn't, multiply everything by an integer (if that doesn't work, then the entire spectrum was not given).

2. Look at the splitting pattern, and include in your part structures the adjacent carbons with an appropriate number of protons, **not underlined**. Simply circle the multiplets:

   (t, 3H): $\underline{CH_3}-CH_2-$

   (s, 6H): $\underline{CH_3}-\underset{|}{\overset{|}{C}}-$, $\underline{CH_3}-\underset{|}{\overset{|}{C}}-$ (3 × $-\underset{|}{\overset{|}{C}}-\underline{CH_2}-\underset{|}{\overset{|}{C}}-$ can be ruled out because there are not enough non-hydrogen-bearing substituents to fit)

   (m, 2H): $\boxed{-\underline{CH_2}-}$

   (t, 1H): $-\underline{CH}-CH_2-$ or $-\underset{|}{\overset{|}{CH}}-\underline{CH}-\underset{|}{\overset{|}{CH}}-$

                 $-\underset{|}{\overset{|}{C}}-$, 2 $\underline{Br}$

3. Look for some correlation between the underlined and non-underlined groups.

   A. The underlined and circled CH_2 group (third set, above) must be the non-underlined CH_2 group of the first and fourth sets:

   $$CH_3-CH_2-\overset{|}{CH}-$$
   $$\text{t, 3H m, 2H t, 1H}$$

   B. The underlined, unsubstituted carbon must be the non-underlined, unsubstituted carbons of the second set:

   $$CH_3-\underset{|}{\overset{|}{C}}-CH_3$$
   $$\text{s, 6H}$$

   C. There is only one way to hook these two pieces together with two bromine atoms:

   $$CH_3-CH_2-CHBr-\underset{CH_3}{\overset{CH_3}{C}}-Br$$

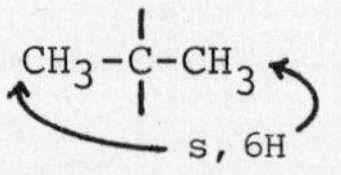

4. Use the chemical shift information as a check, at least, or as further help if the coupling patterns can't solve the problem (as above):

   R_2CH_2 (1.25) with adjacent Br (+0.5) = 1.75

   RCH_3 (0.9) with adjacent Br (+0.5) = 1.4

   $$CH_3—CH_2—CHBr—CBr(CH_3)_2$$

   RCH_3 (0.9)

   R_2CHBr (4.1) with adjacent Br (+0.5) = 4.6

   For many problems, you will be able to "see" the structure much more quickly than this stepwise process would suggest, but this methodical approach often avoids confusion in complex cases.

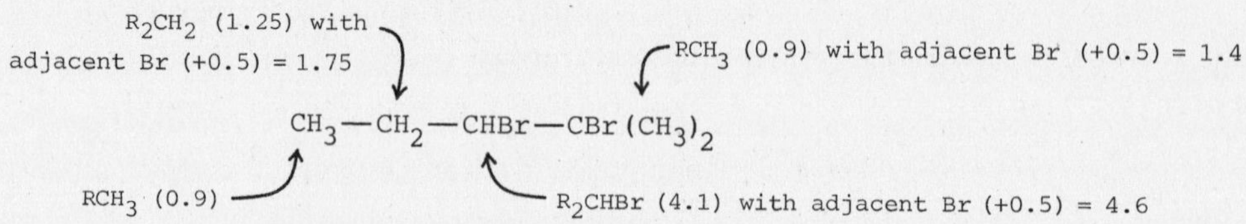

5. For CMR spectra

   The most important piece of information you can obtain from a CMR spectrum is how many different types of carbon atoms there are in the molecule. In many cases, this will tell you whether the structure is symmetrical or non-symmetrical in some way. If given, the multiplicity of the carbon resonance in the proton-**coupled** CMR spectrum will tell you directly if the carbon is a CH_3, CH_2, CH, or quaternary C.

Secondarily, chemical shift information can tell you:

A: Whether the signal corresponds to an alkene or alkane carbon,
     or if there is a heteroatom substituent

B: What nearby regions of the carbon skeleton look like (α-, β-, and γ-steric effects,
     <u>cis</u>/<u>trans</u> stereochemistry of alkenes, etc.)

13.D   Answers to Exercises

13.1 With a spectrometer operating at 250 MHz, the difference between the TMS and CH_3 resonances is 557.5 Hz (2.23 ppm); the difference between the CH_3 and CH_2 resonances is 442.5 Hz:

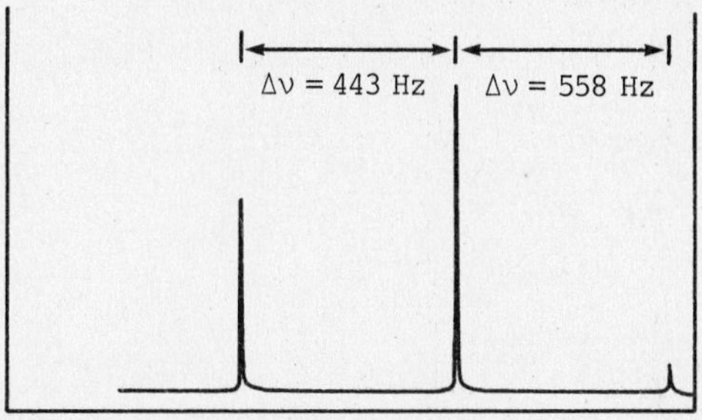

$\Delta\nu = 443$ Hz $\Delta\nu = 558$ Hz

13.2 (a)

$$H-\underset{\underset{Cl}{|}}{\overset{\overset{Cl}{|}}{C}}-\underset{\underset{CH_3}{|}}{\overset{\overset{CH_3}{|}}{C}}-CH_2-Cl$$

one hydrogen = area 1

two hydrogens = area 2

two equivalent methyl groups = area 6

(b)

four equivalent methyl groups = area 12

four equivalent hydrogens = area 4

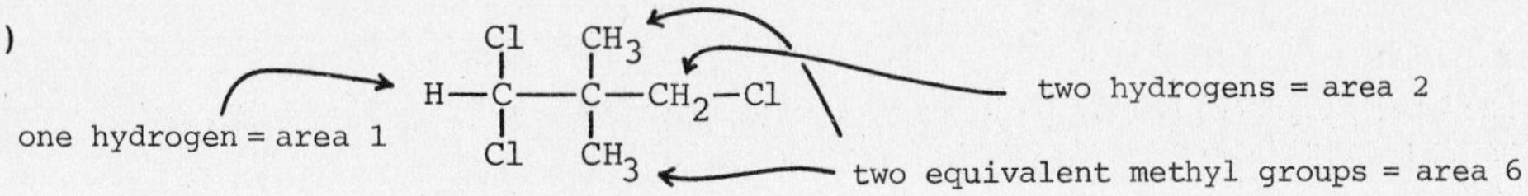

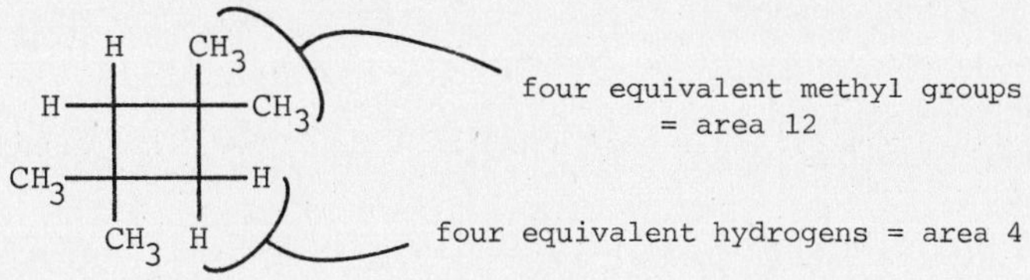

Ratio of peaks = 12:4 = 3:1

(c)   two equivalent methylene groups = area 4

$$CH_3-OCH_2CH_2O-CH_3$$

two equivalent methyl groups = area 6

Ratio of peaks = 6:4 = 3:2

(d)

Ratio of peaks = 3:1:1

13.3 (a)   (b)

1:1   1:1

Area   1   1   9

$(CH_3O)_2CHCH_3$

1:3:3:1   1:1

Area   1   6   3

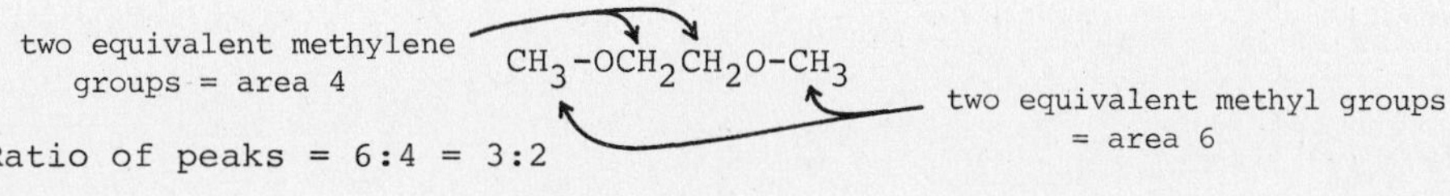

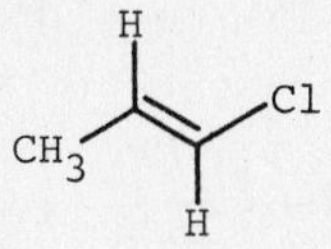

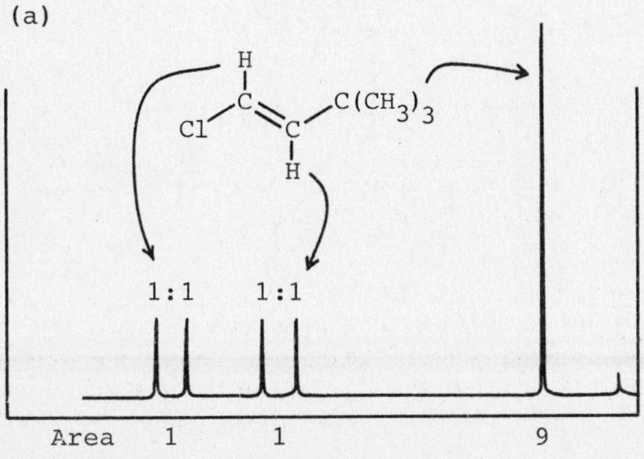

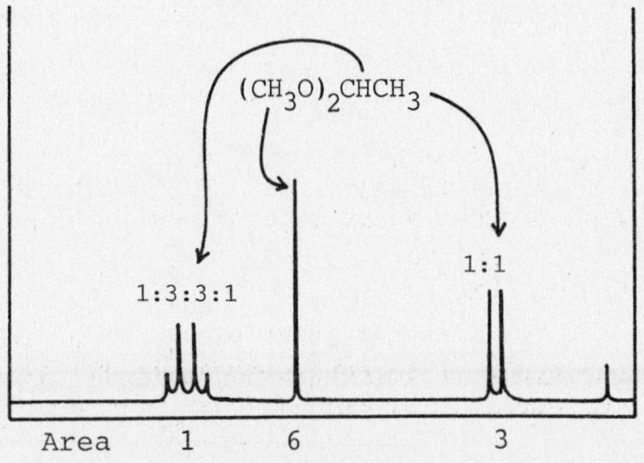

(c)

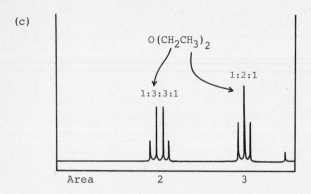

$O(CH_2CH_3)_2$

1:3:3:1

1:2:1

Area   2   3

(d)

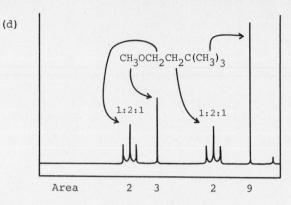

$CH_3OCH_2CH_2C(CH_3)_3$

1:2:1   1:2:1

Area   2   3   2   9

13.5

(a)

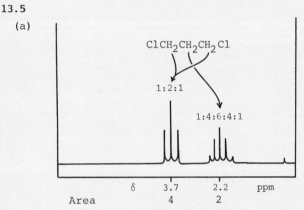

$ClCH_2CH_2CH_2Cl$

1:2:1

1:4:6:4:1

δ   3.7   2.2   ppm

Area   4   2

(b)

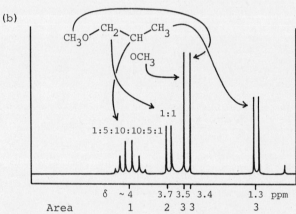

$CH_3O-CH_2-CH-CH_3$

OCH_3

1:1

1:5:10:10:5:1

δ   ~4   3.7 3.5 3.4   1.3   ppm

Area   1   2   3 3   3

NOTE: the resonance for the CH_2 group will not actually be a simple doublet (see explanations for problems #11(b) and #12(f)).

13.6 (a)

H_c H_a H_b

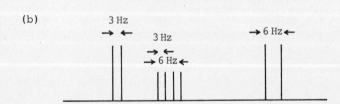

4 Hz   4 Hz   6 Hz

6 Hz

(b)

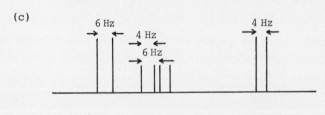

3 Hz   3 Hz   →6 Hz←

→6 Hz←

NOTE: the peaks for H_b will be about twice as tall as those for H_c, which in turn will be about twice as tall as those for H_a.

(c)

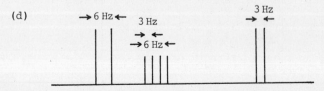

6 Hz   4 Hz   4 Hz

6 Hz

(d)

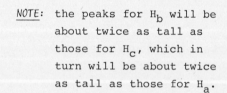

→6 Hz←   3 Hz   3 Hz

→6 Hz←

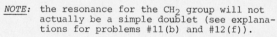

13.7

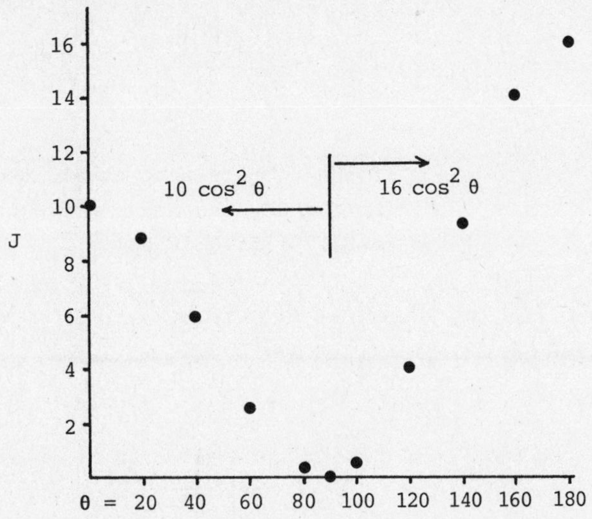

13.8 To a first approximation it will be a triple triplet, split equally by the two adjacent equatorial hydrogens ($J_{axial-equatorial} \approx 3$ Hz) and the two adjacent axial hydrogens ($J_{axial-axial} \approx 10$ Hz):

13.9 δ 0.9 ppm, triplet, 3 hydrogens: CH_3 next to a CH_2 group

1.1 ppm, doublet, 3 hydrogens: CH_3 next to a CH group

1.5 ppm, multiplet, 2 hydrogens: CH_2 next to several hydrogens

1.8 ppm, doublet, J = 2.3 Hz, 1 hydrogen: CH coupled to another CH group; the coupling constant suggests that the coupling is long range, through an acetylene: $\underline{H}C{\equiv}C{-}C\underline{H}\diagup$

2.3 ppm, multiplet, 1 hydrogen: CH next to several hydrogens

The pieces are therefore: $C\underline{H}_3{-}CH_2$, $C\underline{H}_3{-}CH$, $CH_n{-}C\underline{H}_2{-}CH_n$, $\underline{H}C{\equiv}C{-}C\underline{H}\diagup$, $-C\underline{H}(CH_n)$

From the formula, you can determine that there are 2 rings, 2 double bonds, 1 ring and 1 double bond, or 1 triple bond; the evidence above indicates that there is a triple bond. The structure which is consistent with all of the data is 3-methyl-1-propyne:

$$CH_3CH_2\overset{\overset{\textstyle CH_3}{|}}{C}HC{\equiv}CH$$

13.10 At room temperature, you expect a singlet because the resonances from axial and equatorial hydrogens are averaged rapidly by chair $\rightleftharpoons$ chair interconversion.

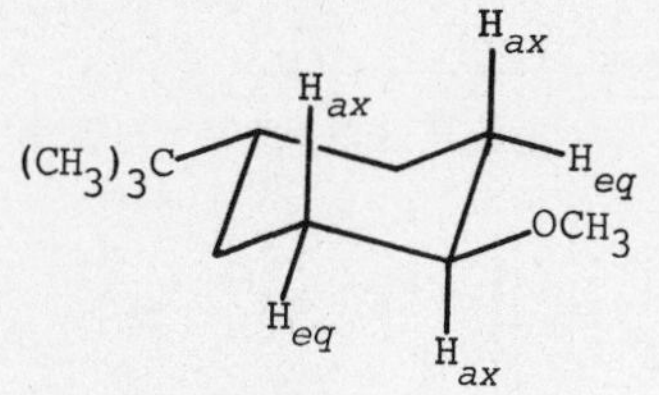

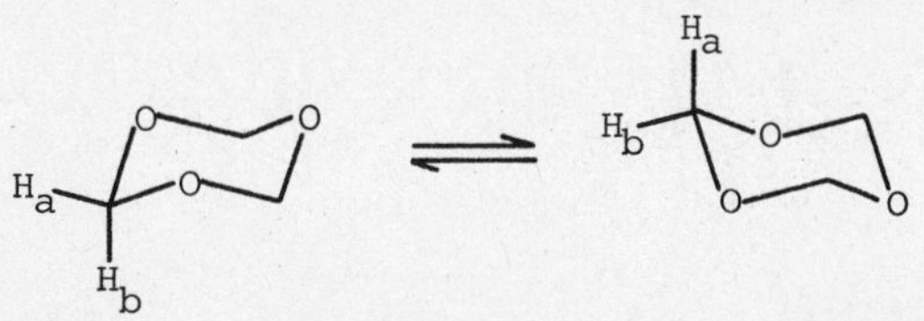

At -100 °C, this interconversion is slow ("frozen out"), and separate resonances for axial and equatorial hydrogens will be seen. Because the axial and equatorial H's are not equivalent, they will split each other and a pair of doublets will be observed.

13.12

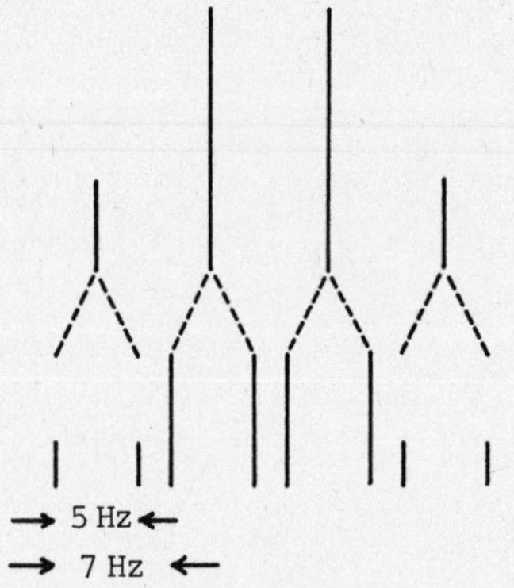

If the two J's were equal, the peak for the CH$_2$ resonance would be a simple sextet, 1:5:10:10:5:1.

→ 5 Hz ←
→ 7 Hz ←

13.13

7 Hz

5 Hz

7 Hz

5 Hz

δ 4.0   δ 2   δ 1.2

CH—   -OH   (CH$_3$)$_2$

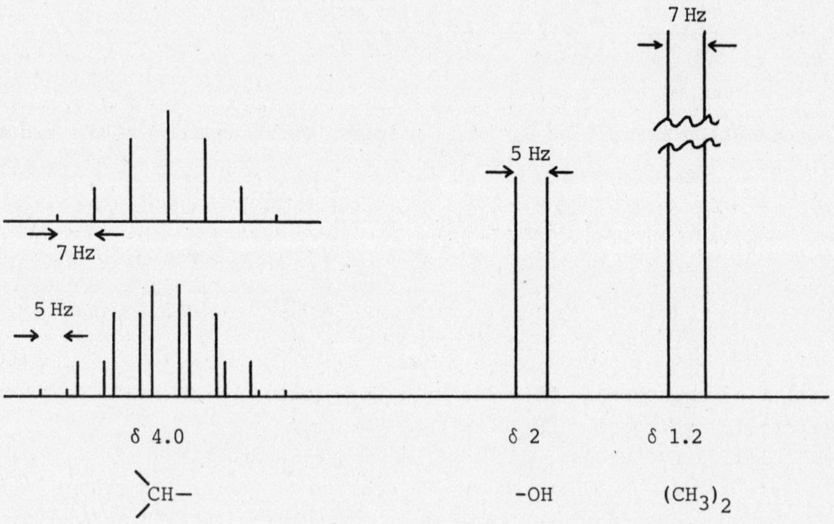

13.14 The fact that the CMR spectrum shows only four resonances indicates that the isomer is a meso compound, i.e., that there is a plane of symmetry that makes the C-1 equivalent to the C-5 carbon, C-2 equivalent to C-4, and the two methyls equivalent. The two isomers below are therefore eliminated by the CMR spectrum:

Cl   Cl   Cl   Cl
OH   OH

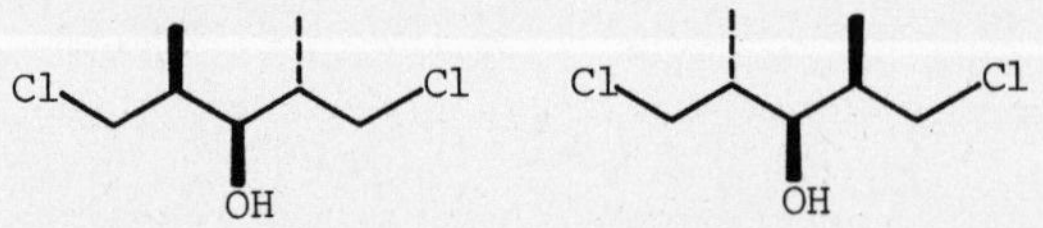

These meso compounds would give four-line CMR spectra:

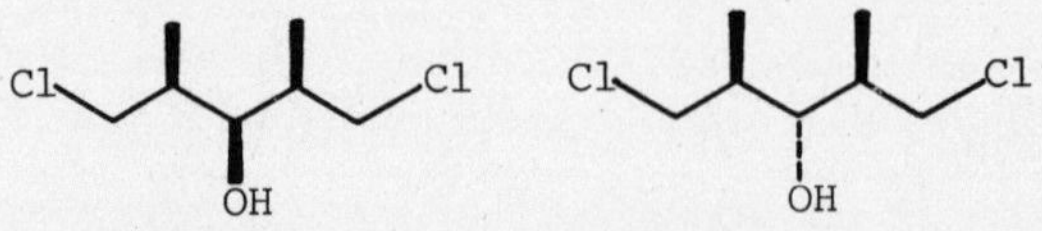

Cl   Cl   Cl   Cl
OH   OH

13.15

OH		OH		OH		OH	
CH$_3$		CH$_2$		CH-CH$_3$		CH$_3$-C-CH$_3$	
		CH$_3$		CH$_3$		CH$_3$	

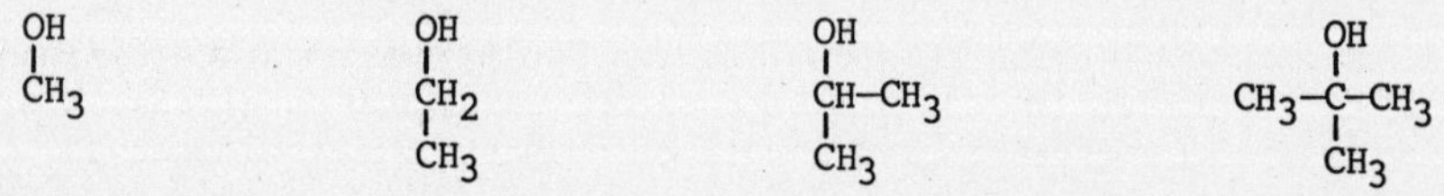

δ   49.3 + 9 = 58   + 9 = 67   + 9 =   76 ←— calculated
     49.3   57.3   63.7   68.7 ←— actual

13.16

	δ for hexane	+	correction	=	estimated δ	(actual δ)
CH_3	13.9		γ, -2.5		11.4	10.9
CH_2	22.9		β, +9.5		32.4	29.5
CH—CH_3	32.0		α, +9.0		41.0	34.3
CH_2	32.0		β, +9.5		41.5	39.0
CH_2	22.9		γ, -2.5		20.4	20.2
CH_3	13.9		none		13.9	13.9

To calculate resonance for the C-3 methyl group: 13.7   [δ (CH_3 in <u>n</u>-pentane)]
+ 9.5   [β-substituent]
- 2.5   [γ-substituent]
= 20.7 ppm   (actual = 18.8 ppm)

Note that the correspondance is not exact, especially for the α-effect. If additional effects such as branching are taken into account, a more accurate prediction can be obtained. Estimations of this sort are usually employed to assign a particular resonance to a particular carbon, rather than to assign structure of an unknown compound. From the practical point of view, application of the α-, β-, and γ-effects as above is enough to confirm or rule out various possibilities.

13.17   The C-3 methylene group of the (<u>Z</u>)-isomer will resonate at lower chemical shift values (will be shifted upfield) relative to that of the (<u>E</u>)-isomer, as a result of the γ-inter-action with the methyl group at the other end of the double bond. For the same reason, the effect on the resonance which corresponds to the methyl substituent on C-3 will be opposite: it will occur at higher chemical shift (downfield) in the (<u>Z</u>)-isomer than in the (<u>E</u>)-isomer.

13.18   The CMR spectrum of cycloheptene will consist of 4 lines, three in the upfield region (δ 20-35 ppm) and one in the alkene region (δ 125-135 ppm).

13.19   (a) δ 1.0, s, 6H: 2 isolated CH_3's
3.4, s, 4H: 2 isolated CH_2's

The only possibility is 1,3-dibromo-2,2-dimethylpropane: $Br-CH_2-\overset{\overset{\displaystyle CH_3}{|}}{\underset{\underset{\displaystyle CH_3}{|}}{C}}-CH_2-Br$

(b) δ 1.0, t, 6H: 2 $C\mathbf{H_3}-CH_2$
2.4, q, 4H: 2 $CH_3-C\mathbf{H_2}-C$

A symmetrical structure is again required: 3,3-dibromopentane, $CH_3-CH_2-\overset{\overset{\displaystyle Br}{|}}{\underset{\underset{\displaystyle Br}{|}}{C}}-CH_2-CH_3$

(c) δ 0.9, d, 6H: $(CH_3)_2CH$
1.5, m, 1H: CH
1.85, t, 2H: $CH-C\mathbf{H_2}-CH$ ($CH_2-C\mathbf{H_2}-C$ won't fit rest of the data)
5.3, t, 1H: chemical shift indicates $CH_2-C\mathbf{H}Br_2$

All the pieces fit together as 1,1-dibromo-3-methylbutane: $(CH_3)_2CHCH_2CHBr_2$

(d) δ 1.0, s, 9H: $(CH_3)_3C$
5.3, s, 1H: $C-CHBr_2$

1,1-dibromo-2,2-dimethylpropane: $(CH_3)_3CCHBr_2$

(e) δ 1.0, d, 6H: $(C\mathbf{H_3})_2)CH$
1.75, m, 1H: C$\mathbf{H}$
3.95, d, 2H: $Br-C\mathbf{H_2}-CH$
4.7, q, 1H: $CH-\underset{\underset{\displaystyle Br}{|}}{C\mathbf{H}}-CH_2$

(f) δ 1.3, m, 2H: $C\mathbf{H_2}$
1.85, m, 4H: 2 CH_2-C-Br
3.35, t, 4H: 2 $CH_2-C\mathbf{H_2}-Br$

1,5-dibromopentane: $BrCH_2CH_2CH_2CH_2CH_2Br$

These fit together only one way:
1,2-dibromo-3-methylbutane, $(CH_3)_2CHCHBrCH_2Br$

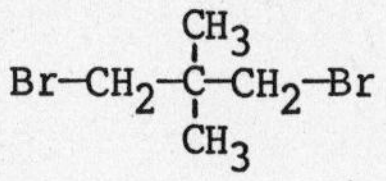

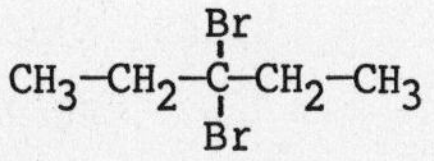

13.E   Answers and Explanations for Problems

1. In the NMR spectrum of ethyl bromide, the methyl hydrogens have δ = 1.7 ppm, the methylene hydrogens have δ = 3.3 ppm, and J=7 Hz. The number of peaks given by the methyl hydrogens is three, with the approximate area ratio of 1:2:1. These peaks are separated by 7 Hz. The number of peaks given by the methylene hydrogens is four, with an approximate area ratio of 1:3:3:1. These peaks are separated by 7 Hz. The total area of the methyl peaks compared to the methylene peaks is in the ratio 3:2. Of these two groups of peaks, the **methylene** peaks are farther downfield. The chemical shift difference between these peaks of 1.6 ppm corresponds in a 180-MHz instrument to 288 Hz and in a 250-MHz instrument to 400 Hz.

2.   (a) δ 0.95, t, 3H: **CH₃**—CH₂
           1.52, sextet, 2H: CH₂—**CH₂**—CH₃
           3.30, s, 3H: **CH₃**—O (you can tell it's a methyl ether from the chemical shift)
           3.40, t, 2H: CH₂—**CH₂**—O

           Structure: methyl propyl ether, CH₃—O—CH₂—CH₂—CH₃

      (b) δ 1.15, s, 1: this can only be an OH
           1.28, s, 9: and this must be a t-butyl group

           Structure: t-butyl alcohol, $(CH_3)_3COH$

      (c) δ 1.20, t, 3H: **CH₃**—CH₂
           3.45, q, 2H: CH₃—**CH₂**—O (you can tell the oxygen is attached to this carbon because of
                                      the chemical shift)

Although there appear to be only 5 hydrogens accounted for by the data given, remember that the areas are a relative ratio only: five hydrogens in a 3:2 ratio could just as well be ten hydrogens in a 6:4 ratio. The structure is diethyl ether:

                                      CH₃—CH₂—O—CH₂—CH₃

      (d) δ 0.90, d, 6H: (**CH₃**)₂CH
           1.78, m, 1H: C**H**—(CHₙ)
           2.45, t, 1H: could be **H**O—CH₂
           3.45, t, 2H: HO—**CH₂**—CH

           Structure: 2-methyl-1-propanol, $(CH_3)_2CH$—CH₂—OH

      (e) δ 1.13, d, 6H: (**CH₃**)₂CH (because of the downfield shift of the methyl groups, there is
                                              probably an oxygen on the CH carbon)
           3.30, s, 3H: **CH₃**—O
           3.65, septet, 1H: (CH₃)₂**CH**—O

           Structure: methyl isopropyl ether, $(CH_3)_2CH$—O—CH₃

      (f) δ 0.95, t, 3H: **CH₃**—CH₂
           1.50, m, 4H: four hydrogens must be 2 CH₂ groups
           2.20, t, 1H: **H**O—CH₂
           3.70, dt, 2H: HO—**CH₂**—CH₂

           Structure: 1-butanol, CH₃—CH₂—CH₂—CH₂—OH

      (g) δ 0.92, t, 3H: **CH₃**—CH₂
           1.18, d, 3H: **CH₃**—CH
           1.45, m, 2H: **CH₂**—(CHₙ)
           1.80, d, 1H: **H**O—CH
           3.75, m, 1H: O—**CH**—(CHₙ) (You know that there is an oxygen attached because of the
                                          chemical shift)
                         OH
                         |
           Structure: 2-butanol, CH₃—CH—CH₂—CH₃

3.   A: two methyls, $CH_3CCl_2CH_3$

B: δ, 1.2 (t, 3H) = $C\underline{H}_3$-CH_2

δ, 1.9 (quint, 2H) = CH_3-$C\underline{H}_2$-CH (<u>or</u> -CH_2-$C\underline{H}_2$-CH_2- but this is inconsistent with the
other information)

δ, 5.8 (t, 1H) = -CH_2-$C\underline{H}X_2$

This is all consistent with $CH_3CH_2CHCl_2$.

C: δ, 1.4 (d, 3H) = $C\underline{H}_3$-CH

δ, 3.8 (d, 2H) = -CH-$C\underline{H}_2$-

δ, 4.3 (sextet, 1H) = CH_3-$C\underline{H}$-CH_2-

$\left.\begin{array}{c} \\ \\ \\ \end{array}\right\}$ CH_3CHCH_2Cl
$\quad\quad\quad\underset{Cl}{|}$

D: δ, 2.2 (quint, 2H) = -CH_2-$C\underline{H}_2$-CH_2- (<u>or</u> CH_3-$C\underline{H}_2$-CH- but this is inconsistent with the
other information)

δ, 3.7 (t, 4H) = -$C\underline{H}_2$-CH_2-$C\underline{H}_2$-

The structure must be $ClCH_2CH_2CH_2Cl$.

4.   (a)   The doublet at δ 1.7 ppm, corresponding to six

hydrogens, suggests two equivalent $C\underline{H}_3$-CH units. Hence, $CH_3\overset{\displaystyle Br}{\underset{\displaystyle |}{C}}H-\overset{\displaystyle Br}{\underset{\displaystyle |}{C}}HCH_3$

The quartet at δ 4.4 ppm is therefore the two equivalent C-H's.

(b)   Again, the doublet at δ 1.7 suggests CH_3CH-, but now there is only one. Hence, the molecule
contains the unit: CH_3CHBr-. Since there is no other methyl, the second bromine must be
at the other end of the chain. Thus the structure is $CH_3\underset{\underset{\textstyle Br}{|}}{C}HCH_2CH_2Br$.

5.   (a)

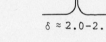

δ ≈ 2.0-2.4

(d)   J ≈ 7 Hz

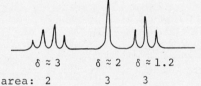

δ ≈ 3   δ ≈ 2   δ ≈ 1.2
area: 2   3   3

(b)   J ≈ 7 Hz

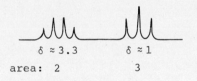

δ ≈ 3.3   δ ≈ 1

area: 2   3

(e)   See problem #4(b).

(c)   See problem #4(a).

6.   Since there are only three separate resonances, there must be some symmetry to the structure.
The doublet in the proton-coupled CMR spectrum corresponds to a CH group, the triplet to a CH_2
and the quartet to CH_3. To add up to ten hydrogens, these must be present as two equivalent
CH_3's, two equivalent CH's, and one CH_2 group:

2,4-dibromopentane, $CH_3-\overset{\underset{\textstyle Br}{|}}{C}H-CH_2-\overset{\underset{\textstyle Br}{|}}{C}H-CH_3$

7.   E and F:

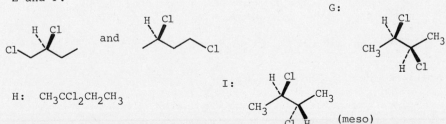

H: $CH_3CCl_2CH_2CH_3$

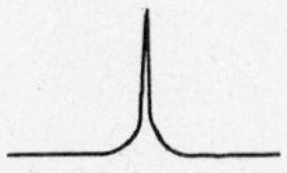

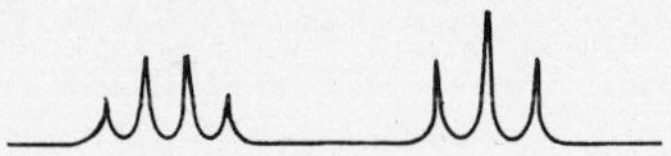

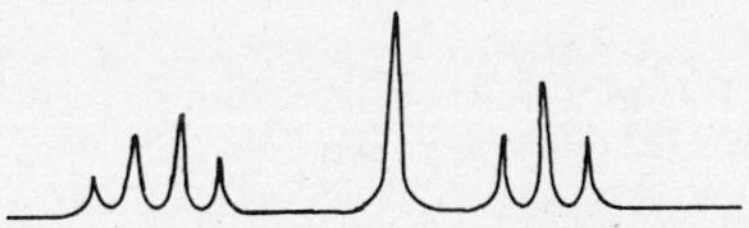

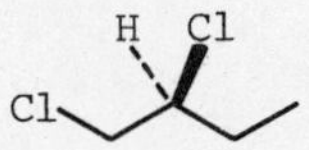

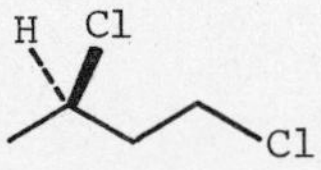

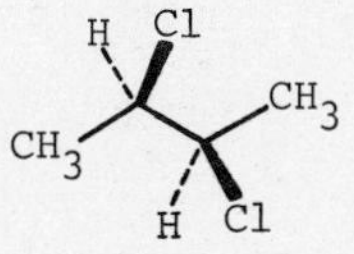

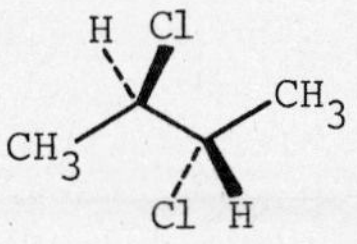

(meso)

8. (a) CH_3-CCl_3

  (b) $HOCH_2-C(CH_3)_3$

  (c) CH_3-CH_2-I

  (d) δ 2.2, quintet, area 2: $CH_2-\underline{CH}_2-CH_2$

    δ 3.7, t, area 4: $2 \times Cl-\underline{CH}_2-CH_2$

    Structure: $Cl-CH_2-CH_2-CH_2-Cl$

  (e) $\begin{array}{c} CH_3 \\ \\ CH_3 \end{array}\!\!CH-OH$

  (f) $Cl-CH_2-C\equiv C-H$ Note the long-range coupling across the triple bond

9. $CH_3-CHCl-CH-Cl_2$ *NOTE*: the resonance at δ 0 ppm is due to tetramethylsilane as chemical shift reference.

10. The peaks 104.5 Hz above and below the main peak for $CHCl_3$ are the doublet due to $^{13}CHCl_3$. The separation of these two peaks corresponds to the carbon-proton coupling constant (209 Hz). In the proton-coupled CMR spectrum of $CHCl_3$, a doublet would appear (at 77 ppm) with the same coupling constant, i.e. with a separation of 209 Hz also.

11. (a) With equal areas under the two peaks in the NMR spectrum, and only two peaks in the CMR spectrum, the molecule must be quite symmetrical. The presence of an ether is suggested by the downfield position (3.6 ppm) of one of the peaks in the NMR spectrum.

  Structure: tetrahydrofuran

  The spectrum of tetrahydrofuran does not show the pair of clean triplets that one would expect from a first order analysis. Although coupling is not observed between the two equivalent CH_2 groups at C-3 and C-4, their interaction has an effect on the patterns of the other CH_2 resonances. This "non-first order" effect, which is sometimes called "virtual coupling", results in a more complicated pattern for both sets of peaks.

  (b) Two peaks in the CMR spectrum: symmetrical structure again. The downfield position of the resonances in both spectra suggest that electronegative elements are present. In the NMR spectrum, the area ratio of 4:1, and the fact that the downfield resonance (δ 4.2) is a quintet, suggests that the compound is 1,2,3-trichloropropane:

  $$Cl-CH_2-\overset{\displaystyle Cl}{\overset{|}{C}H}-CH_2-Cl$$

  (*NOTE*: the resonances for the CH_2 groups are not simple doublets as you might expect. The two hydrogens in each CH_2 are **not** equivalent, and therefore they can have different chemical shifts as well as split each other. The easiest way to convince yourself that the two hydrogens are not equivalent is to make two different models of 1,2,3-trichloropropane, substituting first one and then the other hydrogen on one of the CH_2 groups with bromine (or anything other than hydrogen or chlorine). You will see that the two models you have made are **not** the same, and that they are not enantiomers either. They are diastereomers, hence the relationship between the two hydrogens that you substituted is referred to as **diastereotopic.**)

  (c) The CMR spectrum indicates four carbons, two of which are probably double-bond carbons and two which are sp^3-hydridized; one of the latter contains an electron-withdrawing group because of its position around 63 ppm. The NMR spectrum indicates four types of hydrogens: two on a double bond (δ 5.6 ppm), one OH group (broad, 4.5 ppm), and CH_2 and CH_3 groups. Both of these are downfield from their position in alkanes because they are attached to the double bond, and because the OH is on the CH_2 group. The structure is 2-buten-1-ol:

  $$CH_3-CH=CH-CH_2-OH$$

12. (a) δ 1.0, d, 6H: $(C\underline{H}_3)_2CH$

    2.0, looks like a septet, but could be **nine** peaks, 1H: $(CH_3)_2C\underline{H}-CH_2$

    3.4, d, 2H: $CH-C\underline{H}_2-Cl$

    Structure: $(CH_3)_2CH-CH_2-Cl$

  (b) $CH_3-CH_2-CH_2-CH_2-I$

  (c) The downfield resonances (δ 5.1 and ~5.8 ppm) are characteristic for a vinyl group ($CH_2=CH-$), with a complex non-first order splitting pattern. The remaining two carbons, four hydrogens, and a bromine, must be arranged either as 3-bromo-1-butene or 4-bromo-1-butene:

  $$CH_3-CHBr-CH=CH_2 \qquad\qquad Br-CH_2-CH_2-CH=CH_2$$

These are easily distinguished by the resonances in the upfield portion of the spectrum: the triplet at δ 3.4 and the quartet at δ 2.4 ppm are clearly the CH_2's next to the bromine and the double bond, respectively, in 4-bromo-1-butene. If you look closely at the quartet at δ 2.4 ppm, you can actually see long range coupling to the $=CH_2$ hydrogens: each peak in the quartet is barely perceptible as a triplet.

(d)   The formula C_5H_8O tells you that there are either two π bonds or two rings, or one of each.   The NMR spectrum shows the following:

δ 1.5, s, 6H: probably two equivalent, isolated methyl groups, with the chemical shift suggesting that the carbon they are attached to has the oxygen attached

δ 2.2, s, 1H: could be an acetylenic hydrogen, $\equiv C-H$

δ 2.9, broad, 1H: because it is broad, it is likely to be an OH

The structure is 2-methyl-3-butyn-2-ol:

$$\begin{array}{c} CH_3 \\ | \\ CH_3-C-C\equiv C-H \\ | \\ OH \end{array}$$

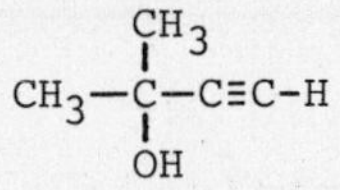

(e)   The formula indicates that there is one double bond or a ring.

δ 1.3, t, 3H: $\underline{CH}_3-CH_2$

3.7, q, 2H: $CH_3-\underline{CH}_2-O$

3.9, dd (see insert to discern pattern), 1H, and
4.0, dd, 1H: two hydrogens at the end of a double bond: $=CH_2$

6.4, dd, 1H: $O-\underline{CH}=CH_2$

The structure is ethyl vinyl ether: $CH_3-CH_2-CH=CH_2$

Notice how the CH= hydrogen is shifted further downfield than a normal olefinic hydrogen because of the electron-withdrawing oxygen substituent. Conversely, the $=CH_2$ hydrogens are shifted upfield in comparison to normal because of the enol ether resonance structure (see below) which puts **more** electron density at that position.

$$CH_3CH_2-O-CH=CH_2 \qquad\qquad CH_3CH_2-\overset{+}{O}=CH-CH_2^-$$

(f)   This is a spectacular spectrum, isn't it?!! Note that the peak areas are in the ratio of 6:1:4:1, which for 24 hydrogens is 12:2:8:2.

δ 1.2, t, 12H: four equivalent methyl groups, attached to CH_2's

1.8, t, 2H: CH_2 next to another CH_2 or between two CH's

3.5, multiplet, 8H: this pattern is actually quite interpretable; if you look

closely, you can see that there are actually four quartets that are overlapping. The quartets arise from coupling to a methyl group. If we imagine that the quartet coupling is "removed", what would be left is a pattern of four lines, shown below, which are known as an "AB pattern". In other words, if you take an AB pattern and split every line into a quartet, you will get the observed multiplet:

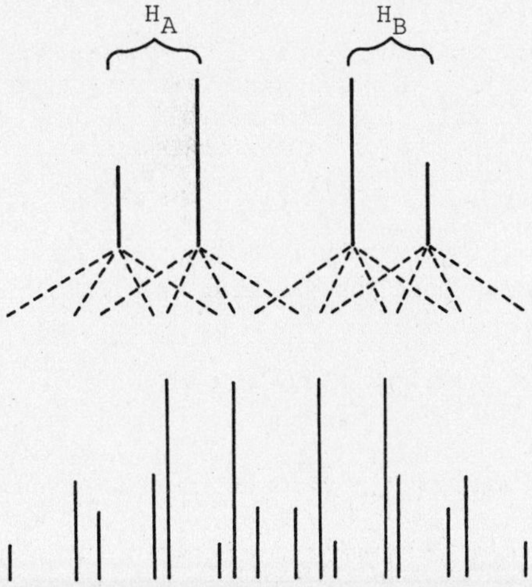

An AB pattern arises from two hydrogens which are strongly coupled to each other; that is, the chemical shift idfference between them is not much greater than their coupling constant. Rather than appearing as a simple pair of doublets, the doublets of an AB pattern "lean" strongly toward each other. The two hydrogens of the CH_2 groups that give rise to this "quartet" of AB patterns are **diastereotopic** because, from their point of view, a carbon near to them is chiral. Again, you can convince yourself of this by making two models of the compound (shown below), substituting first one and then the other hydrogen of one of the CH_2 groups with something else, and comparing the two models that you have made. They will be diastereomers.

δ 4.5, t, 2H: because of the far downfield position, it must be on a carbon with two oxygens: $(RO)_2C\underline{H}-CH_2$

The structure is 1,1,3,3-tetraethoxypropane:

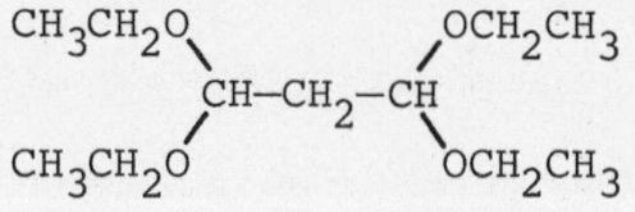

13. There are only four isomers of C_4H_9Br, shown below (X = Br):

1- and 2-Bromobutane will have four resonances in the CMR spectrum; t-butyl bromide will have only two. With only three carbon resonances, there is only one possibility: 1-bromo-2-methyl-propane. The proton NMR spectrum will be similar to that of the chloride; see the spectrum for Problem #12 (a).

14. The four possible compounds are shown for the answer above (X = Cl). The fact that there are four resonances in the CMR spectrum of the compound indicates that it is either 1- or 2-chlorobutane. The proton-coupled CMR spectrum of 1-chlorobutane would show a quartet (for C-4) and three triplets (for carbons 1-3); that of the 2-chloro isomer would show two quartets (C-1 and C-4), a triplet (C-3) and a doublet (C-2).

15. On the NMR time scale, the two methyls are averaged by the chair ⇌ chair interconversion:

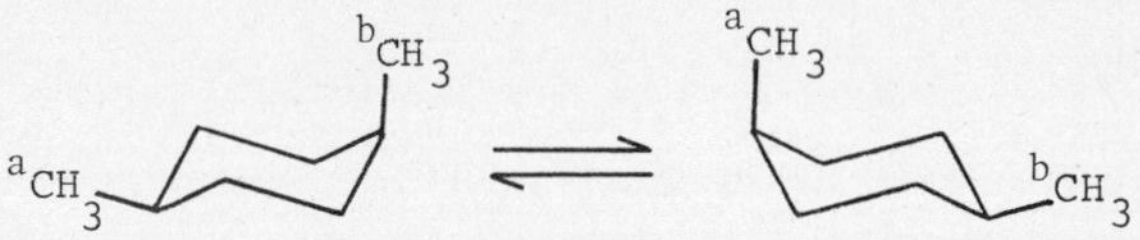

At lower temperatures where this interconversion occurs slowly, separate signals are seen for the two methyls.

16. (a) All of the carbons are CH_2 groups since they are all triplets in the proton-coupled spectrum. The compound must therefore be 5-chloro-1-pentanol: $Cl-CH_2-CH_2-CH_2-CH_2-CH_2-OH$

(b) The fact that there are only four carbon resonances for eight carbons indicates that the compound must be a dibutyl ether. The multiplicity of the four peaks (3 triplets and 1 quartet) shows that the compound is di-n-butyl ether:

$$CH_3-CH_2-CH_2-CH_2-O-CH_2-CH_2-CH_2-CH_3$$

(c) δ 75.1 (d): $\underline{C}$HOH
35.3 (s): $\underline{C}$, with no hydrogens
25.8 (q), much more intense than the others: probably the $\underline{C}H_3$'s of a t-butyl group
18.2 (q): $\underline{C}H_3$

The structure is 3,3-dimethyl-2-butanol:

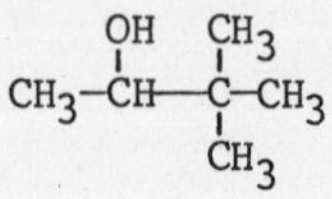

(d) δ 65.5 (d): $\underline{C}H-O$
49.2 (t): $\underline{C}H_2$
25.1 (d): $\underline{C}H$
24.3 and 22.7 (q): $\underline{C}H_3$'s. Since there are 5 resonances and 6 carbons, it is likely that one of the methyl resonances represents two equivalent methyl groups.

The structure is 4-methyl-2-pentanol:

$$CH_3-\overset{\overset{\displaystyle OH}{|}}{CH}-CH_2-\overset{\overset{\displaystyle CH_3}{|}}{CH}-CH_3$$

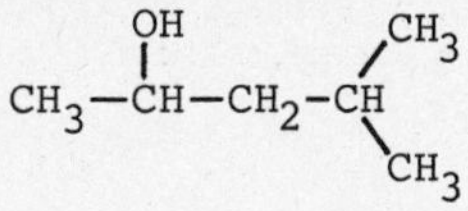

(e) With two types of carbon, the possibilities are obviously limited.

   δ 71.1 (d): CH—O

      33.9 (t): CH₂

With only CH and CH₂ groups, the only reasonable structure is cyclohexane-1,4-diol (from the data given it is difficult to predict whether it is the _cis_ or the _trans_ isomer):

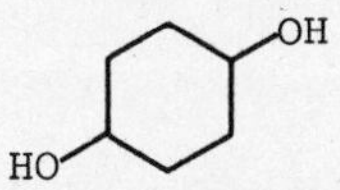

17. The remaining possibilities for simple elimination products from 3-bromo-2,3-dimethylpentane are E- and Z-3,4-dimethyl-2-pentene. These can be readily distinguished from their CMR spectrum: the Z-isomer will have the resonance for the C-3 methyl group downfield from that for the E-isomer; conversely, the C-4 carbon in the Z-isomer will be upfield of that in the E-isomer:

Isomer J:

12.4 20.6
28.5 117.9
17.8 141.0

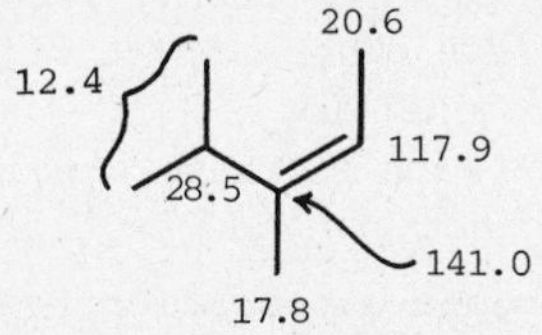

(Z-3,4-dimethyl-2-pentene)

Isomer K:

13.0, 13.1 37.4 116.2
21.6
141.5

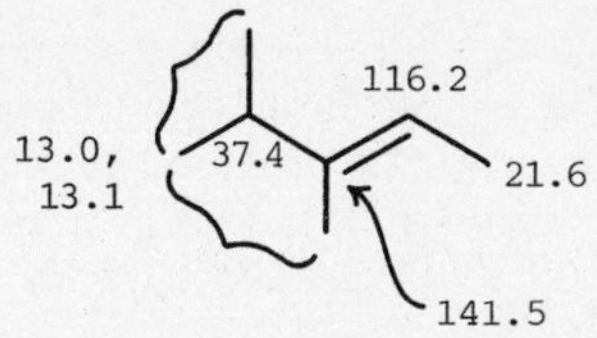

(E-3,4-dimethyl-2-pentene)

18. Isomers L and M: The CMR spectrum indicates one type of methyl and two types of alkene carbon. The structures are therefore the symmetrical stereoisomers of 2,4-hexadiene. Which one is Z,Z- and which is E,E- can be decided from the chemical shifts of the methyl groups: the methyl resonance in the Z,Z-isomer will come upfield of that of the E,E-isomer. Isomer L is therefore Z,Z-2,4-hexadiene, and isomer M is E,E-2,4-hexadiene. Not surprisingly, Isomer N is the unsymmetrical isomer.

Isomer L: Isomer M: Isomer N:

Z,Z-2,4-hexadiene   E,E-2,4-hexadiene   E,Z-2,4-hexadiene

19. The two isomers that can be formed are 3-methylcyclopentene and 4-methylcyclopentene:

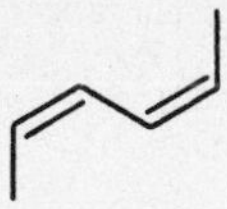

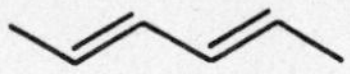

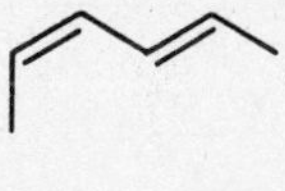

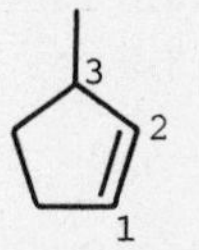

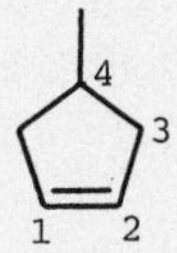

4-Methylcyclopentene is symmetrical and will show only four resonances in the cmr spectrum; every carbon in 3-methylcyclopentene is different, however, and six peaks appear in the CMR spectrum.

20.

	δ		δ	Δδ	
CH₃	13.2	CH₃	13.9	+0.7	(= δ-effect)
CH₂	25.0	CH₂	19.4	−5.6	(= γ-effect)
CH₂	25.0	CH₂	35.3	+10.3	(= β-effect)
CH₃	13.2	CH₂OH	61.7	+48.5	(= α-effect)

Using the known effects of Cl substitution, the following chemical shifts would be predicted:

ClCH₂—CH₂—CH₂—CH₂OH   CH₃—CHCl—CH₂—CH₂OH   CH₃—CH₂—CHCl—CH₂OH
45   30   30   62   25   50   46   57   9   30   66   61

$$\left(\begin{array}{c} & & & \overset{\text{Cl}}{\underset{|}{}} \\ \text{CH}_3 - \text{CH}_2 - \text{CH}_2 - \text{CHOH} \\ 14 \quad\;\; 14 \quad\;\; 46 \quad\;\; 93 \end{array} \right. \quad \text{This molecule is unstable } \Big)$$

4-Chloro-1-butanol certainly corresponds most closely to the observed values.

21. For the same reason that acetylenic hydrogens come in between alkane and alkene hydrogens, the sp-hybridized carbons in an acetylene are shielded by the diamagnetic anisotropy of the π-electron cloud (see Section 13.9 and Figure 13.3 in the Text).

22. Isomer O, with one vinyl hydrogen in the proton nmr spectrum, must be 1-methylcyclohexene; isomers P and Q, with 2 vinyl hydrogens in the proton NMR, must be 3- and 4-methylcyclohexene. Isomer P must be 3-methylcyclohexene because one of the alkene carbons shows a downfield shift from the adjacent methyl group (β-effect). In the isomeric 4-methylcyclohexene (isomer Q), the methyl substituent is further removed from the double bond and has no effect on the resonances of the sp^2-hybridized carbons. It is only by coincidence that these carbons resonate exactly at the same place, since they are not equivalent.

23. (a) The overall apppearance of a CMR spectrum of 2-pentanol doubly labeled at C-2 and C-3 will be of two doublets (^{13}C-2 and ^{13}C-3 will split each other). There will also be much weaker peaks (1% of the intensity of the labeled carbons) for C-1, C-4, and C-5; these minor peaks will be split into double doublets, since each of these carbons will be coupled to the two labeled carbons (and the two coupling constants will be different).

   (b) Since the 2-pentyl cation intermediate undergoes carbocation rearrangement during the course of the dehydration, and the alkene itself isomerizes in the reaction mixture, the <u>trans</u>-2-pentene that is isolated is a mixture of C-2,C-3- and C-3,C-4-^{13}C-labeled material. That which has the ^{13}C-label in the C-2 and C-3 positions is responsible for the doublets at δ 123.6 (J = 70 Hz) and 133.2 (J = 70 Hz) ppm, and the isomer with the label at C-3 and C-4 for the doublets at 25.8 (J = 40 Hz) and 133.2 (J = 40 Hz).

24. The hydrogens are split by the fluorine spins, with J_{HF} = 50 Hz. The spectrum is a triplet since the two fluorines are equivalent. Note that in a different region in the nmr spectrum it is possible to determine the fluorine NMR spectrum, which would also show a triplet with the same coupling constant.

25.
$$\text{CH}_3 - \text{CH}_2 - \text{F}$$
$$\delta\;\; 14.6 \nearrow \qquad\quad \curvearrowright \; 79.3$$

Each resonance is split by ^{19}F (remember, the spectrum is only **proton** decoupled).

26. The excess proportion of α-spins is 3×10^{-5} (Section 13.5) × 0.01 moles = 3×10^{-7} moles (of α-spin converted to β) × 0.017 cal mole^{-1} (Section 13.3)
$$= 5.1 \times 10^{-9} \text{ cal}$$

$$\frac{5.1 \times 10^{-9} \text{ cal}}{1 \text{ cal deg}^{-1} \text{ mL}^{-1}} \times 1 \text{ mL} = 5.1 \times 10^{-9} \text{ deg} \quad \text{(not much!)}$$

13.F   **Supplementary Problems**

S1.   From the molecular formulas and NMR spectral data given below, deduce the structure of each compound.

(a) $C_4H_7Cl_3$; δ 1.4 (s, 3H); 4.0 (s, 4H)
(b) $C_4H_7Cl_3$; δ 1.3 (d, 3H); 2.1 (s, 3H); 4.6 (q, 1H)
(c) $C_4H_8Br_2$; δ 1.0 (d, 3H); 2.5 (m, 1H); 3.3 (d, 4H)
(d) $C_4H_7Br_3$; δ 1.4 (d, 3H); 2.6 (t, 2H); 3.6 (m, 1H), 5.4 (t, 1H)

S2.   Sketch the NMR spectra of the following compounds. Be sure to represent the expected δ for each group of peaks, the relative areas, and the splitting patterns.

(a) $ICH_2CH_2CHCl_2$
(b) $(CH_3)_3CCHClCH_2Cl$
(c) $(CH_3)_2CHCHCH_2Cl$ with Cl substituent
(d) $(CH_3)_2CHCHCl_2$

(e) $(CH_3CH_2)_2CHCH_2Br$

(f)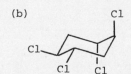

S3.   How many resonances do you expect to see in the CMR spectrum of each of the following compounds at 25 °C?   At -100 °C?

(a)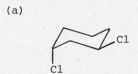

(b)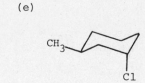

(c)

(d)

(e)

S4.   The NMR spectrum of a rapidly (on the NMR time scale) interconverting mixture of conformational isomers is the weighted average of the spectra of the individual conformations. At low temperature, the chemical shifts of H-1 in axial- and equatorial-chlorocyclohexane are as shown below.   Predict the observed chemical shift of this proton at room temperature.

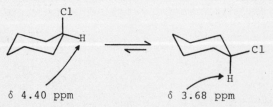

δ 4.40 ppm δ 3.68 ppm

S5.   For 1,1-diphenylpropane, J_{ab} = 7 Hz is in the expected range for acyclic alkanes. In 2-methyl-1,1-diphenylpropane, however, $J_{a'b'}$ is > 10 Hz.

Using the Karplus curve (Fig. 13.27) and Newman projections, offer an explanation for this increase in the coupling constant J.

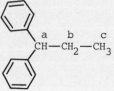

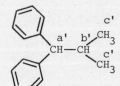

J_{ab} = 7 Hz $J_{a'b'}$ = > 10 Hz

13.G   Answers to Supplementary Problems

S1.   (a) $(ClCH_2)_2CClCH_3$ (b) $CH_3CCl_2CHClCH_3$

(c) $CH_3CH(CH_2Br)_2$ (d) $CH_3CHBrCH_2CHBr_2$

S2.   (a)   (b)

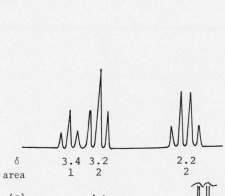

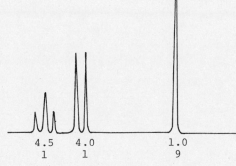

| δ | 3.4 | 3.2 | | 2.2 | | | 4.5 | 4.0 | | 1.0 |
| area | 1 | 2 | | 2 | | | 1 | 1 | | 9 |

(c)   (d)

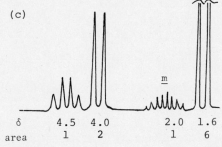

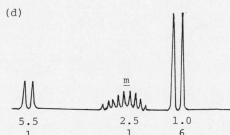

| δ | 4.5 | 4.0 | $\underline{m}$ | 2.0 | 1.6 | | 5.5 | $\underline{m}$ | 2.5 | 1.0 |
| area | 1 | 2 | | 1 | 6 | | 1 | | 1 | 6 |

(e)   (f)

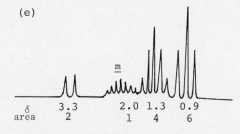

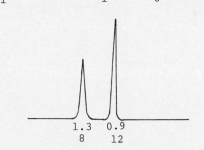

| δ | 3.3 | $\underline{m}$ | 2.0 | 1.3 | 0.9 | | 1.3 | 0.9 |
| area | 2 | | 1 | 4 | 6 | | 8 | 12 |

S3.   (a)   25° C: 4; -100° C: 6   (b)   25° C: 2; -100°C: 3

(c)   25° C: 7; -100° C: 7

(There is too little of the other chair conformation

present at equilibrium to be seen.)

(d)   25° C and -100° C: 3   (e)   25° C: 7; -100° C: 14

S4.

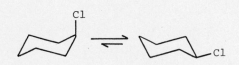

$$\Delta G = -0.5 \text{ kcal mole}^{-1} = -RT \ln K$$

$$K = \frac{[\text{equatorial-Cl}]}{[\text{axial-Cl}]} = 2.3$$

relative
percent: $\dfrac{1}{3.3}$ = 30%; $\dfrac{2.3}{3.3}$ = 70%; $\delta_{average}$ = 0.3 × 4.4 + 0.7 × 3.7 = 3.9 ppm

S5. In 1,1-diphenylpropane, the C_2-C_3 bond has two favored staggered conformations that are in rapid equilibrium, thus averaging J_{ab} to the usual 7-Hz value for acyclic hydrocarbons. In the 2-methyl substituted derivative, only one staggered conformation is favored, with a 180 dihedral angle between $H_{a'}$ and $H_{b'}$.

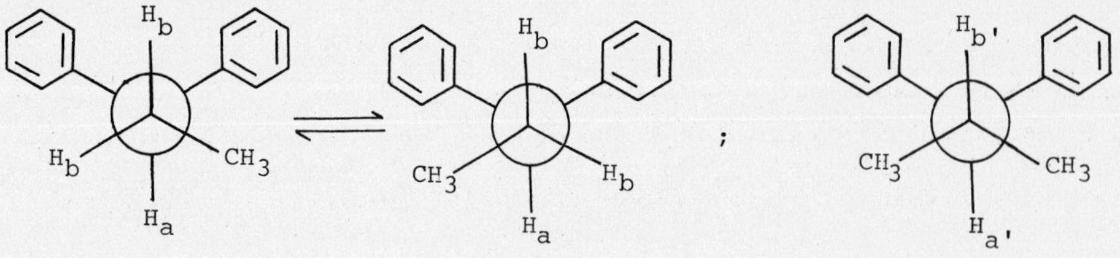

14. ALDEHYDES AND KETONES

14.1 Structure

carbonyl group (hybridization, polarization)

14.2 Nomenclature

Common Names: "-ic acid"   "-aldehyde" $\alpha, \beta, \gamma, \ldots$
IUPAC Names: alkan**al**   alkan**one**
                  -carbaldehyde   oxo-
                  formyl   (numbers, instead of $\alpha, \beta, \gamma, \ldots$)

14.3 Physical Properties

14.4 Nuclear Magnetic Resonance Spectra

$-C\underline{H}=O$ ca. 9.5 ppm

$\overset{O}{\overset{\|}{-C}}C\underline{H}_3$ ca. 2.0 ppm

$R-\overset{O}{\overset{\|}{C}}-R'$ ca. 200 ppm

14.5 Synthesis of Aldehydes and Ketones

Oxidation of Alcohols (see Section 10.6); Cr^{+6} reagents:

$RCH_2OH \longrightarrow RCH=O$ (use CrO_3/pyridine to avoid overoxidation)

$R-\overset{OH}{\overset{|}{CH}}-R' \longrightarrow R-\overset{O}{\overset{\|}{C}}-R'$ ($Na_2Cr_2O_7/H_2SO_4$ (Jones reagent) is most common)

Oxidation of Alkenes (see Section 11.6.E); Ozonolysis:

$$RCH=C\begin{smallmatrix}R'\\R''\end{smallmatrix} \xrightarrow[\text{2. Zn}]{\text{1. } O_3} RCH=O + O=C\begin{smallmatrix}R\\R'\end{smallmatrix}$$

$$\xrightarrow{KMnO_4} RCO_2H + O=C\begin{smallmatrix}R\\R'\end{smallmatrix}$$

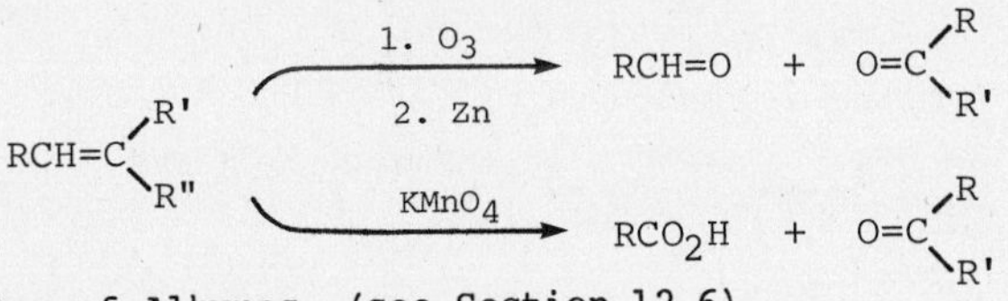

Hydration of Alkynes (see Section 12.6)

$$R-\overset{O}{\overset{\|}{C}}CH_3 \xleftarrow[H_2SO_4]{Hg^{++}} R-C\equiv CH \xrightarrow[\text{2. } H_2O_2,\ OH^-]{\text{1. } B_2H_6} RCH_2CH=O$$

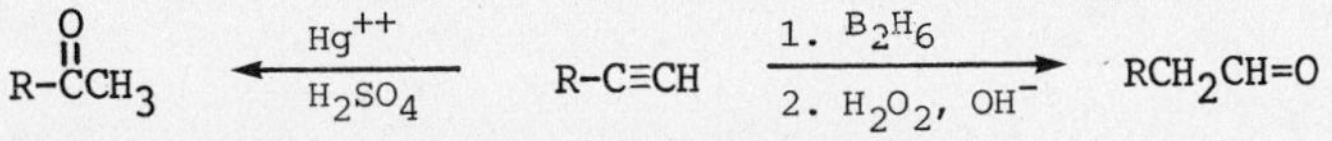

14.6 Enolization (carbonyl compounds as nucleophiles)

A. Keto-Enol Equilibria
    enol, enolate ion   (resonance structures)
    tautomerism:

$$-\overset{}{\underset{}{C}}-\overset{O}{\overset{\|}{C}}-\overset{}{\underset{}{C}}-H \rightleftharpoons -\overset{}{\underset{}{C}}-\overset{OH}{\overset{|}{C}}=C$$

    deuterium exchange:

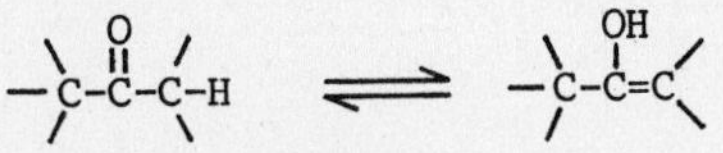

$$-\overset{}{\underset{}{C}}-\overset{O}{\overset{\|}{C}}-\overset{}{\underset{}{C}}-H \underset{D_2O}{\overset{D^+ \text{ or } OD^-}{\rightleftharpoons}} -\overset{}{\underset{}{C}}-\overset{OH}{\overset{|}{C}}-\overset{}{\underset{}{C}}-D$$

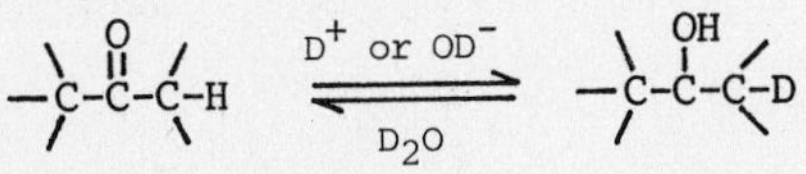

B. Enolate Ions
    pK_a of acetone = 19   ambident anions
    lithium diisopropylamide (LDA)   degree of association
    formation, alkylation, and silylation of enolates

C. Racemization (via enol or enolate)
    chiral center α to carbonyl

D. Halogenation
    autocatalytic   induction period

193

14.7 Addition of Oxygen and Nitrogen Nucleophiles

    A. Carbonyl Hydrates: gem-Diols

        ^{18}O-exchange   inductive effects

        acid-catalyzed vs. base-catalyzed mechanisms

$$R-\overset{\overset{\displaystyle ^{16}O}{\|}}{C}-R' \; + \; H_2{}^{18}O \;\; \rightleftharpoons \;\; R-\overset{\overset{\displaystyle ^{16}OH}{|}}{\underset{\underset{\displaystyle ^{18}OH}{|}}{C}}-R' \;\; \rightleftharpoons \;\; R-\overset{\overset{\displaystyle ^{18}O}{\|}}{C}-R' \; + \; H_2{}^{16}O$$

    B. Acetals and Ketals

        hemiacetal and hemiketal formation (acid- **or** base-catalyzed)

        acetal and ketal formation (acid-catalyzed only)

        protecting group

        enol ether formation and hydrolysis:

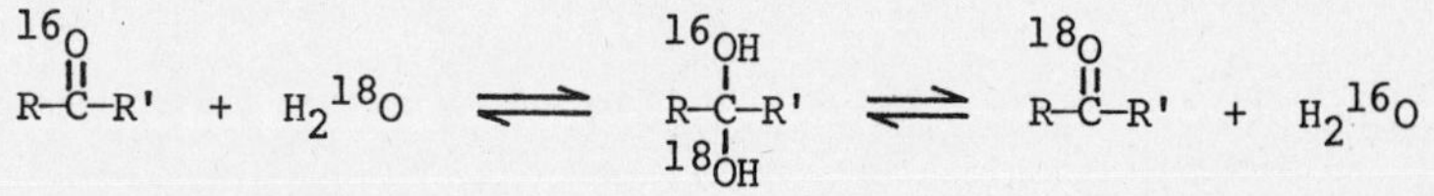

$$R-\overset{\overset{\displaystyle OR'}{|}}{\underset{\underset{\displaystyle OR'}{|}}{C}}-CH \;\; \xrightarrow{\;\Delta\;} \;\; R-\overset{\overset{\displaystyle OR'}{|}}{C}=C \;\; \xrightarrow{\;H_3O^+\;} \;\; R-\overset{\overset{\displaystyle O}{\|}}{C}-CH \; + \; ROH$$
$$+ \; ROH$$

    C. Imines and Related Compounds

        imine = Schiff base   condensation

        hemiaminal = carbinolamine   oximes, hydrazones,
                                             phenyl hydrazones

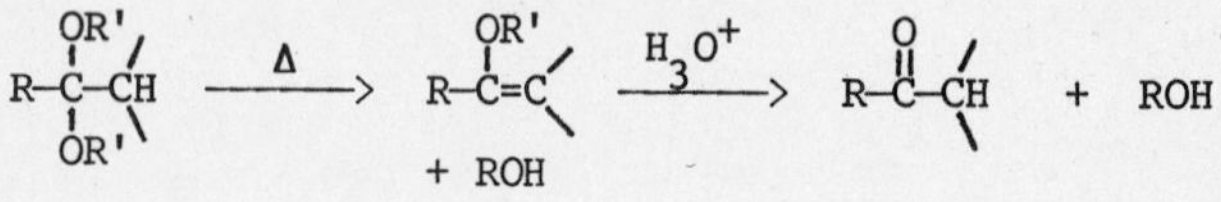

14.8 Addition of Carbon Nucleophiles (carbon-carbon bond-forming reactions)

    A. Addition of Organometallic Reagents: Synthesis of Alcohols

        Grignard reagent   acetylide anion

        alkyllithium reagent

    B. Addition of HCN; cyanohydrin formation

    C. The Aldol Addition Reaction (an important C–C bond-forming reaction)

        α,β-unsaturated aldehydes   cyclic compounds

        intramolecular aldol condensations

        mixed aldol condensations using preformed enolate

    D. Diastereomeric Transition States

        formation of stereoisomers

    E. The Wittig Reaction

        phosphonium salts   oxaphosphetane

        ylide   betaine

        phosphorane

14.9 Oxidation and Reduction

    A. Oxidation of Aldehydes and Ketones

        autooxidation of aldehydes:

$$R-CH=O \; \xrightarrow{\;air\;} \; RCO_2H$$

        Baeyer-Villiger reaction

        migratory aptitudes $(H > C_6H_5 > 3^o > 2^o > 1^o \text{ alkyl} > \text{methyl})$

        peroxycarboxylic acids

    B. Metal Hydride Reduction   (addition of protons **and** electrons)

        lithium aluminum hydride ($LiAlH_4$)   sodium borohydride ($NaBH_4$)

    C. Catalytic Hydrogenation

D. Deoxygenation Reactions

    Wolff-Kishner reduction   Clemmensen reduction

14.B   Important Reactions Introduced

Alkylation and silylation of ketone enolates   (14.6.B)

Equation:

$$R\text{-}\overset{\overset{O}{\|}}{C}\text{-}CH_2\text{-}R' \xrightarrow{\text{LDA}} R\text{-}\overset{\overset{O^-Li^+}{|}}{C}=CH\text{-}R' \quad \begin{cases} \xrightarrow{R''X} R\text{-}\overset{\overset{O}{\|}}{C}\text{-}\underset{\underset{R''}{|}}{C}H\text{-}R' \\[2em] \xrightarrow{Me_3SiCl} R\text{-}\overset{\overset{OSiMe_3}{|}}{C}=CHR' \end{cases}$$

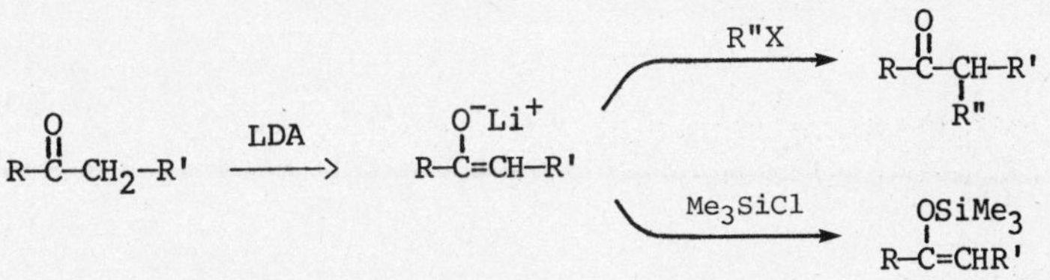

Generality: LDA = lithium diisopropylamide (or other hindered very strong base)

                    R" = methyl or 1° alkyl

Key features: important carbon-carbon bond-forming reaction

                    enolate is strong base, so elimination occurs with 2° or 3° R"X

                    silylation goes on oxygen to give silyl enol ether

Proton exchange of ketones and aldehydes   (14.6.A)

Equation:

$$R\text{-}\overset{\overset{O}{\|}}{C}\text{-}CHR_2 \underset{}{\overset{*H_2O}{\rightleftharpoons}} R\text{-}\overset{\overset{O}{\|}}{C}\text{-}C^*HR_2$$

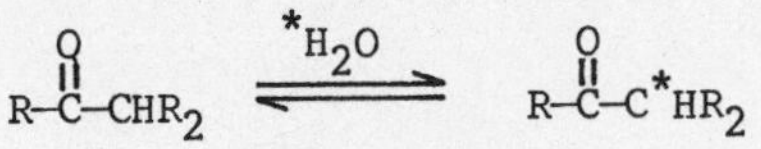

Generality: acid- or base-catalyzed

              $^*H = {}^1H$ (proton exchange), ^2H (deuterium), or ^3H (tritium)

              all α-hydrogens can be exchanged

Key features: useful for determining number of α-hydrogens by exchanging in ^2H

                    useful for making labeled compounds

                    stereocenters α to carbonyl can be isomerized

Halogenation of ketones and aldehydes   (14.6.D)

Equation:

$$R\text{-}\overset{\overset{O}{\|}}{C}\text{-}CHR_2 \xrightarrow{X_2} R\text{-}\overset{\overset{O}{\|}}{C}\text{-}CXR_2$$

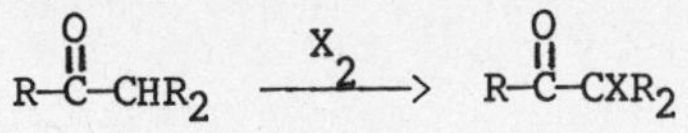

Generality: X = Cl, Br, I

              requires either acid or base catalysis

Key features: with acid catalysis, second and third halogens are introduced more slowly than first

                    with base catalysis, usually replace all α-hydrogens

                    acid-catalyzed process is autocatalytic

Hemiacetal (hemiketal) and acetal (ketal) formation   (14.7.B)

Equation:

$$R\text{-}\overset{\overset{O}{\|}}{C}\text{-}R' \underset{}{\overset{R''OH}{\rightleftharpoons}} R\text{-}\overset{\overset{OH}{|}}{\underset{\underset{OR''}{|}}{C}}\text{-}R' \underset{}{\overset{+\,R''OH}{\rightleftharpoons}} R\text{-}\overset{\overset{OR''}{|}}{\underset{\underset{OR''}{|}}{C}}\text{-}R' + H_2O$$

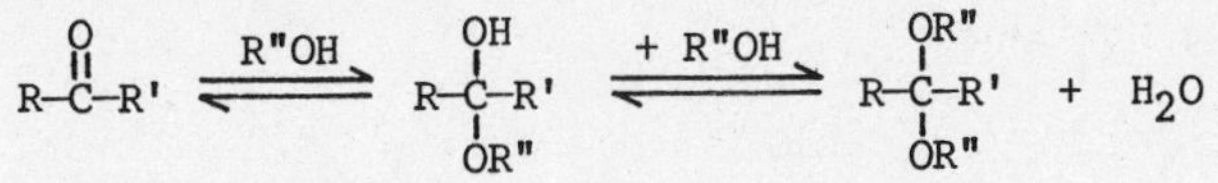

Generality: R, R' = H, alkyl, or aryl; R" = alkyl

Key features: first step acid- **or** base-catalyzed, reversible

                    second step occurs **only** with acid catalysis

                    equilibrium to acetal driven by removal of water

                    acetals useful as protecting groups

Formation of imines and derivatives   (14.7.C)

Equation:

$$R\text{-}\overset{\overset{O}{\|}}{C}\text{-}R' + H_2NY \rightleftharpoons R\text{-}\overset{\overset{NY}{\|}}{C}\text{-}R' + H_2O$$

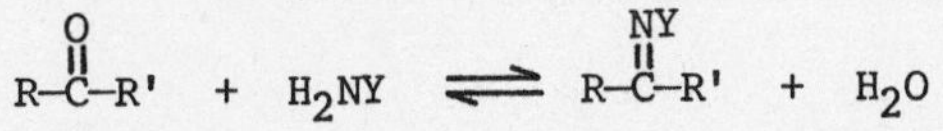

Generality: Y = H, alkyl, aryl, OR (product called an "oxime"), NR_2 (product called a hydrazone)

Key features: reaction occurs via hemiaminal, usually with mild acid catalysis

                equilibrium favors carbonyl compound if Y = H, alkyl

                equilibrium favors imine if Y = aryl, OR, or NR_2

Addition of organometallic reagents to ketones and aldehydes (14.8.A)

Equation:

$$R-\overset{\overset{O}{\|}}{C}-R' \ + \ R''M \ \longrightarrow \ R-\overset{\overset{O^-M^+}{|}}{\underset{R'}{C}}-R'' \ \xrightarrow[\text{workup}]{H_2O} \ R-\overset{\overset{OH}{|}}{\underset{R'}{C}}-R''$$

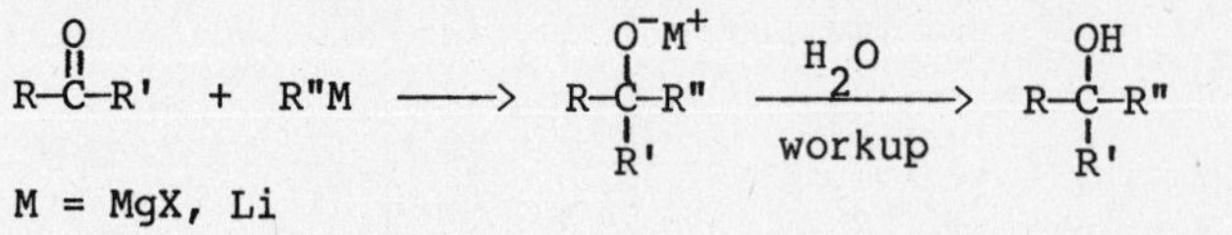

Generality: M = MgX, Li

Key features: very important carbon-carbon bond-forming reaction

                equation often written without specifically indicating aqueous workup

Cyanohydrin formation (14.8.B)

Equation:

$$R-\overset{\overset{O}{\|}}{C}-R' \ + \ HCN \ \longrightarrow \ R-\overset{\overset{OH}{|}}{\underset{CN}{C}}-R'$$

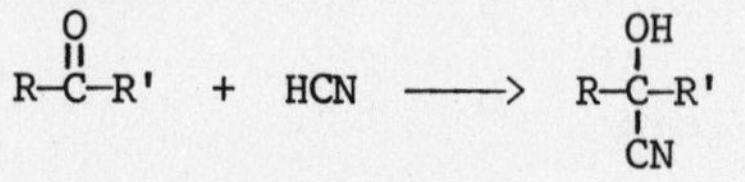

Generality: R, R' = alkyl, aryl, H

Key features: addition catalyzed by cyanide salt

                reaction is reversed in base

Aldol addition reaction (14.8.C)

Equation:

$$R-\overset{\overset{O}{\|}}{C}-R' \ + \ \overset{}{\underset{R}{CH_2}}-\overset{\overset{O}{\|}}{C}-R \ \xrightarrow{\text{catalyst}} \ R-\overset{\overset{OH}{|}}{\underset{R}{C}}-\overset{}{\underset{R}{CH}}-\overset{\overset{O}{\|}}{C}-R \ \xrightarrow{\text{catalyst}} \ \overset{R}{\underset{R'}{C}}=\overset{}{\underset{R}{\overset{\overset{O}{\|}}{C}-R}}$$

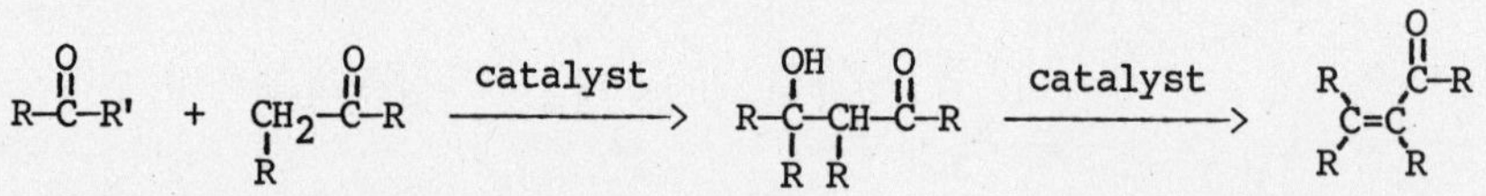

Generality: all R's above = alkyl, aryl, or H

                acid or base catalysis required

Key features: important carbon-carbon bond-forming reaction

                important method for making cyclic compounds (intramolecular reaction)

                often can isolate hydroxy aldehyde or hydroxy ketone intermediate

                mechanism of addition reaction involves enolate attack on carbonyl component (base-
                   -catalyzed), **or** enol attack on protonated carbonyl component (acid-catalyzed)

                mechanism of dehydration reaction involves loss of hydroxide ion from enolate (base-
                   -catalyzed), **or** loss of H_2O from enol (acid-catalyzed)

                usually best for self-condensation of a single aldehyde or ketone
                   (mixed aldol reactions can give bad mixtures)

                mixed aldols reactions can be successful in special circumstances, such as:
                   carbonyl component = a non-enolizable aldehyde

                mixed aldol reactions can also be carried out by preforming enolate with LDA, then
                   adding carbonyl component

Wittig reaction (14.8.E)

Equation:

$$Ph_3PCHR_2 \ \xrightarrow[\substack{\text{(or other}\\\text{strong base)}}]{nBuLi} \ Ph_3\overset{+}{P}\overset{-}{C}R_2 \ \xrightarrow{\overset{\overset{O}{\|}}{R'-C-R'}} \ R_2C=CR'_2 \ + \ Ph_3P=O$$

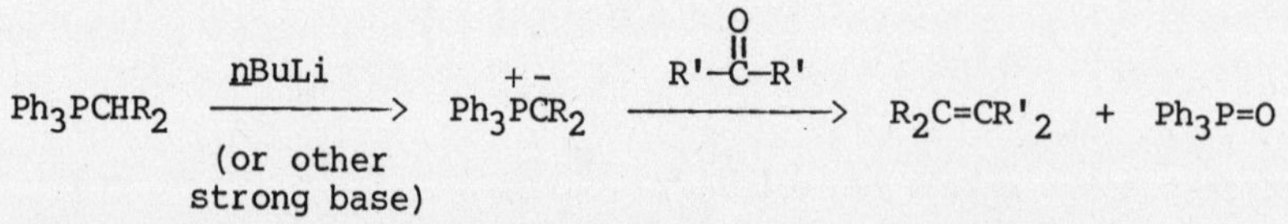

Generality: R, R' = various combinations of alkyl, aryl, or hydrogen

Key features: important reaction for forming carbon-carbon **double** bonds

                reaction proceeds via oxaphosphetane

                $R'_2C=O$ must be unhindered

Oxidation of aldehydes (14.9.A)

Equation:

$$R\text{--}\overset{\overset{\displaystyle O}{\|}}{C}\text{--}H \xrightarrow{[Ox]} R\text{--}\overset{\overset{\displaystyle O}{\|}}{C}\text{--}OH$$

Generality: [Ox] = air (O_2), Ag_2O, H_2O_2, $KMnO_4$, aq. CrO_3, RCO_3H, etc.

Key features: usually a reaction to be avoided, i.e., it often occurs as a side reaction to preparation of aldehydes or on their storage

Baeyer-Villiger oxidation (14.9.A)

Equation:

$$R\text{--}\overset{\overset{\displaystyle O}{\|}}{C}\text{--}R' + R''CO_3H \longrightarrow R\text{--}\overset{\overset{\displaystyle O}{\|}}{C}\text{--}O\text{--}R' + R''CO_2H$$

Generality: R groups = various combinations of alkyl, aryl, or H

Key features: migratory aptitude (i.e. R' vs. R): H > 3° alkyl > 2° alkyl > aryl > 1° alkyl > CH_3

Reduction of aldehydes and ketones (14.9.B and C)

Equation:

$$R\text{--}\overset{\overset{\displaystyle O}{\|}}{C}\text{--}R' \dashrightarrow[\;]{[H]} R\text{--}\overset{\overset{\displaystyle OH}{|}}{\underset{\underset{\displaystyle H}{|}}{C}}\text{--}R'$$

Generality: [H] = $LiAlH_4$, $NaBH_4$; H_2/catalyst (difficult; catalyst = Pd, Pt, etc.)

Key features: important preparation of alcohols

Deoxygenation of aldehydes and ketones (14.9.D)

Equation:

$$R\text{--}\overset{\overset{\displaystyle O}{\|}}{C}\text{--}R' \xrightarrow{\text{[deoxygenation]}} R\text{--}CH_2\text{--}R'$$

Generality: [deoxygenation] = KOH/ H_2NNH_2/ diethyleneglycol/ 240 $^{\circ}$C (Wolff-Kishner reduction) or Zn metal/ conc. HCl (Clemmensen reduction)

Key features: for Wolff-Kishner reduction, aldehyde or ketone must be stable to strong base for Clemmensen reduction, it must be stable to strong acid

14.C   Important Concepts and Hints

Reactions of Double Bonds: C=O vs. C=C

If you are developing an intuitive understanding of organic chemistry, the chapter on aldehydes and ketones should give you a view of its logical foundations as well as its complexity. Intuition is difficult to teach, but as you study this chapter, try to apply the Question-and-Answer outline suggested in Section 9.C of this Study Guide. Hopefully, you will not only see similarities among many of the reactions discussed in this chapter, but also recognize analogies between these reactions and those discussed earlier, in the chapter on alkenes for instance. As an illustration of the sort of analogy we want you to see, study the examples below, in which we've juxtaposed reaction mechanisms from carbonyl and alkene chemistry. There are great differences in the conditions under which these reactions occur, and in their rates and the position of equilibrium, but there is a lot of similarity among the mechanisms.

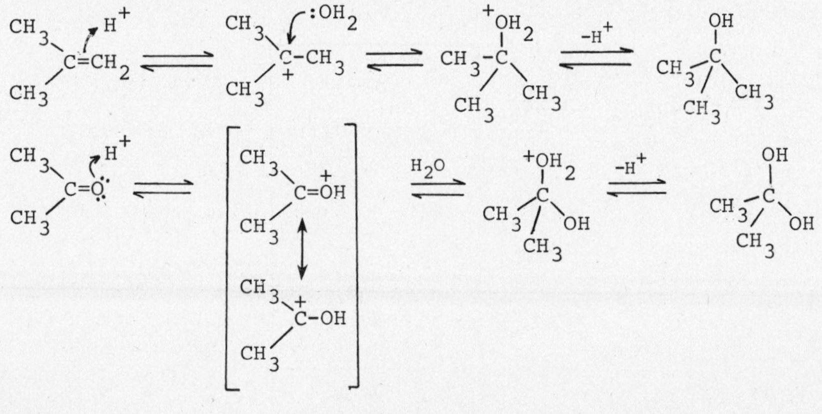

$$CH_3-CH=CH_2 + HCl \rightleftharpoons CH_3-\overset{+}{CH}-CH_3 \xrightarrow{^-Cl} CH_3-\overset{Cl}{\underset{|}{CH}}-CH_3$$

$$CH_3-CH=O + HCN \rightleftharpoons \left[CH_3-CH=\overset{+}{O}H \leftrightarrow CH_3-\overset{+}{C}H-OH \right] \xrightarrow{^-CN} CH_3-\overset{CN}{\underset{|}{CH}}-OH$$

—————

$$CH_3-\overset{OH}{\underset{|}{CH}}-CH_3 \underset{H^+}{\rightleftharpoons} CH_3-\overset{+OH_2}{\underset{|}{CH}}-CH_3 \xrightarrow{-H_2O} CH_3-\overset{+}{CH}-CH_3 \xrightarrow{-H^+} CH_3CH=CH_2$$

$$CH_3-\overset{OH}{\underset{|}{CH}}-NH-NH_2 \underset{H^+}{\rightleftharpoons} CH_3\overset{+OH_2}{\underset{|}{CH}}-NH-NH_2 \xrightarrow{-H_2O} \left[CH_3\overset{+}{CH}NH-NH_2 \leftrightarrow CH_3CH=\overset{+}{NH}-NH_2 \right] \xrightarrow{-H^+} CH_3CH=N-NH_2$$

—————

$$CH_3CH_2CH=CH_2 \underset{H^+}{\rightleftharpoons} CH_3CH_2\overset{+}{C}HCH_3 \xrightarrow{-H^+} CH_3CH=CHCH_3$$

$$CH_3CH_2CH=O \underset{H^+}{\rightleftharpoons} \left[CH_3CH_2CH=\overset{+}{O}H \leftrightarrow CH_3CH_2\overset{+}{C}HOH \right] \xrightarrow{-H^+} CH_3CH=CHOH$$

—————

$$\overset{CH_3}{\underset{CH_3}{>}}C=CH_2 \xrightarrow{Br-Br} \left[\overset{CH_3}{\underset{CH_3}{>}}\overset{Br^+}{\underset{|}{C}}-CH_2 \leftrightarrow \overset{CH_3}{\underset{CH_3}{>}}\overset{Br}{\underset{+}{C}}-CH_2 \right] \xrightarrow[-H^+]{H_2O} \overset{CH_3}{\underset{CH_3}{>}}\overset{Br}{\underset{OH}{C}}-CH_2$$

$$\overset{HO}{\underset{CH_3}{>}}C=CH_2 \xrightarrow{Br-Br} \left[\overset{HO}{\underset{CH_3}{>}}\overset{+}{\underset{|}{C}}\overset{Br}{-CH_2} \leftrightarrow \overset{HO^+}{\underset{CH_3}{>}}C-\overset{Br}{CH_2} \right] \xrightarrow{-H^+} \overset{O}{\underset{CH_3}{>}}C-\overset{Br}{CH_2}$$

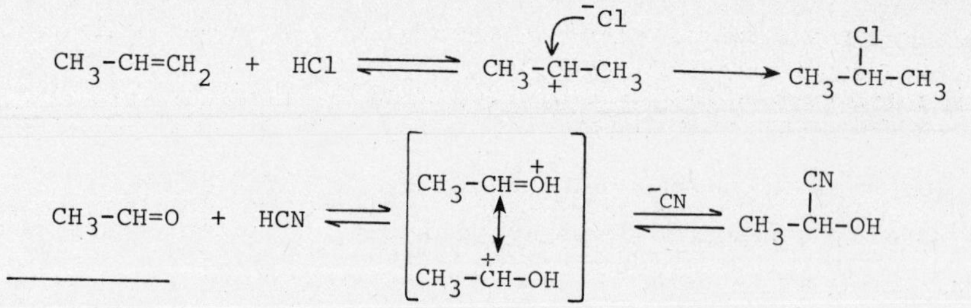

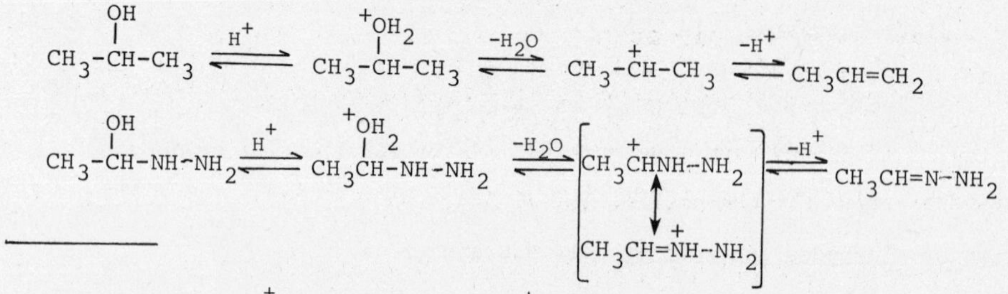

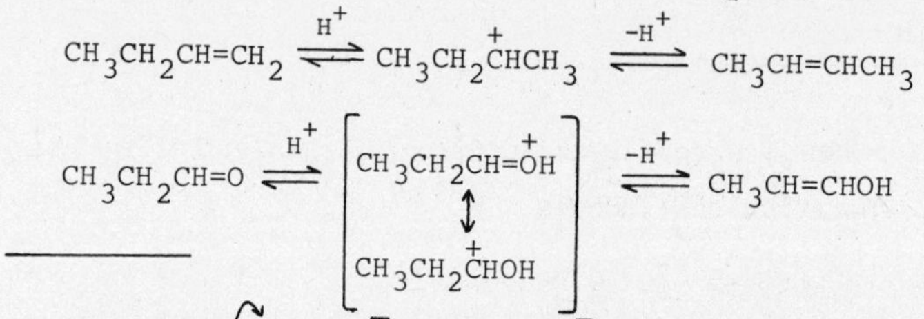

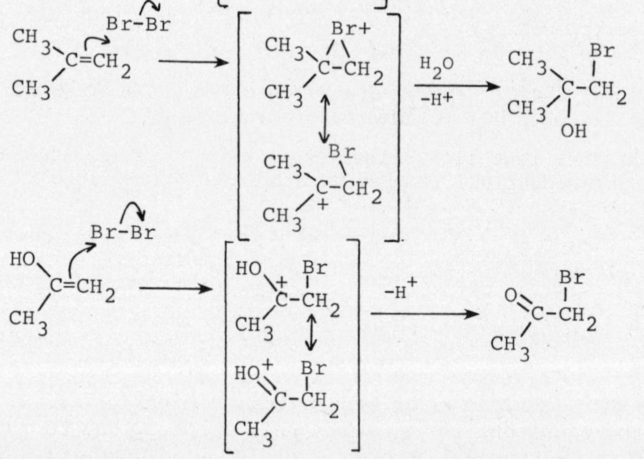

Acid- vs. Base-Catalyzed Reactions

In this chapter you encounter reactions which can be either acid- or base-catalyzed. The equilibration of ketone + alcohol $\rightleftharpoons$ hemiketal, and the bromination of a ketone are just two examples. Usually, the mechanisms of the acid- and base-catalyzed transformations are **electronically** identical; that is, the "electron flow" is the same in both cases. The mechanisms differ only in the sequence of proton addition or loss. For instance, compare the two mechanisms outlined below for the bromination of acetone.

Acid-Catalyzed:

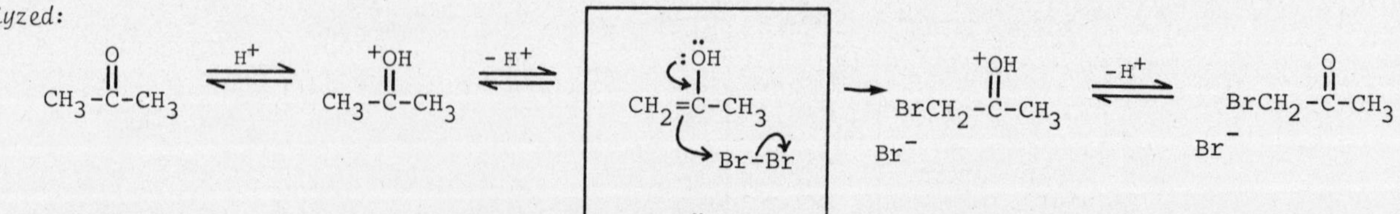

$$CH_3-\overset{O}{\overset{||}{C}}-CH_3 \underset{H^+}{\rightleftharpoons} CH_3-\overset{+OH}{\overset{||}{C}}-CH_3 \underset{-H^+}{\rightleftharpoons} \left[\overset{:\ddot{O}H}{CH_2=C-CH_3} \, Br-Br \right] \rightarrow \overset{+OH}{BrCH_2-\overset{||}{C}-CH_3} \,\, Br^- \underset{-H^+}{\rightleftharpoons} \overset{O}{BrCH_2-\overset{||}{C}-CH_3}$$

Base-Catalyzed:

$$CH_3-\overset{O}{\overset{||}{C}}-CH_3 \xrightarrow{OH^-} \left[\overset{:\ddot{O}:^-}{CH_2=C-CH_3} \, Br-Br \right] \rightarrow \overset{O}{BrCH_2-\overset{||}{C}-CH_3} \,\, Br^-$$

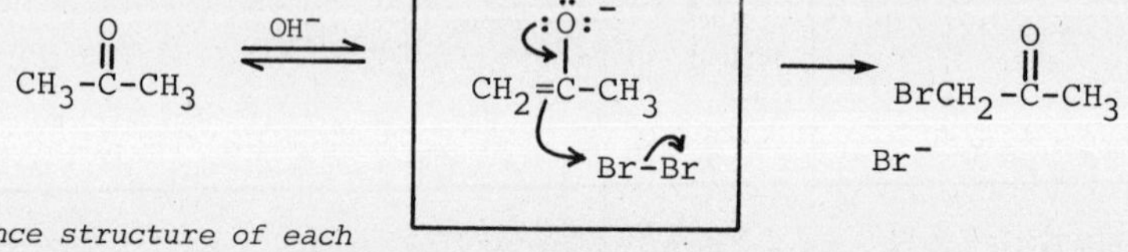

(*NOTE: only the major resonance structure of each
intermediate is drawn.*)

Examine in particular the key steps enclosed in the box; they differ only in the number of protons involved. For another comparison, see the mechanisms of acid- and base-catalyzed hemiacetal formation depicted in Section 14.7.B in the text. You will encounter many more reactions which can proceed by either acid- or base-catalysis in the discussion of carboxylic acid derivatives (Chapter 18).

A few generalizations are useful to keep in mind when you are studying reactions like these, or trying to recall their mechanisms during an exam:

A. In acid-catalyzed reactions, the protons usually go on the molecule before other steps occur (nucleophilic attack, loss of a proton elsewhere (= tautomerization), etc.). Anionic intermediates are **almost never** observed (except counterions of strong acids such as Cl^-, tosylate ion, etc.); enolates and alkoxide ions are not involved as intermediates.

B. In base-catalyzed reactions, proton **removal** usually precedes other steps. Cationic intermediates are rare, unless they are the protonated forms of good bases (ammonium ions, etc); oxonium ions and carbocations are **not** involved as intermediates.

The equations below are examples of **incorrect** mechanisms:

$$CH_3-\overset{O}{\overset{\|}{C}}-CH_2-\overset{OH}{\underset{\|}{C}}(CH_3)_2 \rightleftharpoons CH_3-\overset{O}{\overset{\|}{C}}-CH_2-\overset{+OH_2}{C}(CH_3)_2 \overset{-H^+}{\rightleftharpoons} CH_3-\overset{O^-}{C}=CH-\overset{+OH_2}{C}(CH_3)_2 \overset{-H_2O}{\longrightarrow} CH_3-\overset{O}{\overset{\|}{C}}-CH=C(CH_3)_2$$

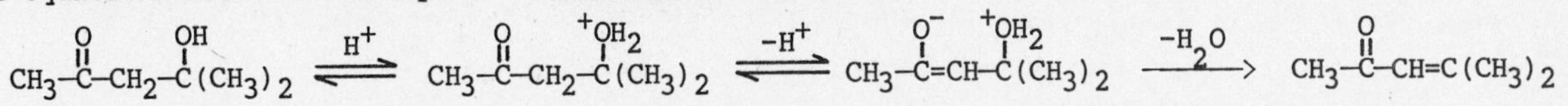

you can't have acid-catalysis (oxonium ion formation) and base-catalysis
(enolate formation) at the same time

$$CH_3-\overset{O}{\overset{\|}{C}}-CH_3 \overset{H^+}{\rightleftharpoons} CH_3-\overset{+OH}{C}-CH_3 \overset{CH_3O^-}{\rightleftharpoons} CH_3-\overset{OH}{\underset{OCH_3}{C}}-CH_3$$

acid base

$$CH_3-\overset{O}{\overset{\|}{C}}-CH_3 \overset{H^+}{\rightleftharpoons} CH_3-\overset{+OH}{C}-CH_3 \overset{HC\equiv C^-Na^+}{\dashrightarrow} CH_3-\overset{OH}{\underset{CH_3}{C}}-C\equiv CH$$

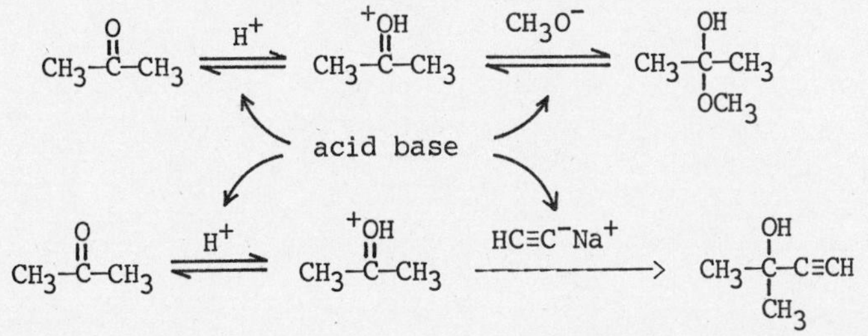

acetylide ion (strong base) will react with
the acid used to protonate ketone

Deprotonation vs. Oxidation; Protonation vs. Reduction

When you convert cyclohexanol to cyclohexanone, all you do is remove two protons, right? Wrong! You also have to remove two electrons, which is why an oxidizing agent (electron acceptor) is required, instead of just a base. Similarly, to convert cyclohexanone back to cyclohexanol, two

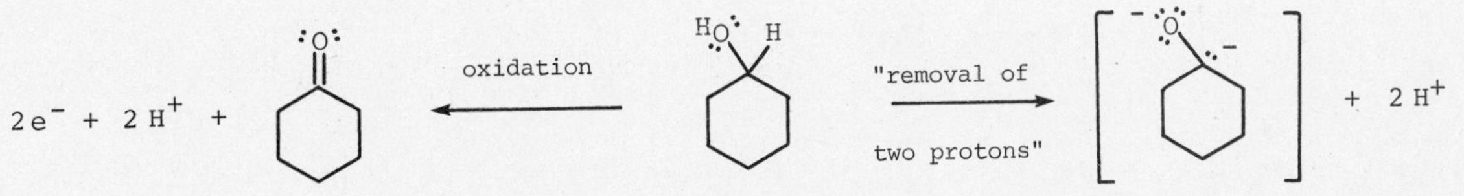

electrons need to be supplied by a reducing agent. The simple addition of two protons by a strong acid (even if possible) would not give cyclohexanol:

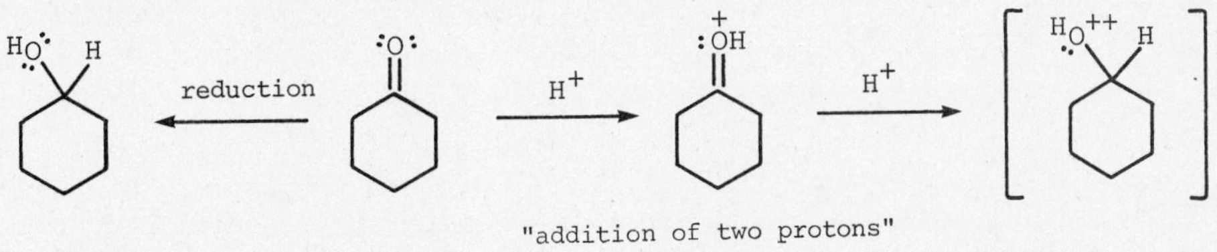

Neither oxidation nor reduction is accomplished with base or acid alone.

14.D Answers to Exercises

14.1

(a)

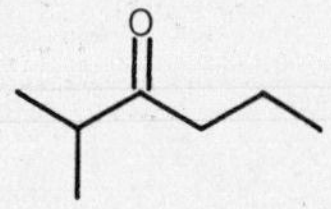

(b)

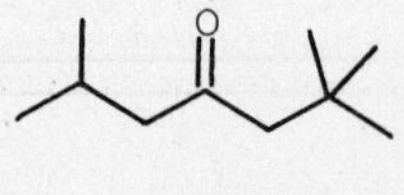

(c) 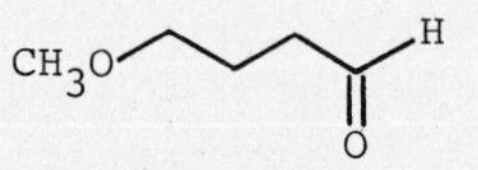 CH_3O

(d)

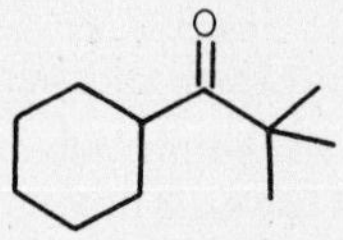

14.2 (a) 2-methyl-3-hexanone

(b) 2,6,6-trimethyl-4-heptanone

(c) 4-methoxybutanal

(d) 1-cyclohexyl-2,2-dimethyl-1-propanone

14.3 3-methylbutanal:

$$CH_3-\overset{\overset{\displaystyle CH_3}{|}}{CH}-CH_2-\overset{\overset{\displaystyle O}{\|}}{C}-H$$

14.4

(a)

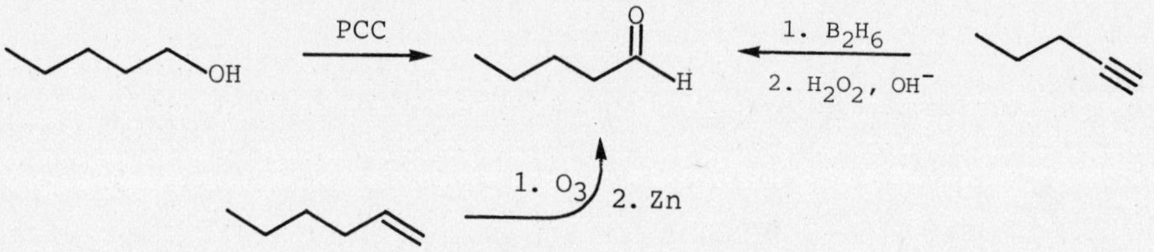

(b)

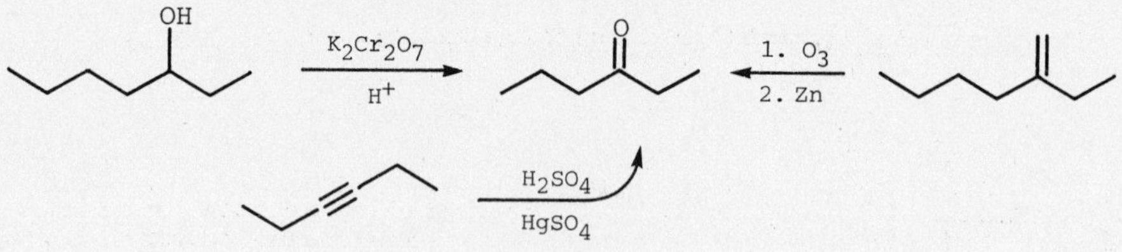

(NOTE: 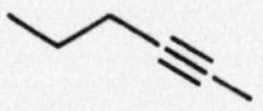 would give a mixture of isomers)

(c)

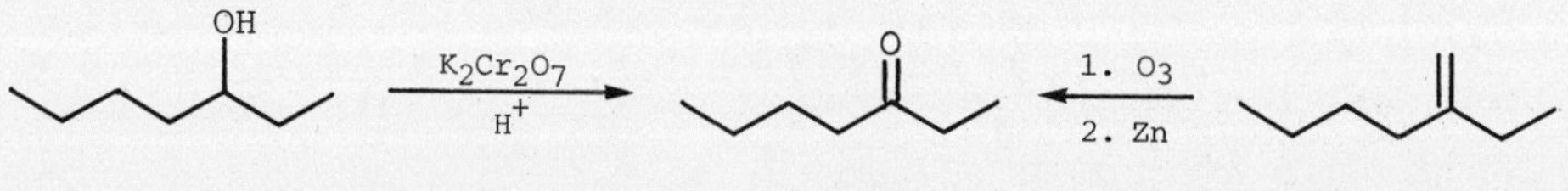

Hydration of any acetylene precursor would
lead to a mixture of isomers

(d)

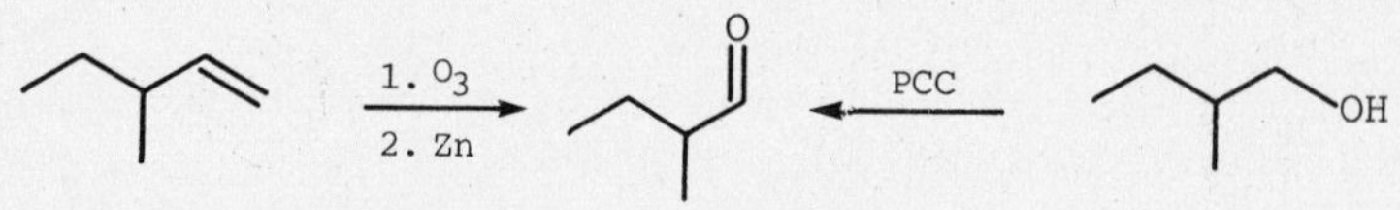

14.5 Rate = k × [OH−] [ketone]   (second-order reaction)

14.6 In one liter of D_2O, there are $2 \times 55.5 = 111$ moles of deuterium atoms. In one liter of a 1-molar solution of 3-pentanone, there are $4 \times 1 = 4$ moles of exchangeable hydrogen atoms. The ratio of deuterium to exchangeable hydrogen is therefore $111/4 = 27.75$. The chance that any one exchangeable position will still have a proton after equilibrium is reached is $1/27.75$; the chance that one out of the four exchangeable positions in 3-pentanone will still have a proton is $4 \times (1/27.75) = 14.4\%$. Therefore 86% of the 3-pentanone molecules will contain four deuteriums and the average per molecule will be $4 \times 0.86 = 3.44$.

14.7 (a) One: (b) One: 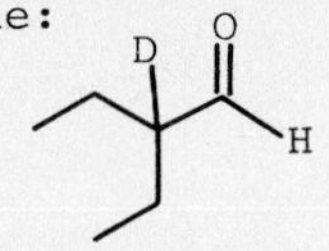   (c) Four:

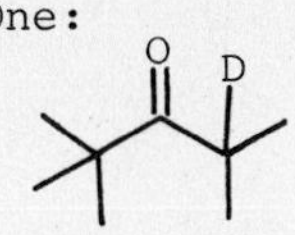

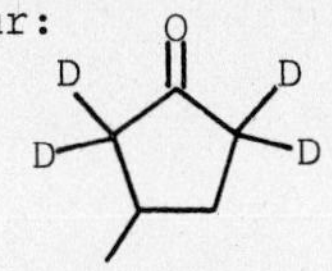

(d) None: an alkene is not deprotonated by hydroxide

14.8   I = $CH_3-\overset{\overset{O}{\|}}{C}-CH_3$ II = $CH_3-\overset{\overset{OH}{|}}{C}=CH_2$ III = $CH_3-\overset{\overset{O^-}{|}}{C}=CH_2$

$$III \underset{K_1}{\overset{}{\rightleftharpoons}} I \overset{K_2}{\rightleftharpoons} II \underset{K_3}{\overset{}{\rightleftharpoons}} III$$

$K_1 = 10^{-pK_a(acetone)} = 10^{-19}$

$K_3 = 10^{-pK_a(enol)}$

$K_2 = \dfrac{[enol]}{[ketone]} = 1.5 \times 10^{-7}$

$K_1 = K_2 \cdot K_3;\quad K_3 = \dfrac{K_1}{K_2} = \dfrac{10^{-19}}{1.5 \times 10^{-7}}$ so that $pK_a(enol) = 12.2$

(more acidic than an alcohol)

The difference in $\Delta H°$ for these two reactions is precisely equal to the difference $\Delta H°_f$ for the two isomeric forms of acetone. *Since the enol form is much less stable, it is more acidic.*

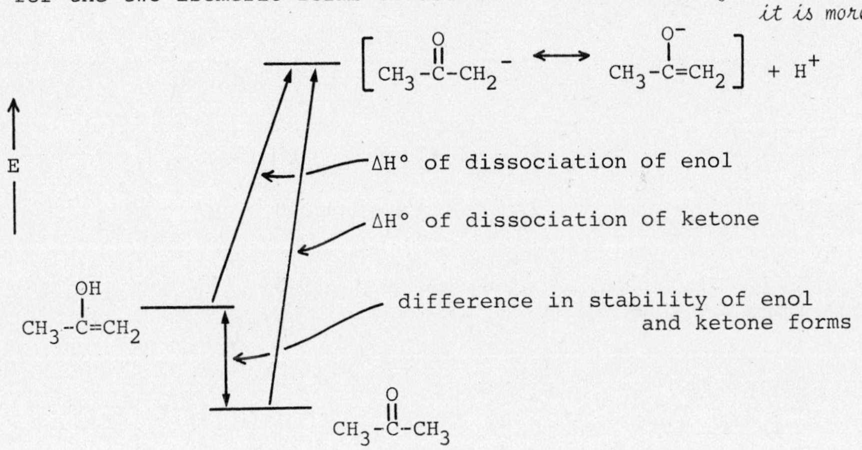

14.9

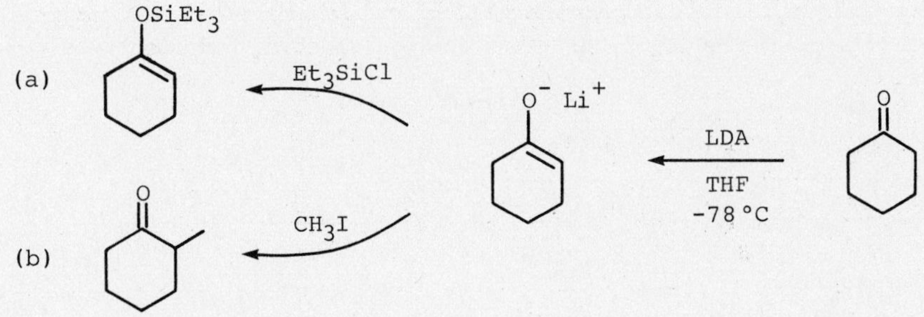

(a)

(b)

14.10 The only ones which will racemize are those which have an enolizable stereocenter; i.e., a stereocenter that (1) is next to a carbonyl group
                          and (2) has a hydrogen substituent:

(a) and (c) will
      racemize:

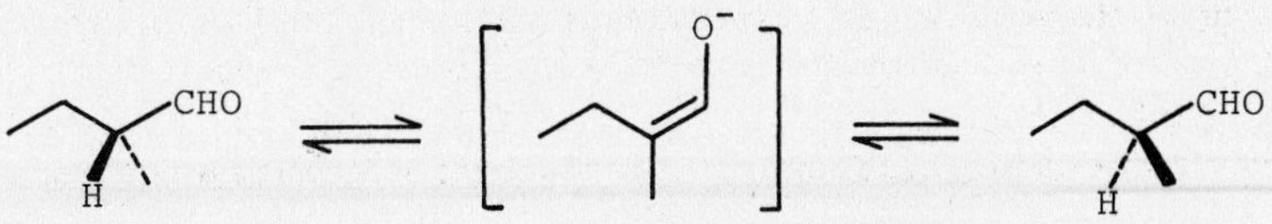

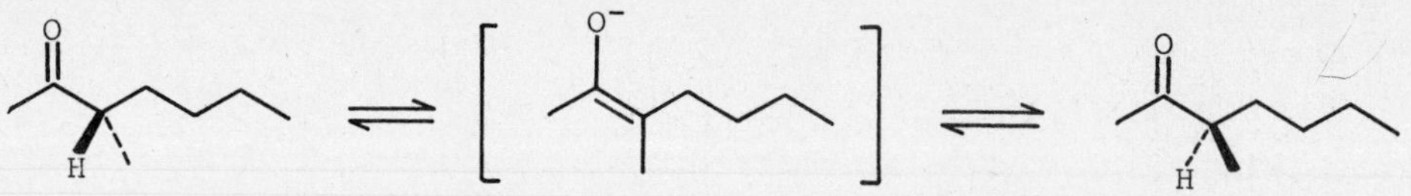

(b) and (d)
will not:

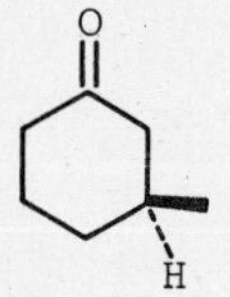

*stereocenter not
next to ketone*

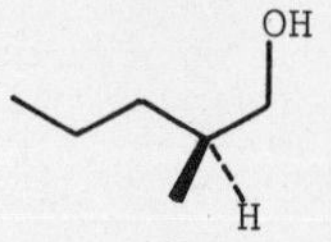

*alcohol unaffected
by base*

14.11

(a)

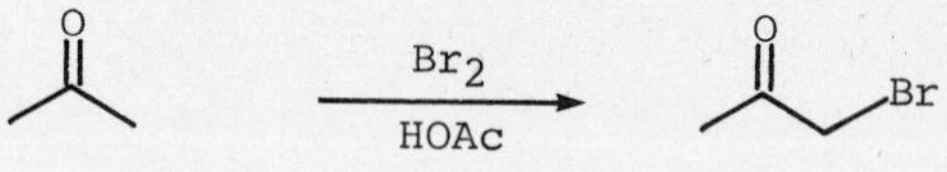

$$\xrightarrow[\text{HOAc}]{Br_2}$$

(b)

[from (a)]

$$\xrightarrow{NaBH_4} \qquad \xrightarrow{NaOH}$$

14.12

$$\underline{K} = \frac{[C(OH)_2]}{[C=O][H_2O]}$$

$$[H_2O] = 55.5 \; ; \quad [C=O] + [C(OH)_2] = 1 \; M$$

$$[C=O] = 1 - [C(OH)_2] \qquad \underline{K} = \frac{[C(OH)_2]}{(1 - [C(OH)_2]) \times 55.5}$$

$$\underline{K} \times 55.5 = [(\underline{K} \times 55.5) + 1] \times [C(OH)_2]$$

For formaldehyde: $\underline{K} = 18$; $[C(OH)_2] = 0.999 \; M$; $[C=O] = 0.001 \; M$
　　ratio $[C(OH)_2]/[C=O] = 999$

For acetaldehyde: $\underline{K} = 0.01$; $[C(OH)_2] = 0.36 \; M$; $[C=O] = 0.64 \; M$
　　ratio $[C(OH)_2]/[C=O] = 0.56$

For acetone: $\underline{K} = 10^{-5}$; $[C(OH)_2] \simeq 1 \times 10^{-5}$; $[C=O] \simeq 1 \; M$
　　ratio $[C(OH)_2]/[C=O] = 10^{-5}$

14.13　　The equilibrium:　　aldehyde + methanol $\rightleftharpoons$ hemiacetal

lies very far on the side of hemiacetal in the case of chloroacetaldehyde, hence there is so little free aldehyde present in the CD_3OD solution that the aldehyde hydrogen does not appear in the NMR spectrum.

14.14　　Hydration of propene:

$$CH_2{=}CH{-}CH_3 \xrightleftharpoons{H^+} CH_3{-}\overset{+}{CH}{-}CH_3 \xrightleftharpoons{H_2O} CH_3{-}\overset{\overset{+}{O}H_2}{CH}{-}CH_3 \xrightleftharpoons{-H^+} CH_3{-}\overset{OH}{CH}{-}CH_3$$

Hydrolysis of ethyl vinyl ether:

$$CH_2{=}CH{-}OEt \xrightleftharpoons{H^+} \left[CH_3{-}\overset{+}{CH}{-}OEt \longleftrightarrow CH_3{-}CH{=}\overset{+}{O}Et \right] \xrightleftharpoons{H_2O} CH_3{-}\overset{\overset{+}{O}H_2}{CH}{-}OEt \xrightleftharpoons{-H^+} CH_3{-}\overset{OH}{CH}{-}OEt \rightleftharpoons$$

In both the hydration of an alkene and the acid catalyzed hydrolysis of an enol ether, the hard step is formation of the initial carbocation intermediate. In the case of an enol ether, the carbocation is stabilized by resonance with the lone pair electrons of the oxygen substituent, therefore it is formed more easily.

14.15　　In the all equatorial isomer, all of the methyls are the same, and all of the CH's are the same:　two signals in the cmr spectrum.

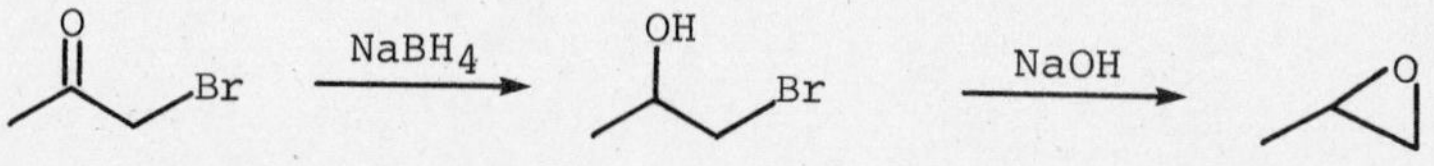

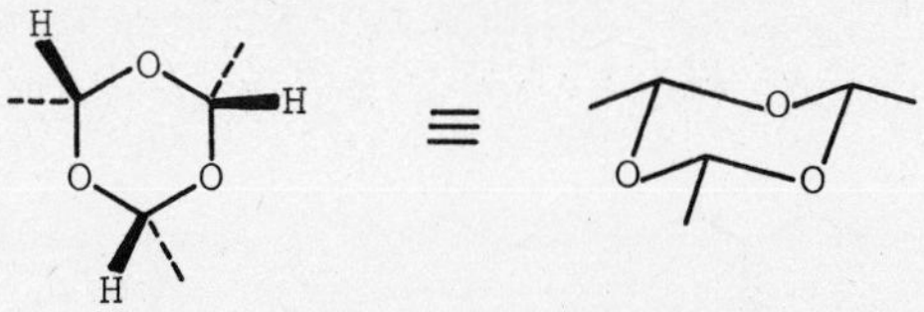

In the other isomer, two of the methyls will be <u>cis</u> to each other and different from the third which is <u>trans</u> to them; likewise, the CH group that is between the two <u>cis</u> methyls is different from those that are between <u>trans</u> methyls; different types of methyl and two different types of CH groups: four signals in the cmr spectrum.

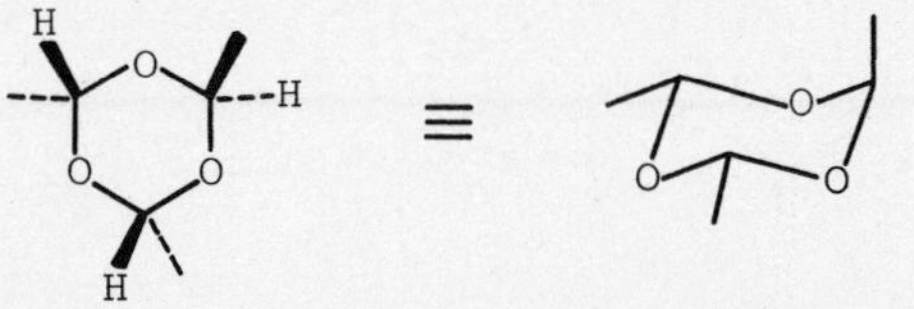

14.16 Because of the sp^2-hybridization of the nitrogen and the aldehyde carbon, there exist <u>cis</u> and <u>trans</u> isomers of the oxime product:

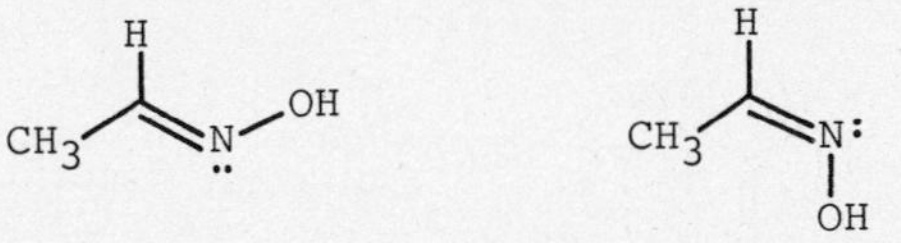

14.17   *rate-limiting step*

$$R_2C=O + H_2NR' \xrightleftharpoons{K_1} R_2C\begin{smallmatrix}O^-\\ NH_2R'\\ + \end{smallmatrix} \xrightleftharpoons{K_2} R_2C\begin{smallmatrix}OH\\ NHR'\end{smallmatrix} \xrightleftharpoons{K_3} R_2C\begin{smallmatrix}+OH_2\\ NHR'\end{smallmatrix} \xrightleftharpoons{k_1} R_2=\overset{+}{N}HR' \rightleftharpoons R_2=NR'$$

ketone + amine   " NH_2^+-O^- "   " NH-OH "   " NH-OH_2^+ "   *immonium ion*   *product*

Rate = $k_1 \times [NH\text{-}OH_2^+]$ $[NH\text{-}OH_2^+] = K_3 \times [H^+] \times [NH\text{-}OH]$

$[NH\text{-}OH] = K_2 \times [NH_2^+\text{-}O^-]$

$[NH_2^+\text{-}O^-] = K_1 \times [\text{ketone}] \times [\text{amine}]$

Therefore, Rate = $k_1 \times K_3 \times K_2 \times K_1 \times [H^+] \times [\text{ketone}] \times [\text{amine}]$

If the first step were rate-limiting:

Rate = $k' \times [\text{ketone}] \times [\text{amine}]$, independent of $[H^+]$

14.18

(a) H_2O $CH_2=O$

(b) H_2O

                                                                        $BrMg$ $\xleftarrow{Mg}$ 1-bromobutane

(c) H_2O

(d) H_2O

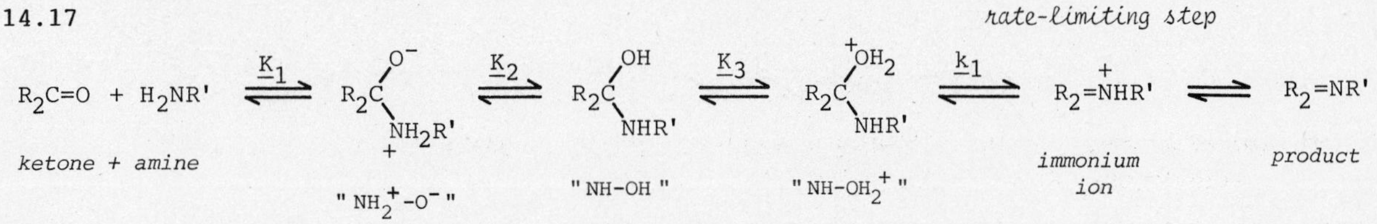

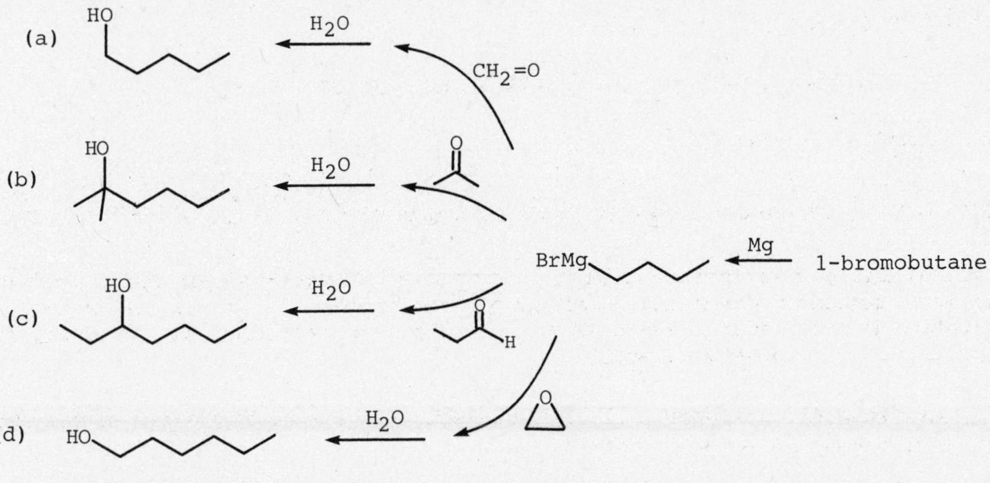

14.19

(a)   + RMgBr ← Mg ← Br

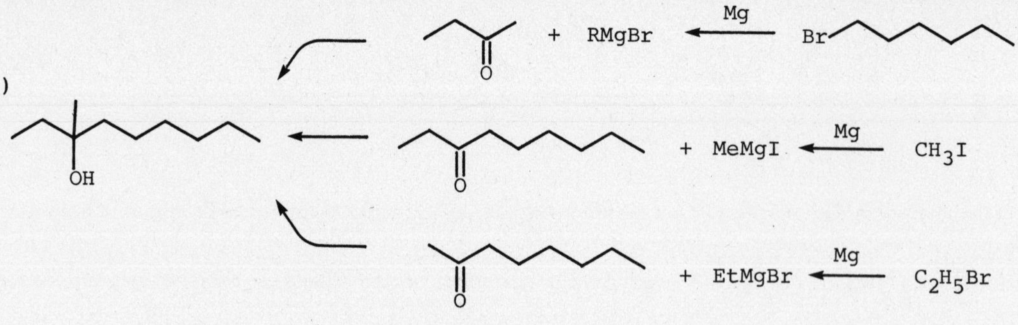

   + MeMgI ← Mg ← CH$_3$I

   + EtMgBr ← Mg ← C$_2$H$_5$Br

(b)   + R'MgBr ← Mg ← Br

   + MeMgI ← Mg ← CH$_3$I

   + EtMgBr ← Mg ← C$_2$H$_5$Br

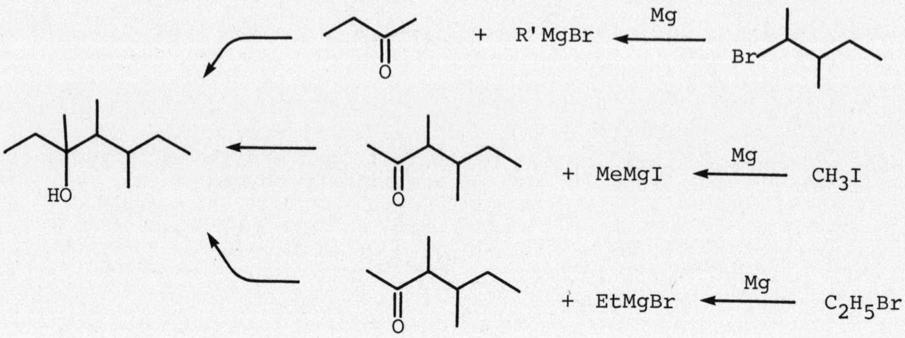

(c)   + nBuMgBr ← Mg ← Br

   + EtMgBr ← Mg ← C$_2$H$_5$Br

   + iBuMgBr ← Mg ← Br

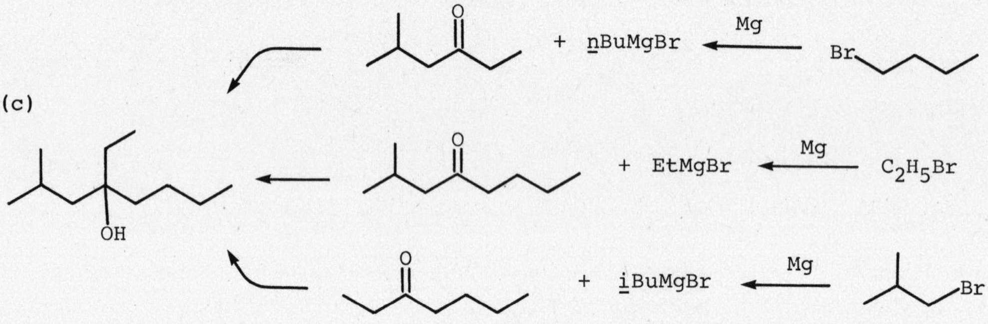

14.20

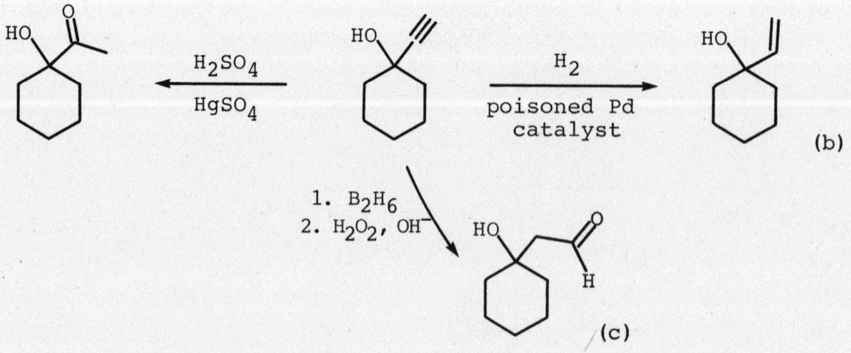

(a) ← H$_2$SO$_4$ / HgSO$_4$ ← → H$_2$ / poisoned Pd catalyst → (b)

1. B$_2$H$_6$
2. H$_2$O$_2$, OH$^-$ → (c)

14.21

(a) → HCN / NaCN → → H$_2$ / PtO$_2$, HCl →

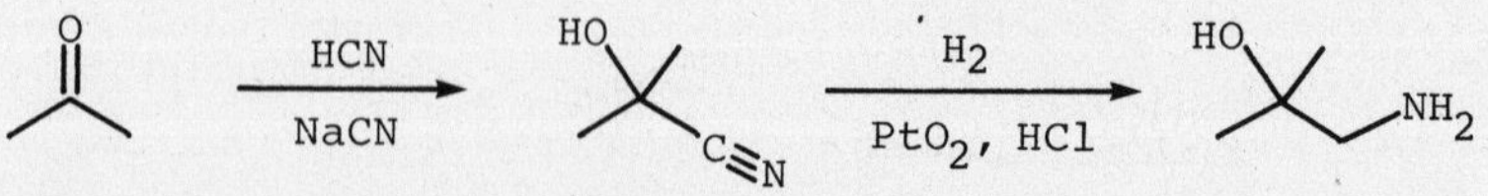

(b) + MgBr →

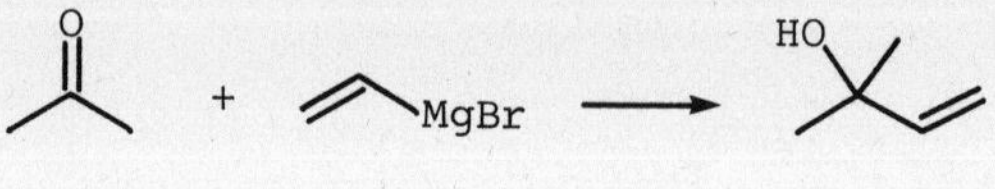

(c)

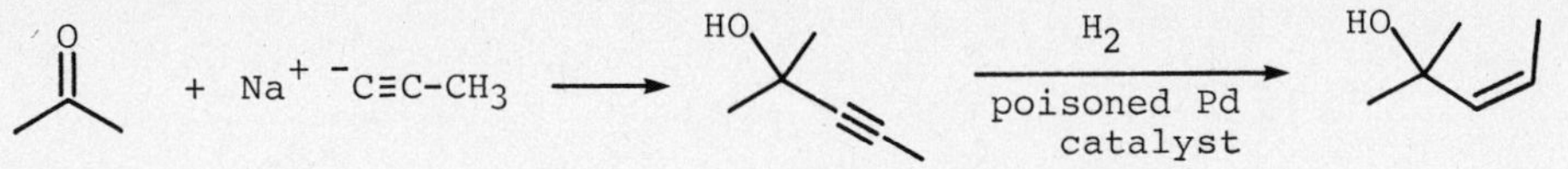

14.22

(a)

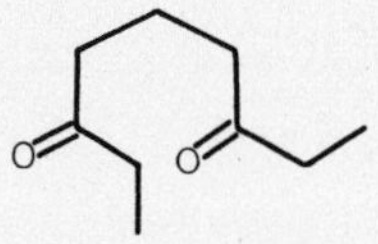

3,7-nonanedione

(b)

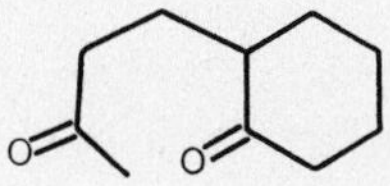

2-(3-oxobutyl)cyclohexanone

14.23

(a) 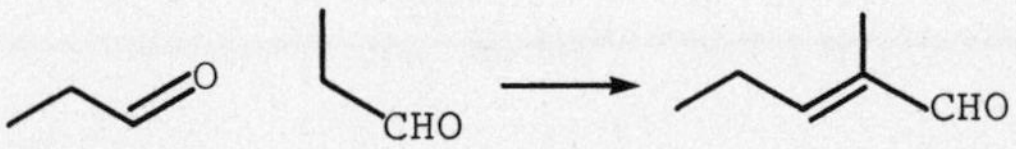 (self-condensation of propanal)

(b) 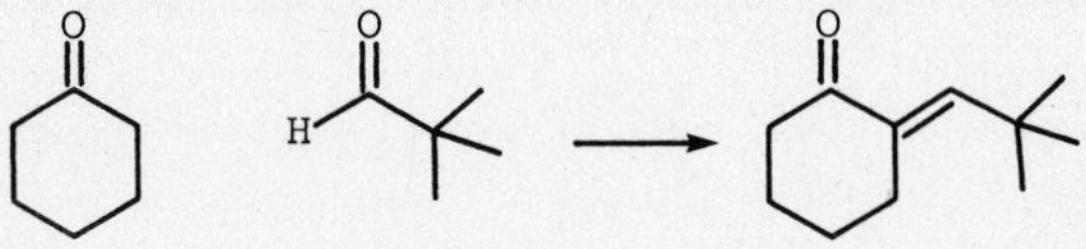 (crossed aldol condensation of cyclo-hexanone and 2,2-dimethylpropanal)

(c) 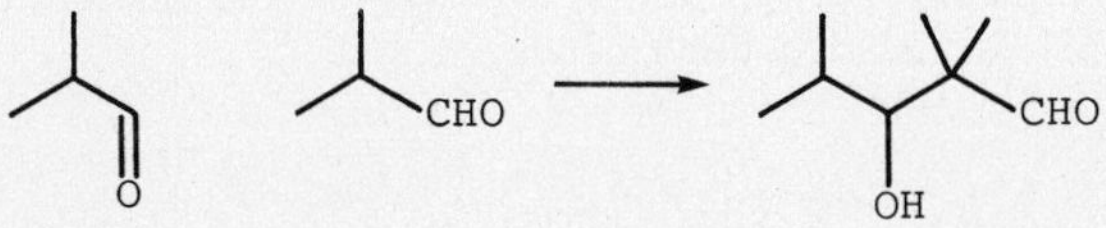 (self-condensation of 2-methylpropanal)

(d)

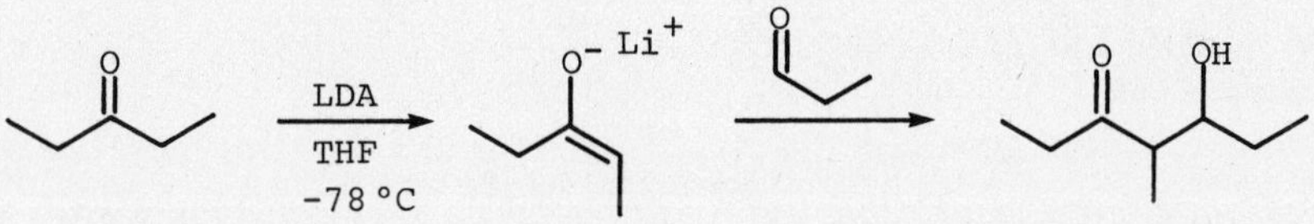

(mixed aldol condensation between 3-pentanone enolate and propanal)

14.24

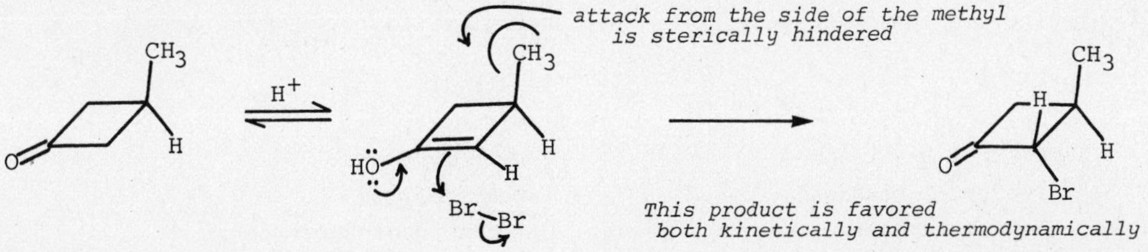

attack from the side of the methyl is sterically hindered

This product is favored both kinetically and thermodynamically

trans-2-bromo-3-methylcyclo-butanone

14.25 (a) $Ph_3P:$ + $(CH_3)_2CHI$ ⟶ $Ph_3\overset{+}{P}CH(CH_3)_2$ $\overset{I^-}{}$ $\xrightarrow{\underline{n}\text{-BuLi}}$ $Ph_3\overset{+}{P}\overset{-}{C}(CH_3)_2$ + $H\overset{O}{\overset{\|}{C}}CH_2CH_3$

$(CH_3)_2C=CHCH_2CH_3$ ⟵

(b) $Ph_3P:$ + $\underline{n}$-BuBr ⟶ $\xrightarrow{nBuLi}$ $Ph_3\overset{+}{P}\overset{-}{C}HCH_2CH_2CH_3$ + $(CH_3)_3C\overset{O}{\overset{\|}{C}}H$ ⟶ $(CH_3)_3CCH=CHCH_2CH_2CH_3$

(c) $Ph_3P:$ + EtI ⟶ $\xrightarrow{nBuLi}$ $Ph_3\overset{+}{P}\overset{-}{C}HCH_3$ + $CH_3\overset{O}{\overset{\|}{C}}CH_2CH_2CH_3$ ⟶ $CH_3CH=\overset{\overset{\displaystyle CH_3}{|}}{C}CH_2CH_2CH_3$

14.26

(a) 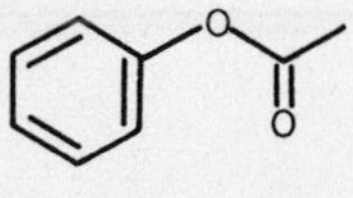 (b) 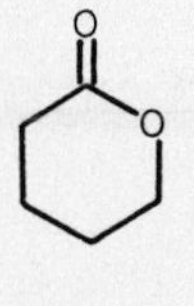 (c) 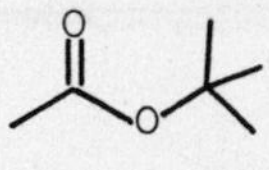 (d)

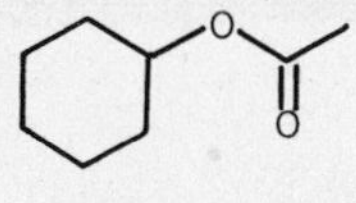

14.27

(a)

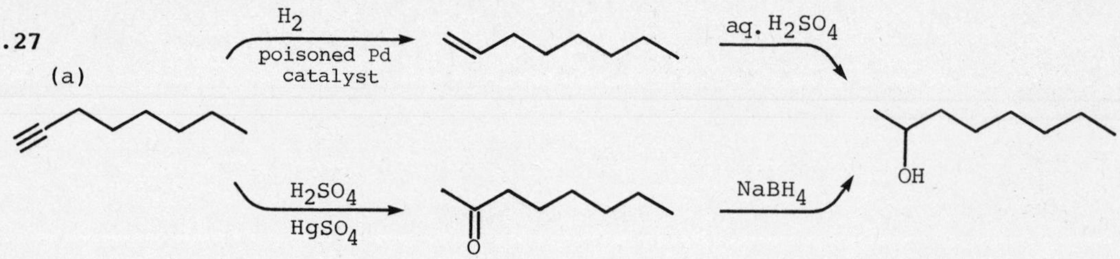

(b)

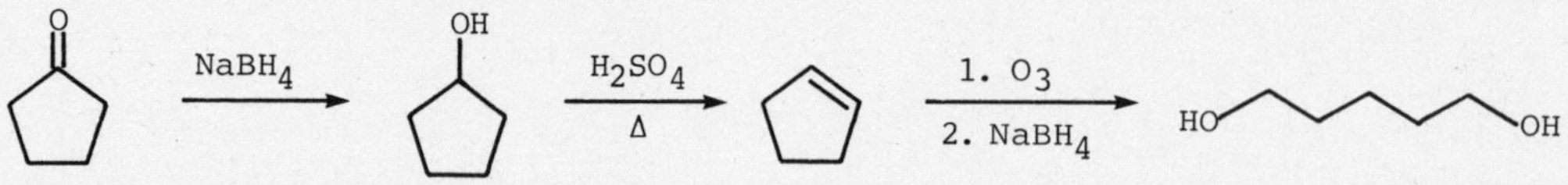

14.28 (a) Clemmensen reduction (1° bromide would not survive the conditions of Wolff-Kishner reduction).

(b) Wolff-Kishner reduction (3° alcohol would not survive Clemmensen reduction conditions).

(c) Neither the Wolff-Kishner reduction nor the Clemmensen reduction would be appropriate for deoxygenation of the carbonyl group of (c); the epoxide group would be destroyed by the strongly basic or acidic conditions.

(d) Both of the methods would work.

14.E Answers and Explanations for Problems

1. (a) methyl ethyl ketone
    (b) propyl isopropyl ketone
    (c) methyl t-butyl ketone
    (d) ethyl neopentyl ketone
    (e) methyl cyclopentyl ketone

    (f) isobutyraldehyde
    (g) α-bromopropionaldehyde
    (h) β-methoxybutyraldehyde
    (i) ethyl vinyl ketone
    (j) methyl cyclopropylmethyl ketone

2. (a) 2-butanone
    (b) 2-methyl-3-hexanone
    (c) 3,3-dimethyl-2-butanone
    (d) 5,5-dimethyl-3-hexanone
    (e) 1-cyclopentylethanone

    (f) 2-methylpropanal
    (g) 2-bromopropanal
    (h) 3-methoxybutanal
    (i) 1-penten-3-one
    (j) 1-cyclopropyl-2-propanone

3. (a) $CH_3\overset{O}{\overset{\|}{C}}CH_2CH(CH_3)_2$

    (b) $CH_3CH_2CH(OC_2H_5)_2$

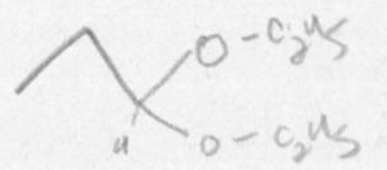

    (c) $CH_3\overset{Cl}{\overset{|}{C}H}CH_2CHO$

    (d)

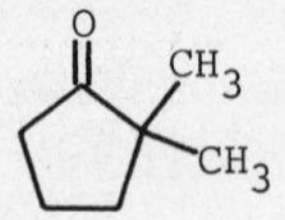

    (e)

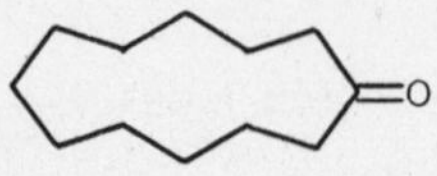

    (f)

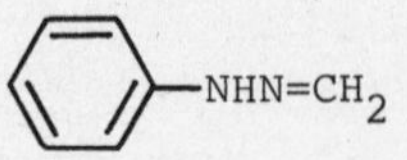

    (g)

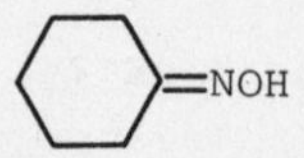

    (h) $(CH_3)_2C=NNH_2$

4. (a)

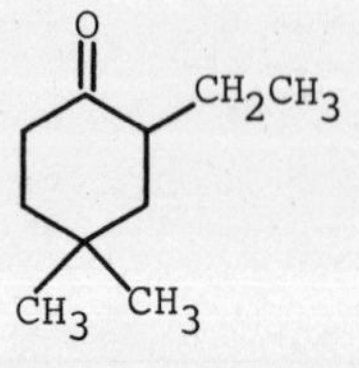

    (b)

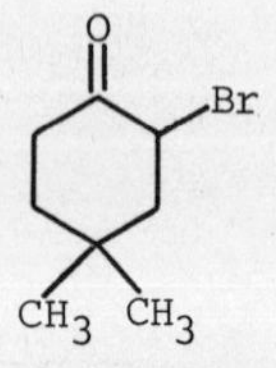

    (c)

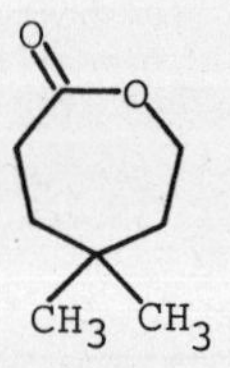

    (d)

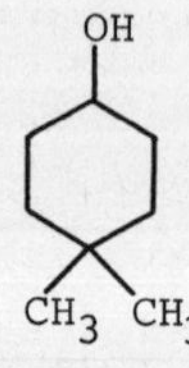

(e)

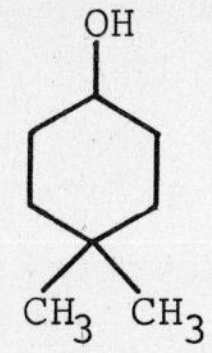

(f)

(g)

(h)

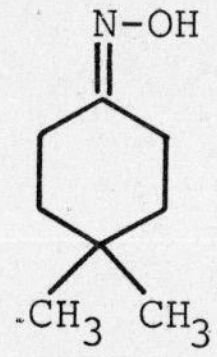

(i)

(j)

(k, l)

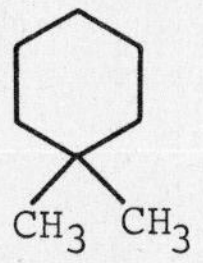

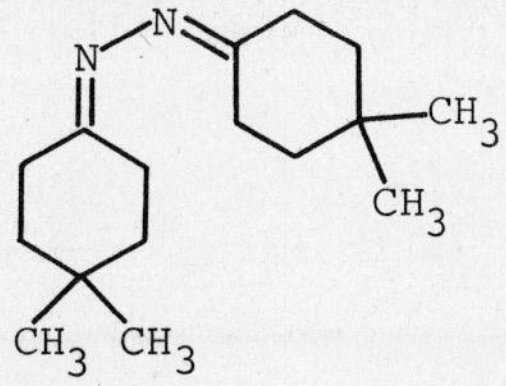

(m)

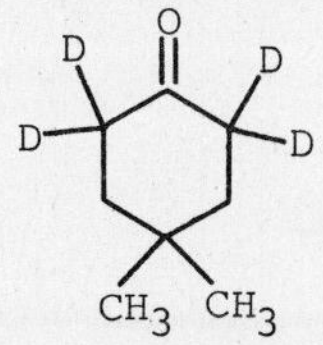

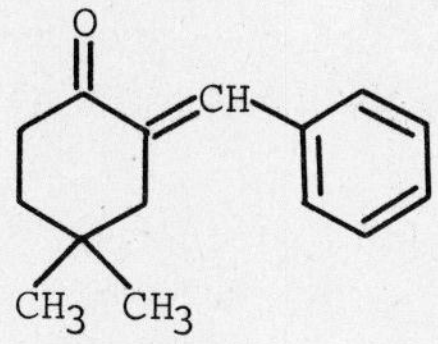

(n)

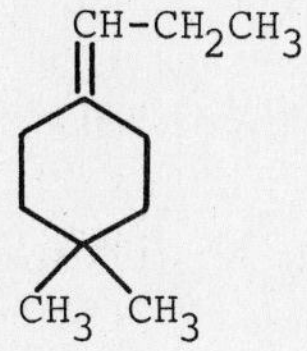

5.

(a)

(b)

(c)

(d, e)

(f)

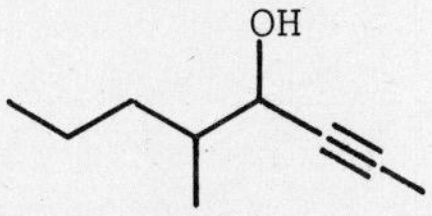

(g)

(h)

(i)

(j) No reaction

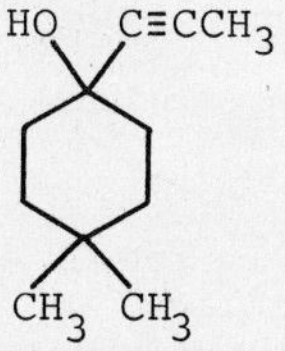

(k, l)

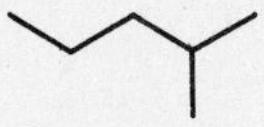

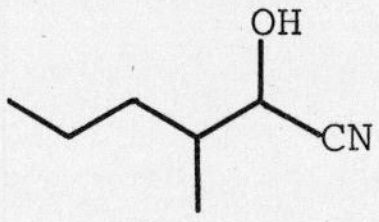

(m)

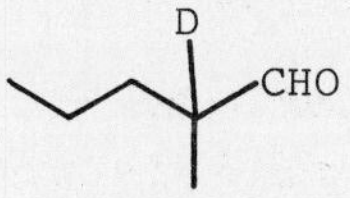

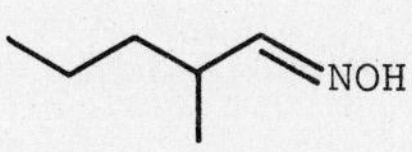

(n)

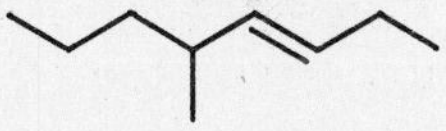

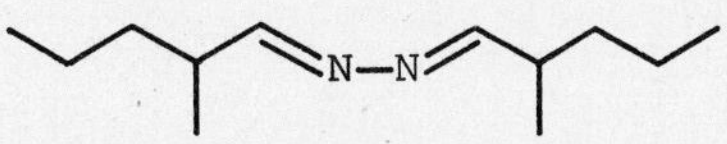

6.

(a)

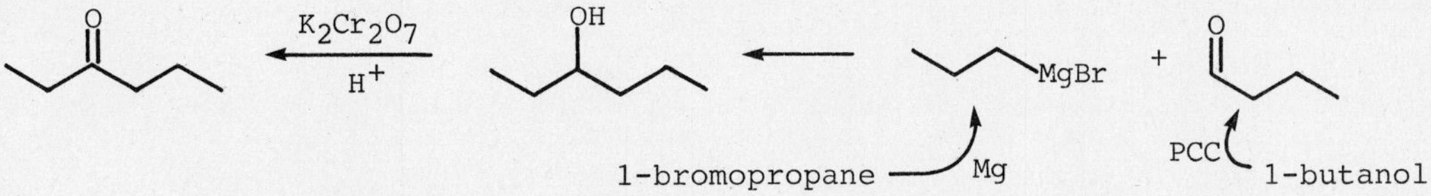

$$\text{(alcohol)} \xrightarrow[\text{H}^+]{\text{K}_2\text{Cr}_2\text{O}_7} \text{(ketone)}$$

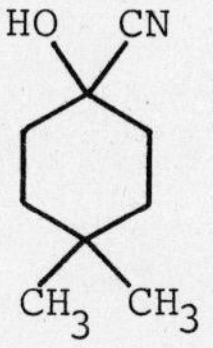

1-bromopropane → Mg → MgBr

PCC ← 1-butanol

(b)

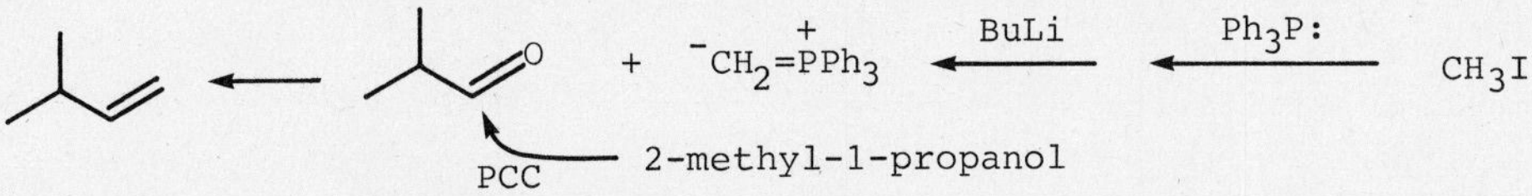

BuLi ← Ph$_3$P:

$^-$CH$_2$=PPh$_3^+$

CH$_3$I

PCC ← 2-methyl-1-propanol

(c)

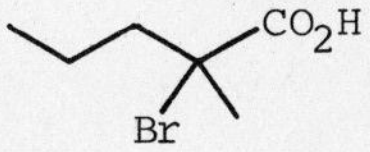

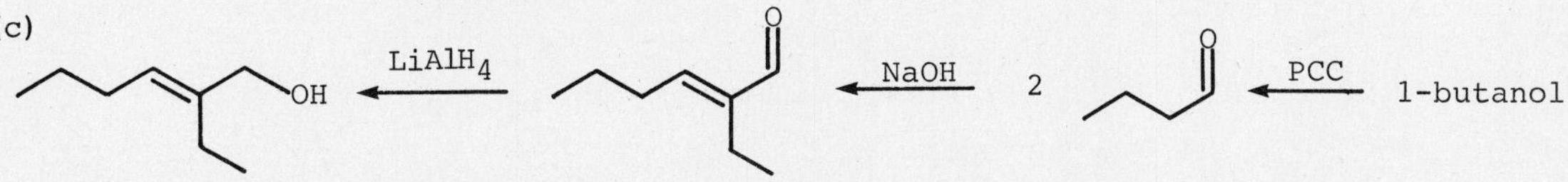

$$\xrightarrow{\text{LiAlH}_4} \text{} \xleftarrow{\text{NaOH}} 2 \xleftarrow{\text{PCC}} \text{1-butanol}$$

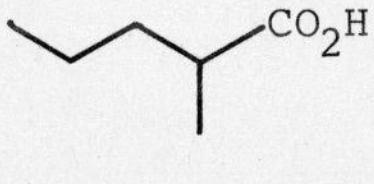

(d)

1. Ph$_3$P:
2. BuLi ← 1-bromopropane

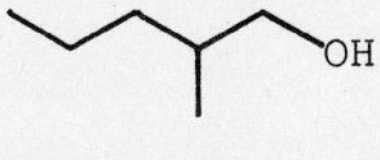

Ph$_3$P$^+$ $^-$

PCC ← 2-butanol

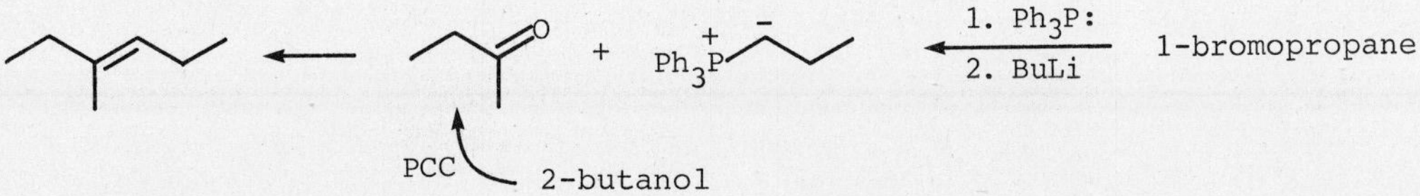

(e)

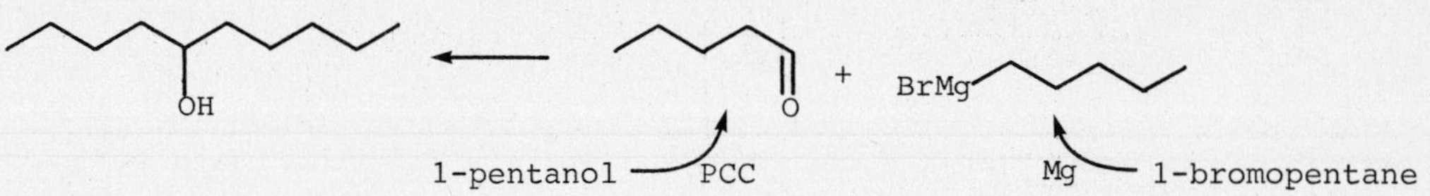

1-pentanol — PCC

1-bromopentane, Mg → BrMg-

(f)

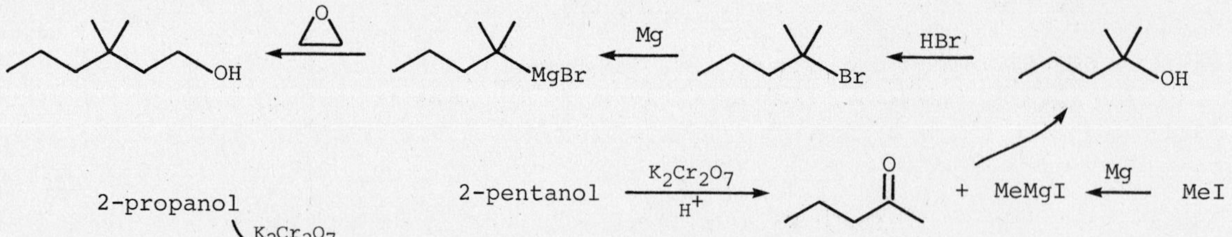

2-pentanol $\xrightarrow[H^+]{K_2Cr_2O_7}$ + MeMgI ← MeI, Mg

HBr, Mg, MgBr

(g)

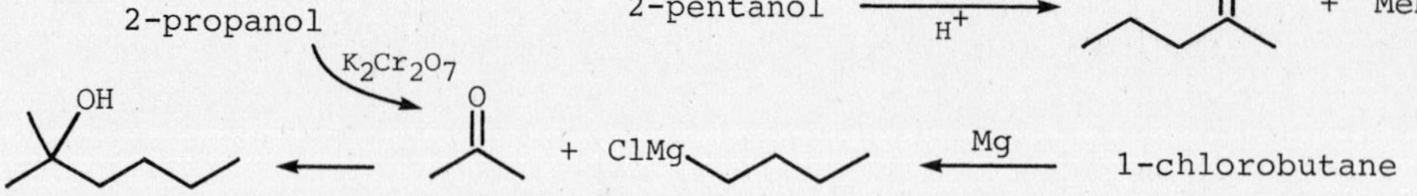

2-propanol

$K_2Cr_2O_7$

+ ClMg- ← 1-chlorobutane, Mg

(h)

MeMgI

$K_2Cr_2O_7$

Br $\xrightarrow[2.\ CH_2=O]{1.\ Mg}$ → OH → PCC → + ClMg- ← 1-chlorobutane, Mg

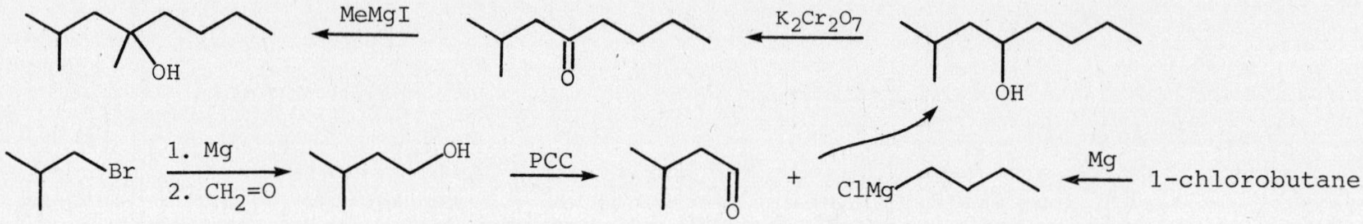

7. (a) $CH_3CH_2CH_2CH_2CHO \xrightarrow[\substack{H_2NNH_2-NaOH \\ (HOCH_2CH_2)_2O \\ \Delta}]{Zn(Hg)-HCl \text{ or}} CH_3CH_2CH_2CH_2CH_3$

(b) $CH_3(CH_2)_3CHO + HC\equiv C^-Na^+ \xrightarrow{NH_3} \xrightarrow{H^+} CH_3(CH_2)_3\overset{\overset{OH}{|}}{C}HC\equiv CH$

(c) $CH_3(CH_2)_3CHO + KCN \xrightarrow{H_2SO_4} CH_3(CH_2)_3\overset{\overset{OH}{|}}{C}HCN$

(d) $CH_3(CH_2)_3CHO \xrightarrow{Ag_2O} \xrightarrow{H_3O^+} CH_3CH_2CH_2CH_2CO_2H$

(e) $2CH_3(CH_2)_3CHO \xrightarrow{KOH} CH_3CH_2CH_2CH_2CH=\overset{\overset{CHO}{|}}{C}-CH_2CH_2CH_3$

$\xrightarrow{H_2-Pd}$ $CH_3CH_2CH_2CH_2CH_2\overset{\overset{CHO}{|}}{C}HCH_2CH_2CH_3$

$\xrightarrow[\substack{(HOCH_2CH_2)_2O \\ (Wolff-Kishner)}]{H_2NNH_2,NaOH,}$ $CH_3CH_2CH_2CH_2CH_2\overset{\overset{CH_3}{|}}{C}HCH_2CH_2CH_3$

(f) $CH_3CH_2CH_2CH_2CHO \xrightarrow{NaBH_4} \xrightarrow{PBr_3} CH_3(CH_2)_4Br$

(g) $CH_3CH_2CH_2CH_2CHO \xrightarrow{NaBH_4} CH_3CH_2CH_2CH_2CH_2OH \xrightarrow[120\,°C]{H_2SO_4} (CH_3CH_2CH_2CH_2CH_2)_2O$

(h) $CH_3CH_2CH_2CH_2CHO + (C_6H_5)_3P=CH_2 \longrightarrow CH_3CH_2CH_2CH_2CH=CH_2$

8. (a)

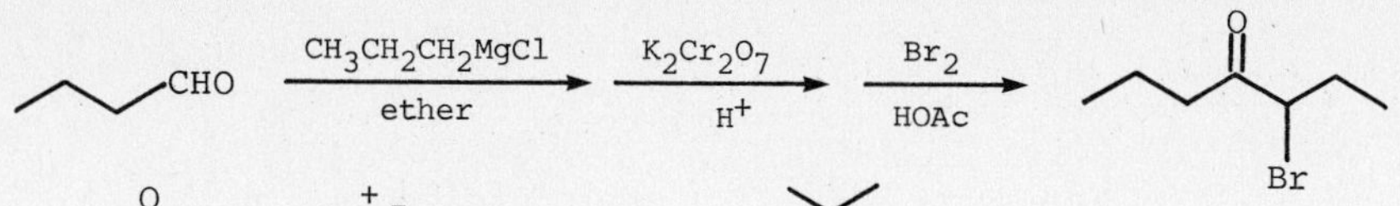

$$\text{CH}_3\text{CH}_2\text{CH}_2\text{MgCl} \quad \text{ether} \xrightarrow{} \quad \text{K}_2\text{Cr}_2\text{O}_7 \quad \text{H}^+ \xrightarrow{} \quad \text{Br}_2 \quad \text{HOAc}$$

(b)

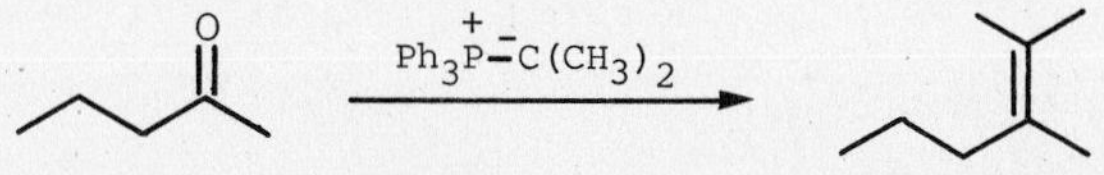

$$\text{Ph}_3\overset{+}{\text{P}}\!\!=\!\!\text{C}(\text{CH}_3)_2$$

(c)

$$\text{NaBH}_4 \quad \text{PBr}_3 \quad \text{Mg} \quad \text{(epoxide)} \quad \text{PCC}$$

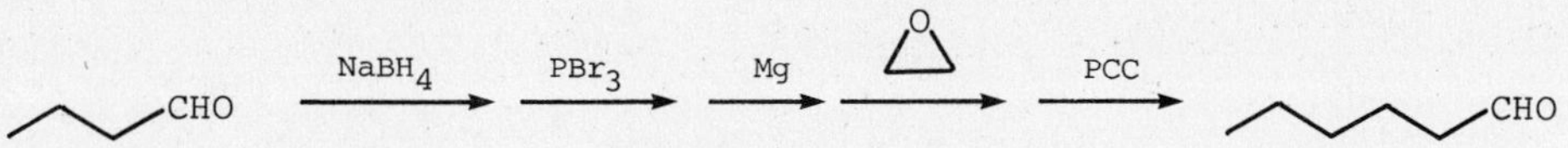

(d)

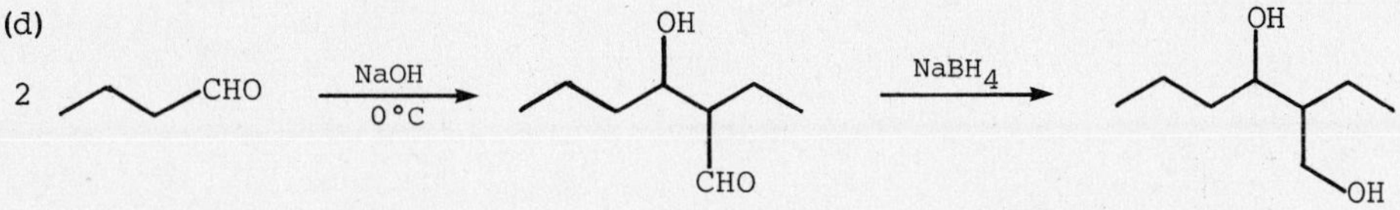

2

$$\xrightarrow[0\,^\circ\text{C}]{\text{NaOH}} \quad \xrightarrow{\text{NaBH}_4}$$

(e)

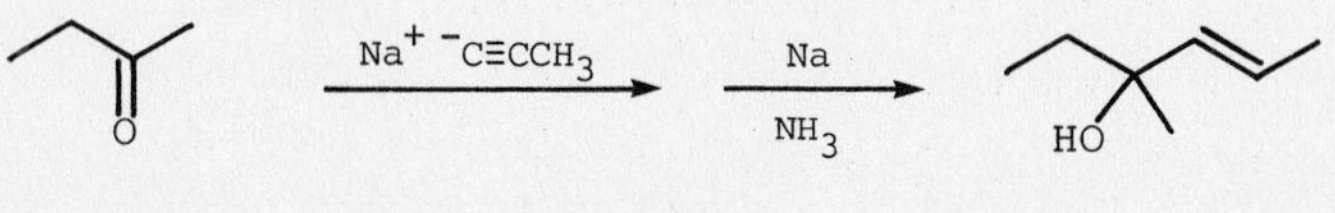

$$\text{Na}^+\ {}^-\text{C}\!\equiv\!\text{CCH}_3 \quad \xrightarrow[\text{NH}_3]{\text{Na}}$$

(f)

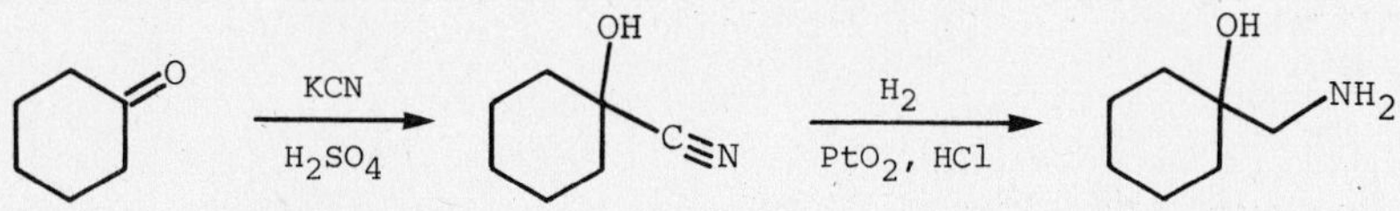

$$\xrightarrow[\text{H}_2\text{SO}_4]{\text{KCN}} \quad \xrightarrow[\text{PtO}_2,\ \text{HCl}]{\text{H}_2}$$

9. (a)

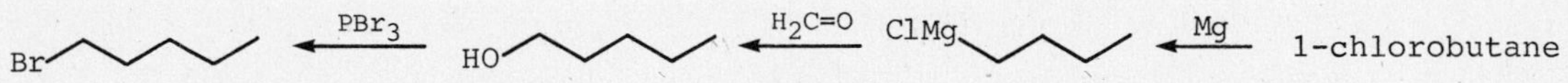

$$\text{Br} \xleftarrow{\text{PBr}_3} \text{HO} \xleftarrow{\text{H}_2\text{C=O}} \text{ClMg} \xleftarrow{\text{Mg}} \text{1-chlorobutane}$$

(b)

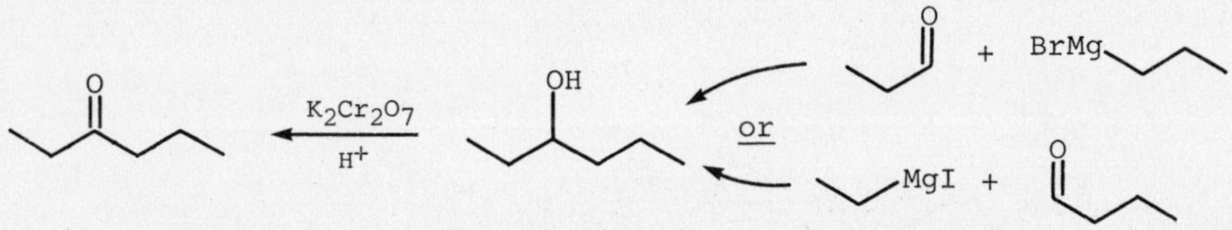

$$\xleftarrow[\text{H}^+]{\text{K}_2\text{Cr}_2\text{O}_7} \qquad + \ \text{BrMg}$$

$$\underline{\text{or}}$$

$$\text{MgI} \ + $$

(c)

$$\xleftarrow[\Delta]{\text{H}_2\text{SO}_4} \quad \xleftarrow{\text{nPrMgCl}} \quad \xleftarrow{\text{K}_2\text{Cr}_2\text{O}_7}$$

$$\text{1-chloropropane} \xrightarrow{\text{Mg}} \text{nPrMgCl} \ + \qquad \text{CHO} \xleftarrow{\text{PCC}} \text{1-butanol}$$

(d)

EtI

$$\xleftarrow{\text{EtMgI}} \quad \xleftarrow[\text{H}^+]{\text{K}_2\text{Cr}_2\text{O}_7} \quad \xleftarrow{} \qquad + \ \text{BrMg}$$

$$\text{PCC} \nearrow \qquad\qquad \text{Mg} \nearrow$$

isobutyl alcohol   isobutyl bromide

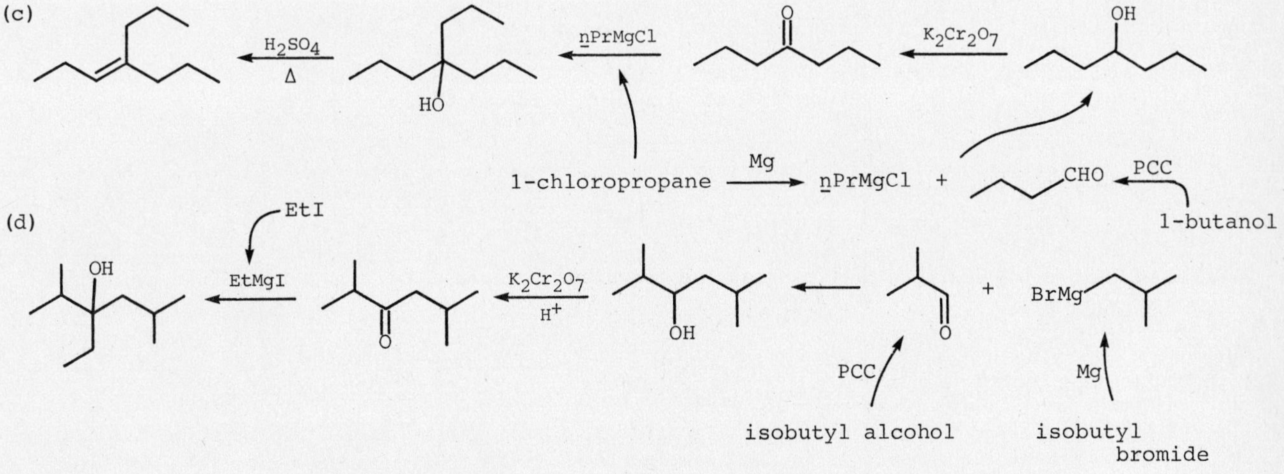

10. (a)

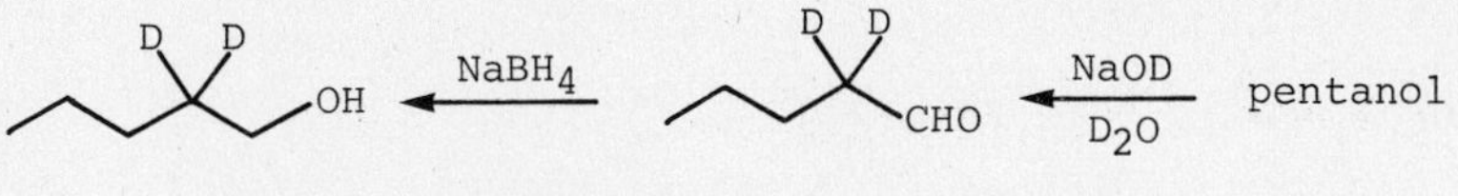

$$\xleftarrow{\text{NaBH}_4} \quad \xleftarrow[\text{D}_2\text{O}]{\text{NaOD}} \quad \text{pentanol}$$

(b)

$$\xleftarrow[\text{Pt}]{\text{D}_2}$$

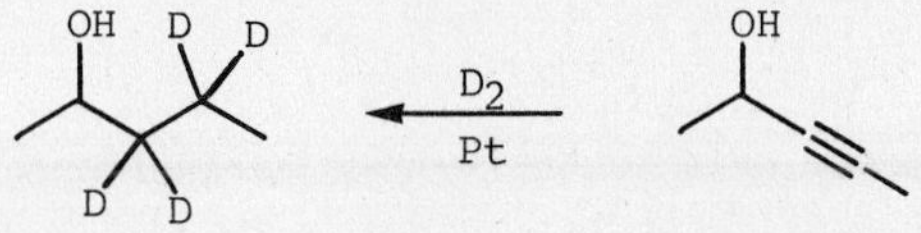

(c)

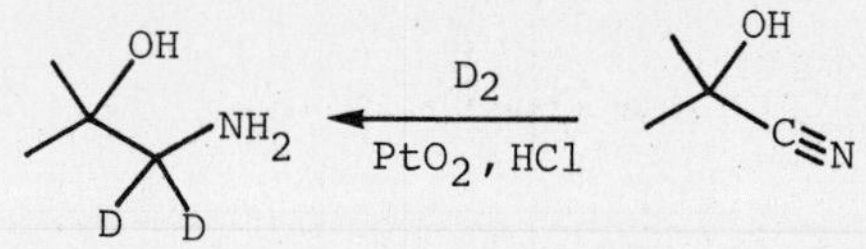

(d)

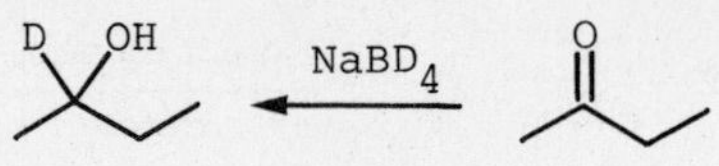

11. (a) It is not possible to make the phosphonium salt pre-
          cursor to the ylide reagent, because neopentyl
          halides are too hindered for S_N2 attack:

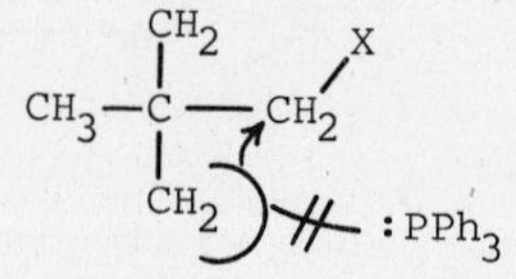

     (b) The four-membered ring is too strained to be formed
          in this reversible reaction:

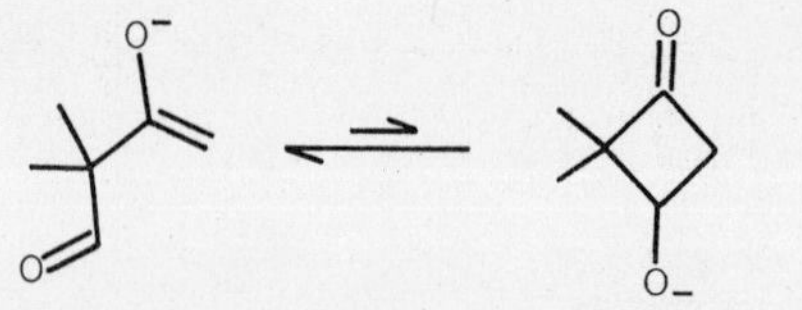

     (c) There would be three other products formed in similar amounts from this
          mixed aldol condensation:

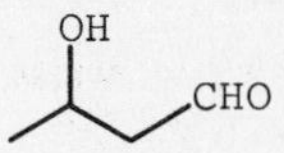

3-hydroxybutanal 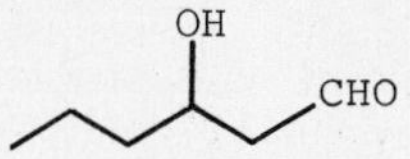   *3-hydroxyhexanal* 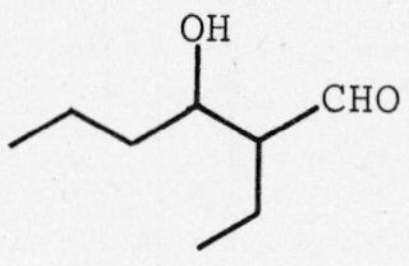   *2-ethyl-*   *2-ethyl-*
                                                    3-hydroxyhexanal   *3-hydroxybutanal*

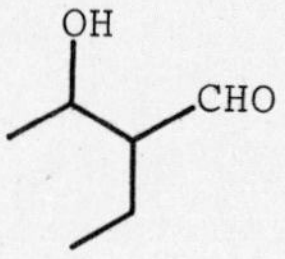

     (d) The acidic conditions of the Clemmensen reduction would lead to loss of the
          alcohol group, with carbocation rearrangement and substitution by chloride.

12.

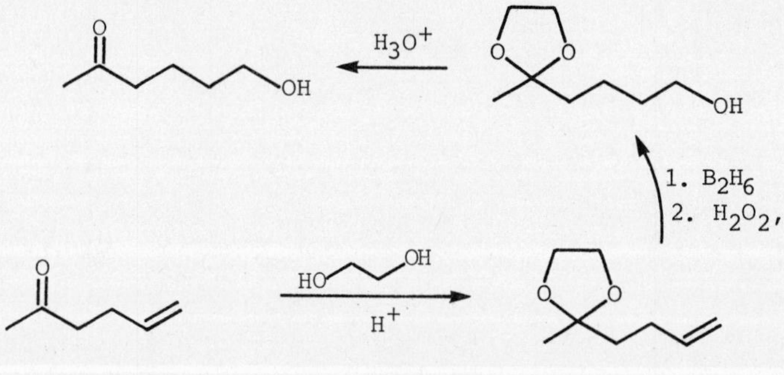

13.   Consider the reaction of a base at the two sites:

     Reaction on oxygen:

     Since the oxygen already has eight electrons, one pair in the double bond must be displaced
     onto carbon as the new bond is formed using the electron pair as the base. The resulting
     intermediate would be a high-energy charge-separated species.

     Reaction on carbon:

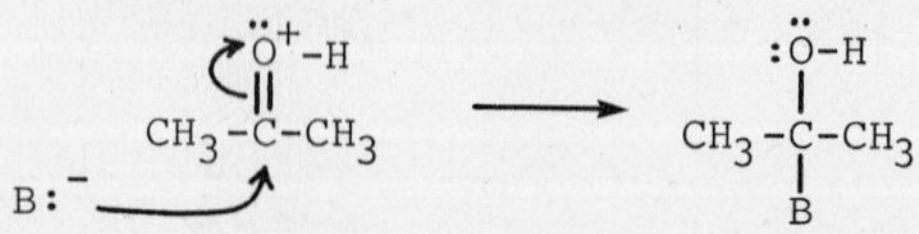

     Again, the carbon already has eight electrons, so one pair in the double bond must be dis-
     placed onto oxygen. However, in this case, the resulting product is neutral, and of much
     lower energy.

This example points up the value of using resonance structures. Of the two contributions to the resonance hybride, the former is more important, since both C and O have octet configurations. However, the latter structure shows that C also has positive character and, to the extent that it has positive character, is electron deficient and can react with a base.

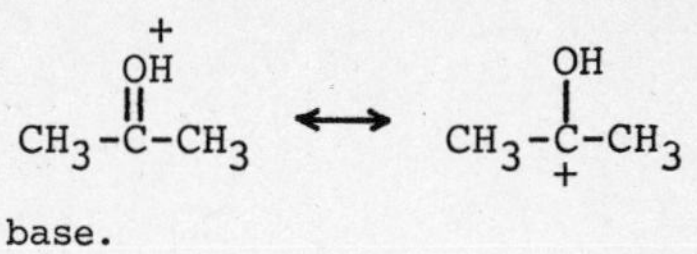

$$CH_3-\overset{\overset{+}{O}H}{\underset{\|}{C}}-CH_3 \longleftrightarrow CH_3-\overset{OH}{\underset{\overset{+}{C}}{|}}-CH_3$$

14. This example is another case of kinetic vs. equilibrium control. The acid-catalyzed reaction involves the more highly substituted enol which is formed faster than its isomer, but 1,3-dibromoacetone is apparently more stable than 1,1-dibromoacetone, perhaps because of steric effects. The important implication in these results is that the acid-catalyzed bromination reaction is reversible.

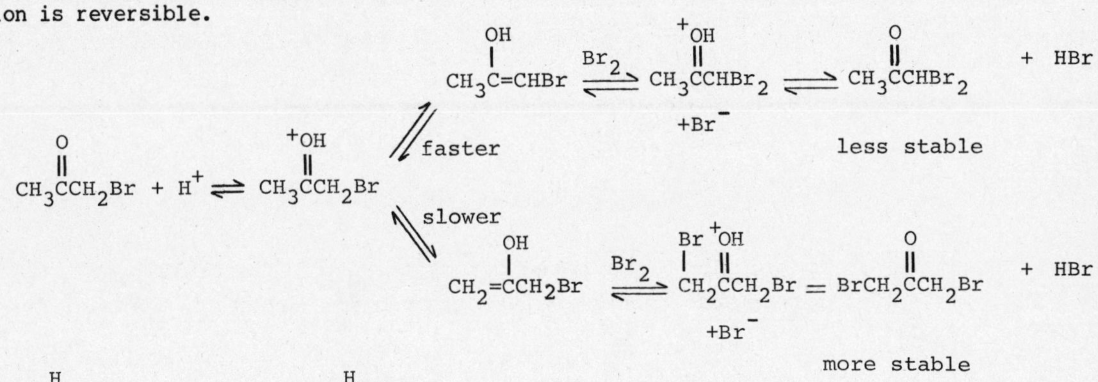

$$CH_3\overset{OH}{\underset{|}{C}}=CHBr \xrightarrow{Br_2} CH_3\overset{+OH}{\underset{\|}{C}}CHBr_2 \rightleftharpoons CH_3\overset{O}{\underset{\|}{C}}CHBr_2 + HBr$$

+Br⁻   less stable

$$CH_3\overset{O}{\underset{\|}{C}}CH_2Br + H^+ \rightleftharpoons CH_3\overset{+OH}{\underset{\|}{C}}CH_2Br$$

↗ faster

↘ slower

$$CH_2=\overset{OH}{\underset{|}{C}}CH_2Br \xrightarrow{Br_2} \overset{Br}{\underset{|}{CH_2}}\overset{+OH}{\underset{\|}{C}}CH_2Br = BrCH_2\overset{O}{\underset{\|}{C}}CH_2Br + HBr$$

+Br⁻

more stable

15.

16.

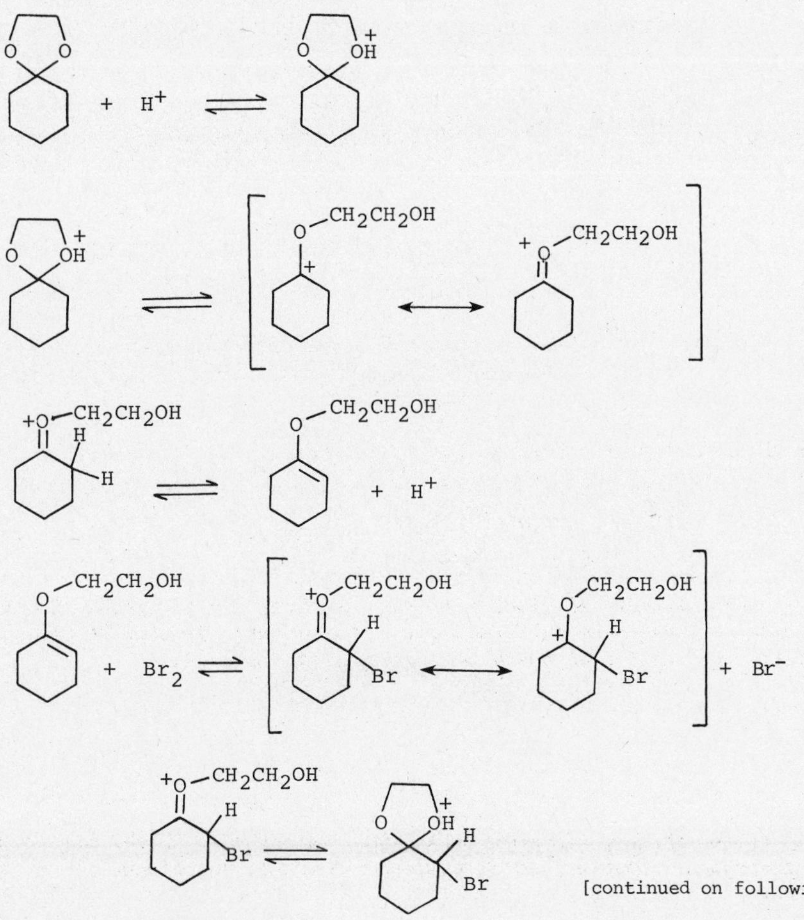

[continued on following page]

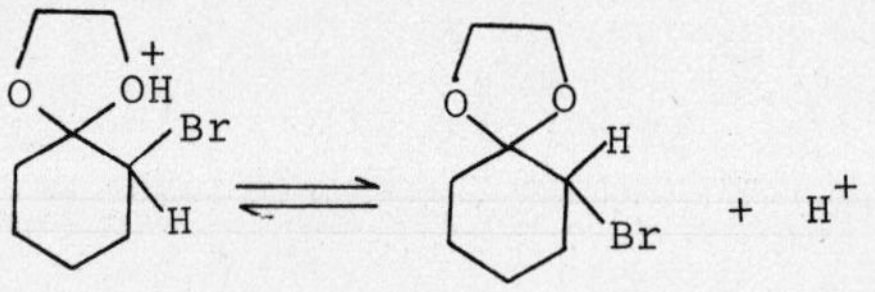

17.

(1) $CH_3\overset{\displaystyle OEt}{\underset{\displaystyle |}{C}}HOEt + H^+ \rightleftharpoons CH_3\overset{\displaystyle \overset{+}{H}OEt}{\underset{\displaystyle |}{C}}HOEt$ (2) $CH_3\overset{\displaystyle \overset{+}{H}OEt}{\underset{\displaystyle |}{C}}HOEt \rightleftharpoons CH_3CH=\overset{+}{O}Et + EtOH$

(3) $CH_3CH=\overset{+}{O}Et + H_2O \rightleftharpoons CH_3\overset{\displaystyle \overset{+}{O}H_2}{\underset{\displaystyle |}{C}}HOEt$ (4) $CH_3\overset{\displaystyle \overset{+}{O}H_2}{\underset{\displaystyle |}{C}}HOEt \rightleftharpoons CH_3\overset{\displaystyle OH}{\underset{\displaystyle |}{C}}HOEt + H^+$

(5) $CH_3\overset{\displaystyle OH}{\underset{\displaystyle |}{C}}HOEt + H^+ \rightleftharpoons CH_3\overset{\displaystyle OH}{\underset{\displaystyle |}{C}}H\overset{+}{O}Et$ (6) $CH_3\overset{\displaystyle OH}{\underset{\displaystyle |}{C}}H\overset{+}{O}Et \rightleftharpoons CH_3\overset{\displaystyle \overset{+}{O}H}{\underset{\displaystyle |}{C}}H + EtOH$
$ \overset{\displaystyle |}{H} \overset{\displaystyle |}{H}$

(7) $CH_3\overset{\displaystyle \overset{+}{O}H}{\underset{\displaystyle ||}{C}}H \rightleftharpoons CH_3CHO + H^+$

18. Greater than unity. The fluorinated carbonyl group is destabilized because the dipolar resonance structure is less stable.

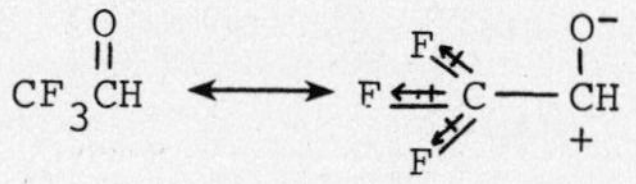

destabilized by electrostatic repulsions between C-F dipoles and C^+.

19. (a) a cyclic acetal

(b) (1) $HOCH_2CH_2CH_2\overset{\displaystyle O}{\underset{\displaystyle ||}{C}}H + H^+ \rightleftharpoons HOCH_2CH_2CH_2\overset{\displaystyle \overset{+}{O}H}{\underset{\displaystyle ||}{C}}H$

(2) $HOCH_2CH_2CH_2\overset{\displaystyle \overset{+}{O}H}{\underset{\displaystyle ||}{C}}H \rightleftharpoons$

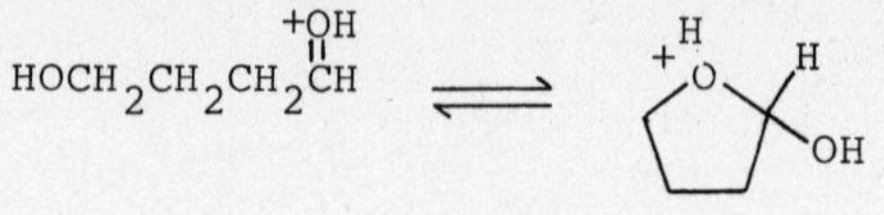

(3)

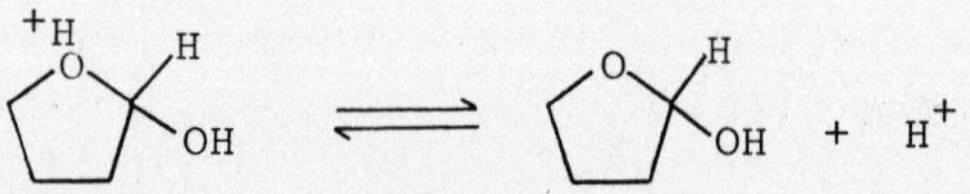

(4)

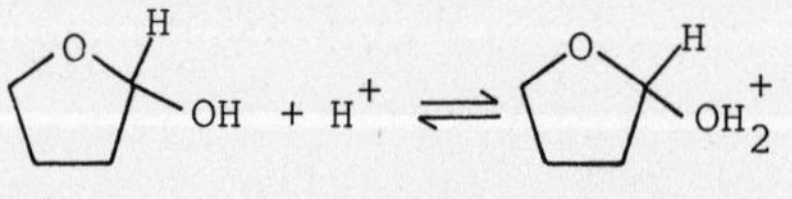

(5)

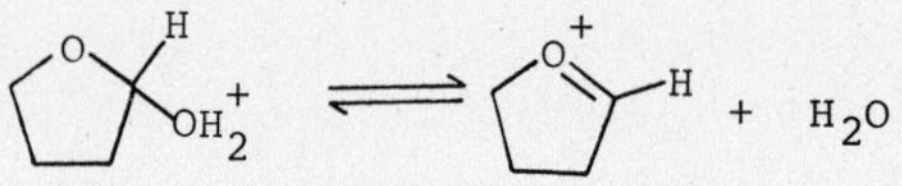

(6)

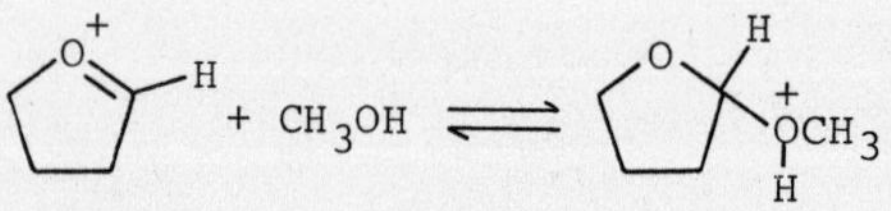

(7)

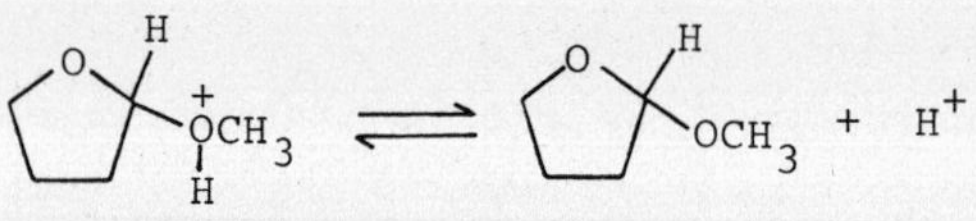

(c) a cyclic hemiacetal

(d) See steps 1)-3) in part (b).

20.

$$CH_3\overset{\overset{O}{\|}}{CH} + H^+ \rightleftharpoons CH_3\overset{\overset{+OH}{\|}}{CH} \qquad CH_3\overset{\overset{+OH}{\|}}{CH} + CH_3CHO \rightleftharpoons CH_3\overset{OH}{\underset{H}{C}}-\overset{+}{O}=CH_3$$

$$CH_3CHOH-\overset{+}{O}=\overset{H}{C}CH_3 + \overset{H}{O}=\overset{}{C}CH_3 \rightleftharpoons CH_3\overset{OH}{\underset{H}{C}}-O-\overset{H}{\underset{CH_3}{C}}-\overset{+}{O}=\overset{H}{C}CH_3 \rightleftharpoons$$

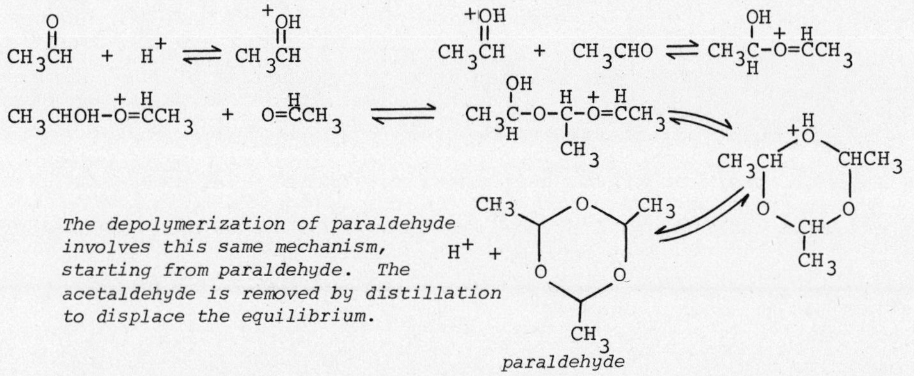

The depolymerization of paraldehyde involves this same mechanism, starting from paraldehyde. The acetaldehyde is removed by distillation to displace the equilibrium.

$$H^+ +$$

paraldehyde

21. (a) $CH_3(CH_2)_8CH_2OH \xrightarrow{PBr_3} CH_3(CH_2)_8CH_2Br \xrightarrow[NH_3]{HC\equiv C^-} CH_3(CH_2)_8CH_2C\equiv CH$

$\Big\downarrow H_2 \;\; \text{Lindlar catalyst}$

$$CH_3(CH_2)_8CH_2CHO \xleftarrow[AcOH]{Zn} \xleftarrow{O_3} CH_3(CH_2)_8CH_2CH=CH_2$$

(b) $CH_3(CH_2)_9CH_2CH_2OH \xrightarrow[\Delta]{Al_2O_3} CH_3(CH_2)_9CH=CH_2 \xrightarrow{O_3} \xrightarrow[AcOH]{Zn}$

$$CH_3(CH_2)_9CHO$$

22.

$$\underset{C_7H_{16}O}{A} \xrightarrow[H_2SO_4]{Na_2Cr_2O_7} \underset{C_7H_{14}O}{B} \xrightarrow{NaOD} C_7H_{12}D_2O$$

$$\xrightarrow{Ag_2O} \text{no reaction}$$

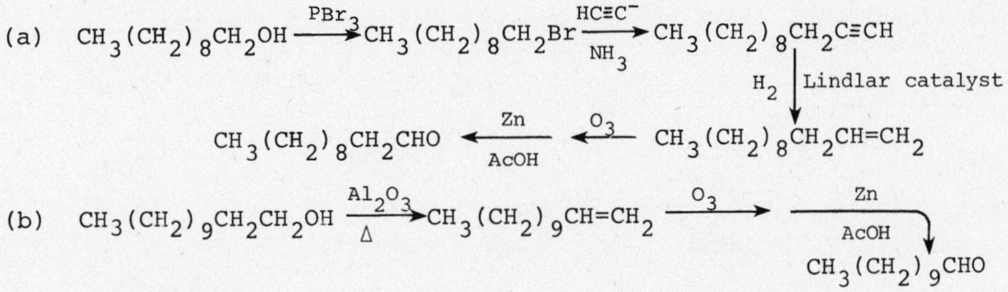

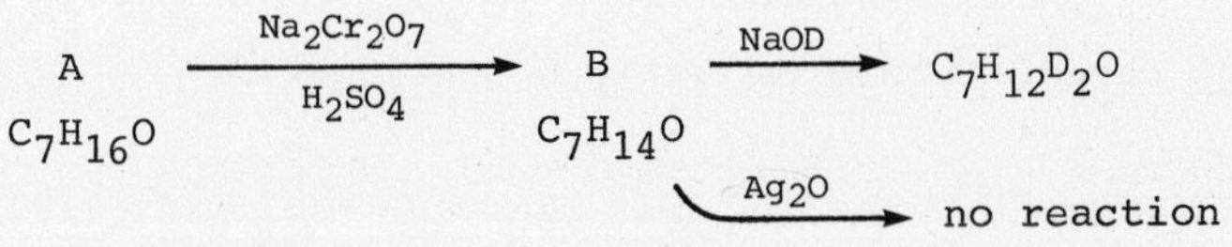

1) **A**, $C_7H_{16}O$: formula indicates no rings or double bonds

2) $A \xrightarrow{Cr^{+6}} B$: A is an alcohol, B is an aldehyde or ketone

3) $B \xrightarrow{Ag_2O}$ no reaction: B is not an aldehyde

4) $B \xrightarrow{NaOD} C_7H_{12}D_2O$: only two hydrogens are exchangeable (α to the carbonyl group of B)

The only possibilities for this latter case are:

$$\underset{CH_3}{\overset{CH_3}{>}}CH-\overset{\overset{O}{\|}}{C}-CH\underset{CH_3}{\overset{CH_3}{<}} \qquad \text{or} \qquad CH_3-\overset{\overset{CH_3}{|}}{\underset{CH_3}{C}}-\overset{\overset{O}{\|}}{C}-CH_2-CH_3$$

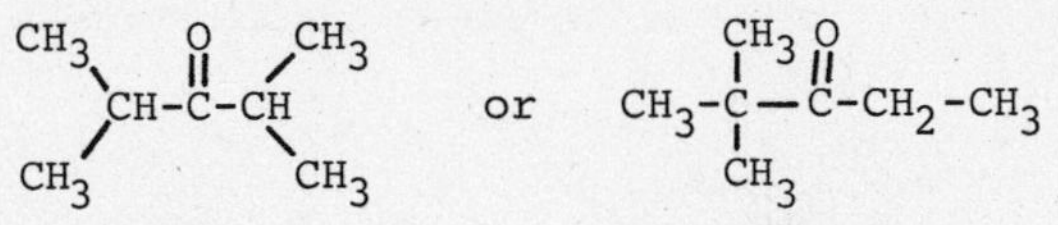

A is therefore $(CH_3)_2CH\overset{OH}{C}HCH_2(CH_3)_2$ or $(CH_3)_3C\overset{OH}{C}HCH_2CH_3$. To distinguish between these two possibilities, further information is needed.

23.

$$\underset{C_{12}H_{22}}{D_1 \text{ and } D_2} \xleftarrow{H_2/Pt} \underset{\substack{C_{12}H_{20} \\ \textit{(optically active)}}}{C} \xrightarrow{O_3} \underset{\substack{C_6H_{10}O \\ \textit{(optically active)}}}{E} \xrightarrow{H_2NOH} \underset{C_6H_{11}NO}{F}$$

$$\searrow{}^{DCl}$$

$$\text{mw } 101$$

NMR: only one methyl, as a doublet

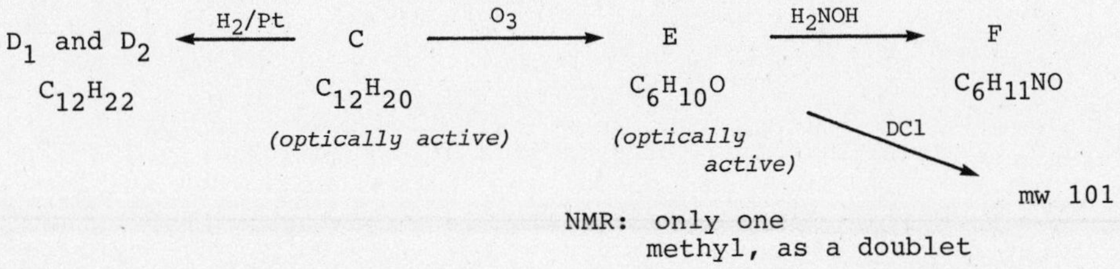

1) C, $C_{12}H_{20}$:   formula indicates three "degrees of unsaturation"; that is: three rings, two rings and one double bond; one ring and two double bonds, or one ring and one triple bond, etc.

2) C $\xrightarrow{H_2/Pt}$ D_1 and D_2, $C_{12}H_{22}$:   hydrogenation adds only two H's, so unsaturation is two rings and one double bond.

3) C $\xrightarrow{O_3}$ E, $C_6H_{10}O$:   C has been cleaved into two molecules of the same formula, E, which is either a ketone or an aldehyde.

4) E, $C_6H_{10}O$:   formula indicates mw 98 and two unsaturations: one C=O and one ring.

5) E $\xrightarrow{DCl}$ mw 101:   there are three exchangeable protons, so E cannot be an aldehyde.

6) E, only one methyl group, as a doublet in NMR: $\rangle$CH-CH$_3$ is part of the structure.

7) There are many ketones of formula $C_6H_{10}O$ with one ring, but only one which satisfies 4), 5), and 6) above:

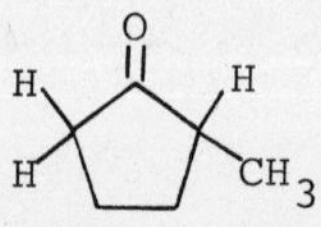

8) E is optically active: it is not a racemic mixture, and the two halves of C must have the same configuration.

9) C could be either:

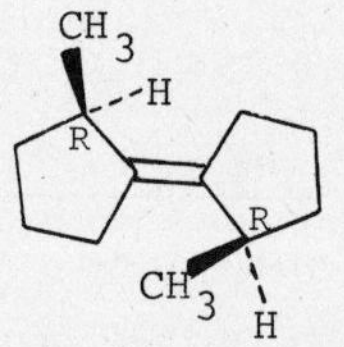

and

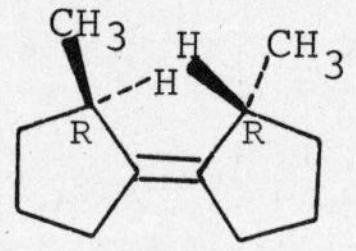

(or the (S,S)-enantiomers)

10) C $\xrightarrow[Pt]{H_2}$ D_1 and D_2:   C is __not__ the *cis* isomer in 9); only the *trans* isomer can give two isomers on hydrogenation:

$\xrightarrow[Pt]{H_2}$ +

$\xrightarrow[Pt]{H_2}$ $\equiv$

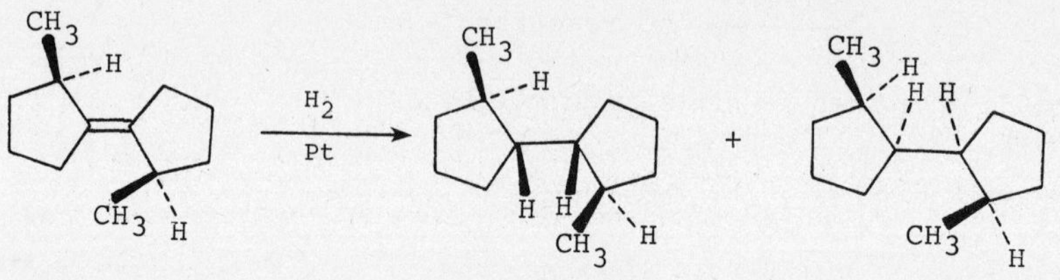

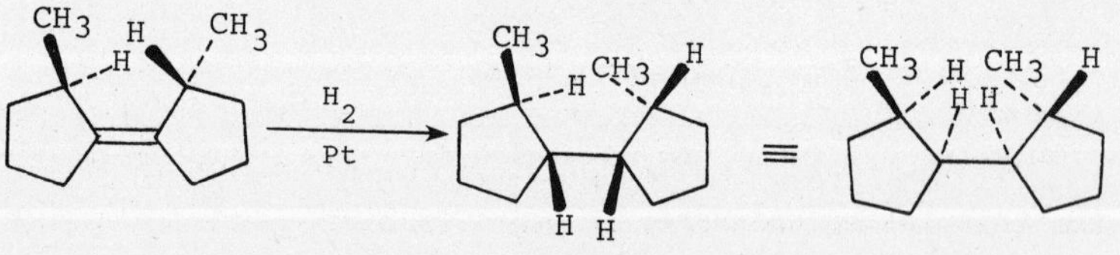

(You can see this easily with models)

11) Finally, F is the oxime:

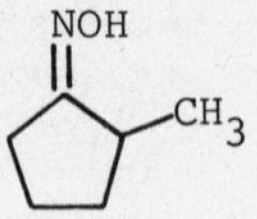

24.   G $\xrightarrow{H_2/Pd}$ H $\xrightarrow{CH_3CO_3H}$ I
       C_6H_8O $C_6H_{10}O$ *(ketone)* $C_6H_{10}O_2$ NMR: only one methyl, as a doublet, δ 1.2

       $\searrow$ NaOD $\rightarrow$ $C_6H_7D_3O$

1) G, C_6H_8O: formula indicates three degrees of unsaturation.

2) G $\xrightarrow{H_2/Pd}$ H, $C_6H_{10}O$: only one saturation is a C=C; that leaves one ring and one C=O.

3)   H $\xrightarrow{\text{NaOD}}$ $C_6H_7D_3O$:   three hydrogens α to C=O.

4)   H $\xrightarrow{\text{CH}_3\text{CO}_3\text{H}}$ I, $C_6H_{10}O_2$: H undergoes the Baeyer-Villiger reaction:

$$-\overset{O}{\underset{\|}{C}}-C \longrightarrow -\overset{O}{\underset{\|}{C}}-O-C$$

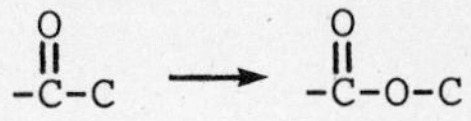

5)   I, NMR: one methyl, doublet at δ 1.2:

$$-O-\overset{H}{\underset{|}{C}}-CH_3$$

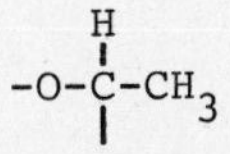

6)   From 3) and 4) above, I must be:

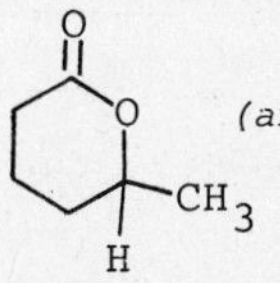

(any smaller ring would require another methyl group)

7)   ∴ H must be

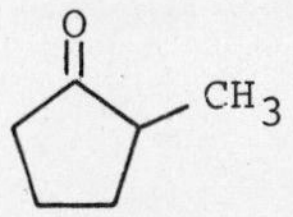

8)   G, nmr: methyl is a singlet: G is

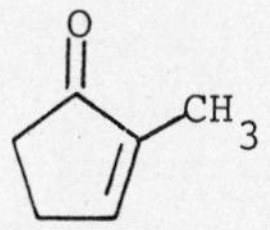

25.

23.9   18.5, 18.9

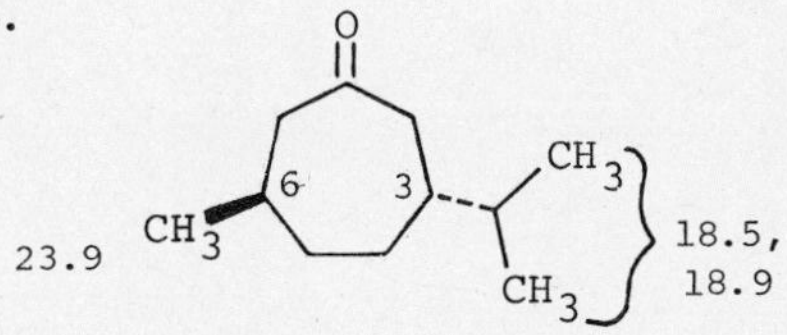

18.5 (q), 18.9 (q), and 23.9 (q) all belong to methyl groups. It is reasonable to assume that the isopropyl methyls are the ones with similar resonances. (Note: the resonances are not identical because the methyls are diastereotopic; see answer to problem #6, Chapter 15.)

41.9   32.0, 34.9

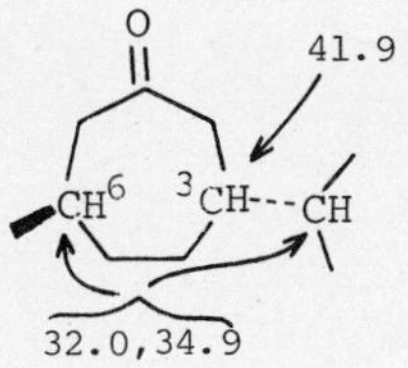

32.0 (d), 34.9 (d), and 41.9 (d) are the CH's. C-3 clearly has the most β-branches and is therefore expected to come the furthest downfield.

51.6   47.0   38.5   32.5

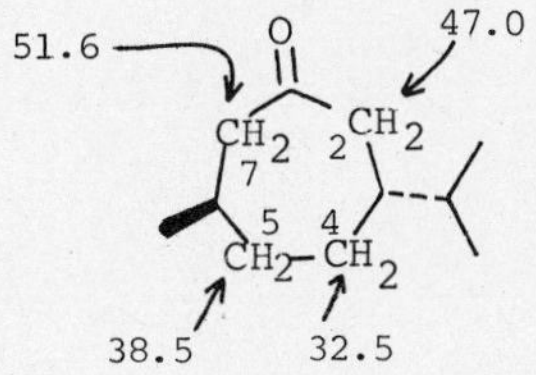

32.5 (t), 38.5 (t), 47.0 (t), and 51.6 (t) are the CH_2's. C-2 and C-7 should be downfield from C-4 and C-5 (presence of electron withdrawing C=O group), therefore they are 47.0 and 51.6. C-2 and C-4 have 2 γ-substitutents more than C-7 and C-5, respectively, because of the isopropyl vs. methyl groups. Therefore they should come ≈5 ppm further upfield.

By comparison, it is clear what the stereochemistry of the 3,6-dimethyl isomer is.

51.6   32.0 or 34.9   23.9   38.5

51.7   31.1   23.7   37.9   K

50.8   29.2   20.9   33.9   J

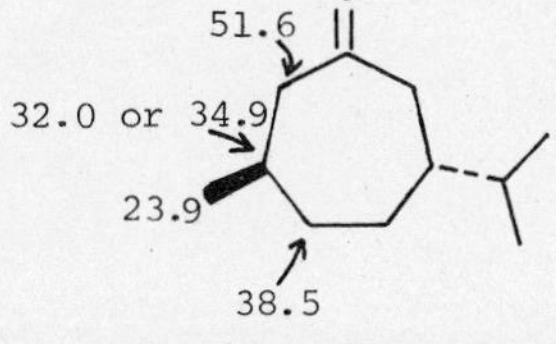

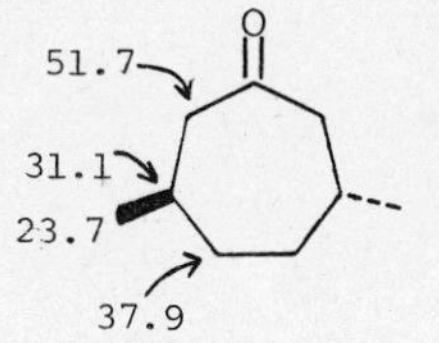

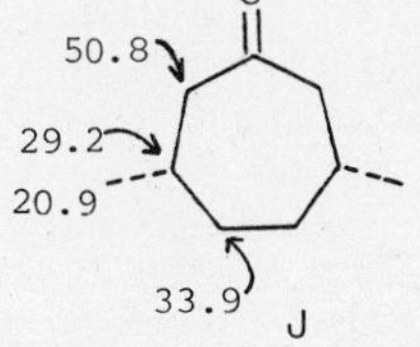

26.

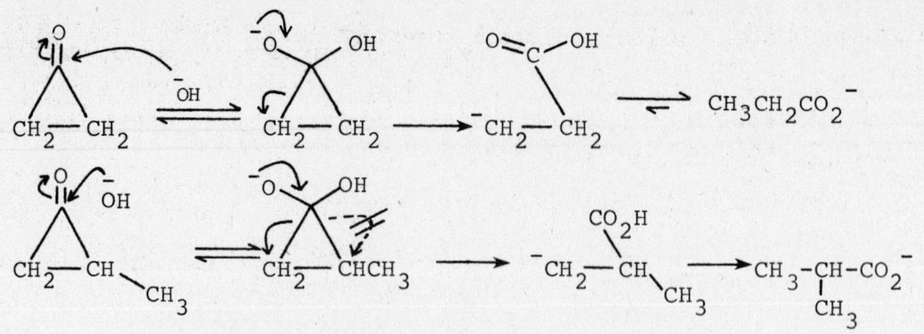

Cleavage occurs to give the more stable, primary carbanion.

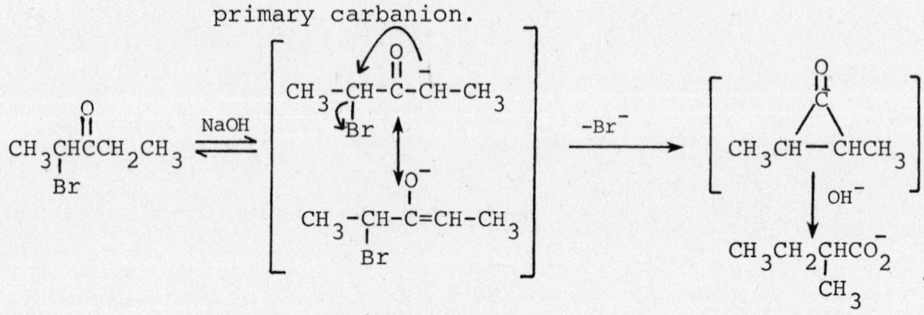

as above

27.

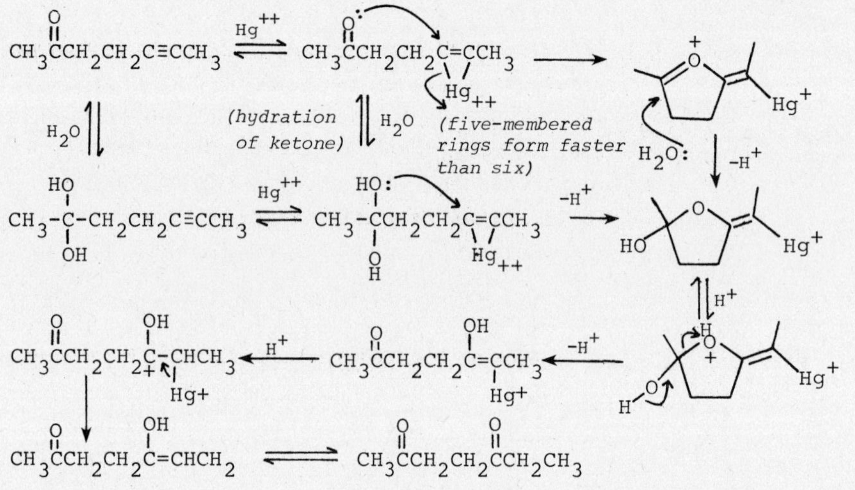

(hydration of ketone)

(five-membered rings form faster than six)

28.

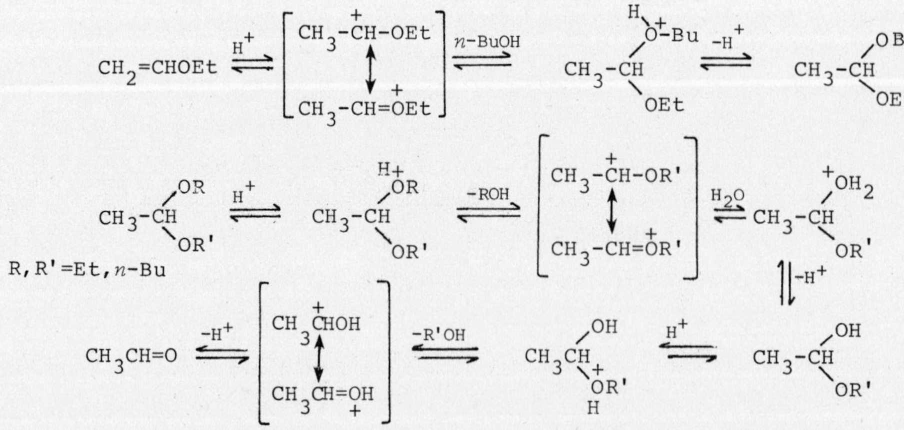

R,R'=Et, n-Bu

The normal conditions for LiAlH$_4$ or NaBH$_4$ reduction of ketones to alcohols are alkaline, and the bromohydrin would cyclize to the epoxide: 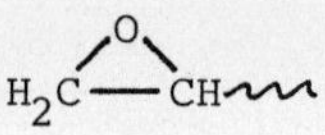 . Protect the alcohol by formation of the mixed acetal, by using ethyl vinyl ether:

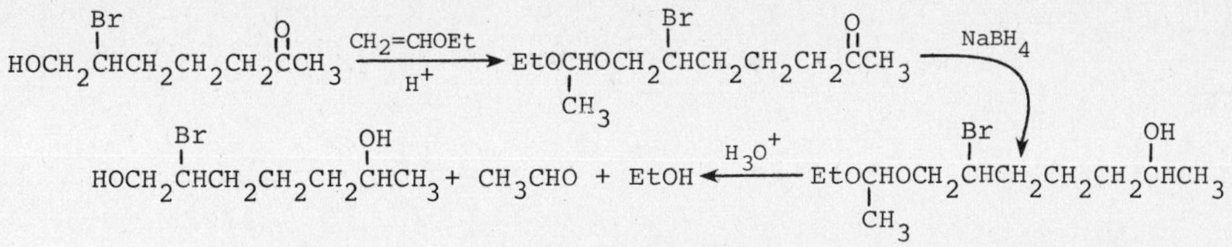

$$HOCH_2CHCH_2CH_2CH_2CCH_3 \xrightarrow[H^+]{CH_2=CHOEt} EtOCHOCH_2CHCH_2CH_2CH_2CCH_3 \xrightarrow{NaBH_4}$$

(with Br, O, and CH₃ substituents)

$$HOCH_2CHCH_2CH_2CH_2CHCH_3 + CH_3CHO + EtOH \xleftarrow{H_3O^+} EtOCHOCH_2CHCH_2CH_2CH_2CHCH_3$$

(with Br, OH, and CH₃ substituents)

29.

(a) 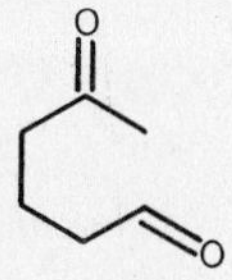   (b) 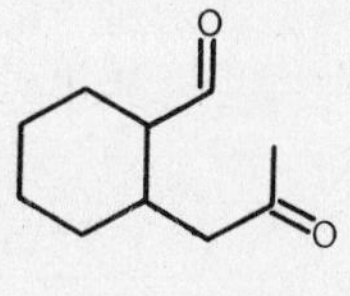   (c) 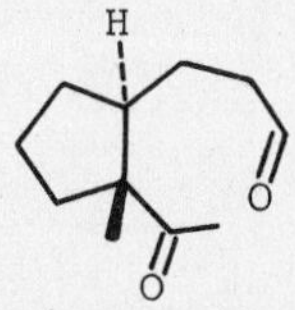   (d)

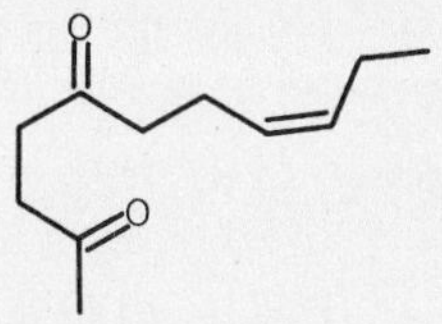

30. The 2.8 Hz coupling corresponds to an equatorial-equatorial or an axial-equatorial H-C-C-H coupling; the 11.8 Hz coupling corresponds to axial-axial coupling. Since the hydrogen at C-5 is axial, the initial bromo compound must have bromine axial (C-6 hydrogen equatorial). This isomerizes to the more stable product with bromine equatorial.

31.

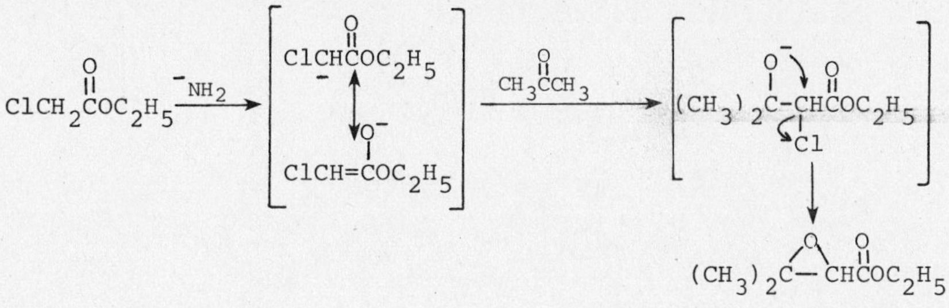

$$ClCH_2COC_2H_5 \xrightarrow{^-NH_2} \left[\begin{array}{c} ClCHCOC_2H_5 \\ \updownarrow \\ ClCH=COC_2H_5 \end{array} \right] \xrightarrow{CH_3CCH_3} \left[(CH_3)_2C-CHCOC_2H_5 \right]$$

(so far, just like an aldol condensation)

$$\downarrow$$

$$(CH_3)_2C-CHCOC_2H_5 + Cl^-$$

32.

$$(CH_3)_2CHCH_2CH + \overset{+}{N}H_4 \rightleftharpoons (CH_3)_2CHCH_2CH \rightleftharpoons (CH_3)_2CHCH_2C-H$$

$$:NH_3 \qquad\qquad \downarrow -H^+$$

$$(CH_3)_2CHCH_2CH \xleftarrow{-H_2O} (CH_3)_2CHCH_2CH \xleftarrow{H^+} (CH_3)_2CHCH_2CH$$

$$-CN \downarrow$$

$$(CH_3)_2CHCH_2CH$$

Reaction scheme with NH₄Cl / HCN:

(cyclic ketone) $\xrightarrow[HCN]{NH_4Cl}$ [intermediate with NH₂, CN] $\rightarrow$ (piperidine ring with CN, N-H, CN)

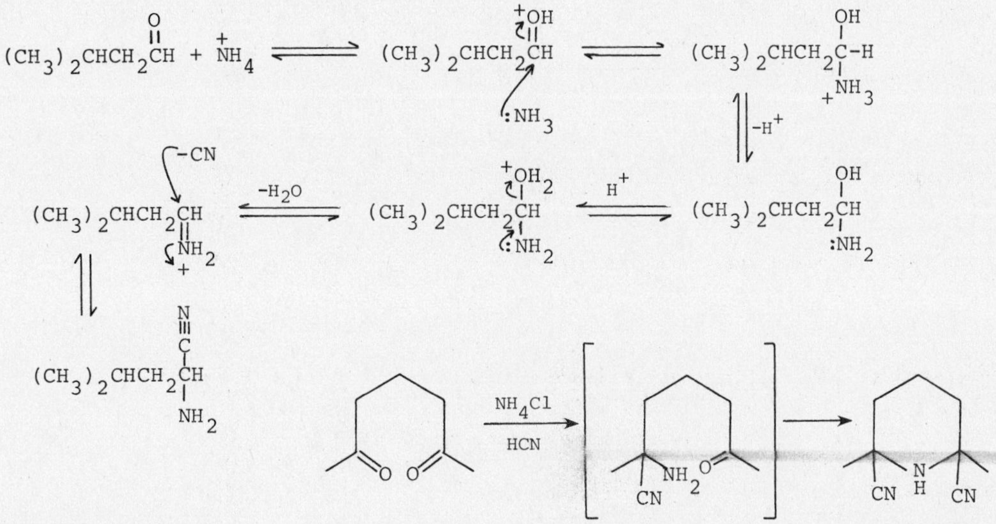

(cis and trans)

14.F   Supplementary Problems

S1. Provide IUPAC names for the following compounds:

(a)   (b) 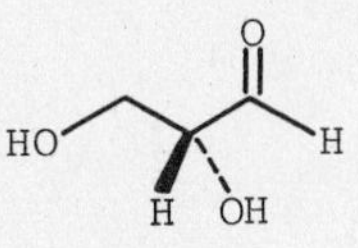   (c)

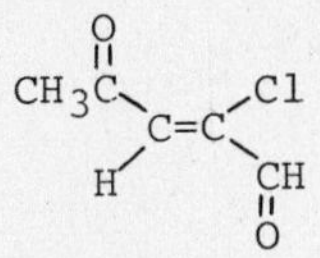

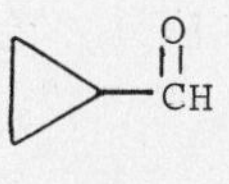

(d) 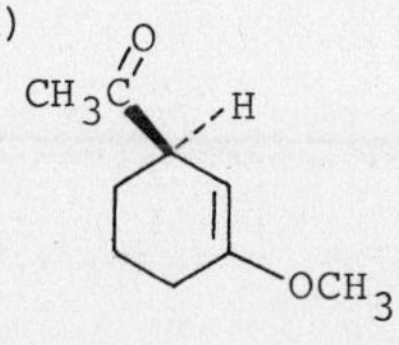   (e) 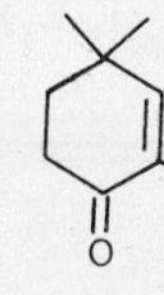   (f)

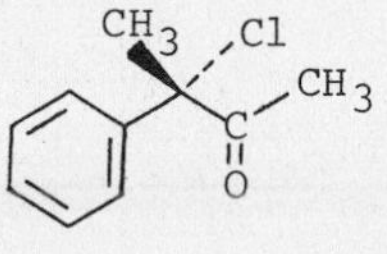

S2. Write the structure of the principal product formed in each of the following reaction sequences.

(a)

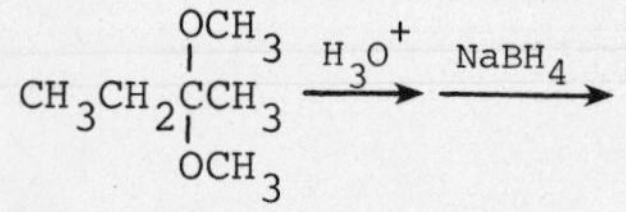

$$CH_3CH_2 \underset{\underset{OCH_3}{|}}{\overset{\overset{OCH_3}{|}}{C}} CH_3 \xrightarrow{H_3O^+} \xrightarrow{NaBH_4}$$

(b)

$$\xrightarrow{CH_3MgBr} \xrightarrow{H_2O} \xrightarrow[H_2SO_4]{K_2Cr_2O_7} \xrightarrow[D_2O]{NaOD}$$

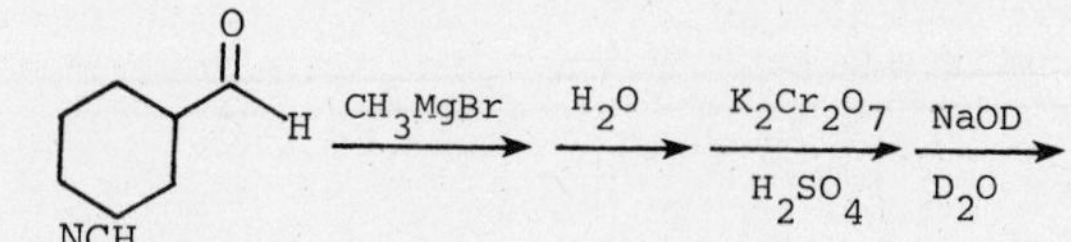

(c) $CH_3CH_2CH_2C\equiv CH \xrightarrow[2.H_2O_2, OH^-]{1.B_2H_6} \xrightarrow{HCN}$

(d)

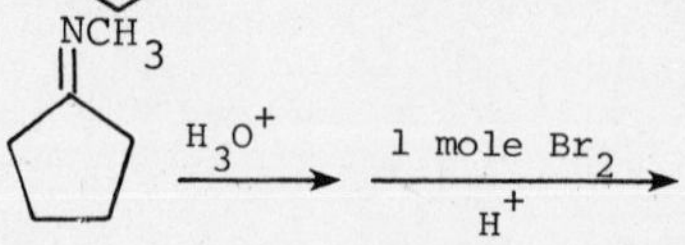

$$\xrightarrow{H_3O^+} \xrightarrow[H^+]{1\ mole\ Br_2}$$

(e)

$$HOCH_2CH_2 \underset{\underset{CH_3}{|}}{\overset{\overset{CH_3}{|}}{C}} CH_2CH_2OH \xrightarrow[\underset{\Delta}{H_2SO_4}]{K_2Cr_2O_7}$$

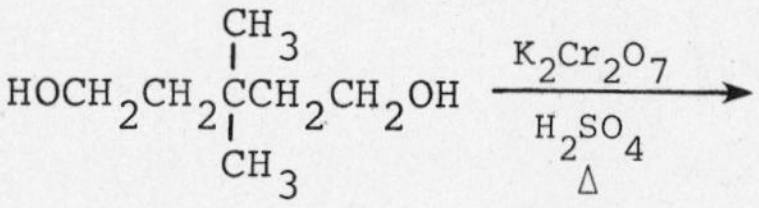

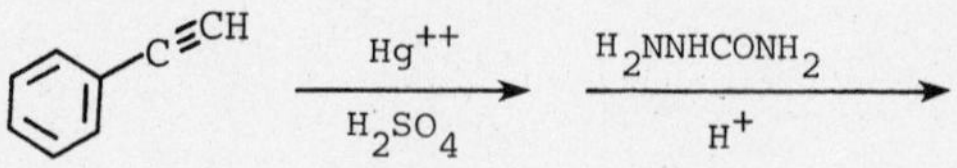

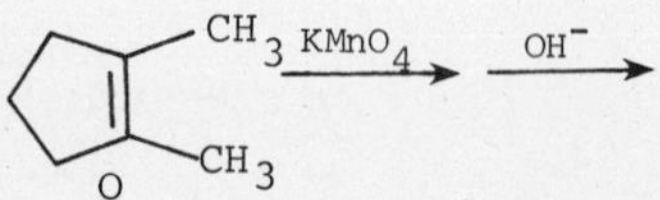

(f)

$$\xrightarrow[H_2SO_4]{Hg^{++}} \xrightarrow[H^+]{H_2NNHCONH_2}$$

(g)

$$\xrightarrow{KMnO_4} \xrightarrow{OH^-}$$

(h) $(CH_3)_2CH\overset{\overset{O}{\|}}{C}CH_3 \xrightarrow{HC\equiv CNa} \xrightarrow{H_2O}$

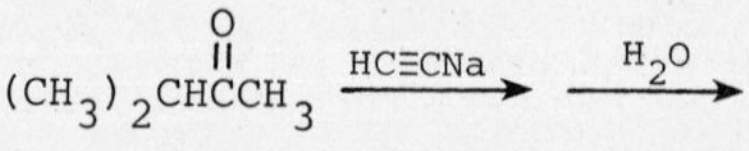

(i)

$$\xrightarrow{LDA} \xrightarrow{CH_3CH_2I} \xrightarrow[KOH, \Delta\Delta]{H_2NNH_2}$$

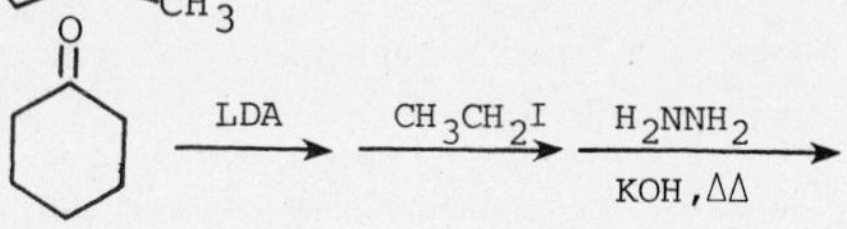

S3. Show how to carry out each of the following transformations. More than one step is involved in each case.

(a)

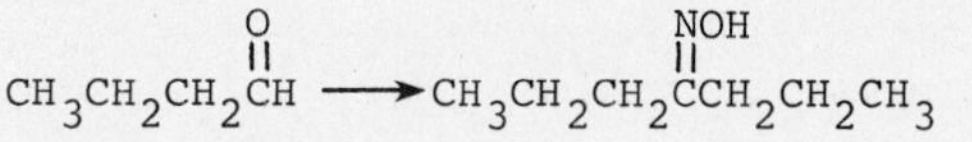

$$CH_3CH_2CH_2\overset{\overset{O}{\|}}{CH} \longrightarrow CH_3CH_2CH_2\overset{\overset{NOH}{\|}}{C}CH_2CH_2CH_3$$

(b)

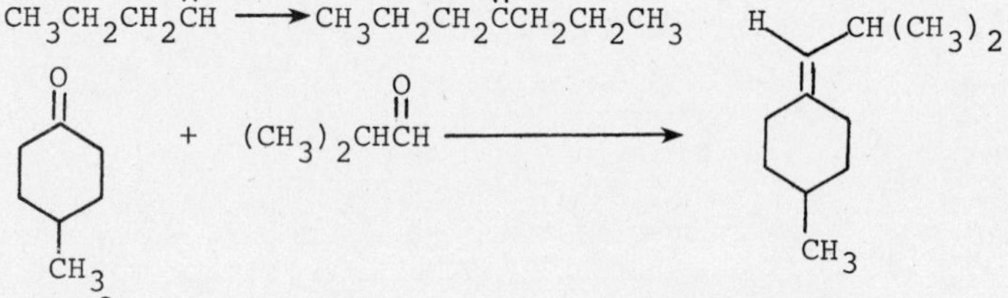

(c)

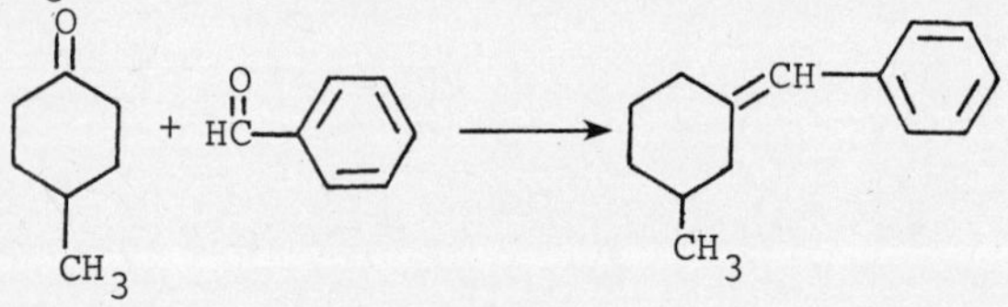

(d) 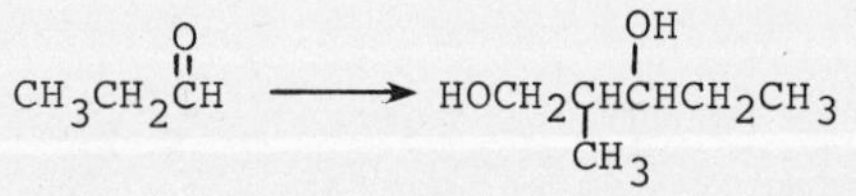 $CH_3CH_2\overset{\overset{O}{\|}}{CH} \longrightarrow HOCH_2\underset{\underset{CH_3}{|}}{\overset{\overset{OH}{|}}{C}H}CHCH_2CH_3$

S4. Show how each of the following compounds can be prepared from materials containing four carbons or less.

(a)

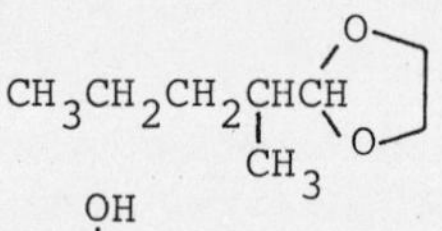

(b) 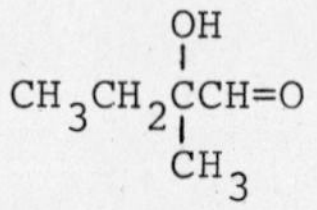 $CH_3CH_2\underset{\underset{CH_3}{|}}{\overset{\overset{OH}{|}}{C}}CH=O$

(c) $CH_3\underset{\underset{OH}{|}}{\overset{}{C}H}CH=CHCH(CH_3)_2$

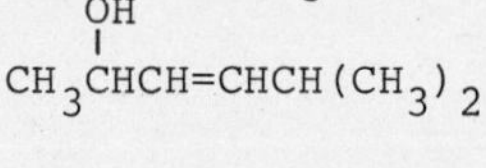

(d) 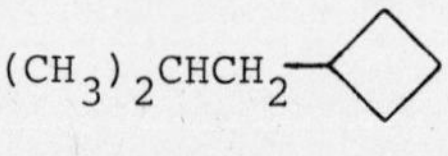 $(CH_3)_2CHCH_2$

S5. On heating cis-6,7-epoxy-2-nonanone with a trace of acid, it is converted to brevicomin, the aggregating pheromone of the female western pine beetle *Dendroctomus brevicomis*:

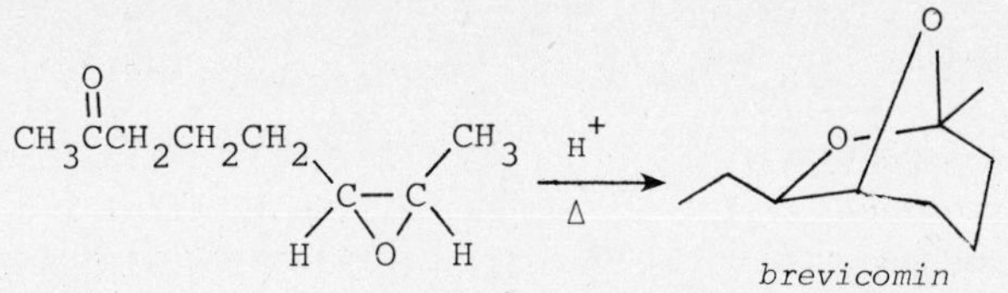

$$CH_3CCH_2CH_2CH_2-\underset{\underset{H}{|}}{C}-\underset{\underset{H}{|}}{C}-CH_3 \quad \xrightarrow[\Delta]{H^+} \quad \text{brevicomin}$$

A proposed synthesis of this epoxyketone is shown below. Each of the proposed steps contains a flaw and will lead to a significant amount of side products. For each step, point out the flaw or likely side reaction. Then, suggest a synthesis which avoids these problems.

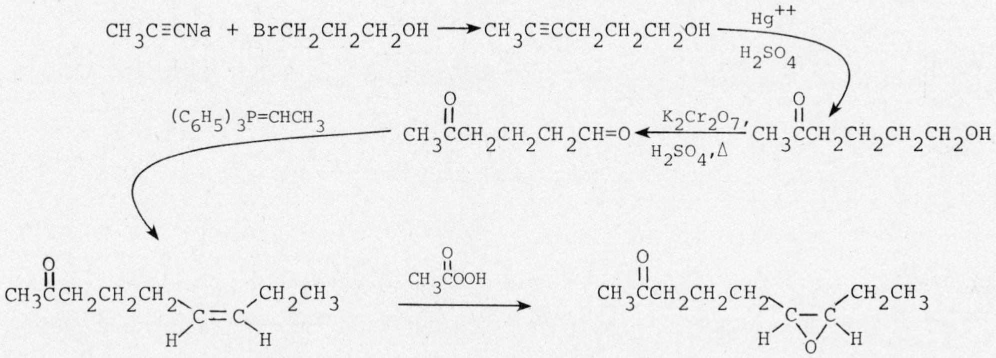

$$CH_3C\equiv CNa + BrCH_2CH_2CH_2OH \longrightarrow CH_3C\equiv CCH_2CH_2CH_2OH \xrightarrow[H_2SO_4]{Hg^{++}}$$

$$(C_6H_5)_3P=CHCH_3 \longleftarrow CH_3CCH_2CH_2CH_2CH=O \xleftarrow[H_2SO_4, \Delta]{K_2Cr_2O_7} CH_3CCH_2CH_2CH_2CH_2OH$$

$$CH_3CCH_2CH_2CH_2-\underset{\underset{H}{\|}}{C}=\underset{\underset{H}{\|}}{C}-CH_2CH_3 \xrightarrow{CH_3COOH} CH_3CCH_2CH_2CH_2-\underset{\underset{H}{|}}{C}-\underset{O}{\underset{H}{|}}-CH_2CH_3$$

S6. Show all the intermediates involved in the following reaction sequence

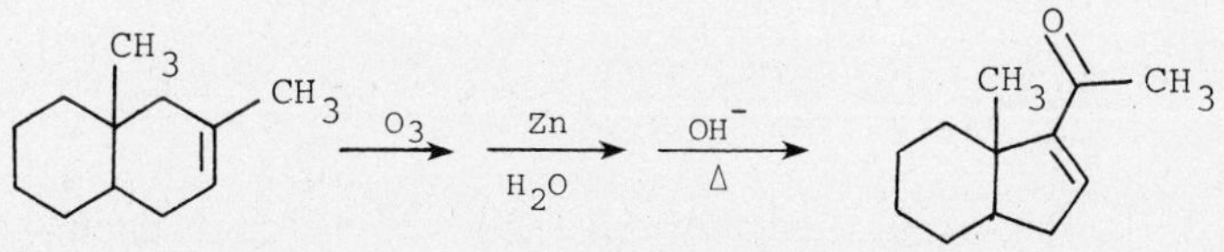

$$\xrightarrow{O_3} \xrightarrow[H_2O]{Zn} \xrightarrow[\Delta]{OH^-}$$

S7. Compound A, of formula C_7H_{14}, reacts with ozone followed by zinc dust to give B and C. B reacts with phenylhydrazine to give a crystalline product of formula $C_8H_{10}N_2$. Compound C does not undergo any reaction with Ag_2O, but it shows a singlet at δ 2.0 in the NMR spectrum. The reaction of B with the ylide formed from ethyltriphenylphosphonium bromide gives two compounds, A and an isomer D. The cmr spectra of A and D are given below:

    A: δ 12.0, 12.8, 20.2, 22.1, 32.7, 118.3, 134.8 ppm
    D: δ 12.0, 12.6, 14.2, 20.4, 41.2, 117.6, 134.7 ppm

What are A,B,C and D?

S8. Suggest a mechanism for the following conversion:

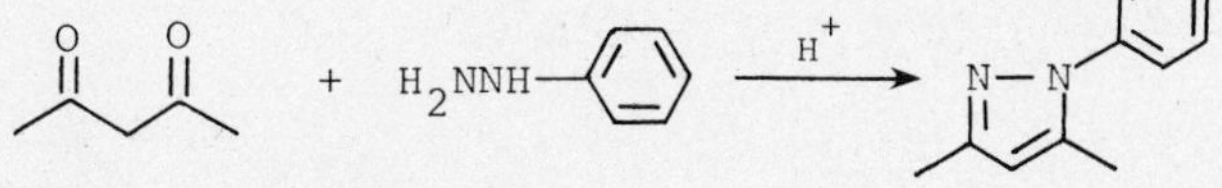

$$\underset{O}{\|} \quad \underset{O}{\|} + H_2NNH-\text{C}_6\text{H}_5 \xrightarrow{H^+} \text{N}-\text{N}-\text{C}_6\text{H}_5$$

S9. Write a mechanism which accounts for the formation of butyrolactone when 1,4-butanediol is treated with CrO_3/pyridine.

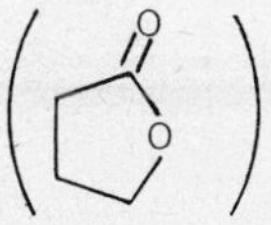

14.G   Answers to Supplementary Problems

S1. (a) ($\underline{Z}$)-2-chloro-4-oxo-2-pentanal
         (b) ($\underline{R}$)-2,3-dihydroxypropanal
         (c) cyclopropanecarbaldehyde

         (d) ($\underline{R}$)-1-methoxy-3-(1-oxoethyl)cyclohexene
         (e) 2,2,4-trimethyl-2-cyclohexenone
         (f) ($\underline{S}$)-3-chloro-3-phenyl-2-butanone

S2.
   (a) $CH_3CH_2CHCH_3$ (with OH)

   (b) (cyclohexane with D and CCD_3, C=O)

   (c) $CH_3CH_2CH_2CH_2CH-C\equiv N$ (with OH)

   (d) (cyclopentanone with Br)

   (e) $HO_2CCH_2CCH_2CO_2H$ (with two CH_3)

   (f) (phenyl) $C=NNHCONH_2$, CH_3

   (g) (cyclohexenone with CH_3)

   (h) $(CH_3)_2CHC-C\equiv CH$ (with OH and CH_3)

   (i) (cyclohexane with CH_2CH_3)

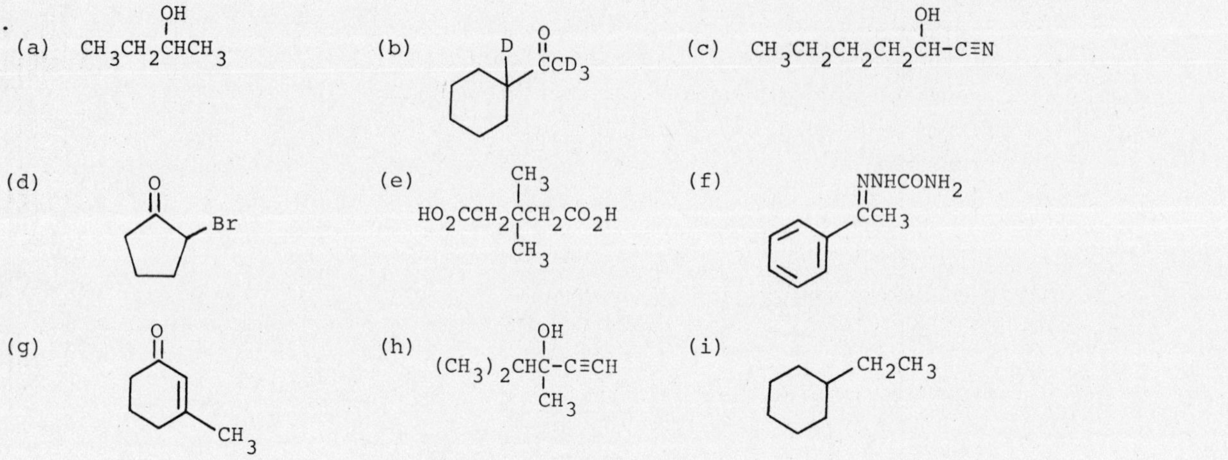

S3. (a) CH_3CH_2CH (C=O) + $NaC\equiv CCH_3$ $\longrightarrow$ $\xrightarrow{H_2O}$ $CH_3CH_2CHC\equiv CCH_3$ (with OH) $\xrightarrow{H_2, Pt}$ $(CH_3CH_2CH_2)_2CHOH$

   $\xrightarrow{K_2Cr_2O_7, H_2SO_4}$

   $(CH_3CH_2CH_2)_2C=NOH$ $\xleftarrow{H_2NOH, H^+}$ $(CH_3CH_2CH_2)_2C=O$

   (b) $(CH_3)_2CHCH$ (C=O) $\xrightarrow{NaBH_4}$ $(CH_3)_2CHCH_2OH$ $\xrightarrow{PBr_3}$ $(CH_3)_2CHCH_2Br$ $\xrightarrow{(C_6H_5)_3P}$

   $(CH_3)_2CHCH_2\overset{+}{P}(C_6H_5)_3$ Br^- $\xrightarrow{n\text{-BuLi}}$ $(CH_3)_2CHCH=P(C_6H_5)_3$ + (4-methylcyclohexanone) $\longrightarrow$ (4-methylcyclohexylidene $=CHCH(CH_3)_2$)

   (c) (4-methylcyclohexanone) + H(C=O)(C_6H_5) $\xrightarrow{NaOH}$ (2-benzylidene-4-methylcyclohexanone $=CHC_6H_5$) $\xrightarrow[BF_3]{HSCH_2CH_2SH}$ (dithiolane spiro structure $=CHC_6H_5$) $\xrightarrow{Raney-Ni}$ (3-methylcyclohexylidene $=CHC_6H_5$)

   (d) $2CH_3CH_2CH$ (C=O) $\xrightarrow{NaOH}$ $HCCHCHCH_2CH_3$ (O, OH, CH_3) $\xrightarrow{NaBH_4}$ $HOCH_2CHCHCH_3$ (OH, CH_3)

S4. (a) $2CH_3CH_2CH$ (C=O) $\xrightarrow{NaOH, \Delta}$ $CH_3CH_2CH=CCH$ (C=O, CH_3) $\xrightarrow{H_2, Pt}$ $CH_3CH_2CH_2CHCH$ (C=O, CH_3) $\xrightarrow[H^+]{HOCH_2CH_2OH}$ $CH_3CH_2CH_2CHCH$ (dioxolane, CH_3)

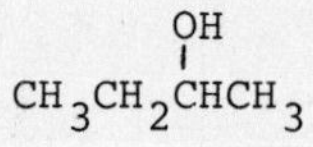

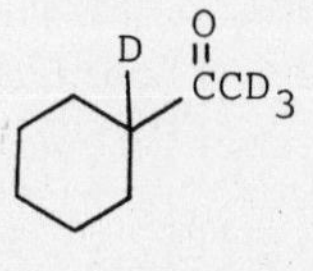

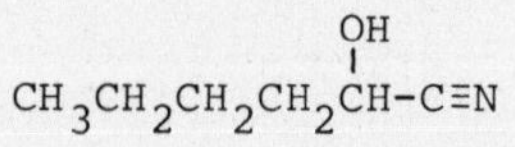

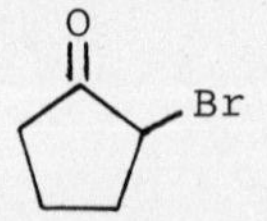

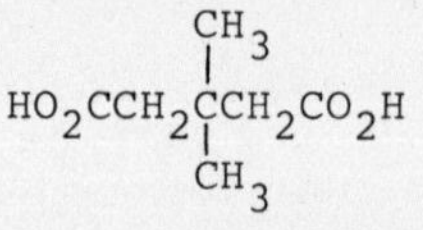

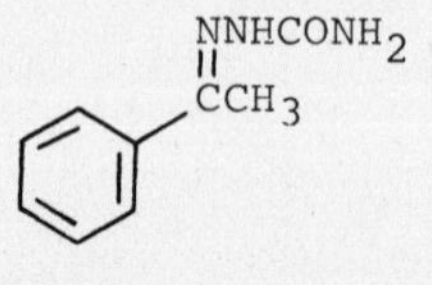

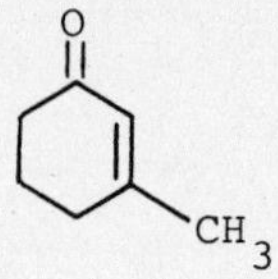

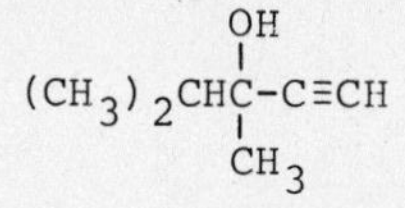

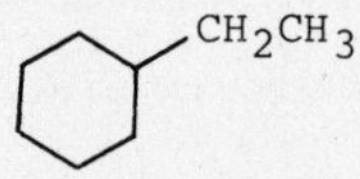

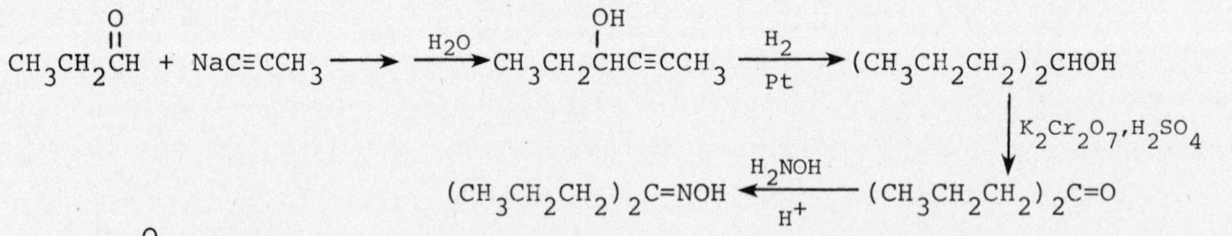

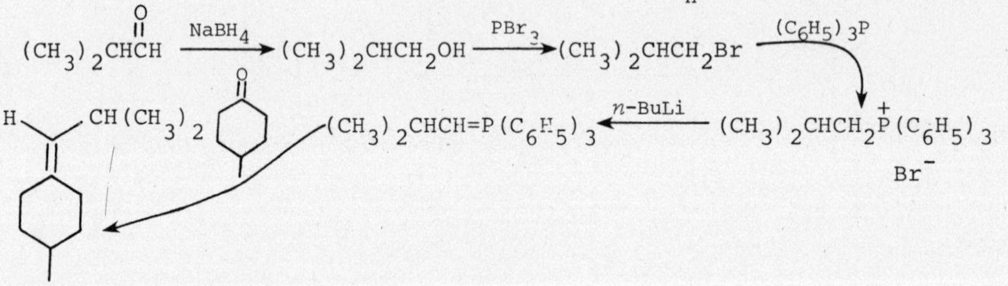

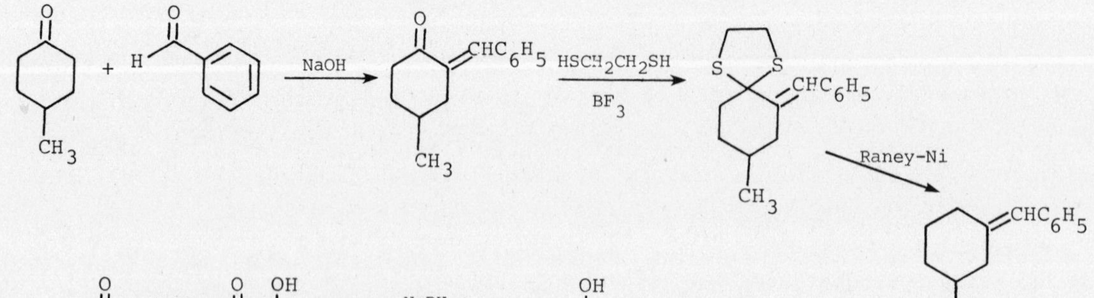

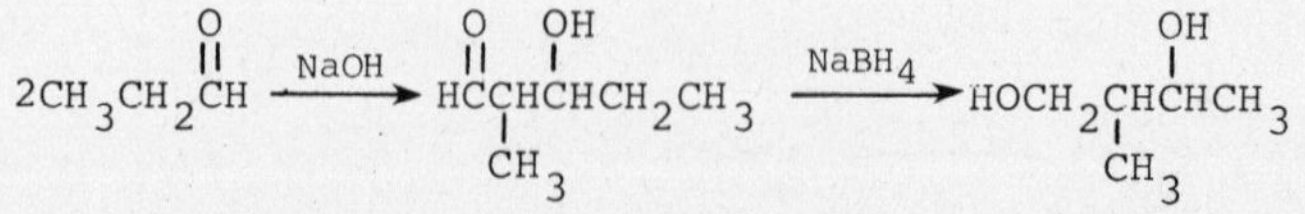

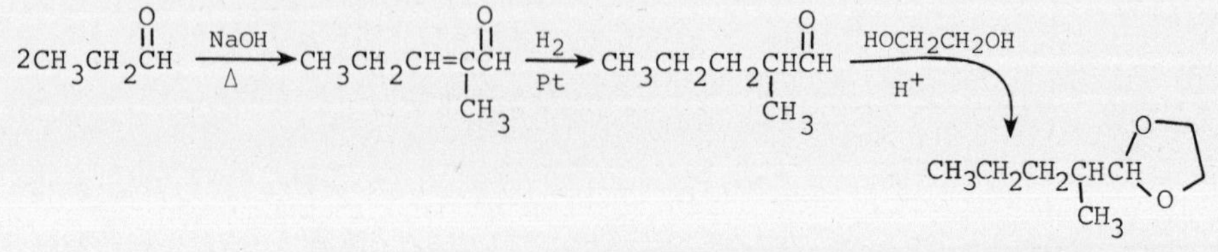

(b) $CH_3CH_2\overset{\overset{O}{\|}}{C}CH_3 + NaC\equiv CH \longrightarrow \overset{H_2O}{\longrightarrow} CH_3CH_2\underset{\underset{CH_3}{|}}{\overset{\overset{OH}{|}}{C}}C\equiv CH \overset{H_2}{\underset{\text{Lindlar catalyst}}{\longrightarrow}} CH_3CH_2\underset{\underset{CH_3}{|}}{\overset{\overset{OH}{|}}{C}}CH=CH_2 \overset{\begin{array}{l}1.O_3\\2.Zn,\\H_2O\end{array}}{\longrightarrow}$

$$CH_3CH_2\underset{\underset{CH_3}{|}}{\overset{\overset{OH}{|}}{C}}-CH=O$$

(c) $CH_3\overset{\overset{O}{\|}}{C}CH_3 \overset{LDA}{\underset{\underset{-78°C}{THF}}{\longrightarrow}} CH_3\overset{\overset{OLi}{|}}{C}=CH_2 \overset{(CH_3)_2CHCH}{\longrightarrow} CH_3\overset{\overset{O}{\|}}{C}CH_2\overset{\overset{OH}{|}}{C}HCH(CH_3)_2 \overset{H^+}{\longrightarrow}$

$$CH_3\overset{\overset{OH}{|}}{C}HCH=CHCH(CH_3)_2 \overset{NaBH_4}{\longleftarrow} CH_3\overset{\overset{O}{\|}}{C}CH=CHCH(CH_3)_2$$

(d) $(CH_3)_2CHCH_2Br + (C_6H_5)_3P: \overset{n-BuLi}{\longrightarrow} (CH_3)_2CHCH=P(C_6H_5)_3$

$$(CH_3)_2CHCH_2\diamondsuit \overset{H_2}{\underset{Pt}{\longleftarrow}} (CH_3)_2CHCH=\diamondsuit$$

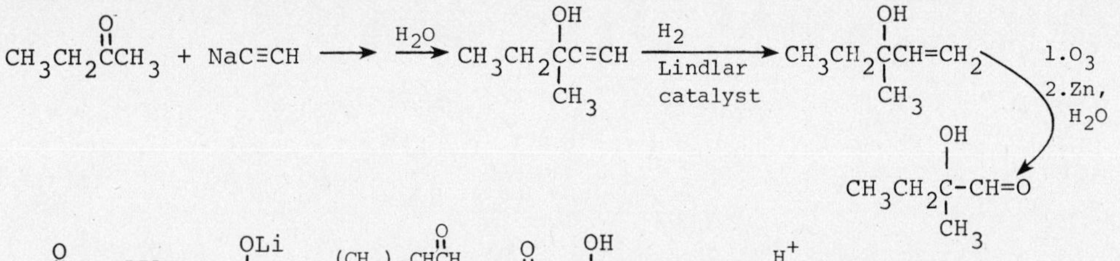

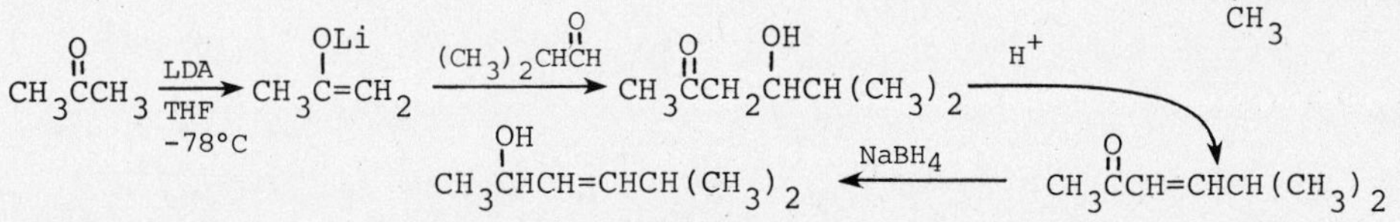

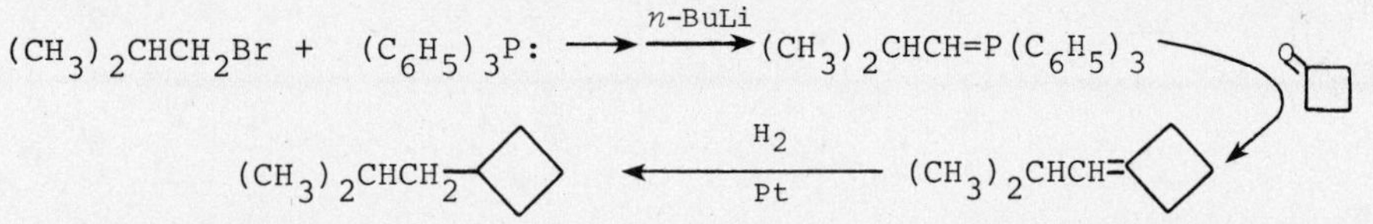

S5. (a) $CH_3C\equiv CNa$ will react with the alcohol: $CH_3C\equiv CNa + ROH \longrightarrow CH_3C\equiv CH$
$$+$$
$$RO^-Na^+$$

(b) Two isomeric ketones can be formed: $CH_3\overset{\overset{O}{\|}}{C}CH_2CH_2CH_2CH_2OH$

and $CH_3CH_2\overset{\overset{O}{\|}}{C}CH_2CH_2CH_2OH$

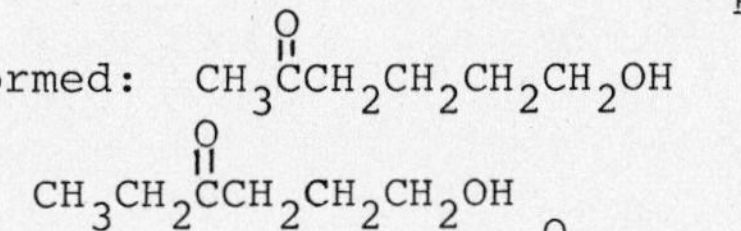

(c) Aldehyde will be overoxidized, to give acid: $CH_3\overset{\overset{O}{\|}}{C}CH_2CH_2CH_2COOH$

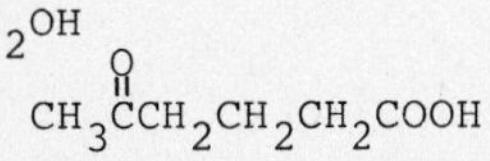

(d) Wittig reagent can react with ketone, too: $CH_3\overset{\overset{CHCH_3}{\|}}{C}CH_2CH_2CH_2---$
and it can also give a mixture of *cis* and *trans* isomers:

$$\cdots CH_2CH_2\underset{H}{\overset{H}{C}}=\underset{H}{\overset{CH_3}{C}}$$

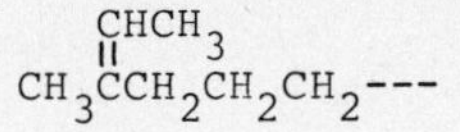

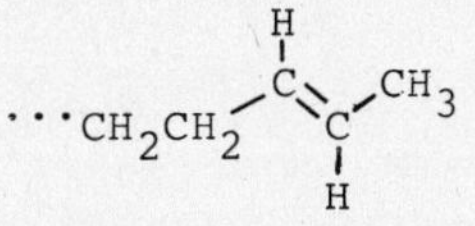

(e) The ketone can undergo Baeyer-Villiger reaction in the presence of a peracid: $CH_3\overset{\overset{O}{\|}}{C}OCH_2CH_2CH_2\cdots$

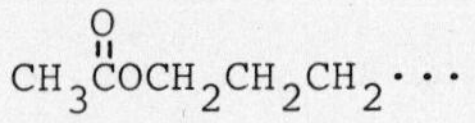

A synthesis that avoids these problems would make use of protecting groups:

$$BrCH_2CH_2CH_2OH + C_2H_5OCH=CH_2 \overset{H^+}{\longrightarrow} BrCH_2CH_2CH_2O\underset{\underset{CH_3}{|}}{C}HOC_2H_5 \overset{HC\equiv CNa}{\longrightarrow}$$

$$\overset{HOCH_2CH_2OH}{\underset{H^+}{\longrightarrow}} CH_3\overset{\overset{O}{\|}}{C}CH_2CH_2CH_2OH \overset{Hg^{++}}{\underset{H_2SO_4}{\longleftarrow}} HC\equiv CCH_2CH_2CH_2O\underset{\underset{CH_3}{|}}{C}HOC_2H_5$$

$$CH_3\overset{\overset{\diamondsuit}{}}{C}CH_2CH_2CH_2OH \overset{Tosyl-Cl}{\underset{pyridine}{\longrightarrow}} CH_3\overset{\overset{\diamondsuit}{}}{C}CH_2CH_2CH_2OTosyl \overset{NaC\equiv CCH_3}{\longrightarrow}$$

$$CH_3\overset{\overset{\diamondsuit}{}}{C}CH_2CH_2CH_2\underset{\underset{H}{|}}{C}=\underset{\underset{H}{|}}{C}\overset{\overset{CH_3}{|}}{} \overset{H_2}{\underset{Lindlar}{\longleftarrow}} CH_3\overset{\overset{\diamondsuit}{}}{C}CH_2CH_2CH_2C\equiv CCH_3$$

$$CH_3\overset{\overset{\diamondsuit}{}}{C}CH_2CH_2CH_2\underset{\underset{H}{|}}{\overset{}{C}}\underset{O}{\diagdown}\underset{H}{\overset{}{C}}\overset{\overset{CH_3}{|}}{} \overset{mild}{\underset{H_3O^+}{\longrightarrow}} \left[CH_3\overset{\overset{O}{\|}}{C}CH_2CH_2CH_2\underset{\underset{H}{|}}{\overset{}{C}}\underset{O}{\diagdown}\underset{H}{\overset{}{C}}\overset{\overset{CH_3}{|}}{} \right] \longrightarrow$$

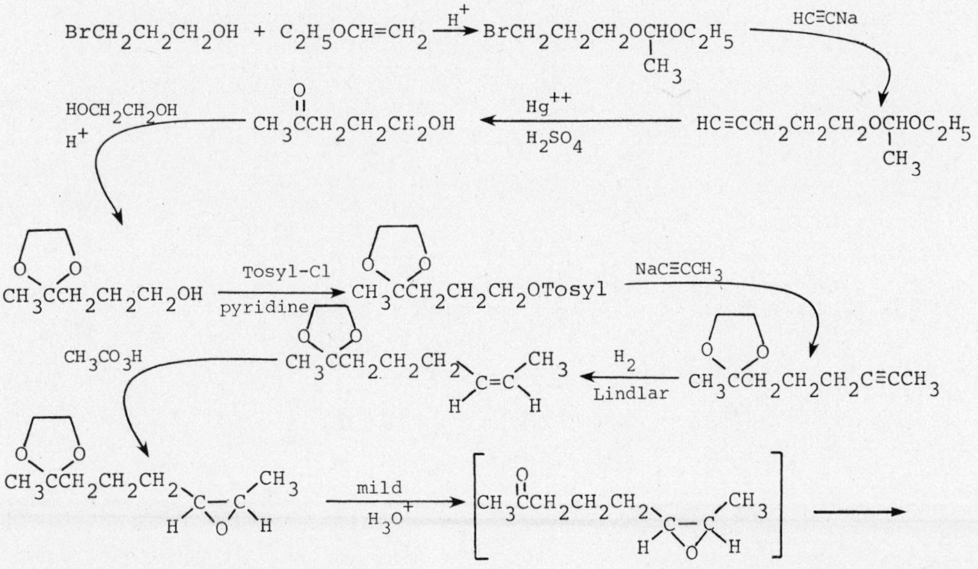

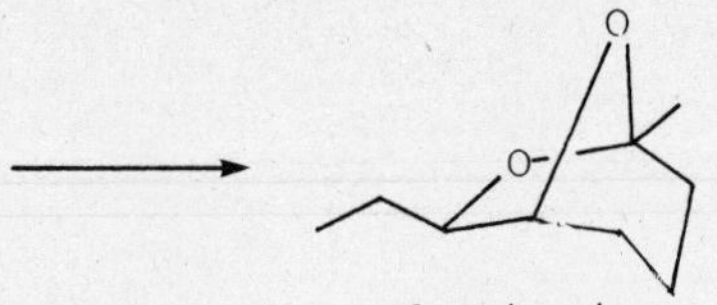

brevicomin

S6.

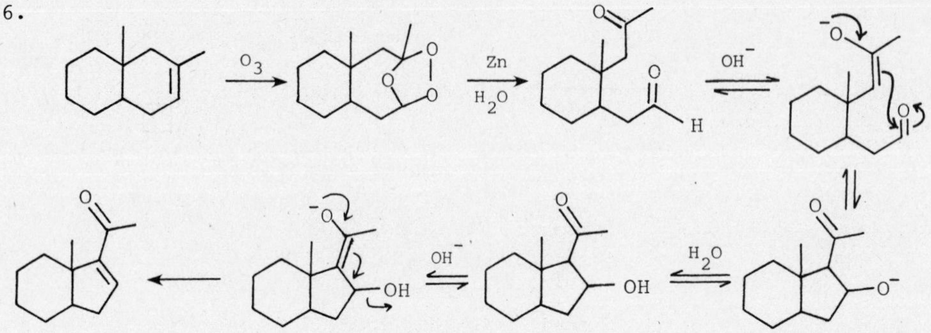

S7.

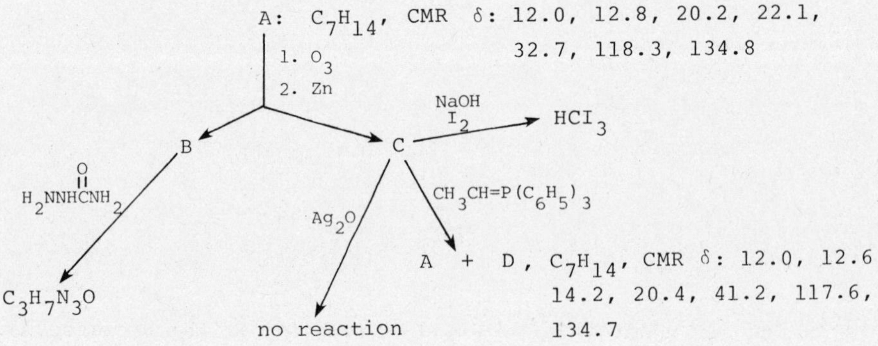

A: C_7H_{14}, CMR δ: 12.0, 12.8, 20.2, 22.1,
                                      32.7, 118.3, 134.8

1) A, C_7H_{14}, cmr δ 118.3, 134.8: A is an alkene.

2) A $\xrightarrow[\text{2. Zn}]{\text{1. O}_3}$ B + C; B + H_2NNH-⬡ ⟶ $C_8H_{10}N_2$ $\left(CH_3CH=NNH\text{-⬡} \right)$: B is
                                                                                              acetaldehyde

3) C $\xrightarrow{Ag_2O}$ n.r.; singlet at δ 2.0: C is a methyl ketone, either

$$CH_3\overset{O}{\overset{\|}{C}}CH_2CH_2CH_3 \text{ or } CH_3\overset{O}{\overset{\|}{C}}CH(CH_3)_2.$$

4) cmr of A shows 7 carbons: no isopropyl group present, so C is

$$CH_3\overset{}{\underset{\underset{O}{\|}}{C}}CH_2CH_2CH_3 .$$

5) A and D are therefore the two stereoisomers of 3-methyl-2-hexene:

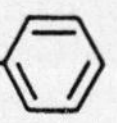

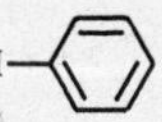

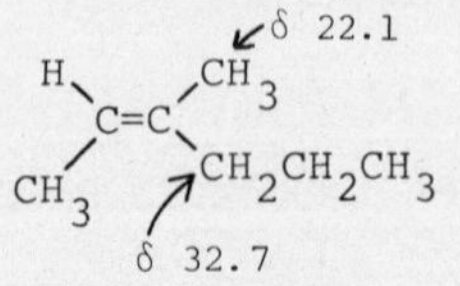

A   D

(A *cis* substitutent causes an upfield shift in the CMR)

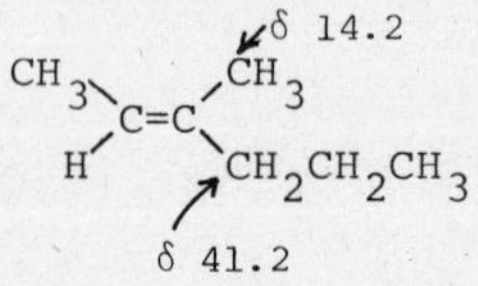

S8.

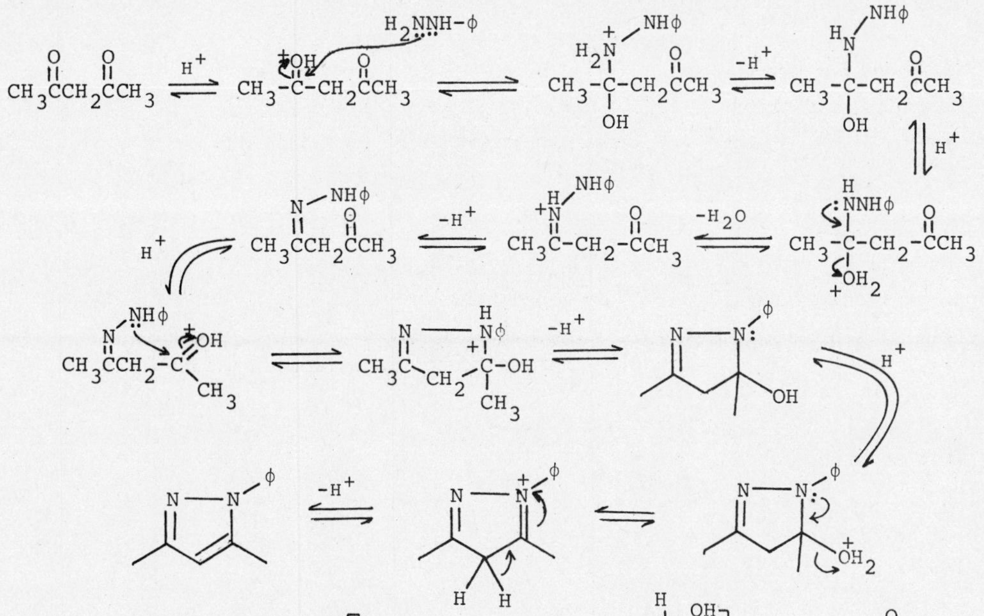

$$CH_3CCH_2CCH_3 \rightleftharpoons CH_3\overset{+}{C}-CH_2CCH_3 \rightleftharpoons CH_3-\overset{+}{C}-CH_2CCH_3 \rightleftharpoons CH_3-C-CH_2CCH_3 \rightleftharpoons$$

with reagents H^+, $H_2NNH-\phi$, $-H^+$, H^+

$$CH_3CCH_2CCH_3 \rightleftharpoons CH_3C-CH_2-CCH_3 \rightleftharpoons CH_3-C-CH_2-CCH_3$$

with $-H^+$, $-H_2O$

$$CH_3CCH_2-C \rightleftharpoons CH_3C=CH_2-C-OH \rightleftharpoons$$

with $-H^+$

$$\rightleftharpoons$$

with H^+, $-H^+$

S9.

$$HOCH_2CH_2CH_2CH_2OH \xrightarrow[\text{pyridine}]{CrO_3} \left[HOCH_2CH_2CH_2CH \rightleftharpoons \right] \longrightarrow$$

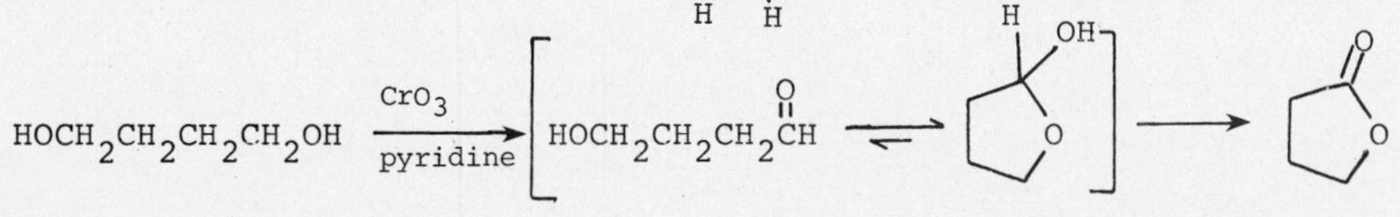

*this is oxidized like
any other 2° alcohol*

15. INFRARED SPECTROSCOPY

15.C   Important Concepts and Hints

What IR Spectroscopy is Good For:

IR spectroscopy is complementary to NMR because it gives you information primarily about functional groups instead of about the carbon skeleton. With this technique you can decide immediately if the compound has a hydroxy group, for example, or a carbonyl, a nitrile, and so on. Often the IR spectrum can tell you additional details about a functional group: Is the double bond cis, trans, or a 1,1-disubstituted olefin? Is the carbonyl group in a five- or six-membered ring, or part of an acyclic ketone?, etc. In the chapter on carboxylic acid derivatives (Chapter 18) you will learn that the position of the carbonyl stretching frequency can tell you even more.

Generally, the IR spectrum will not tell you much about the hydrocarbon backbone of a molecule. All CH_2 and CH_3 groups, for instance, have the same stretching and bending vibrations, and the fundamental vibrational modes of larger structural units are not readily assignable.

What You Should Learn:

The subject of IR spectroscopy has a logical foundation, but its routine application relies primarily on memory. The characteristic absorption frequencies of the various functional groups in organic molecules can be understood from first principles, as pointed out in the introductory sections of the chapter. However, the day-to-day interpretation of infrared spectra relies on simply knowing what IR band corresponds to what functional group. You will have to do a moderate amount of memorization in order to be able to use IR easily in solving problems. Start with Table 15.1, and then expand your knowledge until you are familiar with all the **highlighted entries** in Table 15.3. In subsequent chapters, the IR characteristics of additional functional groups will be presented, and you should add them to your memory.

<u>What</u> <u>you</u> <u>Should</u> <u>Avoid</u>:

The tendency of most students is to "overinterpret" an IR spectrum, and attempt to assign every band that appears. Although much useful information is contained in an IR spectrum, there are a lot of peaks which cannot be identified with any particular functional group and so are not useful in understanding the structure of a compound. When you look at an IR spectrum, you should first pick out the unambiguous peaks (C=O stretch, O-H stretch, aldehyde C-H, for example), and see what you can do with that information and the rest available in the problem. If necessary, you can return to the spectrum and use it to get finer details.

You should also recognize that average absorptions given for a particular vibrational mode are averages for a wide variety of compounds. As with all averages, individual cases can be very different. For example, you should not assume that all <u>trans</u> alkenes will show the C-H out-of-plane bend at exactly 970 cm^{-1}, or that a molecule with a strong band at 1720 cm^{-1} cannot be a six-membered ring ketone.

15.D   Answers to Exercises

15.1

$$\tilde{\nu} = \frac{1}{2\pi c} \sqrt{\frac{f(m_1 + m_2)}{m_1 m_2}}$$

$c = 2.998 \times 10^{10}$ cm sec^{-1}

f (single bond) $= 5 \times 10^5$ dynes cm^{-1}

f (double bond) $= 10 \times 10^5$ dynes cm^{-1}

f (triple bond) $= 15 \times 10^5$ dynes cm^{-1}

If M_1 = atomic weight, then $\dfrac{m_1 + m_2}{m_1 m_2} = \left(\dfrac{M_1 + M_2}{M_1 M_2}\right) \times (6.023 \times 10^{23})$

(a) $\tilde{\nu} = \dfrac{1}{1.884 \times 10^{11}} \sqrt{6.023 \times 10^{23}} \sqrt{f\left(\dfrac{M_1 + M_2}{M_1 M_2}\right)} = 4.12 \sqrt{5 \times 10^5 \times \dfrac{17}{16}}$

$\tilde{\nu} = 3003$ cm^{-1}

(b) 2185 cm^{-1} (c) 1682 cm^{-1} (d) 2060 cm^{-1} (e) 1113 cm^{-1}

(f) 1573 cm^{-1} (g) 1985 cm^{-1} (h) 1074 cm^{-1}

15.2   3090 cm^{-1} indicates an alkene C-H bond:

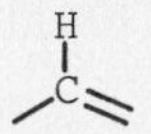

1718 cm^{-1} is an overtone of the strong band at 890 cm^{-1}; these two bands indicate the presence of a 1,1-disubstituted alkene:

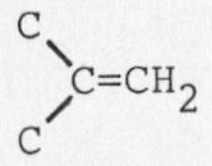

1653 cm^{-1} is consistent with the presence of an alkene.

15.3   Recall that absorption of infrared light can only occur if the dipole moment of the molecule is different in the two vibrational levels. For a symmetrical alkene such as <u>trans</u>-4-octene, there is no dipole moment either before or after excitation of the double bond stretching band, hence this transition is infrared inactive and the band is not observed in the IR spectrum.

15.4   Using the equation of Exercise 15.1: $\tilde{\nu} = 2225$ cm^{-1}

15.5   Because the C-C-O angle in ketene is 180°, the C=O stretching motion requires simultaneous C=C compression, a movement which will be resisted strongly by the C=C bond in comparison with the normal $\underset{C}{\overset{C}{>}}$C=O arrangement. Therefore, the high C=O stretching frequency is to be expected.

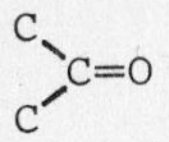

15.E   Answers and Explanations for Problems

1.   (a)   The intense band at ~965 cm^{-1} suggests

$$\underset{H}{\overset{R}{}}C=C\underset{R}{\overset{H}{}}.$$

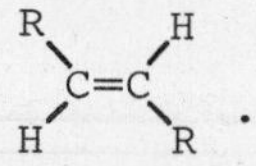

(b)   Bands at 3300, 2150, and 630 cm^{-1} conclusively indicate RC≡CH.

(c)   Broad band at 3350 cm^{-1} shows OH. Complex absorption peaking at 1050 cm^{-1} suggests primary.

(d)   Bands at 3080, 1825, 1640, 995, and 905 cm^{-1} are conclusive evidence for RCH=CH$_2$.

(e)   Broad band at 3400 cm^{-1} shows OH, as does absorption at 1020 cm^{-1} (C–O stretch), probably primary. Sharp band at 2120 cm^{-1} and band at 650 cm^{-1} show terminal acetylene. Thus, there are two functional groups, OH and C≡CH.

(f)   Strong band at 1720 cm^{-1} (C=O stretch) could be an aldehyde or ketone (acyclic or six-membered ring), but the absence of bands at 2720 and 2820 cm^{-1} shows that it is not an aldehyde.

(g)   Strong band at 1725 cm^{-1} (C=O stretch) and bands at 2720 and 2820 cm^{-1} (C–H stretch) are characteristic of the aldehyde group.

2.   IR: sharp bands at 3080, 1640, and 890 cm^{-1} indicate alkene;
strong band at 890 cm^{-1} indicates
specifically a 1,1-disubstituted double bond: $\underset{C}{\overset{C}{}}C=CH_2$

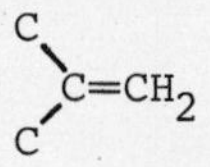

NMR: δ 0.9, singlet, 9 hydrogens; must be a t-butyl group: C(CH$_3$)$_3$

1.7, broad singlet, 3 hydrogens; CH$_3$, with some reason to
be deshielded relative to an alkane, for example on a double bond: $CH_3\!-\!C=$

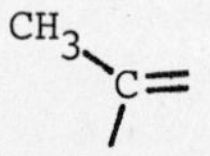

1.9, singlet, 2 hydrogens; CH$_2$ with no adjacent hydrogens

4.6 & 4.8, very little coupling, 1 hydrogen each;
two alkene hydrogens: $\underset{C}{\overset{C}{}}C=CH_2$

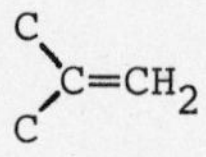

All of this data is consistent only with
the structure 2,4,4-trimethyl-1-pentene:

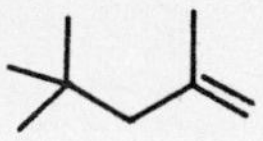

3.   IR: 3400 cm^{-1}, broad: O–H
3100, 1840 (overtone), 1640 (weak) cm^{-1}: an alkene
1150 cm^{-1}: C–O

NMR: δ 1.2, singlet, 6H: two equivalent, isolated methyl groups

2.3, broad, 1H: the O–H

5.0, multiplet, 2H, and 6.0, multiplet, 1H:
this is the common pattern for a vinyl group: $\underset{H}{\overset{C}{}}C=C\underset{H}{\overset{H}{}}$

Structure: 2-methyl-3-buten-2-ol,

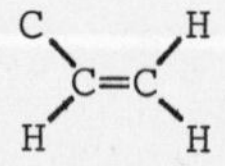

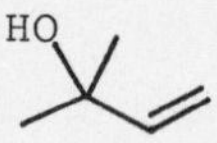

4.   IR: 3400 cm^{-1}, broad: O–H
3300 cm^{-1} (almost hidden by O–H band), weak band at 2140 cm^{-1}, and strong band at 660 cm^{-1}:
terminal acetylene, C≡C–H

NMR: δ 1.5, singlet, 6H: two equivalent, isolated methyl groups

2.2, singlet, 1H: the O–H

2.9, singlet, 1H: consistent with C≡C–H

Structure: 2-methyl-3-butyn-2-ol,

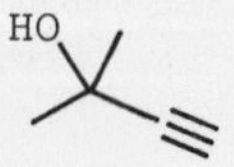

5.   IR: 3350 cm^{-1}, broad: O–H

NMR: δ 0.8, two doublets, 12H: two diastereotopic pairs of methyl groups next to a CH group, probably two isopropyl groups: 2 $(CH_3)_2CH-$ *(see answer to following problem)*

1.0-2.0, m, 6H: CH's and CH_2's

3.6, broad, 1H: hydrogen next to an O—H group

(the OH resonance is broad and falls under the multiplet of the CH's)

Structure: 2,6-dimethyl-4-heptanol

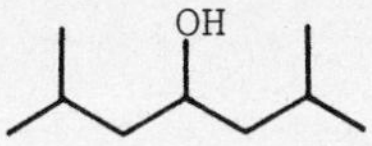

6. <u>IR</u>: 3450 cm^{-1}, broad: O—H

1710 cm^{-1}, strong: ketone, acyclic or in six-membered ring

(1100 cm^{-1}, sharp: suggests that alcohol is 2°)

<u>CMR</u>: δ 212.7: confirms presence of ketone

76.8: carbon with O—H group

30.7: could be the methyl of a methyl ketone

26.4: CH

7.1 & 8.5: non-equivalent, upfield methyl groups

A reasonable structure is 4-methyl-3-hydroxy-2-pentanone:

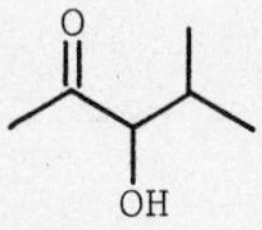

Note that the two methyls of the isopropyl group are non-equivalent
because of the stereocenter which is in the molecule. (Make two
models, one with a CD_3 in place of one of the methyls, and second with it in place of the other; note that
these two models represent _diastereomers_.) The word that is used to describe the relationship between
these two methyls is _diastereotopic_, and one of the consequences of their non-equivalence is the fact that
their resonances come at different positions in the NMR spectrum.

7. (a) <u>IR</u>: 3400 cm^{-1}, broad: O—H

1160 cm^{-1}: tertiary O—H

<u>CMR</u>: 7.9: shielded methyl(s)

25.5: methyl on electron-withdrawing carbon

33.5: CH_2(s) on electron-withdrawing carbon

72.6: C—OH

Since this compound is isomeric with that in part (b), and the CMR spectrum of (b) shows six
separate resonances, there must be two sets of equivalent carbons in the structure of (a).

Structure: 3-methyl-3-pentanol

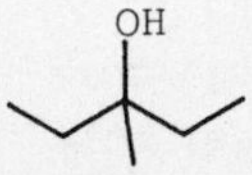

(b) <u>IR</u>: 3400 cm^{-1}, broad: O—H

There are too many bands in the 1020-1160 cm^{-1} region to tell whether the
alcohol is primary, secondary, or tertiary

<u>CMR</u>: six resonances indicate that the alcohol cannot be derived

from the 2,2-dimethylbutyl skeleton, because symmetry would

result in fewer than six peaks. For the same reason, the

following alcohols can also be ruled out:

$$C-C-C-C$$
(with C above and C below the second carbon)

$$CH_3CH_2CH_2\overset{\displaystyle CH_3}{\underset{\displaystyle CH_3}{C}}-OH \qquad HO-CH_2CH_2CH\overset{\displaystyle CH_3}{\underset{\displaystyle CH_3}{<}} \qquad HO-CH_2CH(CH_2CH_3)_2 \qquad CH_3\overset{\displaystyle OH}{C}(CH_2CH_3)_3 \qquad HO-\overset{\displaystyle CH_3}{\underset{\displaystyle CH_3}{C}CH(CH_3)_2}$$

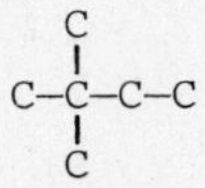

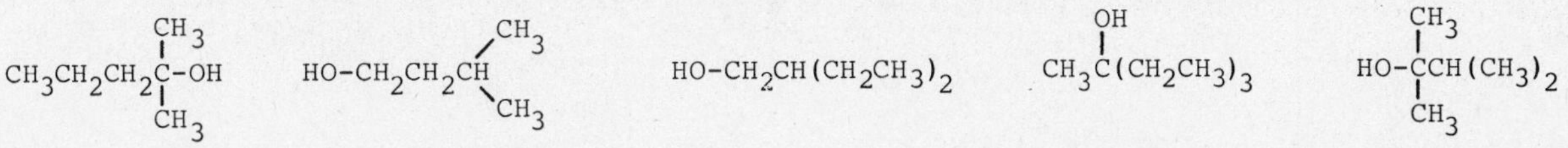

<u>CMR</u>: no resonance at δ < 20 ppm indicates that there is no CH_3 at the end of a chain
without a β-substituent. This rules out some more possibilities:

$$CH_3CH_2CH_2CH_2CH_2CH_2-OH \qquad CH_3CH_2CH_2CH_2\overset{\displaystyle OH}{CHCH_3} \qquad CH_3CH_2\overset{\displaystyle OH}{\underset{\displaystyle CH_3}{CHCHCH_3}}$$

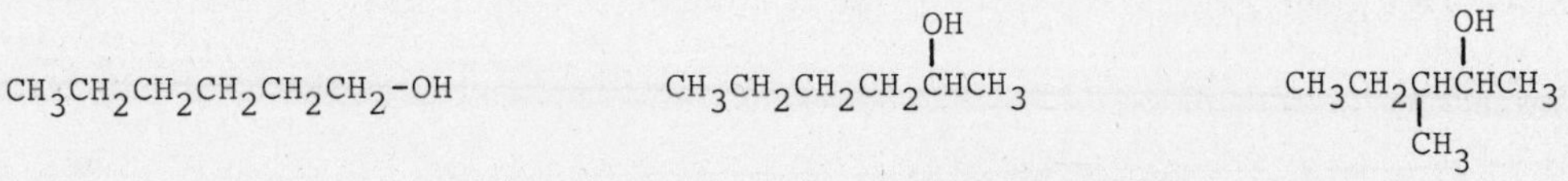

$$\underset{OH}{CH_3CH_2CH_2\overset{\mid}{C}HCH_2CH_3} \qquad (CH_3)_2\overset{\mid}{\underset{OH}{C}}HCHCH_2CH_3 \qquad CH_3CH_2CH_2\overset{\mid}{\underset{CH_3}{C}}HCH_2\text{-}OH \qquad CH_3CH_2\overset{\mid}{\underset{CH_3}{C}}HCH_2CH_2\text{-}OH$$

The only possibilities that remain are:

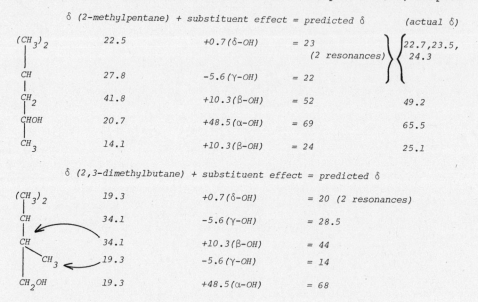

$$CH_3\text{—}\overset{\mid}{\underset{CH_3}{C}}H\text{—}CH_2\text{—}\overset{\mid}{\underset{OH}{C}}H\text{—}CH_3 \qquad \text{and} \qquad CH_3\text{—}\overset{\mid}{\underset{\underset{CH_3}{\mid}}{C}}H\text{—}\overset{\mid}{\underset{OH}{C}}H\text{—}CH_2\text{—}OH$$

(NOTE: in both of these compounds, the two methyls of the isopropyl group are diastereotopic (see answer to problem #6) and therefore are non-equivalent.)

To distinguish between these two possibilities, estimate the CMR chemical shifts using Table 13.3 and the α-, β-, and γ-substituent effects of OH (see problem #20, Chapter 13):

δ (2-methylpentane) + substituent effect = predicted δ   (actual δ)

	δ	substituent effect	predicted δ	actual δ
$(CH_3)_2$	22.5	+0.7 (δ-OH)	= 23 (2 resonances)	22.7, 23.5, 24.3
CH	27.8	-5.6 (γ-OH)	= 22	
CH_2	41.8	+10.3 (β-OH)	= 52	49.2
CHOH	20.7	+48.5 (α-OH)	= 69	65.5
CH_3	14.1	+10.3 (β-OH)	= 24	25.1

δ (2,3-dimethylbutane) + substituent effect = predicted δ

	δ	substituent effect	predicted δ
$(CH_3)_2$	19.3	+0.7 (δ-OH)	= 20 (2 resonances)
CH	34.1	-5.6 (γ-OH)	= 28.5
CH	34.1	+10.3 (β-OH)	= 44
CH_3	19.3	-5.6 (γ-OH)	= 14
CH_2OH	19.3	+48.5 (α-OH)	= 68

The chemical shifts predicted for 4-methyl-2-pentanol clearly fit the data best.

Notice that the only piece of information gathered from the IR spectrum was that the compound is an alcohol. Nevertheless, that was crucial, because it eliminated from consideration all sixteen ethers which have the formula $C_6H_{14}O$.

8. (a) CH_3Cl, $\oint = 2.83 \times 10^5$, $DH^O = 84$ kcal mole^{-1}
         CH_3Br, $\oint = 2.29 \times 10^5$, $DH^O = 70$ kcal mole^{-1}
         CH_3I, $\oint = 1.83 \times 10^5$, $DH^O = 56$ kcal mole^{-1}

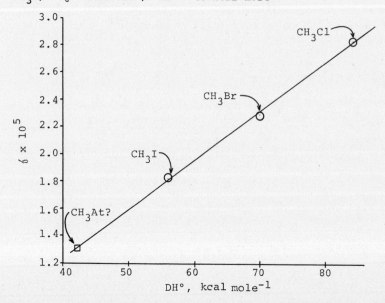

(b) Notice that DH° goes down by 14 kcal mole^{-1} from CH_3Cl to CH_3Br and from CH_3Br to CH_3I. If we project this incremental change to CH_3At, then DH° $\approx$ 42 kcal mole^{-1}, and f from the above graph is $\approx 1.3 \times 10^5$ dynes cm^{-1}.

$$\tilde{\upsilon} = 4.120\sqrt{1.3 \times 10^5 \, \frac{12+210}{12 \cdot 210}} = 441 \text{ cm}^{-1}$$

(c) For CH_3SH, the Hooke's Law model gives $f = 2.56 \times 10^5$ dynes cm^{-1}. From the graph in part a, this corresponds to DH° $= 76.5$ kcal mol^{-1}.

9. <u>IR</u>: 3350, 1080 cm^{-1}: O—H

            1175 cm^{-1}, strong: C—F

<u>CMR</u>: two carbons, each split into a quartet; each carbon coupled to three fluorines

<u>Structure</u>: 3,3,3-trifluoroethanol, CF_3CH_2OH

10. The O–O stretch is not infrared active <u>if</u> the molecule exists in a conformation where there is no dipole moment change.

    i.e.

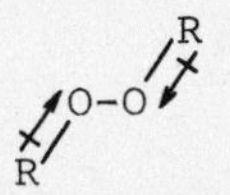

For a gauche conformation, there is a change in dipole moment and the band is active.

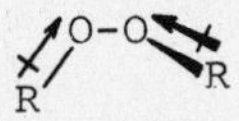

For a 900 cm^{-1} stretch, $f = 3.82 \times 10^5$ dynes cm^{-1}. The value is lower due to the low DH° of O-O bond.

11. $\dfrac{dE}{dr} = 2f(r-r_0)$ $\dfrac{d^2E}{dr^2} = 2f$

The larger the force constant the greater the change of E with r; i.e., the sharper the curvature. But f is also related to the energy difference between vibrational levels. Compare:

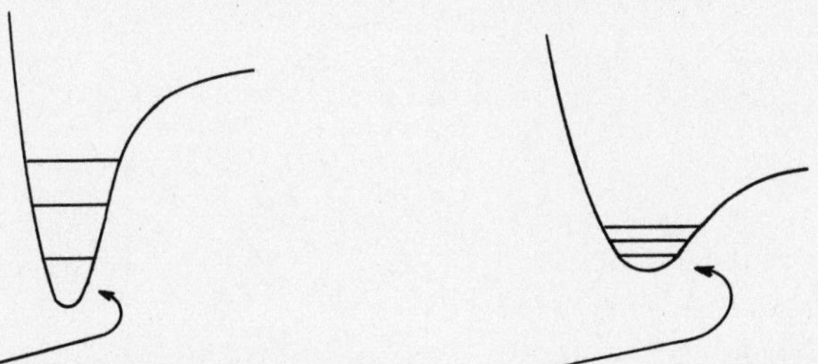

large f, sharp curve, large spacings between levels, strong bond (large DH°)

small f, wide curve, small spacings between levels, weak bond (small DH°)

15.F Supplementary Problems

S1. IR spectral bands and some nmr characteristics are given for four isomers of formula C_6H_{12}. What can you deduce about the structures from the information for each?

(a) IR: 1170, 1374, 1450, 2900 cm^{-1} (all strong); nmr: single resonance.

(b) IR: 960 (s), 1374 (w), 1450, 2940 (s) cm^{-1}; nmr: only ethyl and vinyl protons.

(c) IR: 885, 1370 (w), 1640, 2900, 3000 (w) cm^{-1}; nmr: only ethyl and vinyl protons.

(d) IR: 1450 (s), 2950 (s) cm^{-1}; nmr: single resonance.

S2. What are the structures of the compounds in the sequence below? Assign the resonances.

$$ A \xrightarrow{KMnO_4} B \ + \ CO_2 \xrightarrow{NaBH_4} C \xrightarrow[\Delta]{H_2SO_4} D \xrightarrow[Pt]{H_2} E $$

IR:	886(s)	1450		1067(s)	1440	nmr:
						singlet
	1445	1714(s)		1450	1645(vw)	
	1618	2875		2860	2865	
	2860	2950(s)		2940	3000	
	2940			3300(s)		
	3082					

S3. How could you use IR spectroscopy to distinguish between the following pairs of isomers?

(a) $HOCH_2CH_2CH_2CH_2\overset{\overset{\displaystyle O}{||}}{C}H$ and [image of tetrahydropyran with OH]

(b) [image of cyclopentane-1,2-diol, trans] and [image of cyclopentane-1,2-diol, cis]

(c) [image of cyclopentanone] and [image of cyclobutanecarbaldehyde]

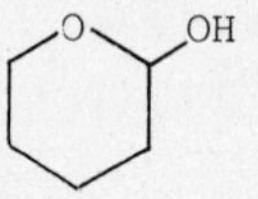

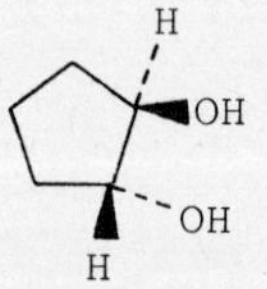

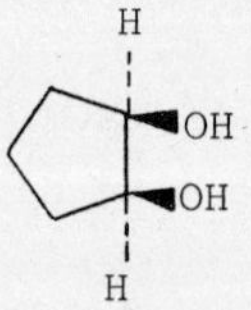

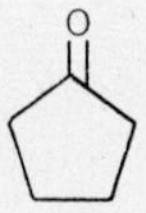

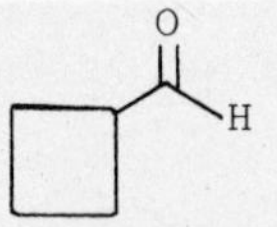

S4. Some IR and nmr spectral properties of five isomers of C_4H_8O are given below. Assign the structures for each isomer.

(a) IR: 1176, 1370, 1718, 3000 cm^{-1}; nmr: singlet (3H) at 2.0 ppm.

(b) IR: 962(s), 1000, 1075, 1666, 2860, 2940, 3300(br) cm^{-1}; nmr: 2 resonances (1H each) between 5 and 6 ppm.

(c) IR: 1724, 2718, 2825, 2878, 2970 cm^{-1}; nmr: triplet (1H) at 9.5 ppm.

(d) IR: 917(s), 1450, 1640(w), 2860, 2940, 3300(br) cm^{-1}; nmr: 3 resonances (1H each) between 5 and 6 ppm, doublet (3H) at 1.0 ppm.

(e) IR: 806, 962, 1030, 1200, 1312, 1612(s), 2950, 3000 cm^{-1}; nmr: indicates presence of ethyl group.

15.G   Answers to Supplementary Problems

S1.   (a) and (d): nmr: single resonance. The only possibilities are

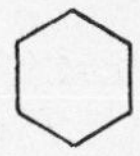

and   . These are hard to assign by IR: the symmetrically-

substituted double bond and the lack of vinyl hydrogens mean that no
characteristic olefinic absorbances will appear in the spectrum of 2,3-
dimethyl-2-butene. However, spectrum (a) has a band at 1374 cm^{-1}, characteristic of -CH$_3$ rocking, indicating that (a) is the olefin. Spectrum (d)
therefore corresponds to cyclohexane.

(b) and (c): nmr indicates only ethyl and vinyl hydrogens present. There
are three possibilities: (CH$_3$CH$_2$)$_2$C=CH$_2$ and *cis*- and *trans*-3-hexene.
Spectrum (b) has a strong band at 960 cm^{-1}, consistent with the C-H out-
of-plane bending absorption expected for *trans*-3-hexene; (c) has bands
at 885 and 1640 cm^{-1}, which are what you would expect to find in the
spectrum of 2-ethyl-1-butene (C-H out-of-plane bending and C=C stretching,
respectively).

S2.

| A | B | C | D | E |

886 (C-H bend)	1450 (CH$_2$ scissor)	1067 (C-O stretch)	1440 (CH$_2$ scissor)	
1445 (CH$_2$ scissor)	1714 (C=O stretch)	1450 (CH$_2$ scissor)	1645 (C=C stretch)	
1618 (C=C stretch)	2875,2950 (C-H stretch)	2860,2940 (C-H stretch)	2865 (alkane C-H)	
2860,2940 (alkane C-H stretch)		3300 (O-H stretch)	3000 (alkene C-H)	
3082 (alkene C-H stretch)				

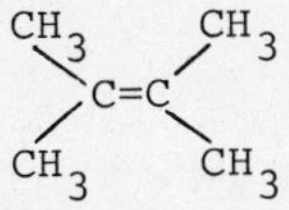

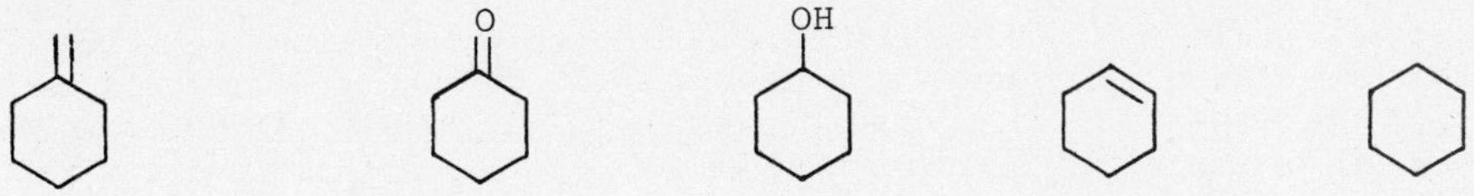

S3.   (a) Open chain form will show strong band due to C=O stretch at 1725 cm^{-1};
        cyclic hemiacetal form will not.

(b) *Cis* isomer will show intramolecular hydrogen-bonded O-H stretch (3250-
    3450 cm^{-1}) at all concentrations; *trans* isomer will show only free O-H
    stretch (3620-3640 cm^{-1}) at low concentration.

(c) Ketone: C=O stretch at 1745 cm^{-1}, no bands in region 2700-2850 cm^{-1}.
    Aldehyde: C=O stretch at 1725 cm^{-1}, two medium bands for H-CO stretch
    at 2720, 2820 cm^{-1}.

S4.   (a) CH$_3$CH$_2$CCH$_3$ (b) CH$_3$C=CCH$_2$OH   (c) CH$_3$CH$_2$CH$_2$CH   (d) CH$_3$CHCH=CH$_2$
                    ‖   H   H   ‖   OH
                    O   O

(e) CH$_3$CH$_2$OCH=CH$_2$

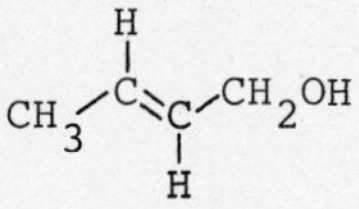

16. ORGANIC SYNTHESIS

16.A   Chapter Outline and Important Terms Introduced

16.1   Introduction

16.2   Considerations in Synthesis Design

     1. Construction of the proper carbon skeleton
     2. Placement of desired functional groups in their proper place
     3. Control of stereochemistry where relevant

16.3   Planning a Synthesis
     retrosynthesis   synthetic equivalents: synthons
     synthetic tree

16.4   Protecting Groups

16.5   Industrial Syntheses
     process development

16.B   Important Reactions Introduced: (none in this chapter)

16.C   Important Concepts and Hints

    To many organic chemists, the best examples of the elegance and creativity of chemistry are found in synthesis. It is in designing a synthesis of a complex molecule, and carrying it out in the laboratory, that many chemists find their greatest fulfillment. Although you are introduced to this topic with relatively simple molecules as targets, the field has advanced to the extent that we can confidently design syntheses of molecules that are bewilderingly complex. The successful synthesis of Vitamin B_{12} by the late R.B. Woodward, A. Eschenmoser, and their research groups is a spectacular example of what the chemist can now accomplish.

    For the most part, organic chemists choose as their synthetic targets compounds isolated from natural sources, or compounds similar to them. Such syntheses are pursued in order to produce compounds of potentially valuable biological activity, to assist in structure determination, to demonstrate the usefulness of a new reaction sequence, or, one suspects in some cases, for the fun of it. The development of efficient syntheses of less complex, commercially important compounds is an equally challenging aspect of organic synthesis. In this regard, elegance and creativity are measured by the simplicity and economy of the processes, their energy efficiency, the absence of byproducts, etc.

    Regardless of the type of synthesis you are trying to develop, you must be able to think logically and you must know a broad range of organic reactions. With these two abilities, as well as practice, you will develop an intuition for organic synthesis and be able to appreciate the creative possibilities. Chapter 16 outlines the logical processes involved in synthesis design; the rest of the text provides you with the background knowledge of reactions (your repertoire). It's up to you to practice synthesis problems and develop the necessary intuition.

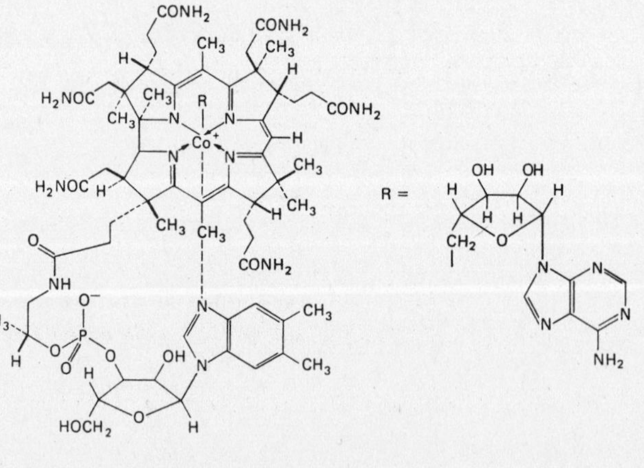

The suggestion that you should work synthesis problems backwards was made in Section 12.B of this Study Guide, and is discussed in more detail in Chapter 16 of the Text. An example of the sort of thing that happens when you work a synthesis problem **forward** is the following scheme, taken from an actual answer to a midterm exam question:

$$\text{cyclohexane} \xrightarrow[h\nu]{Br_2} \text{bromocyclohexane} \xrightarrow[C_2H_5OH]{KOH} \text{cyclohexene} \xrightarrow[H_2SO_4]{\text{dilute}} \text{cyclohexanol} \xrightarrow{PBr_3} \text{bromocyclohexane} \xrightarrow{NaCN} \text{cyclohexyl-CN}$$

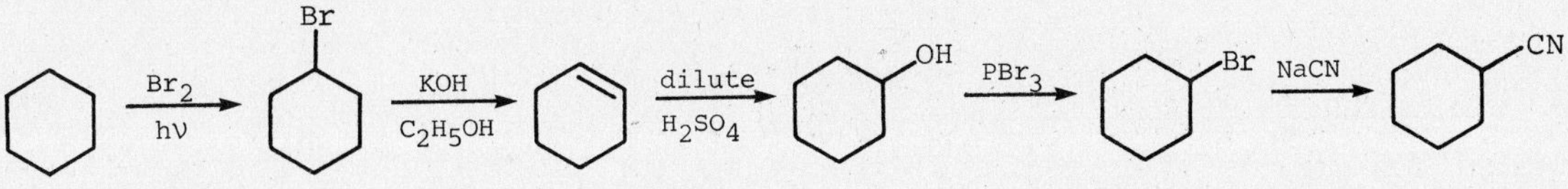

Because the student was thinking "What can I make from this compound?" at each stage, he wasted three steps converting bromocyclohexane into bromocyclohexane!

A more subtle mistake that we all make arises from the usual human tendency to stop looking for something once we think we've found it. Often you will think of a way to carry out a transformation, without evaluating it closely to determine whether there are any potential side reactions. Examples of reactions which appear at first glance to accomplish their intended conversion are shown below. Also listed are the side products expected or the incompatibility of functional groups which make these transformations poor choices. You should always look for such problems and, if you find them, continue to search for another route.

$$(CH_3)_2CH-CH_2-CH(CH_3)_2 + Br_2 \xrightarrow{h\nu} \cancel{} (CH_3)_2CH-CHBr-CH(CH_3)_2 + HBr$$

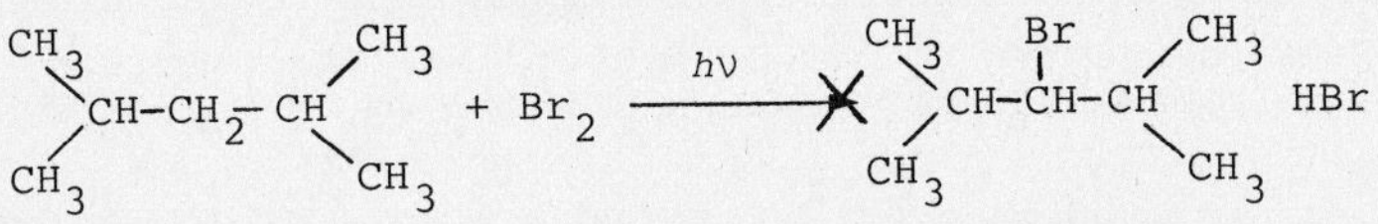

(Bromination is selective for 3° position)

$$CH_3CH_2CHBrCH_2CH_2CH_3 \xrightarrow[EtOH]{KOH} \cancel{} CH_3CH_2\overset{\displaystyle H}{\underset{}{C}}=\overset{\displaystyle CH_2CH_3}{\underset{\displaystyle H}{C}}$$

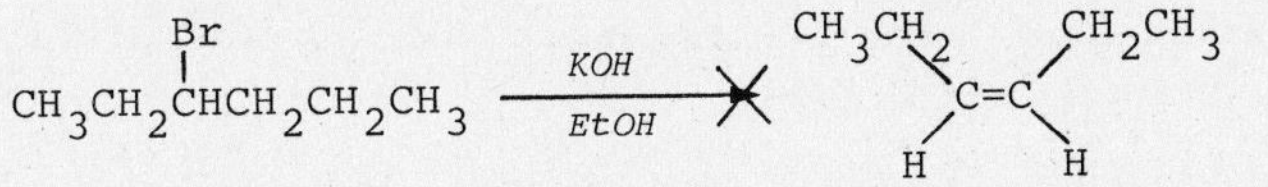

(Three other isomers will be produced, too)

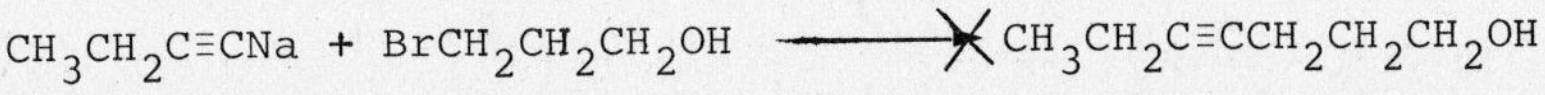

$$CH_3CH_2C\equiv CNa + BrCH_2CH_2CH_2OH \xrightarrow{} \cancel{} CH_3CH_2C\equiv CCH_2CH_2CH_2OH$$

(Acetylide ion will be protonated by hydroxy proton)

$$2\ HCCH_2CH_2Br \xrightarrow{NaOH} \cancel{} \underset{\displaystyle CH_2Br}{HCCHCHCH_2CH_2Br}$$

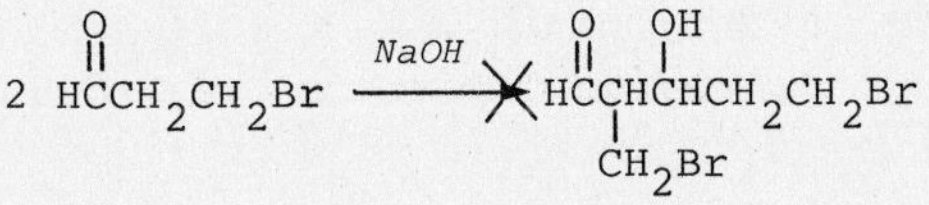

(Bromide will undergo substitution or elimination under the basic conditions)

$$CH_3CCH_2CH_2CH=CH_2 \xrightarrow[HBr]{Br_2} \cancel{} \underset{\displaystyle Br}{CH_3CCHCH_2CH=CH_2}$$

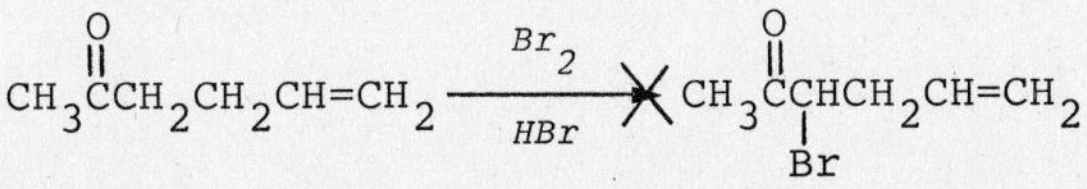

(Double bond will undergo bromine addition)

$$\underset{\displaystyle Br}{CH_2CHCH_2CH_2CH_2Br} \xrightarrow{Mg} \cancel{} \underset{\displaystyle Br}{CH_3CHCH_2CH_2CH_2MgBr}$$

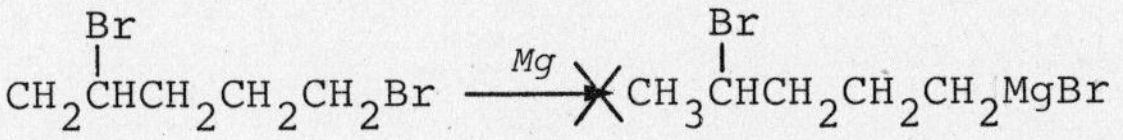

(The other bromide will react, too)

These are only examples to show you the sort of difficulties to look out for.

16.D   Answers to Exercises

16.1   R—Y $\xrightarrow{\ ?\ }$ R—Z

NOTE: *this matrix was constructed based on reactions presented in Chapters 1-16; () indicates entries that would be changed based on reactions introduced in subsequent chapters.*

R—Z

	RH	RBr	ROH	RCH$_2$OH	RCHO	RCOCH$_3$	RCN
RH	X	–*	–	–	–	–	–
RBr	1	X	1	1	1	1	1
ROH	+	1	X	+	+	+	+
RCH$_2$OH	+	(–)	(–)	X	1	+	(–)
RCHO	1	(–)	(–)	1	X	+	(–)
RCOCH$_3$	+	(–)	+	(–)	(–)	X	–
RCN	+	(–)	(–)	(–)	1	(–)	X

R—Y (row label at left)

* Although some RH can be converted to RBr by free radical bromination, the reaction is not general because some RH do not react and others give impractical mixtures.

16.2   4-Methylpentanenitrile: the possible carbon-carbon connections to build up the six-carbon skeleton are indicated below, with the asterisk showing where the functional group is located in the product:

1. $\underset{C}{\overset{C}{\diagdown}}$C—C—C—C*

2. $\underset{C}{\overset{C}{\diagdown}}$C   C—C—C*

3. $\underset{C}{\overset{C}{\diagdown}}$C—C   C—C*

4. $\underset{C}{\overset{C}{\diagdown}}$C—C—C   C*

The most logical connection is 4: making the new bond next to the nitrile functional group. You can use the displacement reaction of an alkyl halide with cyanide ion to accomplish this:

+ NaCN ⟶

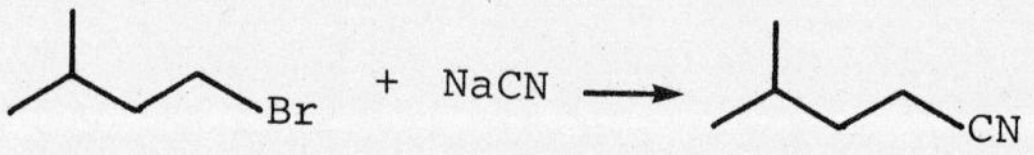

16.3   (a) Acetylene is a synthon for the -COCH$_3$ group, via the following sequence:

$$HC\equiv CH \xrightarrow{NaNH_2} Na^+\ {}^-C\equiv CH \xrightarrow{RX} R-C\equiv CH \xrightarrow[HgSO_4]{H_2SO_4} R-\overset{O}{\overset{\|}{C}}-CH_3$$

(b) Cyanide is the best synthon for -CH$_2$NH$_2$, via the following reactions:

$$R-X + Na^+\ {}^-C\equiv N \longrightarrow R-C\equiv N \xrightarrow[PtO_2,\ H^+]{H_2} R-CH_2-NH_2$$

(c) Formaldehyde: R—MgX + CH$_2$=O $\xrightarrow{\quad}$ $\xrightarrow{H_2O}$ R—CH$_2$—OH

(d) Propyne: $HC\equiv C-CH_3 \xrightarrow{NaNH_2} Na^+\ {}^-C\equiv C-CH_3 \xrightarrow{RX} R-C\equiv C-CH_3$

Na/NH$_3$ H$_2$ poisoned Pd catalyst

$$\underset{H}{\overset{R}{\diagdown}}C=C\underset{CH_3}{\overset{H}{\diagup}} \qquad \underset{H}{\overset{R}{\diagdown}}C=C\underset{H}{\overset{CH_3}{\diagup}}$$

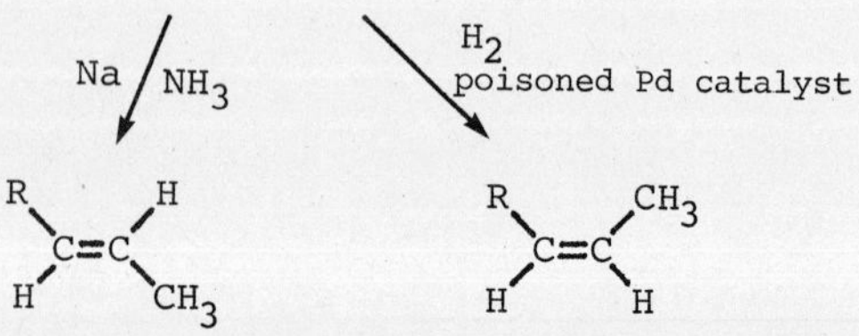

16.4 1-Heptene: If we are only going to consider combinations that will give the seven-carbon skeleton by formation of **one** carbon-carbon bond (with starting materials of five carbons or less), the possibilities are indicated below, with the asterisk showing where the functional group is located in the product:

1. C–C C–C–C–C$\overset{*}{-}$C
2. C–C–C C–C–C$\overset{*}{-}$C
3. C–C–C–C C–C$\overset{*}{-}$C
4. C–C–C–C–C C$\overset{*}{-}$C

Review the methods available for introduction of a carbon-carbon double bond:

(a) Dehydration of an alcohol   (b) Elimination of an alkyl halide

Both of these can be ruled out for the same reasons as in Example 16-3 in the Text.

(c) Partial hydrogenation of an alkyne: $R-C\equiv CH \xrightarrow[\substack{\text{poisoned} \\ \text{Pd catalyst}}]{H_2} R-CH=CH_2$

This is particularly attractive, since the alkyne can be used to form the carbon-carbon bond via combination 4.

(d) Wittig reaction: this will form the carbon-carbon double bond, but it does not correspond to any of the disconnections given above, and would necessitate **two** C-C bond forming reactions.

As indicated in (c), the route via 1-heptyne is desirable, since alkylation of a primary halide with sodium acetylide will afford this in one step:

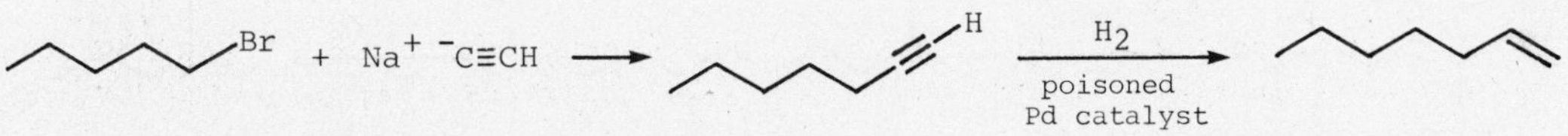

16.5 Non-3-yn-1-ol: as pointed out in the text, oxirane is a synthon for the CH_2CH_2OH group, via the following reaction:

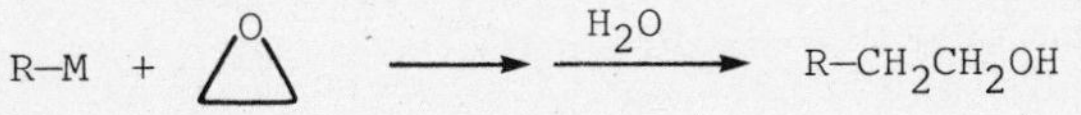

The appropriate precursor to "R—M" in this case would be 1-heptyne, which was an intermediate in the 1-heptene synthesis which was outlined in Exercise 16.4:

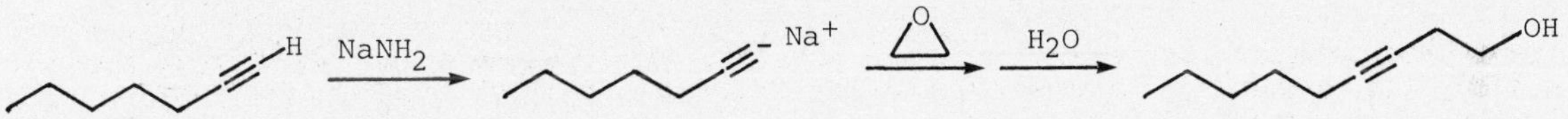

16.6 2,9-Dimethyldecan-5-ol: with twelve carbons in the target, at least two carbon-carbon bond-forming reactions will be required. If we consider only combination strategies that use two five-carbon units and a two-carbon unit, the most reasonable connection we look for is:

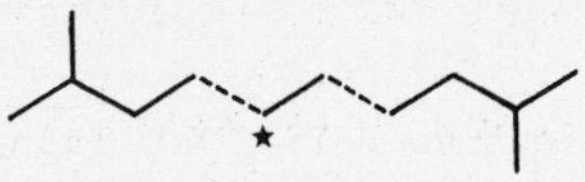

Review methods for introduction of an alcohol group:

(a) Hydration of an alkene: $RCH=CHR' \xrightarrow[\substack{\underline{or}\ 1.\ B_2H_6 \\ 2.\ H_2O_2,\ OH^-}]{aq.\ H_2SO_4} R\overset{OH}{\underset{|}{C}}H-CH_2R'$

(b) Reduction of a ketone: $R-\overset{O}{\overset{\|}{C}}-R' \longrightarrow R-\overset{OH}{\underset{|}{C}}H-R'$

(c) Hydrolysis of an alkyl halide: $R-\overset{X}{\underset{|}{C}}H-R' \xrightarrow{OH^-} R-\overset{OH}{\underset{|}{C}}H-R'$

(d) Grignard (or other organometallic reaction):

$R-MgX + H-\overset{O}{\overset{\|}{C}}-R' \longrightarrow \xrightarrow{H_2O} R-\overset{OH}{\underset{|}{C}}H-R'$

This problem is a particularly good one for illustrating the fact that there are often several good routes to a given target. Compare the following routes, which rely on either (a), (b), or (d) above. We can rule out (c), because from the point of view of synthesis, halides are usually made from alcohols, and not vice versa.

A. [via (a)]

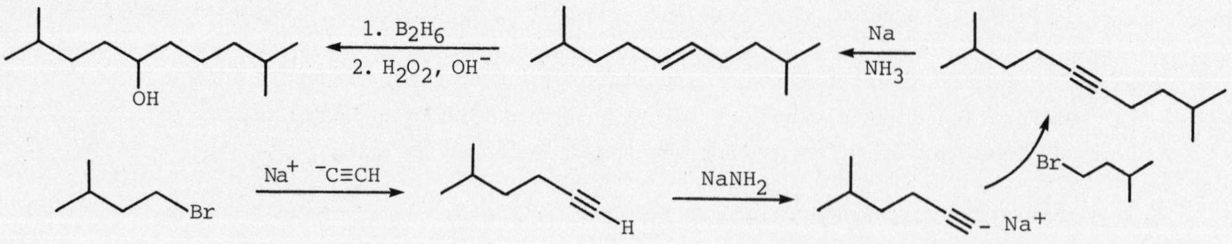

1. B_2H_6
2. H_2O_2, OH^-

$\dfrac{Na}{NH_3}$

Na^+ $^-C{\equiv}CH$

$NaNH_2$

In this route, we recognize that the alkene precursor to the alcohol can be **symmetrical**, therefore it doesn't matter which end the OH group ends up on. The alkene in turn is available from the alkyne, which allows us to make easily the carbon-carbon bonds required by our connection strategy. Note that several equally good alternatives are available for partial reduction of the triple bond and hydration of the alkene.

B. [via (b)]

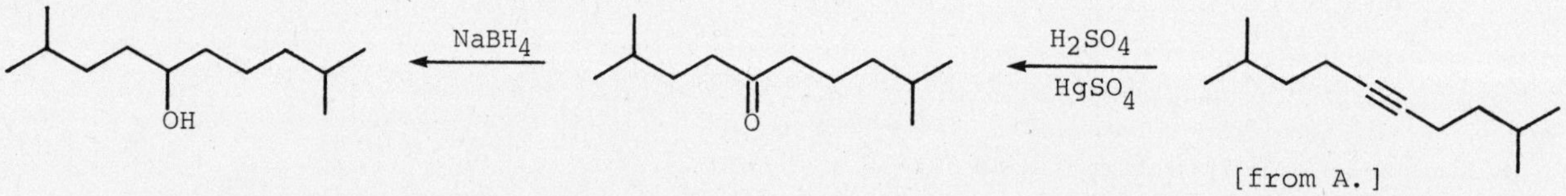

$NaBH_4$

$\dfrac{H_2SO_4}{HgSO_4}$

[from A.]

In terms of number of steps, this method is the same as A., and has a similar advantage in that it uses the same starting materials.

C. [via (d)]

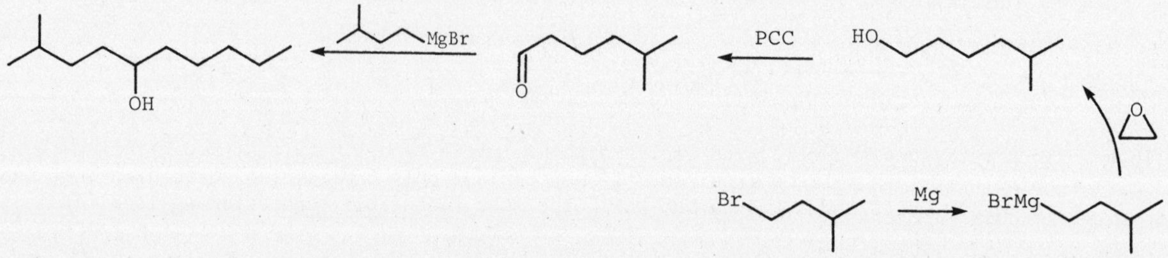

MgBr

PCC

$\dfrac{Mg}{}$ BrMg

This sequence relies on Grignard reactions for the carbon-carbon bond forming reactions, and takes advantage of oxirane as a synthon for the O–C–C– unit.

D. The following synthesis is given as an example of a route that is workable, but since it involves quite a few more steps than the ones above, it is a poor answer.

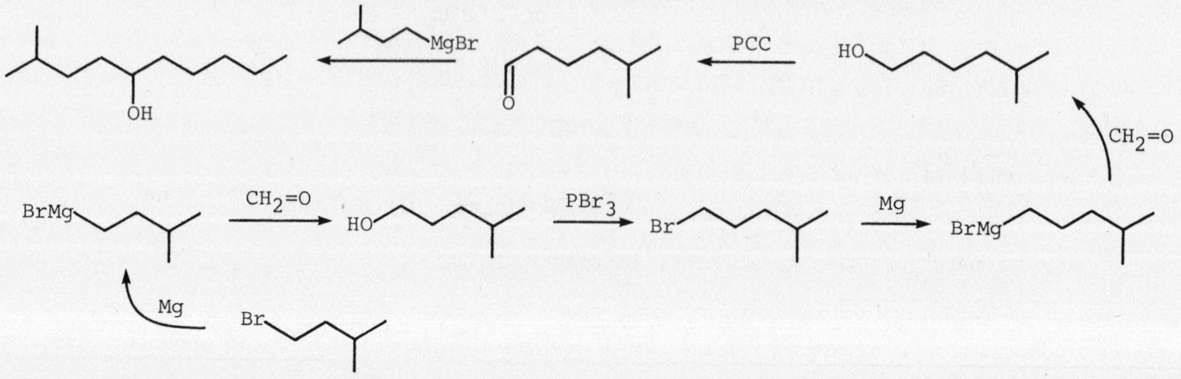

MgBr

PCC

$CH_2{=}O$

BrMg

$CH_2{=}O$ HO

PBr_3 Br

Mg BrMg

Mg

Br

16.7 4-(Deuteriomethyl)nonane: In this case, we need to introduce the deuterium atom specifically on the sidechain methyl group, so we have to consider connection strategies that will leave functionality on that carbon. Working the synthesis backward, we realize that 2-propyl-1-heptanol is a key intermediate:

$$\xleftarrow{\text{LiAlD}_4} \qquad \xleftarrow{\text{PBr}_3}$$

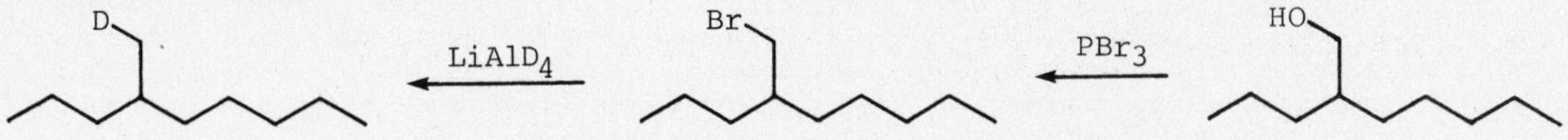

A reaction which forms a carbon-carbon bond **adjacent** to an oxygenated carbon is required, and the most appropriate is the aldol condensation:

$$\xleftarrow[\text{Pt}]{\text{H}_2} \qquad \xleftarrow{\text{NaOH}} \quad 2 \quad \text{CHO}$$

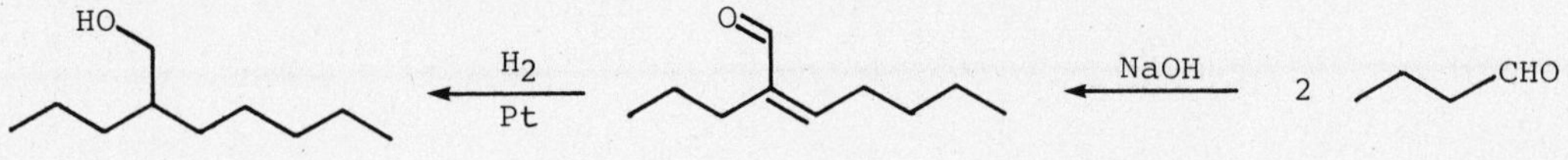

16.8 From the point of view of carbon-carbon bond formation, a Grignard reaction is the obvious choice:

$$\text{R-CH}_2\text{-Br} \ + \ \text{Mg} \ \longrightarrow \ \text{R-CH}_2\text{-MgBr} \ \xrightarrow{\triangle} \ \xrightarrow{\text{H}_2\text{O}} \ \text{R-CH}_2\text{CH}_2\text{CH}_2\text{-OH}$$

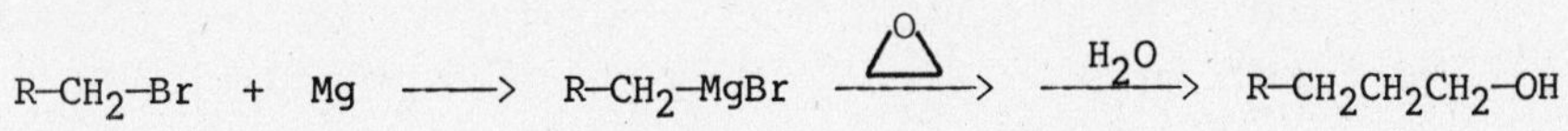

However, since the ketone at the 2-position of the starting material will itself react with a Grignard reagent, it must be protected during the synthesis:

$$\xleftarrow{\text{H}_3\text{O}^+} \qquad \xleftarrow{\text{H}_2\text{O}} \ \xleftarrow{\triangle} \qquad \xuparrow{\text{Mg}}$$

$$\xrightarrow[\text{H}^+]{\text{HO} \frown \text{OH}}$$

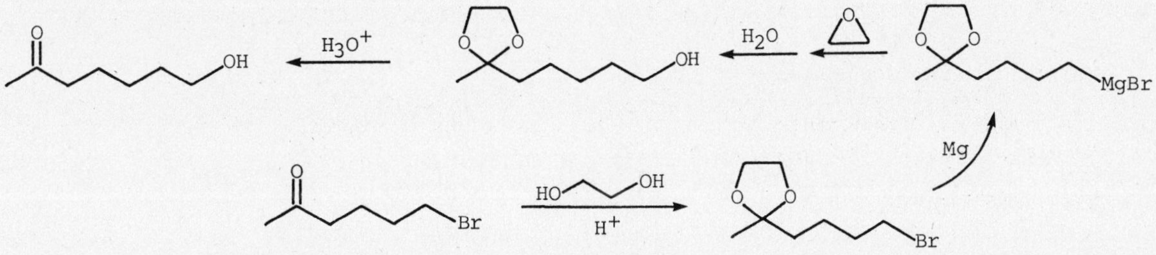

16.9 In this case, the alcohol group must be protected both during the Grignard reaction as well as during the subsequent oxidation of the side chain hydroxyl group to the ketone.

$$\xleftarrow{\text{H}_3\text{O}^+} \qquad \xleftarrow{\ } \qquad \xuparrow{\underline{n}\text{-BuMgBr}}$$

$$\xrightarrow[\text{Et}_3\text{N}]{\text{Me}_3\text{SiCl}}$$

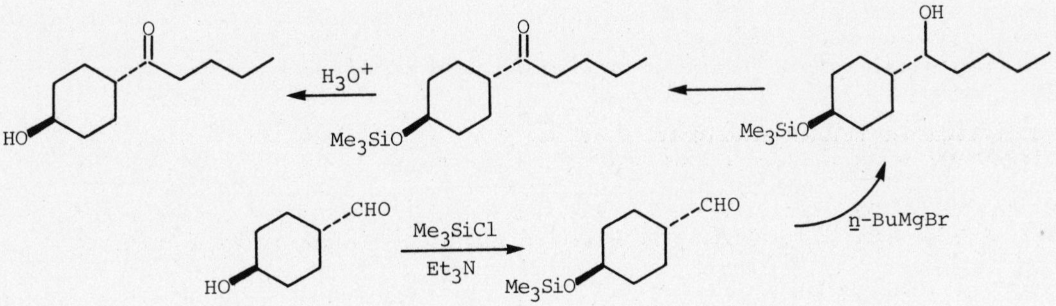

16.E   Answers and Explanations for Problems

NOTE: *for most synthesis problems, especially the more complex ones, there is more than one "correct" answer. Two or three routes can be devised which will lead to the target compound. Often one route will stand out above the others because it is shorter, or avoids low-yield reactions or isomeric products. Always try to find such a route, because that one is "more correct" as an answer. In this Study Guide, we cannot list every conceivable way to make the target compound, and your answer may differ from the one depicted here. Look at our explanations carefully, and learn to evaluate possible syntheses by comparison of yours with ours.*

1. (a) $CH_3(CH_2)_5OH \xleftarrow{H_2O} CH_3(CH_2)_5OMgBr \xleftarrow{CH_2=O} CH_3(CH_2)_4MgBr \xleftarrow[ether]{Mg} CH_3(CH_2)_4Br$

$CH_3(CH_2)_3MgBr$

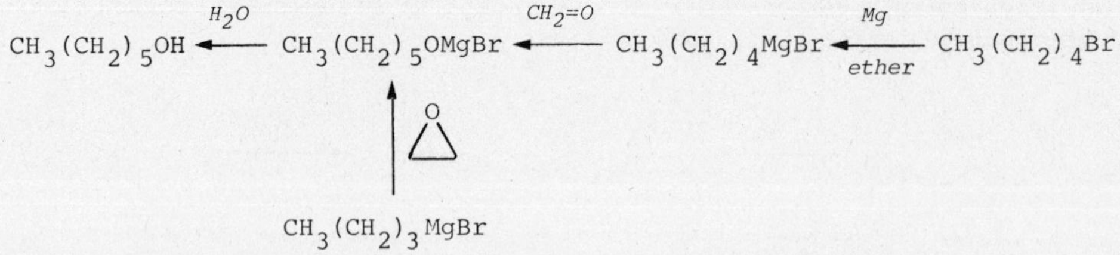

(b) $CH_3(CH_2)_3\overset{OH}{\underset{|}{C}}HCH_3 \xleftarrow{H_2O} CH_3(CH_2)_3\overset{OMgX}{\underset{|}{C}}HCH_3 \xleftarrow{or}$

$CH_3(CH_2)_3\overset{O}{\overset{||}{C}}H + CH_3MgI$

$CH_3(CH_2)_3MgBr + H\overset{O}{\overset{||}{C}}CH_3$

(c) $CH_3CH_2CH_2\overset{OH}{\underset{|}{C}}HCH_2CH_3 \xleftarrow{H_2O} CH_3CH_2CH_2\overset{OMgBr}{\underset{|}{C}}HCH_2CH_3 \xleftarrow{or}$

$CH_3CH_2CH_2\overset{O}{\overset{||}{C}}H + BrMgCH_2CH_3$

$CH_3CH_2CH_2MgBr + H\overset{O}{\overset{||}{C}}CH_2CH_3$

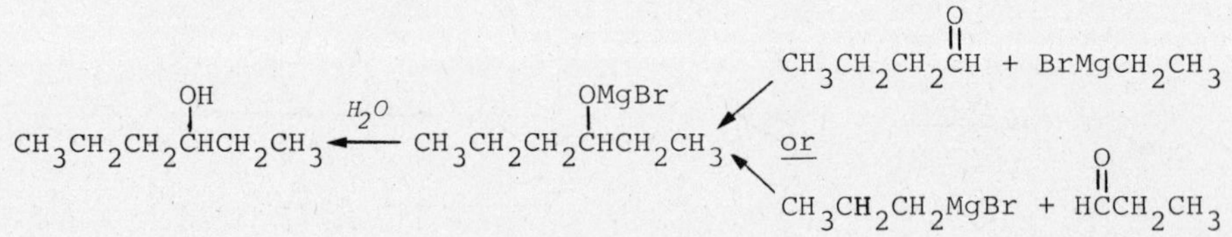

(d) $CH_3(CH_2)_4C\equiv CH \xleftarrow{} CH_3(CH_2)_4Br + NaC\equiv CH$

(e)

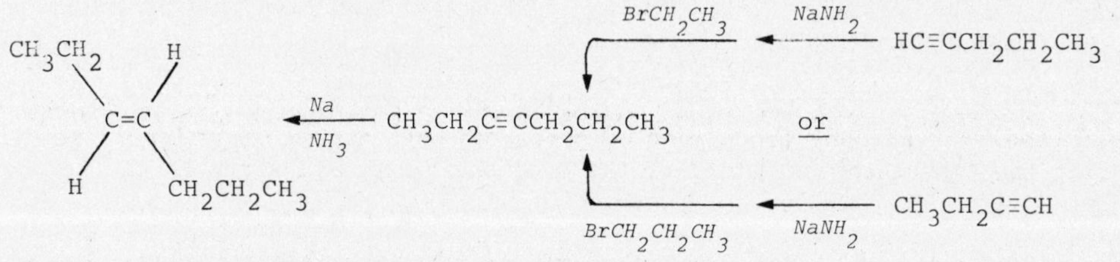

$\underset{H}{\overset{CH_3CH_2}{}}C=C\underset{CH_2CH_2CH_3}{\overset{H}{}}$ $\xleftarrow[NH_3]{Na} CH_3CH_2C\equiv CCH_2CH_2CH_3 \xleftarrow[]{} $

$\xleftarrow[]{BrCH_2CH_3 \quad NaNH_2} HC\equiv CCH_2CH_2CH_3$

or

$\xleftarrow[BrCH_2CH_2CH_3]{NaNH_2} CH_3CH_2C\equiv CH$

(Any route involving elimination of an alcohol or a halide would give some cis-isomer, too.)

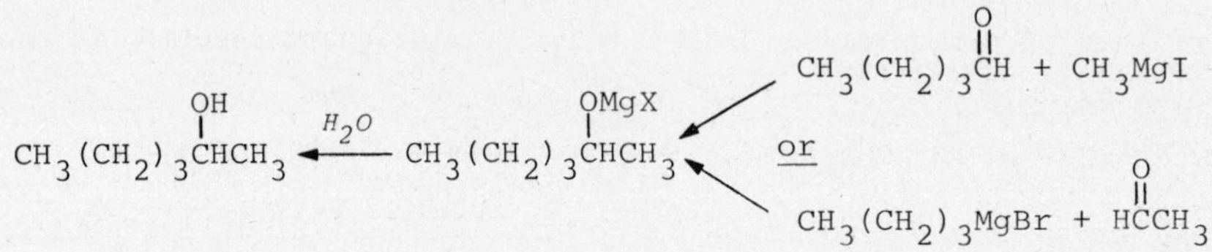

(f)

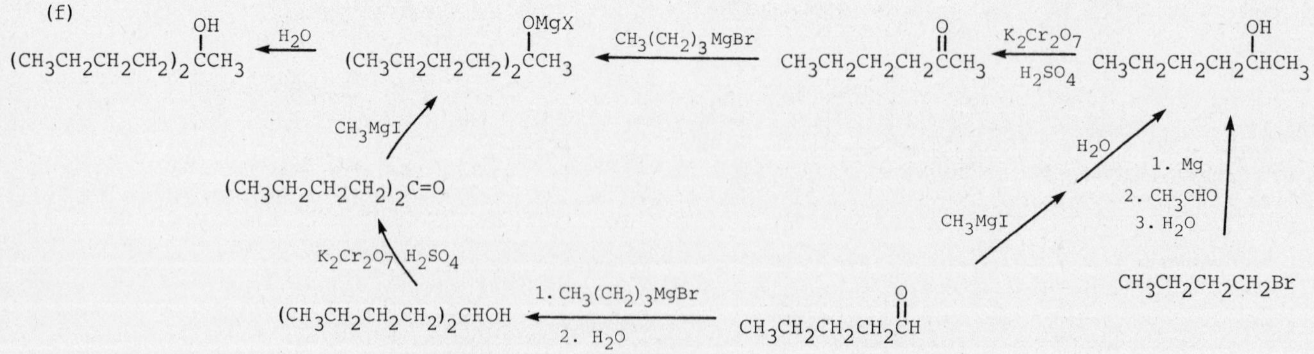

$(CH_3CH_2CH_2CH_2)_2\overset{OH}{\underset{|}{C}}CH_3 \xleftarrow{H_2O} (CH_3CH_2CH_2CH_2)_2\overset{OMgX}{\underset{|}{C}}CH_3 \xleftarrow{CH_3(CH_2)_3MgBr} CH_3CH_2CH_2CH_2\overset{O}{\overset{||}{C}}CH_3 \xleftarrow[H_2SO_4]{K_2Cr_2O_7} CH_3CH_2CH_2CH_2\overset{OH}{\underset{|}{C}}HCH_3$

CH_3MgI

$(CH_3CH_2CH_2CH_2)_2C=O$

$K_2Cr_2O_7 \quad H_2SO_4$

$(CH_3CH_2CH_2CH_2)_2CHOH \xleftarrow[2. H_2O]{1. CH_3(CH_2)_3MgBr} CH_3CH_2CH_2CH_2\overset{O}{\overset{||}{C}}H$

CH_3MgI $\begin{array}{l}H_2O\\1.\ Mg\\2.\ CH_3CHO\\3.\ H_2O\end{array}$

$CH_3CH_2CH_2CH_2Br$

Note that in many instances a number of similar, equally valid routes are available. In Section 18.7.D of the Text, you will find the reaction depicted here, which would be the best way to prepare 5-methyl-5-nonanol:

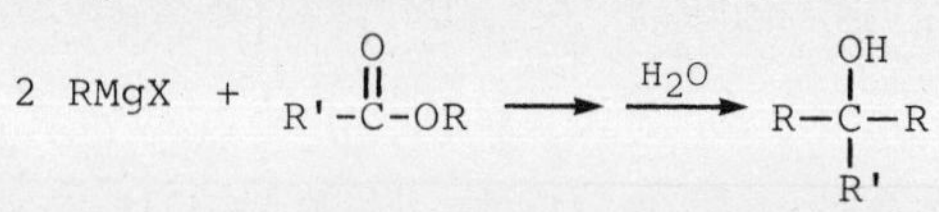

$2\ RMgX + R'-\overset{O}{\overset{||}{C}}-OR \xrightarrow{H_2O} R-\overset{OH}{\underset{\underset{R'}{|}}{C}}-R$

(g) $(CH_3)_2\overset{\overset{OH}{|}}{C}CH_2CH_2CH_2CH(CH_3)_2$

1st decision: which C-C bond to form

$(CH_3)_2\overset{\overset{O}{\|}}{C}CH_2\text{----}CH_2CH_2CH(CH_3)_2$ *or* $(CH_3)_2\overset{\overset{O}{\|}}{C}CH_2CH_2\text{----}CH_2CH(CH_3)_2$

　　　4 carbons　　　5 carbons　　　　　　　　5 carbons　　　4 carbons

The first choice is the best, because the functional group in the product is closest to the bond to be formed.

2nd decision: what C-C bond-forming reaction to choose

$(CH_3)_2\overset{\overset{O}{\|}}{CH}CH + MCH_2CH_2CH(CH_3)_2 \longrightarrow \xrightarrow{H_2O} (CH_3)_2\overset{\overset{OH}{|}}{CH}CHCH_2CH_2CH(CH_3)_2$

This reaction would put the hydroxy group in the wrong place. You could correct this, but the sequence would involve several steps and would therefore be inefficient:

$(CH_3)_2\overset{\overset{OH}{|}}{CH}CHCH_2CH_2CH(CH_3)_2 \xrightarrow{H_2SO_4} (CH_3)_2C=CHCH_2CH_2CH(CH_3)_2 \xrightarrow[H_2SO_4]{dilute} (CH_3)_2\overset{\overset{OH}{|}}{C}CH_2CH_2CH_2CH(CH_3)_2$

　　　　　　　　　　　　　　　　　　　　　　(major)

$+$

$(CH_3)_2CHCH=CHCH_2CH(CH_3)_2$ *(minor)*

Alternatively,

$\overset{CH_3}{\underset{CH_3}{}}C\overset{O}{\diagup\diagdown}CH_2 + MCH_2CH_2CH(CH_3)_2 \longrightarrow \xrightarrow{H_2O} (CH_3)_2\overset{\overset{OH}{|}}{C}CH_2CH_2CH_2CH(CH_3)_2$

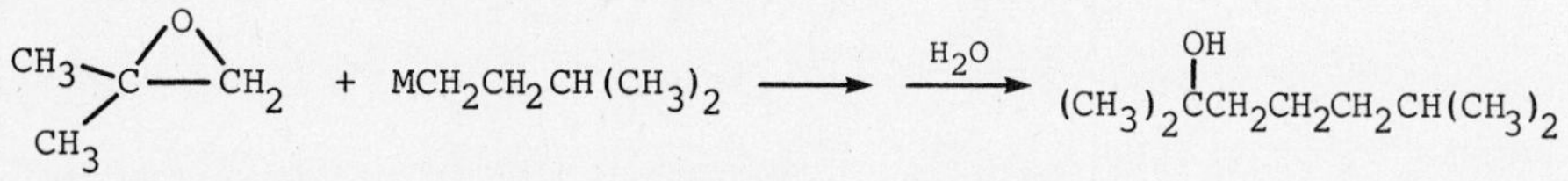

This reaction gives the desired products directly.

FINAL DECISION: what M should be: MgX or Li

With an epoxide such as this one, Grignard reagents often induce rearrangement prior to addition. The organolithium reaction is therefore the better choice.

$(CH_3)_2C\overset{O}{\diagup\diagdown}CH_2 \xrightarrow{RMgBr} \left[(CH_3)_2\overset{\overset{O}{\|}}{CH}CH \right] \xrightarrow{H_2O} (CH_3)_2\overset{\overset{OH}{|}}{CH}CHCH_2CH_2CH(CH_3)_2$

$\xrightarrow{RLi} (CH_3)_2\overset{\overset{OLi}{|}}{C}CH_2CH_2CH_2CH(CH_3)_2 \xrightarrow{H_2O} (CH_3)_2\overset{\overset{OH}{|}}{C}CH_2CH_2CH_2CH(CH_3)_2$

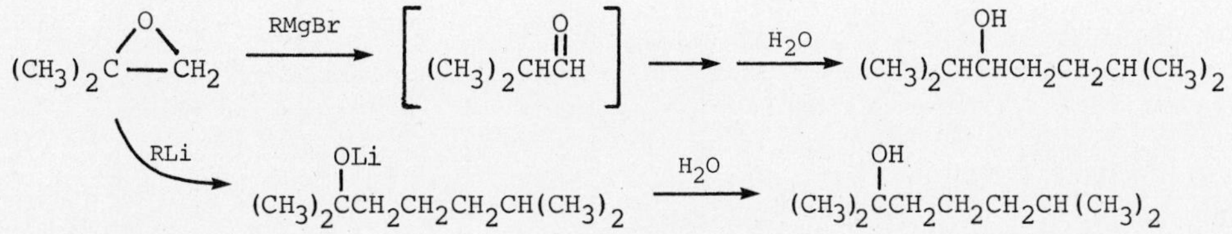

Many other routes can be imagined, such as the multistep sequence below, but the extra steps required make them very inefficient, and therefore poor solutions to the problem.

$BrMgCH_2CH_2CH(CH_3)_2 \xrightarrow[2.\,H_2O]{1.\,CH_2=O} HO(CH_2)_3CH(CH_3)_2 \xrightarrow[2.\,Mg]{1.\,PBr_3} BrMg(CH_2)_3CH(CH_3)_2 \xrightarrow[2.\,H_2O]{1.\,(CH_3)_2C=O} (CH_3)_2\overset{\overset{OH}{|}}{C}(CH_2)_3CH(CH_3)_2$

(h)   *First decision:*
　　　which C-C bond to form:

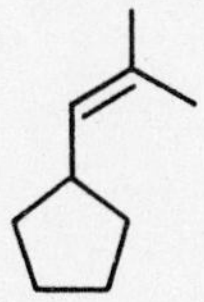

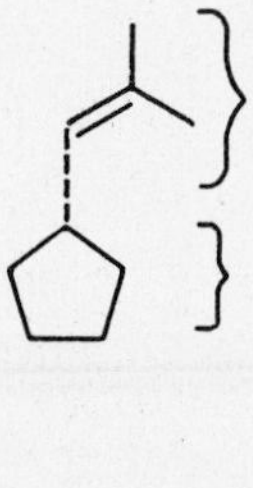

　　　　　　　　　　　　　　　　　　　　} 4 carbons

　　　　　　　　　　　　　　　　　　　　} 5 carbons

This would be efficient from the point of view of requiring only one C-C bond-forming step. The most obvious way to do this would involve a Grignard reaction and dehydration sequence:

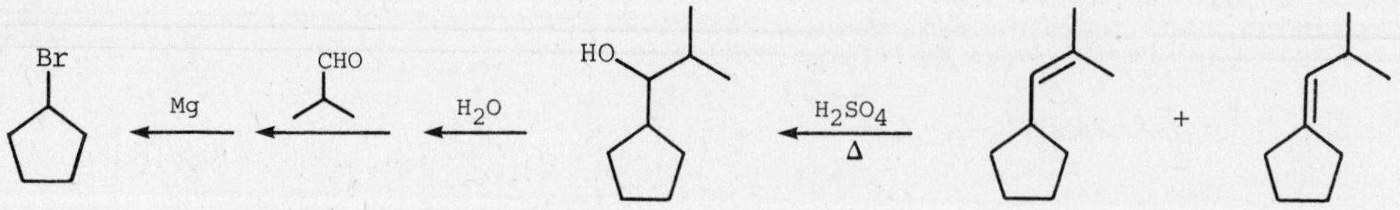

However, this route leads to two double bond isomers (in comparable amounts) which would be hard to separate.

The best general method for introducing a double bond in a specific position is the Wittig reaction. Using this reaction, the last step in the synthesis would be:

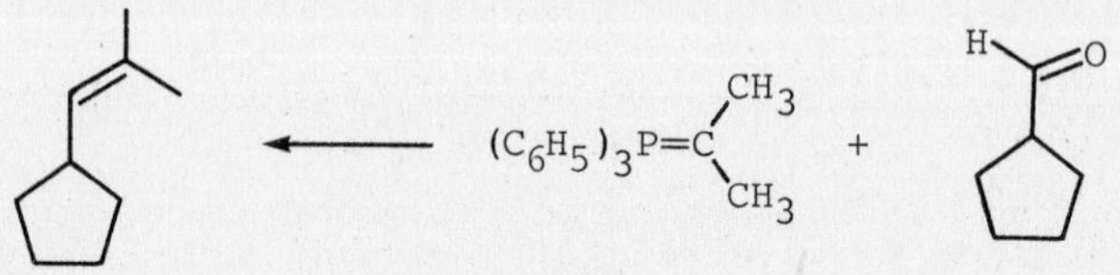

$(C_6H_5)_3P=C\begin{smallmatrix}CH_3\\CH_3\end{smallmatrix}$ +

The aldehyde would be synthesized as follows:

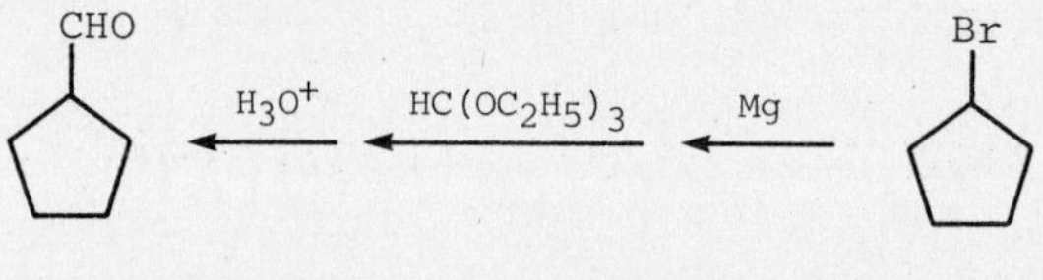

$\xleftarrow{H_3O^+}$ $\xleftarrow{HC(OC_2H_5)_3}$ $\xleftarrow{Mg}$

2. (a)

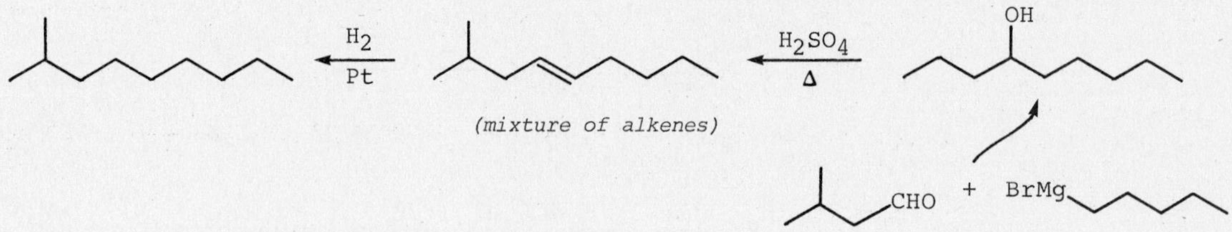

$\xleftarrow{\begin{smallmatrix}H_2\\Pt\end{smallmatrix}}$ $\xleftarrow{\begin{smallmatrix}H_2SO_4\\\Delta\end{smallmatrix}}$

(mixture of alkenes)

CHO + BrMg—

(b)

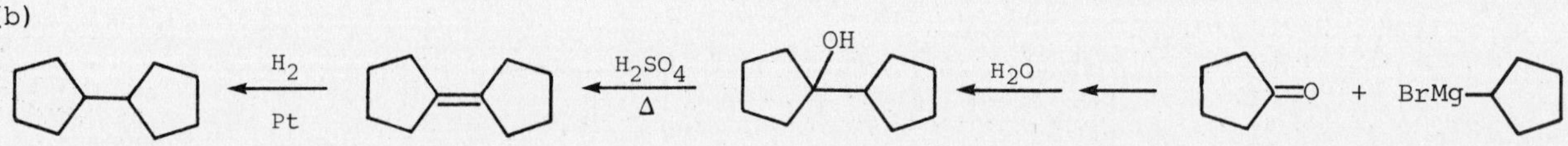

$\xleftarrow{\begin{smallmatrix}H_2\\Pt\end{smallmatrix}}$ $\xleftarrow{\begin{smallmatrix}H_2SO_4\\\Delta\end{smallmatrix}}$ $\xleftarrow{H_2O}$ =O + BrMg—

(NOTE: the hydroxyl could also be removed the same way it was in part (a).)

(c) $(CH_3)_2CH(CH_2)_6CH(CH_3)_2$

1st decision:
which C-C bonds to form: $(CH_3)_2CHCH_2CH_2$---CH_2-CH_2---$CH_2CH_2CH(CH_3)_2$

5 carbons   2 carbons   5 carbons

2nd decision: what reaction to use (take the symmetry of the molecule as a hint)

$(CH_3)_2CHCH_2CH_2Br + NaC\equiv CH \longrightarrow (CH_3)_2CHCH_2CH_2C\equiv CH \xrightarrow[]{NaNH_2 \quad BrCH_2CH_2CH(CH_3)_2}$

$(CH_3)_2CH(CH_2)_6CH(CH_3)_2 \xleftarrow[Pt]{H_2} (CH_3)_2CHCH_2CH_2C\equiv CCH_2CH_2CH(CH_3)_2$

(d) Don't forget the aldol condensation!

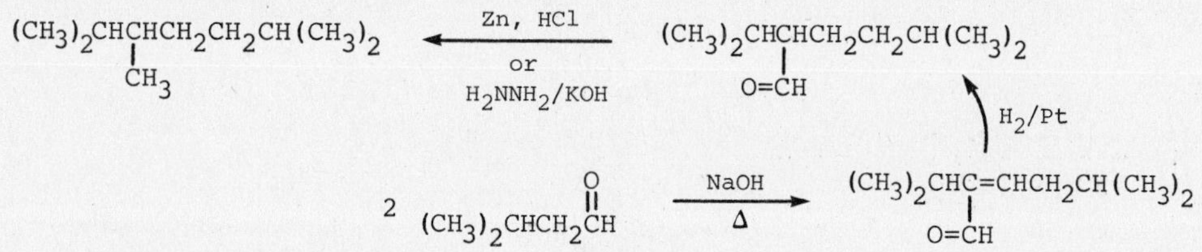

$(CH_3)_2CHCHCH_2CH_2CH(CH_3)_2$ $\xleftarrow[H_2NNH_2/KOH]{\text{Zn, HCl or}}$ $(CH_3)_2CHCHCH_2CH_2CH(CH_3)_2$
      CH_3 $O=CH$

$\uparrow H_2/Pt$

$2\ \ (CH_3)_2CHCH_2\overset{O}{\overset{\|}{C}}H$ $\xrightarrow[\Delta]{NaOH}$ $(CH_3)_2CHC=CHCH_2CH(CH_3)_2$
                                                            $O=CH$

(e)
      CH_3 CH_3
$CH_2=CHCH_2CHCH_2CH_2CH_3$ $\xleftarrow[3.\ H_2O]{1.\ PBr_3 \atop 2.\ Mg}$ $CH_2=CHCH_2\overset{CH_3}{\underset{OH}{C}}CH_2CH_2CH_3$ $\xleftarrow{H_2O}$ $CH_3\overset{O}{\overset{\|}{C}}CH_2CH_2CH_3$

                                                                  + $CH_2=CHCH_2MgBr$

(f) $((CH_3)_2CHCH_2CH_2)_3CH$ $\xleftarrow[3.\ H_2O]{1.\ HBr \atop 2.\ Mg}$ $((CH_3)_2CHCH_2CH_2)_3COH$ $\leftarrow$

$\xleftarrow[H_2SO_4]{H_2/Pt\ \ \text{or}}$ $(CH_3)_2CHCH_2CH_2MgBr$

$(CH_3)_2CHCH_2CH_2\overset{O}{\overset{\|}{C}}H$ $\xrightarrow[2.\ H_2O]{1.\ (CH_3)_2CHCH_2CH_2MgBr}$ $((CH_3)_2CHCH_2CH_2)_2CHOH$ $\xrightarrow[H_2SO_4]{K_2Cr_2O_7}$ $((CH_3)_2CHCH_2CH_2)_2C=O$

$\uparrow PCC$

$(CH_3)_2CHCH_2CH_2CH_2OH$ $\xleftarrow{CH_2=O}$ $(CH_3)_2CHCH_2CH_2MgBr$

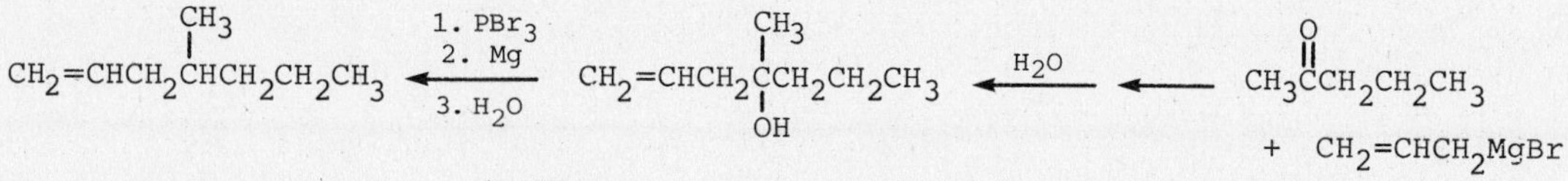

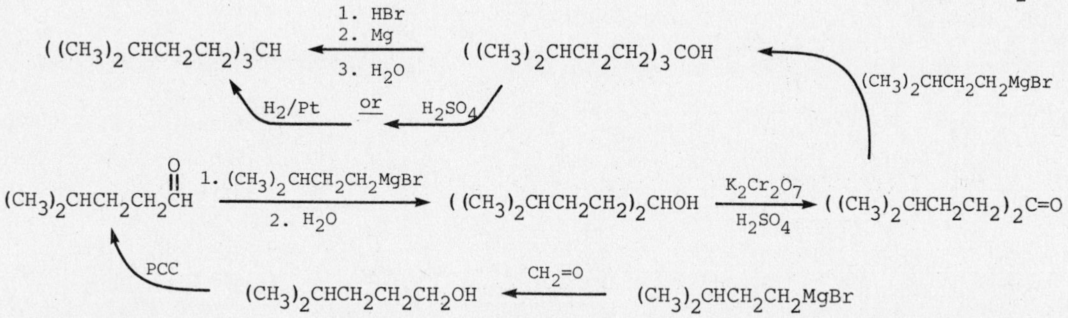

(In Section 18.7.D of the Text, you will learn that the most efficient way to do this is: $3\ RMgBr + R'\overset{O}{\overset{\|}{O}}COR' \xrightarrow{H_2O} R_3COH$

3. (a)
$\underset{CH_3}{\overset{H}{C}}=\underset{H}{\overset{CH_2CH_2CH_3}{C}}$ $\xleftarrow[NH_3]{Na}$ $CH_3-C\equiv C-CH_2CH_2CH_3$ $\xleftarrow{CH_3I}$ $NaC\equiv CCH_2CH_2CH_3$ $\xleftarrow{NaNH_2}$ $HC\equiv CCH_2CH_2CH_3$

See comments to Problem #1(e).

(b)
   $CH_2CH_2CH_2CH_3$ (cyclopentane with OH and H) $\xleftarrow{H_2O}$ $\leftarrow$ epoxide $+ LiCH_2CH_2CH_2CH_3$ (via: Li$^+$ $^-$R)

(c)
$\underset{H}{\overset{CH_3CH_2CH_2}{C}}=\underset{H}{\overset{CH_2CH_2CH_3}{C}}$ $\xleftarrow[\substack{\text{poisoned} \\ \text{Pd catalyst}}]{H_2}$ $CH_3CH_2CH_2C\equiv CCH_2CH_2CH_3$ $\leftarrow$ $CH_3CH_2CH_2C\equiv CNa$ $+$ $BrCH_2CH_2CH_3$

See comments to Problem #1(e).

(d)
$CH_3CH_2\overset{OH\ \ H}{\underset{H\ \ OH}{C-C}}CH_2CH_3$ $\xleftarrow[H_2O]{OsO_4}$ $CH_3CH_2\underset{H}{\overset{H}{C}}=\overset{C}{\underset{CH_2CH_3}{}}$ CH_2CH_3

$\uparrow H_3O^+$ $\uparrow Na/NH_3$

                                 CH_3CH_2Br
                    $CH_3CH_2C\equiv CCH_2CH_3$ $\leftarrow$ $+$
                                 $CH_3CH_2C\equiv CNa$

                         $\downarrow H_2$ $\substack{\text{poisoned Pd} \\ \text{catalyst}}$

$CH_3CH_2\overset{CH_2CH_3}{\underset{H\ \ O\ \ H}{C-C}}$ $\xleftarrow{CH_3CO_3H}$ $\underset{H}{\overset{CH_3CH_2}{C}}=\underset{H}{\overset{CH_2CH_3}{C}}$

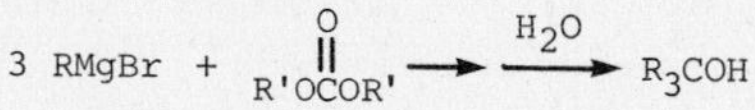

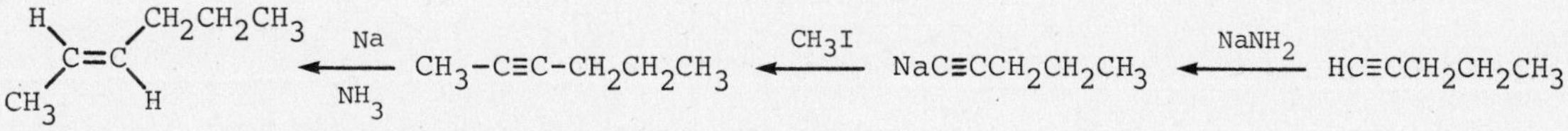

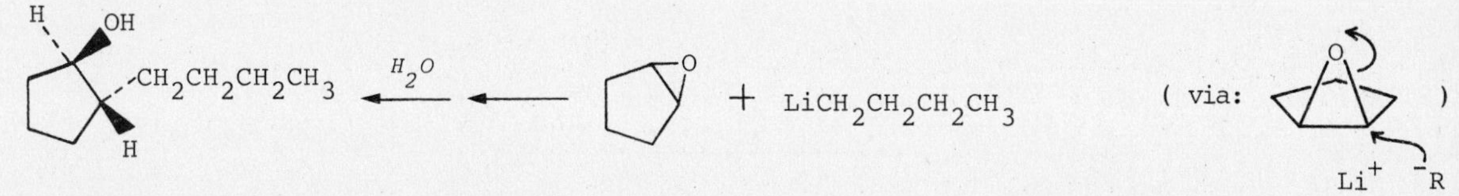

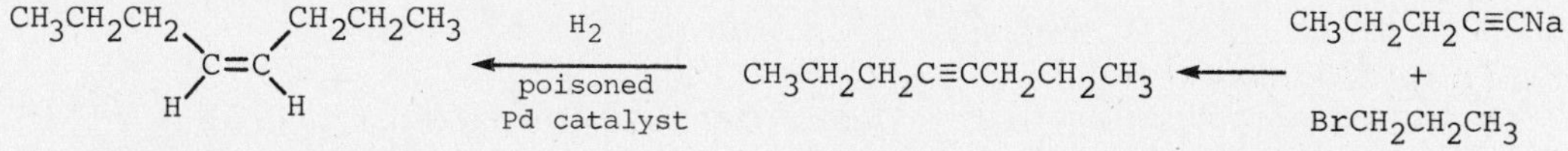

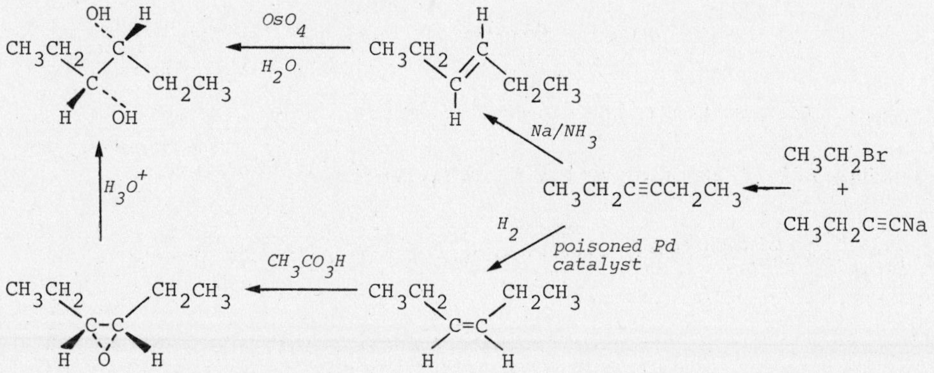

(This is good to work through with models.)

(e) [structure: H, OH / CH₃ / H / CH₃ — CH₂CH₂CH₂CH₃] ←—H_2O— [cis epoxide with CH₃, H, CH₃ groups] $+$ $LiCH_2CH_2CH_2CH_3$

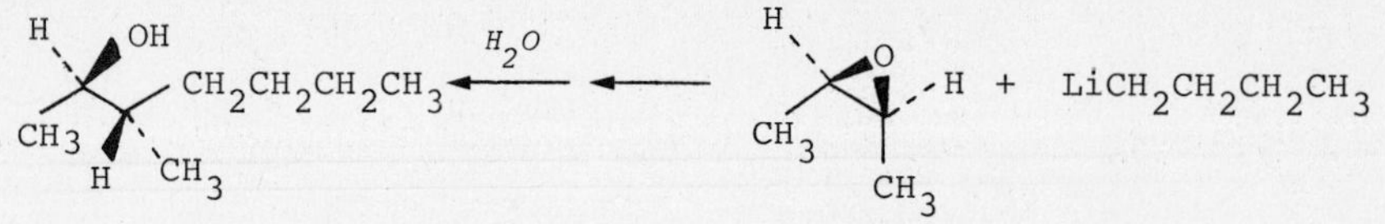

(The trans epoxide would give the (2RS, 3RS) diastereomer.)

(f) [cyclopentane with OH and CH=CHCH₂CH₃ group] ←—$\dfrac{H_2}{\text{poisoned Pd catalyst}}$— [cyclopentane with OH and C≡CCH₂CH₃] ←—H_2O— [cyclopentanone] $+$ $NaC\equiv CCH_2CH_3$

(g) [cyclopropane: CH₃CH₂, H, H, CH₂CH₃] ←—$\dfrac{CH_2I_2}{Zn\text{-}Cu}$— [alkene CH₃CH₂ and CH₂CH₃, cis] ←—$\dfrac{Na}{NH_3}$— $CH_3CH_2C\equiv CCH_2CH_3$

(from part (d))

4. (a) $HOCH_2CH_2CH_2$—C(H)(CH₃)—CH_2CH_3 (S) ←—H_2O— [epoxide] $BrMgCH_2$—C(H)(CH₃)—CH_2CH_3 (S) ←—Mg— $BrCH_2$—C(H)(CH₃)—CH_2CH_3 (S)

(b) $CH_3CH_2CH_2$—C(CN)(H)(CH₃) (R) ←—$NaCN$— $CH_3CH_2CH_2$—C(CH₃)(Br)(H) (S)   *(S_N2 reaction, with inversion)*

(c) H_3C—C(H)(OH)—CH_2-$C(CH_3)_3$ ←—H_2O— [epoxide with CH₃, CH₂, O, H] $+$ $LiC(CH_3)_3$

(d) [but-2-yne chain with D, H at stereocenter product] ←—$Na^+ {}^-C\equiv CCH_2CH_2CH_3$— [CH with D, H, Br]

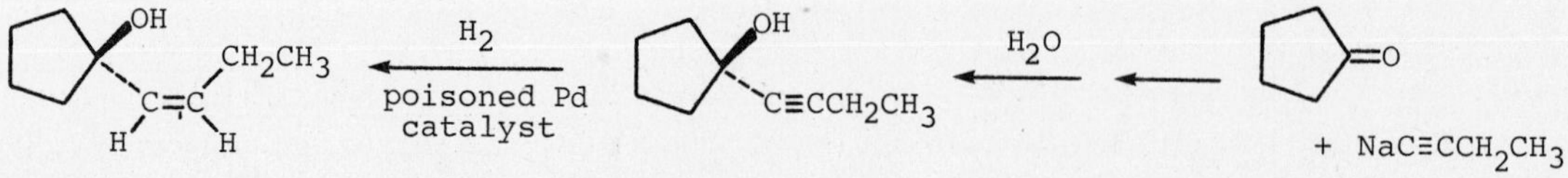

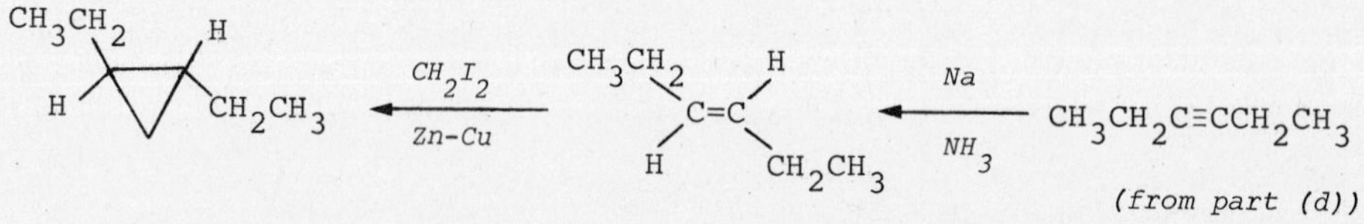

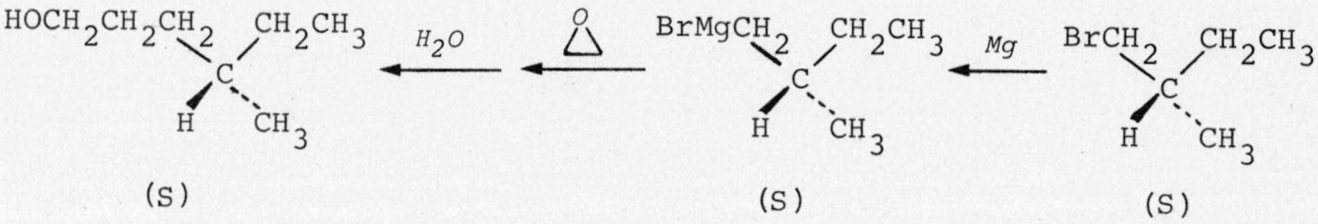

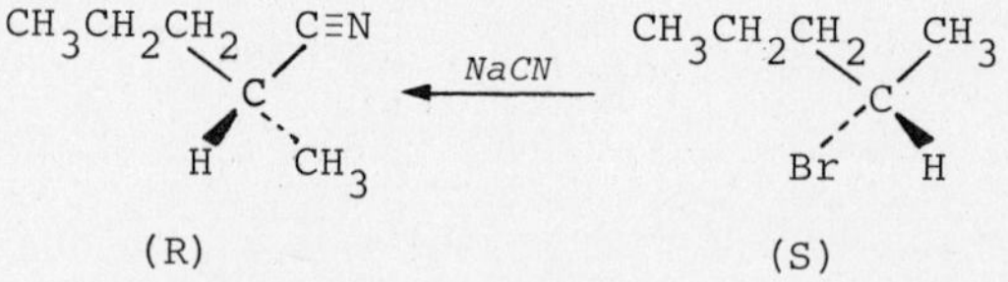

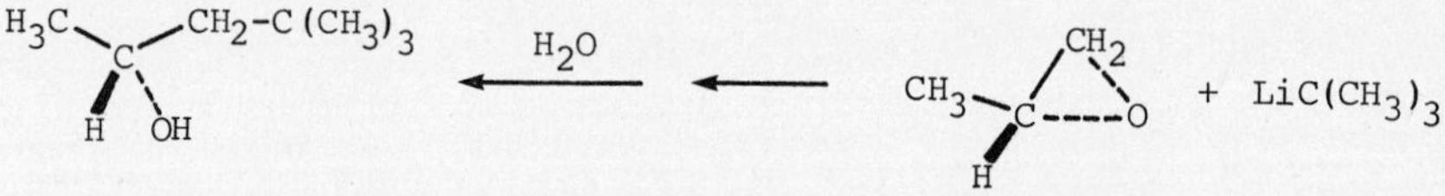

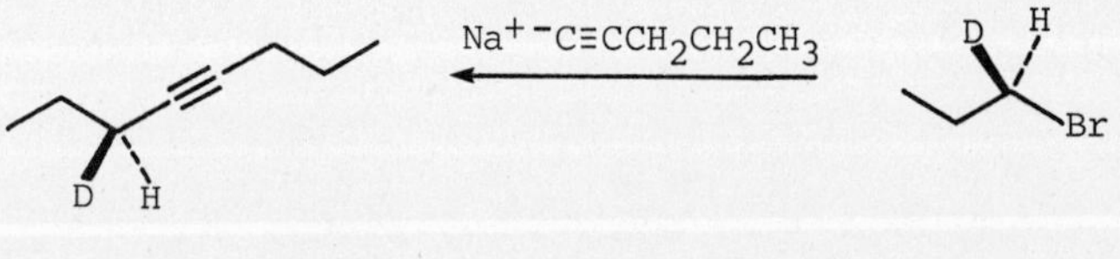

5. (a) The aldehyde must be protected during the strongly basic elimination reaction, otherwise it will undergo aldol condensation reactions.

[CH₂=CH–CH₂CH₂CHO] ←—H_3O^+— [allyl-1,3-dioxolane] ←—$\dfrac{t\text{-BuOK}}{t\text{-BuOH}}$— [Br–(CH₂)₄–1,3-dioxolane] ←—$\dfrac{HO\text{–CH}_2\text{CH}_2\text{–}OH}{H^+}$— [Br–(CH₂)₄–CHO]

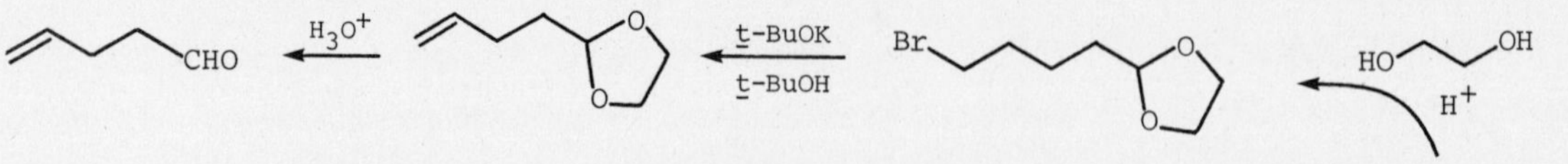

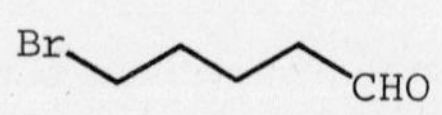

(b) The hydroxyl group in the starting material must be protected during the Grignard and oxidation reactions.

HO–(chain)–OH with OH ←—H_3O^+— Me_3SiO–(chain)–$OSiMe_3$ with OH ←—Me_3SiO–(chain)–$MgBr$—

HO–(chain)–Br —$\dfrac{1.\ Me_3SiCl,\ Et_3N}{2.\ Mg}$→ Me_3SiO–(chain)–$MgBr$ —$CH_2{=}O$→ Me_3SiO–(chain)–OH —PCC→ Me_3SiO–(chain)–CHO

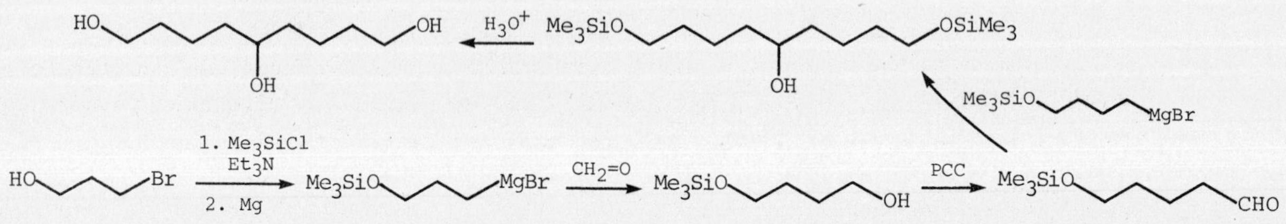

(c) The aldehyde must be protected to avoid cyanohydrin formation.

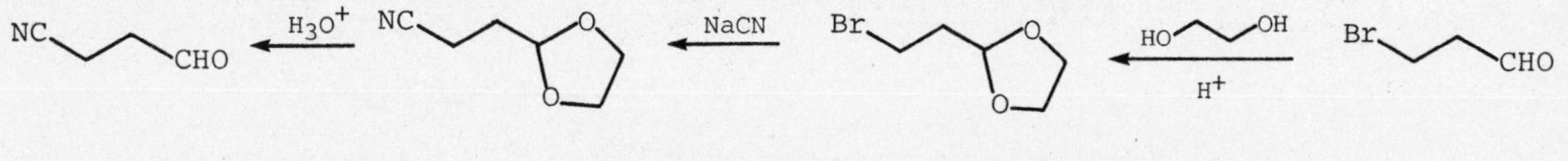

6. (a) The logical approach to the cis-olefin involves partial hydrogenation of the alkyne, after assembly of the alkyne by alkylation of acetylide anions:

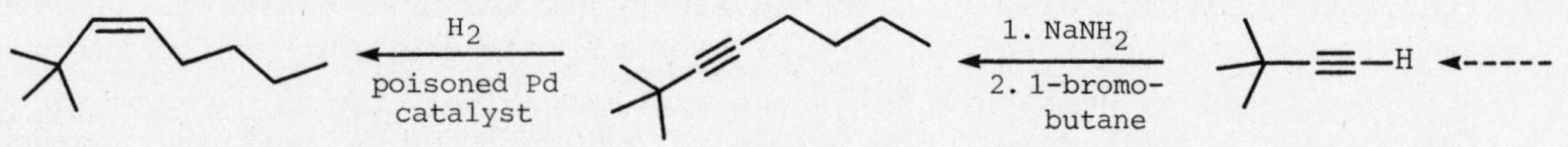

This route will be successful from t-butyl acetylene on to the target, but will not work for the synthesis of t-butylacetylene itself. Attempted alkylation of a tertiary halide with the strongly basic acetylide anion will lead exclusively to elimination:

$$(CH_3)_3C\text{-}Br \;+\; Na^+\;{}^-C{\equiv}CH \longrightarrow CH_2{=}C(CH_3)_2 \;+\; HC{\equiv}CH \;+\; NaBr$$

The acetylene must therefore be formed in another way; the most reasonable is via the alkene:

$$(CH_3)_3C\text{-}CH{=}CH_2 \xrightarrow{Br_2} (CH_3)_3C\text{-}CHBr\text{-}CH_2Br \xrightarrow{NaNH_2} (CH_3)_3CC{\equiv}C^-\;Na^+$$

The alkene in turn is available by a number of methods:

$$Ph_3\overset{+}{P}\text{-}\overset{-}{C}H_2 \;+\; (CH_3)_3CCHO \longrightarrow (CH_3)_3C\text{-}CH{=}CH_2$$

$$(CH_3)_3CCH_2Br \xrightarrow{Mg} \xrightarrow{CH_2=O} (CH_3)_3CCH_2CH_2OH \xrightarrow{PBr_3} (CH_3)_3CCH_2CH_2Br \xrightarrow[tBuOH]{tBuOK} (CH_3)_3C\text{-}CH{=}CH_2$$

(b) Two possibilities which involve various protecting or masking groups are shown below:

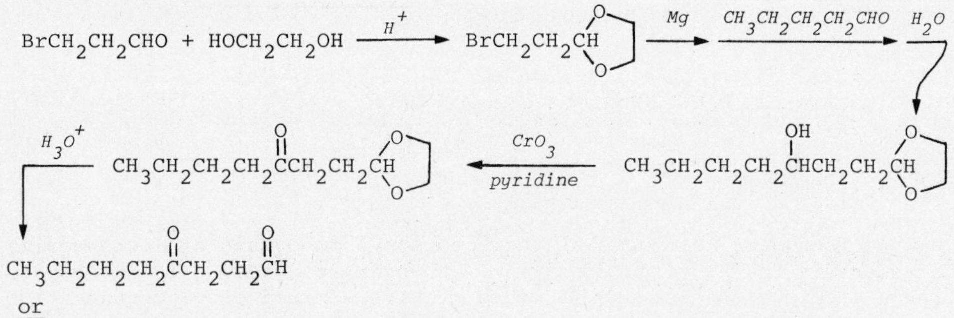

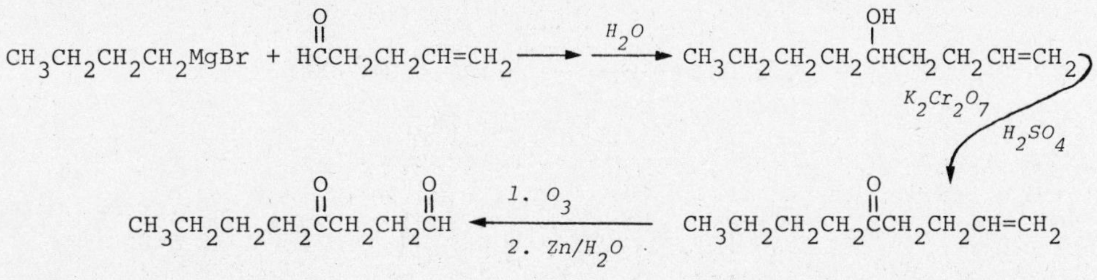

(c) The desired target is a six-carbon keto alcohol. Thus, we must add one carbon at least. Since the material is an alcohol, we may consider a Grignard synthesis. It is a secondary alcohol, so there are two possible combinations:

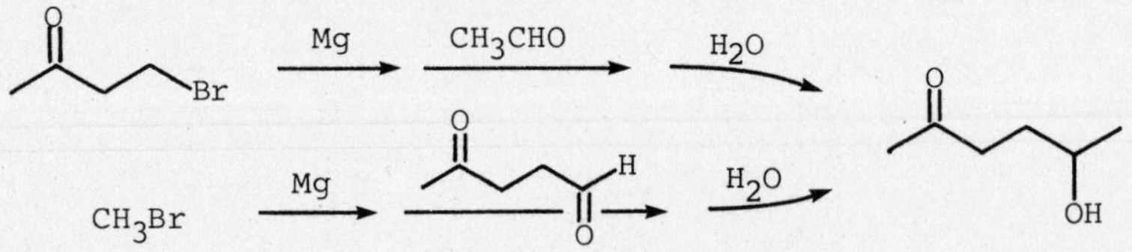

In the latter route, we have a problem of selectivity. The Grignard reagent CH_3MgBr can react with either carbonyl group. Although aldehydes are more reactive than ketones, the Grignard reagent is so reactive it will probably not show much selectivity.

In the first route, we have a different problem: the Grignard reagent *can react with itself*. Polymerization will result. A simple way out of this dilemma is to **protect** the carbonyl group in 4-bromo-2-butanone so that it cannot react with a Grignard reagent. This may be done by converting it into a ketal, which does not react with Grignard reagents:

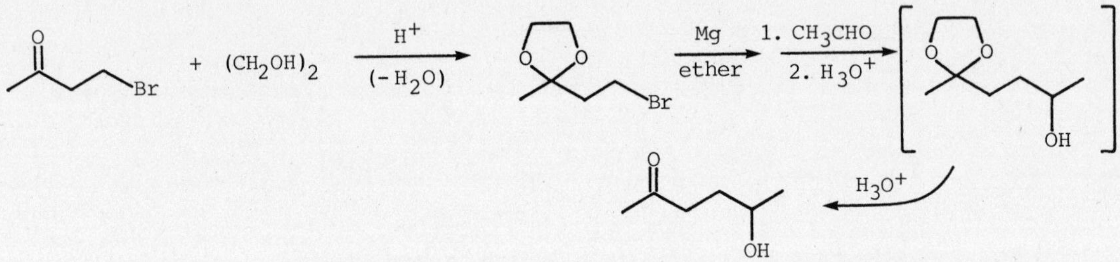

(d) The target: $(CH_3)_2C{=}CH\overset{\overset{\displaystyle CH_2CH_3}{|}}{C}{=}CHCH_2CH_2CH_3$ (no stereochemistry specified).

The major challenge is to introduce the double bonds in the correct positions. Routes that involve dehydration of alcohols or elimination of alkyl halides will lead to other isomers in addition to the desired one. The best way to introduce a double bond in a specific position is via the Wittig reaction. With this in mind, you can imagine two carbonyl compounds which would give the desired product:

$$2\ O{=}CHCH_2CH_2CH_3 \xrightarrow[\Delta]{NaOH} O{=}CH{-}\overset{\overset{\displaystyle CH_3CH_2}{|}}{C}{=}CHCH_2CH_2CH_3 \xrightarrow{(CH_3)_2C=P(C_6H_5)_3} (CH_3)_2C{=}CH\overset{\overset{\displaystyle CH_3CH_2}{|}}{C}{=}CH_2CH_2CH_3$$

$$(CH_3)_2C{=}O + CH_3\overset{\overset{\displaystyle O}{\|}}{C}CH_2CH_3 \xrightarrow[\Delta]{NaOH} (CH_3)_2C{=}CH\overset{\overset{\displaystyle CH_3CH_2}{|}}{C}{=}O \xrightarrow{(C_6H_5)_3P=CHCH_2CH_2CH_3} (CH_3)_2C{=}CH\overset{\overset{\displaystyle CH_3CH_2}{|}}{C}{=}CH_2CH_2CH_3$$

You should recognize that both of these carbonyl compounds are potentially available in one step via the aldol condensation. However, the ketone is clearly a less desirable intermediate because it would require a mixed aldol condensation, leading to many products in addition to the desired one.

(e) $(CH_3)_2C{=}CHCHO + NaC{\equiv}CCH_2CH_3 \longrightarrow \xrightarrow{H_2O} (CH_3)_2C{=}CH\overset{\overset{\displaystyle OH}{|}}{C}HC{\equiv}CCH_2CH_3$

(f) $(CH_3CH_2)_2C{=}O + NaC{\equiv}CCH{=}CH_2 \longrightarrow (CH_3CH_2)_2\overset{\overset{\displaystyle OH}{|}}{C}C{\equiv}CCH{=}CH_2$

(g) The easiest way to form the carbon-carbon bond in this case would be to use a Grignard reaction:

$$\text{"}HOCH_2CH_2CH_2MgBr\text{"} + H\overset{\overset{\displaystyle O}{\|}}{C}CH_2CH(CH_3)_2 \longrightarrow \xrightarrow{H_2O} HOCH_2CH_2CH_2\overset{\overset{\displaystyle OH}{|}}{C}HCH_2CH(CH_3)_2$$

However, this Grignard reagent cannot be made, because of the presence of a hydroxy group in the molecule.   (A simple proton transfer reaction would

destroy the reagent: $HOCH_2CH_2CH_2MgBr$ $\xrightarrow{fast!}$ $BrMgOCH_2CH_2CH_3$.)

For this reason, we must protect the hydroxy group:

$HOCH_2CH_2CH_2Br$ $\xrightarrow[Et_3N]{Me_3SiCl}$ $Me_3SiOCH_2CH_2CH_2Br$ $\xrightarrow{Mg}$ $Me_3SiOCH_2CH_2CH_2MgBr$ $\xrightarrow{\overset{\overset{O}{\parallel}}{HCCH_2CH(CH_3)_2}}$

$HOCH_2CH_2CH_2\overset{\overset{OH}{|}}{C}HCH_2CH(CH_3)_2$ $\xleftarrow{H_3O^+}$ $Me_3SiOCH_2CH_2CH_2\overset{\overset{OH}{|}}{C}HCH_2CH(CH_3)_2$ $\xleftarrow{H_2O}$

16.F Supplementary Problems

S1. Using monofunctional starting materials having five carbons or less, and any other reagents, outline efficient syntheses of the following compounds.

(a) $(CH_3)_2CHCH_2CH=\overset{\overset{\displaystyle |}{CH_2C(CH_3)_3}}{C}CH_2CH_2CH_2CH_3$

(b) $(CH_3)_2\overset{\overset{Br}{|}}{C}(CH_2)_6\overset{\overset{Br}{|}}{C}(CH_3)_2$

(c) $CH_3CH_2\overset{\overset{\displaystyle |}{CH_2SCH_3}}{C}=CHCH_2CH_3$

(d) $CH_3\overset{\overset{OH}{|}}{C}HCH_2CH_2CH_2\overset{\overset{O}{\parallel}}{C}CH_3$

(e) $(CH_3)_2C=\overset{\overset{\displaystyle CH=CH_2}{|}}{\underset{\displaystyle CH_3}{C}}$

(f) $CD_3\overset{\overset{O}{\parallel}}{C}CH_2CH_2\overset{\overset{O}{\parallel}}{C}CH_3$

(g) $(CH_3)_2CHCH_2CH_2CH_2\overset{\overset{OH}{|}}{C}HCH_2OH$

(h). $\overset{\displaystyle HOCH_2CH_2}{\underset{\displaystyle H}{}}C=C\overset{\displaystyle H}{\underset{\displaystyle CH_2CH_2OH}{}}$

(i) $\overset{Br \quad CHBrCH_3}{\text{(cyclopentane ring)}}$

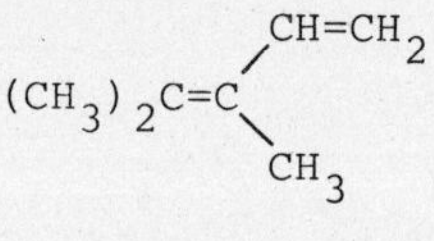

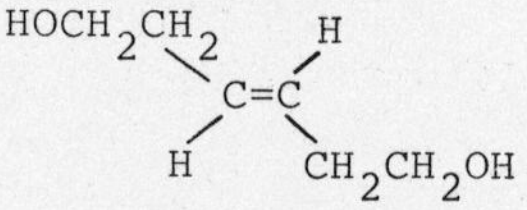

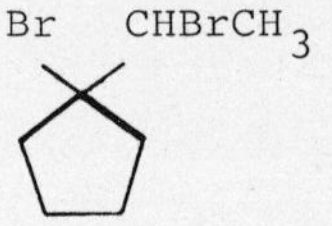

(j) $((CH_3)_2CHCH_2)_2CHCN$

(k) $CH_3C(CH_2Br)_3$

(l) $CH_3CH_2CH_2\overset{\overset{\displaystyle H\cdots OH}{}}{\underset{\displaystyle HO\cdots H}{C}}CH_2CH_2CH_3$

(m)   (cyclopropane ring with CH_3 CH_3 and CH_2OCH_3)

(n)   (cyclopentane ring with CH_3 and $\overset{\overset{O}{\parallel}}{C}CH_3$)

(o) $CH_3CH_2\overset{\overset{\displaystyle CO_2H}{|}}{\underset{\displaystyle OH}{C}}CH_2CH_2CH_3$

(p) $\overset{\displaystyle CH_3CH_2}{\underset{\displaystyle Cl}{}}C=C\overset{\displaystyle H}{\underset{\displaystyle CH_2CH_3}{}}$

(q)   (cyclopentane ring with $=C(CH_3)CH_3$ and OCH_2CH_3)

(r) $\overset{\displaystyle D}{\underset{\displaystyle H}{}}C=C\overset{\displaystyle H}{\underset{\displaystyle CH_2CH_2CH_2CH_3}{}}$

(s) $CH_2=CHCH_2CH_2-$ (cyclobutane ring)

(t)   (cyclopentene ring with $CH_2CH_2CH_3$ and $CH_2CH_2CH_3$)

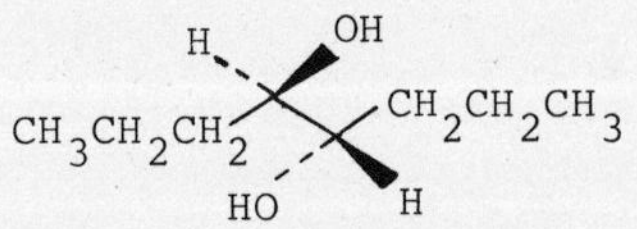

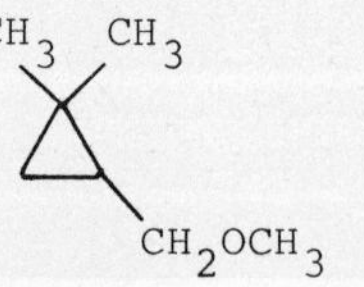

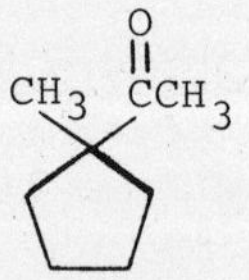

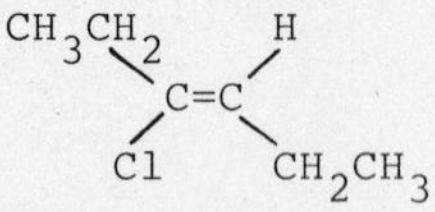

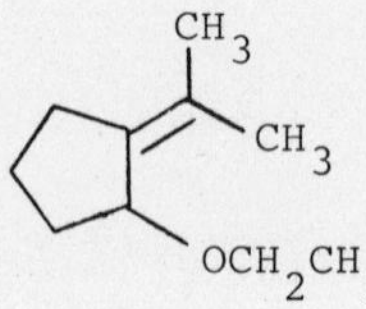

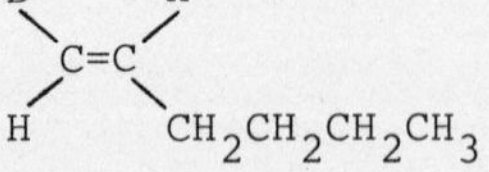

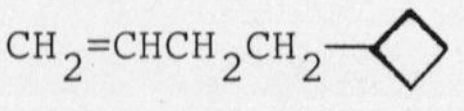

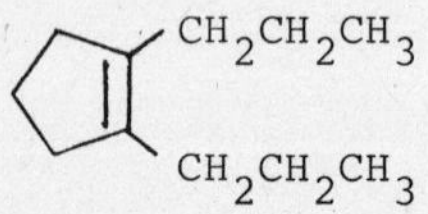

(u) $(CH_3CH_2)_2CHC\equiv CCH(CH_2CH_3)_2$

(v) $HON=CHCH_2CH_2CH_2CH=NOH$

(w)   (bicyclic ring with CH_2CH_3 and $C\overset{\displaystyle Cl}{\underset{\displaystyle Cl}{}}$)

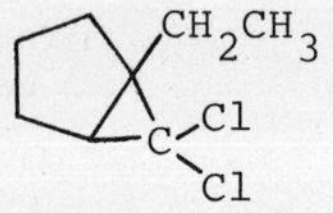

(x)

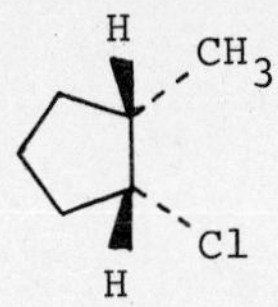

(y)

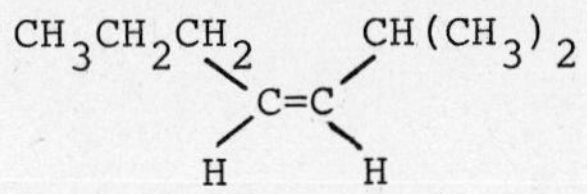

$$CH_3CH_2CH_2 \quad CH(CH_3)_2$$
$$C=C$$
$$H \qquad\qquad H$$

(z) $(CH_3)_2CHCH_2\overset{OH}{\underset{|}{CH}}-\overset{OH}{\underset{|}{\underset{CH_2CH_2CH_3}{C}}}-\overset{OH}{\underset{|}{CH}}CH_2CH_2CH_2CH_3$

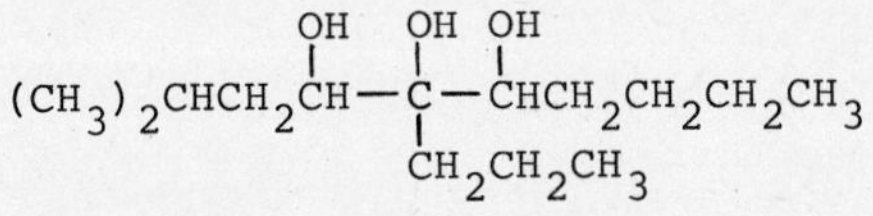

16.G   Answers to Supplementary Problems

S1. (a) $(CH_3)_2CHCH_2CH=\overset{\underset{|}{CH_2C(CH_3)_3}}{C}CH_2CH_2CH_2CH_3 \longleftarrow (CH_3)_2CHCH_2CH=P(C_6H_5)_3 + \overset{O}{\overset{\|}{C}}\overset{\underset{|}{CH_2C(CH_3)_3}}{}CH_2CH_2CH_2CH_3$

$\uparrow$ $\underline{n}$-$BuLi$

$\uparrow$ $(C_6H_5)_3P$

$(CH_3)_2CHCH_2CH_2Br$

$K_2Cr_2O_7 \,\Big|\, H_2SO_4$ $\uparrow$

$(CH_3)_3CCH_2MgBr + \overset{O}{\overset{\|}{H}C}CH_2CH_2CH_2CH_3 \xrightarrow{\quad} \xrightarrow{H_2O} (CH_3)_3CCH_2\overset{OH}{\underset{|}{CH}}CH_2CH_2CH_2CH_3$

(b) $(CH_3)_2\overset{Br}{\underset{|}{C}}(CH_2)_6\overset{Br}{\underset{|}{C}}(CH_3)_2 \xleftarrow[h\nu]{2\ Br_2} (CH_3)_2CH(CH_2)_6CH(CH_3)_2 \xleftarrow[Pt]{H_2}$

$\longrightarrow NaC\equiv CNa \xrightarrow{2\ (CH_3)_2CHCH_2CH_2Br} (CH_3)_2CHCH_2CH_2C\equiv CCH_2CH_2CH(CH_3)_2$

$HC\equiv CH + 2\ NaNH_2$

(c) $CH_3CH_2\overset{}{\underset{\underset{CH_2SCH_3}{|}}{C}}=CHCH_2CH_2CH_3 \xleftarrow{NaSCH_3} CH_3CH_2\overset{}{\underset{\underset{CH_2Br}{|}}{C}}=CHCH_2CH_2CH_3 \xleftarrow{PBr_3} CH_3CH_2\overset{}{\underset{\underset{CH_2OH}{|}}{C}}=CHCH_2CH_2CH_3$

$NaBH_4 \uparrow$

$2\ CH_3CH_2CH_2\overset{O}{\overset{\|}{C}}H \xrightarrow[\Delta]{NaOH} CH_3CH_2\overset{}{\underset{\underset{O=CH}{|}}{C}}=CHCH_2CH_2CH_3$

(d) $CH_3\overset{OH}{\underset{|}{CH}}CH_2CH_2\overset{O}{\overset{\|}{C}}CH_3 \longleftarrow CH_3\overset{O}{\overset{\triangle}{CH}CH_2} + CH_2=\overset{OLi}{\underset{|}{C}}CH_3 \xleftarrow[\substack{THF \\ -78^\circ\ C}]{LDA} CH_3\overset{O}{\overset{\|}{C}}CH_3$

(e) $(CH_3)_2C=\overset{\underset{\underset{CH_3}{|}}{CH=CH_2}}{C} \xleftarrow[-H_2O]{H_2SO_4} (CH_3)_2\overset{\underset{\underset{CH_3}{|}}{OH}}{CH}CH=CH_2 \xleftarrow{H_2O}$

$\uparrow$

$(CH_3)_2CH\overset{O}{\overset{\|}{C}}CH_3 + BrMgCH=CH_2$

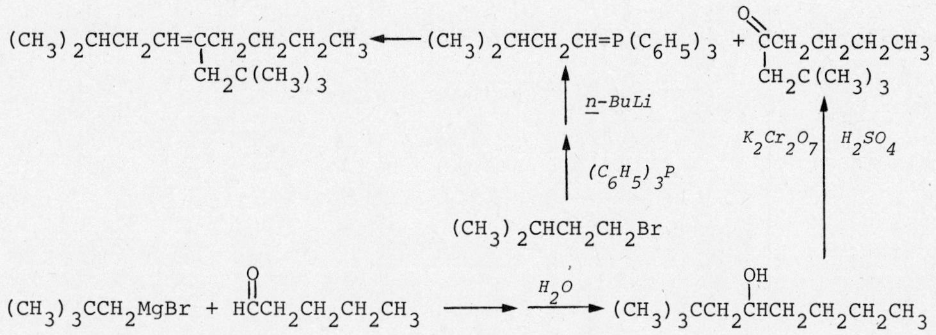

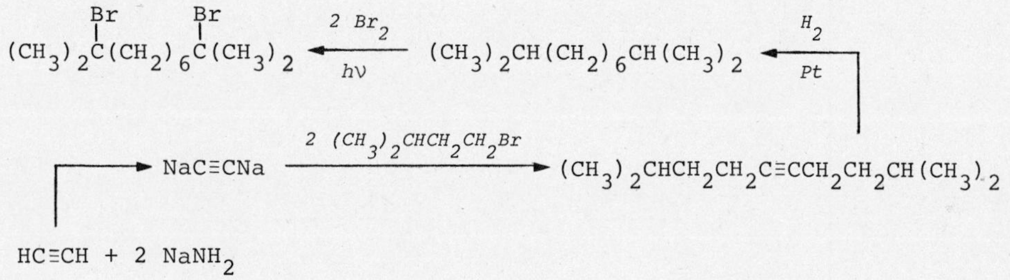

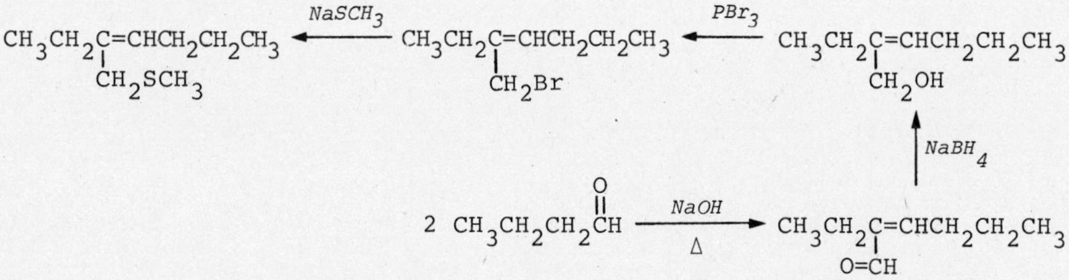

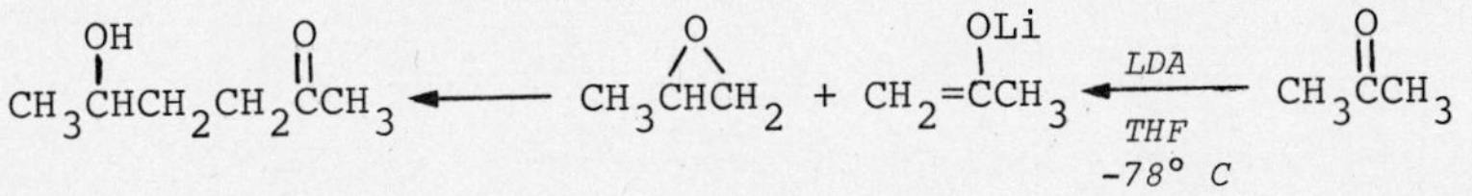

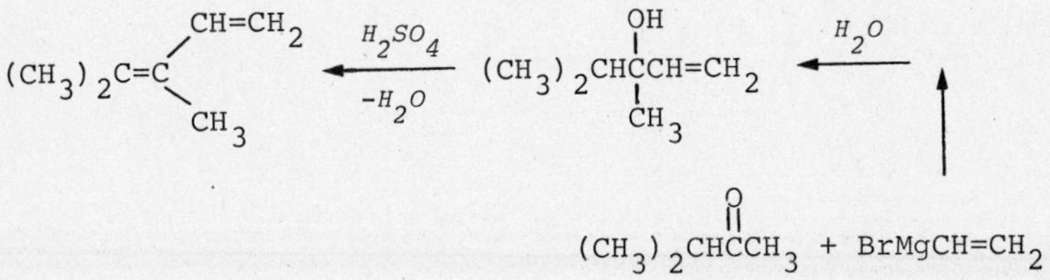

(f) $CD_3CCH_2CH_2CCH_3$ $\xrightarrow[pyridine]{CrO_3}$ $CD_3CHCH_2CH_2CHCH_3$ $\xleftarrow[Pt]{H_2}$ $CD_3CHC=CCHCH_3$

(the two left carbonyls and the center OH/OH groups)

$CD_3CHC=CCHCH_3$ (with OH, OH) $\xleftarrow{H_2O}$

CH_3CH (O) $\xrightarrow[D_2O]{D^+}$ CD_3CH (O)

$HC\equiv CNa$ $\xrightarrow{HCCH_3 \ (O)}$ $HC\equiv CCHCH_3$ (ONa) $\xrightarrow{NaNH_2}$ $NaC\equiv CCHCH_3$ (ONa)

(g) $(CH_3)_2CHCH_2CH_2CH_2CHCH_2OH$ (OH) $\xleftarrow[H_2O_2]{OsO_4}$ $(CH_3)_2CHCH_2CH_2CH_2CH=CH_2$ $\xleftarrow[\text{poisoned Pd catalyst}]{H_2}$

$(CH_3)_2CHCH_2CH_2C\equiv CCH_3$ $\xrightarrow[\Delta]{NaNH_2}$ $(CH_3)_2CHCH_2CH_2CH_2C\equiv CNa$ $\xrightarrow{H_2O}$ $(CH_3)_2CHCH_2CH_2CH_2C\equiv CH$

$(CH_3)_2CHCH_2CH_2Br + NaC\equiv CCH_3$

(h) $HOCH_2CH_2$ \ / H (C=C) H / \ CH_2CH_2OH $\xleftarrow[NH_3]{Na}$ $HOCH_2CH_2C\equiv CCH_2CH_2OH$ $\xleftarrow{}$ $2\ CH_2-CH_2$ (O) $+ NaC\equiv CNa$

$2\ NaNH_2 \uparrow$

$HC\equiv CH$

(i) Br, CHBrCH$_3$ on cyclopentane ring $\xleftarrow[CCl_4]{Br_2}$ H, CH_3 (=CH$_3$) cyclopentane $\xleftarrow{}$ cyclopentanone $+ CH_3CH=P(C_6H_5)_3$ $\xleftarrow[2.\ \underline{n}\text{-BuLi}]{1.\ P(C_6H_5)_3}$ CH_3CH_2Br

(j) $((CH_3)_2CHCH_2)_2CHCN$ $\xleftarrow{NaCN}$ $((CH_3)_2CHCH_2)_2CHBr$ $\xleftarrow{PBr_3}$

$(CH_3)_2CHCH_2CH$ (O) $+ BrMgCH_2CH(CH_3)_2$ $\xrightarrow{}$ $\xrightarrow{H_2O}$ $((CH_3)_2CHCH_2)_2CHOH$

(k) $CH_3C(CH_2Br)_3$ $\xleftarrow{3\ PBr_3}$ $CH_3C(CH_2OH)_3$ $\xleftarrow{NaOH,\ CH_2O}$ CH_3CH (O)

(l) $CH_3CH_2CH_2$ (H, OH / HO, H) C $CH_2CH_2CH_3$ $\xleftarrow{H_3O^+}$ $CH_3CH_2CH_2$ epoxide $CH_2CH_2CH_3$ (H) $\xleftarrow{CH_3CO_3H}$

$CH_3CH_2CH_2C\equiv CCH_2CH_2CH_3$ $\xrightarrow{Na/NH_3}$ $CH_3CH_2CH_2$ (H) C=C (H) $CH_2CH_2CH_3$

$NaC\equiv CNa + 2\ CH_3CH_2CH_2Br$

(m) $CH_3\ CH_3$ cyclopropane with CH_2OCH_3 $\xleftarrow[Zn-Cu]{CH_2I_2}$ $(CH_3)_2C=CHCH_2OCH_3$ $\xleftarrow{}$ $(CH_3)_3C=CHCH_2Br + NaOCH_3$

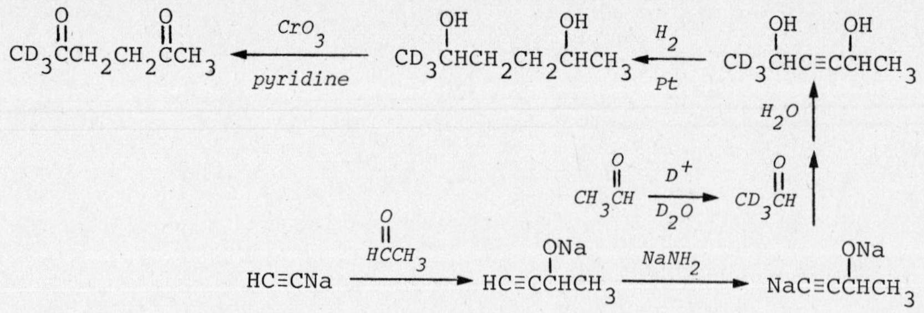

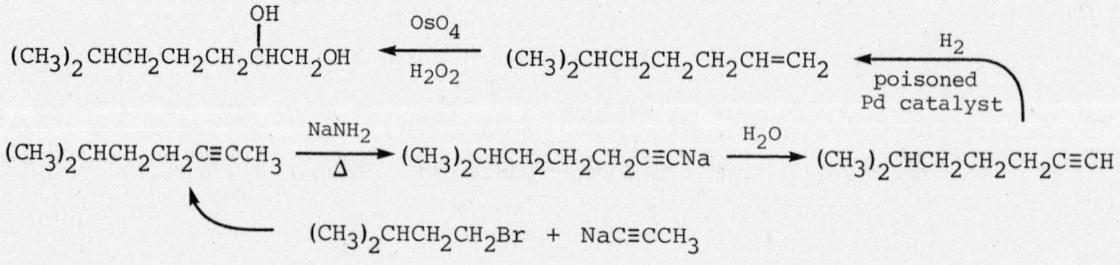

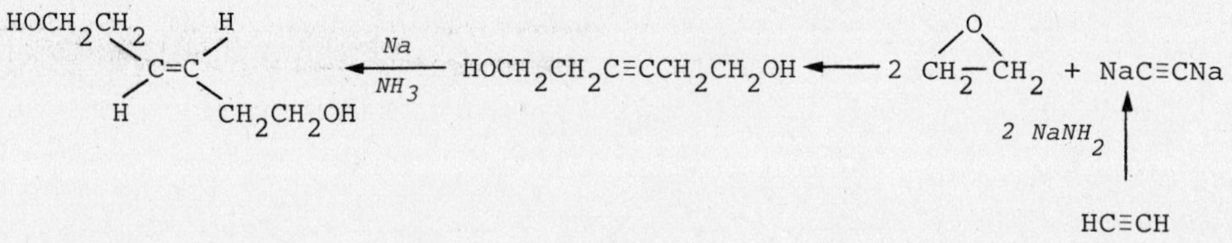

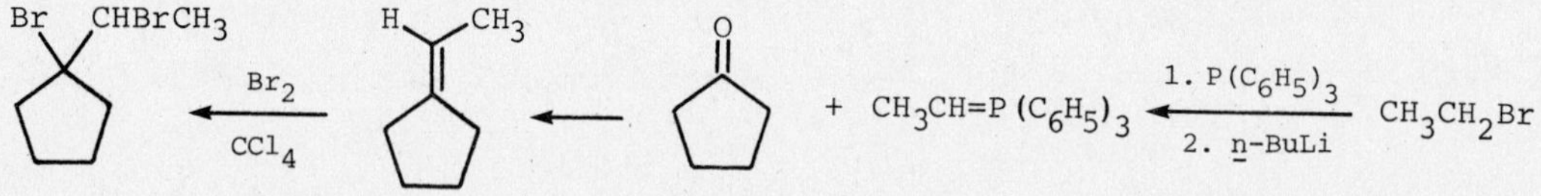

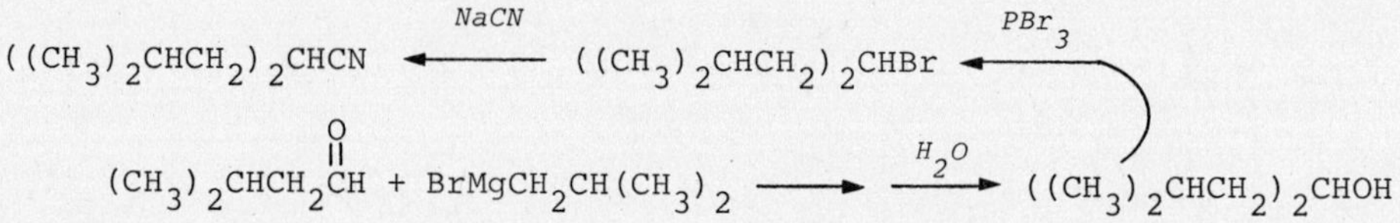

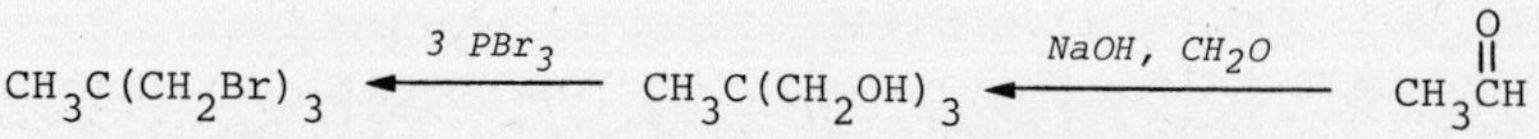

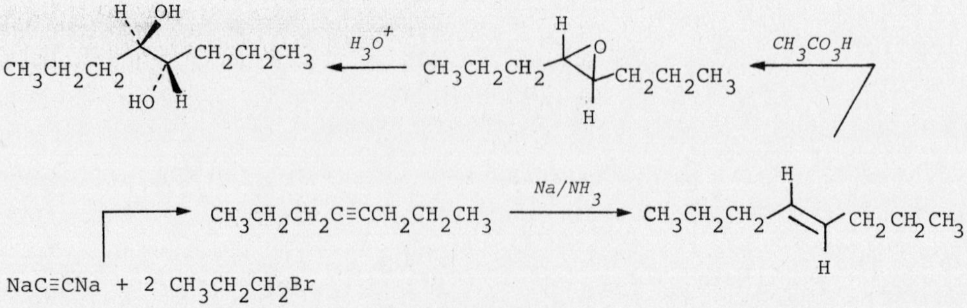

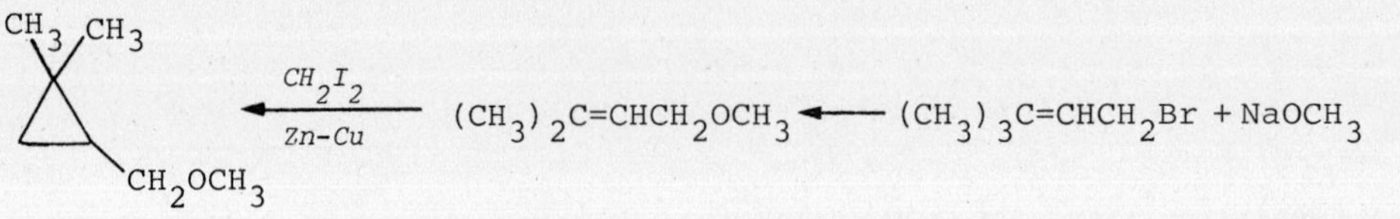

(n) $\underset{CH_3}{\overset{O}{\parallel}}CCH_3$ $\xrightarrow[pyridine]{CrO_3}$ $\underset{CH_3}{\overset{OH}{\mid}}CHCH_3$ $\xleftarrow[]{H_2O}$ $\xleftarrow[]{\overset{O}{\parallel}{CH_3CH}}$ $CH_3\ MgBr$ $\xleftarrow{Mg}$ $\xleftarrow{HBr}$

$CH_3MgI +$ $\overset{O}{\bigcirc}$ $\longrightarrow$ $\xrightarrow{H_2O}$ $\underset{}{\overset{CH_3\ OH}{\bigcirc}}$

(o) $\underset{OH}{\overset{CO_2H}{CH_3CH_2\overset{\mid}{\underset{\mid}{C}}CH_2CH_2CH_3}}$ $\xleftarrow[\Delta]{H_3O^+}$ $\underset{OH}{\overset{CN}{CH_3CH_2\overset{\mid}{\underset{\mid}{C}}CH_2CH_2CH_3}}$ $\xleftarrow{HCN}$ $\overset{O}{\overset{\parallel}{CH_3CH_2CCH_2CH_2CH_3}}$

$\qquad\qquad\qquad\qquad\qquad\qquad\qquad\qquad\qquad\qquad\qquad\qquad\qquad\qquad K_2Cr_2O_7 \mid H_2SO_4$

$CH_3CH_2MgBr + \overset{O}{\overset{\parallel}{HCCH_2CH_2CH_3}}$

$\underline{or}$ $\qquad\qquad\qquad\qquad\qquad\qquad$ $\xrightarrow{H_2O}$ $\underset{OH}{\overset{}{CH_3CH_2\overset{\mid}{C}HCH_2CH_2CH_3}}$

$\overset{O}{\overset{\parallel}{CH_3CH_2CH}} + BrMgCH_2CH_2CH_3$

(p) $\underset{Cl}{\overset{CH_3CH_2}{\diagdown}}C=C\underset{CH_2CH_3}{\overset{H}{\diagup}}$ $\xleftarrow{KOt\text{-}Bu}$ $\underset{H}{\overset{CH_3CH_2}{\diagdown}}\overset{\diagup Cl}{\underset{\diagdown Cl}{C-C}}\underset{CH_2CH_2CH_3}{\diagup}$ $\xleftarrow[CCl_4]{Cl_2}$ $\underset{H}{\overset{CH_3CH_2}{\diagdown}}C=C\underset{H}{\overset{CH_2CH_3}{\diagup}}$

$\qquad\qquad\qquad\qquad\qquad\qquad\qquad\qquad\qquad\qquad\qquad\qquad\qquad\qquad H_2$

$NaC{\equiv}CNa + 2\ CH_3CH_2Br \longrightarrow CH_3CH_2C{\equiv}CCH_2CH_3$

(q) $\underset{OCH_3}{\overset{\overset{\textstyle CH_3}{\diagup}C{\diagdown}CH_3}{\bigcirc}}$ $\xleftarrow{(CH_3)_2C=P(C_6H_5)_3}$ $\underset{OCH_3}{\overset{O}{\bigcirc}}$ $\xleftarrow[H_2SO_4]{K_2Cr_2O_7}$ $\underset{OCH_3}{\overset{OH}{\bigcirc}}$ $\xleftarrow[H^+]{CH_3OH}$ $\overset{}{\bigcirc}{O}$

$\qquad\qquad\qquad\qquad\qquad \xleftarrow{nBuLi}\ \xleftarrow{P(C_6H_5)_3}\ CH_3CHICH_3$

(r) $\underset{H}{\overset{D}{\diagdown}}C=C\underset{CH_2CH_2CH_2CH_3}{\overset{H}{\diagup}}$ $\xleftarrow[\Delta]{CH_3CO_2D}$ $\underset{H}{\overset{R_2B}{\diagdown}}C=C\underset{CH_2CH_2CH_2CH_3}{\overset{H}{\diagup}}$ $\xleftarrow{B_2H_6}$

$HC{\equiv}CNa + BrCH_2CH_2CH_2CH_3 \longrightarrow HC{\equiv}CCH_2CH_2CH_2CH_3$

(s) $CH_2{=}CHCH_2CH_2{-}\square$ $\xleftarrow[\Delta]{Al_2O_3}$ $HOCH_2CH_2CH_2CH_2{-}\square$ $\xleftarrow{H_2O}$ $\xleftarrow{\overset{O}{\triangle}}$

$BrMg{-}\square$ $\xrightarrow{\overset{O}{\triangle}}$ $\xrightarrow{H_2O}$ $HOCH_2CH_2{-}\square$ $\xrightarrow{PBr_3}$ $\xrightarrow{Mg}$ $BrMgCH_2CH_2{-}\square$

$\uparrow{Mg}$

$Br{-}\square$

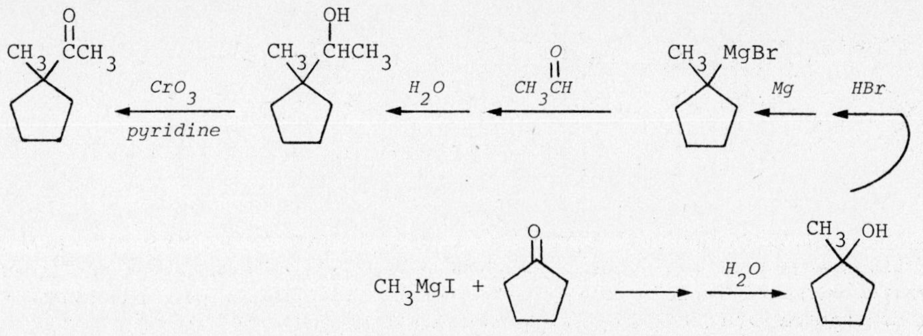

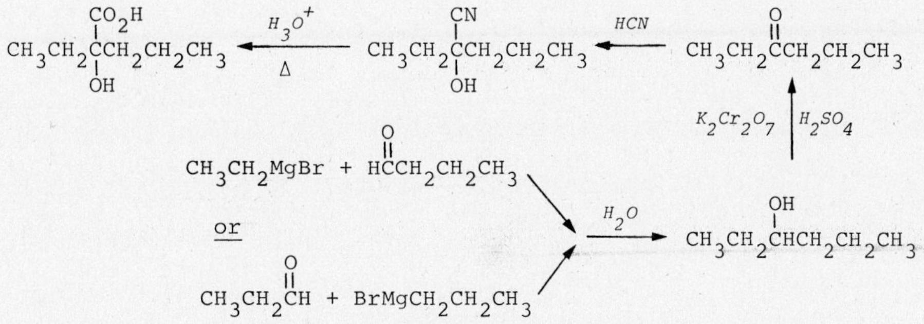

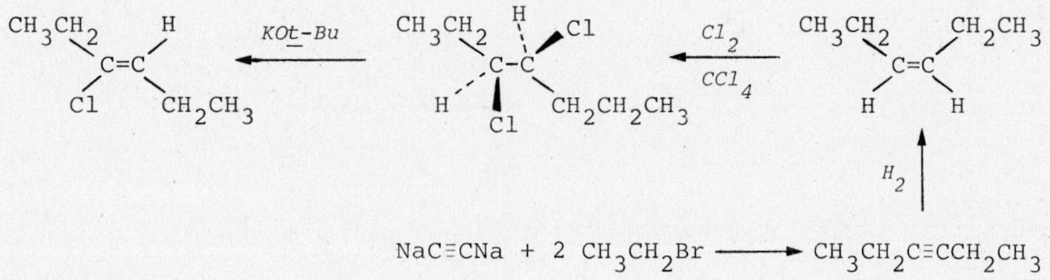

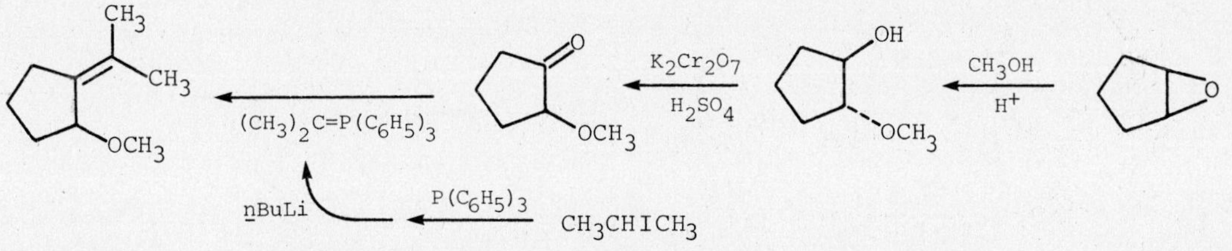

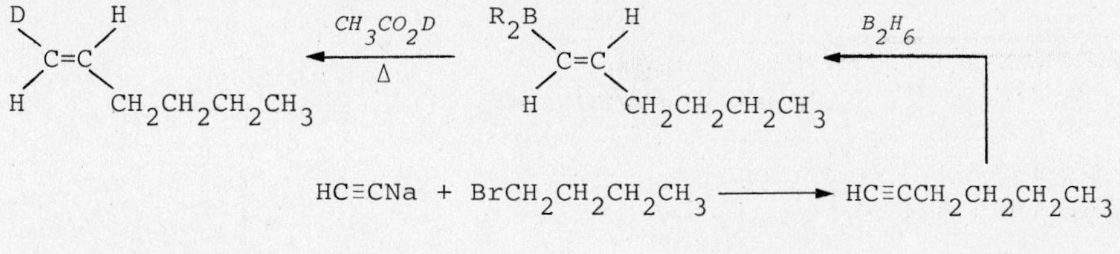

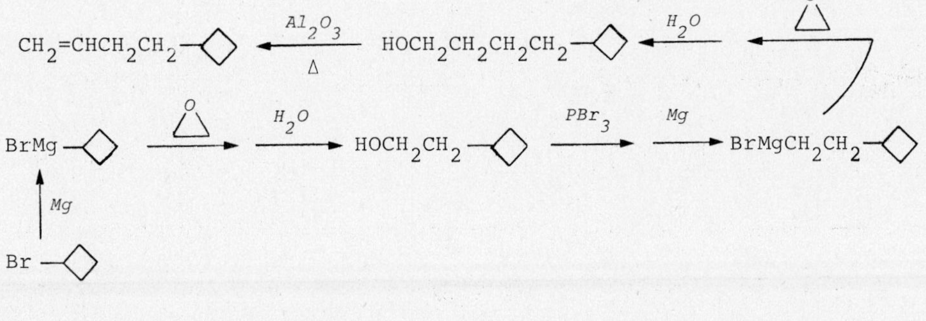

(t) [structure: cyclopentene with CH₂CH₂CH₃ groups] $\xleftarrow{H_2SO_4}$ [structure: cyclopentanol with OH, CH₂CH₂CH₃, and CH₂CH₂CH₃] $\xleftarrow{H_2O}$ $\xleftarrow{BrMgCH_2CH_2CH_3}$

[cyclopentanone structure] $\xrightarrow[\substack{THF \\ -78°\ C}]{LDA}$ [structure with OLi] $\xrightarrow{BrCH_2CH_2CH_3}$ [cyclopentanone with CH₂CH₂CH₃]

(u) $(CH_3CH_2)_2CHC{\equiv}CCH(CH_2CH_3)_2$ $\xleftarrow{NaNH_2}$ $(CH_3CH_2)_2CHCHCHCH(CH_2CH_3)_2$ (with Br above and Br below) $\xleftarrow[CCl_4]{Br_2}$

$(CH_3CH_2)_2CHCH{=}CHCH(CH_2CH_3)_2$

$\xrightarrow{CrO_3,\ pyridine}$ $(CH_3CH_2)_2CHCH{=}O$

$+$

$\xrightarrow{CH_2=O}$ $\xrightarrow{H_2O}$ $(CH_3CH_2)_2CHCH_2OH$

$(CH_3CH_2)_2CHCH{=}P(C_6H_5)_3$

$(CH_3CH_2)_2CHMgBr$ 1. PBr_3
                         2. $(C_6H_3)_3P$

(v) $HON{=}CHCH_2CH_2CH_2CH{=}NOH$ $\xleftarrow[H^+]{2\ H_2NOH}$ $\overset{O}{\overset{\|}{H}}CCH_2CH_2CH_2C\overset{O}{\overset{\|}{H}}$ $\xleftarrow[2.\ Zn]{1.\ O_3}$ [cyclopentene structure]

(w) [bicyclic structure with CH₂CH₃, CH₃, CCl₂] $\xleftarrow[NaOH]{HCCl_3}$ [cyclopentene with CH₂CH₃] $\xleftarrow[\Delta]{H_2SO_4}$ [cyclopentanol with OH, CH₂CH₃] $\xleftarrow[2.\ H_2O]{1.\ BrMgCH_2CH_3}$ [cyclopentanone structure]

(x) [cyclopentane with H, CH₃, Cl, H] $\xleftarrow{PCl_3}$ [cyclopentane with H, CH₃, OH, H] $\xleftarrow{H_2O}$ $\xleftarrow{CH_3Li}$ [epoxide cyclopentane structure]

  $\uparrow$

1. B_2H_6 | 2. $H_2O_2,\ OH^-$

[cyclopentene with CH₃] $\xleftarrow[\Delta]{H_2SO_4}$ $\xleftarrow{CH_3MgI}$ [cyclopentanone structure]

(y) [alkene: CH₃CH₂CH₂ and CH(CH₃)₂ on C=C with H, H] $\xleftarrow{H_2}$ $CH_3CH_2CH_2C{\equiv}CCH(CH_3)_2$ $\longleftarrow$

$CH_3CH_2CH_2Br\ +\ NaC{\equiv}CCH(CH_3)_2$

(z) $(CH_3)_2CHCH_2\overset{OH}{C}H{-}\overset{OH}{\underset{CH_2CH_2CH_3}{C}}{-}\overset{OH}{C}HCH_2CH_2CH_2CH_3$ $\xleftarrow[H_2O_2]{OsO_4}$ $(CH_3)_2CHCH_2\overset{OH}{C}HC{=}CHCH_2CH_2CH_2CH_3$ (with CH₂CH₂CH₃ below)

$\uparrow H_2O$

$2\ CH_3CH_2CH_2CH_2C\overset{O}{\overset{\|}{H}}$ $\xrightarrow[\Delta]{NaOH}$ $HC\overset{O}{\overset{\|}{C}}{=}CHCH_2CH_2CH_3$ (with CH₂CH₂CH₃ below) $\xrightarrow{(CH_3)_2CHCH_2MgBr}$

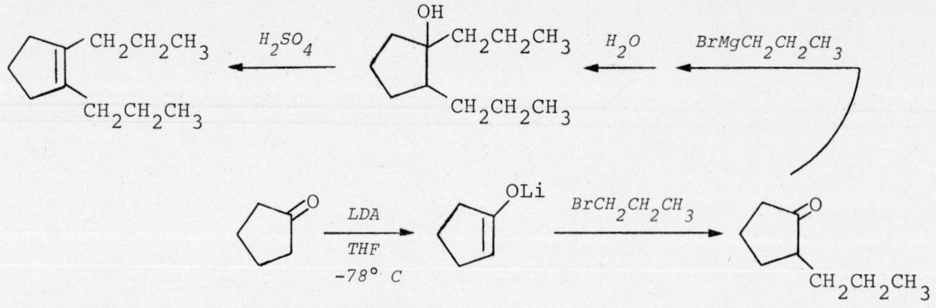

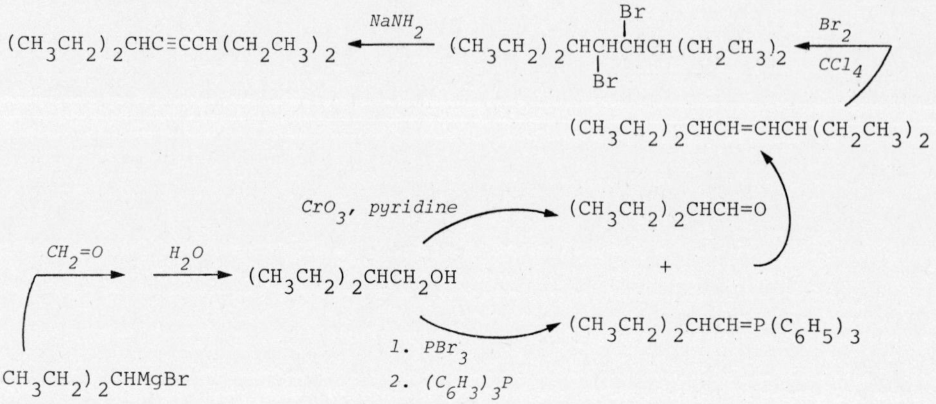

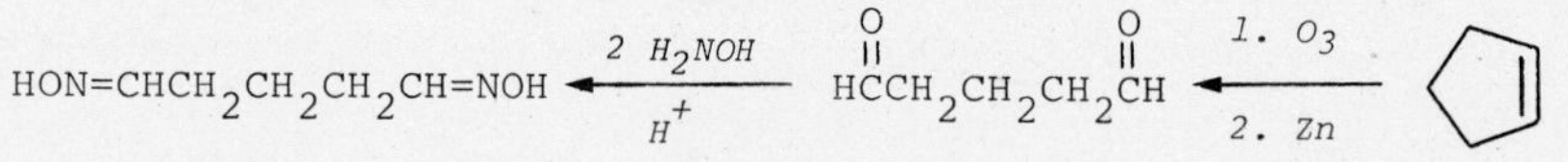

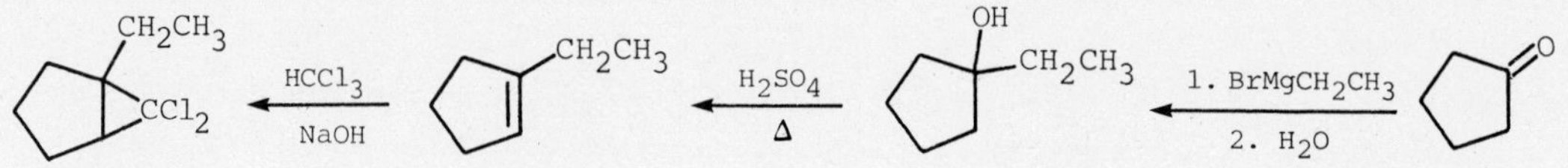

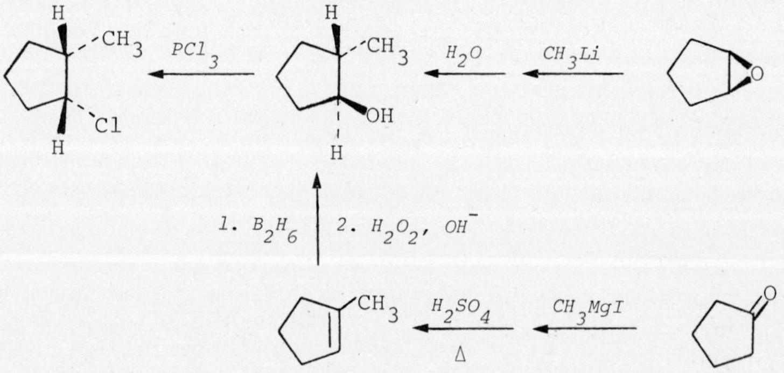

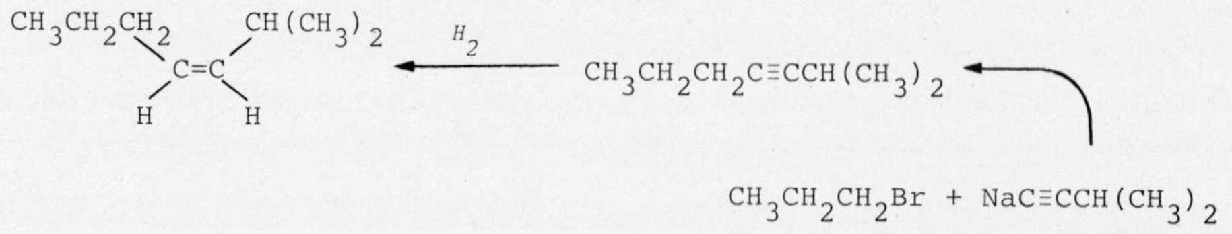

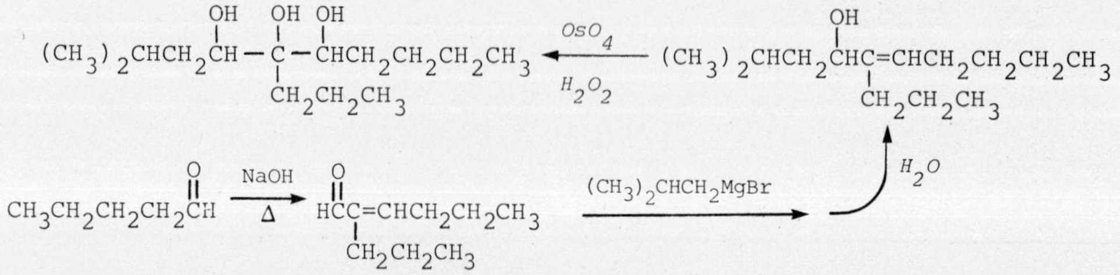

17. CARBOXYLIC ACIDS

17.A Chapter Outline and Important Terms Introduced

17.1 <u>Structure</u>
  carboxy group

17.2 <u>Nomenclature</u>
  -oic acid   1,2,3,... vs. α,β,γ,...

17.3 <u>Physical Properties</u>

17.4 <u>Acidity</u> (pK_a of acetic acid = 4.7)

  A. Ionization
        conjugated system   resonance stabilization
  B. Inductive Effects
  C. Salt Formation
        -ate
  D. Soaps
        micelle   alkanesulfonates
        biodegradable

17.5 <u>Spectroscopy</u>

  A. Nuclear Magnetic Resonance
        CH_3CO_2H 2 ppm CH_3CO_2H 10-13 ppm
  B. Infrared
        C=O 1710-1760 cm^{-1} O-H 2400-3400 cm^{-1}

17.6 <u>Synthesis</u>

  A. Hydrolysis of Nitriles
        acid- or base-catalyzed
  B. Carbonation of Organometallic Reagents
  C. Oxidation of Primary Alcohols or Aldehydes

17.7 <u>Reactions</u>

  A. Reactions Involving the O-H Bond
        esterification with diazomethane
        alkylation of salts
  B. Reactions Involving the Hydrocarbon Side Chain
        bromination of α-position
  C. Formation of Esters
        esterification (<— **important mechanism**)
        tetrahedral intermediate
  D. Formation of Acyl Halides
  E. Reaction with Ammonia: Formation of Amides
  F. Reduction of the Carboxy Group
  G. One-Carbon Degradation of Carboxylic Acids
        Hunsdiecker reaction   Kochi reaction

17.8 <u>Natural Occurrence of Carboxylic Acids</u>

17.B Important Reactions Introduced

<u>Hydrolysis of nitriles</u> (17.6.A)

Equation:

$$R-C{\equiv}N \;+\; H_2O \xrightarrow[\text{}]{\text{catalysis}} R\overset{\overset{\displaystyle O}{\|}}{C}-NH_2 \longrightarrow RCO_2H \;+\; NH_3$$

Generality: R = alkyl, aryl

Key features: acid- or base-catalyzed, heat required
                reaction can be stopped at amide intermediate

Reaction of organometallic reagents with carbon dioxide   (17.6.B)

Equation:
$$R\text{-}M + CO_2 \longrightarrow RCO_2^-M^+ \xrightarrow{H^+} RCO_2H$$

Generality: R = alkyl, aryl; M = Li or MgX

Key features: useful synthesis of carboxylic acids

Oxidation of primary alcohols (or aldehydes) to carboxylic acids   (17.6.C)

Equation:
$$R\text{-}CH_2OH \xrightarrow{[Ox]} [R\text{-}CH\text{=}O] \xrightarrow{[Ox]} RCO_2H$$

Generality: $[Ox] = KMnO_4$, aq. Cr^{+6}, HNO_3

Key features: often a side reaction in oxidation of 1° alcohols to aldehydes

Esterification of carboxylic acids with diazomethane   (17.7.A)

Equation: $RCO_2H + CH_2N_2 \longrightarrow RCO_2CH_3 + N_2$

Generality: R = alkyl, aryl, H, etc.

Key features: useful and convenient on small scale
                dangerous on large scale (diazomethane is toxic and explosive)

Alkylation of carboxylate anions   (17.7.A)

Equation: $RCO_2^-M^+ + R'\text{-}X \longrightarrow RCO_2\text{-}R' + M^+X^-$

Generality: R' = alkyl

Key features: typical S_N2 displacement reaction (R' = 1° > 2° >> 3° alkyl)
                useful method for replacing R'-X bond with O-R bond with inversion

α-Halogenation of carboxylic acids   (17.7.B)

Equation:
$$RCH_2CO_2H + X_2 \xrightarrow{PX_3} RCHXCO_2H$$

Generality: X = Cl, Br

Key features: reaction occurs via enol of intermediate acyl halide

Esterification of carboxylic acids   (17.7.C)

Equation:
$$RCO_2H + HOR' \xrightleftharpoons{H^+} RCO_2R' + H_2O$$

Generality: R' = alkyl

Key features: mechanism is important to know (addition/elimination reaction)
                acid-catalyzed equilibrium process, often driven to product by removal of water
                oxygen in H_2O product comes from the carboxylic acid OH

Formation of acyl halides   (17.7.D)

Equation:
$$RCO_2H \xrightarrow{[reagent]} RCOX$$

Generality: R = alkyl, aryl; [reagent] = $SOCl_2$, PCl_3, PBr_3, PCl_5

Amide formation from ammonium carboxylate salts (17.7.E)

Equation: $RCO_2H + H_3N \longrightarrow RCO_2^-NH_4^+ \xrightarrow{\Delta} RCONH_2 + H_2O$

Generality: carboxylic acid must be stable to heat

Key features: not commonly used; employed only for simple cases

Reaction of carboxylic acids and esters with lithium aluminum hydride (LiAlH$_4$) (17.7.F)

Equation: $RCO_2R' + LiAlH_4 \longrightarrow RCH_2OH + R'OH$

Generality: R = alkyl, aryl; R' = alkyl, aryl, or H

Degradation of carboxylic acids to alkyl halides (17.7.G)

Equation: $RCO_2H \longrightarrow R-X + CO_2$

Generality: reagent = Br_2 with Ag^+ or Hg^{++} salt of acid (Hunsdiecker reaction)
                         $Pb(OAc)_4 + LiCl$ (Kochi reaction)

Key features: proceeds via $RCO_2\cdot$ and $R\cdot$ radicals

17.C   Important Concepts and Hints

An important new type of reaction mechanism is introduced in this chapter: the nucleophilic displacement of a substituent on a carbonyl group. The acid-catalyzed formation of an ester from a carboxylic acid and an alcohol is the most important example of this type. The mechanism involves first **addition** of the nucleophile to the carbon-oxygen double bond, and then **elimination** of the leaving group to regenerate the carbonyl group. The full scope of this substitution mechanism will become apparent in the following chapter, when it will be discussed at length. For the moment, you should examine closely the comparison of the esterification reaction and the formation, then decomposition of a hemiketal. It's a good analogy, and it helps tie this new mechanism in with one you've seen before.

Aside from that, no other new concepts are introduced in this chapter. The effects of electron-withdrawing substituents on acidity was presented in the chapter on alcohols (Section 10.4), and the synthetic reactions which lead to carboxylic acids have been introduced previously. Although the reactions of carboxylic acids are for the most part new, their mechanisms involve the nucleophilic displacement, enolization, or carbonyl-addition mechanisms you have seen before. Consequently there is little else for us to comment on in this section of the Study Guide. This situation will become more common in subsequent chapters of this book, although we will still make (hopefully) helpful comments where appropriate.

17.D   Answers to Exercises

17.1   (a) 5-chloropentanoic acid   (c) 2-iodo-4-methylhexanoic acid
            (b) 5,5-dimethylhexanoic acid   (d) 2,4-pentadienoic acid
                                                              (or penta-2,4-dienoic acid)

17.3 $pK_a = -\log K_a = 3.75$

$$\frac{[H^+][HCO_2^-]}{[HCO_2H]} = 1.77 \times 10^{-4} \qquad [H^+] = [HCO_2^-] = x; \qquad [HCO_2H] = 0.1 - x$$

$$\frac{x^2}{0.1 - x} = 1.77 \times 10^{-4}; \qquad x = [HCO_2^-] = 4.12 \times 10^{-3} \underline{M}$$

17.4

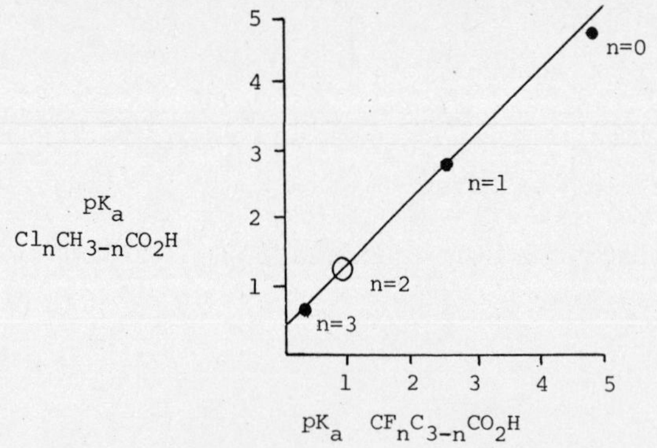

pK_a predicted for $F_2CHCO_2H = 0.9$

17.5 $K = \dfrac{[RCO_2^-]}{[RCO_2H][OH^-]} = 1.3 \times 10^9 \ M^{-1}$

pH	$[OH^-]$	Ratio: $[RCO_2^-]/[RCO_2H]$
2	10^{-12}	1.3×10^{-3}
4	10^{-10}	0.13
6	10^{-8}	13
8	10^{-6}	1300

17.6   2,2-Dimethylbutanoic acid:

NMR (CMR):   δ 0.95 (9.5) ⟶

1.25 (24.8)

CH_3

$CH_3 — CH_2 — C — CO_2H$ ⟵ 12.5

1.50 (33.7) ⟶

CH_3

(43.0)

(182.2)

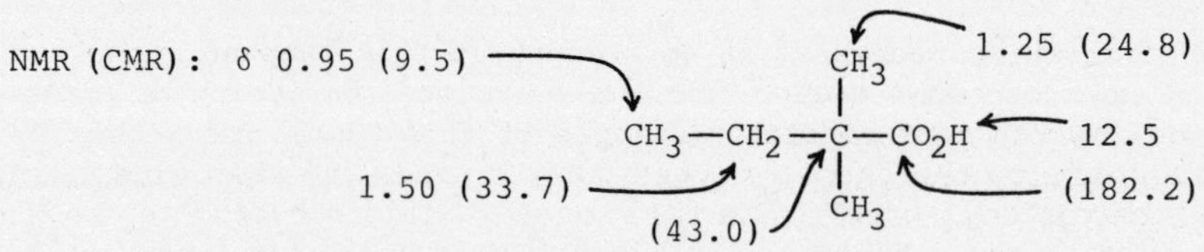

17.7   (b) and (d)   2-Methylpentanoic acid and 7-methyloctanoic acid can be prepared by this route:

$\xrightarrow{\text{NaCN}} \xrightarrow{\text{H}_3\text{O}^+}$ (structures)

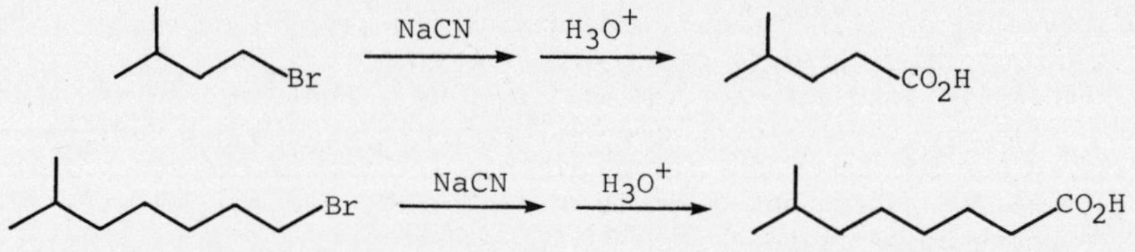

(a) and (c)   2,2-Dimethylpropanoic acid and 1-methylcyclohexanecarboxylic acid **cannot** be prepared via the alkylation of cyanide ion with a tertiary halide; cyanide ion is too basic, and elimination is the major reaction:

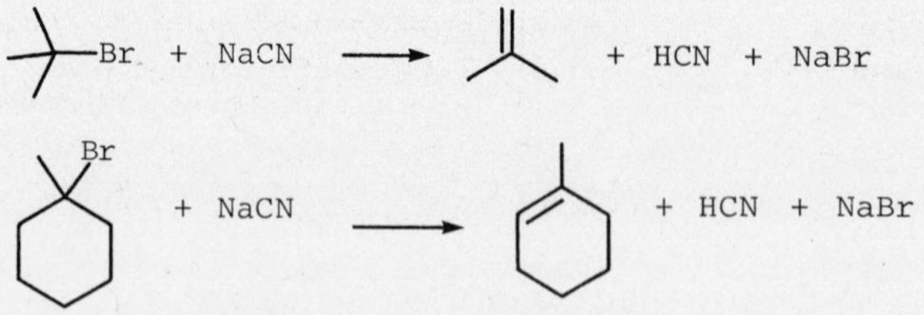

—Br + NaCN ⟶ + HCN + NaBr

+ NaCN ⟶ + HCN + NaBr

17.8

(a) $\xleftarrow[\text{2. H}^+]{\text{1. CO}_2}$ $\xleftarrow{\text{Mg}}$ $\xleftarrow{\text{HCl}}$ $\xleftarrow{\text{MeMgI}}$

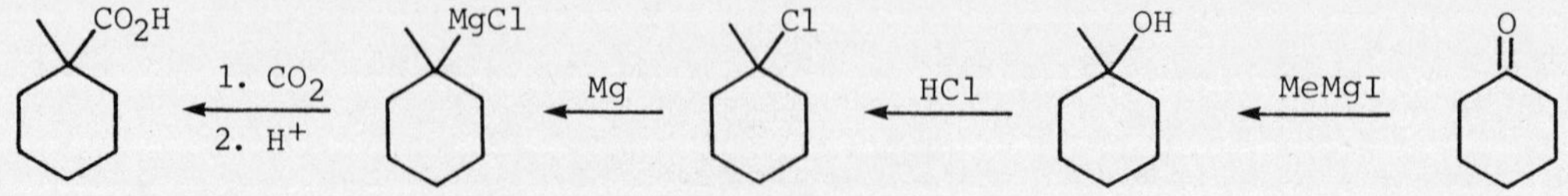

(b) $(CH_3)_3CCO_2H \xleftarrow[\text{CO}_2]{\text{H}^+} (CH_3)_3CMgBr \xleftarrow{\text{Mg}} (CH_3)_3CBr \xleftarrow[\text{h}\nu]{\text{Br}_2} (CH_3)_3CH$

(c) 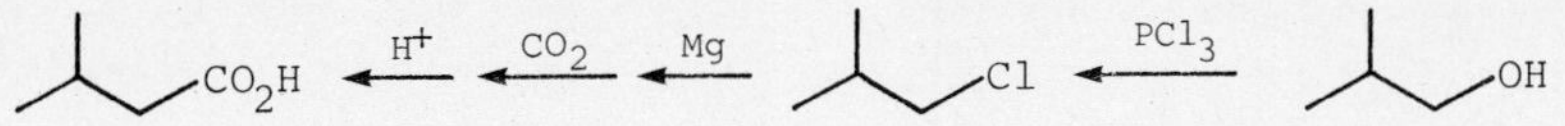

17.9 $3\ CH_3CH_2OH + 4\ KMnO_4 + 4\ H^+ \longrightarrow 3\ CH_3CO_2H + 4\ MnO_2 + 4\ K^+ + 5\ H_2O$

17.10 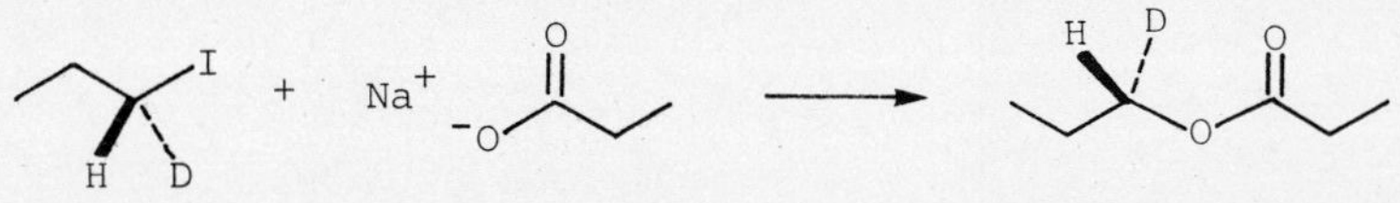

(S)-1-deuteriopropyl propanoate

17.11 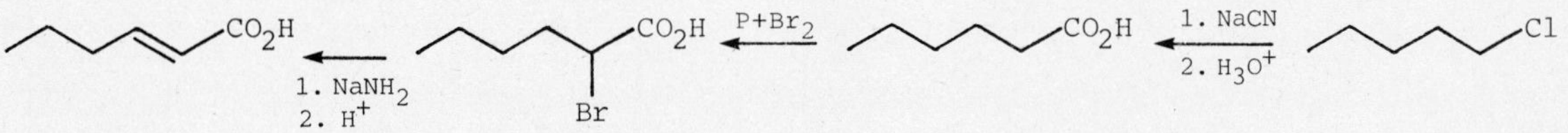

17.12

slow step (k)

$$RCO_2H + H^+ \overset{K}{\rightleftharpoons} \underset{\underline{\underline{1}}}{R\text{-}\overset{\overset{+}{O}H}{\overset{\|}{C}}OH} + CH_3OH \overset{k}{\rightleftharpoons} R\text{-}C(OH)(OH)\text{-}\overset{+}{H}OCH_3$$

Rate = $\underline{k} \times [CH_3OH] \times [\underline{\underline{1}}]$ $[\underline{\underline{1}}] = \underline{K} \times [RCO_2H] \times [H^+]$

Rate = $\underline{k} \times \underline{K} \times [CH_3OH] \times [RCO_2H] \times [H^+]$

17.13

$$CH_3CH_2CH_2CO_2^-\ NH_4^+ \overset{K}{\rightleftharpoons} CH_3CH_2CH_2CO_2H + NH_3$$

pK_a: 9.24, 4.82

$$K_a(NH_4^+) = \frac{[NH_3][H^+]}{[NH_4^+]} = 10^{-9.24}$$

$$K_a(RCO_2H) = \frac{[RCO_2^-][H^+]}{[RCO_2H]} = 10^{-4.82}$$

$$K = \frac{[RCO_2H][NH_3]}{[RCO_2^-][NH_4^+]} = \frac{K_a(NH_4^+)}{K_a(RCO_2H)} = 10^{-4.42} = 1.51 \times 10^{-5}$$

17.14 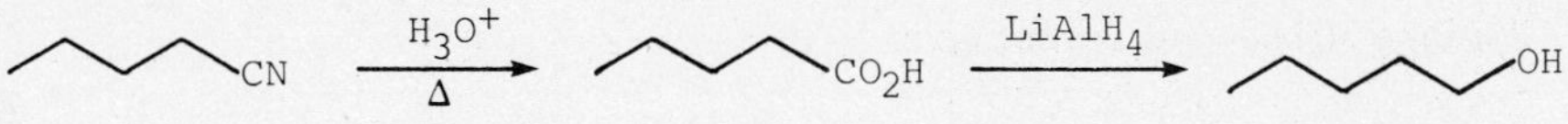

17.15 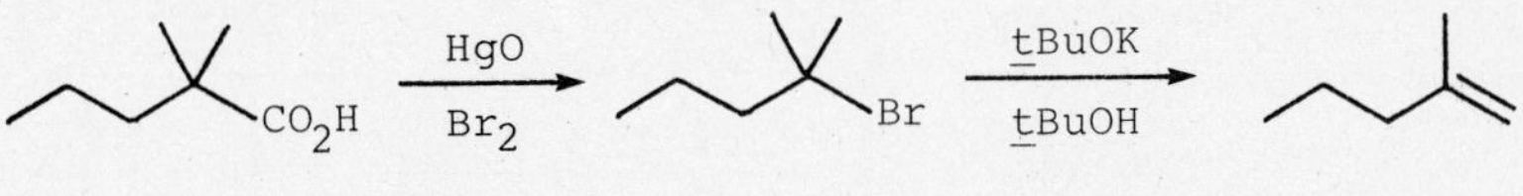

17.E   Answers and Explanations for Problems

1.   <u>IUPAC</u>

(a) 3-methylpentanoic acid   (e) 2-hydroxybutanoic acid

(b) 2,2-dimethylpropanoic acid   (f) decanoic acid
       (NOTE: trivial name is pivalic acid)   (g) cyclobutanecarboxylic acid

(c) 4-bromobutanoic acid   (h) 3-methoxybutanoic acid

(d) iodoacetic acid   (i) 3,4-dimethylpentanoic acid
       (NOTE: iodoethanoic acid is a sys-   (j) cyanoacetic acid
       tematic name that is never used in
       practice)

2.

(a) $CH_3CHClCH_2CO_2H$ (with Cl substituent)

(b) $CH_3(CH_2)_4CO_2H$

(c) $CH_3CH(OCH_3)CH_2CH_2CO_2H$

(d) cyclopentane-CO_2H

(e) $Br-CH_2CH_2CO_2H$

(f) CH_3CH_2 and CO_2H on a cis double bond, $C=C$ with H, H

(g) structure with H, OH and CO_2H on an alkene chain

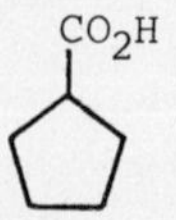

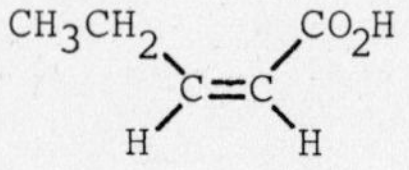

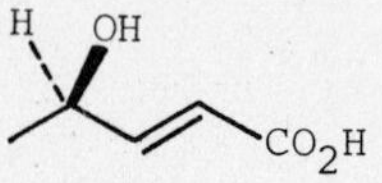

(h) $BrCH_2CHClCO_2H$

3.

(a) cyclohexyl–CH_2OH

(b) cyclohexane with Br and CO_2H

(c) cyclohexyl–CO_2CH_3

(d) cyclohexyl–$CO_2CH(CH_3)_2$

(e) cyclohexyl–$C(=O)NH_2$

(f) cyclohexyl–$C(=O)NHCH_3$

(g) cyclohexyl–$C(=O)Cl$

(h) cyclohexyl–$C(=O)Br$

(i) No reaction

(j) cyclohexyl–$C(=O)O^-\ Na^+$

(k) cyclohexyl–Br

(l) cyclohexyl–Cl

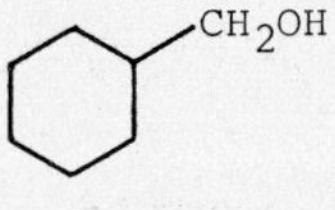

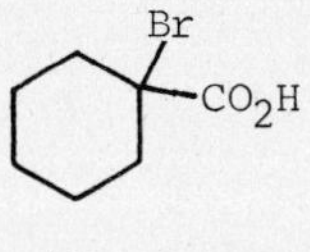

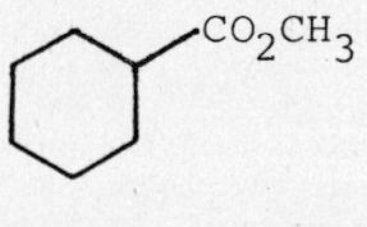

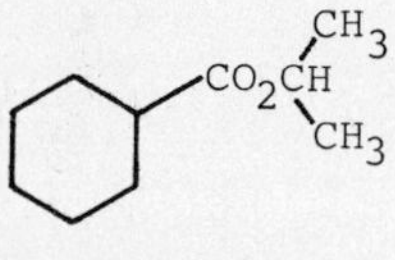

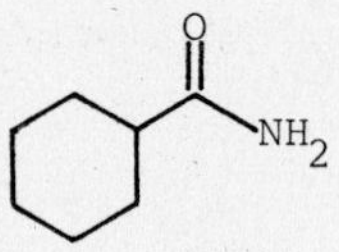

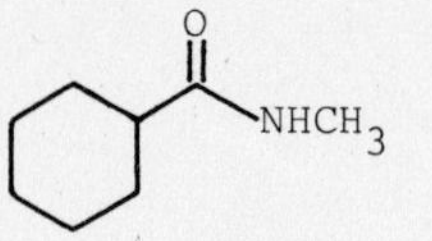

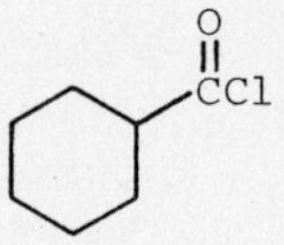

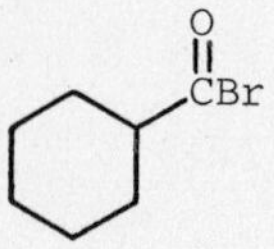

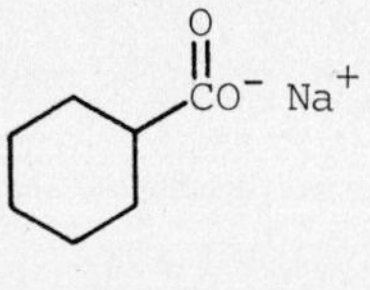

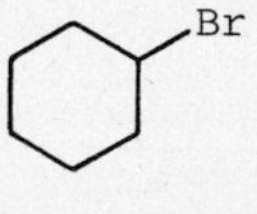

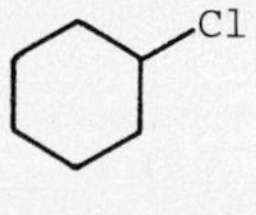

4.

(a) Grignard (displacement reaction is poor with a tertiary halide).

(b) cyanide   (reaction of $BrCH_2CH_2CH_2Br$ with Mg leads to cyclopropane).

(c) cyanide   (the Grignard reagent reacts with carbonyl group).

(d) Grignard (displacement reaction is slow with neopentyl halides).

(e) Both methods work well.

(f) cyanide   (Grignard reagent reacts with -OH).

5.

(a) $CH_3-C(CH_3)_2-CH_3$ $\xrightarrow[h\nu]{Br_2}$ $(CH_3)_3CCH_2Br$ $\xrightarrow[ether]{Mg}$ $(CH_3)_3CCH_2MgBr$

$(CH_3)_3CCH_2COOH \xleftarrow[\quad]{H^+ \quad CO_2}$

(b) $(CH_3)_3CCH_2COOH$ (from a) $\xrightarrow[P]{Br_2}$ $\xrightarrow{H_2O}$ $(CH_3)_3CCHBrCOOH$

(c) $(CH_3)_3CCH_2MgBr$ (from a) $\xrightarrow{CH_2O}$ $\xrightarrow{H^+}$ $(CH_3)_3CCH_2CH_2OH$

or $(CH_3)_3CCH_2COOH$ (from a) $\xrightarrow{LiAlH_4}$ $\xrightarrow{H^+}$

(d) $(CH_3)_3CCH_2CO_2H$ [from (a)] $\xrightarrow[\Delta]{SOCl_2}$ $(CH_3)_3CCH_2COCl$

6. (a) $CH_3CH_2CH_2CHO$ $\xrightarrow{Ag_2O \text{ or } HNO_3}$ $CH_3CH_2CH_2CO_2H$

(b) $CH_3CH_2CH_2CHO$ $\xrightarrow{\text{dilute } OH^-}$ $CH_3CH_2CH_2CH=\overset{\overset{\displaystyle CHO}{|}}{C}CH_2CH_3$ $\xrightarrow{Ag_2O}$ $CH_3CH_2CH_2CH=\overset{\overset{\displaystyle CO_2H}{|}}{C}CH_2CH_3$

(c) $CH_3CH_2CH_2CHO$ $\xrightarrow{HCN}$ $CH_3CH_2CH_2\overset{\overset{\displaystyle OH}{|}}{C}HCN$ $\xrightarrow[\Delta]{H^+}$ $CH_3CH_2CH_3\overset{\overset{\displaystyle OH}{|}}{C}HCO_2H$

(d) $CH_3CH_2CH_2CHO$ $\xrightarrow[LiAlH_4]{NaBH_4 \text{ or}}$ $CH_3CH_2CH_2CH_2OH$ $\xrightarrow{PBr_3}$ $CH_3CH_2CH_2CH_2Br$ $\xrightarrow[ether]{Mg}$ $\xrightarrow[2.\ H^+]{1.\ CO_2}$ $CH_3CH_2CH_2CH_2CO_2H$

7. (a) $LiAlH_4$

(b) $(CH_3)_2CHCH_2CO_2H$ $\xrightarrow{LiAlH_4}$ $(CH_3)_2CHCH_2CH_2OH$ $\xrightarrow{PBr_3}$ $\xrightarrow{CN^-}$ $\xrightarrow[\Delta]{H^+ \text{ or } OH^-}$ $(CH_3)_2CHCH_2CH_2CO_2H$

(c) $(CH_3)_2CHCH_2CH_2CO_2H$ [from (b)] $\xrightarrow{LiAlH_4}$ $(CH_3)CHCH_2CH_2CH_2OH$ $\xrightarrow{PBr_3}$ $\xrightarrow[ether]{Mg}$ $\xrightarrow{CH_2=O}$ $(CH_3)_2CHCH_2CH_2CH_2CH_2OH$

$(CH_3)_2CHCH_2CH_2\overset{\overset{\displaystyle}{|}}{\underset{\underset{\displaystyle Br}{|}}{C}}HCH_2Br$ $\xleftarrow{Br_2}$ $(CH_3)_2CHCH_2CH_2CH=CH_2$ $\xleftarrow[\Delta]{Al_2O_3}$ $(CH_3)_2CHCH_2CH_2CH_2CH_2OH$

(d) $(CH_3)_2CHCH_2CO_2H$ $\xrightarrow[Br_2]{P}$ $(CH_3)_2CHCHBrCO_2H$ $\xrightarrow{CH_3OH}{H^+,\ \Delta}$ $(CH_3)_2CHCHBrCO_2CH_3$ $\xrightarrow[CH_3OH]{CH_3ONa}$

$(CH_3)_2C=CHCO_2CH_3$

(e) 1. CH_3Li (f) NH_3, Δ (g) Ag_2O, Br_2
2. H_2O

8. (a) [cyclohexane ring]$=CH_2$ $\xrightarrow[OH^-]{B_2H_6}{H_2O_2}$ [cyclohexane ring]$-CH_2OH$ $\xrightarrow{PBr_3}$ $\xrightarrow[ether]{Mg}$ $\xrightarrow[2.\ H^+]{1.\ CO_2}$ [cyclohexane ring]$-CH_2CO_2H$

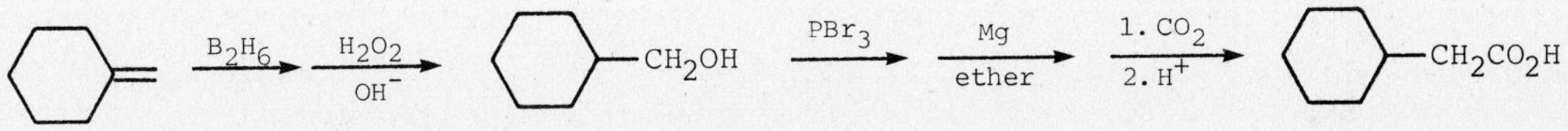

(b) $(CH_3)_3CCH=CH_2$ $\xrightarrow{KMnO_4}$ $(CH_3)_3CCO_2H$

$\underline{or}$ $\xrightarrow[CH_3CO_2H]{O_3}{Zn}$ $(CH_3)_3CCHO$ $\xrightarrow{Ag_2O}$

(c) $CH_3COCH_2CH_2C(CH_3)_2Br$ $\xrightarrow[H^+]{HOCH_2CH_2OH}$ [dioxolane ring]$CH_3-C-CH\ CH\ C(CH_3)_2Br$ $\xrightarrow[ether]{Mg}$ $\xrightarrow[2.\ H^+]{1.\ CO_2}$

$CH_3\overset{\overset{\displaystyle O}{\|}}{C}CH_2CH_2-\overset{\overset{\displaystyle CH_3}{|}}{\underset{\underset{\displaystyle CH_3}{|}}{C}}-CO_2H$ $\xleftarrow[H_2O]{H^+}$ [dioxolane ring]$CH_3-C-CH_2CH_2C(CH_3)_2CO_2H$

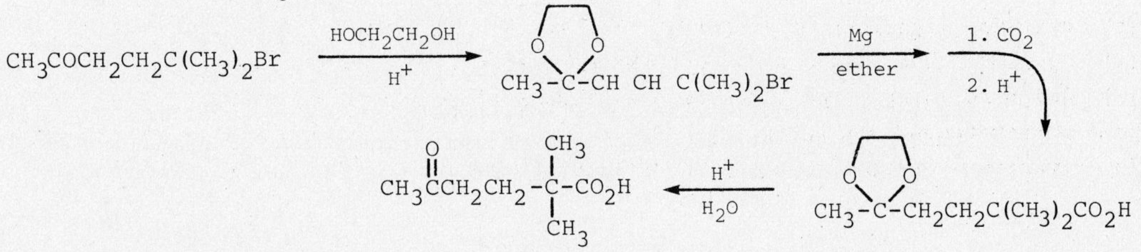

(d) $CH_3CH_2CO_2H$ $\xrightarrow{LiAlH_4}$ $CH_3CH_2CH_2OH$ $\xrightarrow{PBr_3}$ $CH_3CH_2CH_2Br$ $\xrightarrow{CN^-}$ $\xrightarrow[\Delta]{H^+ \text{ or } OH^-}$ $CH_3CH_2CH_2CO_2H$

(e) $CH_3CH_2CH_2CO_2H$ $\xrightarrow[Br_2]{Ag_2O}$ $CH_3CH_2CH_2Br$ $\xrightarrow{OH^-}$ $CH_3CH_2CH_2OH$ $\xrightarrow{HNO_3}$ $CH_3CH_2CO_2H$

(f) $CH_3CH_2CH_2Br$ [from (e)] $\xrightarrow{N_3^-}$ $CH_3CH_2CH_2N_3$

9. The dissociation equilibrium can be written as: $AcOH \rightleftharpoons H^+ + AcO^-$

with $\underline{K} = \dfrac{[H^+][AcO^-]}{[AcOH]} = 1.8 \times 10^{-5}$

If we make the simplification that each H comes from ionization of AcOH, then $[H^+] = [AcO^-]$. Also, $[AcOH]_{total} = [AcOH] + [AcO^-]$.

The equation then becomes:
$$\underline{K} = \frac{[AcO^-]^2}{[AcOH]_{total} - [AcO^-]} = 1.8 \times 10^{-5}$$

$$[AcO^-]^2 + (1.8 \times 10^{-5})[AcO^-] - (1.8 \times 10^{-5})[AcOH]_{total} = 0$$

This can be solved using the solution to the quadratic equation:

$$x = \frac{-b \pm \sqrt{b^2 - 4ac}}{2a}$$

where $x = [AcO^-]$
$a = 1$
$b = 1.8 \times 10^{-5}$
and $c = -(1.8 \times 10^{-5})[AcOH]_{total}$

(a) $[AcOH]_{total} = 0.1$ M: $[AcO^-]/[AcOH] = 0.0135 = 1.35\%$
(b) $[AcOH]_{total} = 0.01$ M: $[AcO^-]/[AcOH] = 0.0433 = 4.33\%$
(c) $[AcOH]_{total} = 0.001$ M: $[AcO^-]/[AcOH] = 0.1435 = 14.35\%$

A simpler way to solve the problem is to recognize that only a small fraction of AcOH dissociates, so that $[AcOH] \approx [AcOH]_{total}$:

$$\frac{[AcO^-]^2}{[AcOH]_{total}} = 1.8 \times 10^{-5} ; \qquad [AcO^-] = \sqrt{(1.8 \times 10^{-5})[AcOH]_{total}}$$

Using this equation, the following ratios are obtained:

(a) $[AcOH]_{total} = 0.1$ M: $[AcO^-]/[AcOH] = 0.0134 = 1.34\%$
(b) $[AcOH]_{total} = 0.01$ M: $[AcO^-]/[AcOH] = 0.0424 = 4.24\%$
(c) $[AcOH]_{total} = 0.001$ M: $[AcO^-]/[AcOH] = 0.134 = 13.4\%$

Note that the percent dissociation increases as the concentration decreases. Because dissociation is a unimolecular reaction, its rate will be unaffected by concentration; recombination on the other hand is a bimolecular reaction and is therefore slower in more dilute solution. The position of equilibrium therefore shifts toward dissociation in dilute solution.

10. $pK_a = -\log K_a$

(a) 4.85   (b) 4.20   (c) 1.26   (d) 0.64   (e) 3.68

11.   (a) $CH_3CH_2O^-$

In acetate ion the negative charge is shared between two oxygens, whereas in ethoxide ion the charge is essentially localized on a single oxygen. Ethoxide ion is therefore relatively less stable and has a greater tendency to react with a proton.

(b) $CH_3CH_2CH_2CO_2^-$

β-Chloropropionate is stabilized by the electron-attracting inductive effect of chlorine.

(c) $ClCH_2CH_2CO_2^-$

In α-chloropropionate ion, the chlorine is closer to the center of negative charge and provides greater stabilization.

(d) $FCH_2CO_2^-$

Two electron-attracting fluorines provide greater stabilization of the anion than one does.

(e) $CH_3CH_2CH_2CO_2^-$

The ethynyl group has a somewhat electron-attracting inductive effect compared to an alkyl group, and provides greater stabilization of an anion.

(f) $CH_3CO_2^-$

HCl is a stronger acid than acetic acid, hence acetate ion is a stronger base than chloride ion. The reason that HCl is the stronger acid is, however, more difficult to explain. HCl is a stronger acid than CH_3CO_2H even in the gas phase, but the difference, $\Delta pK = 4-5$, is smaller than in aqueous solution, $\Delta pK = 11$. This difference means that the solvation energy of Cl^- is greater than that for $CH_3CO_2^-$. The greater acidity of HCl in the gas phase appears to be due in part to the greater bond strength of CH_3CO_2-H compared to H-Cl, and in part to the higher electron affinity of $Cl\cdot$ compared to $CH_3CO_2\cdot$.

12.
$$HO_2CCH_2CH_2\overset{\overset{\displaystyle Cl}{|}}{C}HCH_2\underline{COOH} \qquad \text{more acidic (Cl is closer)}$$

13. Compare the effect of chlorine substitution on pK_a for the various isomers:

pK_a (butanoic acid) $- pK_a$ (2-chlorobutanoic acid) $= 1.90$ } ratio $= 2.55$

pK_a (" ") $- pK_a$ (3-chlorobutanoic acid) $= 0.77$ } ratio $= 2.56$

pK_a (" ") $- pK_a$ (4-chlorobutanoic acid) $= 0.30$

pK_a (butanoic acid) $- pK_a$ (3-cyanobutanoic acid) $= 0.38$,   therefore

pK_a (" ") $- pK_a$ (2-cyanobutanoic acid)   is expected to be $2.55 \times 0.38 = 0.97$:

$4.82 - 0.97 = 3.85 =$ calculated pK_a of 2-cyanobutanoic acid.

Note that the pK_a of 2-cyanobutanoic acid has yet to be determined experimentally.

14.

$$CH_3CH_2\overset{\overset{\displaystyle O}{||}}{C}OH + H^+ \rightleftharpoons CH_3CH_2\overset{\overset{\displaystyle +OH}{||}}{C}OH$$

$$CH_3CH_2\overset{\overset{\displaystyle +OH}{||}}{C}HO + H_2{}^{18}O \rightleftharpoons CH_3CH_2\overset{\overset{\displaystyle OH}{|}}{\underset{\underset{\displaystyle OH}{|}}{C}}{}^{-18}OH_2{}^+ \rightleftharpoons CH_3CH_2\overset{\overset{\displaystyle OH}{|}}{\underset{\underset{\displaystyle OH}{|}}{C}}{}^{-18}OH + H^+ \rightleftharpoons CH_3CH_2\overset{\overset{\displaystyle +OH_2}{|}}{\underset{\underset{\displaystyle OH}{|}}{C}}{}^{-18}OH$$

$$H^+ + CH_3CH_2\overset{\overset{\displaystyle {}^{18}O}{||}}{C}OH \rightleftharpoons H_2O + CH_3CH_2\overset{}{\underset{\underset{\displaystyle OH}{|}}{C}}={}^{18}OH^+$$

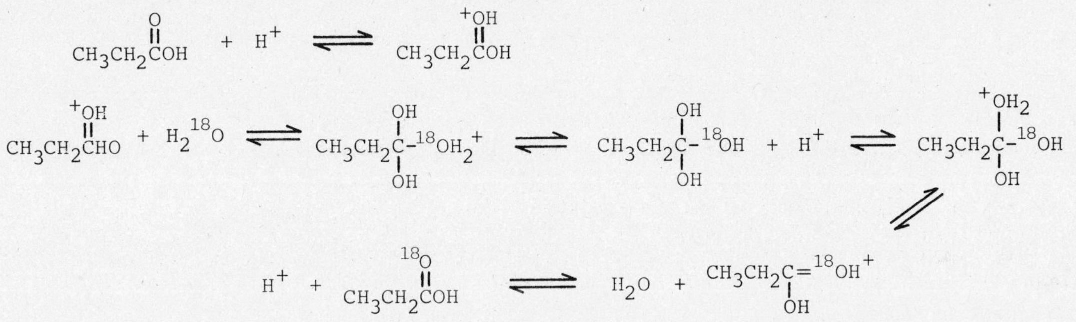

15.

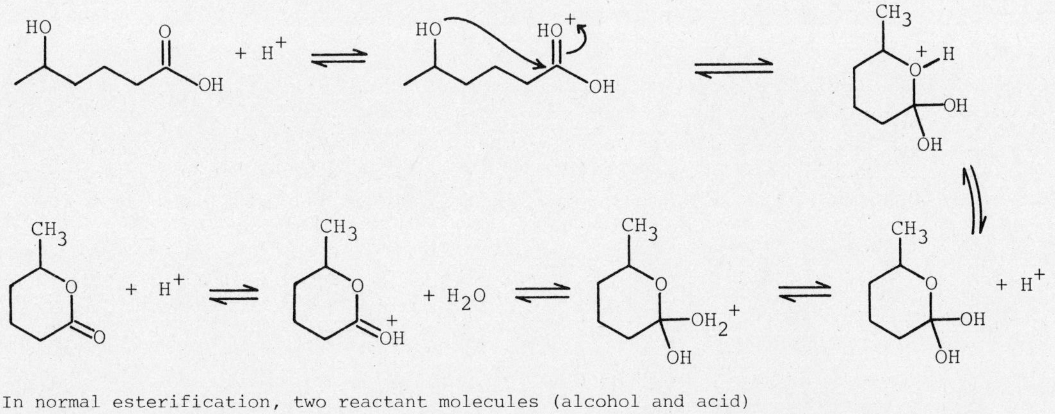

In normal esterification, two reactant molecules (alcohol and acid) give two product molecules (ester and water), with a consequent $\Delta S°$ of about zero. In the present cyclization, one molecule gives two. The additional freedom of motion of the products corresponds to a positive $\Delta S°$ and a larger equilibrium constant.

16.

$$CH_3CH_2CO_2H + D^+ \rightleftharpoons CH_3CH_2\overset{\overset{\displaystyle +OD}{||}}{C}OH \rightleftharpoons H^+ + CH_3CH_2\overset{\overset{\displaystyle OD}{|}}{C}=O$$

$$CH_3CH_2\overset{\overset{\displaystyle O}{||}}{C}OD + D^+ \rightleftharpoons CH_3CH_2\overset{\overset{\displaystyle +OD}{||}}{C}OD \rightleftharpoons H^+ + CH_3CH=C\overset{\nearrow OD}{\searrow_{OD}}$$

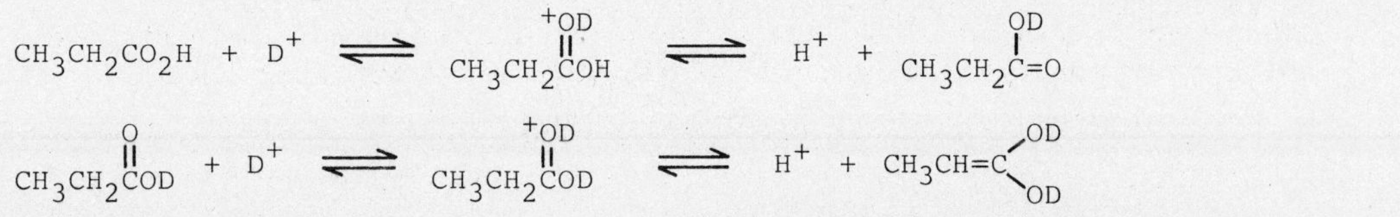

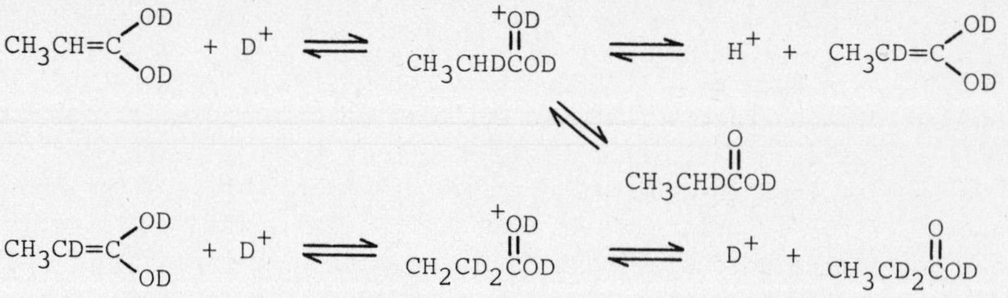

17. ΔH°(gas) = -4.6 kcal mole^{-1}. The liquid phase involves solvation energies not present in the ideal gas state. The reactants are solvated more strongly than the products, probably because of hydrogen-bonding, and the esterification reaction is less exothermic.

18. (a) The C-Cl dipole stabilizes the carboxylate ion by electrostatic attraction.

(b) Trigonometry gives the following geometric results:

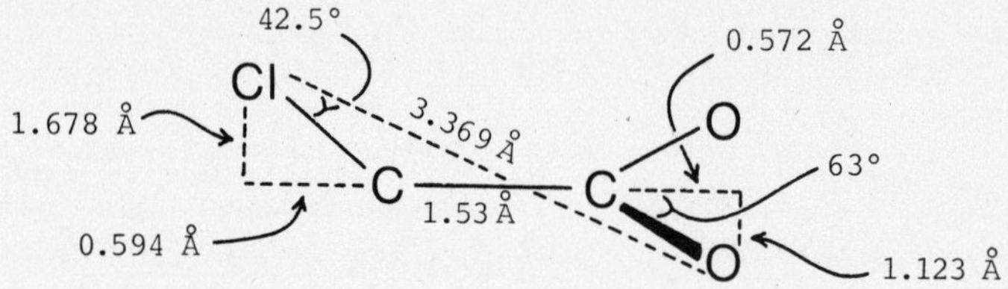

$$E = \frac{(q=0.5)(\mu=1.9)(\cos 42.5^{\circ})}{(3.369)^2} (69 \text{ kcal mole}^{-1}) = 4.3 \text{ kcal mole}^{-1}$$

This result is per oxygen. Total stabilization of both oxygens is 8.5 kcal mole^{-1}. The acidity difference between $ClCH_2CO_2H$ and CH_3CO_2H in the gas phase corresponds to an energy difference of about 13 kcal mole^{-1}; hence, even this crude electrostatic calculation on one conformer gives a result of the right order of magnitude.

17.F Supplementary Problems

S1. Give the IUPAC name for each of the following compounds:

(a) $DCH_2CH_2CH_2CO_2H$

(b)

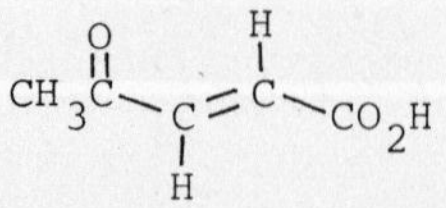

(c)

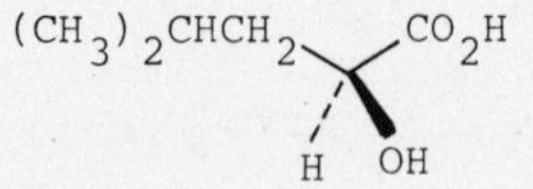

(d)

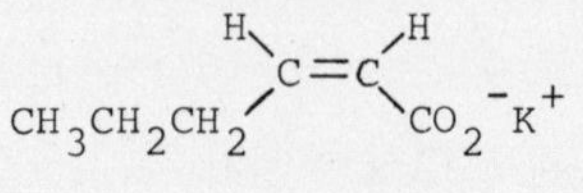

(e)

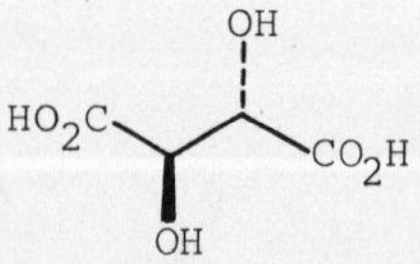

(f)

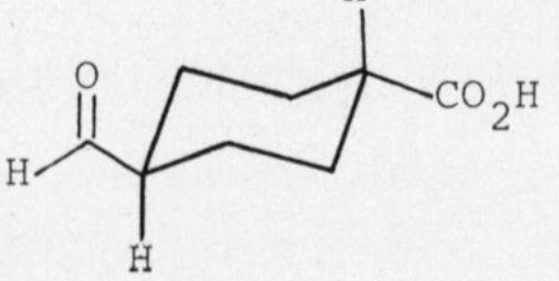

(g) $CH_2=C=CH-CO_2H$

S2. Write the structure for each of the following compounds:

(a) γ,γ-dibromobutyric acid

(b) 3-chloro-2-hydroxypropanoic acid

(c) sodium 4-hydroxybutanoate

(d) 2-oxopropanoic acid

(e) ammonium valerate

(f) cis-cyclopentane-1,2-dicarboxylic acid

S3. What is the major organic product of each of the following reaction
     sequences?

(a) $(CH_3)_2CHCO_2H$ $\xrightarrow[Cl_2, \Delta]{PCl_3}$ $\xrightarrow{H_2O}$

(b) 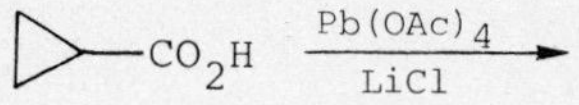 $-CO_2H$ $\xrightarrow[LiCl]{Pb(OAc)_4}$

(c) $(CH_3)_3CCH_2C\equiv N$ $\xrightarrow[\Delta]{H_3O^+}$ $\xrightarrow{AgO}$ $\xrightarrow{I_2}$

(d) $CH_2=CHCH_2CH_2CH_2CO_2H$ $\xrightarrow{LiAlH_4}$ $\xrightarrow[H^+]{CH_3CO_2H}$

(e) $HO_2C-C\equiv C-CO_2H$ $\xrightarrow{CH_2N_2}$ $\xrightarrow{1\ mole\ Br_2}$

(f) 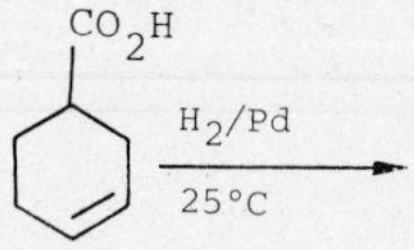
     $\xrightarrow[25°C]{H_2/Pd}$

(g)
     $\xrightarrow{PCl_3}$ $\xrightarrow{CH_3OH}$

(h)
     $\xrightarrow{KMnO_4}$ $\xrightarrow{NaOH}$

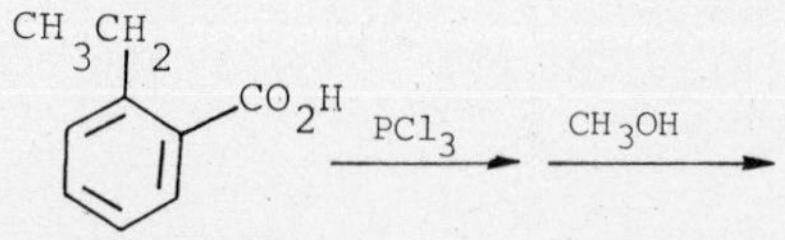

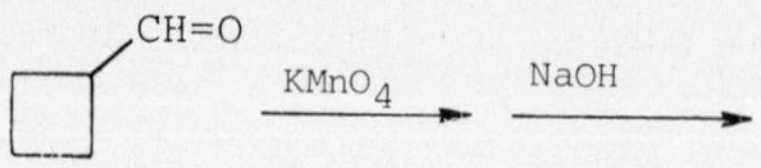

S4. Show how to carry out the following conversions:

(a) $CH_3CH_2CH_2CO_2H \longrightarrow CH_3CH_2CH_2CH_2CH_2OH$

(b) $CH_3CH_2CH_2CO_2H \longrightarrow CH_3CH=CHCO_2H$

(c)  $-CH_2OH \longrightarrow$ $-Br$

(d) $(CH_3)_2CHCH_2CH=CH_2 \longrightarrow (CH_3)_2CHCH_2\overset{OH}{\underset{|}{C}HCO_2H}$

(e) 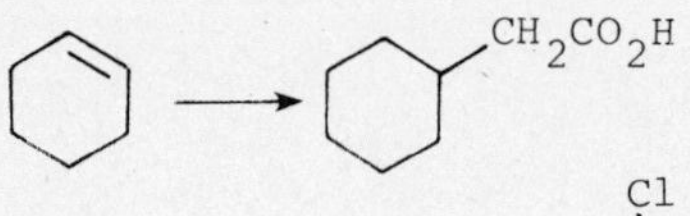 $\longrightarrow$ ^{CH_2CO_2H}

(f) $CH_3CH_2CH_2CH_2Cl \longrightarrow CH_3CH_2CH_2\overset{Cl}{\underset{|}{C}HCO_2CH_3}$

(g) $CH_3CH_2CH_2CO_2H \longrightarrow CH_3\overset{Br\ Br}{\underset{|\ \ |}{CHCHC}}O_2CH_3$

(h) 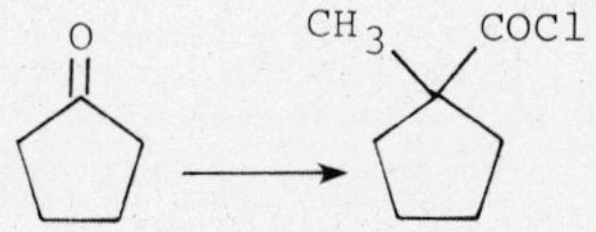 $\longrightarrow$

(i) $(CH_3)_3CCH_2\overset{O}{\overset{||}{C}}CH_3 \longrightarrow (CH_3)_3CCH_2O\overset{O}{\overset{||}{C}}CH_3$

S5. Show how to synthesize the following compounds using starting materials
     of five carbons or less and any other reagents:

(a) $(CH_3)_3CCH_2CO_2CH(CH_3)_2$

(b) $(CH_3)_2CHCH_2CH_2CH_2CH_2CO_2H$

(c) $CH_3CH_2CH_2\overset{CO_2CH_3}{\underset{|}{C}H}CH_2CH_2CH_2CH_3$

(d)

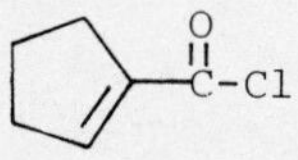

(e) $CH_3CH_2CH_2\underset{\overset{|}{H}}{\overset{}{C}}=C\underset{\overset{|}{H}}{\overset{CO_2H}{C}}$

(f)

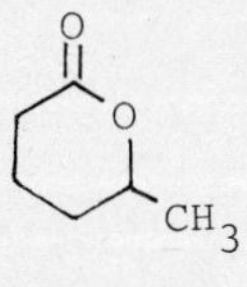

(g) $CH_3CH_2\overset{CH_3}{\underset{\overset{|}{OCH_3}}{CHCHC}}\equiv CCO_2CH_3$

(h) 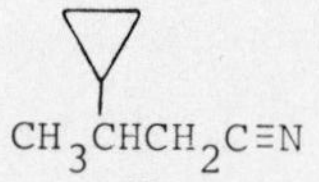 $CH_3CHCH_2C\equiv N$

(i)

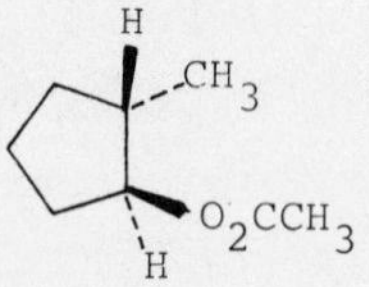

(j) $CH_3CH_2CO_2CH_2CH_2CH_2CH_2O_2CCH_2CH_3$

S6. Calculate the pH when chloroacetic acid is dissolved in water at 1.0 M concentration;
     at 0.1 M; at 0.001 M.

S7.   In a solution which is 1.0 $\underline{M}$ in dichloroacetic acid and 1.0 $\underline{M}$ in acetic acid, what are the concentrations of dichloroacetate and acetate ions?

S8.   Determine the structure of each of the compounds in the sequence below:

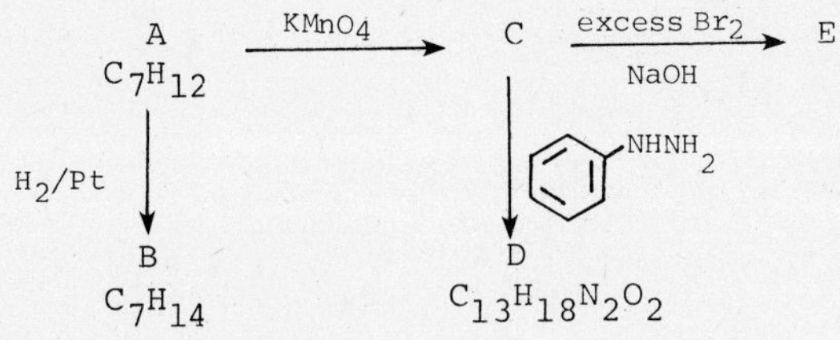

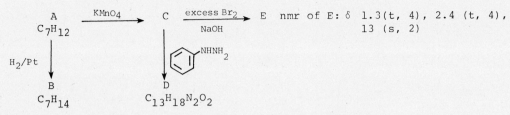

$$\begin{array}{c} A \\ C_7H_{12} \end{array} \xrightarrow{KMnO_4} C \xrightarrow[NaOH]{excess\ Br_2} E \quad nmr\ of\ E:\ \delta\ 1.3(t,\ 4),\ 2.4\ (t,\ 4),\ 13\ (s,\ 2)$$

H_2/Pt ↓

$$\begin{array}{c} B \\ C_7H_{14} \end{array} \qquad \qquad \begin{array}{c} D \\ C_{13}H_{18}N_2O_2 \end{array}$$

S9.   Write a mechanism for the following transformation:

$$HO-\overset{O}{\overset{\|}{C}}-CH_2-CH_2-\overset{O}{\overset{\|}{C}}-OH \xrightarrow[\Delta]{(H^+)} \quad \text{(lactone)} \quad +\quad H_2O$$

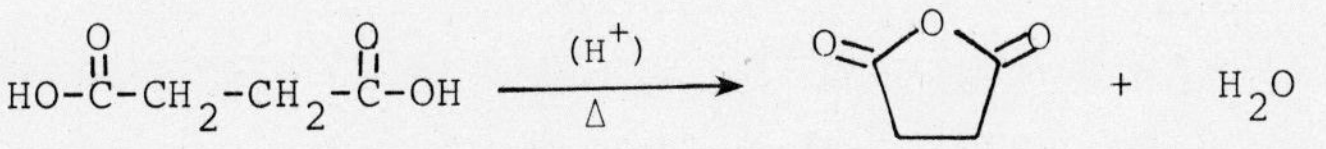

S10. Predict the major product of the following reaction and justify your answer:

$$CH_3CH=CHCO_2H\ +\ Br_2 \xrightarrow[solvent]{CH_3OH}$$

S11. Rank the following compounds in order of increasing acidity:

F_2CHCO_2H $HOCH_2CH_2CO_2H$ $CH_3CH_2CH_2CH_2OH$ $CH_3CH_2\overset{CH_3}{\underset{CH_3}{\overset{|}{\underset{|}{C}}}}-CO_2H$ $ClCH_2CO_2H$

$CF_3CO_2CH_3$ CF_3CH_2OH $CH_3CH_2CO_2H$

17.G   Answers to Supplementary Problems

S1.   (a)   4-deuteriobutanoic acid
      (b)   ($\underline{E}$)-4-oxo-2-pentanoic acid
      (c)   ($\underline{S}$)-2-hydroxy-4-methylpentanoic acid
      (d)   potassium ($\underline{Z}$)-2-hexenoate

      (e)   ($\underline{R},\underline{S}$)-2,3-dihydroxybutanedioic acid
            (or $\underline{meso}$-)
      (f) $\underline{trans}$-4-formylcyclohexanecarboxylic acid
      (g)   2,3-butadienoic acid

S2.   (a) $Br_2CHCH_2CH_2CO_2H$

      (b) $ClCH_2\overset{OH}{\overset{|}{C}}HCO_2H$

      (c) $HOCH_2CH_2CH_2CO_2^-\ Na^+$

      (d) $CH_3\overset{O}{\overset{\|}{C}}CO_2H$

      (e) $CH_3CH_2CH_2CH_2CO_2^-\ NH_4^+$

      (f)   cyclopentane with H and CO_2H substituents (cis-1,2-cyclopentanedicarboxylic acid)

S3.   (a) $(CH_3)_2\overset{Cl}{\overset{|}{C}}CO_2H$

      (b)   cyclopropane–Cl

      (c) $(CH_3)_3CCH_2I$

      (d) $CH_2=CHCH_2CH_2CH_2CH_2O_2CCH_3$

      (e) $\underset{Br}{\overset{CH_3O_2C}{\diagdown}}C=C\underset{CO_2CH_3}{\overset{Br}{\diagup}}$

      (f)   cyclohexane–CO_2H

      (g) CH_3CH_2 benzene ring CO_2CH_3 (ortho)

      (h)   cyclobutane–$CO_2^-Na^+$

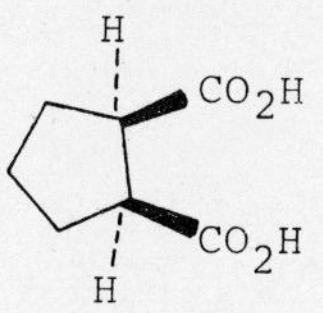

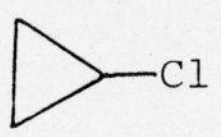

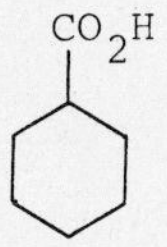

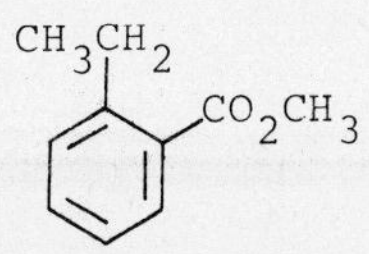

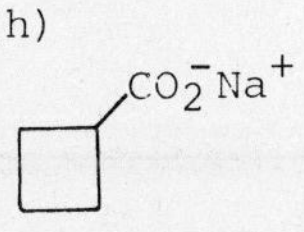

S4.

(a) $CH_3CH_2CH_2CO_2H \xrightarrow{LiAlH_4} \xrightarrow{H_2O} CH_3CH_2CH_2CH_2OH \xrightarrow{PBr_3} \xrightarrow{Mg} \xrightarrow{CH_2=O} \xrightarrow{H_2O} CH_3CH_2CH_2CH_2CH_2OH$

(b) $CH_3CH_2CH_2CO_2H \xrightarrow[\Delta]{P + Br_2} \xrightarrow{H_2O} CH_3CH_2\overset{Br}{\underset{|}{C}HCO_2H} \xrightarrow[HOC_2H_5]{NaOC_2H_5} \xrightarrow{H^+} CH_3CH=CHCO_2H$

(c) cyclopentyl-$CH_2OH \xrightarrow{KMnO_4}$ cyclopentyl-$CO_2H \xrightarrow[2. Br_2]{1. HgO}$ cyclopentyl-Br

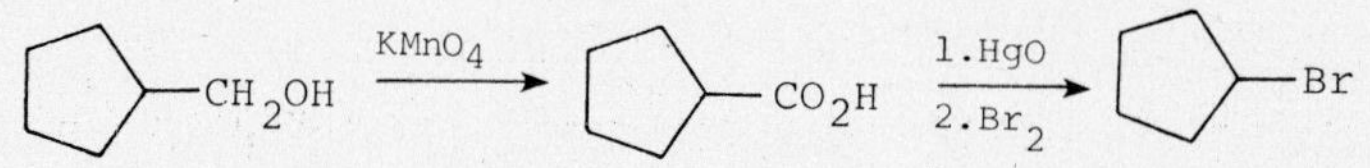

(d) $(CH_3)_2CHCH_2CH=CH_2 \xrightarrow[2. Zn]{1. O_3} (CH_3)_2CHCH_2\overset{O}{\overset{||}{C}}H \xrightarrow{HCN} (CH_3)_2CHCH_2\overset{OH}{\underset{|}{C}HC\equiv N} \xrightarrow[\Delta]{H_3O^+}$ $(CH_3)_2CHCH_2\overset{OH}{\underset{|}{C}HCO_2H}$

(e) cyclohexene $\xrightarrow{HBr}$ cyclohexyl-$Br \xrightarrow{Mg} \xrightarrow{\triangle^O} \xrightarrow{H_2O}$ cyclohexyl-$CH_2CH_2OH \xrightarrow{HNO_3}$ cyclohexyl-CH_2CO_2H

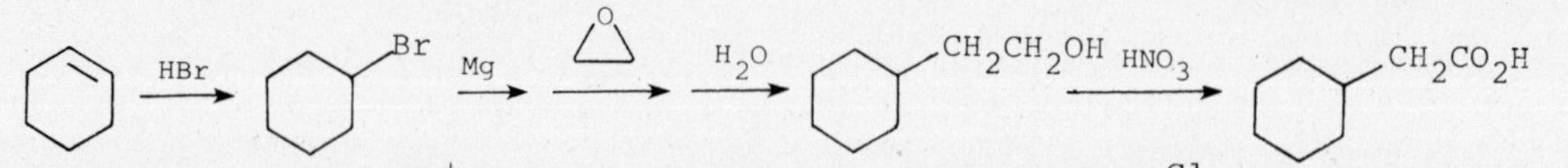

(f) $CH_3CH_2CH_2CH_2Cl \xrightarrow{NaCN} \xrightarrow{H_3O^+} CH_3CH_2CH_2CH_2CO_2H \xrightarrow{P + Cl_2} \xrightarrow{H_2O} CH_3CH_2CH_2\overset{Cl}{\underset{|}{C}HCO_2H} \xrightarrow[CH_3OH]{H^+}$ $CH_3CH_2CH_2\overset{Cl}{\underset{|}{C}HCO_2CH_3}$

(g) $CH_3CH=CHCO_2H \xrightarrow{Br_2} CH_3\overset{Br}{\underset{|}{C}H}-\overset{Br}{\underset{|}{C}HCO_2H} \xrightarrow[CH_3OH]{H^+} CH_3\overset{Br}{\underset{|}{C}H}-\overset{Br}{\underset{|}{C}HCO_2CH_3}$

[from (b)]

(h) cyclopentanone $\xrightarrow{CH_3MgI} \xrightarrow{HCl}$ (1-methyl-1-chlorocyclopentane) $\xrightarrow{Mg} \xrightarrow{CO_2} \xrightarrow{H^+}$ (1-methylcyclopentanecarboxylic acid) $\xrightarrow{SOCl_2}$ (1-methylcyclopentanecarbonyl chloride)

(i) $(CH_3)_3CCH_2\overset{O}{\overset{||}{C}}CH_3 \xrightarrow{CH_3CO_3H} (CH_3)_3CCH_2O\overset{O}{\overset{||}{C}}CH_3$

S5.

(a) $(CH_3)_3CCH_2CO_2CH(CH_3)_2 \xleftarrow[H^+]{(CH_3)_2CHOH} (CH_3)_3CCH_2CO_2H \xleftarrow{H^+} \xleftarrow{CO_2} \xleftarrow{Mg} (CH_3)_3CCH_2Br$

(Note: $(CH_3)_3CCH_2Br \xrightarrow{NaCN}$ ⊘ very slow, because of hindrance from β-branching.)

(b) $(CH_3)_2CHCH_2CH_2CH_2CH_2CO_2H \xleftarrow[\Delta]{H_3O^+} \xleftarrow{NaCN} \xleftarrow{PBr_3} (CH_3)_2CHCH_2CH_2CH_2CH_2OH \xleftarrow{H_2O}$ $\xleftarrow{\triangle^O}$

$(CH_3)_2CHCH_2CH_2Br \xleftarrow{Mg}$

(c) $CH_3CH_2CH_2\overset{CO_2CH_3}{\underset{|}{C}H}(CH_2)_4CH_3 \xleftarrow[H^+]{CH_3OH} CH_3CH_2CH_2\overset{CO_2H}{\underset{|}{C}H}(CH_2)_4CH_3 \xleftarrow[Pt]{H_2}$

$\xleftarrow{Ag_2O} 2\ CH_3CH_2CH_2CH_2\overset{O}{\overset{||}{C}}H \xrightarrow{NaOH} CH_3CH_2CH_2\overset{O}{\underset{|}{\overset{||}{C}H}}C=CHCH_2CH_2CH_2CH_3$

(d) cyclopentenyl-$COCl \xleftarrow{SOCl_2}$ cyclopentenyl-$CO_2H \xleftarrow[\Delta]{H_3O^+} \xleftarrow{H_2SO_4}$ (1-cyano-1-hydroxycyclopentane) $\xleftarrow{HCN}$ cyclopentanone

(e) $CH_3CH_2CH_2\underset{H}{\overset{CO_2H}{C}}=\underset{H}{C} \xleftarrow[\substack{poisoned \\ Pd\ catalyst}]{H_2} CH_3CH_2CH_2C\equiv CCO_2H \xleftarrow{H_2O} \xleftarrow{CO_2} \xleftarrow[\Delta]{CH_3MgBr} CH_3CH_2CH_2C\equiv CH$

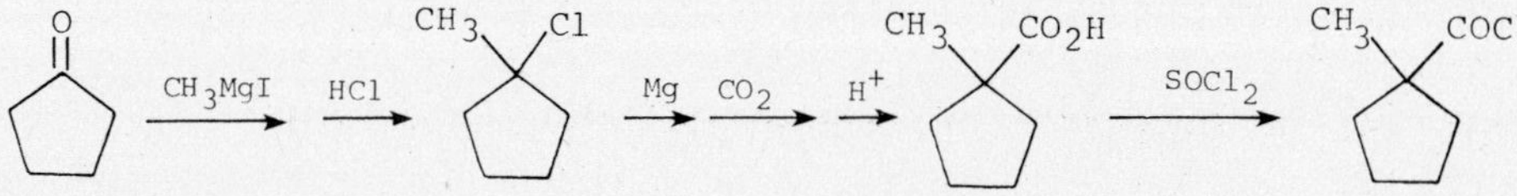

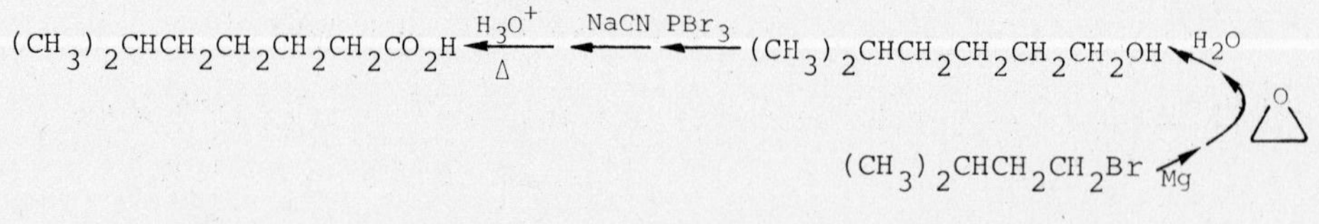

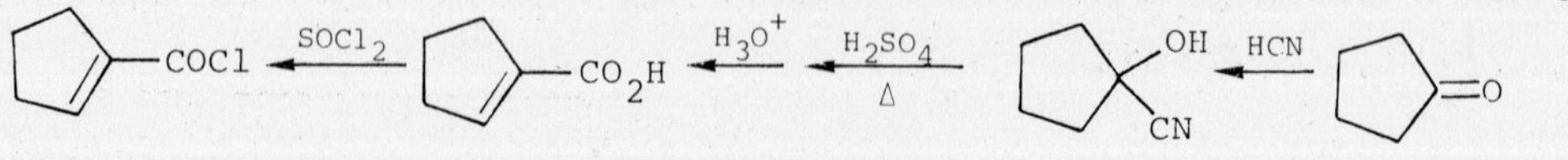

(f) [structure: lactone] $\xleftarrow{CH_3CO_3H}$ [2-methylcyclopentanone] $\xleftarrow{CH_3I}$ [enolate OLi] $\xleftarrow[\substack{THF \\ -78°C}]{LDA}$ [cyclopentanone]

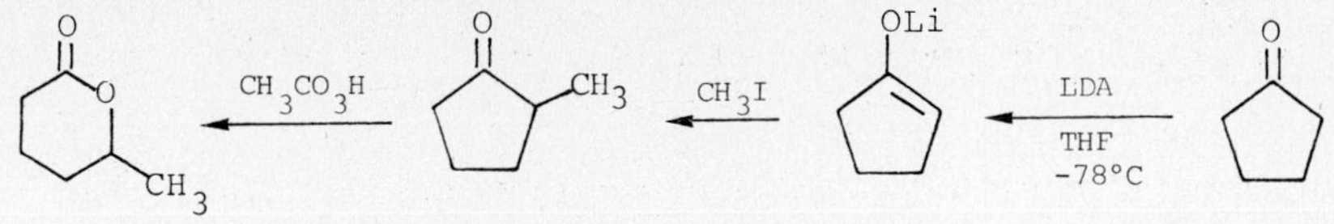

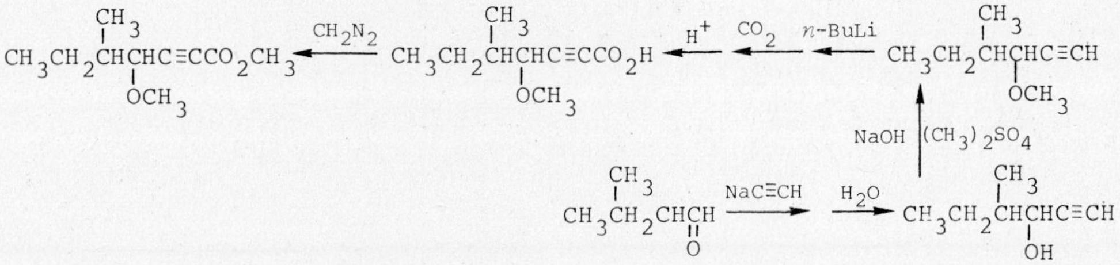

(g) $CH_3CH_2\underset{OCH_3}{\overset{CH_3}{CHCHC\equiv CCO_2CH_3}}$ $\xleftarrow{CH_2N_2}$ $CH_3CH_2\underset{OCH_3}{\overset{CH_3}{CHCHC\equiv CCO_2H}}$ $\xleftarrow[CO_2]{H^+}$ $\xleftarrow{n\text{-BuLi}}$ $CH_3CH_2\underset{OCH_3}{\overset{CH_3}{CHCHC\equiv CH}}$

$\downarrow NaOH \; (CH_3)_2SO_4$

$CH_3CH_2\overset{CH_3}{\underset{O}{CHCH}}$ $\xrightarrow{NaC\equiv CH}$ $\xrightarrow{H_2O}$ $CH_3CH_2\overset{CH_3}{\underset{OH}{CHCHC\equiv CH}}$

(h) [cyclopropyl] $CH_3-CH-CH_2C\equiv N$ $\xleftarrow{NaCN}$ $\xleftarrow{PBr_3}$ [cyclopropyl] $CH_3-CH-CH_2OH$ $\xleftarrow[CH_2=O]{H_2O}$ $\xleftarrow{Mg}$ [cyclopropyl] $\underset{CHCH_3}{\overset{Br}{|}}$

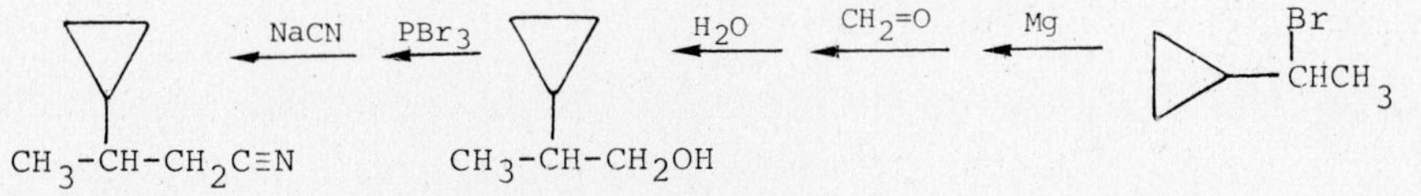

(i) [cyclopentane with H, CH_3, O_2CCH_3, H] $\xleftarrow[H^+]{CH_3CO_2H}$ [cyclopentane with H, CH_3, OH, H] $\xleftarrow[CH_3Li]{H_2O}$ [cyclopentene oxide]

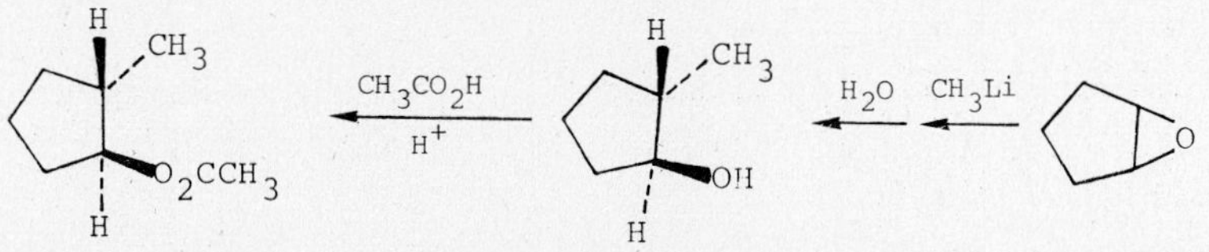

j) $CH_3CH_2\overset{O}{\overset{\|}{C}}OCH_2CH_2CH_2CH_2O\overset{O}{\overset{\|}{C}}CH_2CH_3$ $\xleftarrow{CH_3CH_2COCl}$ $HOCH_2CH_2CH_2CH_2OH$

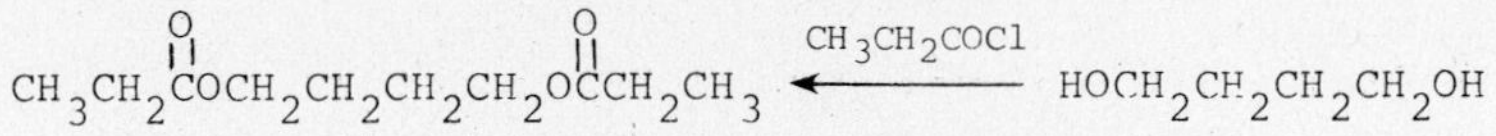

S6. K_a of chloroacetic acid is 1.4×10^{-3} $\underline{M}$ (Table 17.3).

at 1.0 $\underline{M}$ $\dfrac{[H^+][ClCH_2CO_2^-]}{[ClCH_2CO_2H]} = 1.4 \times 10^{-3}$ $[H^+] = [ClCH_2CO_2^-] = X$

$[ClCH_2CO_2H] = 1.0 - X$

$\dfrac{X^2}{1-X} = 1.4 \times 10^{-3}$ $X^2 + 1.4 \times 10^{-3}X - 1.4 \times 10^{-3} = 0$;

$X = \dfrac{-1.4 \times 10^{-3} \pm \sqrt{(1.4 \times 10^{-3})^2 + 5.6 \times 10^{-3}}}{2} = 3.67 \times 10^{-2}$;   pH = 1.44

at 0.1 $\underline{M}$: $\dfrac{X^2}{0.1 - X} = 1.4 \times 10^{-3}$; $X^2 + 1.4 \times 10^{-3}X - 1.4 \times 10^{-4} = 0$;

$X = 2.23 \times 10^{-2}$; pH = 1.65

at 0.001 $\underline{M}$: $\dfrac{X^2}{1 \times 10^{-3} - X} = 1.4 \times 10^{-3}$; $X^2 + 1.4 \times 10^{-3}X - 1.4 \times 10^{-6} = 0$;

$X = 1.35 \times 10^{-3}$; pH = 2.87

S7. Because dichloroacetic acid is a much stronger acid than acetic acid, only a very small amount of the acetic acid will be ionized; that is, essentially all of the protons will come from the dichloroacetic acid:

$\dfrac{[H^+][Cl_2CHCO_2^-]}{[Cl_2CHCO_2H]} = 5.5 \times 10^{-2}$ $[H^+] \simeq [Cl_2CHCO_2^-] = X$, $[Cl_2CHCO_2H] = 1 - X$

$\dfrac{X^2}{1-X} = 5.5 \times 10^{-2}$; $X = \dfrac{-5.5 \times 10^{-2} \pm \sqrt{(5.5 \times 10^{-2})^2 + 0.22}}{2} = 0.21$ $\underline{M}$ =

$[Cl_2CHCO_2^-] = [H^+]$; pH = 0.68.

$$\frac{[H^+][CH_3CO_2^-]}{[CH_3CO_2H]} = 1.8 \times 10^{-5} = \frac{(0.21)y}{1-y}; \quad y = 8.6 \times 10^{-5} = [CH_3CO_2^-]$$

$$\frac{[Cl_2CH_2CO_2^-]}{[CH_3CO_2^-]} = \frac{0.21}{8.6 \times 10^{-5}} = 2.44 \times 10^3$$

S8.

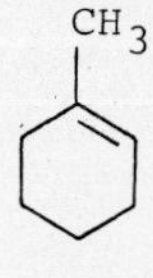

A (1-methylcyclohexene) B (methylcyclohexane)

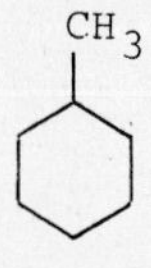

$CH_3CCH_2CH_2CH_2CH_2CO_2H$ (with =O on C)
C

$CH_3CCH_2CH_2CH_2CH_2CO_2H$ (with =NNHC$_6$H$_5$ on C)
D

$HO_2CCH_2CH_2CH_2CH_2CO_2H$
E

S9.

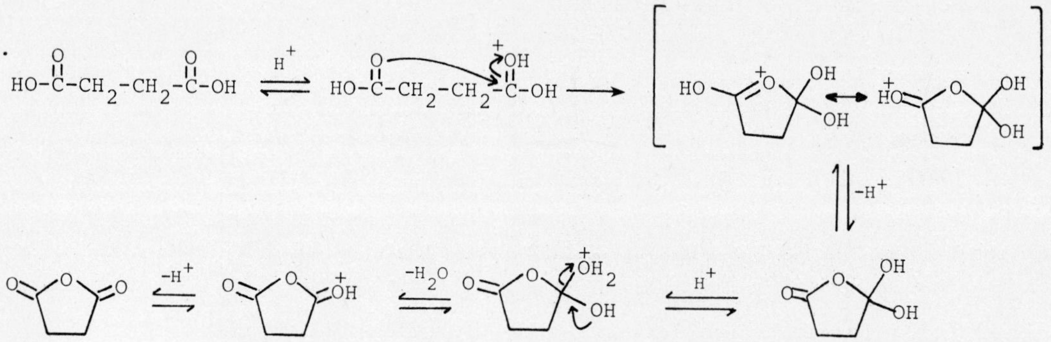

$HO-C-CH_2-CH_2-C-OH$ (each C with =O) $\rightleftharpoons$ H^+ $\rightarrow$ ... $\rightarrow$ [cyclic resonance structures] $\xrightarrow{-H^+}$

... anhydride / lactone intermediates ... $\xleftarrow{-H^+}$ ... $\xrightarrow{-H_2O}$ ... $\xleftarrow{H^+}$ ...

S10.

$CH_3-CH=CH-CO_2H \xrightarrow{Br-Br}$
[$CH_3-\overset{+}{CH}-CH-CO_2H$ (Br) $\longleftrightarrow$ $CH_3-CH-CH-CO_2H$ (bridged $\overset{+}{Br}$) $\longleftrightarrow$ $CH_3-CH-\overset{+}{CH}-CO_2H$ (Br)]
    1   2   3

$\xrightarrow[-H^+]{CH_3OH}$

$CH_3CH-CH-CO_2H$ (Br, OCH$_3$)

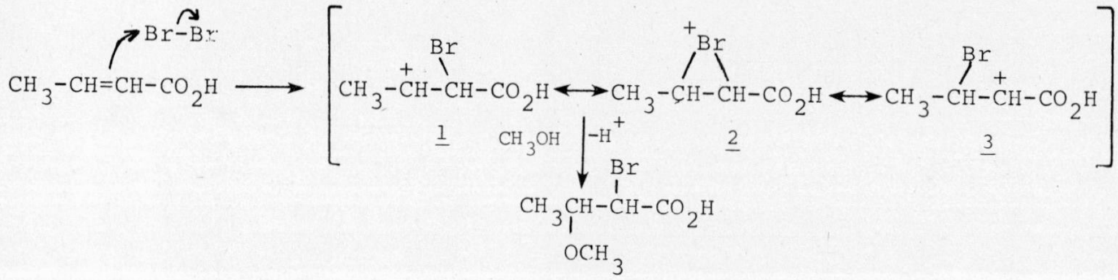

Resonance structure 3 is the *least* favored, because it puts a positive charge next to an already partially positive center: the carbonyl group. Therefore, "Markovnikov orientation" in this case favors nucleophilic attack at the β- and not the α-position.

S11. *least* acidic $CF_3CO_2CH_3$ (no ionizable hydrogens)

$CH_3CH_2CH_2CH_2OH$

CF_3CH_2OH

$CH_3CH_2\underset{CH_3}{\overset{CH_3}{C}}-CO_2H$

$CH_3CH_2CO_2H$

$HOCH_2CH_2CO_2H$

$ClCH_2CO_2H$

most acidic F_2CHCO_2H

18. DERIVATIVES OF CARBOXYLIC ACIDS

18.A   Chapter Outline and Important Terms Introduced

18.1   <u>Structure</u>

      esters   acid anhydrides
      amides   [nitriles]
      acyl halides   double bond character

18.2   <u>Nomenclature</u>

      alkyl alkanoate   alkanoic anhydride
      alkanamide   -carboxamide
      alkanoyl halide   -carbonyl halide

18.3   <u>Physical Properties</u>

18.4   <u>Spectroscopy</u>
   A. Nuclear Magnetic Resonance
   B. Infrared

       -CO$_2$R   1735 cm^{-1} lactones
       -COCl   1800 cm^{-1} lactams

         O   O
         ‖   ‖
       -C-O-C- 1820, 1760 cm^{-1} -CONR$_2$ 1650-1690 cm^{-1}

18.5   <u>Basicity of the Carbonyl Oxygen</u>
      contribution of resonance structures   O-protonation of amides

18.6   <u>Hydrolysis, Nucleophilic Addition-Elimination</u>
      acid catalysis vs. base catalysis
      sequence of bond-making vs. bond-breaking steps
      nucleophilic addition-elimination mechanism

18.7   <u>Other Nucleophilic Substitution Reactions</u>

   A. Reaction with Alcohols
       ester formation from acyl halides
       transesterification
   B. Reaction with Amines and Ammonia
       amide formation from acyl halides or esters
   C. Reaction of Acyl Halides and Anhydrides with Carboxylic Acids and Carboxylate Salts.
                           Synthesis of Anhydrides.
   D. Reaction with Organometallic Compounds
       ketone formation from acyl halides
       tertiary alcohol formation from esters

18.8   <u>Reduction</u>

      acid chloride to aldehyde
      ester to alcohol (Bouveault-Blanc reaction)
      amide to amine
      secondary amide to aldehyde
      nitrile to amine

18.9   <u>Acidity of the α-Protons</u>

        O   O   O
        ‖   ‖   ‖
    CH$_3$CCH$_3$ pK$_a$ 19   CH$_3$COCH$_3$, CH$_3$CN pK$_a$ 25   CH$_3$CN(CH$_3$)$_2$ pK$_a$ 30
    enolate formation   Claisen condensation
    Reformatsky reaction   acetoacetic ester condensation

18.10 <u>Reactions of Amides That Occur on Nitrogen</u>
         amide ionization:

$$R-\overset{\overset{\textstyle O}{\|}}{C}-NH_2 \;\rightleftharpoons\; R-\overset{\overset{\textstyle O}{\|}}{C}-NH^- \;+\; H^+ \qquad pK_a \; 15$$

         nitrile formation

18.11 <u>Pyrolytic Eliminations</u>
         ester pyrolysis   syn elimination
         xanthate ester pyrolysis (Chugaev reaction)

18.12 <u>Waxes and Fats</u>
         A. Waxes (spermaceti, bee's wax, carnauba wax)
         B. Fats
             fatty acids   phosphatidic acids
             triglycerides   lipid bilayer
             saponification

18.B   Important Reactions Introduced

<u>Hydrolysis of carboxylic acid derivatives</u> (18.6)

Equation:
$$R-\overset{\overset{\textstyle O}{\|}}{C}-Y \;+\; H_2O \;\longrightarrow\; R-\overset{\overset{\textstyle O}{\|}}{C}-OH \;+\; H-Y$$

Generality: Y = halogen, OR', NR'_2, O_2CR'
Key features: for $Y = OR'$, NR'_2: acid- or base-catalyzed (NR'_2 requires vigorous conditions)

<u>Reaction of carboxylic acid derivatives with alcohols</u> (18.7.A)

Equation:
$$R-\overset{\overset{\textstyle O}{\|}}{C}-Y \;+\; HOR' \;\longrightarrow\; R-\overset{\overset{\textstyle O}{\|}}{C}-OR' \;+\; H-Y$$

Generality: R = H, alkyl, aryl, OR; R' = alkyl
              Y = Cl or O_2CR (often with pyridine or Et_3N as reagent)
              $Y = OR'$ (transesterification, acid- or base-catalyzed)

Key features: equilibrium process for $Y = OR'$

<u>Reactions of carboxylic acid derivatives with amines</u> (18.7.B)

Equation:
$$R-\overset{\overset{\textstyle O}{\|}}{C}-Y \;+\; 2\; HNR'_2 \;\longrightarrow\; R-\overset{\overset{\textstyle O}{\|}}{C}-NR'_2 \;+\; HY$$

Generality: R = alkyl, aryl, H, or OR; R' = alkyl, aryl, or H
              Y = Cl, O_2CR, OR''

Key features: **not** acid-catalyzed

<u>Reactions of acyl halides and anhydrides with carboxylic acids</u> (18.7.C)

Equation:
$$R-\overset{\overset{\textstyle O}{\|}}{C}-Y \;+\; R'CO_2H \; (\text{or } R'CO_2^-Na^+) \;\longrightarrow\; R-\overset{\overset{\textstyle O}{\|}}{C}-O-\overset{\overset{\textstyle O}{\|}}{C}-R' \;+\; H-Y$$

Generality: Y = Cl, O_2CR (anhydride exchange)

<u>Reaction of carboxylic acid derivatives with organometallic reagents</u> (18.7.D)
       To give alcohols:

Equation:

$$\begin{array}{c} O \\ \| \\ R-C-Y \end{array} + \ 2\ R'M \ \longrightarrow \ \begin{array}{c} OH \\ | \\ R-C-R' \\ | \\ R' \end{array} + \ MY$$

Generality: Y = Cl, O_2CR, OR"; R' = alkyl, aryl; M = Li, MgX

Key features: reaction proceeds via addition/elimination to give ketone, then another addition
                reaction to give alcohol

To give ketones:

Equation:

$$\begin{array}{c} O \\ \| \\ R-C-Cl \end{array} + \ R'M \ \longrightarrow \ \begin{array}{c} O \\ \| \\ R-C-R' \end{array} + \ MCl$$

Generality: R'M = Grignard (RMgX) or organocuprate (R'_2CuLi)

Key features: reaction with Grignard reagent must be carried out at -78 ^{O}C to avoid formation of
                3° alcohol

Reduction of carboxylic acid derivatives (18.8)

To aldehyde:

Equation:

$$\begin{array}{c} O \\ \| \\ R-C-Y \end{array} \xrightarrow{\text{[H]}} \begin{array}{c} O \\ \| \\ R-C-H \end{array}$$

Generality: Y = Cl, [H] = H_2/Pd-BaSO$_4$-poison (quinoline): Rosenmund reduction
                Y = Cl, [H] = LiAlH(OtBu)$_3$
                Y = NR'$_2$, [H] = LiAlH(OEt)$_3$

Key features: these special reagents are required to avoid over-reduction to alcohol

To alcohol:

Equation:

$$\begin{array}{c} O \\ \| \\ R-C-Y \end{array} \xrightarrow{\text{[H]}} R-CH_2-OH$$

Generality: Y = Cl, O_2CR, OR'
                [H] = LiAlH$_4$, LiBH$_4$

Reduction of amides to amines (18.8)

Equation:

$$\begin{array}{c} O \\ \| \\ R-C-NR'_2 \end{array} \xrightarrow{\text{LiAlH}_4} RCH_2NR'_2$$

Generality: R, R' = alkyl, aryl, or H

Alkylation of ester enolates (18.9)

Equation:

$$RCH_2-CO_2R' + LDA \longrightarrow \begin{array}{c} OLi \\ | \\ RCH=COR' \end{array} \xrightarrow{R"X} \begin{array}{c} R\diagdown \\ \quad CH-CO_2R' \\ R"\diagup \end{array}$$

Generality: R = H, alkyl, aryl; R' = alkyl; R" = methyl or 1^O alkyl

Key features: similar to alkylation of ketone enolate, but ester enolate is more reactive

Reaction of ester enolates with ketones and aldehydes (18.9)

Equation: RCH$_2$CO$_2$R'

$$\begin{array}{c} \searrow^{LDA} \\ \nearrow_{Zn} \end{array} \left[\begin{array}{c} O^-M^+ \\ | \\ RCH=COR' \end{array} \right] \xrightarrow{\begin{array}{c} O \\ \| \\ R"-C-R" \end{array}} \begin{array}{c} OH \\ | \\ R"-C-CH-CO_2R' \\ | \quad | \\ R" \ R \end{array}$$

RCHCO$_2$R'
|
Br

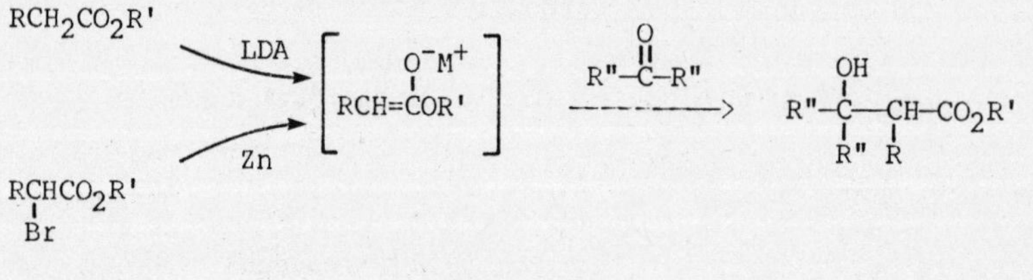

Generality: R, R', R" = various alkyl groups

Key features: similar to aldol addition reaction

Claisen condensation = acetoacetic ester condensation (18.9)

Equation:

$$2 \ RCH_2CO_2R' \ \xrightarrow{R'O^-} \ RCH_2-\overset{\displaystyle O}{\overset{\|}{C}}-\underset{\underset{\displaystyle R}{|}}{CH}-CO_2R'$$

Generality: R = H, alkyl, aryl; R' = alkyl

Key features: mixed condensations are practical only if only one ester can enolize

Formation of nitriles from amides (18.10)

Equation:

$$R-\overset{\displaystyle O}{\overset{\|}{C}}-NH_2 \ \xrightarrow{[-H_2O]} \ R-C{\equiv}N$$

Generality: R = alkyl, aryl

reagent = $SOCl_2$, $POCl_3$, P_2O_5, Ac_2O

Pyrolytic elimination of ester derivatives (18.11)

Equation:

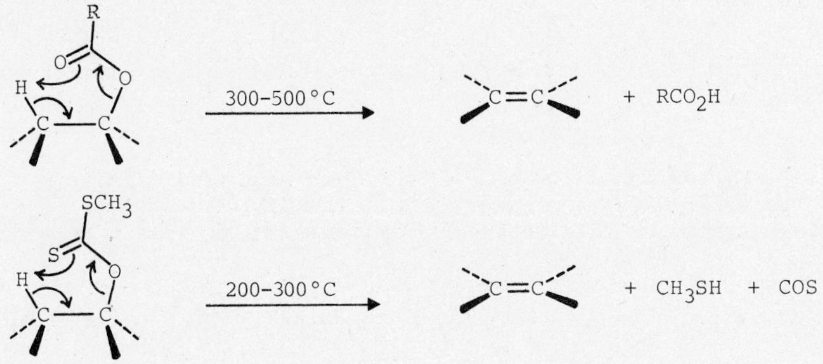

300–500 °C

$$\diagup C=C \diagdown \ + \ RCO_2H$$

200–300 °C

$$\diagup C=C \diagdown \ + \ CH_3SH \ + \ COS$$

(Chugaev reaction)

Generality: 1°, 2°, 3° alcohols

Key features: **syn** stereochemistry of elimination
neutral conditions for thermal elimination
xanthate ester made from ROH + CS_2 + base + CH_3I

18.C   Important Concepts and Hints

Addition-Elimination Mechanism.   The addition-elimination mechanism for substitution reactions of carboxylic acids was introduced in Chapter 17. Its importance is emphasized by the number of reactions discussed in this chapter which proceed by this mechanism. It holds the same importance in the chemistry of carboxylic acid derivatives as the S_N2 mechanism holds for substitution reactions of alkyl systems.

The addition-elimination mechanism applies to both acidic and basic reaction conditions, and examples can be found in which the same overall transformation is catalyzed by either one. Ester and amide hydrolysis are two examples; for both of them, you should compare closely the acid- and base-catalyzed mechanisms (see Section 18.6, and the answer to the Exercise at the end of that section), and be familiar with their similarities and differences (see Section 17.B of this Study Guide for a similar comparison in another reaction sequence).

You should also be completely familiar with the general aspects of the mechanisms which hold under acidic and basic conditions, as depicted below.

Acidic Conditions:

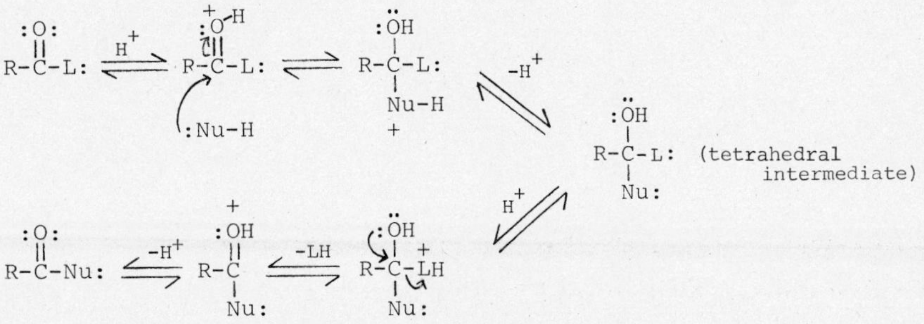

Basic Conditions:

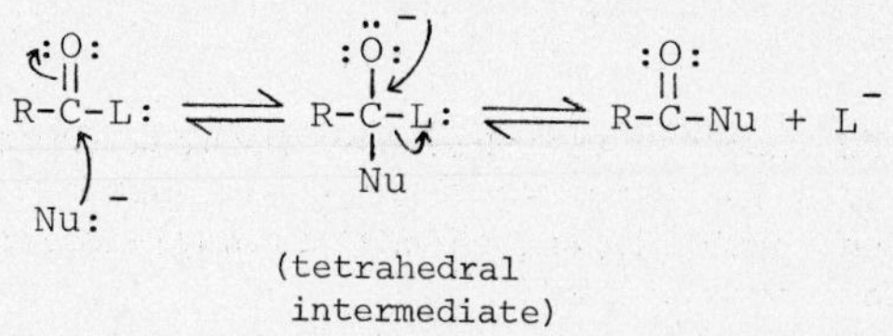

Notice the symmetry of these sequences: the steps leading to the formation of the tetrahedral intermediate are simply reversed in going from there to the product.

There are some reactions in which the distinction is somewhat blurred; for example, in the addition of ammonia to an acid chloride. In this case the nucleophile attacks before it loses its proton (as in the "acidic mechanism") and the leaving group departs before it gains one (as in the "basic mechanism"):

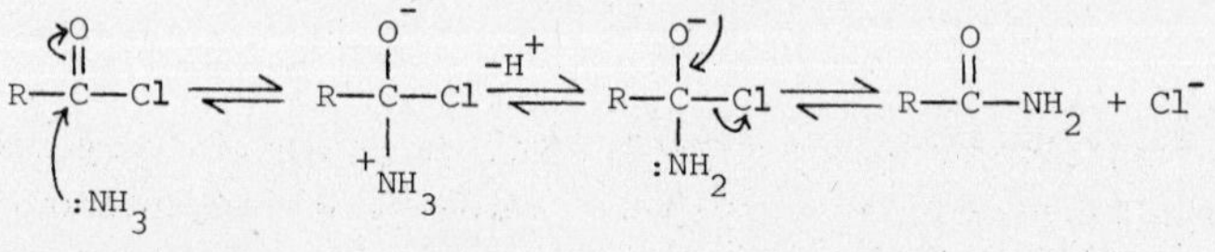

Because of the symmetrical nature of these sequences, the reactions could conceivably go in either direction. In fact, the reaction:

$$\text{ester} + \text{water} \overset{H^+}{\rightleftharpoons} \text{acid} + \text{alcohol}$$

is such an equilibrium process (see Section 17.7.C). There is a convenient way to predict which way the equilibrium lies for reactions which proceed by the **basic** mechanism: compare the pK_a's of "$Nu:^-$" and "L^-"; the reaction will go in the direction which generates the least basic (most stable) leaving group:

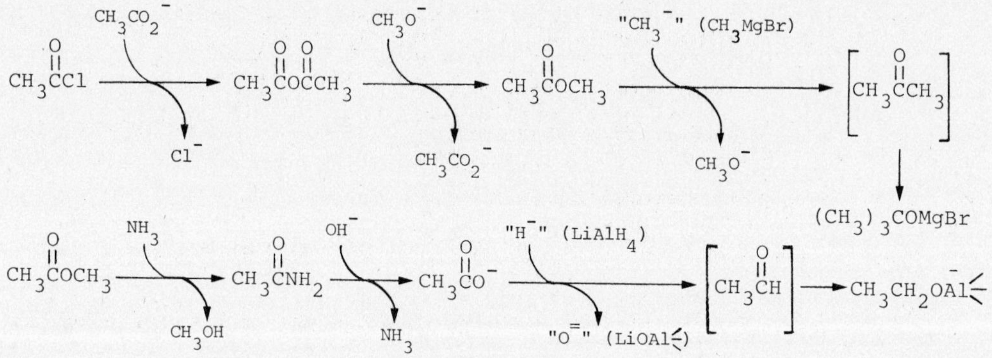

For acid-catalyzed amide hydrolysis, and for reactions with hydroxide ion, additional reactions of the products serve to remove one of the components of the equilibrium, thereby driving it completely to one side:

reaction	equilibrium	additional reaction
acid-catalyzed hydrolysis of amides	$R\overset{O}{\overset{\|}{C}}NH_2 + H_2O \overset{H^+}{\rightleftharpoons} R\overset{O}{\overset{\|}{C}}OH + NH_3$	$\overset{H^+}{\longrightarrow} R\overset{O}{\overset{\|}{C}}OH + NH_4^+$
base-catalyzed hydrolysis of esters, amides	$R\overset{O}{\overset{\|}{C}}L + H_2O \overset{OH^-}{\rightleftharpoons} R\overset{O}{\overset{\|}{C}}OH + HL$ (L = OR' or NR'_2)	$\overset{OH^-}{\longrightarrow} R\overset{O}{\overset{\|}{C}}O^- + HL$

18.D   Answers to Exercises

18.1 The dipolar resonance structure has a double bond between the carbonyl and the Y group. Therefore, the more important this resonance structure is, the greater the degree of shortening of the carbonyl-to-Y bond relative to the single bond model, CH_3-Y.

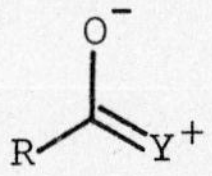

CH_3-NH_2 vs. $CH_3\overset{O}{\overset{\|}{C}}-NH_2$ $\overset{O}{\overset{\|}{C}}$-N   bond shorter by 0.11 Å

CH_3-OCH_3 vs. $CH_3\overset{O}{\overset{\|}{C}}-OCH_3$ $\overset{O}{\overset{\|}{C}}$-O   bond shorter by 0.06 Å

CH_3-F vs. $CH_3\overset{O}{\overset{\|}{C}}-F$ $\overset{O}{\overset{\|}{C}}$-F   bond shorter by 0.01 Å

There is a direct correlation between the basicity of Y^- and the degree of bond shortening.

18.2   (a)   methyl hexanoate, hexanamide, hexanoyl chloride, hexanoic anhydride

(b)   methyl 4-methylpentanoate, 4-methylpentanamide, 4-methylpentanoyl chloride, 4-methylpentanoic anhydride

(c)   methyl 4-pentenoate, 4-pentenamide, 4-pentenoyl chloride, 4-pentenoic anhydride

(d)   methyl 3-bromopropanoate, 3-bromopropanamide, 3-bromopropanoyl chloride, 3-bromopropanoic anhydride

(e)   2-methylpropyl 4-methylpentanoate

(f)   N,N-diethyl-4,4-dimethylpentanamide

18.3

IR, 1740 cm^{-1}

NMR δ 0.9   1.2-1.9   2.3   5.0 CH_3 1.25 ppm

$CH_3-CH_2-CH_2-CH_2-CH_2-\overset{O}{\overset{\|}{C}}-O-CH$

CMR δ 14.3   23.4 25.5   32.9 33.9   172.0   65.6 CH_3 20.2 ppm

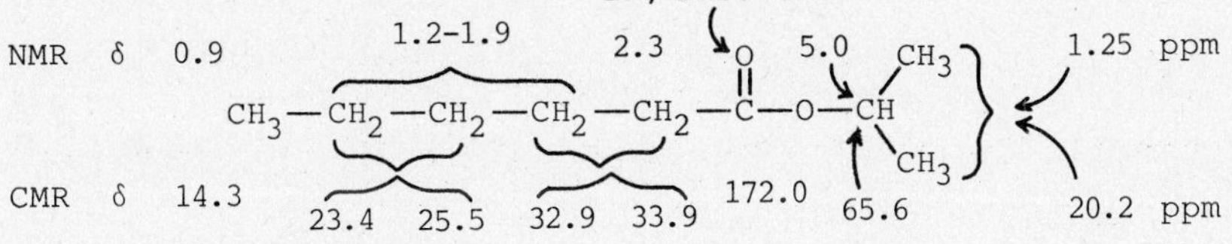

18.4   There is a good correlation:

$\overset{O}{\overset{\|}{C}}$-NH$_2$ bond shorter than CH_3-NH_2 by 0.11 Å; pK_a of conjugate acid: 0.0

$\overset{O}{\overset{\|}{C}}$-OCH$_3$ bond shorter than CH_3-OCH_3 by 0.06 Å; pK_a of conjugate acid: -6.5

$\overset{O}{\overset{\|}{C}}$-F   bond shorter than CH_3-F by 0.01 Å; pK_a of conjugate acid: ~ -9

18.5   *Acid-Catalyzed:*

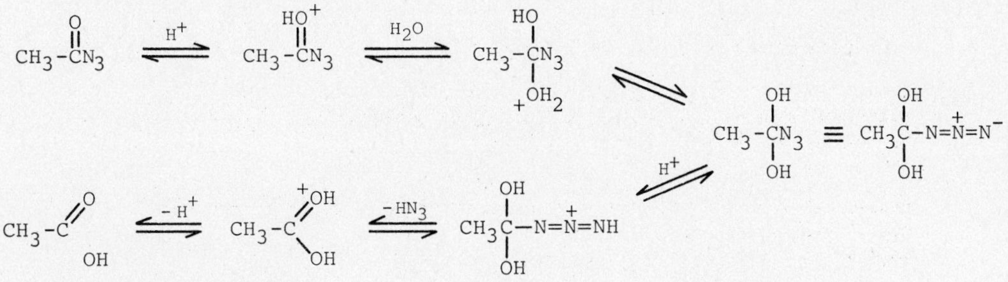

Base-promoted:

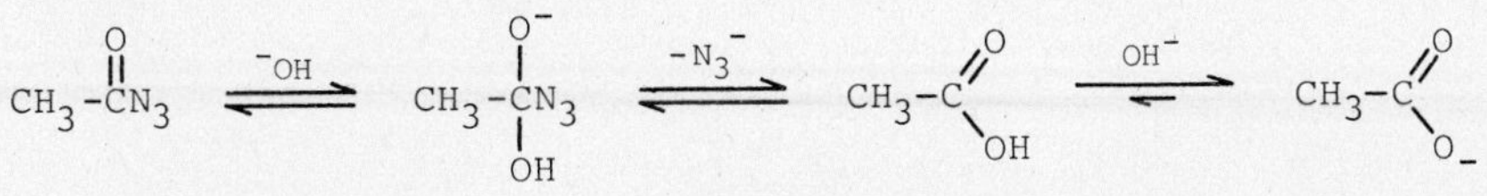

18.6

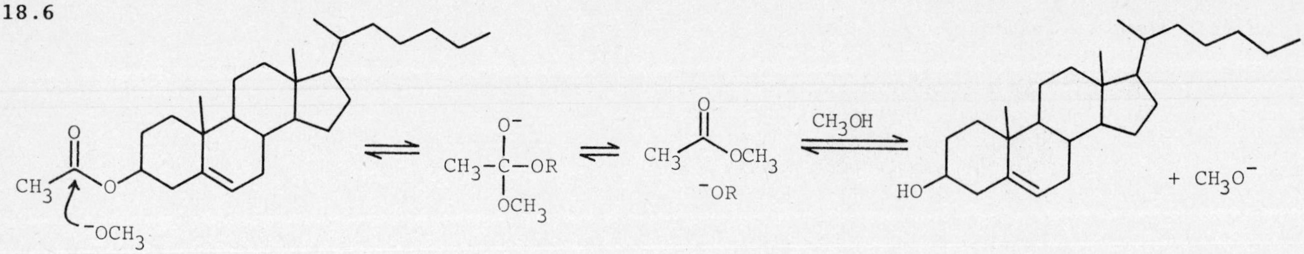

18.7

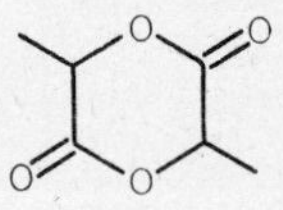

18.8

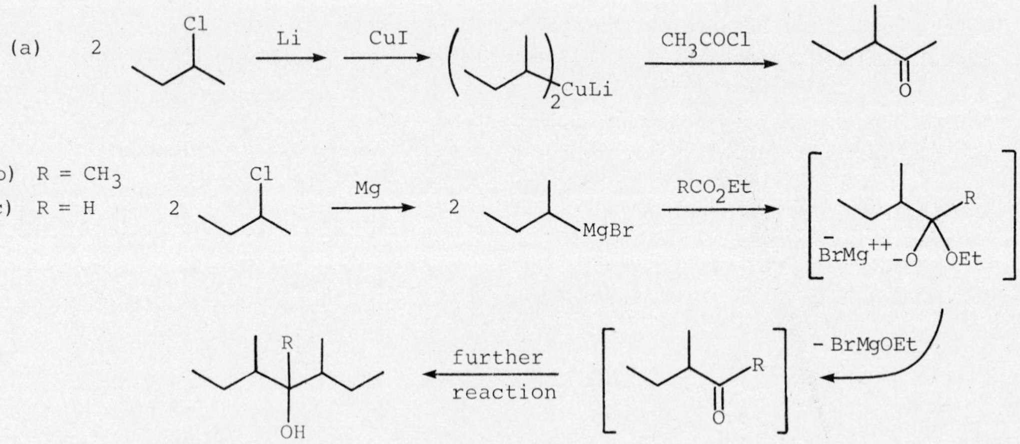

(a) 2 $\xrightarrow{\text{Li}}$ $\xrightarrow{\text{CuI}}$ $\left(\underset{2}{}\right)_2\text{CuLi}$ $\xrightarrow{\text{CH}_3\text{COCl}}$

(b) $R = CH_3$
(c) $R = H$ 2 $\xrightarrow{\text{Mg}}$ 2 -MgBr $\xrightarrow{\text{RCO}_2\text{Et}}$ $\left[\right]$

$\xleftarrow{\text{further reaction}}$ $\left[\right]$ $\xleftarrow{-\text{BrMgOEt}}$

18.9

(a) $H_2/Pd\text{-}BaSO_4\text{-quinoline}$ (Rosenmund reduction)   or $LiAlH(O\underline{t}\text{-}Bu)_3$
(b) $LiAlH_4$ or $LiBH_4$
(c) $LiAlH_4$
(d) $LiAlH(OC_2H_5)_3$

18.10

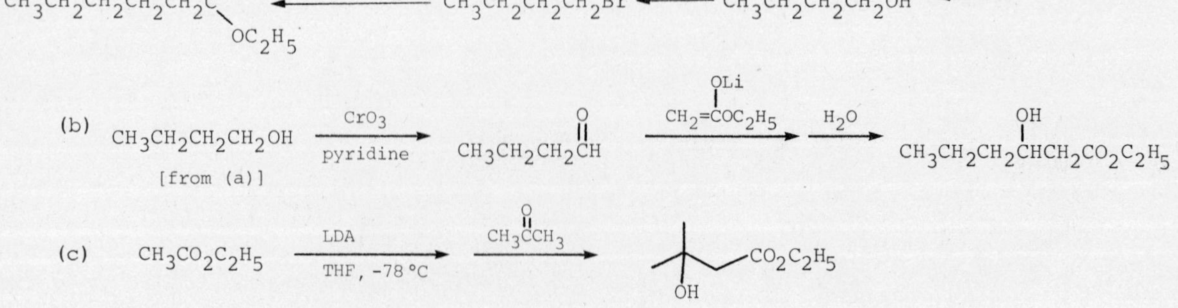

(a) $CH_3CO_2C_2H_5 \xrightarrow{LiAlH_4} \xrightarrow{H_2O} C_2H_5OH \xrightarrow{PBr_3} CH_3CH_2Br$

$CH_3CO_2C_2H_5 \xrightarrow{LiN\textit{i}Pr_2}$ $\xrightarrow{CH_3CH_2Br} CH_3CH_2CH_2CO_2C_2H_5 \xrightarrow{LiAlH_4}$

$CH_3CH_2CH_2CH_2CH_2\overset{O}{\underset{OC_2H_5}{C}} \xleftarrow{CH_2=C(OLi)(OC_2H_5)} CH_3CH_2CH_2CH_2Br \xleftarrow{PBr_3} CH_3CH_2CH_2CH_2OH \xleftarrow{H_2O}$

(b) $CH_3CH_2CH_2CH_2OH$ [from (a)] $\xrightarrow[\text{pyridine}]{CrO_3} CH_3CH_2CH_2\overset{O}{C}H \xrightarrow[\text{H}_2\text{O}]{CH_2=C(OLi)C_2H_5} CH_3CH_2CH_2\overset{OH}{C}HCH_2CO_2C_2H_5$

(c) $CH_3CO_2C_2H_5 \xrightarrow[\text{THF, -78°C}]{LDA} \xrightarrow{CH_3\overset{O}{C}CH_3}$

(d) $CH_3CO_2C_2H_5 \xrightarrow[\text{EtOD}]{EtO^-} CD_3CO_2C_2H_5$

(e) $CH_3CO_2C_2H_5$ $\xrightarrow[\substack{THF \\ -78°C}]{LDA}$ $\xrightarrow{LiAlH_4}$

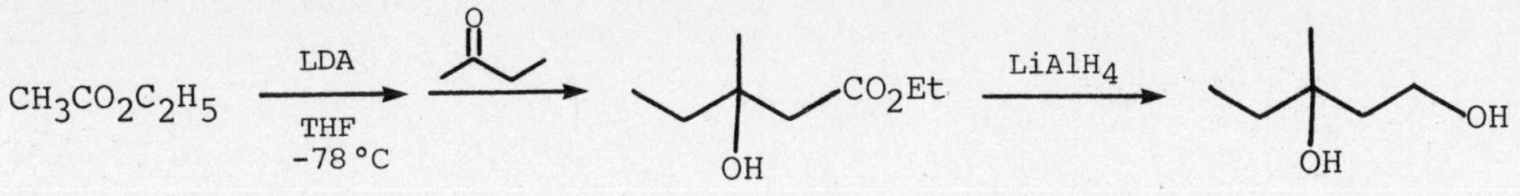

(f) $C_2H_5O_2CCH_3$ + $HCO_2C_2H_5$ $\xrightarrow{EtO^-}$ $C_2H_5O_2CCH_2\overset{\overset{\displaystyle O}{\|}}{C}H$

18.11   Product

Starting Material	C_2H_5Br	$CH_3CH_2CO_2H$	$CH_3CH_2CONH_2$	$CH_3CH_2C{\equiv}N$
C_2H_5Br		17.6		9.2
$CH_3CH_2CO_2H$	17.7.G		17.7.E	
$CH_3CH_2CONH_2$		18.6		18.10
$CH_3CH_2C{\equiv}N$		18.6	18.6	

18.12

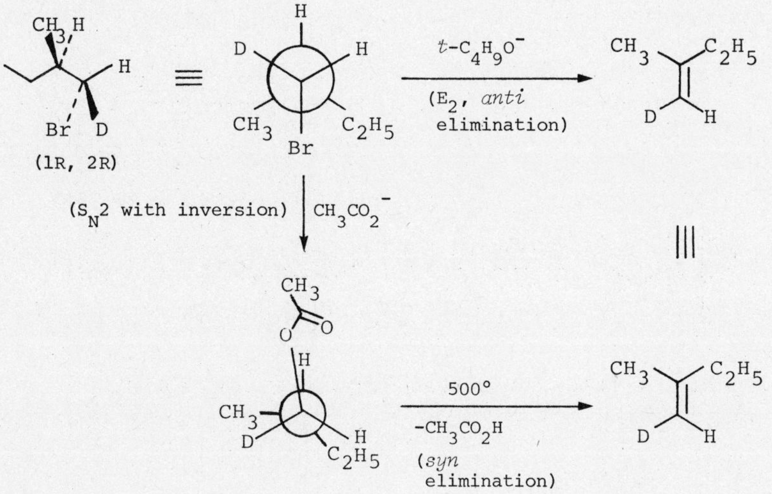

18.E   Answers and Explanations for Problems

1.   (a)   propyl 3-ethylpentanoate
    (b)   ethyl cyclohexanecarboxylate
    (c)   ethyl cyclopentanecarboxylate
    (d)   propanoyl chloride
    (e)   butanoic anhydride

    (f)   N-methylpropanamide
    (g)   N-cyclohexyl-2-methylpropanamide
    (h)   methyl 2-chlorobutanoate
    (i)   3-methylpentanoyl bromide
    (j)   cyclohexyl ethanoate
             (cyclohexyl acetate is used more commonly)

2.   (a)   (b) $H\overset{\overset{\displaystyle O}{\|}}{C}N(CH_3)_2$ (c) $CH_3CH_2CH_2\overset{\overset{\displaystyle O}{\|}}{C}OC_2H_5$ (d) $ClCH_2CH_2CO_2CH_3$

(e) $CH_3CH_2\overset{\overset{\displaystyle O}{\|}}{C}O\overset{\overset{\displaystyle O}{\|}}{C}CH_2CH_3$ (f) $CH_3\overset{\overset{\displaystyle O}{\|}}{C}O\overset{\overset{\displaystyle O}{\|}}{C}H$ (g)   (h) $CH_3CH_2CH_2\overset{\overset{\displaystyle O}{\|}}{C}Br$

(i)   (j) $\underset{\displaystyle CH_3CH_2CH_2CHCH_2CO_2H}{\overset{\displaystyle CHO}{|}}$ (k) $CH_3\overset{\overset{\displaystyle O}{\|}}{C}CH_2CO_2C_2H_5$ (l) $CH_3\overset{\overset{\displaystyle O}{\|}}{C}NHBr$

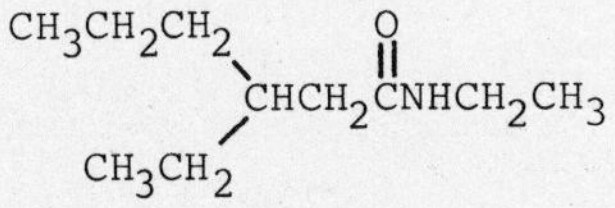

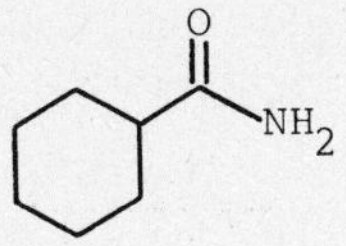

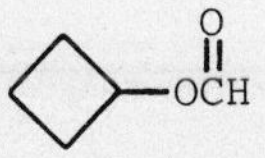

3. Acetic acid is a weak acid and a weak base as shown by:

$$CH_3CO_2H \rightleftharpoons H^+ + CH_3CO_2^-$$

$$K_2 = \frac{[CH_3CO_2^-][H^+]}{[CH_3CO_2H]} = 1.8 \times 10^{-5}$$

$$CH_3C(OH)_2^+ \rightleftharpoons H^+ + CH_3CO_2H$$

$$K_1 = \frac{[H^+][CH_3CO_2H]}{[CH_3C(OH)_2^+]} = 10^6$$

Make the assumption that in 0.1 M HCl, <u>most</u> of the acetic acid is unionized; that is, present as CH_3CO_2H.

(a)
$$\frac{[CH_3CO_2^-] \cdot 10^{-1}}{[CH_3CO_2H]} = 1.8 \times 10^{-5}$$

$$\frac{[CH_3CO_2^-]}{[CH_3CO_2H]} = 1.8 \times 10^{-4}$$

% as $CH_3CO_2^- = 0.018\%$

(b)
$$\frac{[CH_3CO_2H] \cdot 10^{-1}}{[CH_3C(OH)_2^+]} = 10^6$$

$$\frac{[CH_3CO_2H]}{[CH_3C(OH)_2^+]} = 10^7$$

$$\frac{[CH_3C(OH)_2^+]}{[CH_3CO_2H]} = 10^{-7}$$

% as $CH_3C(OH)_2^+ = 0.00001\%$

(% as $CH_3CO_2H \cong 99.98\%$)

4.

$$CH_3\overset{O}{\overset{\|}{C}}OH_2^+ \rightleftharpoons H^+ + CH_3CO_2H \qquad K' = \frac{[H^+][CH_3CO_2H]}{\left[CH_3\overset{O}{\overset{\|}{C}}OH_2^+\right]} = 10^{12} \qquad \text{(eq. 1)}$$

$$CH_3\overset{+OH}{\overset{\|}{C}}OH \rightleftharpoons H^+ + CH_3CO_2H \qquad K_1 = \frac{[H^+][CH_3CO_2H]}{\left[CH_3\overset{+OH}{\overset{\|}{C}}OH\right]} = 10^6 \qquad \text{(eq. 2)}$$

Rearranging:
$$\frac{\left[CH_3\overset{+OH}{\overset{\|}{C}}OH\right]}{[H^+][CH_3CO_2H]} = 10^{-6} \qquad \text{(eq. 3)}$$

Multiply eq. 1 × eq. 3:
$$\frac{[H^+][CH_3CO_2H]}{\left[CH_3\overset{O}{\overset{\|}{C}}OH_2^+\right]} \cdot \frac{\left[CH_3\overset{+OH}{\overset{\|}{C}}OH\right]}{[H^+][CH_3CO_2H]} = 10^{12} \cdot 10^{-6}$$

$$\frac{\left[CH_3\overset{+OH}{\overset{\|}{C}}OH\right]}{\left[CH_3\overset{O}{\overset{\|}{C}}OH_2^+\right]} = 10^6$$

5. The formula $C_7H_{13}O_2Br$ shows that the molecule has one ring or double bond. The infrared band at 1740 cm^{-1} strongly suggests an ester, which would account for both oxygens: $-\overset{O}{\overset{\|}{C}}-O-$ We make the hypothesis that the compound is a bromine-containing ester.

Some of the NMR bands may be: δ 1.0 (3H) triplet: $\underline{CH_3}-CH_2-$

1.3 (6H) doublet: $(\underline{CH_3})_2CH-$

A possible structure that fits this information is:

$$CH_3CH_2\underset{\underset{\text{δ 2.1 (2H) multiplet}}{\uparrow}}{\overset{\overset{\text{Br}}{|}}{CH}}-\underset{\underset{\text{δ 4.2 (1H) triplet}}{\uparrow}}{\overset{\overset{O}{\|}}{C}}-O-CH\overset{\overset{CH_3}{}}{\underset{\underset{}{CH_3}}{}} \quad \leftarrow \text{δ 4.6 (1H) multiplet}$$

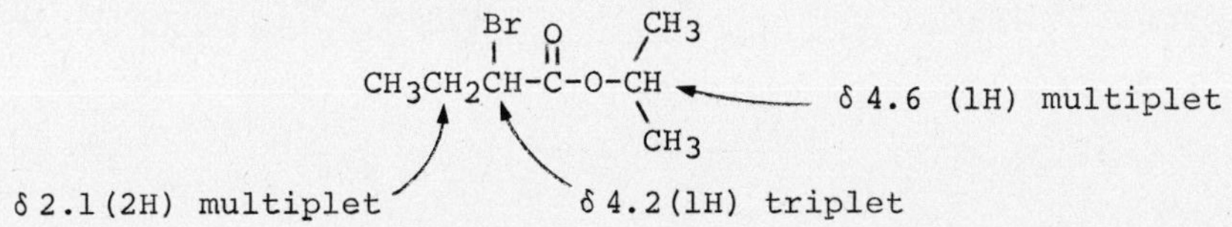

6. Formula, $C_6H_{11}BrO_2$, indicates one double bond or one ring.

   IR: no OH
        1740 cm^{-1} (strong) suggests ester

   NMR: δ 1.3 (t, 3H) and δ 4.2 (q, 2H) must be CH_3CH_2; furthermore, the downfield position of the CH_2 resonance (δ 4.2 ppm) means that it must be attached to an electronegative atom.

   δ 1.9 (s, 6H): two equivalent, isolated methyl groups; downfield position of resonance (δ 1.8 ppm) indicates that the methyl groups are attached to an electron-withdrawing carbon.

   From this information, we conclude that the structural pieces are:

   $$CH_3CH_2-X \qquad \overset{\overset{O}{\|}}{-C}-O- \qquad CH_3-\overset{\overset{Y}{|}}{\underset{\underset{Z}{|}}{C}}-CH_3 \qquad -Br$$

   Structure:
   $$CH_3-CH_2-O-\overset{\overset{O}{\|}}{C}-\overset{\overset{CH_3}{|}}{\underset{\underset{CH_3}{|}}{C}}-Br$$

7. (a) $CH_3CH=CH_2$ + CH_3CO_2H (b) [cyclohexene] + CH_3SH (c) [cyclopentene]—CH_3 + CH_3SH

   (d) $CH_3CH_2CH_2CO_2^-$ Na^+ (e) [benzyl]NH_2 (f) [phenyl]—CN

8.

   (a) $(CH_3)_3C-\overset{\overset{O}{\|}}{C}-ND_2$ (b) [steroid structure with CO_2CH_3 and HO] + $CH_3\overset{\overset{O}{\|}}{C}-OCH_3$ (c) [decalin structure]—CH_2OH

   (d) $CH_3CH_2\overset{\overset{O}{\|}}{C}\overset{\overset{}{|}}{\underset{\underset{CH_3}{|}}{CH}}CO_2C_2H_5$ (e) $CH_3CH_2\overset{\overset{OH}{|}}{CH}CH_2CO_2CH_3$ (f) $CH_3CH_2\overset{\overset{OH}{|}}{CH}\overset{\overset{}{|}}{\underset{\underset{CH_3}{|}}{CH}}CO_2C_2H_5$

9. (a) $CH_3CH_2CH_2CO_2H \xrightarrow[\text{or } PCl_5]{SOCl_2} CH_3CH_2CH_2\overset{\overset{O}{\|}}{C}Cl$

   (b) $CH_3CH_2CH_2\overset{\overset{O}{\|}}{C}OH \xrightarrow{NaOH} CH_3CH_2CH_2\overset{\overset{O}{\|}}{C}O^-\ Na^+ \xrightarrow{CH_3CH_2CH_2\overset{\overset{O}{\|}}{C}-Cl}$

   (c) $CH_3CH_2CH_2CO_2H \xrightarrow{SOCl_2} \xrightarrow{CH_3CH_2CH_2CH_2OH}$

   or $\xrightarrow[H^+]{CH_3CH_2CH_2CH_2OH}$ $\begin{pmatrix} CH_3CH_2CH_2CO_2H \\ \downarrow LiAlH_4 \\ CH_3CH_2CH_2CH_2OH \end{pmatrix}$

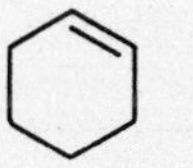

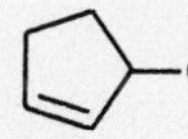

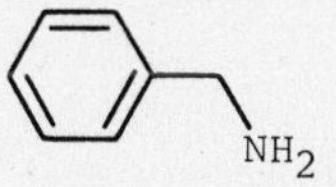

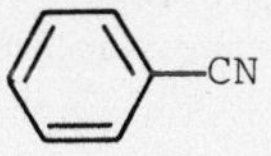

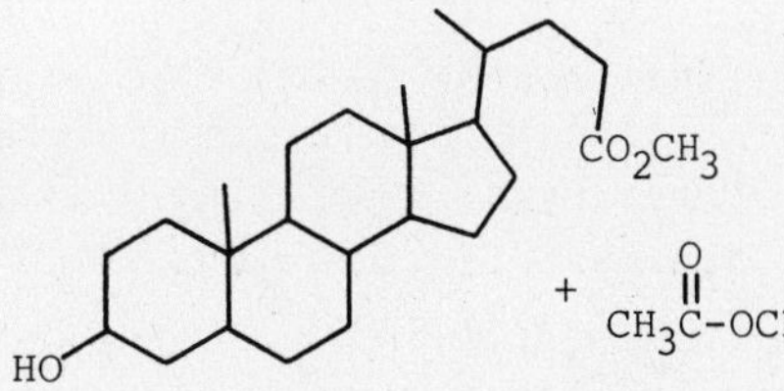

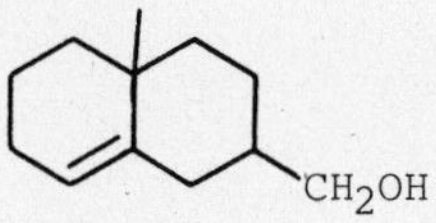

(d) $CH_3CH_2CH_2CO_2H$ + $(CH_3)_2NH$ $\xrightarrow{170°C}$

   $\underline{or}$ $\xrightarrow{SOCl_2}$ $\xrightarrow[\text{OH}^-]{(CH_3)_2NH}$

(e) $CH_3CH_2CH_2\overset{\displaystyle O}{\overset{\|}{C}}OH$ $\xrightarrow{NH_3}$ $\xrightarrow{170°C}$ $CH_3CH_2CH_2\overset{\displaystyle O}{\overset{\|}{C}}NH_2$ $\xrightarrow[\Delta]{P_2O_5}$ $CH_3CH_2CH_2C\equiv N$

(f) $CH_3CH_2CH_2CN$ [from (e)] $\xrightarrow[NH_3]{H_2/\text{catalyst}}$ $CH_3CH_2CH_2CH_2NH_2$

   $\underline{or}$ $CH_3CH_2CH_2\overset{\displaystyle O}{\overset{\|}{C}}NH_2$ $\xrightarrow[\text{ether}]{LiAlH_4}$ $CH_3CH_2CH_2CH_2NH_2$

(g) $CH_3CH_2CH_2CO_2H$ $\xrightarrow[Br_2]{HgO}$ $CH_3CH_2CH_2Br$ (h) $CH_3CH_2CH_2CO_2H$ $\xrightarrow[\substack{2.\ HN(C_2H_5)_2 \\ 3.\ LiAlH_4}]{1.\ SOCl_2}$ $CH_3CH_2CH_2CH_2N(C_2H_5)_2$

10.

(a) $CH_3CH_2CH_2\overset{\displaystyle O}{\overset{\|}{C}}OH$ $\xrightarrow{SOCl_2}$ $CH_3CH_2CH_2\overset{\displaystyle O}{\overset{\|}{C}}Cl$ $\xrightarrow{\left(CH_3\overset{\displaystyle CH_3}{\overset{|}{C}H}CH_2\right)_2CuLi}$

(b) $CH_3CH_2CH_2\overset{\displaystyle O}{\overset{\|}{C}}OH$ $\xrightarrow[H^+]{CH_3OH}$ $CH_3CH_2CH_2CO_2CH_3$ $\xrightarrow{CH_3MgBr}$ $\xrightarrow{H_3O^+}$ $CH_3CH_2CH_2\overset{\displaystyle CH_3}{\underset{CH_3}{\overset{|}{\underset{|}{C}}OH}}$

(c) $CH_3CH_2CH_2CO_2H$ $\xrightarrow{SOCl_2}$ $\xrightarrow{LiAlH(O\underline{t}Bu)_3}$ $CH_3CH_2CH_2CHO$

(d) $CH_3CH_2CH_2CO_2H$ $\xrightarrow{LiAlH_4}$ $CH_3CH_2CH_2CH_2OH$

(e) $CH_3CH_2CH_2CO_2H$ $\xrightarrow[C_2H_5OH]{H^+}$ $CH_3CH_2CH_2CO_2C_2H_5$ $\xrightarrow{NaOC_2H_5}$ $CH_3CH_2CH_2\overset{\displaystyle O}{\overset{\|}{C}}\underset{CH_2CH_3}{\overset{|}{C}H}CO_2C_2H_5$ $\xrightarrow{LiAlH_4}$

(f) $CH_3CH_2CH_2CO_2C_2H_5$ $\xrightarrow[\text{THF, }-78°C]{LiN(\underline{i}\text{-Pr})_2}$ $\xrightarrow{CH_3CH_2CH_2\overset{\displaystyle O}{\overset{\|}{C}}H}$ $\xrightarrow{H_2O}$ $CH_3CH_2CH_2\underset{CH_2CH_3}{\overset{OH}{\overset{|}{C}H}}\overset{|}{C}HCO_2C_2H_5$
   [from (e)]

(g) See answer to (e).

11.

(a) $H_2N-\overset{\displaystyle O}{\overset{\|}{C}}-Cl$ + CH_3O^- $\longrightarrow$ $H_2N-\overset{\displaystyle O}{\overset{\|}{C}}-OCH_3$ + Cl^-

   After addition of CH_3O^-, the intermediate is: $H_2N-\underset{OCH_3}{\overset{O^-}{\overset{|}{\underset{|}{C}}}}-Cl$

   This may decompose in three ways. The three leaving groups
   are NH_2^-, CH_3O^-, Cl^-. The best leaving group is Cl^-, so the product is:

   $H_2N-\underset{OCH_3}{\overset{O^-}{\overset{|}{\underset{|}{C}}}}-Cl$ $\longrightarrow$ $H_2N-\overset{\displaystyle O}{\overset{\|}{C}}-OCH_3$ + Cl^-

(b) $CH_3O-\overset{\displaystyle O}{\overset{\|}{C}}-Cl$ + NH_2^- $\longrightarrow$ $CH_3O-\overset{\displaystyle O}{\overset{\|}{C}}-NH_2$ + Cl^- ; same reasoning as in (a).

12.

(a) $CH_3CO_2CH_3$ $\xrightarrow[\text{THF, }-78°C]{LiN(\underline{i}\text{-Pr})_2}$ $CH_2=\underset{OCH_3}{\overset{OLi}{\overset{|}{\underset{|}{C}}}}$ $\xrightarrow{(CH_3)_2CHCH_2CH_2Br}$ $(CH_3)_2CHCH_2CH_2CH_2CO_2CH_3$

(b) $CH_2=\underset{OC_2H_5}{\overset{OLi}{\overset{|}{\underset{|}{C}}}}$ + $CH_3CH_2CH_2\overset{\displaystyle O}{\overset{\|}{C}}H$ $\longrightarrow$ $\xrightarrow{H_2O}$ $CH_3CH_2CH_2\overset{OH}{\overset{|}{C}}HCH_2CO_2C_2H_5$

(c)

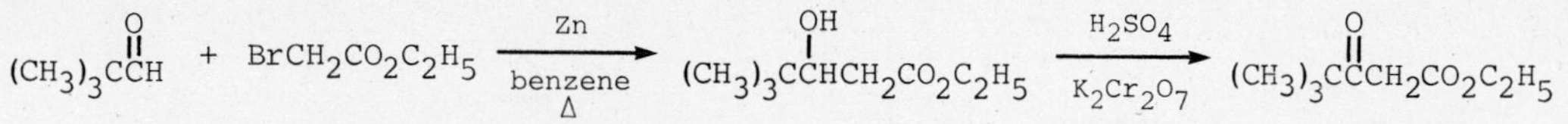

$$(CH_3)_3CCH \overset{O}{\underset{}{\parallel}} + BrCH_2CO_2C_2H_5 \xrightarrow[\substack{benzene \\ \Delta}]{Zn} (CH_3)_3C\underset{OH}{\overset{}{\underset{|}{C}}}CHCH_2CO_2C_2H_5 \xrightarrow[K_2Cr_2O_7]{H_2SO_4} (CH_3)_3C\overset{O}{\underset{}{\parallel}}CCH_2CO_2C_2H_5$$

> (*NOTE*: although only one ester would be enolizable, a mixed Claisen condensation would not be a good choice, because the ethyl acetate enolate would condense faster with ethyl acetate itself than with the sterically more congested ethyl 2,2-dimethylpropanoate.)

(d)

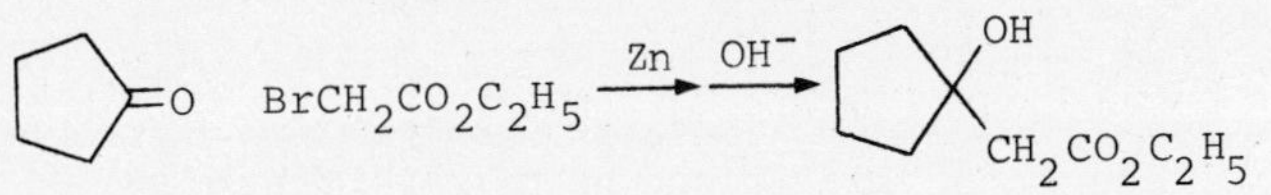

(or via lithium enolate)

13.

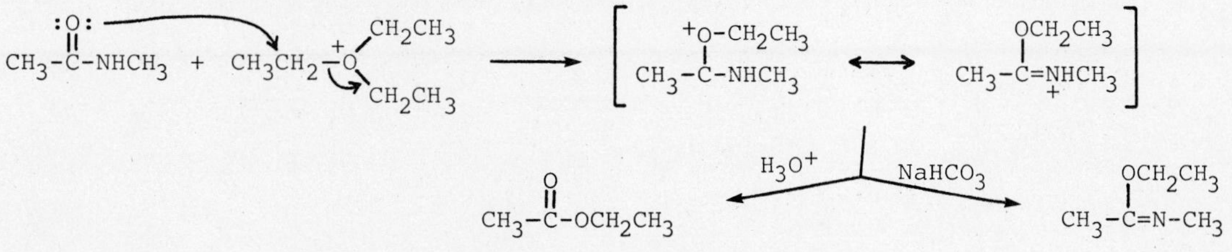

14.

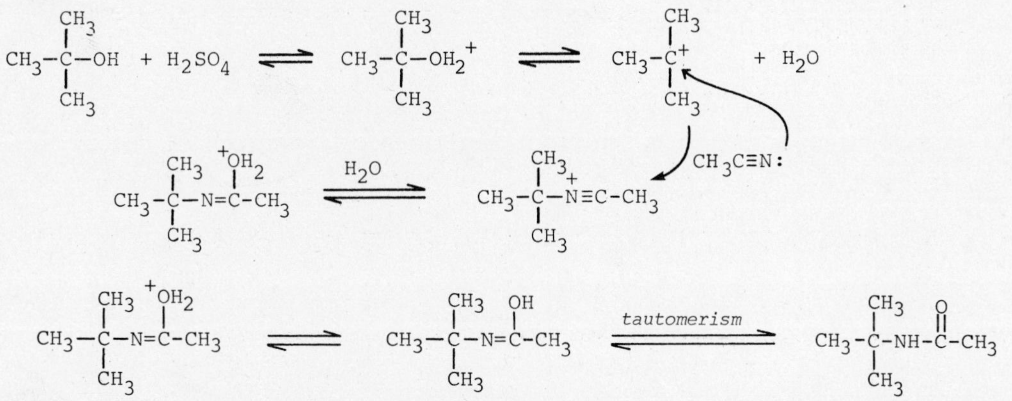

With 2-methyl-2,4-pentanediol, the tertiary carbocation forms more easily than the secondary carbocation. After addition of acetonitrile, the resulting cation reacts *intramolecularly* with the other hydroxyl group. The product is a heterocyclic compound, called a *tetrahydrooxazine*.

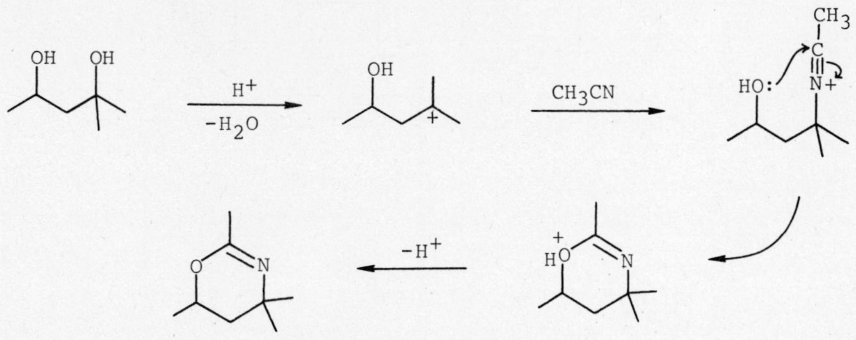

15.

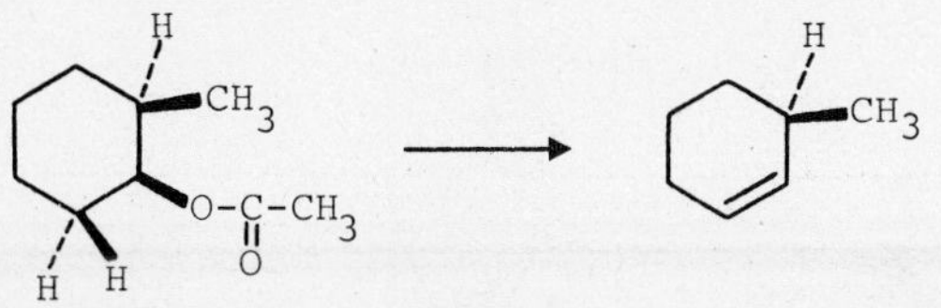

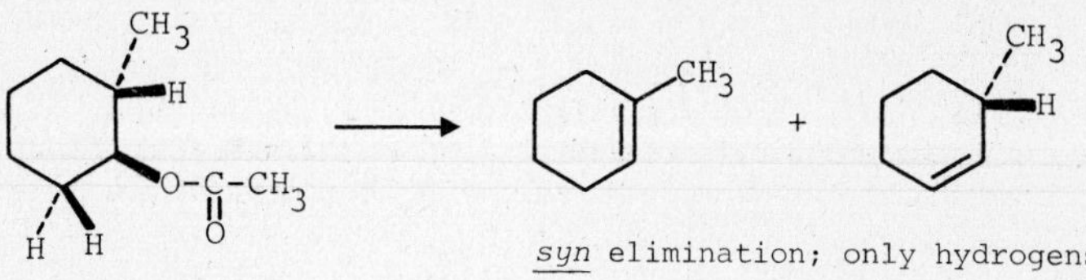

syn elimination; only hydrogens on the same side of the
ring can be removed.

16. The reaction has a favorable entropy (positive ΔS^o) because one molecule gives rise to two. The reaction has a relatively high energy of activation; hence, a high temperature is required. Furthermore, from $\Delta G^o = \Delta H^o - T\Delta S^o$, the favorable entropy can give rise to a favorable equilibrium constant at sufficiently high temperature, despite being endothermic.

17.

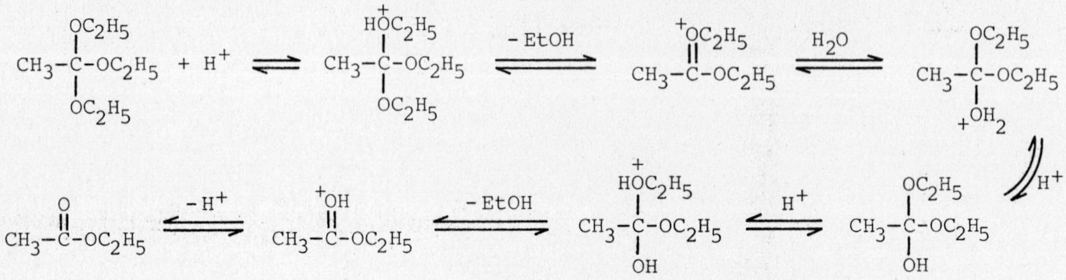

18.

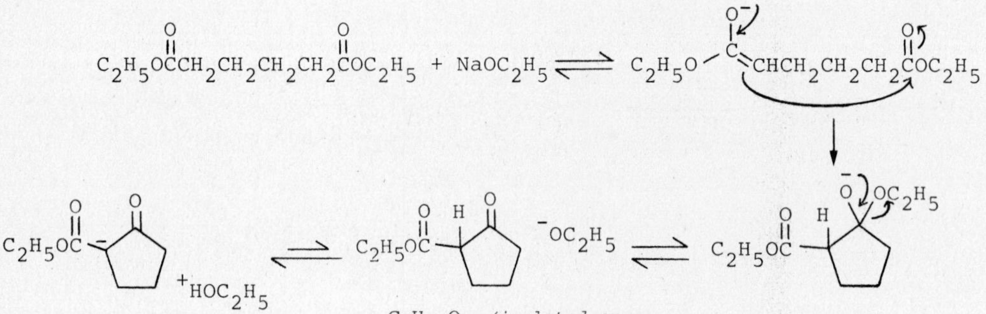

$C_8H_{12}O_3$ *(isolated on acidification)*

19.

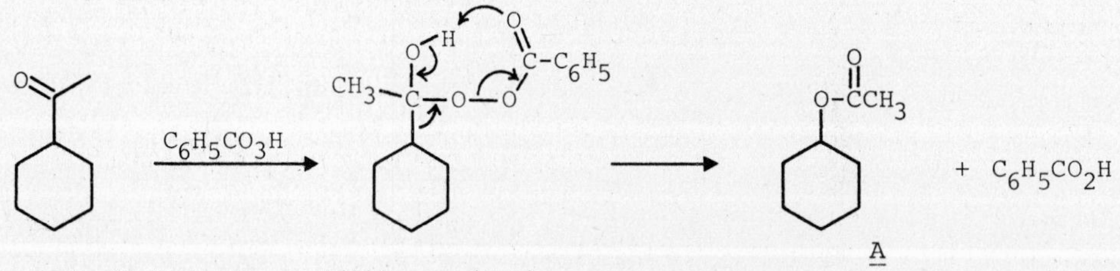

$+ C_6H_5CO_2H$

Note that the Baeyer-Villiger oxidation occurs
exclusively with migration of the cyclohexyl group.

20. (a) S_N2 reaction with inversion of configuration.

(b) Convert to a sulfonate ester and displace with sodium methoxide.

21.

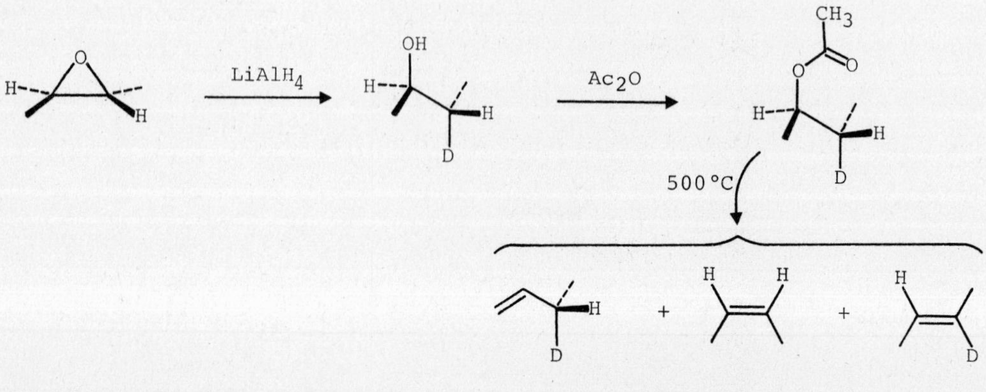

18.F   Supplementary Problems

S1.   Give the IUPAC name of each of the following compounds.

(a) $CH_3CH_2\overset{\overset{\displaystyle CH_3}{|}}{C}HC\overset{\overset{\displaystyle O}{\parallel}}{N}HCH_3$

(e) $CH_3CH_2CH_2\overset{\overset{\displaystyle O}{\parallel}}{C}C\equiv N$

(b)

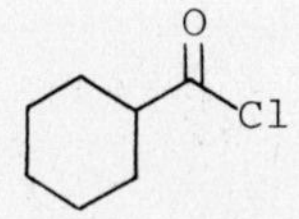

(f) $CH_3CH_2\overset{\overset{\displaystyle O}{\parallel}}{C}NHBr$

(c) $(CH_3)_2CH\overset{\overset{\displaystyle O}{\parallel}}{C}O\overset{\overset{\displaystyle O}{\parallel}}{C}CH(CH_3)_2$

(g)

(d) $CH_2=CH-CH=CH-\overset{\overset{\displaystyle O}{\parallel}}{O}CCH_3$

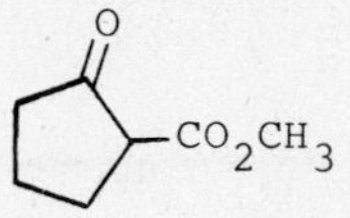

(h)

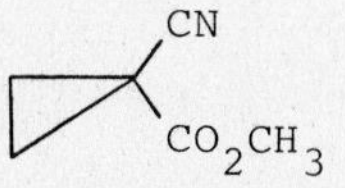

S2.   Provide IUPAC names for juvenile hormone and juvabione (Section 17.8.)
      (Don't forget stereochemistry.)

S3.   What is the major product of each of the following reaction sequences?

(a) $CH_3CH_2\overset{\overset{\displaystyle O}{\parallel}}{C}OCH_3 \xrightarrow{NH_3} \xrightarrow{LiAlH_4} \xrightarrow{CH_3CH_2\overset{\overset{\displaystyle O}{\parallel}}{C}Cl}$

(b) $(CH_3)_2CHCHO \xrightarrow{Ag_2O} \underset{\Delta}{\xrightarrow{P\ +\ Br_2}} \xrightarrow{HOCH(CH_3)_2}$

(c) 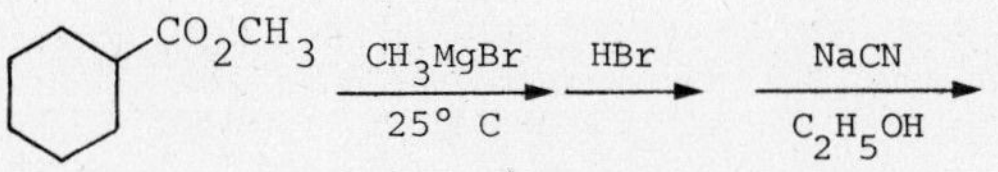 $\underset{25°\ C}{\xrightarrow{CH_3MgBr}} \xrightarrow{HBr} \underset{C_2H_5OH}{\xrightarrow{NaCN}}$

(d) $CH_3CH_2CH_2CH_2CO_2H \underset{Br_2}{\xrightarrow{AgO}} \xrightarrow{Na^+\ ^-O_2CCH_3} \xrightarrow{500°\ C}$

(e) $CH_3CH_2CO_2C(CH_3)_3 \underset{\substack{THF \\ -78°\ C}}{\xrightarrow{LDA}} \xrightarrow{CH_3CH_2\overset{\overset{\displaystyle O}{\parallel}}{C}H} \xrightarrow{CH_3CH_2\overset{\overset{\displaystyle O}{\parallel}}{C}Cl}$

(f) 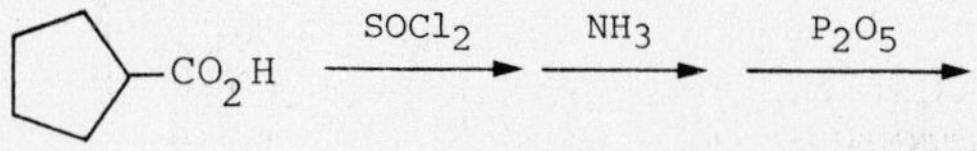 $\xrightarrow{SOCl_2} \xrightarrow{NH_3} \xrightarrow{P_2O_5}$

(g) $(CH_3)_2CHCH_2CO_2H \xrightarrow{SOCl_2} \xrightarrow{LiAlH(O\text{-}\underline{t}Bu)_3} \xrightarrow{H_2O}$

(h) 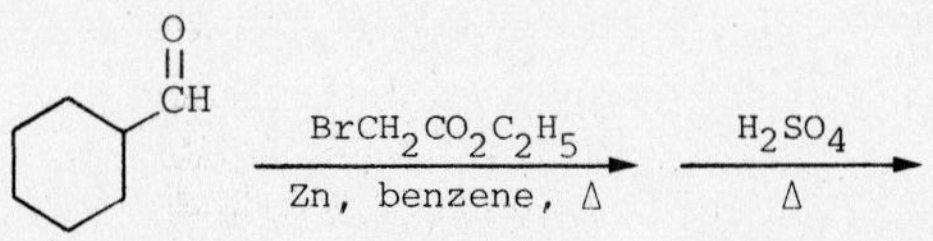 $\underset{Zn,\ benzene,\ \Delta}{\xrightarrow{BrCH_2CO_2C_2H_5}} \underset{\Delta}{\xrightarrow{H_2SO_4}}$

S4.   Show how to carry out the following transformations.

(a)

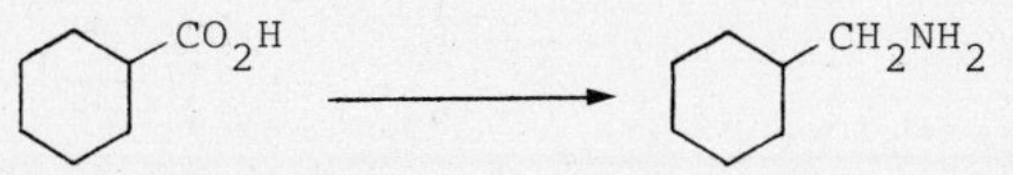

(b) $(CH_3)_2CHCH_2CH_2OH \longrightarrow (CH_3)_2CHCH_2CH_2\overset{\overset{\displaystyle}{}}{C}HCO_2CH(CH_3)_2$
      $\underset{CH_3}{|}$

(c)

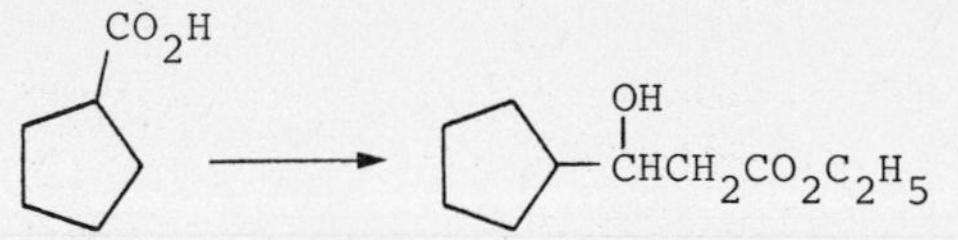

$$\underset{\text{cyclopentane-}CO_2H}{} \longrightarrow \underset{\text{cyclopentane-}CHCH_2CO_2C_2H_5}{\overset{OH}{|}}$$

(d)

$$\text{(lactone)} \longrightarrow CH_3\overset{O}{\overset{||}{C}}OCH_2CH_2CH_2CH_2O\overset{O}{\overset{||}{C}}CH_3$$

(e) $(CH_3)_2CHCH_2OH \longrightarrow ((CH_3)_2CHCH_2)_3CBr$

(f)

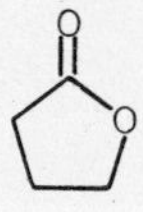

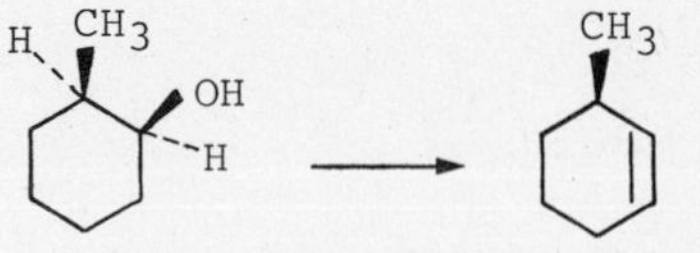

$$\underset{}{} \longrightarrow \underset{}{}$$ (g) $BrCH_2CH_2CH_2Br \longrightarrow \underset{}{}$

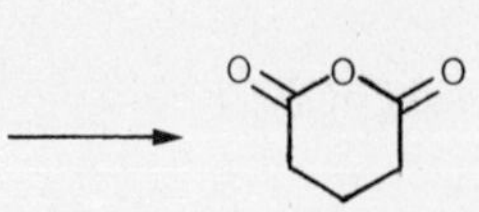

(h) $CH_3CH_2CH_2CO_2C_2H_5 \longrightarrow CH_3CH_2CH_2\overset{OH}{\overset{|}{C}}HCHCH_2CH_3$
$$\underset{CH_2OH}{|}$$

S5. (a) Provide structures for A-D below, and assign all the spectral
     information.

$$A \xrightarrow[\text{2. H}^+]{\text{1. NaOCH}_3} B \xrightarrow{\text{SOCl}_2} C \xrightarrow[\text{quinoline poison}]{\text{H}_2\text{Pd-BaSO}_4} D$$

IR: 1725,1820 cm^{-1} IR: 1740,1710,   IR: 1735,1785 cm^{-1} IR: 1725,1740 cm^{-1}
                             2500-3000(br) cm^{-1}
NMR: δ 2.0(quintet,
2H), 2.8(t,4H)   NMR: δ 3.8(3H),
                             13(s,1H) (and
                             resonances for
                             6 other H's)

(b) When compound **D** is treated with HCN and a trace of base, compound **E** is formed. The
     NMR spectrum of **E** reveals the presence of only seven hydrogens; the IR spectrum shows
     bands at 1735 and 2130 cm^{-1}. Propose a structure for **E** and write a reasonable mechanism
     for its formation.

S6. Reaction of acetonitrile in methanol with dry HCl gives initially methyl acetimidate hydro-
     chloride (**1**) and then methyl orthoacetate (**2**). Write a mechanism for this reaction.

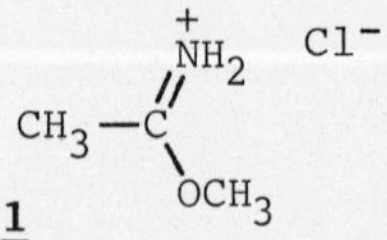

$$CH_3-\overset{\overset{+}{N}H_2}{\underset{OCH_3}{C}}\ Cl^-$$ $$CH_3C(OCH_3)_3$$

1   **2**

S7. Methyl acetimidate (**3**) is hydrolyzed in aqueous sodium hydroxide to give mainly
     acetamide and methanol. In aqueous acid, it hydrolyzes to give primarily
     methyl acetate and ammonia. Write mechanisms for these reactions and explain
     why different products are seen in acid and base.

$$CH_3-\overset{NH}{\underset{OCH_3}{C}}$$

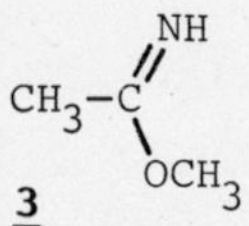

3

S8. Write a mechanism for the following transformation. (**HINT:** see Problem #18 in this chapter)

$$\underset{}{} \xrightarrow[\Delta]{\text{NaOCH}_3} \xrightarrow[\text{(work up)}]{\text{H}^+} \underset{}{}$$

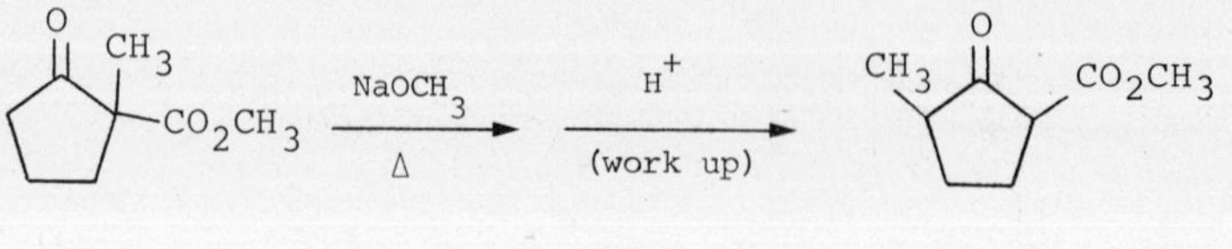

S9. Starting with benzoic acid (**4**), propanoic acid, dimethylamine ($(CH_3)_2NH$), and any needed reagents, outline a synthesis of propoxyphene (the active ingredient in Darvon®).

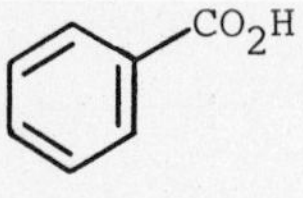

$$\underline{4}$$

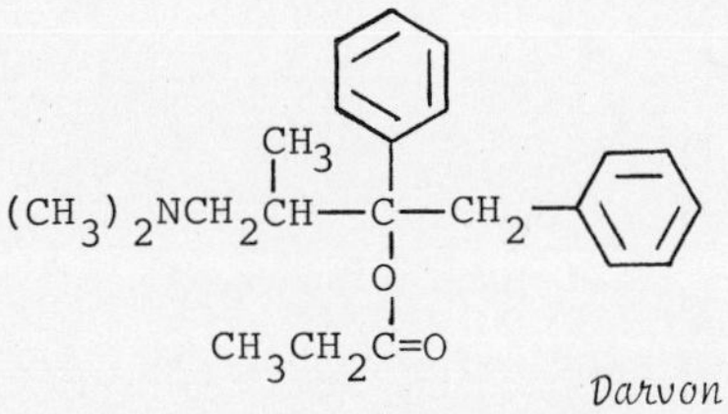

$$(CH_3)_2NCH_2CH \overset{CH_3}{\underset{\underset{CH_3CH_2C=O}{O}}{-C}}-CH_2 \text{—phenyl}$$

Darvon

S10. A useful preparation of deuterioethanol (C_2H_5OD) involves refluxing diethyl carbonate with D_2O and a small amount of strong acid. Why is this preparation so convenient?

S11. Trimyristin is a white crystalline fat, mp 54-55°, obtainable from nutmeg, and is the principal constituent of nutmeg butter. Hydrolysis of trimyristin with hot aqueous sodium hydroxide gives an excellent yield of myristic acid, mp 52-53°, as the only fatty acid. What is the structure of trimyristin?

18.G   Answers to Supplementary Problems

S1. (a) N-2-dimethylbutanamide   (e) 2-oxopentanenitrile
        (b) cyclohexanecarbonyl chloride   (f) N-bromopropanamide
        (c) 2-methylpropanoic anhydride   (g) methyl 2-oxocyclopentanecarboxylate
        (d) 1,3-butadienyl acetate   (h) methyl 1-cyanocyclopropanecarboxylate

S2. Juvenile hormone: methyl (<u>Z</u>)-10,11-epoxy-7-ethyl-3,11-dimethyl-(<u>E</u>,<u>E</u>)-2,6-tridecadienoate

        Juvabione: methyl (<u>R</u>)-4-((<u>R</u>)-1,5-dimethyl-3-oxohexyl)-1-cyclohexenecarboxylate

S3. (a) 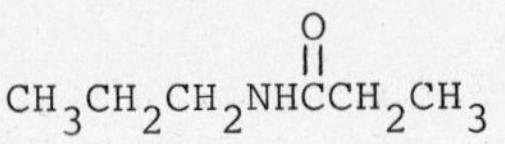 $CH_3CH_2CH_2NHCCH_2CH_3$ (with C=O)   (b) 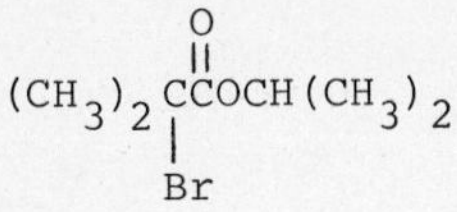 $(CH_3)_2CCOCH(CH_3)_2$ (with C=O and Br)

        (c)

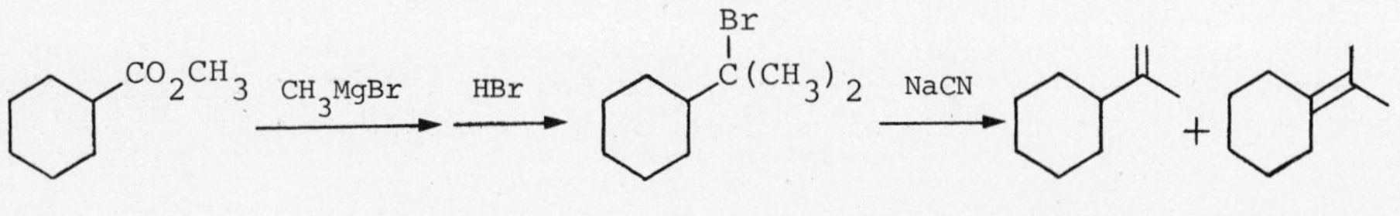

$$\text{(E2, not } S_N2 \text{ . . .)}$$

        (d) $CH_3CH_2CH=CH_2$ (e)

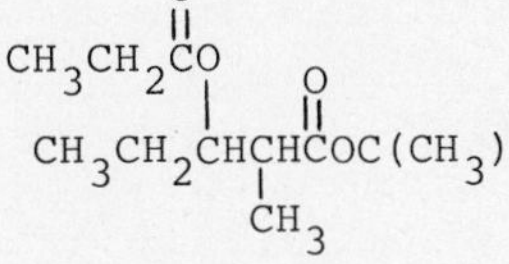

        (f) 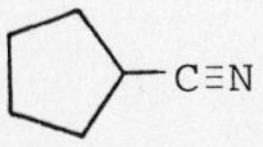 cyclopentyl-$C\equiv N$ (g) 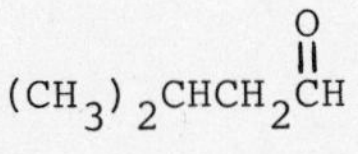 $(CH_3)_2CHCH_2CH$ (with C=O)   (h) 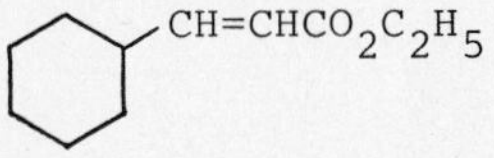 cyclohexyl-$CH=CHCO_2C_2H_5$

S4. (a)

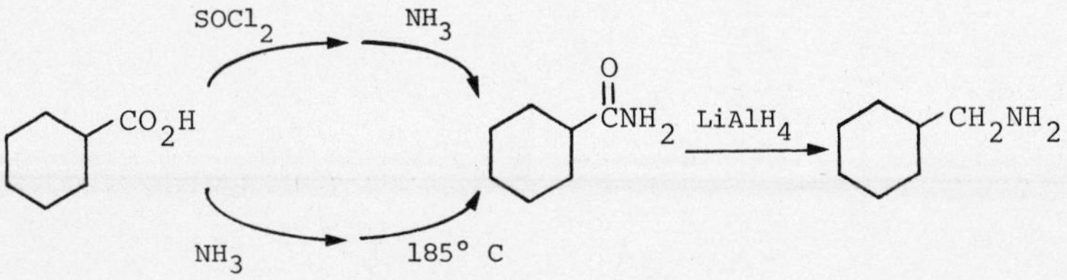

(b) $(CH_3)_2CHCH_2CH_2OH \xrightarrow{PBr_3} (CH_3)_2CHCH_2CH_2Br$

$+$

$(CH_3)_2CHCH_2CH_2\overset{O}{\overset{\|}{C}}HCOCH(CH_3)_2$ $\xleftarrow{}$ $CH=\overset{OLi}{\overset{|}{C}}OCH(CH_3)_2$ $\xleftarrow[\text{THF}]{\text{LDA}}$ $CH_2\overset{O}{\overset{\|}{C}}OCH(CH_3)_2$
$\quad\quad\quad\overset{|}{C}H_3$ $\quad\quad\quad\overset{|}{C}H_3$ $\quad\quad -78°\,C$ $\quad\quad\overset{|}{C}H_3$

(c) (*among several ways*)

cyclopentane-CO_2H $\xrightarrow{SOCl_2}$ $\xrightarrow[\text{quinoline}]{H_2/Pd\text{-}BaSO_4}$ cyclopentane-$\overset{O}{\overset{\|}{C}}H$ $\xrightarrow[\text{Zn}]{BrCH_2CO_2C_2H_5}$ cyclopentane-$\overset{OH}{\overset{|}{C}}HCH_2CO_2C_2H_5$

(d) lactone $\xrightarrow{LiAlH_4}$ $\xrightarrow{H_2O}$ $HOCH_2CH_2CH_2CH_2OH$ $\xrightarrow[\text{pyridine}]{2\ (CH_3\overset{O}{\overset{\|}{C}})_2O}$ $CH_3\overset{O}{\overset{\|}{C}}OCH_2CH_2CH_2CH_2O\overset{O}{\overset{\|}{C}}CH_3$

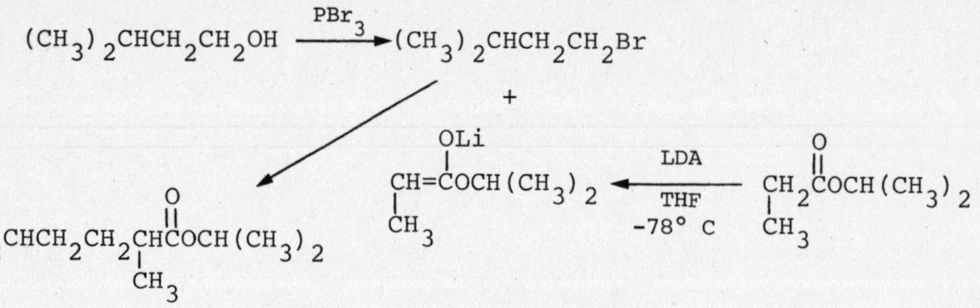

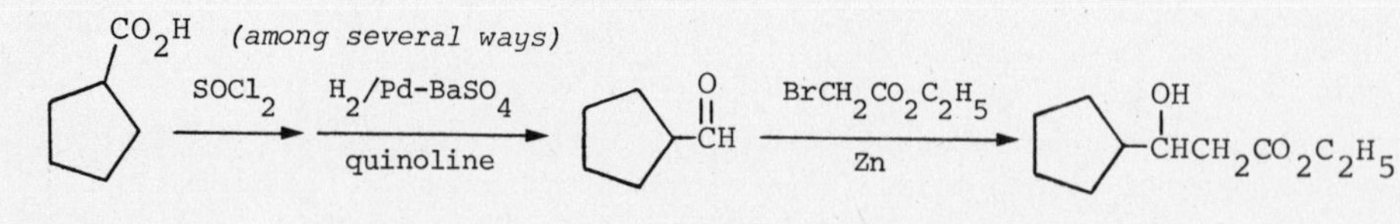

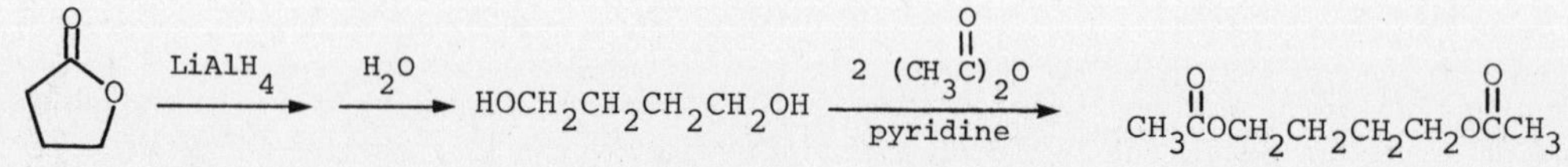

(e) $(CH_3)_2CHCH_2OH \xrightarrow{PBr_3} \xrightarrow{Mg} \xrightarrow{(CH_3O)_2C=O} \xrightarrow{HBr} ((CH_3)_2CHCH_2)_3C\text{-}Br$

(f) cyclohexane structure (H, CH3, OH, H) $\xrightarrow[\text{CS}_2]{NaOH} \xrightarrow{CH_3I} \xrightarrow{\Delta}$ cyclohexene with CH3 (*syn elimination*)

(g) $BrCH_2CH_2CH_2Br \xrightarrow{2\ NaCN} \xrightarrow[\Delta]{H_3O^+} HO_2CCH_2CH_2CH_2CO_2H \xrightarrow[\Delta]{(CH_3\overset{O}{\overset{\|}{C}})_2O}$ glutaric anhydride

(h) $2\ CH_3CH_2CH_2CO_2C_2H_5 \xrightarrow{NaOC_2H_5} CH_3CH_2CH_2\overset{O}{\overset{\|}{C}}\overset{}{C}HCH_2CH_3 \xrightarrow{LiAlH_4} \xrightarrow{H_2O} CH_3CH_2CH_2\overset{OH}{\overset{|}{C}}HCHCH_2CH_3$
$\quad\quad\quad\quad\quad\quad\quad\quad\quad\quad\quad\quad\quad\quad\quad\quad\quad\overset{|}{C}O_2C_2H_5 \quad\quad\quad\quad\quad\quad\quad\quad\quad\quad\quad\quad\quad\quad\quad\overset{|}{C}H_2OH$

S5. (a)

	anhydride	ester	acid	ester	acid chloride
	1755, 1820 cm^{-1}	1740	1710, 2500–3000	1735	1785

A: glutaric anhydride structure

B: $CH_3OCCH_2CH_2CH_2CO\text{-}H$

C: $CH_3OCCH_2CH_2CH_2CCl$

δ2.8(t)

δ2.0(quartet)

δ3.8

δ13

	ester	aldehyde
	1740	1725

D: $CH_3OCCH_2CH_2CH_2CH$

(b) $CH_3\overset{O}{\overset{\|}{O}C}CH_2CH_2CH_2\overset{O}{\overset{\|}{C}}H + HCN \longrightarrow CH_3\overset{O}{\overset{\|}{O}C}CH_2CH_2CH_2\overset{OH}{\overset{|}{C}}HCN \xrightarrow[\rightleftharpoons]{\text{base}} CH_3\overset{O}{\overset{\|}{O}C}CH_2CH_2CH_2\overset{O^-}{\overset{|}{C}}HCN$

6-ring lactone   nitrile
     1735   2130

lactone-CN structure $\rightleftharpoons$ $CH_3O-\overset{-O}{...}\overset{H}{...}CN$ cyclic structure

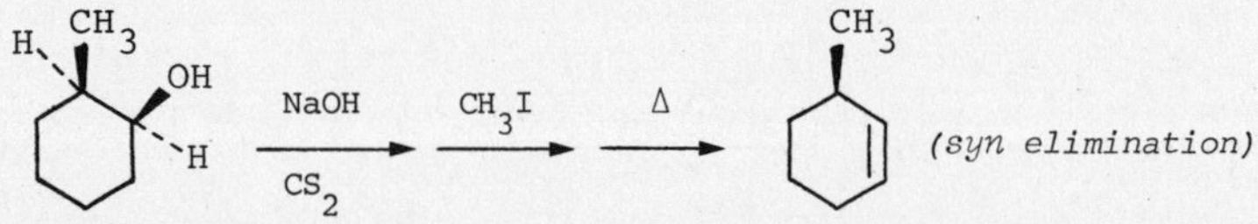

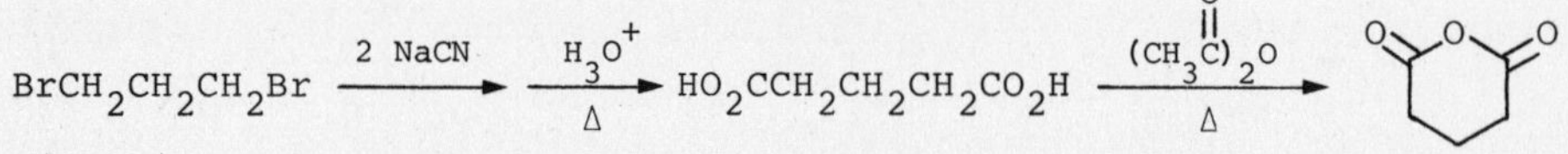

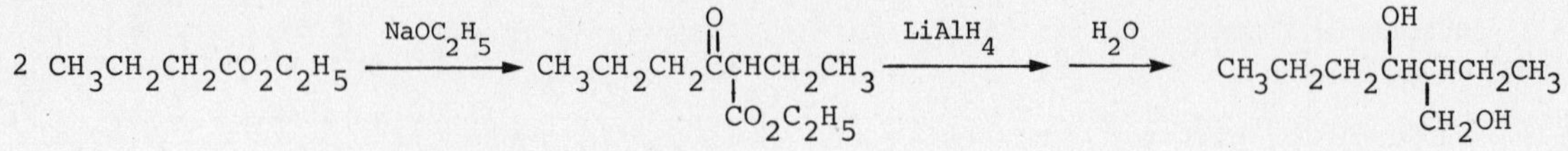

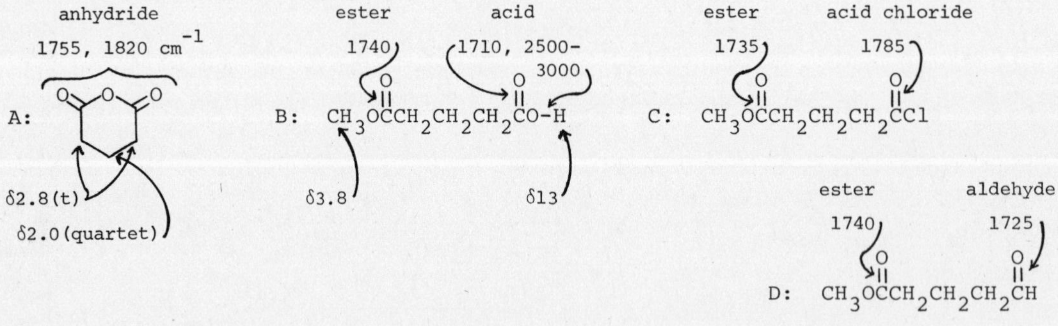

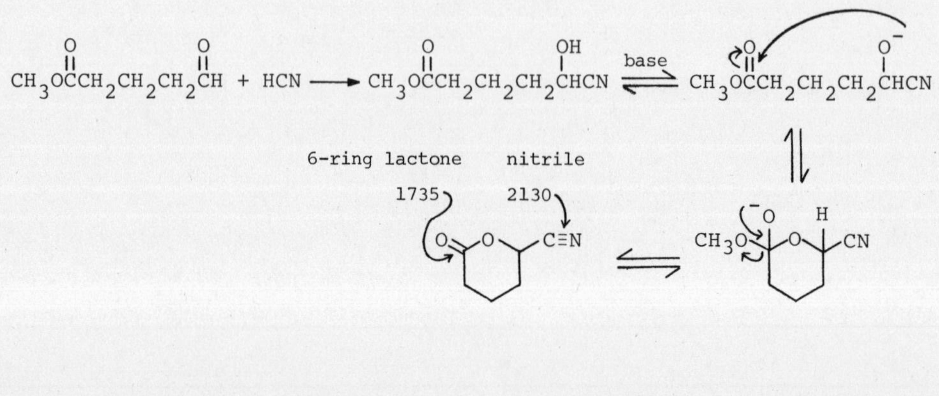

S6. $CH_3C \equiv N \rightleftharpoons CH_3C \equiv \overset{+}{N}H \rightleftharpoons CH_3C \overset{NH}{\underset{HOCH_3}{||}} \xleftarrow{-H^+} CH_3C \overset{NH}{\underset{OCH_3}{||}} \xrightarrow{H^+} CH_3\overset{+}{\underset{OCH_3}{C}}NH_2 \rightleftharpoons CH_3\overset{NH_2}{\underset{HOCH_3}{C}OCH_3}$

$CH_3\ddot{O}H$

CH_3OH

$CH_3\underset{HOCH_3}{\overset{OCH_3}{C}OCH_3} \xleftarrow{CH_3OH} \left[CH_3\overset{+OCH_3}{\underset{OCH_3}{C}} \leftrightarrow CH_3\overset{OCH_3}{\underset{+OCH_3}{C}} \right] \xrightarrow{-NH_3} CH_3\overset{+NH_3}{\underset{:OCH_3}{C}OCH_3} \xrightarrow{H^+} CH_3\overset{NH_2}{\underset{OCH_3}{C}OCH_3}$

$-H^+$

$CH_3C(OCH_3)_3$

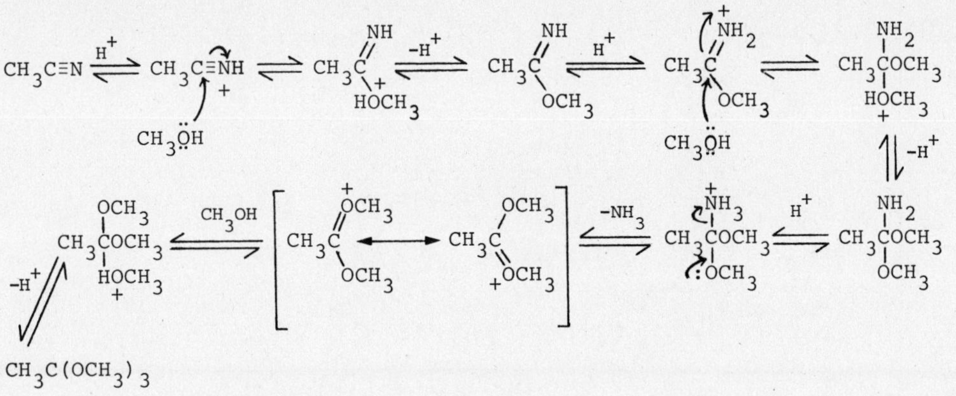

S7. 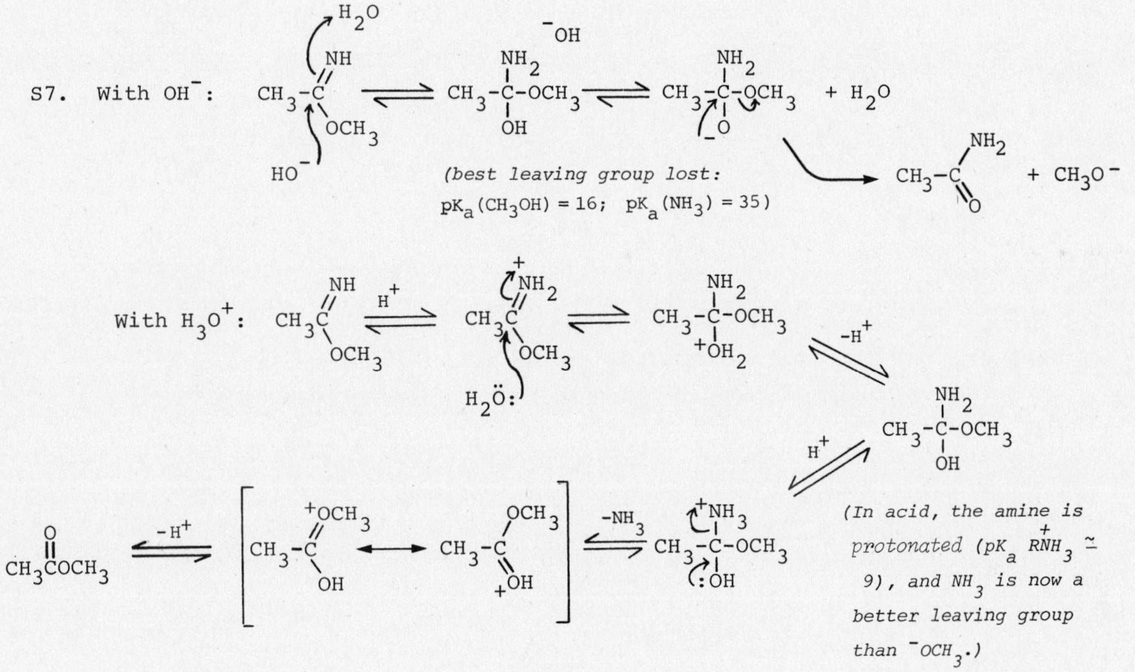 With OH^-: $CH_3-\overset{NH}{\underset{OCH_3}{C}} \rightleftharpoons CH_3-\overset{NH_2}{\underset{OH}{C}-OCH_3} \rightleftharpoons CH_3-\overset{NH_2}{\underset{O^-}{C}-OCH_3} + H_2O$

H_2O ^-OH

HO^-

(best leaving group lost:

$pK_a(CH_3OH) = 16; pK_a(NH_3) = 35)$

$\longrightarrow CH_3-\overset{NH_2}{\underset{O}{C}} + CH_3O^-$

With H_3O^+: $CH_3C \overset{NH}{\underset{OCH_3}{||}} \xrightarrow{H^+} CH_3\overset{+NH_2}{\underset{OCH_3}{C}} \rightleftharpoons CH_3-\overset{NH_2}{\underset{+OH_2}{C}-OCH_3} \xrightarrow{-H^+}$

$H_2\ddot{O}:$

$CH_3-\overset{NH_2}{\underset{OH}{C}-OCH_3}$

H^+

$CH_3\overset{O}{\underset{||}{C}}CH_3 \xleftarrow{-H^+} \left[CH_3-\overset{+OCH_3}{\underset{OH}{C}} \leftrightarrow CH_3-\overset{OCH_3}{\underset{+OH}{C}} \right] \xrightarrow{-NH_3} CH_3-\overset{+NH_3}{\underset{:OH}{C}-OCH_3}$

(In acid, the amine is
protonated (pK_a $R\overset{+}{N}H_3 \cong$
9), and NH_3 is now a
better leaving group
than $^-OCH_3$.)

S8. CH_3O^-

CH_3O^-

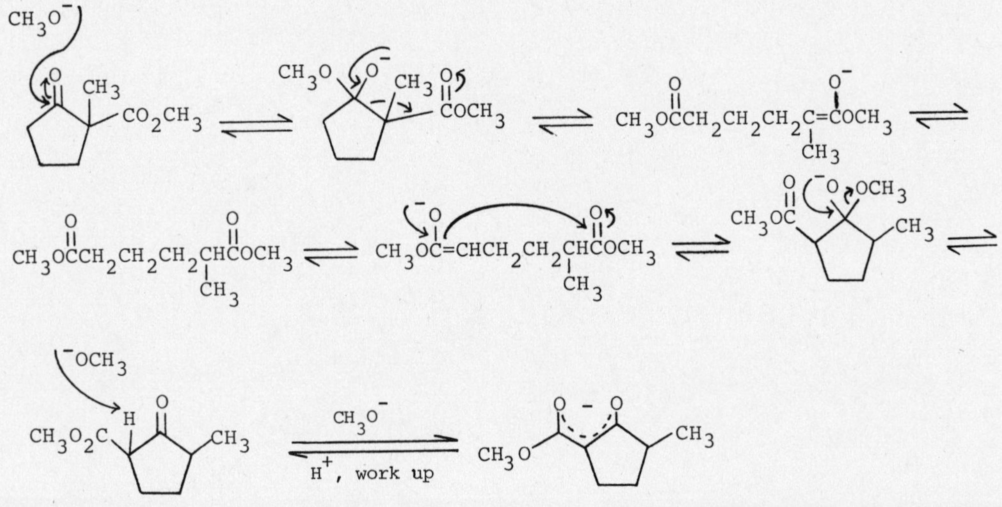

H^+, work up

S9.   This is clearly a case where you have to work backward!

1)   What part of the target came from which starting material?

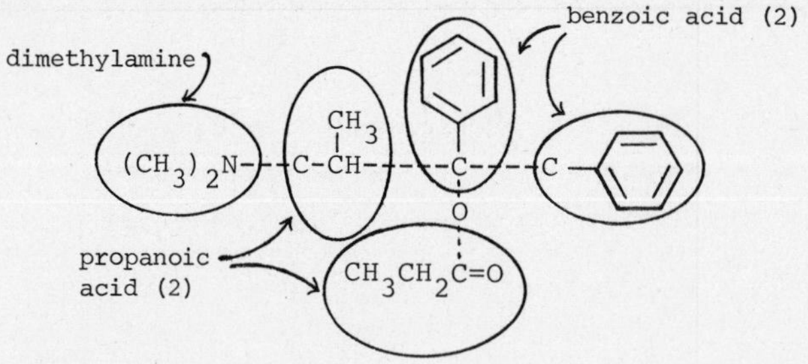

2)   The CH_2 next to the nitrogen could come from $LiAlH_4$ reduction of the amide, and the propanoate ester from the 3° alcohol:

$$(CH_3)_2NCH_2CH \overset{\displaystyle CH_3}{\underset{\displaystyle CH_3CH_2CO_2}{}} \overset{\displaystyle Ph}{\underset{\displaystyle }{C}} -CH_2Ph \quad \xleftarrow[H^+]{CH_3CH_2CO_2H} \quad (CH_3)_2NCH_2CH \overset{\displaystyle CH_3}{} \overset{\displaystyle Ph}{\underset{\displaystyle OH}{C}} -CH_2Ph \quad \xleftarrow[LiAlH_4]{excess}$$

$$(CH_3)_2N-\overset{\displaystyle O}{\overset{\|}{C}}-\overset{\displaystyle CH_3}{\underset{\displaystyle }{CH}}-\overset{\displaystyle Ph}{\underset{\displaystyle OH}{C}}-CH_2Ph$$

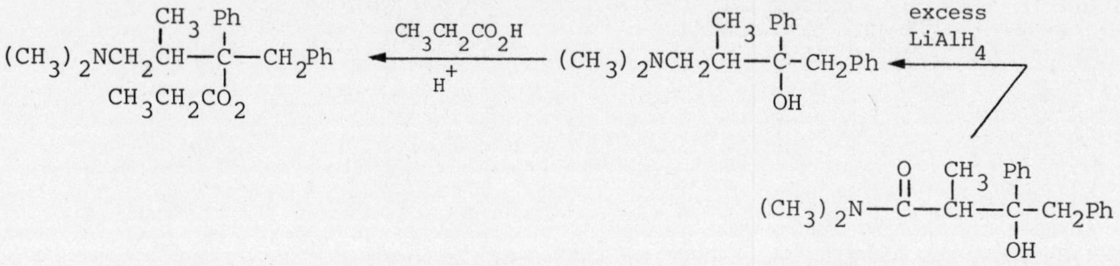

3)   The hydroxyl β to the carbonyl suggests that an ester-enolate or Reformatsky reaction could be used to form the carbon-carbon bond.

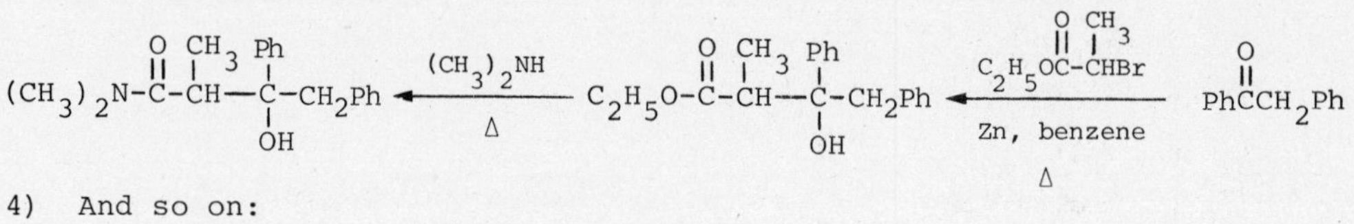

$$(CH_3)_2N-\overset{\displaystyle O}{\overset{\|}{C}}-\overset{\displaystyle CH_3}{\underset{\displaystyle }{CH}}-\overset{\displaystyle Ph}{\underset{\displaystyle OH}{C}}-CH_2Ph \quad \xleftarrow[\Delta]{(CH_3)_2NH} \quad C_2H_5O-\overset{\displaystyle O}{\overset{\|}{C}}-\overset{\displaystyle CH_3}{\underset{\displaystyle }{CH}}-\overset{\displaystyle Ph}{\underset{\displaystyle OH}{C}}-CH_2Ph \quad \xleftarrow[\substack{Zn,\ benzene \\ \Delta}]{C_2H_5O\overset{\displaystyle O}{\overset{\|}{C}}-\overset{\displaystyle CH_3}{\underset{\displaystyle }{CHBr}}} \quad PhC\overset{\displaystyle O}{\overset{\|}{C}}CH_2Ph$$

4)   And so on:

$$CH_3CH_2CO_2H \quad \xrightarrow{P,\ Br_2} \quad \xrightarrow{C_2H_5OH} \quad CH_3\overset{\displaystyle Br}{\underset{\displaystyle }{CH}}CO_2C_2H_5$$

S10. $C_2H_5O\overset{O}{\overset{\|}{C}}OC_2H_5 + D_2O \longrightarrow C_2H_5OD + \left[C_2H_5O\overset{O}{\overset{\|}{C}}OD \right] \longrightarrow C_2H_5OD + CO_2$

The only other product is gaseous CO_2.

S11. $CH_3(CH_2)_{12}COOCH_2$
      $CH_3(CH_2)_{12}COOCH$
      $CH_3(CH_2)_{12}COOCH_2$

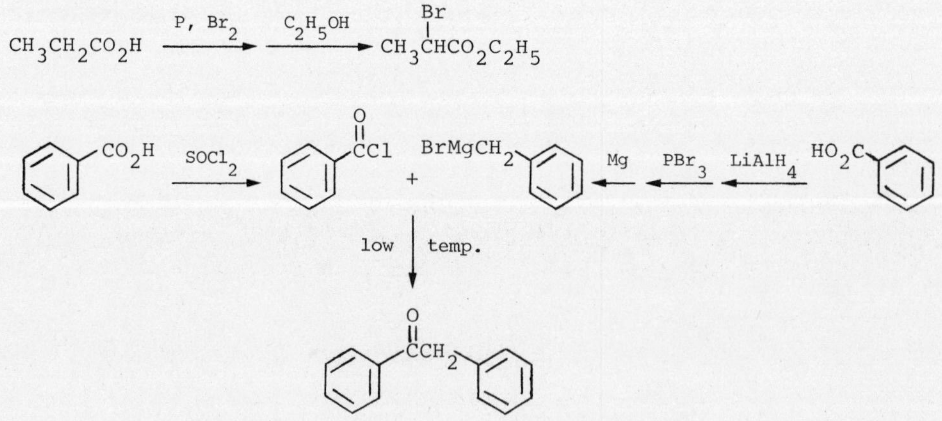

19. CONJUGATION

19.A Chapter Outline and Important Terms Introduced

(*** *NOTE*: *except for the Diels-Alder reaction, most of the reactions discussed in this chapter are not "new". What is different about them is how they proceed in conjugated systems.*)

19.1 Allylic Systems

A. Allylic Cations (resonance structures)

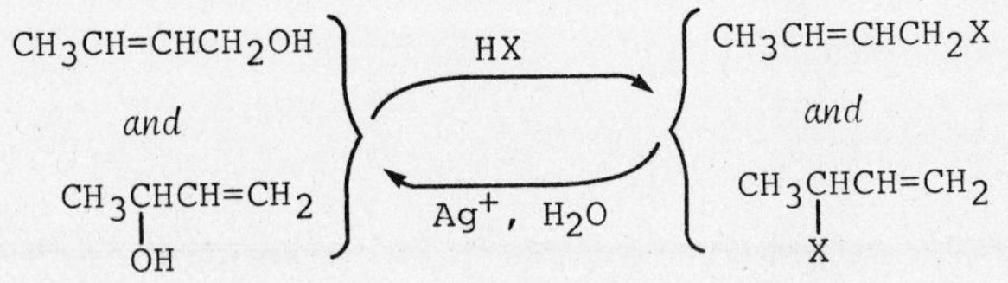

$$CH_3CH=CHCH_2OH$$

and

$$CH_3CHCH=CH_2$$
$$\quad\quad |$$
$$\quad\quad OH$$

HX $\longrightarrow$ Ag$^+$, H$_2$O

$$CH_3CH=CHCH_2X$$

and

$$CH_3CHCH=CH_2$$
$$\quad\quad |$$
$$\quad\quad X$$

allylic rearrangements

B. S$_N$2 Reactions

with or without rearrangement
S$_N$2' reactions

C. Allylic Anions

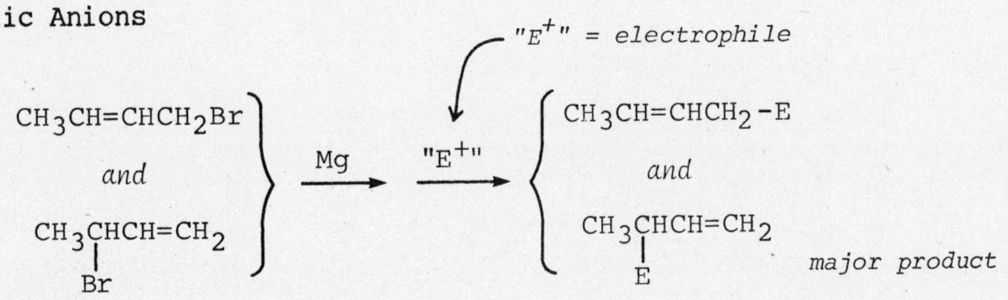

"E$^+$" = electrophile

$$CH_3CH=CHCH_2Br$$

and

$$CH_3CHCH=CH_2$$
$$\quad\quad |$$
$$\quad\quad Br$$

Mg   "E$^+$" $\longrightarrow$

$$CH_3CH=CHCH_2-E$$

and

$$CH_3CHCH=CH_2$$
$$\quad\quad |$$
$$\quad\quad E$$ *major product*

dilution principle
conjugated carbons

D. Allylic Radicals

allylic bromination

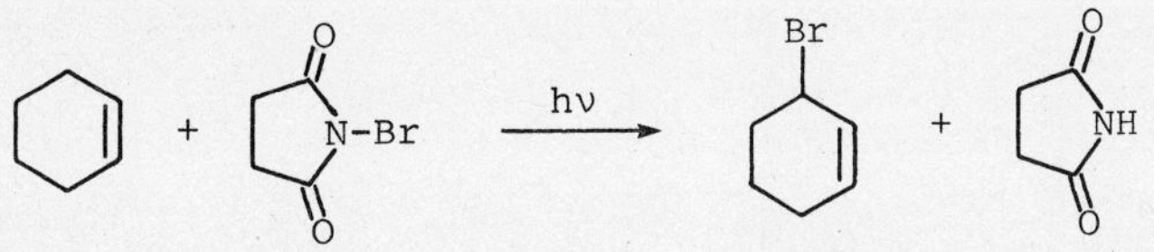

19.2 Dienes

A. Structure and Stability

conjugated vs. unconjugated dienes
isolated double bonds

B. Addition Reactions

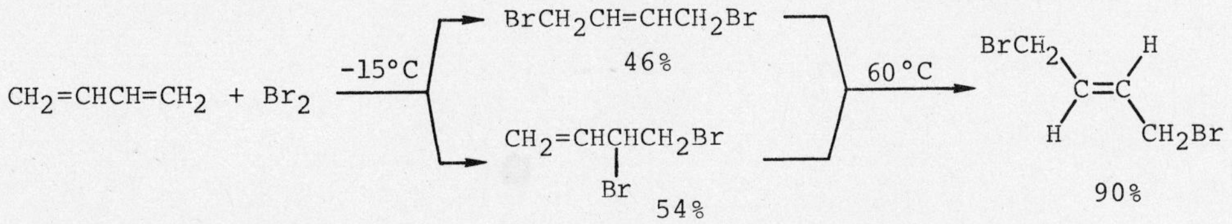

$$CH_2=CHCH=CH_2 + Br_2$$

$-15°C$

$$BrCH_2CH=CHCH_2Br$$
46%

$$CH_2=CHCHCH_2Br$$
$$\quad\quad\quad |$$
$$\quad\quad\quad Br \quad 54\%$$

$60°C$

90%

kinetic vs. thermodynamic control

C. 1,2-Dienes: Allenes

sp-hybridization of central carbon
stereoaxis
cumulated double bonds

D. Preparation of Dienes
    (dehydration, Grignard coupling, Wittig reaction, etc.)

19.3 Unsaturated Carbonyl Compounds

A. Unsaturated Aldehydes and Ketones

α,β- vs. β,γ-unsaturation:

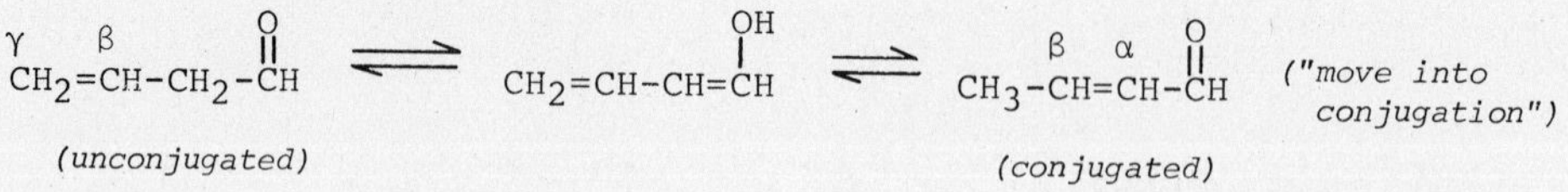

(unconjugated)   (conjugated)   ("move into
                                                                                        conjugation")

formation via aldol condensation:

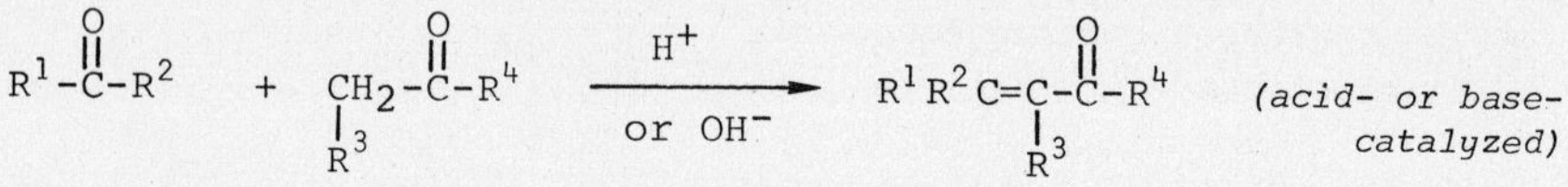

(acid- or base-
catalyzed)

ease of oxidation of allylic alcohols:

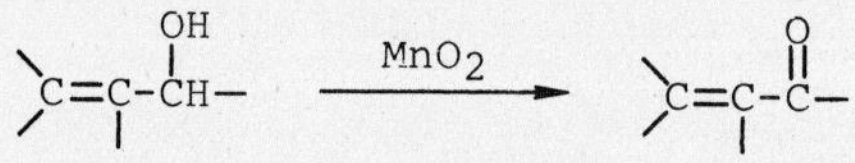

1,2-additions (normal additions) vs. 1,4-additions (conjugate
                                                          additions):

cuprates vs. organolithium (and Grignard) reagents:

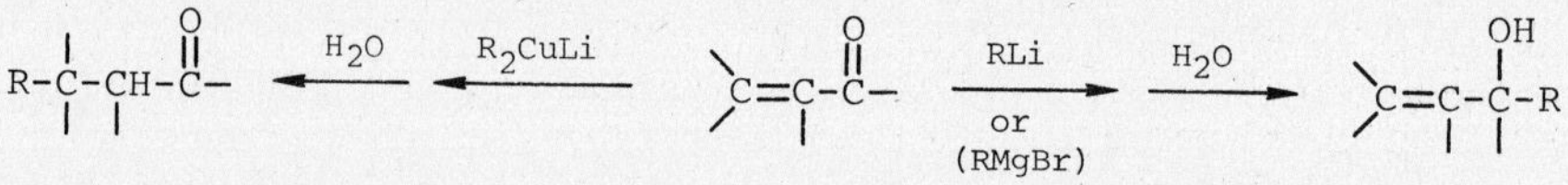

reduction methods

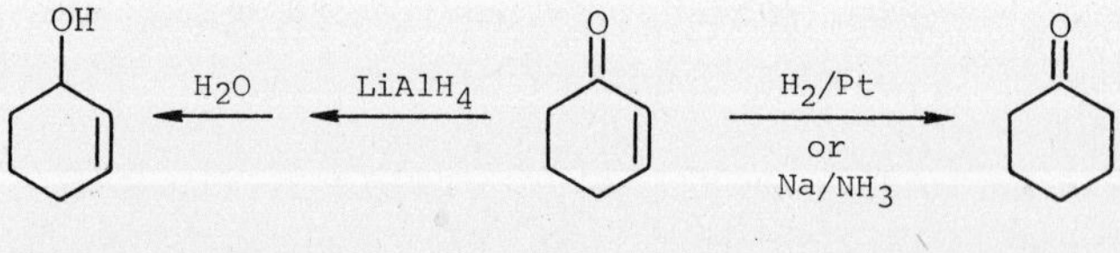

B. Unsaturated Carboxylic Acids and Derivatives
    cross-conjugated
    Perkin reaction

C. Ketenes

$CH_2=C=O$ + HNu: $\longrightarrow$ $CH_3-\overset{O}{\overset{\|}{C}}-Nu$

19.4 Higher Conjugated Systems (trienes)

19.5 The Diels-Alder Reaction

cycloaddition reaction   [4+2] vs. [2+2] or [4+4] cycloaddition reactions
head-to-head vs.   exo vs. endo stereochemistry
  head-to-tail orientation   bicyclic products available

19.B Important Reactions Introduced

> NOTE: Except for the Diels-Alder reaction, most of the reactions discussed in this chapter are not
> "new". What is different about them is how they proceed in conjugated systems.

Diels-Alder reaction (19.5)

Equation:

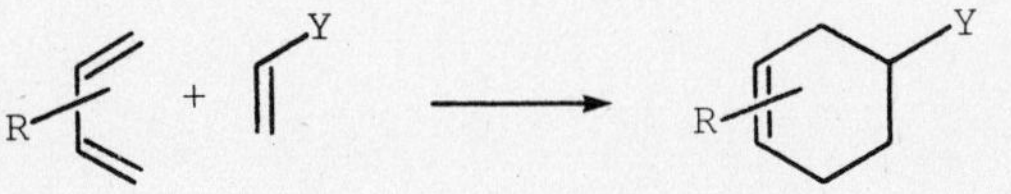

Generality: Y = usually an electron-withdrawing group
               R = a variety of substituents, cyclic diene, etc.

Key features: cycloaddition reaction
               often proceeds with specific orientation, i.e., the two ends which are best able to
                   stabilize radical species end up bonded to each other
               often proceeds with specific stereochemistry, i.e. endo or exo
               important reaction for forming cyclic and bicyclic compounds

19.C Important Concepts and Hints

Conjugation, or the Double Bond Relay

You are familiar by now with many of the reactions of carbon-carbon double bonds and of
carbonyl groups. When both functional groups are present in one molecule, the same reactions can
usually be observed. However, when the p-orbitals of a double bond overlap with those of an
adjacent double bond or carbonyl group, special chemical behavior is often seen. Unusual reactivity is also observed if an intermediate or transition state involves the formation of an sp^2-hybridized carbon adjacent to a double bond (allylic system). All of this comes under the heading
of conjugation. One of the ways to understand conjugation intuitively is to think of it in the
following way: any chemical behavior which involves an sp^2-hybridized carbon can be relayed two
carbons away by an adjacent double bond. The following summary illustrates this point:

S_N1 Substitution (carbocation intermediate)

alkyl system:

allylic system:

S_N2 Substitution

alkyl system:

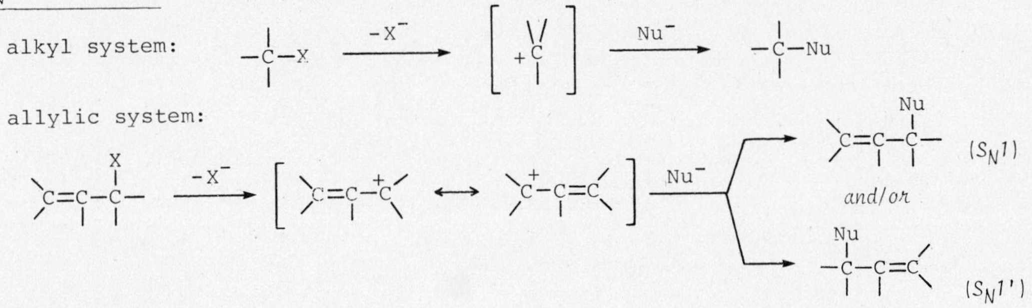

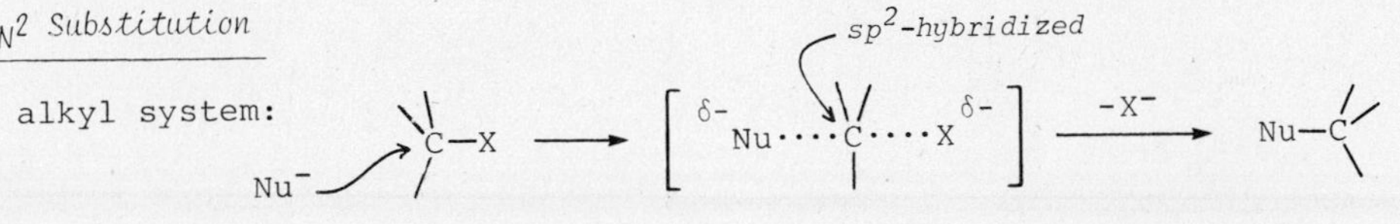

allylic system:

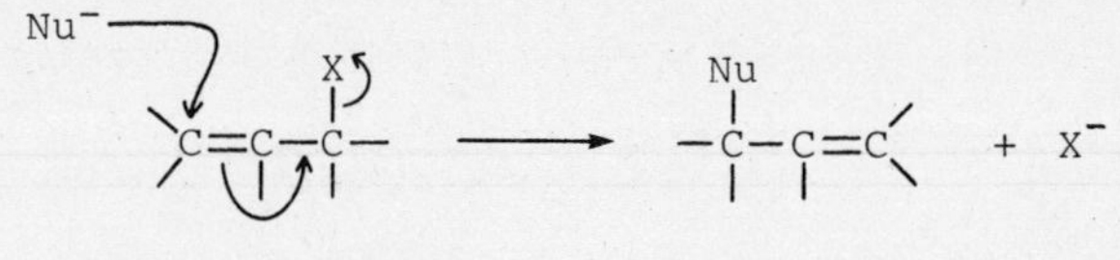

$$S_N2'$$

(also S_N2 without allylic rearrangement)

Grignard Reaction (carbanion intermediate)

alkyl system:

$$-\overset{|}{\underset{|}{C}}-X \xrightarrow{\ Mg\ } -\overset{|}{\underset{|}{C}}-MgX \xrightarrow{\ E^+\ } -\overset{|}{\underset{|}{C}}-E$$

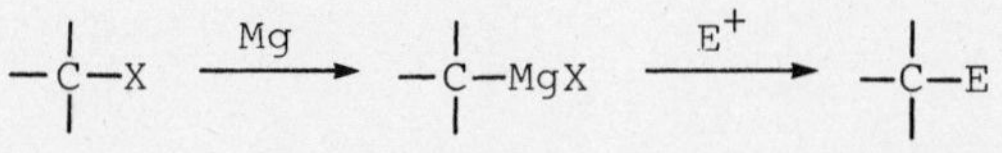

$"E^+"$ = electrophile

allylic system:

and/or

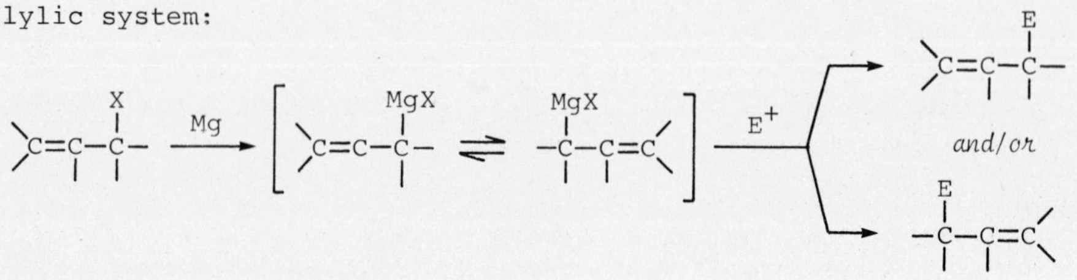

Free-Radical Halogenation (radical intermediate)

alkyl system:

$$-\overset{|}{\underset{|}{C}}-H \xrightarrow{\ X\cdot\ } -\overset{|}{\underset{|}{C}}\cdot \xrightarrow{\ X_2\ } -\overset{|}{\underset{|}{C}}-X$$

allylic system:

and/or

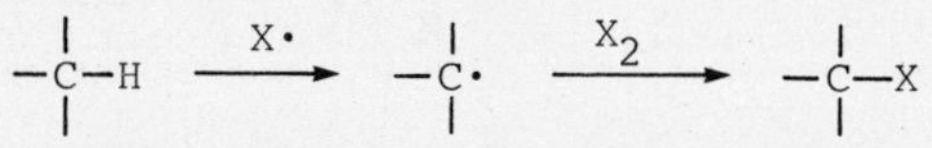

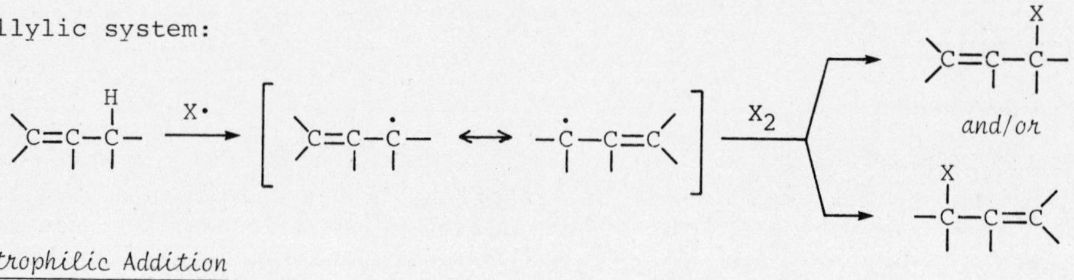

Electrophilic Addition

isolated double bond:

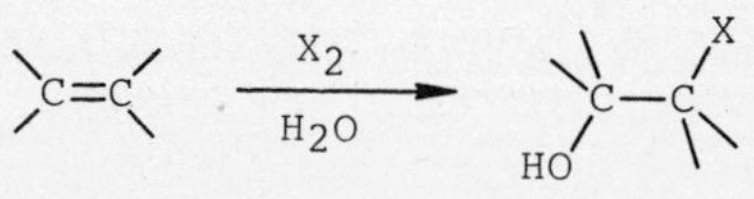

$$\xrightarrow[H_2O]{X_2}$$

conjugated diene:

$$\xrightarrow[H_2O]{X_2}$$

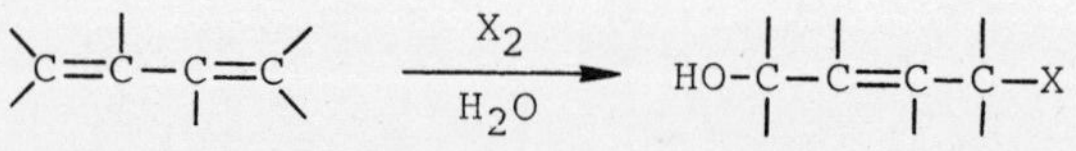

(normal addition can also occur)

Ketone Enolization

isolated carbonyl group:

Base

$$\rightleftharpoons$$

α,β-unsaturated carbonyl group:

Base

γ β α

$$\rightleftharpoons$$

$$\left(\quad \text{Base} \quad \rightleftharpoons \quad can\ still\ occur \right)$$

α'

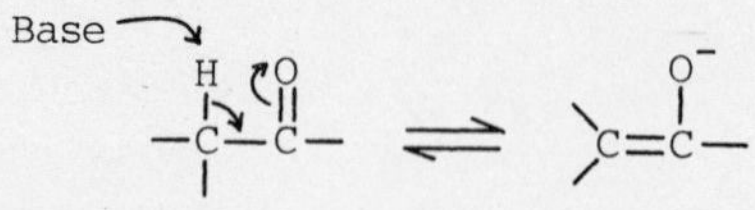

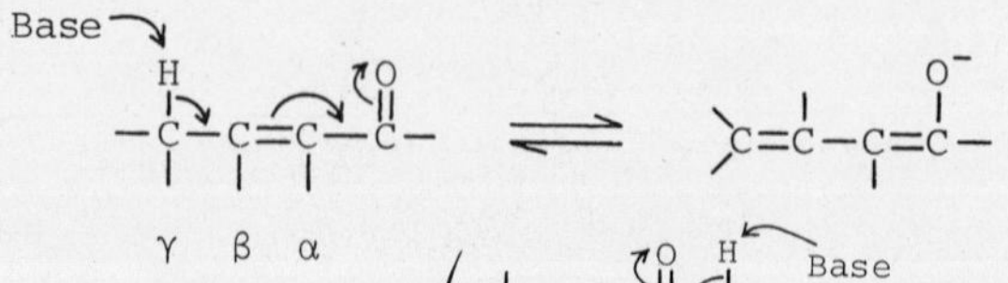

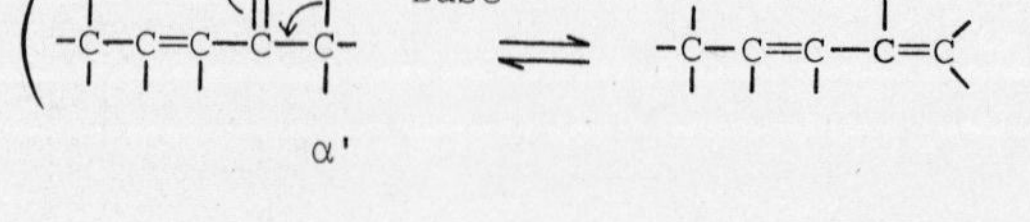

Addition to a Carbonyl

isolated carbonyl group:

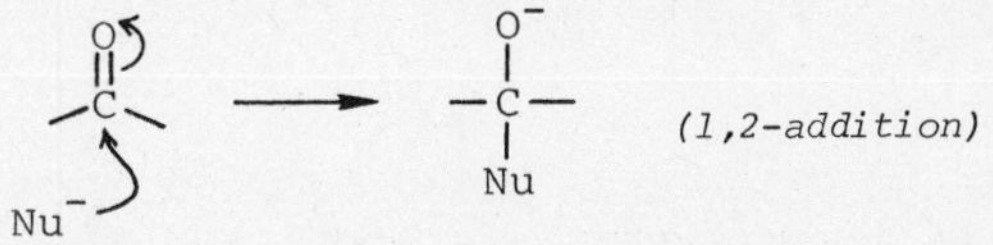

α,β-unsaturated carbonyl group:

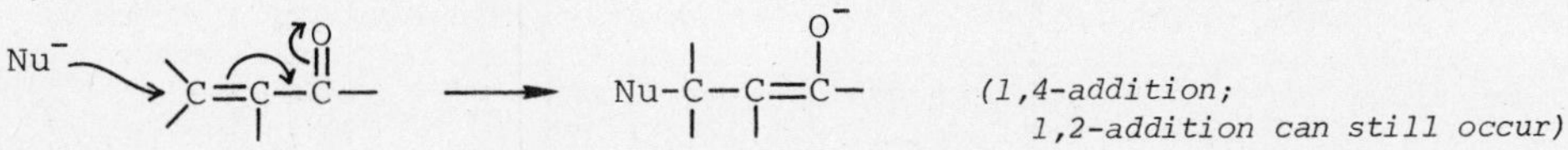

Notice how in each case a reaction which can occur at one carbon atom can take place at the other end of a double bond which is conjugated to it. This does not mean that **all** reactions of allylic systems involve rearrangement, or that all additions to α,β-unsaturated carbonyl compounds are 1,4-; the "normal" modes of reaction are observed as well. Often by choosing specific reaction conditions or reagents, you can favor one over the other.

The Diels-Alder Reaction, or Electrons-going-around-in-a-circle

In contrast to the Diels-Alder reaction, reactions which look similar but involve four or eight electrons in a circle (rather than six) occur only in exceptional circumstances:

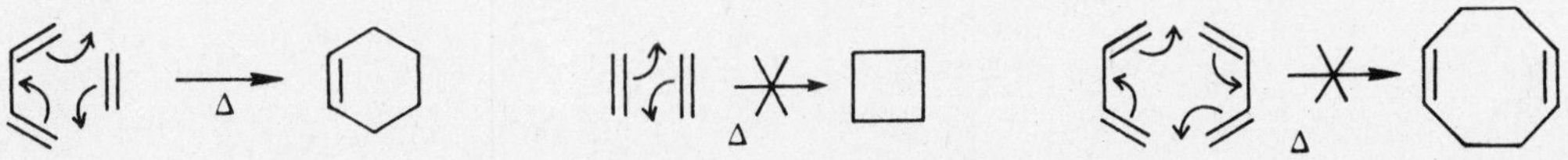

You have seen one other reaction which involves "six-electrons-in-a-cyclic-system": the pyrolysis of acetate (and xanthate) esters. The analogous four-electron transformation does not occur:

You will encounter additional cases such as this one, in which systems involving six electrons in a cyclic arrangement (in π-bonds (for example, benzene) or in transition states (the pyrolysis illustrated above is an example)) are favored relative to the analogous four- or eight-electron systems. A unifying explanation for this phenomenon is given in Chapter 21.

19.D   Answers to Exercises

19.1

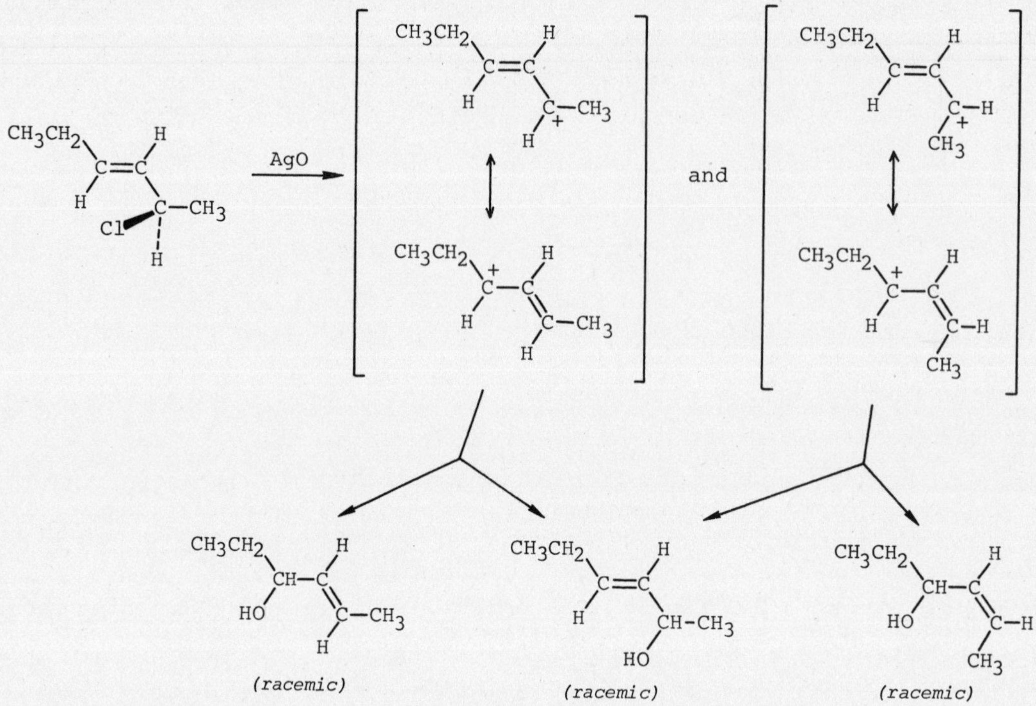

CH_3CH_2 ... (reaction with AgO) ...

(racemic)   (racemic)   (racemic)

19.2

$$(CH_3)_3CMgCl + ClCH_2CH=CH_2 \longrightarrow (CH_3)_3CCH_2CH=CH_2$$

$$(CH_3)_2CHCH_2MgCl + ClCH_2CH=CH_2 \longrightarrow (CH_3)_2CHCH_2CH_2CH=CH_2$$

19.3

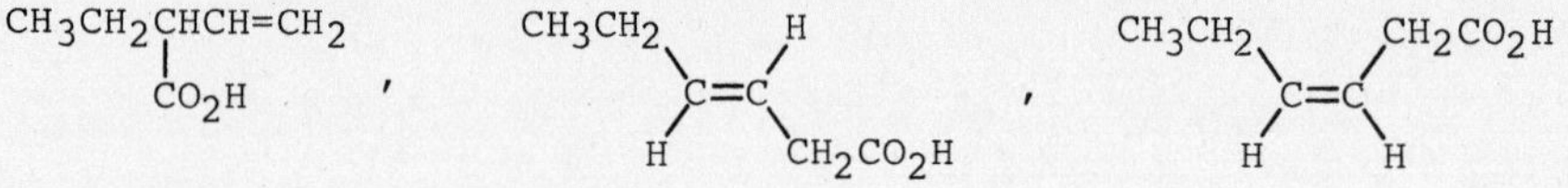

$CH_3CH_2CHCH=CH_2$ with CO_2H ,   ...,   ...

19.4

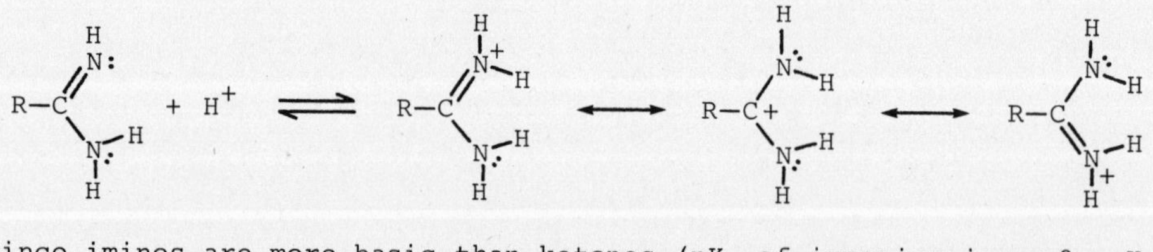

Since imines are more basic than ketones (pK_a of immonium ion ≈ 9, pK_a of protonated acetone ≈ -7), amidines are expected to be more basic than amides. In fact they are: pK_a of protonated acetamidine $= 12.5$; pK_a of protonated acetamide $= 0$.

19.5 From the theory of absolute rates (Section 4.4 in the Text):

$$k = \nu^{\ddagger}e^{-\Delta G^{\ddagger}/RT}$$

Assuming that the proportionality constant, $\nu^{\ddagger}$, is the same for both reactions, the ratio of the two rate constants will be given by:

$$\frac{k_A}{k_B} = \frac{\nu^{\ddagger}e^{-\Delta G^{\ddagger}_A/RT}}{\nu^{\ddagger}e^{-\Delta G^{\ddagger}_B/RT}} = e^{-(\Delta G^{\ddagger}_A - \Delta G^{\ddagger}_B)/RT} = e^{-\Delta\Delta G^{\ddagger}/RT} = e^{-(\Delta\Delta H^{\ddagger} - T\Delta\Delta S^{\ddagger})/RT}$$

For $\Delta\Delta H^{\ddagger} = 10$ kcal mole^{-1} and $\Delta\Delta S^{\ddagger} = 20$ e.u.,

at $300\,°K$, $k_A/k_B = 0.0012$

at $700\,°K$, $k_A/k_B = 1.79$

This exercise serves to emphasize the importance of entropy at higher temperatures. At 300 ^{O}K, the **enthalpy** of activation, $\Delta H^{\ddagger}$, is the major contribution to the free energy of activation ($\Delta G^{\ddagger} = \Delta H^{\ddagger} - T \times \Delta S^{\ddagger}$). Since $\Delta H^{\ddagger}$ is more unfavorable for A ($\Delta \Delta H^{\ddagger} = +10$ kcal mole^{-1}), the reaction of A proceeds more slowly than that of B at the lower temperature. At 700 ^{O}K, the **entropy** of activation, which is multiplied by the temperature ($T \times \Delta S^{\ddagger}$) becomes dominant. Since the entropy of activation is more favorable for A ($\Delta \Delta S^{\ddagger} = +20$ e.u.), the reaction of A proceeds faster at the higher temperature.

19.6

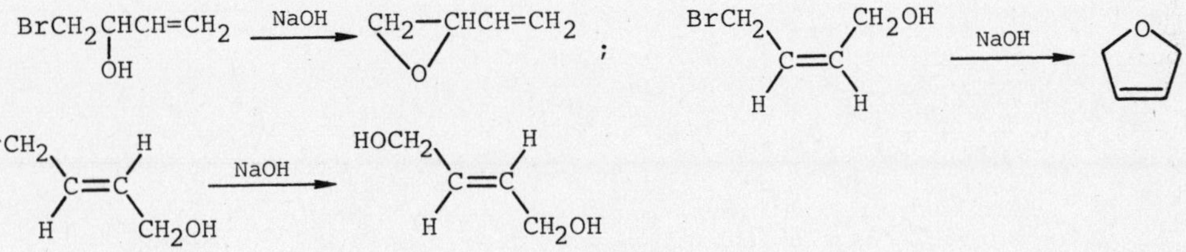

$$BrCH_2CHCH=CH_2 \ (OH) \xrightarrow{NaOH} CH_2-CHCH=CH_2 \ (O) \quad ; \quad BrCH_2C=CCH_2OH \ (H,H) \xrightarrow{NaOH} \ \text{(furan-type ring)}$$

$$BrCH_2C=C \ (H, CH_2OH) \xrightarrow{NaOH} HOCH_2C=C \ (H, CH_2OH)$$

19.9

(a) (chlorocyclohexene) + (vinyl)MgBr $\longrightarrow$ (vinylcyclohexene)

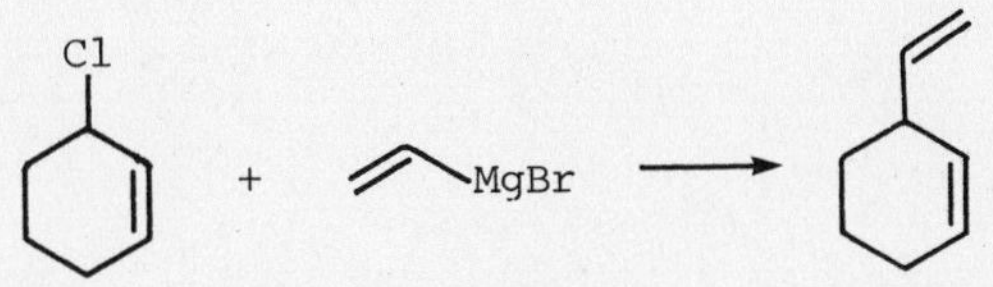

(b) (chlorocyclohexene) + $Ph_3P:$ $\longrightarrow$ $\xrightarrow{BuLi}$ Ph_3P^+ (phosphonium ylide) $\xrightarrow{\text{(acetone)}}$ (isopropylidene cyclohexene)

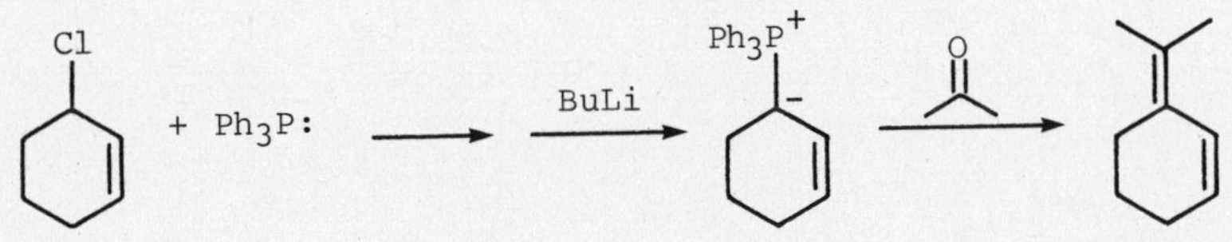

19.10

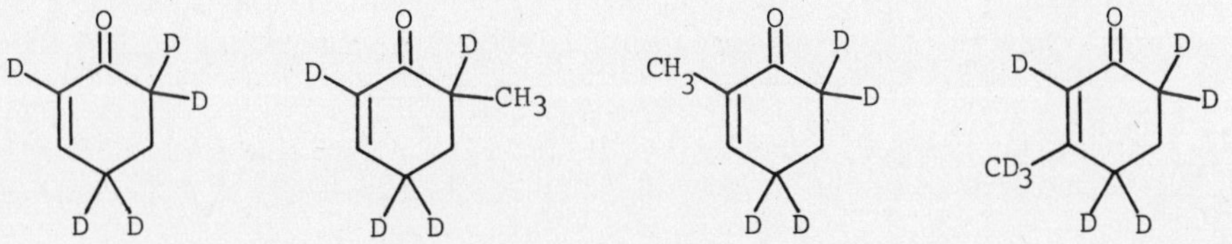

(deuterated cyclohexenones structures)

19.11

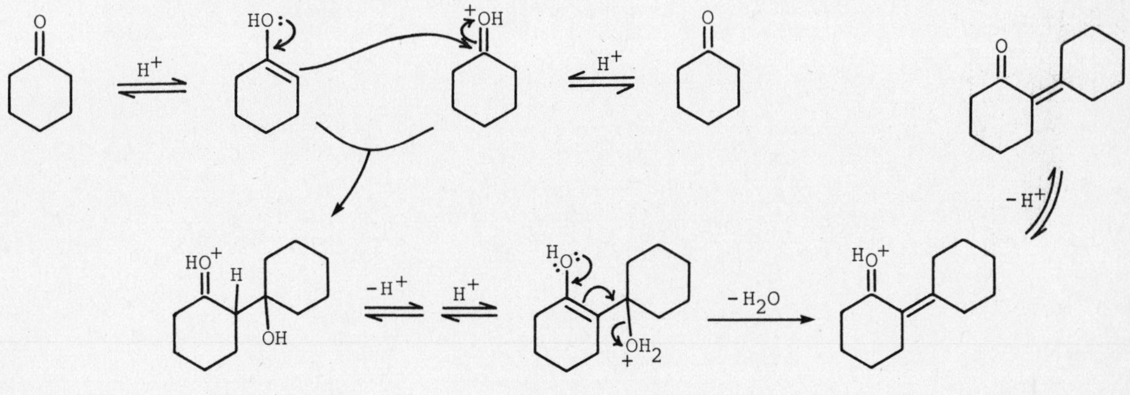

$$\text{(cyclohexanone)} \xrightleftharpoons{H^+} \text{(enol)} \cdots \text{(protonated)} \xrightleftharpoons{H^+} \text{(cyclohexanone)} \qquad \text{(cyclohexylidenecyclohexanone)}$$

$\xrightleftharpoons[H^+]{-H^+}$ $\xrightarrow{-H_2O}$ $\xrightarrow{-H^+}$

19.12

$$2 \ \text{(acetone)} \xrightarrow{H^+} \text{(mesityl oxide)} \xrightarrow[Et_3Al]{HCN} \text{(keto nitrile)} \xrightarrow[\Delta]{H_3O^+} \text{(keto acid, } CO_2H)$$

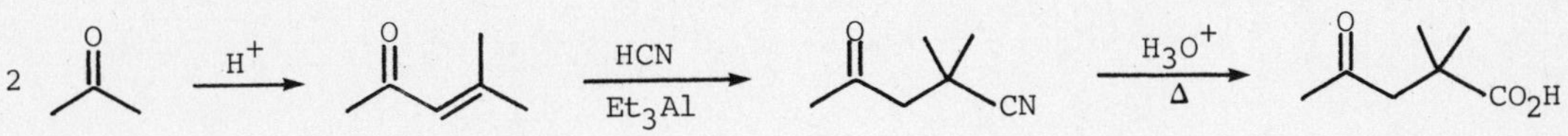

19.13

(a) HO—[structure: 3-ethyl-hept-4-en-3-ol type with HO] ⟵ EtLi

(b) [structure: ketone with ethyl branch] ⟵ EtMgBr, CuI

[central ketone: CH₃CH₂COCH=CHCH₃ (hex-4-en-3-one)]

19.14

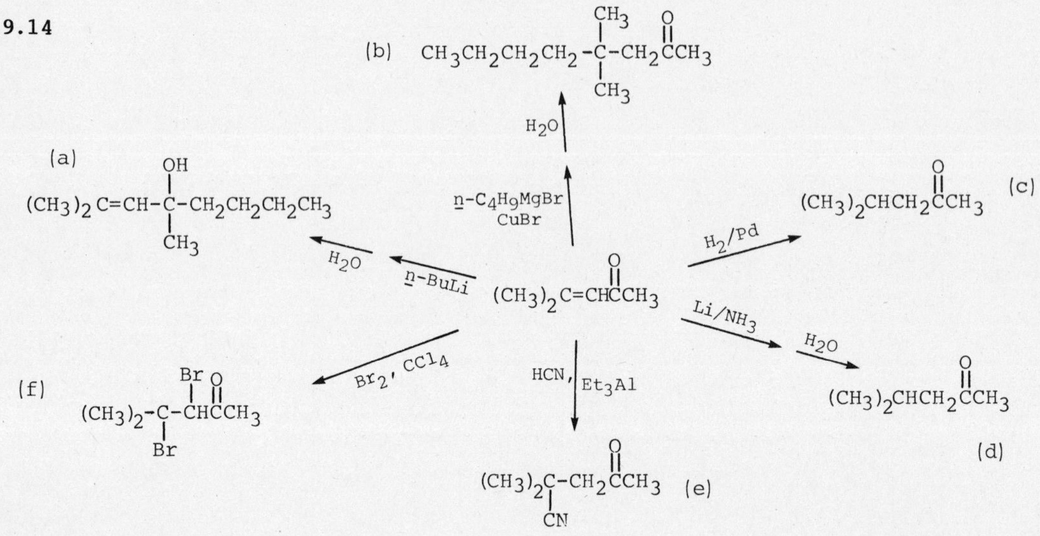

(b) $CH_3CH_2CH_2CH_2-\underset{\underset{CH_3}{|}}{\overset{\overset{CH_3}{|}}{C}}-CH_2\overset{O}{\overset{||}{C}}CH_3$

$\uparrow$ H_2O

(a) $(CH_3)_2C=CH-\underset{\underset{CH_3}{|}}{\overset{\overset{OH}{|}}{C}}-CH_2CH_2CH_2CH_3$

⟵ H_2O ⟵ $\underline{n}$-BuLi

$\underline{n}$-C₄H₉MgBr / CuBr

(c) $(CH_3)_2CHCH_2\overset{O}{\overset{||}{C}}CH_3$ ⟵ H_2/Pd

$(CH_3)_2C=CHCCH_3$

H_2/Pd →

Li/NH₃ → H_2O →

(d) $(CH_3)_2CHCH_2\overset{O}{\overset{||}{C}}CH_3$

(f) $(CH_3)_2-\underset{\underset{Br}{|}}{\overset{\overset{Br}{|}\ \overset{O}{\overset{||}{}}}{C}}-CHCCH_3$ ⟵ Br_2, CCl₄

HCN, Et₃Al ↓

(e) $(CH_3)_2\underset{\underset{CN}{|}}{C}-CH_2\overset{O}{\overset{||}{C}}CH_3$

19.15   Ethanol:

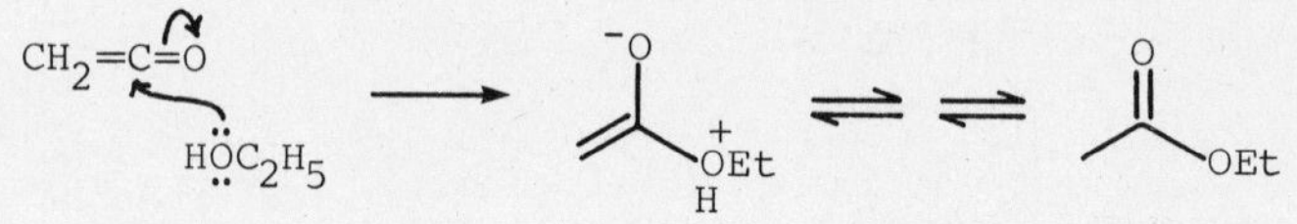

$CH_2=C=O$ with $HO\ddot{C}_2H_5$ → [enol-type] $\overset{-O}{\underset{\overset{+}{O}Et}{}}$ with H ⇌⇌ $\overset{O}{\overset{||}{C}}$—OEt

Acetic acid:

$CH_2=C=O + HO_2CCH_3$ ⇌ $CH_2=\overset{+}{C}OH$ with $^-O_2CCH_3$ → [OH ester] ⇌⇌ [anhydride]

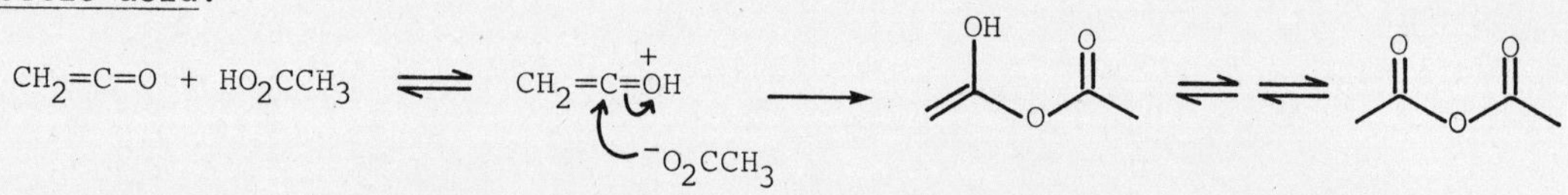

19.16   Not including $\underline{cis}$ and $\underline{trans}$ isomers:

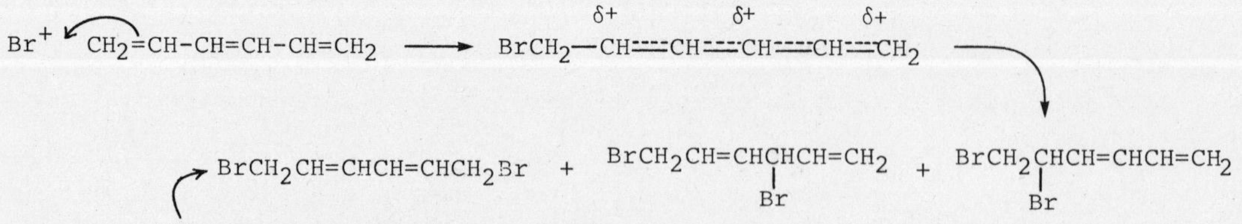

Br^+ ⟵ $CH_2=CH-CH=CH-CH=CH_2$ → $BrCH_2-\overset{\delta+}{CH}{=\!=\!=}CH{=\!=\!=}\overset{\delta+}{CH}{=\!=\!=}CH{=\!=\!=}\overset{\delta+}{CH_2}$

$BrCH_2CH=CHCH=CHCH_2Br$ + $BrCH_2CH=CHCHCH=CH_2$ (Br) + $BrCH_2CHCH=CHCH=CH_2$ (Br)

This isomer is expected to be the major
product at equilibrium, because it is conjugated and has the more highly
substituted double bonds.

19.17

(a) [cyclohexene ring with CH₃, CO₂Me, CO₂Me substituents]

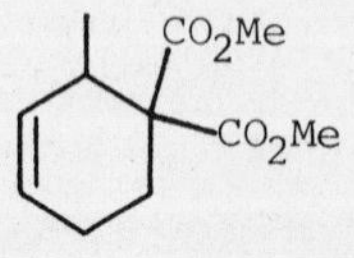

(b) [cyclohexene ring with CHO and MeO substituents]

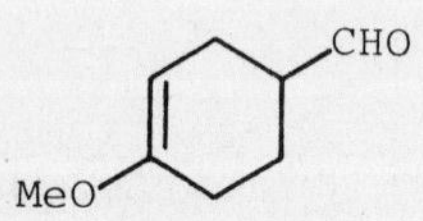

19.18   (a) bicyclo[2.2.2]oct-5-en-2-one

(b) 7,7-dichlorobicyclo[3.2.0]hept-3-en-6-one

19.19

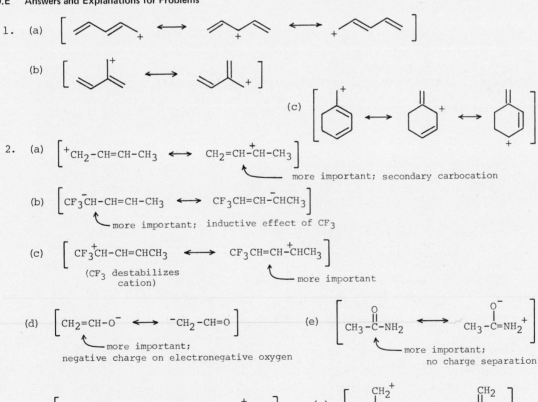

CH₂=CHO₂CCH₃

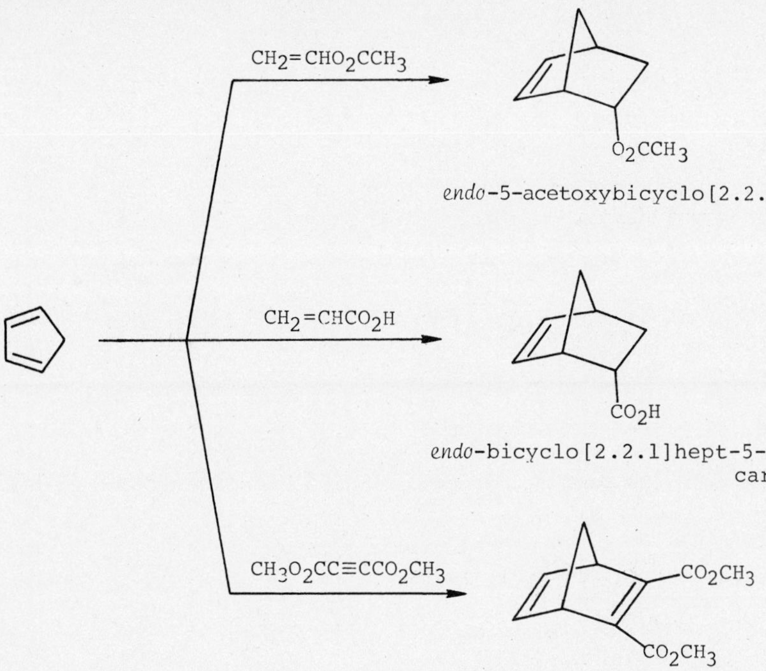

$endo$-5-acetoxybicyclo[2.2.1]hept-2-ene

CH₂=CHCO₂H

$endo$-bicyclo[2.2.1]hept-5-ene-2-
carboxylic acid

CH₃O₂CC≡CCO₂CH₃

dimethyl bicyclo[2.2.1]hepta-2,5-
diene-2,3-dicarboxylate

19.E   Answers and Explanations for Problems

1. (a) $[\quad \searrow\!\!\diagup\!\!\searrow + \quad \longleftrightarrow \quad \searrow\!\!\diagup + \quad \longleftrightarrow \quad + \quad]$

    (b) $[\quad \longleftrightarrow \quad]$

    (c) $[\quad \longleftrightarrow \quad \longleftrightarrow \quad]$

2. (a) $[\ ^{+}\text{CH}_2\text{-CH=CH-CH}_3 \quad \longleftrightarrow \quad \text{CH}_2\text{=CH-}\overset{+}{\text{C}}\text{H-CH}_3 \ ]$
        more important; secondary carbocation

    (b) $[\ \text{CF}_3\overset{-}{\text{C}}\text{H-CH=CH-CH}_3 \quad \longleftrightarrow \quad \text{CF}_3\text{CH=CH-}\overset{-}{\text{C}}\text{HCH}_3 \ ]$
        more important; inductive effect of CF₃

    (c) $[\ \text{CF}_3\overset{+}{\text{C}}\text{H-CH=CHCH}_3 \quad \longleftrightarrow \quad \text{CF}_3\text{CH=CH-}\overset{+}{\text{C}}\text{HCH}_3 \ ]$
        (CF₃ destabilizes
        cation)   more important

    (d) $[\ \text{CH}_2\text{=CH-O}^- \quad \longleftrightarrow \quad ^-\text{CH}_2\text{-CH=O} \ ]$
        more important;
        negative charge on electronegative oxygen

    (e) $[\ \text{CH}_3\text{-}\overset{\overset{\text{O}}{\|}}{\text{C}}\text{-NH}_2 \quad \longleftrightarrow \quad \text{CH}_3\text{-}\overset{\overset{\text{O}^-}{\|}}{\text{C}}\text{=NH}_2^+ \ ]$
        more important;
        no charge separation

    (f) $[\ \text{CH}_2\text{=CH-OCH}_3 \quad \longleftrightarrow \quad ^-\text{CH}_2\text{-CH=}\overset{+}{\text{O}}\text{CH}_3 \ ]$
        more important;
        no charge separation

    (g) $[\quad \longleftrightarrow \quad]$
        more important;
        secondary carbocation

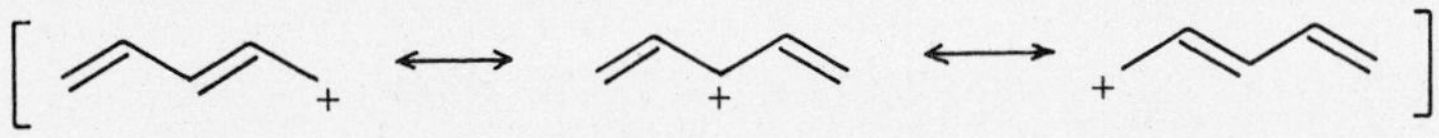

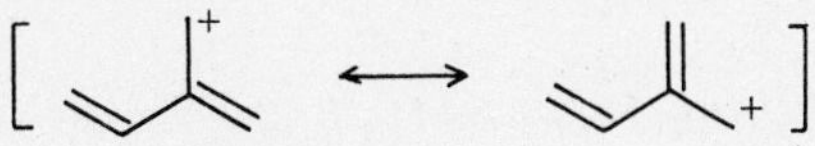

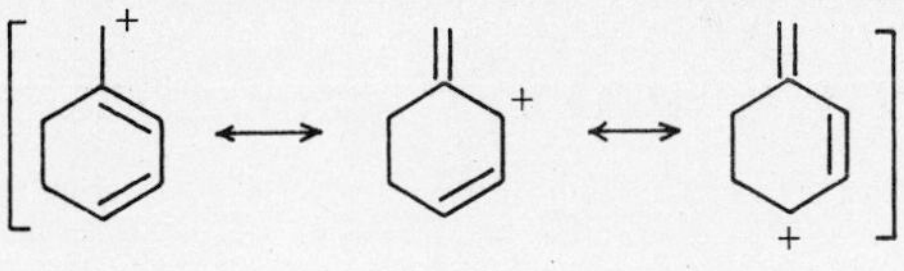

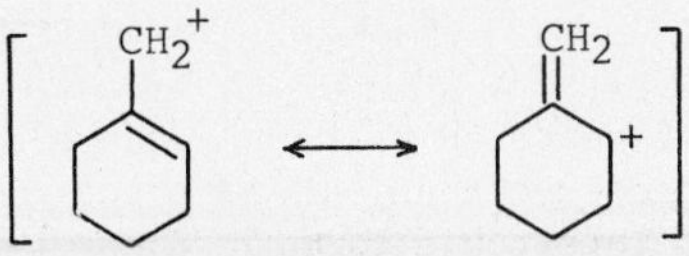

3.

(a) CH_3CH_2MgBr + $Br-CH_2CH=CH_2$ $\longrightarrow$

(b) 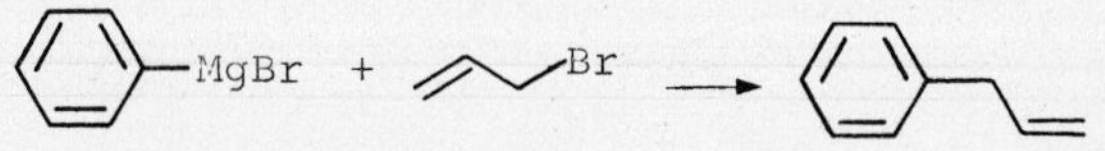 —MgBr + Br $\longrightarrow$

(c) 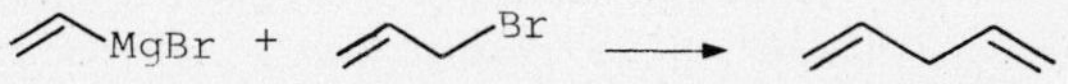 MgBr + Br $\longrightarrow$

(d) $(CH_3)_3CMgBr$ + Br $\longrightarrow$ $(CH_3)_3CCH_2CH=CH_2$

4.

(a) $CH_3CH=CHCH_2OH$ $\xrightarrow{MnO_2}$ $CH_3CH=CHCHO$

(b) $CH_3CH_2CH_2CH_2OH$ $\xrightarrow{MnO_2}$ no reaction

(c) $HOCH_2CH_2CH=CHCH_2OH$ $\xrightarrow{MnO_2}$ $HOCH_2CH_2CH=CHCHO$

(d) 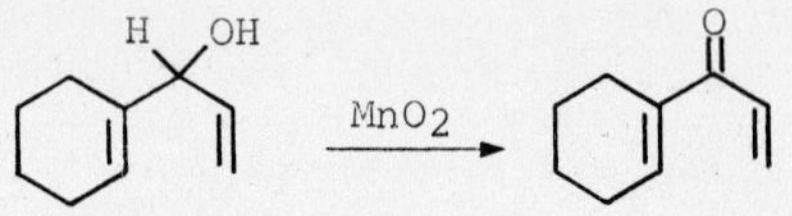 $\xrightarrow{MnO_2}$

(e) 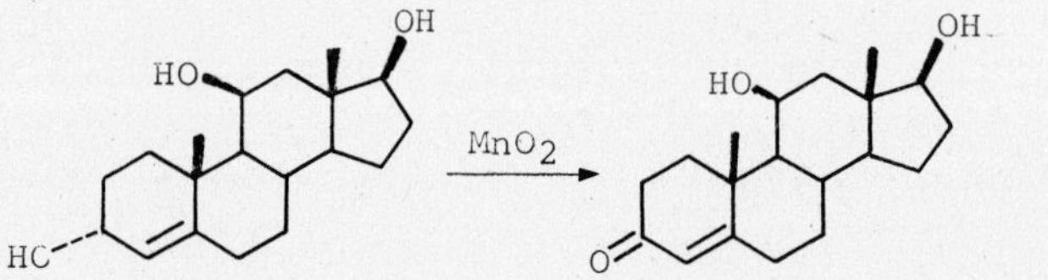 $\xrightarrow{MnO_2}$

(f) $CH_3C\equiv C\overset{OH}{\underset{}{C}}HCH_3$ $\xrightarrow{MnO_2}$ $CH_3C\equiv C\overset{O}{\underset{}{C}}CH_3$

5. Abstraction of the allylic H gives the allyl free radical.

$$C_5H_{11}CH_2CH=CH_2 + Br\cdot \longrightarrow C_5H_{11}\dot{C}HCH=CH_2$$

There are two isomeric allylic radicals:

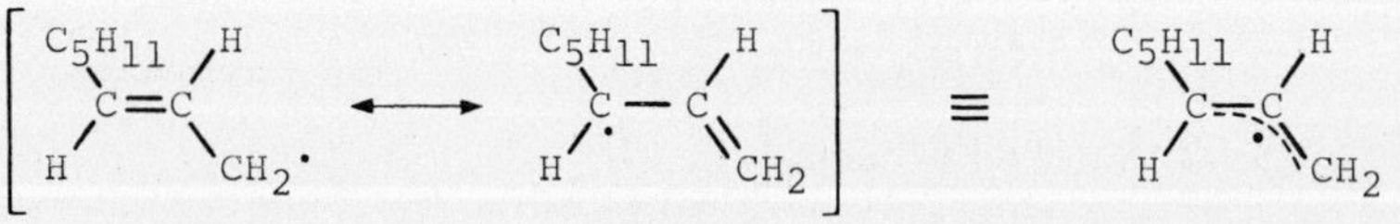

allylic radical A, *transoid*

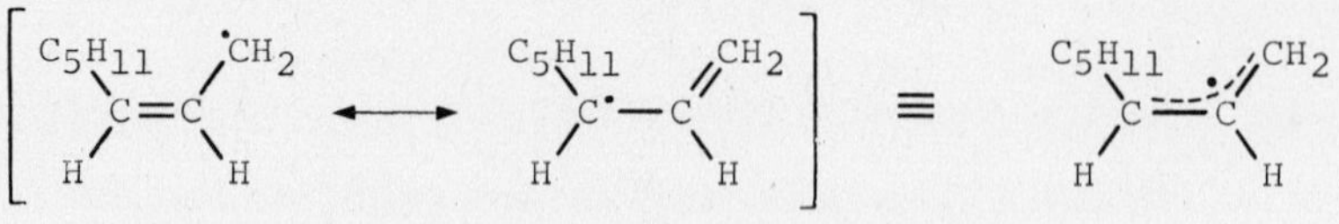

allylic radical B, *cisoid*

If either A or B reacts with Br_2 at C-3, the same product is produced:

$$A \text{ or } B + Br_2 \longrightarrow C_5H_{11}\overset{Br}{\underset{|}{C}}HCH=CH_2 + Br\cdot$$

However, if reaction with Br_2 occurs at C-1, then the **transoid** allylic radical A gives trans-1-bromo-2-octene, whereas the **cisoid** allylic radical B gives cis-1-bromo-2-octene. The barrier to interconversion of these two isomeric radicals is about 10 kcal mole^{-1}, much higher than the activation energy for reaction of either with Br_2 (see Chapter 6).

6.

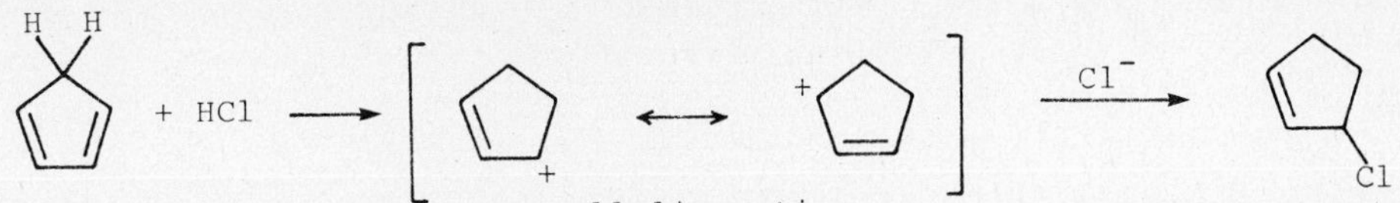

The 4-chloro isomer can only occur by way of the normal secondary carbocation, which is not as stable as the allylic cation which gives the 3-chloro isomer.

i.e.,

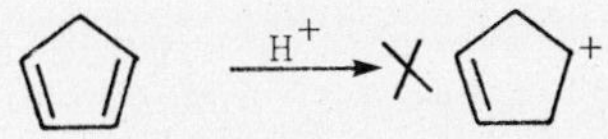

(higher energy; not formed)

7.

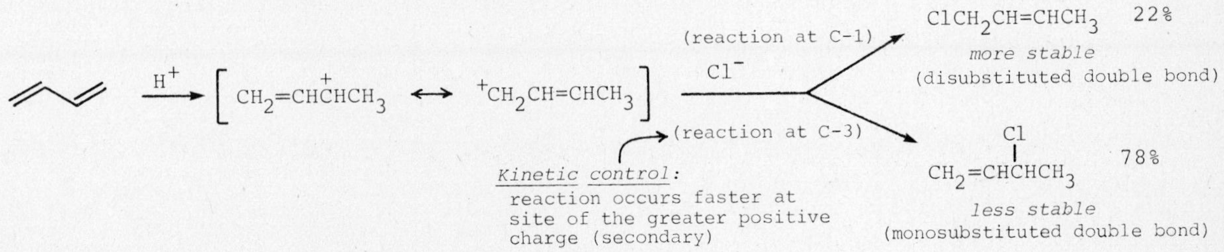

$$CH_2=CH\overset{+}{C}HCH_3 \longleftrightarrow {}^+CH_2CH=CHCH_3$$

(reaction at C-1)

$ClCH_2CH=CHCH_3$ 22%
more stable
(disubstituted double bond)

(reaction at C-3)

Kinetic control:
reaction occurs faster at site of the greater positive charge (secondary)

$CH_2=CHCHCH_3$ (with Cl substituent)   78%
less stable
(monosubstituted double bond)

If equilibration is allowed to occur, the *thermodynamic mixture* is produced. Equilibration occurs by ionization <u>back</u> to the carbocation.

8.

(a)

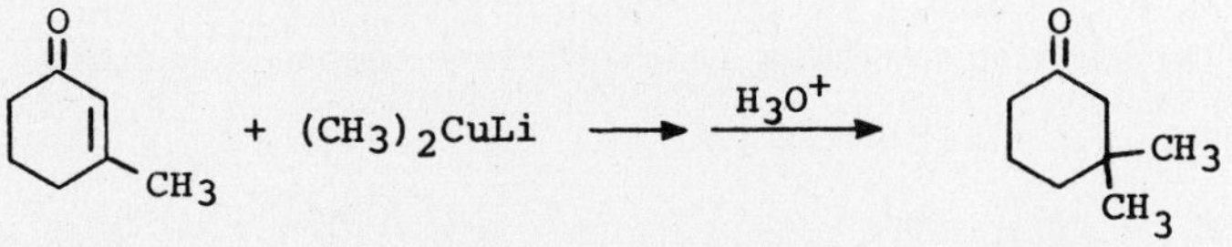

(b)

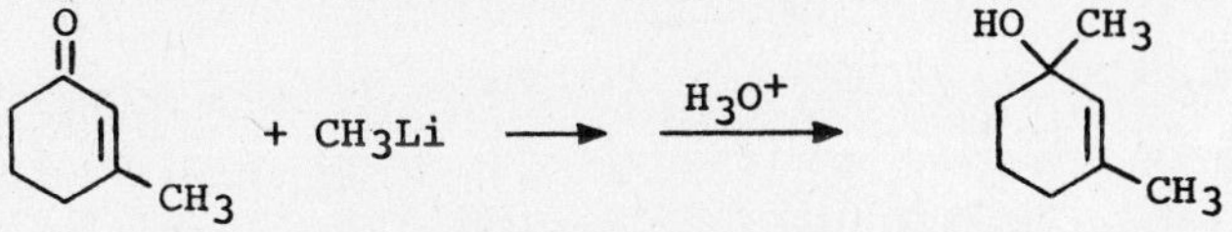

(c)

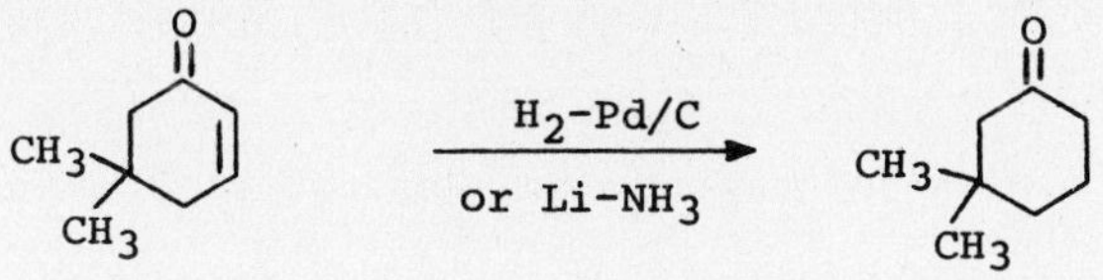

(d)

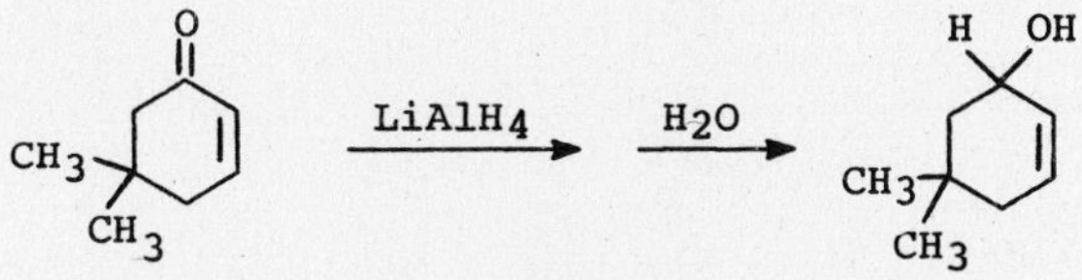

(e)

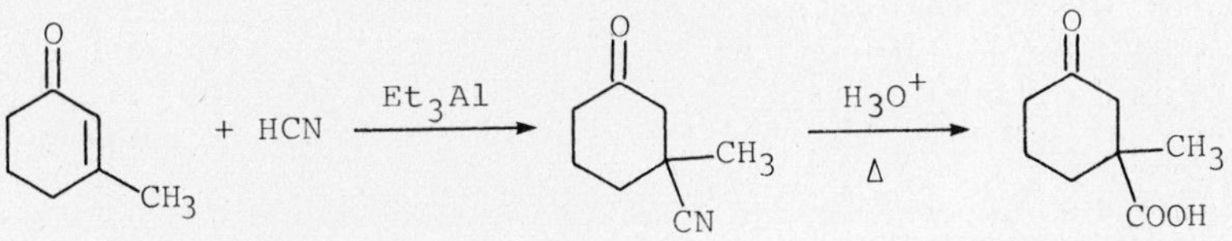

9. (a) $Ba^{14}CO_3 + H_2SO_4 \longrightarrow BaSO_4 + H_2O + {}^{14}CO_2$

$$CH_2=CHBr + Mg \xrightarrow{ether} CH_2=CHMgBr \xrightarrow[\quad]{{}^{14}CO_2} \xrightarrow{H_3O^+} CH_2=CH{-}^{14}CO_2H \xrightarrow{LiAlH_4} \xrightarrow{H_2O} CH_2=CH{-}^{14}CH_2OH$$

$$CH_2=CH{-}^{14}CH_2OH \xrightarrow{SOCl_2} \left.\begin{array}{c} CH_2=CH{-}^{14}CH_2Cl \\ \underline{or} \\ {}^{14}CH_2=CH{-}CH_2Cl \end{array}\right\} \xrightarrow{KMnO_4} CO_2 + HO\overset{O}{\overset{\|}{C}}CH_2Cl$$

Collect and count the CO_2. If rearrangement is complete, the CO_2 will have 100% of the ^{14}C. If there is no rearrangement, it will have 0% of the ^{14}C.

(b) $CH_2=CHCO_2CH_3 + LiAlD_4 \longrightarrow \xrightarrow{H_2O} CH_2=CH-CD_2OH$

Nmr will show only the vinyl H's and the OH. Recall that δ (OH) is concentration-dependent.

$CH_2=CHCD_2OH \xrightarrow{SOCl_2} CH_2=CHCD_2Cl + CD_2=CHCH_2Cl$

not rearranged   *rearranged*

The nmr spectrum will show a mixture of two chlorides. One component shows only vinyl H's as a complex multiplet, while the other shows a vinyl H (triplet) and $-CH_2Cl$ (doublet) with an area ratio of 1:2. The $-CH_2Cl$ group will appear at about $\delta=4$ (3 for $-CH_2Cl$ plus 1 for allylic)

10.

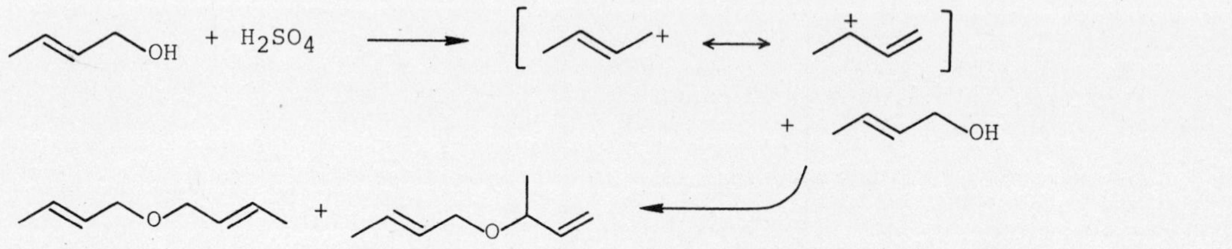

Of course the allylic cation can also react with water to give the isomeric alcohol:

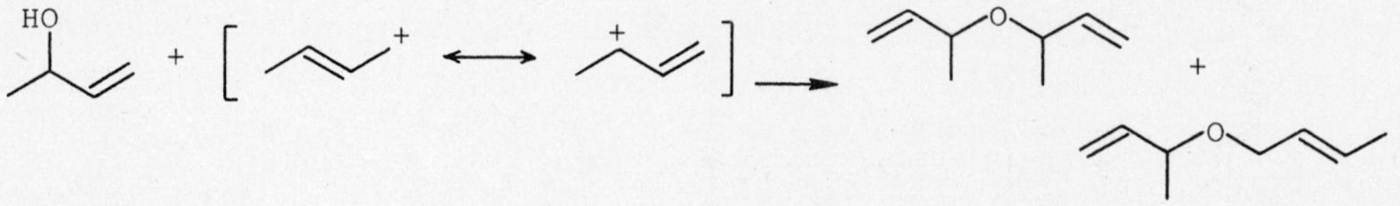

11. (a) $CH_3CH_2CH_2C{\equiv}CH \rightleftharpoons CH_3CH_2C{\equiv}CCH_3 \rightleftharpoons CH_3CH_2CH=C=CH_2$ (175°C; 448 °K)

    A, 1.3%   B, 95.2%   C, 3.5%

Take B, the most stable, as the point of reference. The equilibrium constant for the equilibrium between B and A is:

$$K = [A]/[B] = 1.3/95.2 = 0.0136$$

$\Delta G° = -RT \ln K = -1.987 \times 448 \times (-4.30)$ cal mole^{-1}

$\Delta G° = +3.83$ kcal mole^{-1}

Similarly, the equilibrium constant for B $\rightleftharpoons$ C is:

$$K = [C]/[B] = 3.5/95.2 = 0.0367$$

$\Delta G° = -1.987 \times 448 \times (-3.30)$ cal mole^{-1}

$\Delta G° = +2.94$ kcal mole^{-1}

Note that allene C is more stable than the 1-alkyne and less stable than the internal alkyne.

Mechanism:

$RCH_2C{\equiv}CH + OH^- \rightleftharpoons \left[R-\overset{..}{\overset{-}{C}}H-C{\equiv}CH \longleftrightarrow R-CH=C=\overset{..}{\overset{-}{C}}H \right]$

$\left[R-CH{=\!\!=}C{\equiv}CH \right]^- + H_2O \rightleftharpoons R-CH=C=CH_2 + OH^-$

$R-CH=C=CH_2 + OH^- \rightleftharpoons \left[R-\overset{..}{\overset{-}{C}}=C=CH_2 \longleftrightarrow R-C{\equiv}C-\overset{..}{\overset{-}{C}}H_2 \right]$

$\left[R-C{\equiv}C{=\!\!=}CH_2 \right]^- + H_2O \rightleftharpoons R-C{\equiv}CCH_3 + OH^-$

(b) In the case of $Na^+NH_2^-$, the amide ion is so basic that it converts the terminal alkyne completely to the carbanion, thus shifting the equilibrium quantitatively in this direction.

$$R-CH_2C{\equiv}CH\ +\ NH_2^-\ \rightleftharpoons\ RCH_2C{\equiv}C^-\ +\ NH_3 \qquad K \approx 10^{10}$$
$$pK_a = 25 \qquad\qquad\qquad\qquad pK_a = 34$$

12.

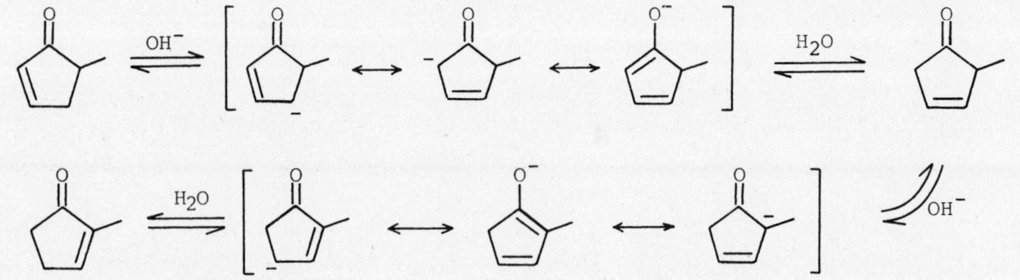

The β,γ- form is common to two α,β- forms in this case. Note that the analogous transformation is not possible for a cyclohexenone:

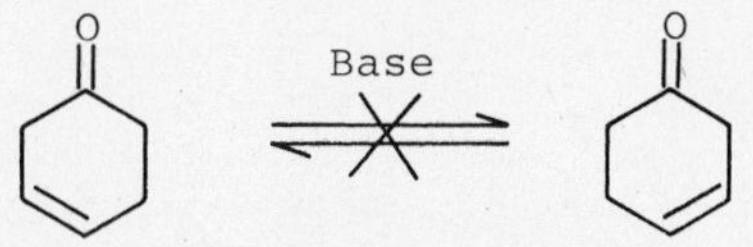

13.

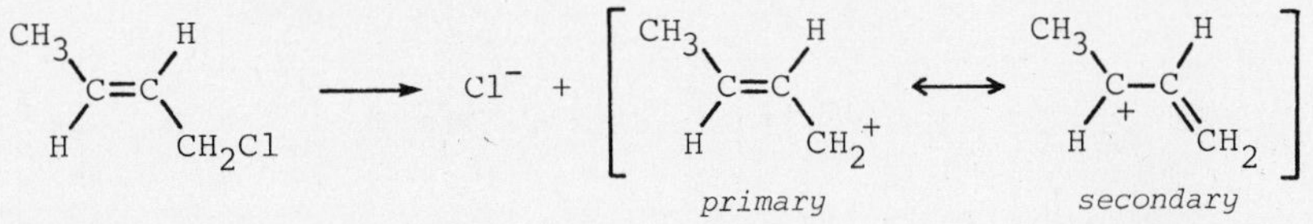

$\Delta H^\circ = +161$ kcal mole^{-1}

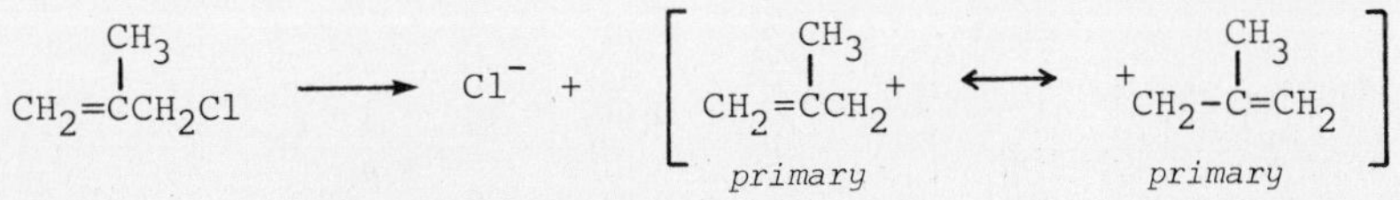

$\Delta H^\circ = +169$ kcal mole^{-1}

The allylic cation from 1-chloro-2-butene has the dual character of primary and secondary carbocations. That from 3-chloro-2-methyl-1-propene is primary-primary.

14.

(a)

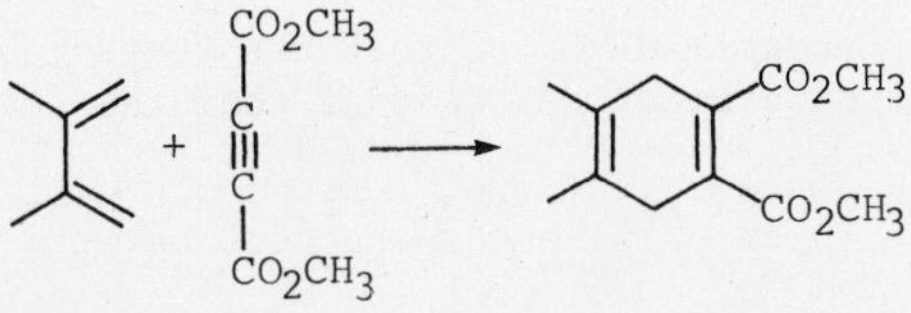

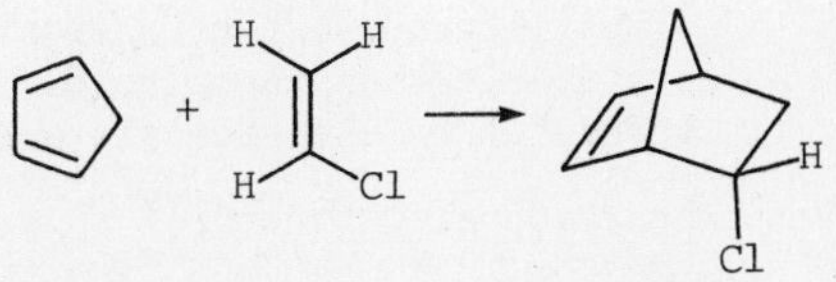

(b)

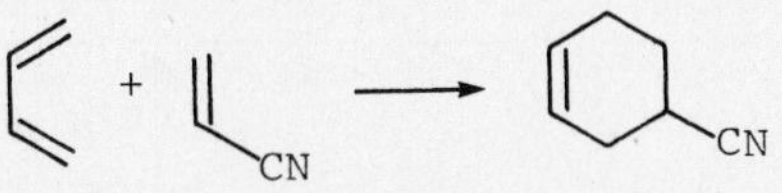

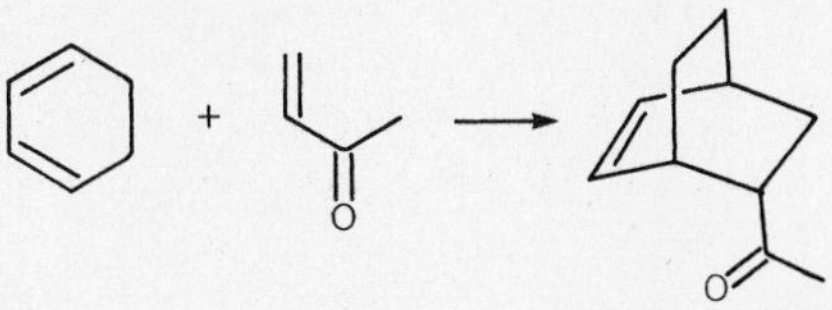

(c)

(d)

(e)

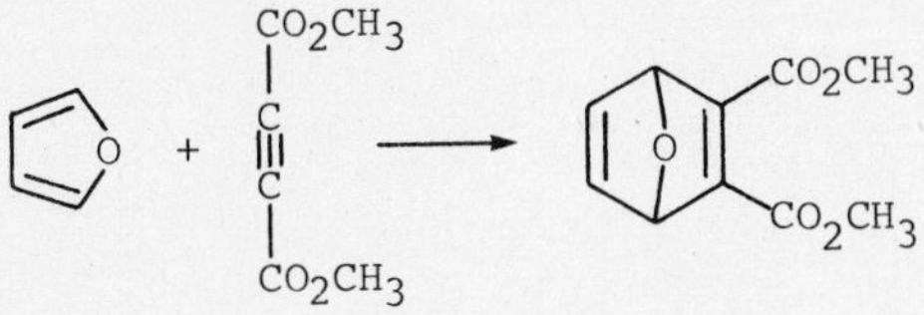

(f)

(g)

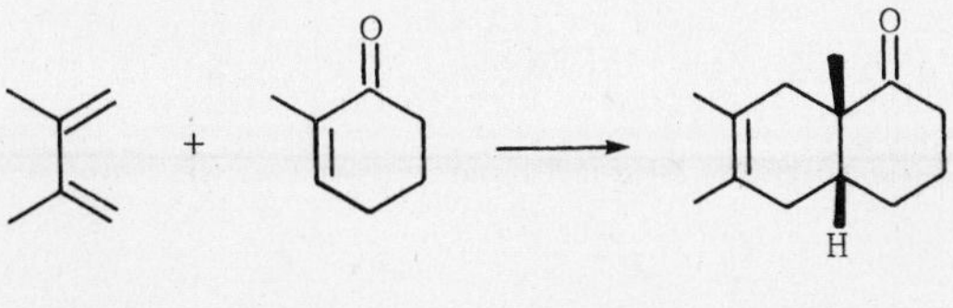

(h)

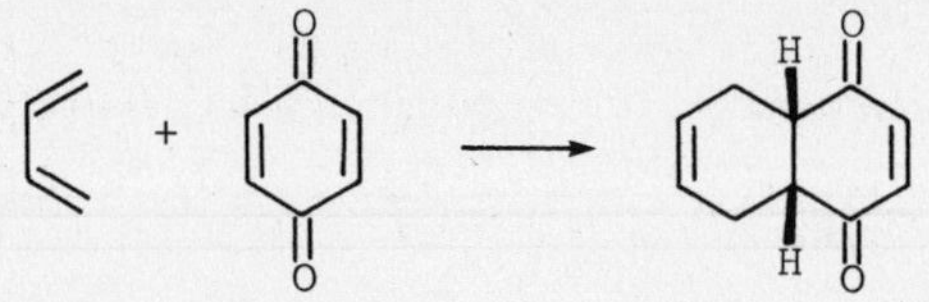

15.

(a)

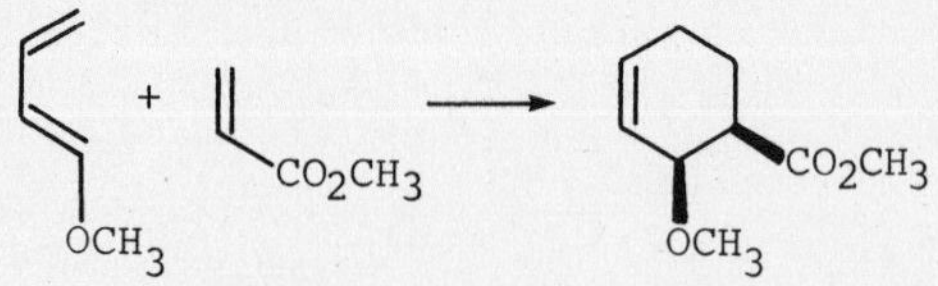

(b)

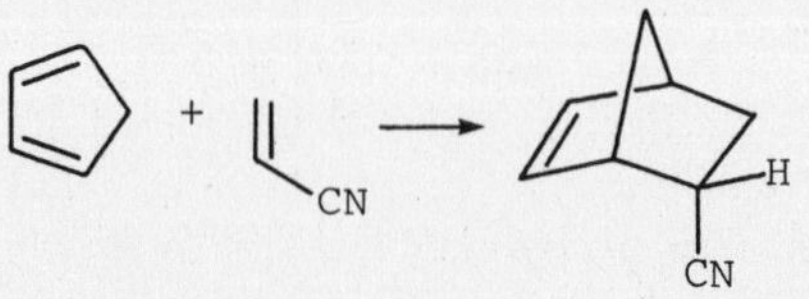

(c)

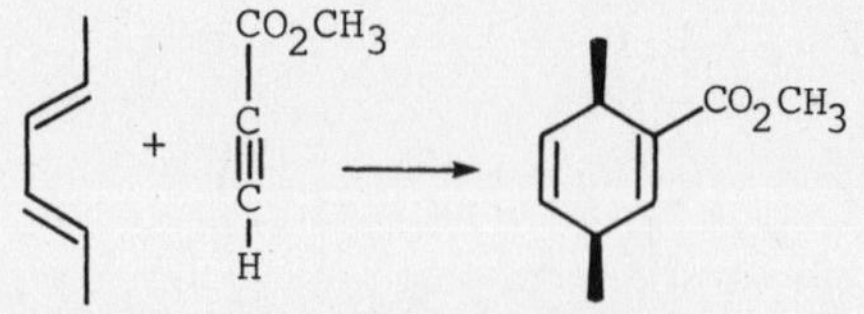

16. (a) $(CH_3)_3COH + OH^- \rightleftharpoons (CH_3)_3CO^- + H_2O$

$(CH_3)_3CO^- + Cl-Cl \rightleftharpoons (CH_3)_3COCl + Cl^-$

(b)

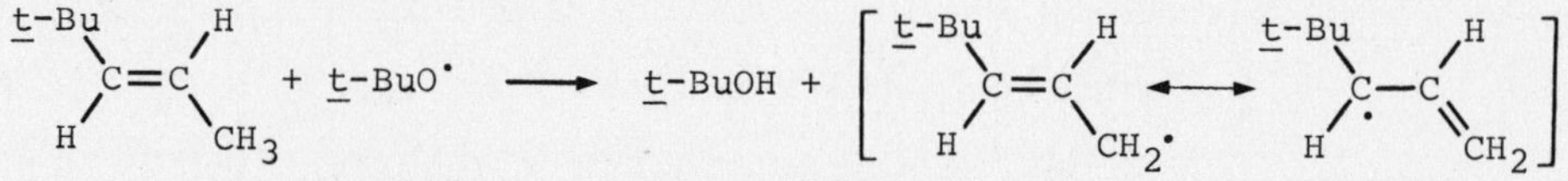

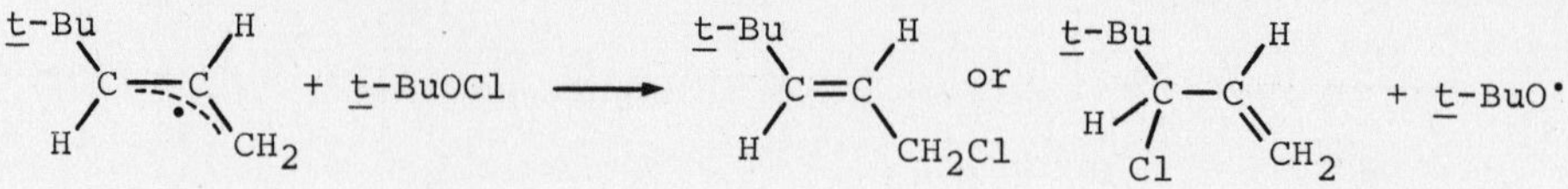

(c) This experiment shows that the <u>transoid</u> $\rightleftharpoons$ <u>cisoid</u> equilibration at -78 °C must be slower than reaction of the radical with <u>t</u>-BuOCl.

(d) The first experiment shows either that the two types of allylic radical (see problem #5) do not interconvert to a significant extent at -78 °C, or that the <u>transoid</u> radical is more stable than the <u>cisoid</u>. The second experiment establishes that the rates of inter-conversion of the radicals are slow.

(e) The resonance structures show that there is "double-bond character" between C-2 and C-3:

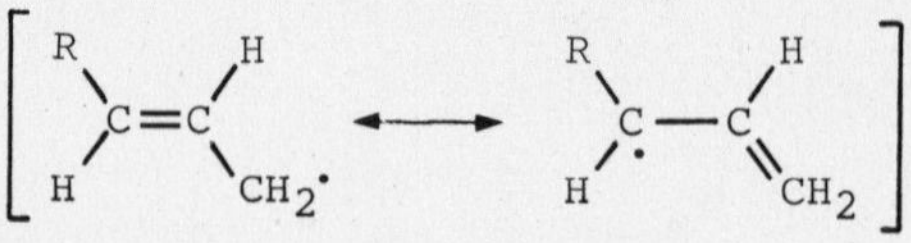

17.

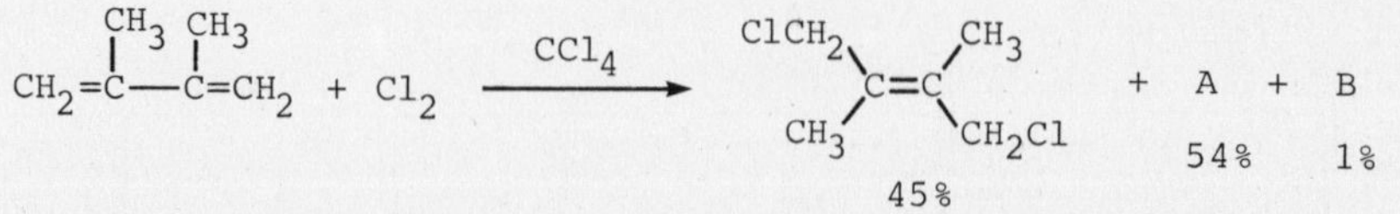

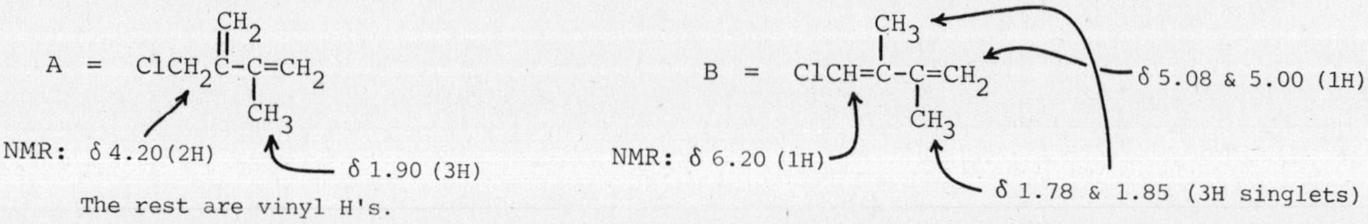

$CH_2=C-C=CH_2 + Cl_2 \xrightarrow{CCl_4}$ + A + B

45%   54% 1%

A = ClCH₂C-C=CH₂

NMR: δ 4.20 (2H)   δ 1.90 (3H)

The rest are vinyl H's.

B = ClCH=C-C=CH₂

NMR: δ 6.20 (1H)   δ 5.08 & 5.00 (1H)

δ 1.78 & 1.85 (3H singlets)

Mechanism (A + B):

$$CH_2=\overset{\overset{\displaystyle CH_3}{|}}{C}-\overset{\overset{\displaystyle |}{CH_3}}{C}=CH_2 + Cl_2 \longrightarrow ClCH_2-\overset{\overset{\displaystyle CH_3}{|}}{\underset{+}{C}}-\overset{\overset{\displaystyle |}{CH_3}}{C}=CH_2 \xrightarrow{-H^+}$$

$$ClCH_2-\overset{\overset{\displaystyle CH_2}{\|}}{C}-\overset{\overset{\displaystyle |}{CH_3}}{C}=CH_2 \qquad \text{A}$$

$$ClCH=\overset{\overset{\displaystyle CH_3}{|}}{C}-\overset{\overset{\displaystyle |}{CH_3}}{C}=CH_2 \qquad \text{B}$$

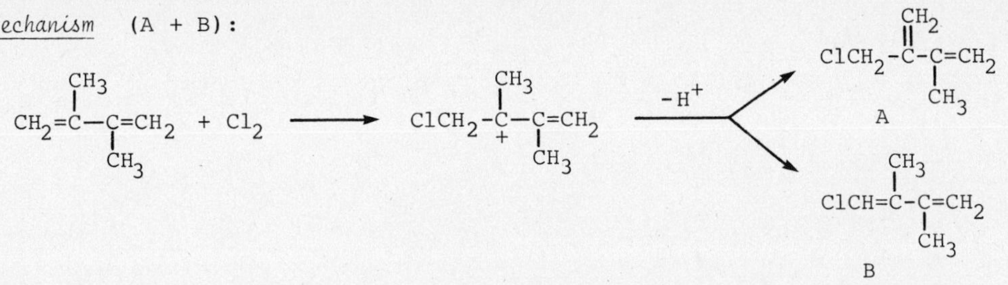

18.

The two peaks of the doublet at δ 1.60 are due to these two methyls, which are not equivalent.

One is _cis_ to CH_2MgBr and one is _trans_ to it.

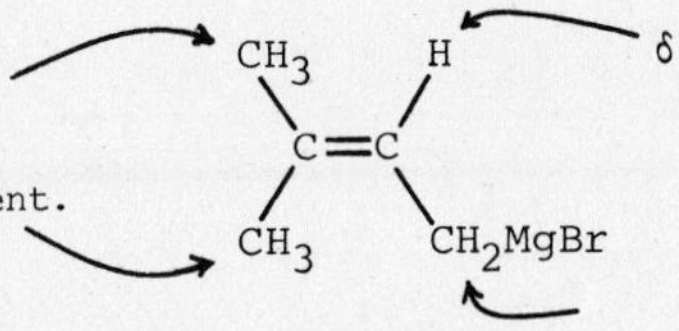

δ 5.6 triplet (1H)
(vinyl H)

δ 0.6 doublet (2H)
(upfield because of negative charge in carbanion)

At room temperature, the two methyl groups become equivalent on the NMR time scale by the following mechanism.

$$\overset{(a)\ CH_3}{\underset{(b)\ CH_3}{}}C=C\overset{H}{\underset{CH_2MgBr}{}} \rightleftharpoons \overset{(a)\ CH_3}{\underset{(b)\ CH_3}{}}\overset{|}{\underset{MgBr}{C}}-CH=CH_2 \rightleftharpoons \overset{(a)\ CH_3}{\underset{(b)\ CH_3}{}}C=C\overset{CH_2MgBr}{\underset{H}{}}$$

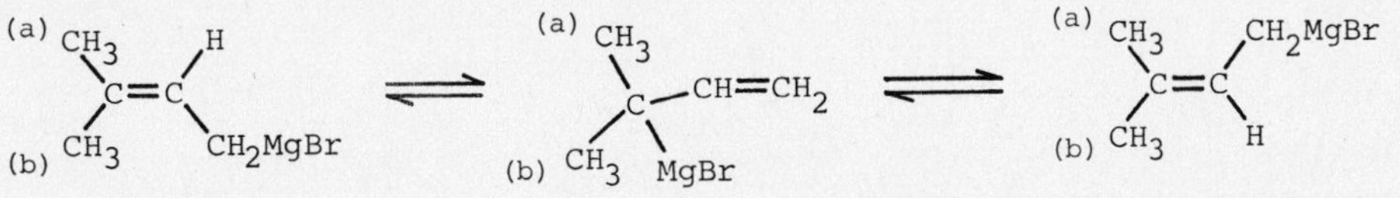

(present only in small amount)

The equilibria are rapid at room temperature.

19. Radical chain mechanism. The propagation steps are:

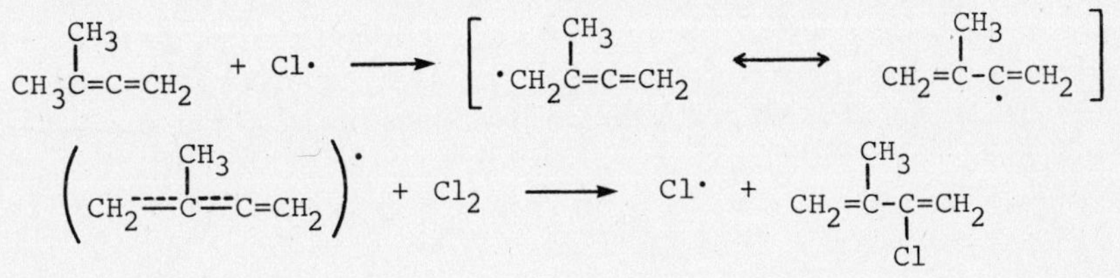

$$CH_3\overset{\overset{\displaystyle CH_3}{|}}{C}=C=CH_2 + Cl\cdot \longrightarrow \left[\cdot CH_2\overset{\overset{\displaystyle CH_3}{|}}{C}=C=CH_2 \longleftrightarrow CH_2=\overset{\overset{\displaystyle CH_3}{|}}{C}-\overset{\cdot}{C}=CH_2 \right]$$

$$\left(CH_2\overset{\overset{\displaystyle CH_3}{|}}{\underset{\cdots}{C}}\cdots C=CH_2 \right)^{\cdot} + Cl_2 \longrightarrow Cl\cdot + CH_2=\overset{\overset{\displaystyle CH_3}{|}}{C}-\underset{Cl}{C}=CH_2$$

20.

$$HOCH_2\underset{OH}{CH}CH_2OH + H^+ \rightleftharpoons HO-CH_2\underset{+OH_2}{CH}CH_2OH \rightleftharpoons HO-CH_2\underset{+}{CH}CH_2-OH \overset{-H^+}{\Longleftarrow}$$

$$O=CH-CH=CH_2 \underset{-H^+}{\rightleftharpoons} \overset{+}{HO}=CH-CH=CH_2 \underset{-H_2O}{\rightleftharpoons} HO-CH=CH-CH_2OH_2^+ \underset{-H^+}{\rightleftharpoons} HO-CH=CH-CH\ OH \rightleftharpoons O=\overset{\overset{\displaystyle H}{|}}{C}-CH_2CH_2OH$$

21.

45% $\rightleftharpoons$ 55%

86% $\rightleftharpoons$ 14%

steric hindrance

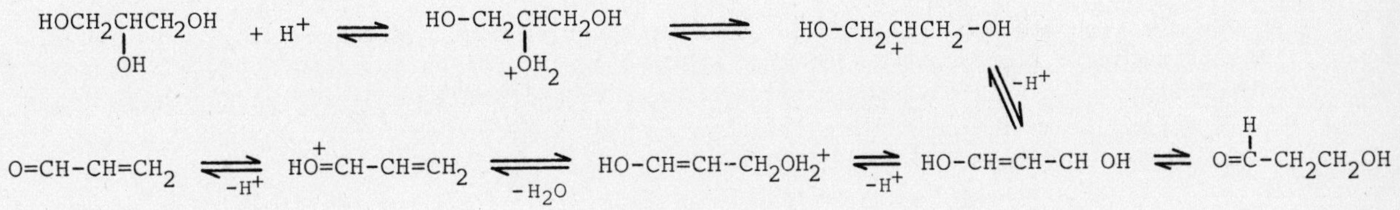

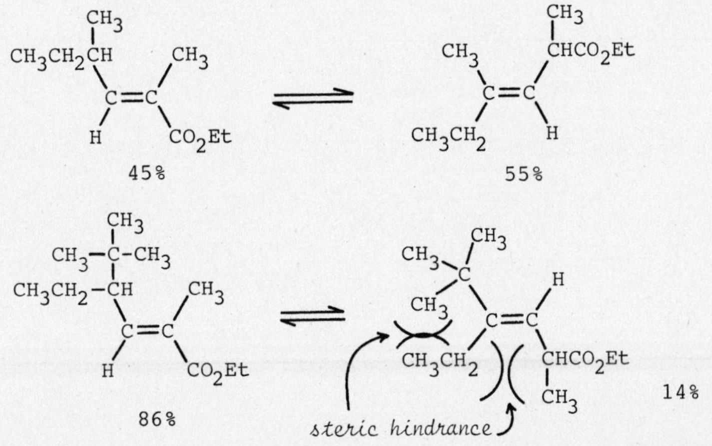

Steric hindrance is greater in the R = t-Bu case and is clearly evident using molecular models.

19.F   Supplementary Problems

S1.   What is the major product to result from each of the following reaction sequences?

(a) 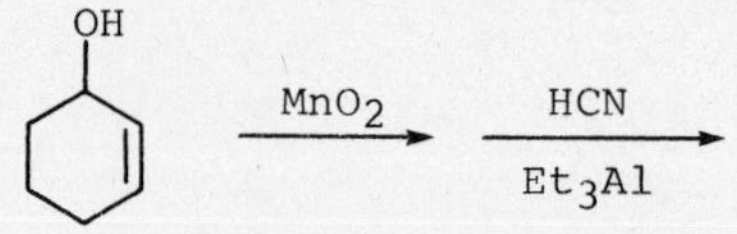 $\xrightarrow{MnO_2}$ $\xrightarrow[Et_3Al]{HCN}$ (b) 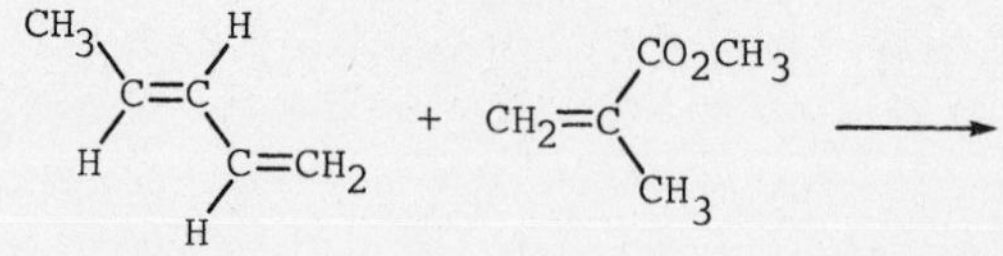   + $CH_2=C\overset{CO_2CH_3}{\underset{CH_3}{}}$ $\longrightarrow$

(c) $(CH_3)_3C\overset{O}{C}H$ + $(CH_3CO)_2O$ $\xrightarrow[180°]{CH_3CO_2Na}$ $\xrightarrow{Br_2}$

(d) 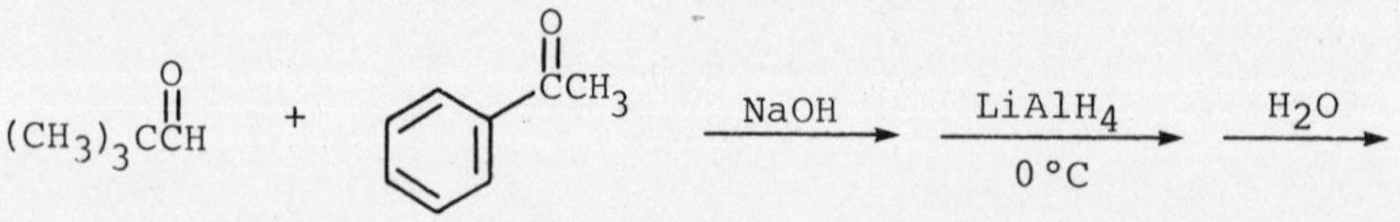 $(CH_3)_3C\overset{O}{C}H$ + $\xrightarrow{NaOH}$ $\xrightarrow[0°C]{LiAlH_4}$ $\xrightarrow{H_2O}$

(e) $CH_3CH=CHCH_2Br$ $\xrightarrow[ether]{Mg}$ $\xrightarrow{CO_2}$ $\xrightarrow[H^+]{CH_3OH}$ $\xrightarrow{CH_3O^-}$

(f) $(CH_3)_2C=CHCH=CH_2$ $\xrightarrow[0°C]{HCl}$ $\xrightarrow{50°C}$ (g) 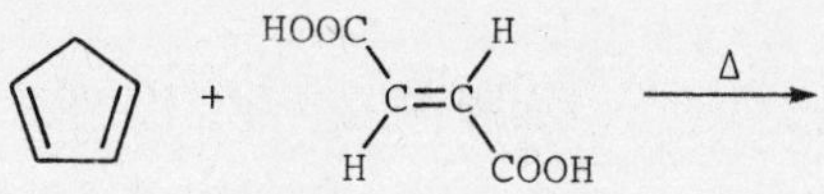   + $\underset{H}{\overset{HOOC}{}}C=C\underset{COOH}{\overset{H}{}}$ $\xrightarrow{\Delta}$

S2.   Of the following three Diels-Alder reactions, one gives only a single product and the other two each give a mixture of two isomeric products. Write the products of each reaction, and indicate the major product for the reactions which give mixtures.

(a) 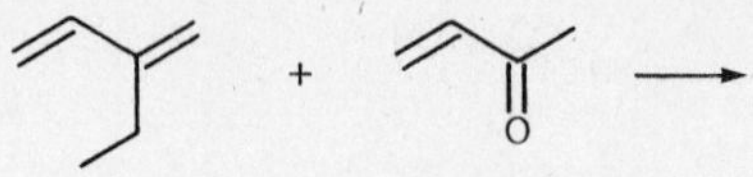   + $\longrightarrow$ (c) 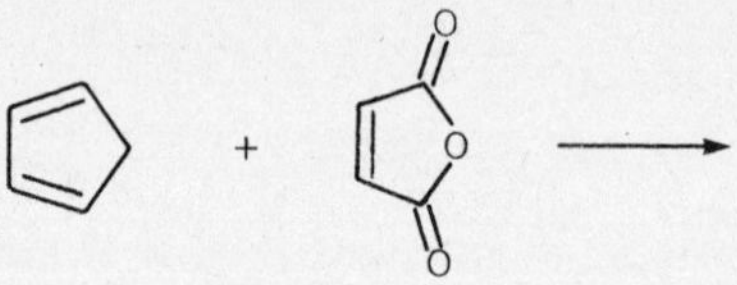   + $\longrightarrow$

(b) 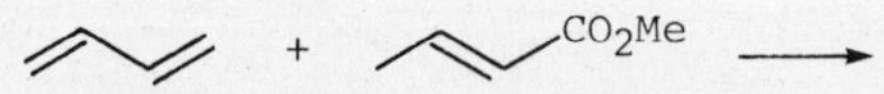   + $\longrightarrow$

S3.   The reaction sequence illustrated below was carried out to prepare methyl 1-cyclohexene-carboxylate. A product was obtained which shows an α,β-unsaturated ester function in the infrared (ν_{max} = 1710, 1660 cm^{-1}). However, the elemental analysis of the product was incorrect (both %C and %H were too high). What is wrong with the sample? How may the synthesis be modified to eliminate the problem?

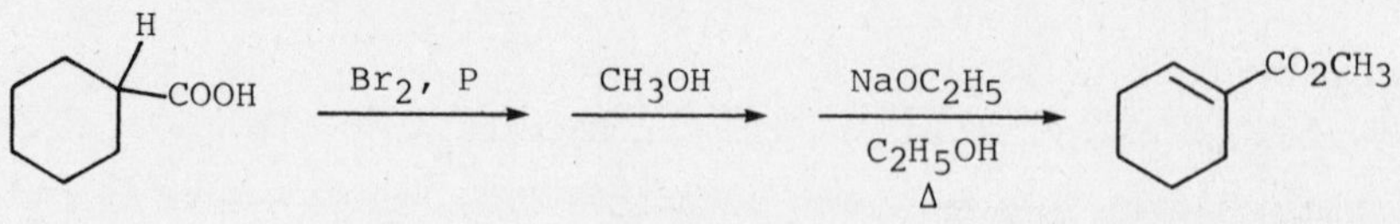

$\xrightarrow{Br_2, P}$ $\xrightarrow{CH_3OH}$ $\xrightarrow[\underset{\Delta}{C_2H_5OH}]{NaOC_2H_5}$

S4.   Provide an explanation for the following differences in chemical behavior.

(a) $ClCH=CHCH_3$ +   NaCN $\longrightarrow$ no reaction

$ClCH=CH\overset{O}{C}CH_3$ +   NaCN $\longrightarrow$ $NC-CH=CH\overset{O}{C}CH_3$

(b) $CH_3OCH_2CH_2CH_3 \xrightarrow{\text{KO}\underline{t}\text{-Bu}}$ no reaction

$CH_3OCH_2CH_2CO_2CH_3 \xrightarrow{\text{KO}\underline{t}\text{-Bu}} CH_2=CHCO_2CH_3 + CH_3OH$

(c)

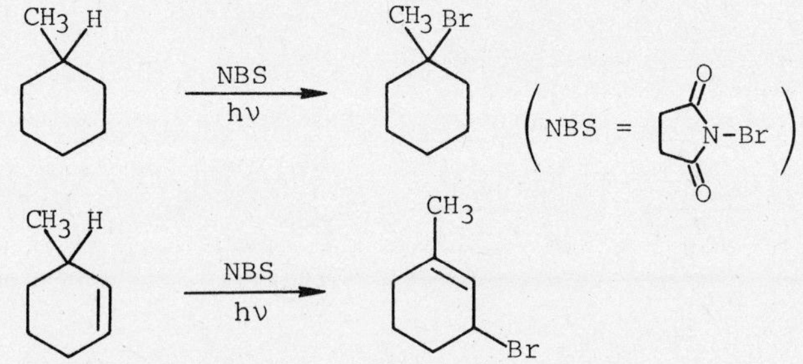

[1,1-dimethylcyclohexane with H] $\xrightarrow[h\nu]{\text{NBS}}$ [1-bromo-1-methylcyclohexane] $\left(\text{NBS} = \text{N-bromosuccinimide} \right)$

[1-methylcyclohex-2-ene] $\xrightarrow[h\nu]{\text{NBS}}$ [1-methyl-3-bromocyclohexene]

(d)

[1-methylcyclopentanol] $\xrightarrow[\text{H}_2\text{SO}_4, \, 0°C]{K_2Cr_2O_7}$ no reaction

[1-methyl-2-cyclopentenol] $\xrightarrow[\text{H}_2\text{SO}_4, \, 0°C]{K_2Cr_2O_7}$ [3-methyl-2-cyclopentenone]

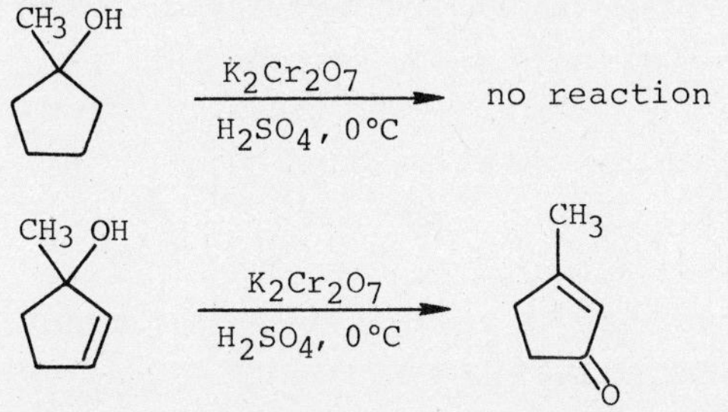

S5. The C=O stretch in the infrared spectrum of conjugated ketones comes at lower frequency than that for the analogous saturated systems. Explain why.

1710 cm^{-1} $CH_3-\overset{O}{\overset{||}{C}}-CH_2CH(CH_3)_2$

1695 cm^{-1} $CH_3-\overset{O}{\overset{||}{C}}-CH=C(CH_3)_2$ 1625 cm^{-1}

S6. Using Appendices I and II, calculate the change in enthalpy expected for the propagation steps of the free-radical chlorination of ethane, ethylene, and propene to give ethyl chloride, vinyl chloride, and allyl chloride, respectively.

S7. The prostaglandins are a class of compounds whose occurrence, structures, and potent biological effects have been studied and elucidated only within recent years. They are found throughout the body, and are implicated in many diverse biological processes, often at nanomolar (10^{-9} M) concentrations. PGE$_2$, the most potent of the prostaglandins, is unstable in the presence of base: it loses water to give PGA$_2$, which then isomerizes to the physiologically inactive PGB$_2$ isomer.
Write a reasonable structure for PGA$_2$, as well as step-by-step mechanisms for these two transformations.

[Structure of PGE$_2$] $\xrightarrow[-\text{H}_2\text{O}]{\text{OH}^-}$ PGA_2 $\xrightarrow{\text{OH}^-}$ [Structure of PGB$_2$]

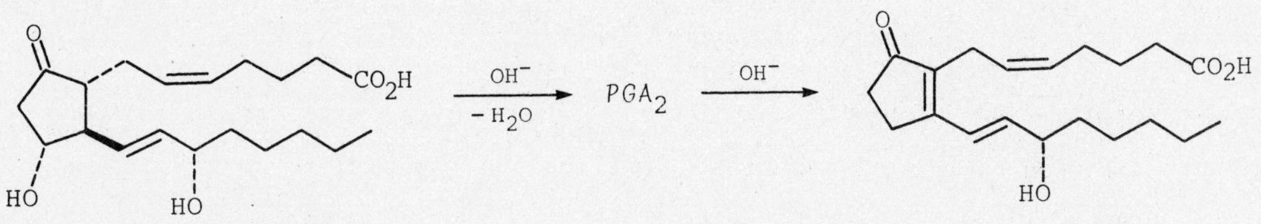

PGE$_2$ *PGB$_2$*

S8. When 2-methyl-3-cyclohexenone is treated with base, it readily isomerizes to 2-methyl-2-cyclohexenone. Similar treatment of bicyclo[2.2.2]oct-5-en-2-one does not produce any reaction, however. Why do these two compounds differ so much in reactivity?

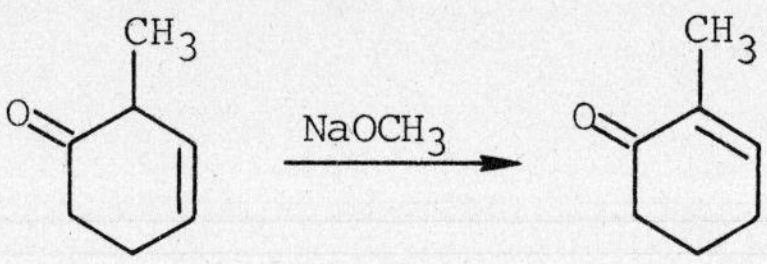

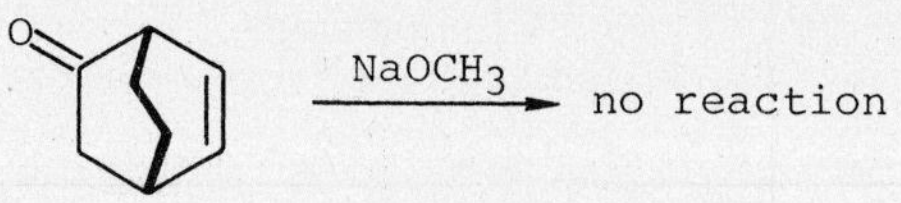

S9. Write a mechanism for the following transformation.

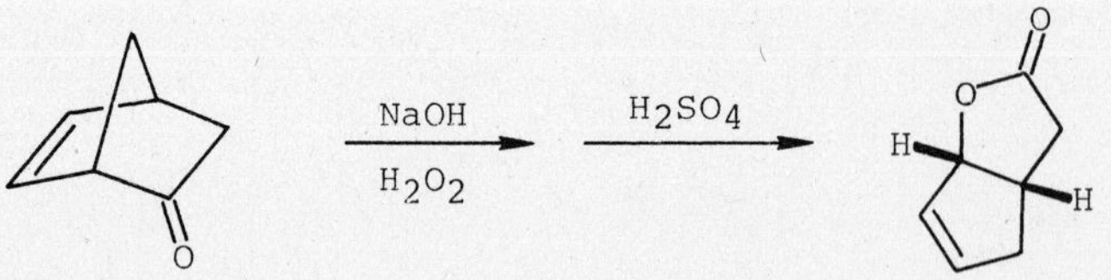

S10. Compound A ($C_7H_{14}O$) has a strong absorption in its infrared spectrum at 3400 cm^{-1}. It reacts with acetic anhydride to give a new compound (B, $C_9H_{16}O_2$), which shows an infrared absorption at 1735 cm^{-1}. Compound A reacts with Na_2CrO_4 in acetic acid to give C, which has an infrared band at 1710 cm^{-1}. Compound C reacts with bromine in acetic acid to give D ($C_7H_{11}BrO$). With excess bromine in aqueous NaOH, C gives a tetrabromo compound (E, $C_7H_8Br_4O$). Compound D reacts with potassium t-butoxide in refluxing t-butyl alcohol to give F, which has infrared absorptions at 1685 and 1670 cm^{-1}. When either C or F is treated with $NaOCH_3$ in CH_3OD, it is found to exchange four of its protons for deuterium. What are compounds A-F?

19.G   Answers to Supplementary Problems

S1.   (a)

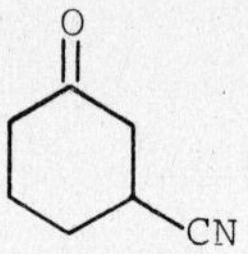

(c)

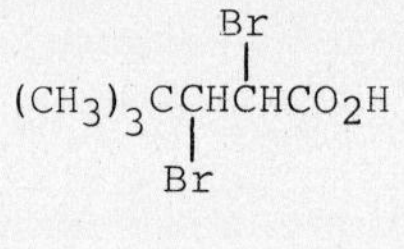

(b)

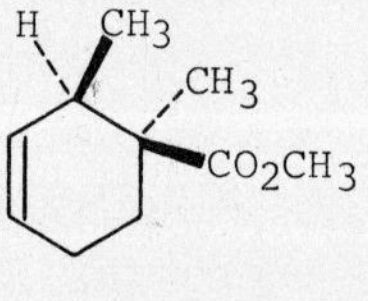

(d)

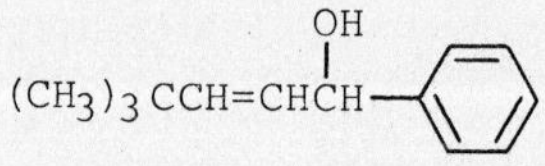

(e)

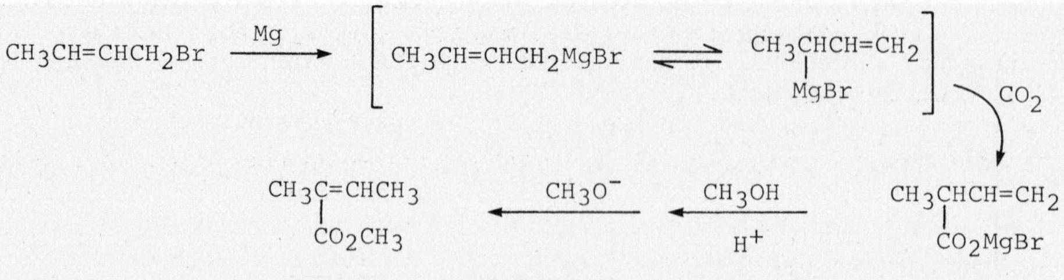

(f)

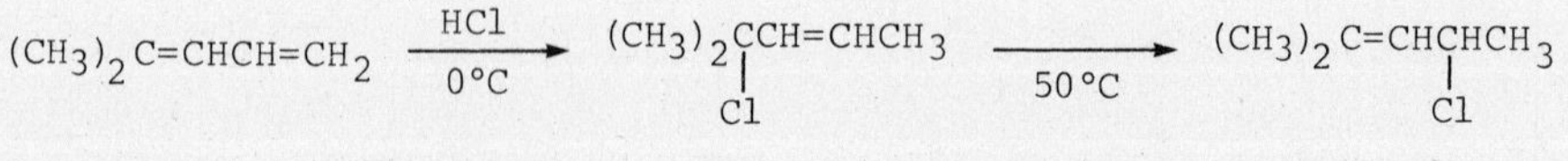

(g)

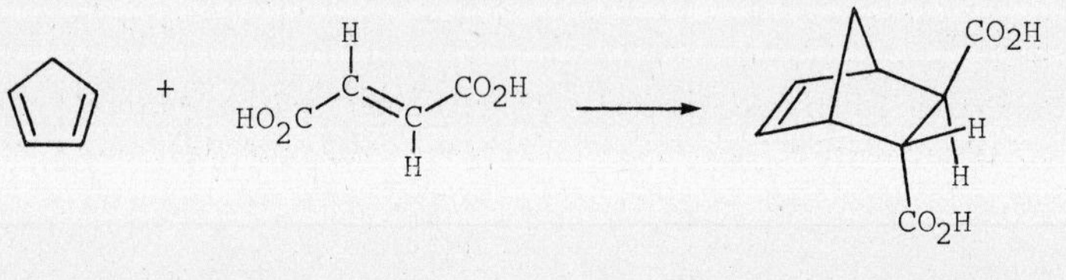

S2. (a)

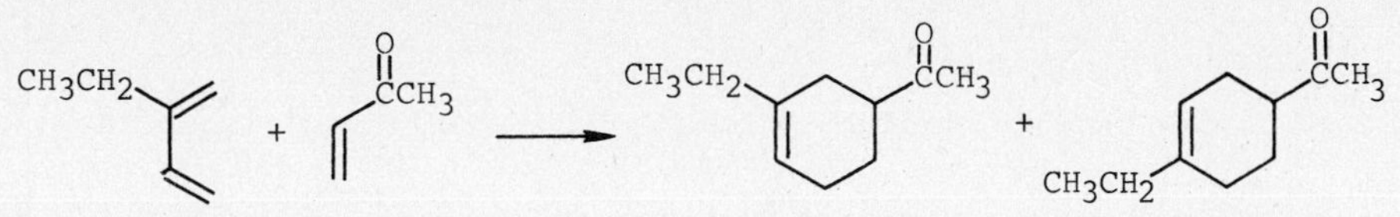

CH$_3$CH$_2$ + (acetyl vinyl ketone) → (cyclohexene with CH$_3$CH$_2$ and COCH$_3$ substituents)

major + (cyclohexene isomer with CH$_3$CH$_2$ and COCH$_3$ substituents)

minor

(b)

(butadiene) + (methyl acrylate CO$_2$CH$_3$) → (cyclohexene with CO$_2$CH$_3$ and CH$_3$ substituents, H shown) *only product*

(c)

(cyclopentadiene) + (maleic anhydride) → (bicyclic anhydride endo) *major* + (bicyclic anhydride exo) *minor*

S3. The methyl group has been lost through ester exchange with the NaOC$_2$H$_5$/C$_2$H$_5$OH used in the last step (see next page). This can be avoided by using NaOCH$_3$/CH$_3$OH to accomplish the elimination.

(cyclohexene-CO$_2$CH$_3$) + C$_2$H$_5$OH $\xrightleftharpoons{\text{NaOC}_2\text{H}_5}$ (cyclohexene-CO$_2$C$_2$H$_5$)

excess

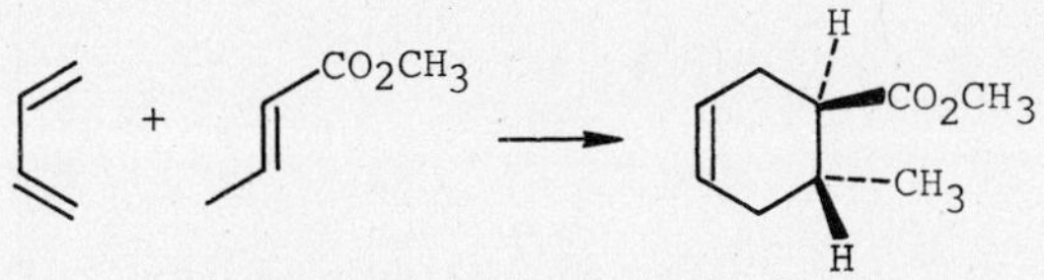

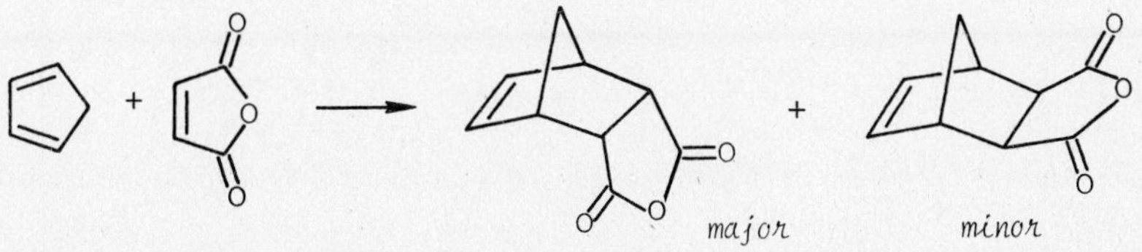

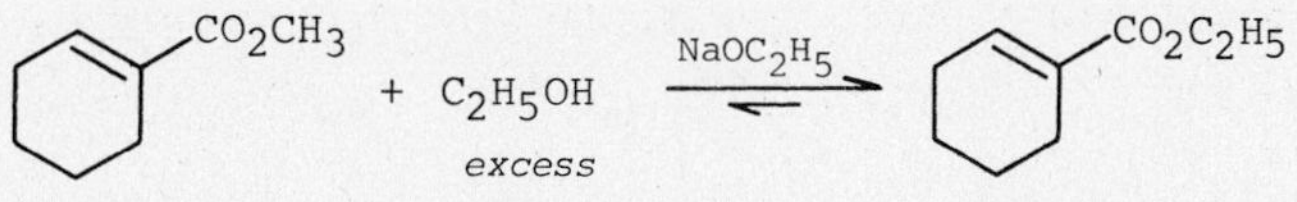

S4. (a) The chloroketone can undergo substitution by a conjugate addition-elimination sequence. Such a mechanism is not possible for 1-chloropropene.

ClCH=CH–CCH$_3$ (with CN$^-$) $\rightleftharpoons$ (intermediate with Cl, NC, CH–CH=CCH$_3$, O$^-$) $\rightleftharpoons$ NC–CH=CH–CCH$_3$

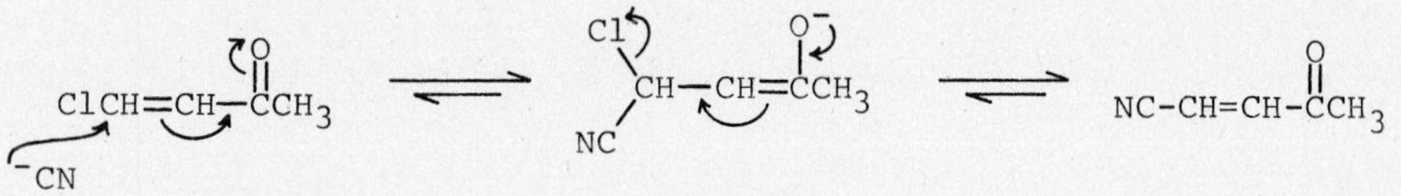

(b) The β-methoxyester can undergo elimination via an enolate, as in the second step of an aldol condensation. Again, the simple alkyl system cannot react in this manner.

CH$_3$OCH$_2$–CH–COCH$_3$ (H, Base) $\rightleftharpoons$ CH$_3$O–CH$_2$–CH=C–OCH$_3$ (O$^-$) $\rightleftharpoons$ CH$_2$=CH–COCH$_3$

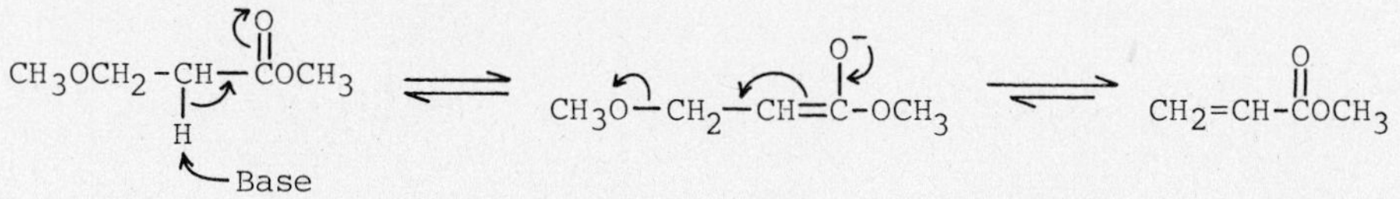

(c) In both free radical reactions, the hydrogen atom-abstraction is selective for the tertiary hydrogen. In the case of 3-methylhexene, this produces an allylic radical, which can subsequently react at the other end of the original double bond.

(cyclohexene with H, CH$_3$) $\xrightarrow{\text{Br}\cdot}$ [(allylic radical resonance structures)] $\xrightarrow{\text{Br}_2}$ (cyclohexene with CH$_3$ and Br)

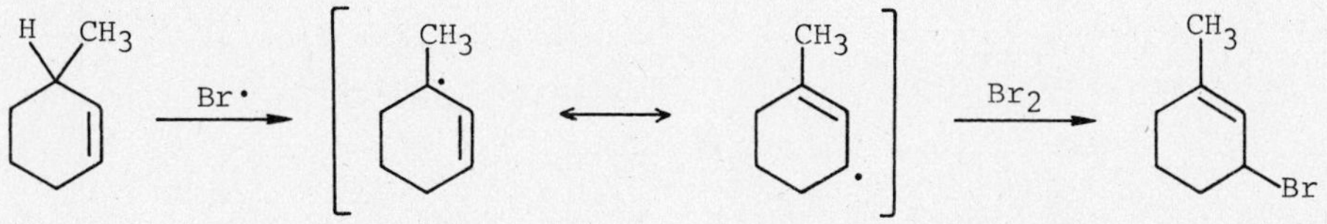

(d) Tertiary alcohols are not oxidized under mild conditions, but the tertiary allylic alcohol can undergo ionization, allylic isomerization, and then oxidation:

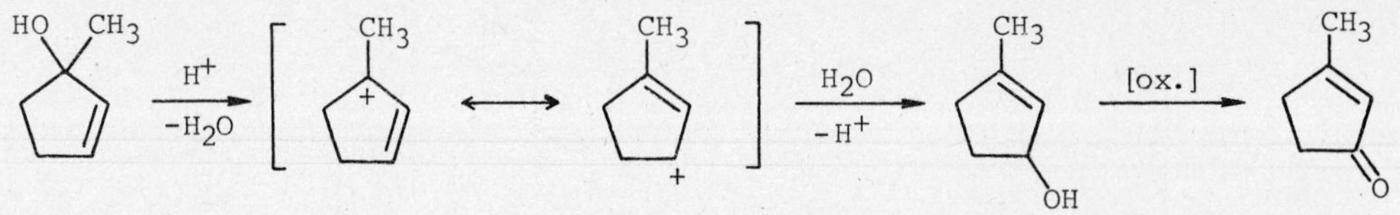

S5. Because of the contribution of resonance structures which have a C-O single bond, there is slightly less double-bond character in the carbonyl bond of an enone:

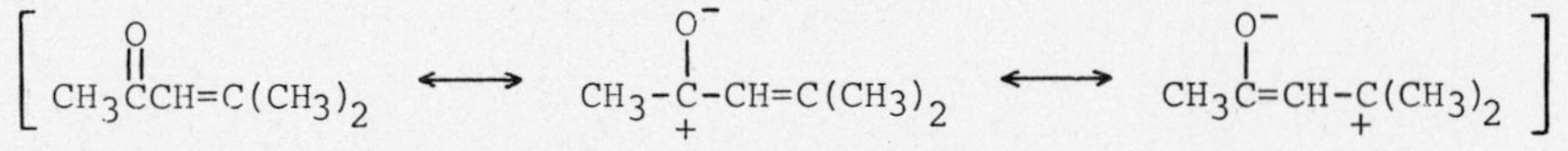

$$\left[\; CH_3\overset{O}{\overset{\|}{C}}CH=C(CH_3)_2 \longleftrightarrow CH_3-\overset{O^-}{\underset{+}{C}}-CH=C(CH_3)_2 \longleftrightarrow CH_3\overset{O^-}{\underset{}{C}}=CH-\underset{+}{C}(CH_3)_2 \; \right]$$

S6.

$$CH_3-CH_3 \; + \; Cl\cdot \longrightarrow CH_3CH_2\cdot \; + \; HCl \qquad \Delta H^\circ \; (kcal \; mole^{-1})$$
$\Delta H^\circ_f = \quad -20.2 \qquad 28.9 \qquad\qquad 26 \qquad\quad -22.1 \qquad\qquad +5$

$$CH_3-CH_2\cdot \; + \; Cl_2 \longrightarrow CH_3CH_2Cl \; + \; Cl\cdot$$
$\Delta H^\circ_f = \qquad 26 \qquad\quad 0 \qquad\qquad -26.1 \qquad\; 28.9 \qquad\qquad -23$

$$CH_2=CH_2 \; + \; Cl\cdot \longrightarrow CH_2=CH\cdot \; + \; HCl$$
$\Delta H^\circ_f = \qquad 12.5 \qquad 28.9 \qquad\qquad 70 \qquad\quad -22.1 \qquad\qquad +7$

$$CH_2=CH\cdot \; + \; Cl_2 \longrightarrow CH_2=CHCl \; + \; Cl\cdot$$
$\Delta H^\circ_f = \qquad 70 \qquad\quad 0 \qquad\qquad\; 8.6 \qquad\quad 28.9 \qquad\qquad -33$

$$CH_2=CH-CH_3 \; + \; Cl\cdot \longrightarrow CH_2=CH-CH_2\cdot \; + \; HCl$$
$\Delta H^\circ_f = \qquad 4.9 \qquad\quad 28.9 \qquad\qquad\quad 39 \qquad\quad -22.1 \qquad\qquad -17$

$$CH_2=CH-CH_2\cdot \; + \; Cl_2 \longrightarrow CH_2=CH-CH_2Cl \; + \; Cl\cdot$$
$\Delta H^\circ_f = \qquad 39 \qquad\qquad 0 \qquad\qquad\qquad 0^* \qquad\quad 28.9 \qquad\qquad -10$

$$*\text{Calculate } \Delta H^\circ_f(CH_2=CHCH_2Cl) = \Delta H^\circ_f(CH_2=CH-CH_2\cdot) + \Delta H^\circ_f(Cl\cdot) - DH^\circ(allyl-Cl)$$
$$= \qquad 39 \qquad + \quad 28.9 \quad - \quad 68 \quad = \quad 0$$

S7.

PGE₂   PGA₂

PGB₂

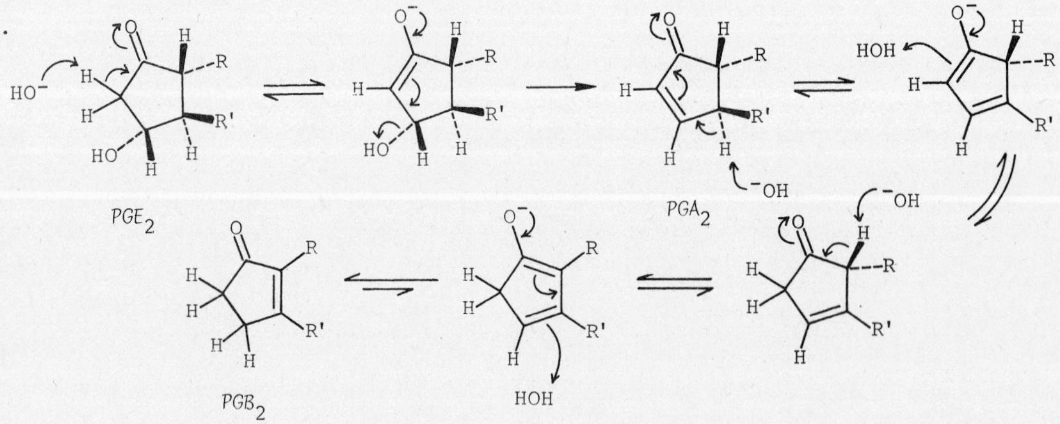

S8. Enolization and subsequent conjugation of the enone system both require that all the atoms involved are able to line up their p-orbitals:

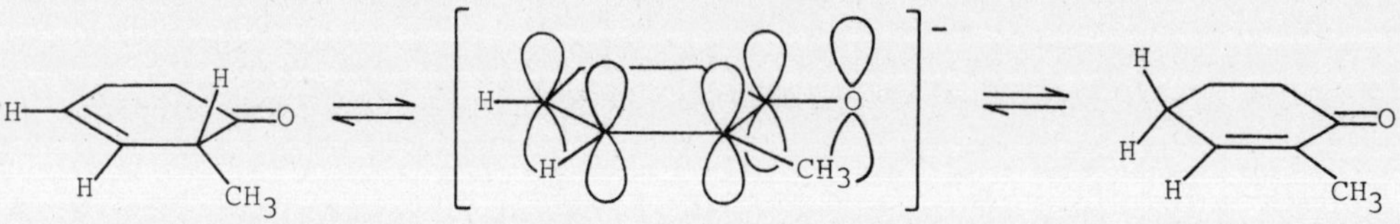

This sort of configuration is not possible for the bicyclic β,γ-enone:

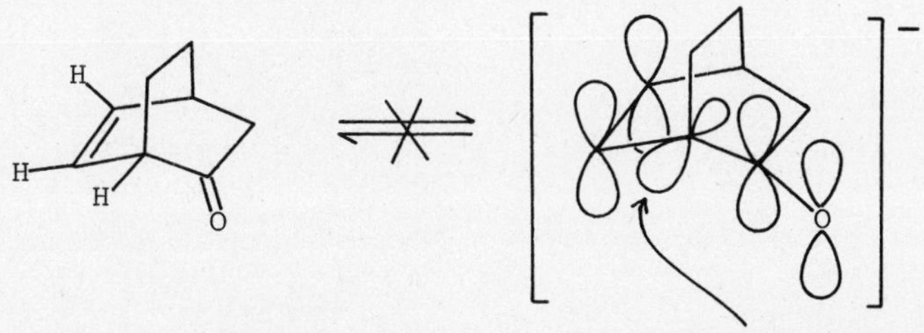

This orbital is perpendicular to the
other p-orbitals and cannot overlap with them

(The generalization that bicyclic systems
cannot have a double bond at the bridgehead carbon is known as Bredt's rule.

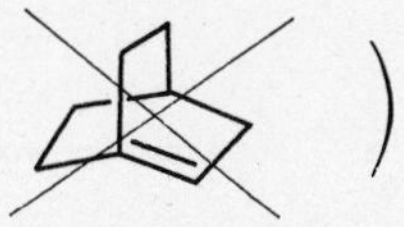

S9.

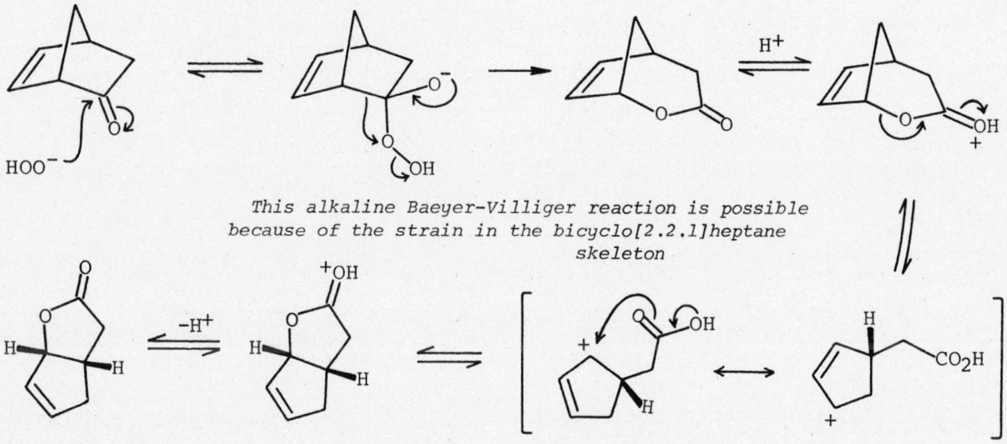

This alkaline Baeyer-Villiger reaction is possible
because of the strain in the bicyclo[2.2.1]heptane
skeleton

S10.

$$A \xrightarrow[H^+]{Cr^{+6}} C \xrightarrow[CH_3CO_2H]{Br_2} D$$

A
$C_7H_{14}O$
(IR: 3400 cm^{-1})

C
(IR: 1710 cm^{-1},
four exchangeable H's)

D
$C_7H_{11}BrO$

A → (Ac$_2$O) → B

C → (NaOH, excess Br$_2$) → E

D → (KOt-Bu, t-BuOH, Δ) → F

B
$C_9H_{16}O_2$
(IR: 1735 cm^{-1})

E
$C_7H_8Br_4O$

F
(IR: 1685, 1670 cm^{-1},
four exchangeable H's)

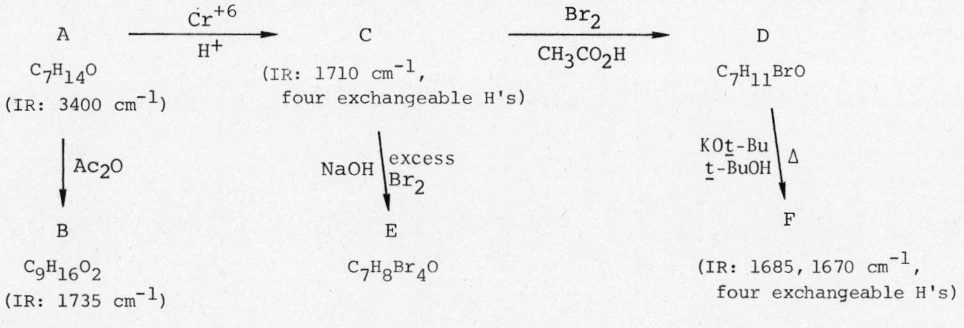

1) Formula for A ($C_7H_{14}O$): indicates one degree of unsaturation.

2) IR of A (3400 cm^{-1}), as well as the fact that reaction of A with Ac$_2$O
   gives B ($C_7H_{14}O + CH_3CO_2H - H_2O = C_9H_{16}O_2$ with IR 1735 cm^{-1} (indicates ester)):
   indicates A is an alcohol.

3) A reacts with Cr^{+6}, H$^+$ to give C (IR 1710 cm^{-1}): indicates B is an acyclic
   or six-membered ring ketone.

4) C has four exchangeable H's: indicates C is $-CH_2-\overset{O}{\underset{\|}{C}}-CH_2-$ or $\underset{}{>}CH-\overset{O}{\underset{\|}{C}}-CH_3$

5) C reacts with excess Br$_2$ and NaOH to give E ($C_7H_8Br_4O$):
   indicates that C is <u>not</u> a methyl ketone (which would give $-CO_2H + HCBr_3$).

6) $\quad C \xrightarrow[H^+]{Br_2} \xrightarrow[\underline{t}-BuOH]{KO\underline{t}-Bu}$ F (IR 1685, 1670 cm^{-1}): indicates that F is a conjugated ketone.

7) F has four exchangeable H's: indicates F must be

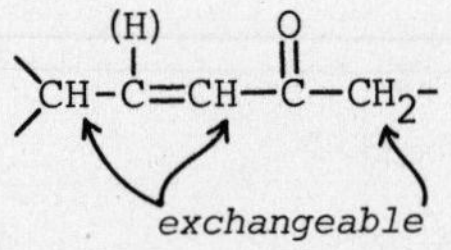

$$\underset{exchangeable}{\overset{(H)}{\underset{\displaystyle\nwarrow\quad\nwarrow\quad\quad\nwarrow}{CH-C=CH-\overset{O}{\overset{\|}{C}}-CH_2-}}}$$

8) There is only one way to put all these facts together with seven carbons:

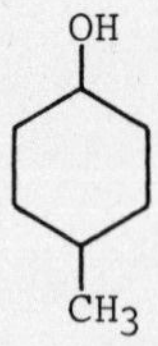

A 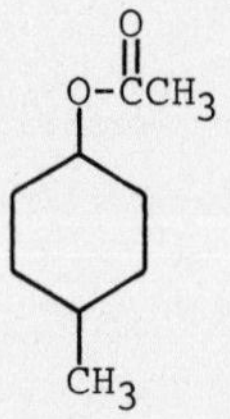 $\qquad$ B 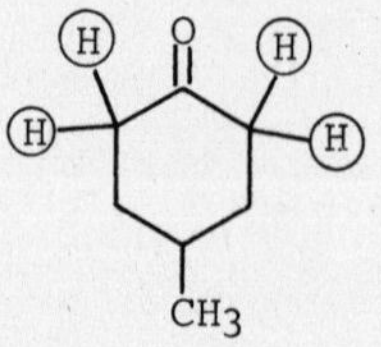 $\qquad$ C

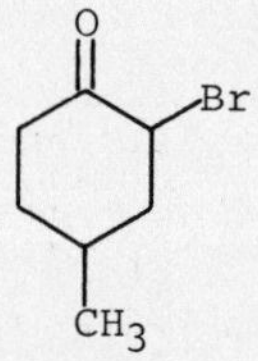

D 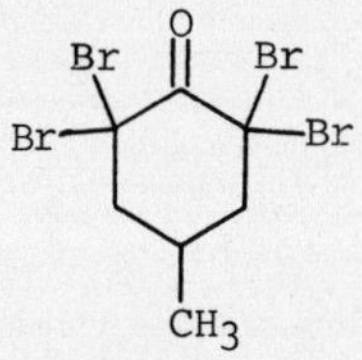 $\qquad$ E 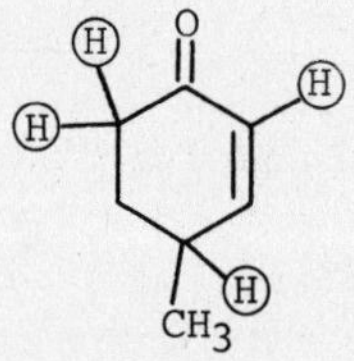 $\qquad$ F

$\textcircled{H}$ = exchangeable H's

20. BENZENE AND THE AROMATIC RING

20.A   Chapter Outline and Important Terms Introduced

20.1   Benzene

    A. The Benzene Enigma
        phenyl
        aromatic

    B. Resonance Energy of Benzene
        delocalization energy
        empirical resonance energy
        aromatic stability
        cyclic system of six π-electrons

    C. Symbols for the Benzene Ring

    D. Formation of Benzene
        dehydrogenation of cyclohexane

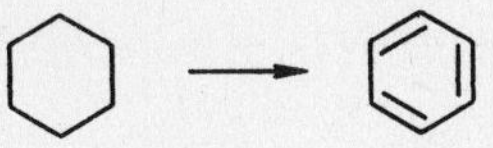

        (using Pd or Pt/Δ; or S, Δ)

        hydroforming process

      hexane,
        heptane 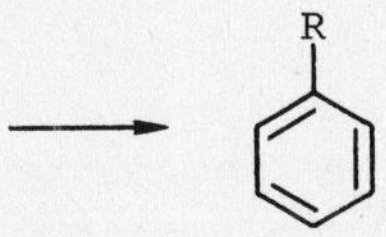
        (using Cr_2O_3 or Pt as catalyst;
                      industrial process)

20.2   Substituted Benzenes

    A. Nomenclature
        ortho-, meta-, and para-   phenyl, tolyl, xylyl, mesityl
          (o-, m-, p-)
        arene   benzyl

    B. Korner's Absolute Method (for telling o-, m-, and p- apart)

20.3   NMR and CMR Spectra
    ring current

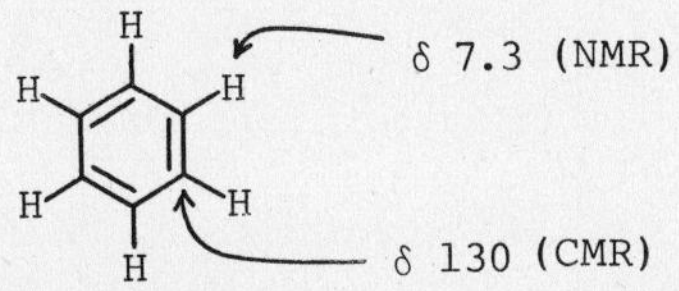

        δ 7.3 (NMR)

        δ 130 (CMR)

20.4   Dipole Moments in Benzene Derivatives

20.5   Side-Chain Reactions

    A. Free Radical Halogenation

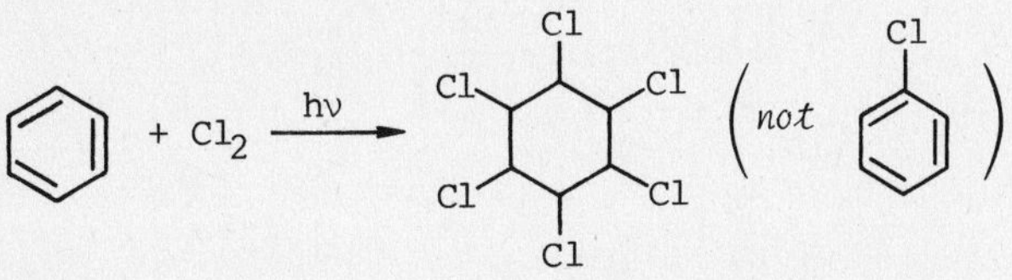

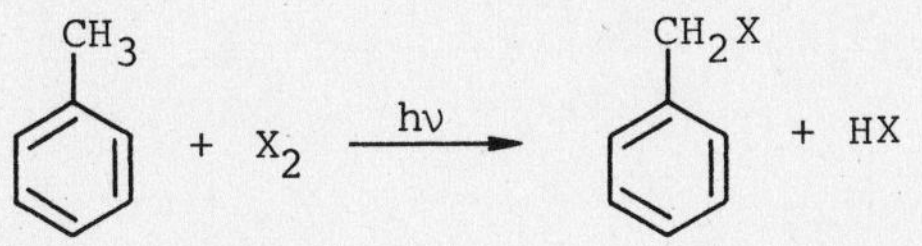

        benzyl radical

B. Benzylic Displacement and Carbocation Reactions

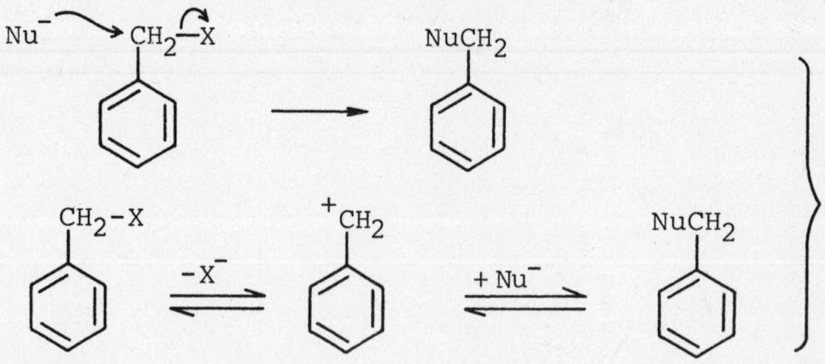

both S_N1 and S_N2 are fast

C. Oxidation

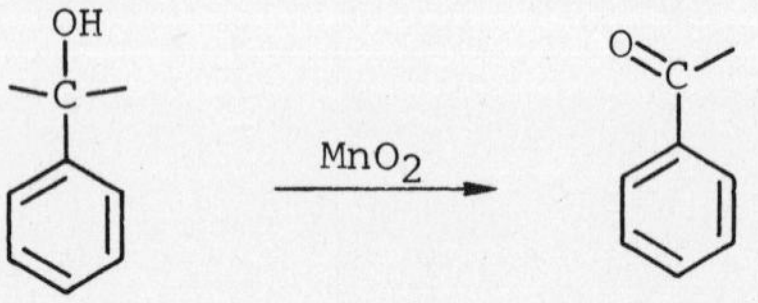

(as easy as allylic alcohol)

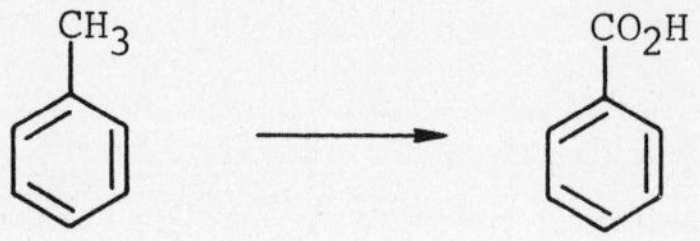

(using $Na_2Cr_2O_7/H_2SO_4$ or $KMnO_4$; at least one benzylic H is needed)

D. Acidity of Alkylbenzenes

benzylic carbanion — pK_a of toluene ~41

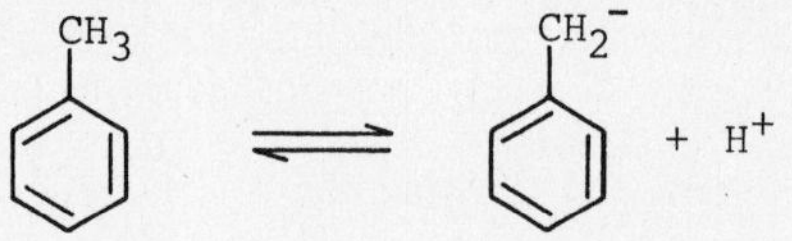

20.6 Reduction

A. Catalytic Reduction

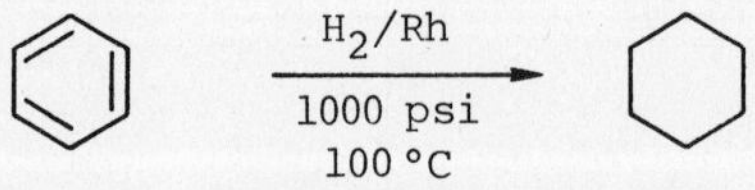

(can't stop short of complete hydrogenation)

B. Hydrogenolysis of Benzylic Groups

C. Birch Reduction (dissolving metal reduction)

20.7 Aromatic Transition States

pericyclic reactions

Cope rearrangement

Claisen rearrangement

sigmatropic rearrangements

20.B Important Reactions Introduced

<u>NOTE:</u> *Many of the reactions which occur at benzylic positions [20.5, Side-Chain Reactions] have been discussed earlier. They are different in the case of benzylic systems only because of the benzene π-system and the increased stability of benzylic carbocations, radicals, and carbanions.*

<u>Hydrogenolysis of benzylic groups</u> (20.6.B)

Equation:

$$Ar-\overset{|}{\underset{|}{C}}-Y \xrightarrow[Pd,\ H+]{H_2} Ar-\overset{|}{\underset{|}{C}}-H$$

Generality: Ar = aryl (i.e. phenyl, tolyl, xylyl, etc.)

Y = halogen, OH, OR, O_2CR

Key features: useful way to make alkyl benzenes

benzylic esters and ethers can be used as protected versions of carboxylic acids and alcohols, since the benzyl group can be cleaved under neutral conditions

Birch reduction   (20.6.C)

alkyl-substituted benzenes:

(via cyclohexadienyl anion)

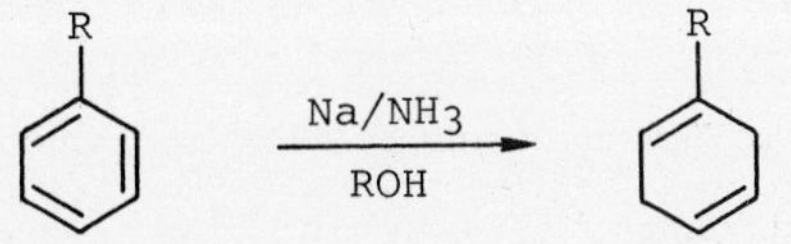

alkoxy-substituted benzenes:

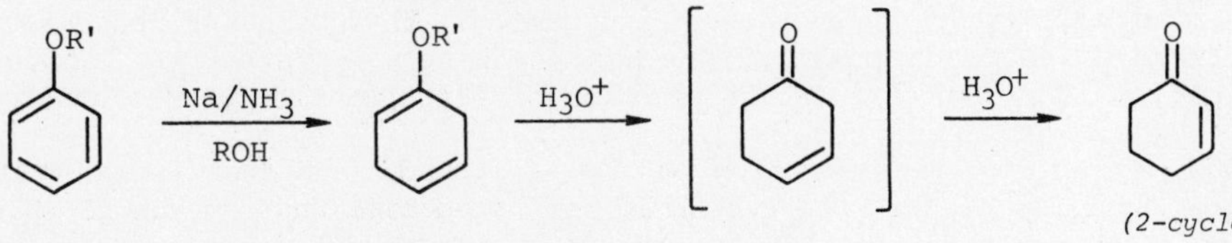

(2-cyclohexenone synthesis)

carbonyl-substituted benzenes:

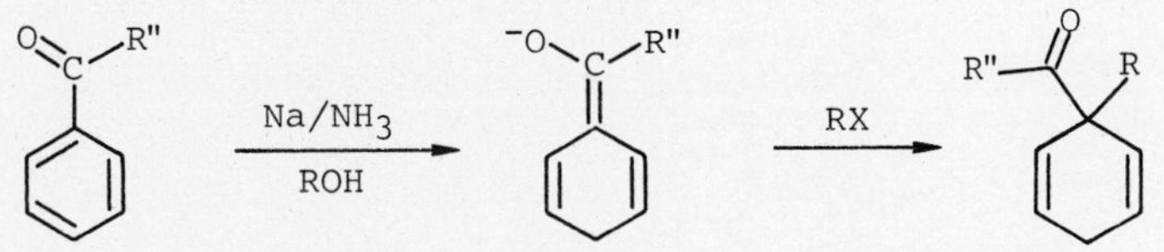

(R" = O$^-$, alkyl)

alkenyl-substituted benzenes (conjugated):

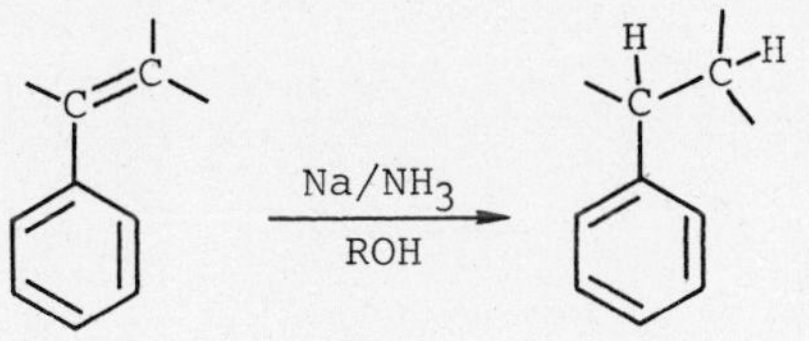

Generality: if substituent is an alkenyl group (e.g. vinyl), it will be reduced too

substituent must not be any other easily reduced group (such as X, NO_2)

Key features: dissolving metal reduction, using Li or Na metal in liquid ammonia as solvent gives 1,4-cyclohexadiene derivatives

for Y = OR', product can be hydrolyzed with aq. H$^+$ to give α,β-unsaturated ketone

[3,3] Sigmatropic rearrangements   (20.7)

Equation:

Generality: R = various substituents
$Y = CH_2$ = Cope rearrangement
Y = O = Claisen rearrangement

Key features: pericyclic reaction with aromatic transition state (4n + 2 electrons)

20.C   Important Concepts and Hints

This chapter introduces you to the benzene ring and some of its chemistry. You will notice in this and subsequent chapters that derivatives of benzene (aryl compounds) react quite differently from the alkyl compounds discussed in earlier chapters. To give you an overview of these differences, and a brief justification as to why they occur, we can divide the reactions into three groups: reactions of aryl σ-bonds, reactions on the ring which involve the π-electrons, and reactions on carbons directly attached to the ring (benzylic positions).

I. Reactions of Aryl σ-Bonds:

Because such reactions involve an sp^2- instead of an sp^3-hybrid orbital, they are usually more difficult; for example, free radical halogenation is not successful with benzene.

II. Reactions on the Ring which Involve the π-Electrons:

Hydrogenation of the π-system of the benzene ring is substantially more difficult than it is for the π-bond of an alkene. Furthermore, electrophilic addition, which is so important for alkenes, does not occur in aryl compounds except under unusual conditions. This behavior reflects the extra stability, known as aromatic stabilization, of the benzene ring's π-system. In Chapter 22, you will see that **substitution** is the most important reaction of electrophiles with aromatic systems, rather than addition.

The Birch reduction is an important reaction of aryl compounds (and acetylenes) which simple alkenes do not undergo. At first glance, the fact that aryl compounds undergo the Birch reduction while alkenes are stable to such conditions would seem to conflict with the idea that the benzene π-system is more stable than that of an alkene. However, the first, and hardest, step in these reductions is the addition of an electron to the lowest-energy antibonding molecular orbital. For benzene, this orbital is lower in energy than that of an alkene, and benzene can accept the electron more readily. It is not until the next step that aromatic stabilization of the π-system is lost by protonation.

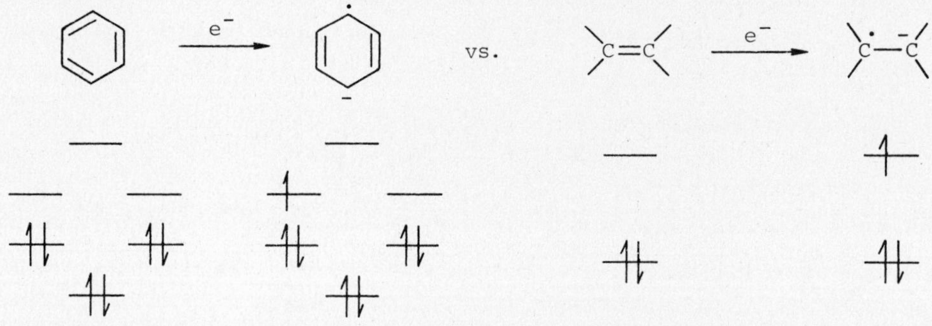

III. Reactions Occurring at Benzylic Positions:

This class of reactions receives the most attention in Chapter 20, and it serves to tie in chemistry that you have learned from previous chapters with aromatic compounds. Because the π-system of the benzene ring can stabilize a p-orbital at the benzylic position via conjugation, it makes virtually every reaction at such a position easier (i.e., faster) than for the alkyl counterpart. Reactions which involve cations (S_N1 reactions; oxidation of alkyl side chains), radicals (free radical halogenations; MnO_2 oxidation of benzylic alcohols; hydrogenolysis of benzylic groups), anions (acidity), or even sp^2-hybridized transition states (S_N2 reactions) are all accelerated by the overlap of the π-system of the ring with the p-orbital on the benzylic carbon. This overlap is depicted in Figure 20.10 for the benzyl radical.

The subject of aromaticity extends beyond derivatives of benzene alone, as pointed out in the last part of this chapter. Huckel's 4n+2 rule, and our more sophisticated understanding of molecular orbital interactions which underly it, help to describe many cyclic transition states (Cope and Claisen rearrangements) as well as other cyclic conjugated systems (elaborated in Section 21.3 in the Text).

20.D   Answers to Exercises

20.1

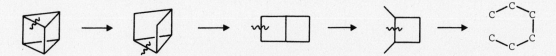

20.2   There are three structural isomers of prismane substituted with two different groups:

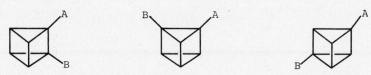

Two of these are chiral and would be capable of being resolved into enantiomers:

Of course, since benzene is planar, no simple disubstituted derivative is chiral and none of them would be resolvable.

20.3

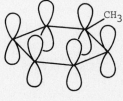

No. of π electrons: 6   6   6

No. of p orbitals: 6   6   5

Toluene   *Pyridine*   *Pyrrole*

20.4

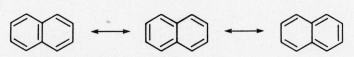

        each resonance structure has six π electrons
        in each of its two rings

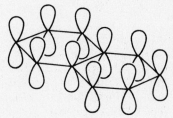

10 π electrons total
10 p orbitals

20.5

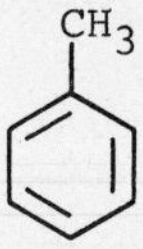

toluene
(methylbenzene)

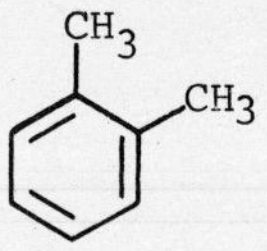

o-xylene
(1,2-dimethylbenzene)

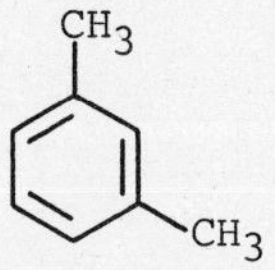

m-xylene
(1,3-dimethylbenzene)

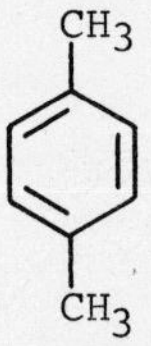

p-xylene
(1,4-dimethylbenzene)

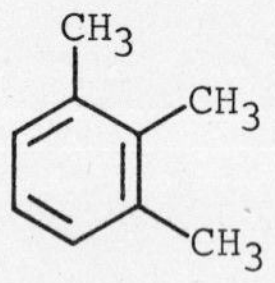

1,2,3-trimethylbenzene
(hemimellitene)

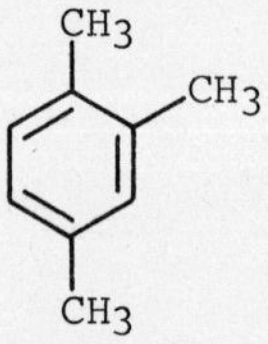

1,2,4-trimethylbenzene

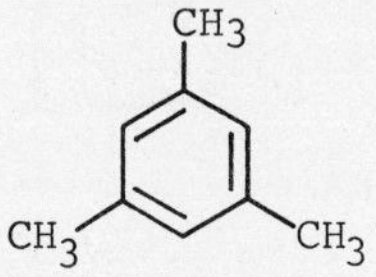

1,3,5-trimethylbenzene
(mesitylene)

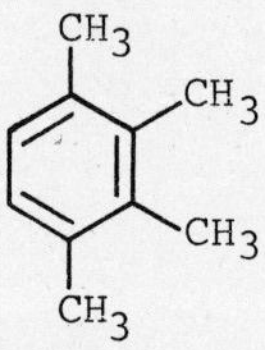

1,2,3,4-tetramethylbenzene
(prehitnene)

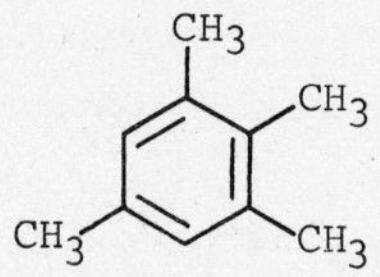

1,2,3,5-tetramethyl-
benzene
(isodurene)

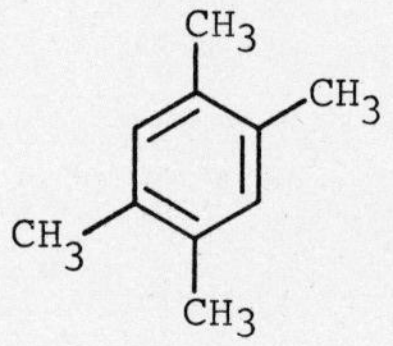

1,2,4,5-tetramethylbenzene
(durene)

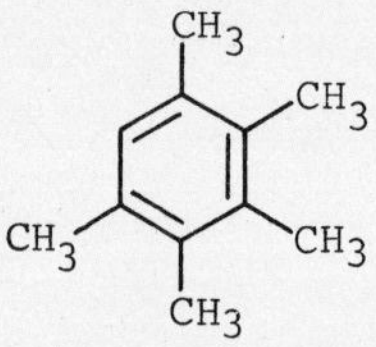

pentamethylbenzene

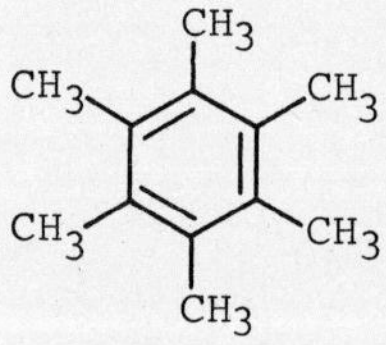

hexamethylbenzene

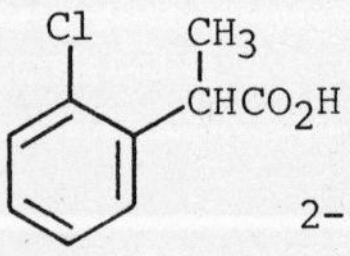

2-(2-chlorophenyl)-
propanoic acid

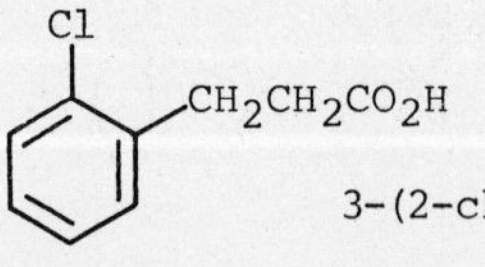

3-(2-chlorophenyl)pro-
panoic acid

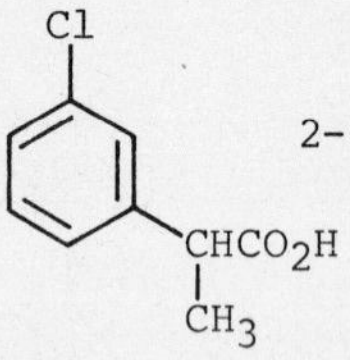

2-(3-chlorophenyl)-
propanoic acid

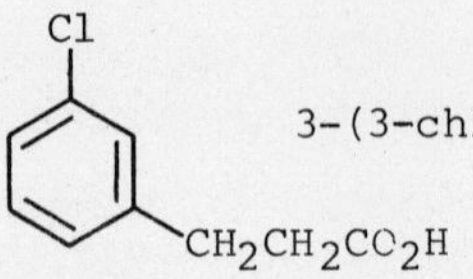

3-(3-chlorophenyl)propanoic
acid

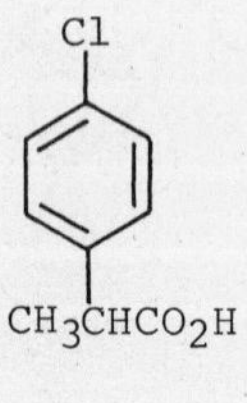

2-(4-chlorophenyl)-
propanoic acid

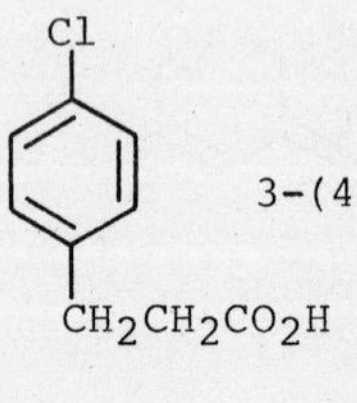

3-(4-chlorophenyl)propanoic
acid

(common names: α-(o-chlorophenyl)propionic acid, etc.)

20.6

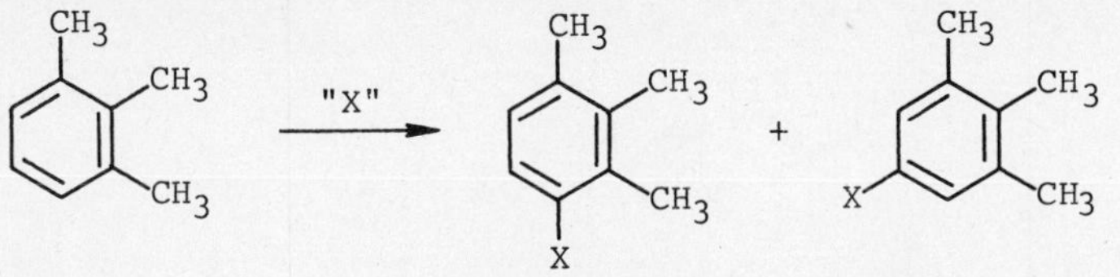

two possible products

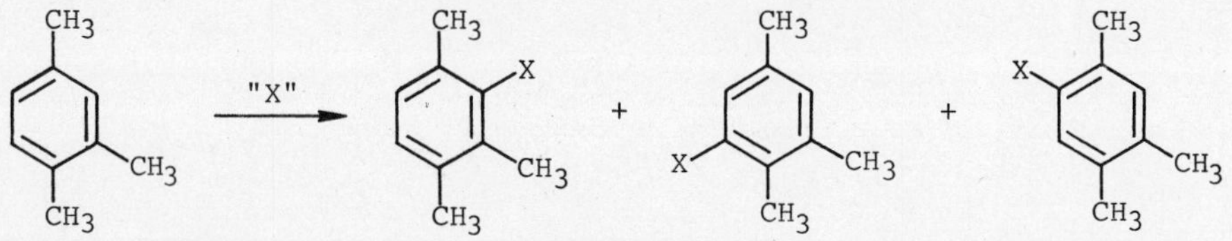

three possible products

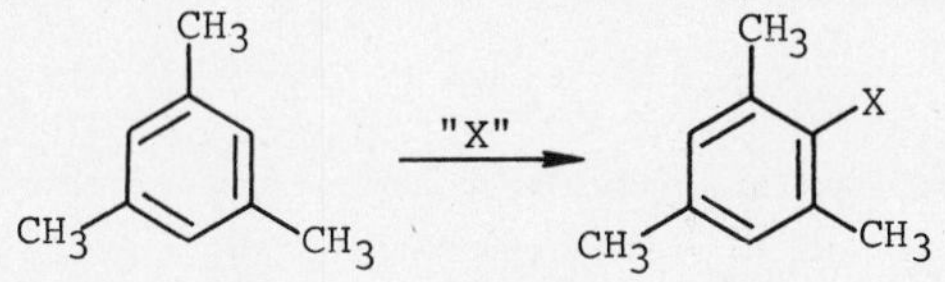

only one product is possible

20.7

(a)

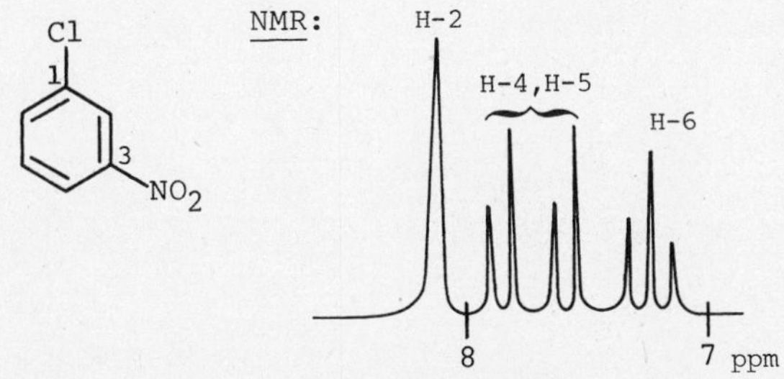

NMR:

On a 60-MHz instrument, there would be overlap, and a significantly more complex spectrum.

<u>CMR</u>: six lines between 125 and 150 ppm.

(b)

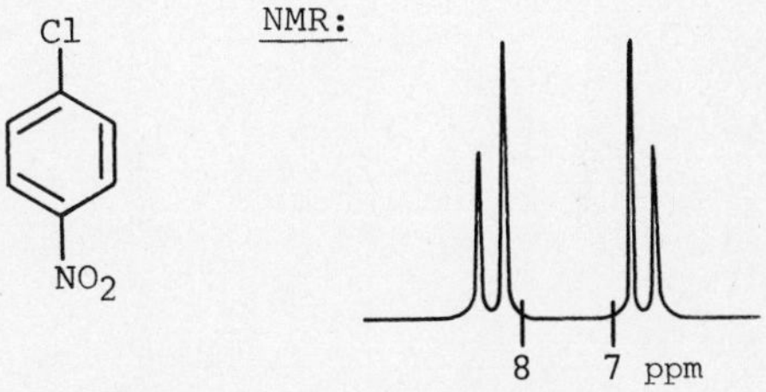

NMR:

<u>CMR</u>:

four lines between 125 and 150 ppm

20.8

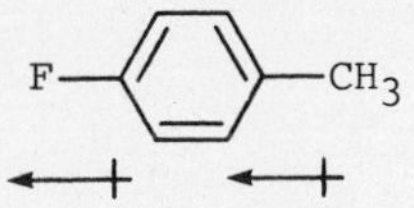

1.63 D + 0.37 D = 2.00 D   (actual value = 2.01 D)

20.9

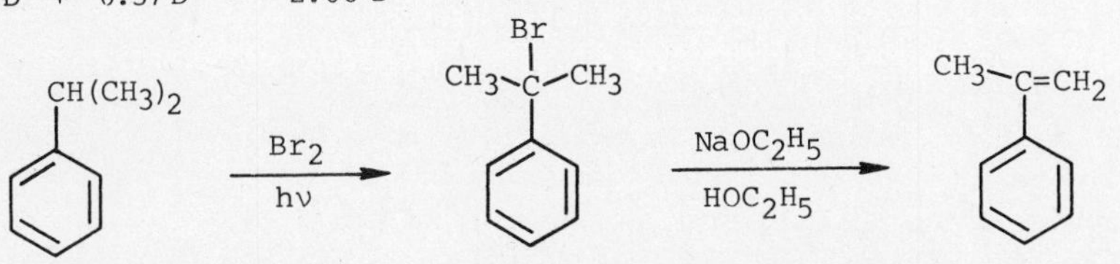

20.10

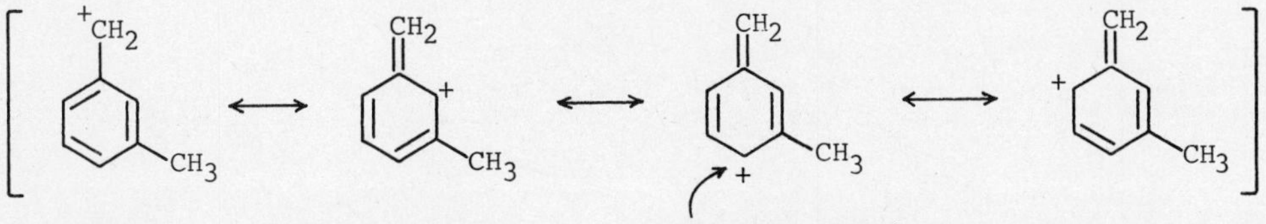

Relative stability: *nearly equal*   *nearly equal*   "secondary" cation *(less stable)*   *nearly equal*

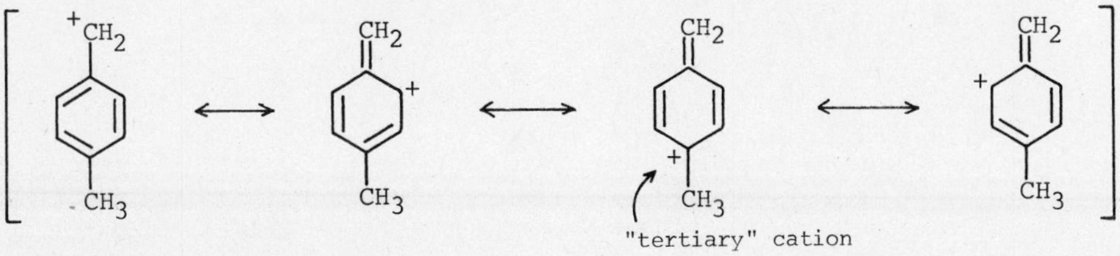

"tertiary" cation *(more stable)*

The <u>p</u>-methylbenzyl cation is more stable.

20.11

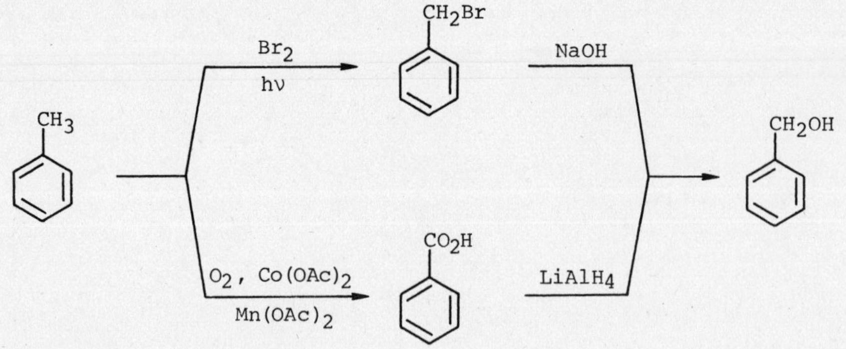

20.12

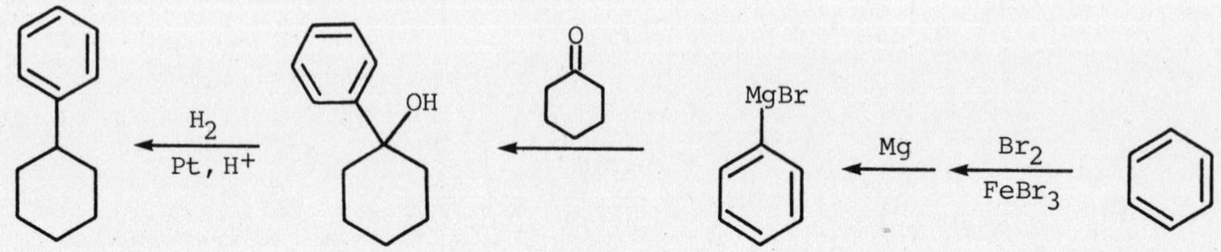

20.13

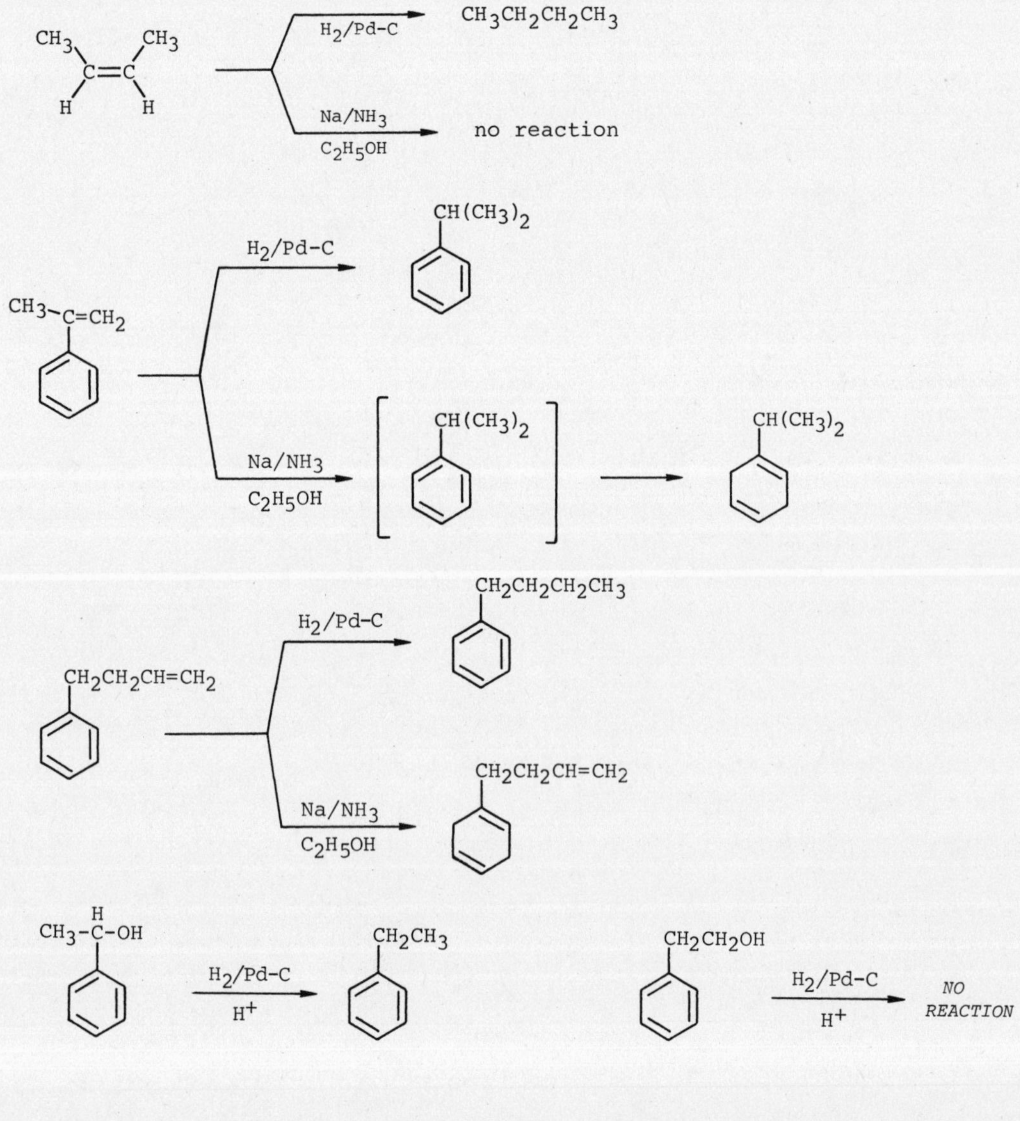

20.14

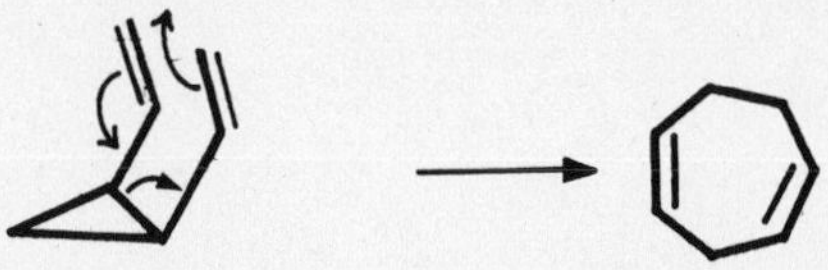

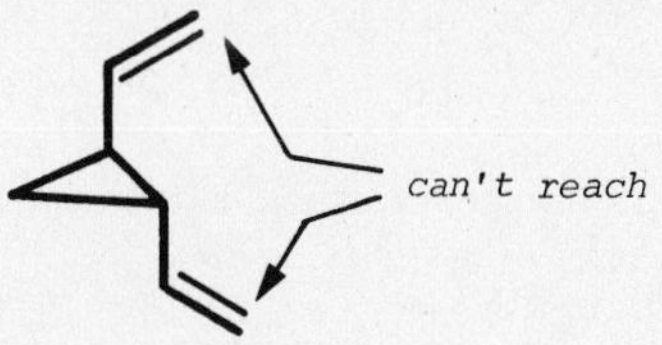

In the *cis* isomer, the vinyl groups are
sterically positioned for reaction

can't reach

trans isomer

20.15

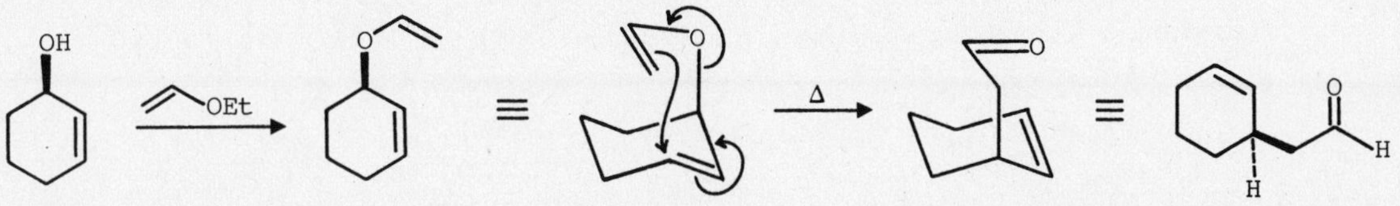

(R)-2-cyclohexeneethanal

20.16 (a)

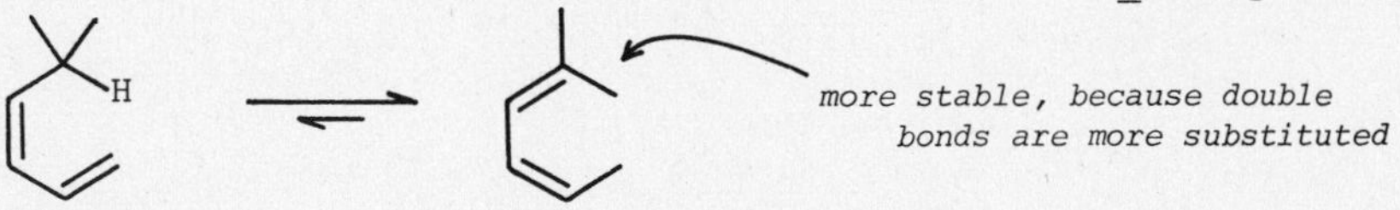

*more stable, because double
bonds are more substituted*

The transition states for the forward and reverse reactions are the same.

(b)

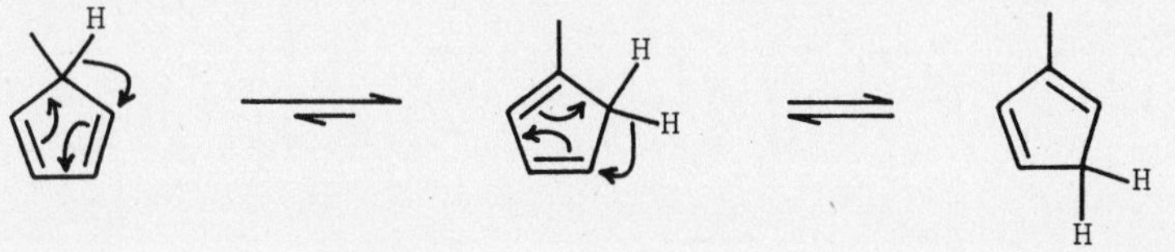

All of the rearrangements are [1.5]sigmatropic rearrangements.

20.E Answers and Explanations for Problems

1. (a)

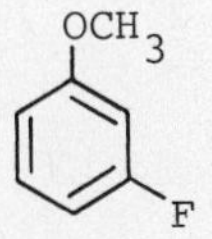

(b)

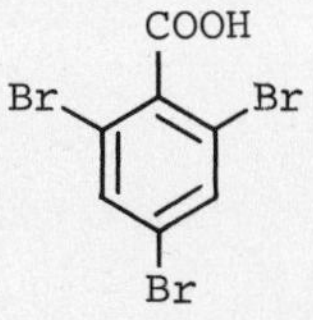

(c)

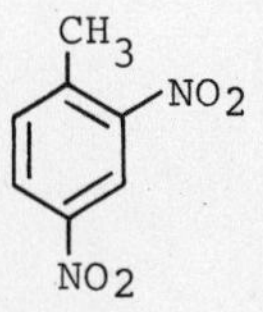

(d)

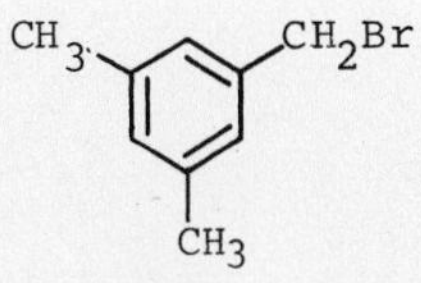

(e)

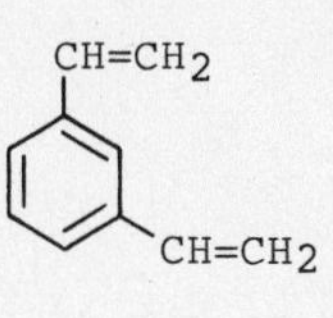

(f)

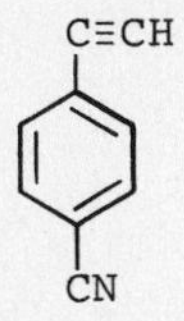

(g)

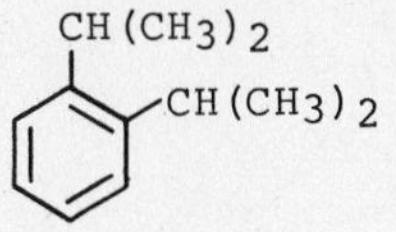

(h)

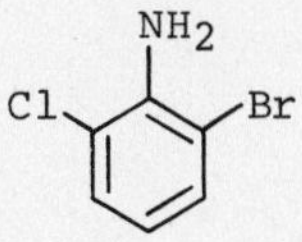

2.   (a) 1,1,1-trichloro-2,2-di(4-chlorophenyl)ethane
         (the abbreviation "DDT" comes from the old, non-systematic name: dichlorodiphenyltrichloroethane)

   (b) p-bromopropylbenzene   (e) 2-(p-nitrophenyl)butane
   (c) 3-bromo-4-iodocumene   (f) 2-(m-chlorophenyl)-3-methylbutane
   (d) 2-bromo-4-ethyltoluene   (g) diphenyl-(4-methylphenyl)methanol

(h) p-bromochlorobenzene   (k) 4-bromo-2,6-dimethylbenzoic acid

(i) 4-bromo-3-fluoro-2-iodotoluene   (l) 1,2,4-trimethylbenzene

(j) m-methoxybenzaldehyde or m-anisaldehyde

3. (a) No. There would be two isomers of the form

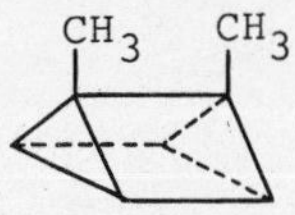

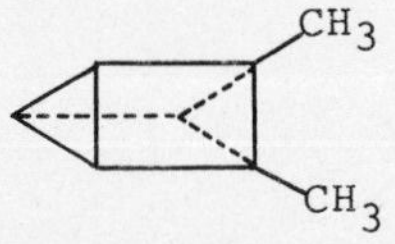

(b) The two structures are resonance structures as symbolized by

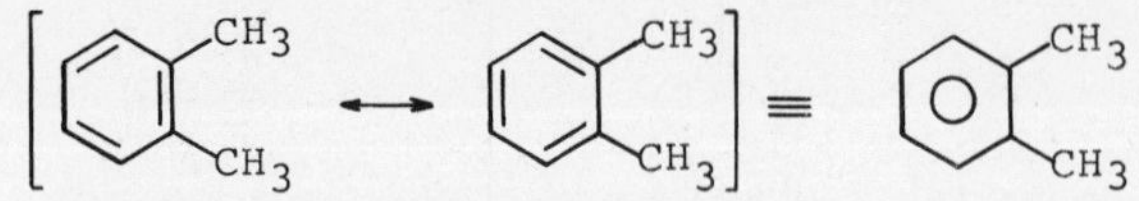

4.

$$\underline{\Delta H^\circ_f}$$

CH≡CH   54.3 kcal mole^{-1}

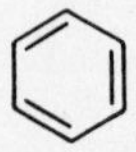

19.8 kcal mole^{-1}

3 HC≡CH ⇌ $\Delta H^\circ = -3(54.3) + 19.8 = -143.1$ kcal mole^{-1}

The negative value for ΔS° reflects the loss in freedom of motion when three separate compounds form one.

$$\Delta G^\circ = \Delta H^\circ - T\Delta S^\circ$$

At 298 °K: $\Delta G^\circ = -143.1$ kcal mole^{-1} - (298 deg × -79.7 cal deg^{-1} mole^{-1})

$\Delta G^\circ = -143.1$ kcal mole^{-1} + 23.8 kcal mole^{-1} = -119.3 kcal mole^{-1}

The equilibrium lies far to the right, but the probability is very small that three acetylenes can collide at the same time with the proper orientation for reaction.

5. (a)   + H$_2$ ⟶ $\Delta H^\circ = -28.4$ kcal mole^{-1}

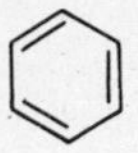

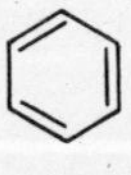

∴ + 3H$_2$ ⟶ $\Delta H^\circ_{calc.} = 3 \times (-28.4) = -85.2$ kcal mole^{-1}

-85.2 - (-49.3) = -35.9 kcal mole^{-1}

Empirical resonance energy = 35.9 kcal mole^{-1}

(b) + H$_2$ ⟶ $\Delta H^\circ = -23.3$ kcal mole^{-1}

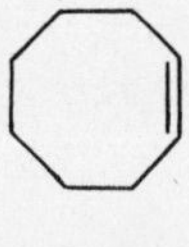

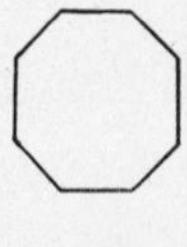

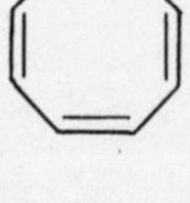

+ 4H$_2$ ⟶ $\Delta H^\circ = -100.9$ kcal mole^{-1}

-93.2 - (-100.9) = +7.7 kcal mole^{-1}

Empirical resonance energy = -7.7 kcal mole^{-1}

The negative value implies that the four double bonds in the tetraene are less stable than 4 × 1 double bonds; i.e., this value represents a <u>destabilization</u> energy or negative resonance energy. This means that not only is there no stabilization energy (resonance), but that cyclooctatetraene is probably more strained because of the four double bonds.

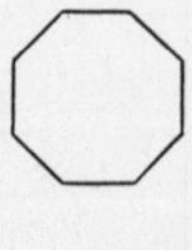

(c)

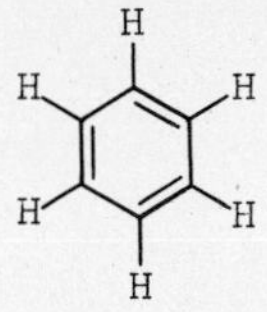

$6 \times E(C-H) = 6 \times 99 = 594$ kcal mole^{-1}

$3 \times E(C-C) = 3 \times 83 = 249$ kcal mole^{-1}

$3 \times E(C=C) = 3 \times 146 = \underline{438}$ kcal mole^{-1}

calc. ΔH°_{atom} $= 1281$ kcal mole^{-1}

Empirical resonance energy $= 1318-1281 = 37$ kcal mole^{-1}

6.

$$C_6H_6 + Cl^\cdot \longrightarrow C_6H_5^\cdot + HCl$$

$\Delta H^\circ_f =$ 19.8   28.9   79   -22.1 $\Delta H^\circ = +8$ kcal mole^{-1}

$$C_6H_5^\cdot + Cl_2 \longrightarrow C_6H_5Cl + Cl^\cdot$$

$\Delta H^\circ_f =$ 79   0   12.2   28.9 $\Delta H^\circ = -38$ kcal mole^{-1}

Although the overall reaction is highly exothermic, the first step is endothermic and occurs quite slowly in comparison to other chlorination reactions. The overall reaction proceeds cleanly and in high yield at 300-400 °C.

7.

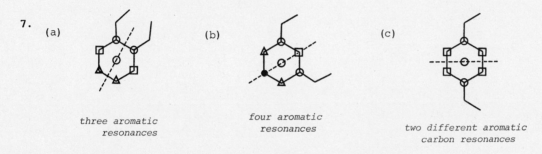

(a)   (b)   (c)

three aromatic   *four aromatic*   *two different aromatic*
resonances   *resonances*   *carbon resonances*

8.   One xylene (m-) is given by three different Br isomers:

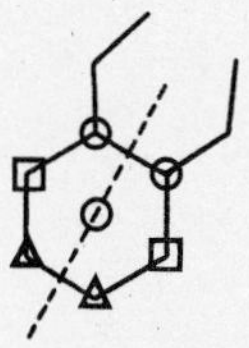

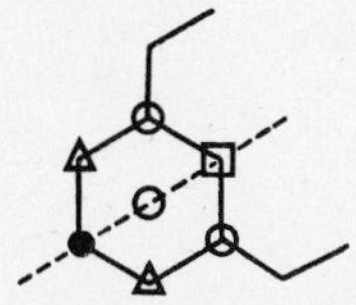

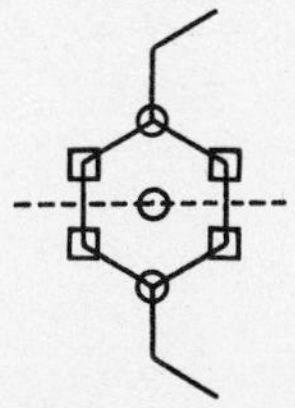

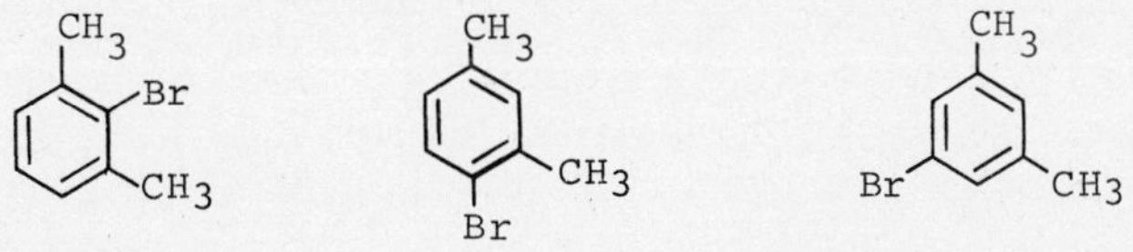

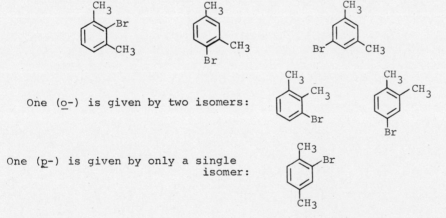

One (o-) is given by two isomers:

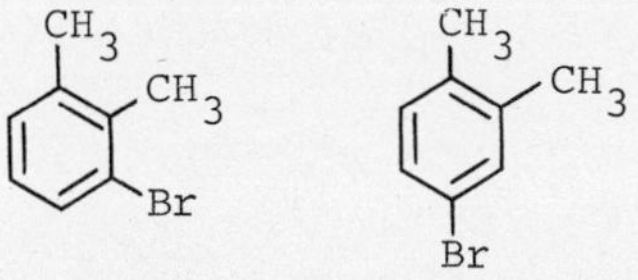

One (p-) is given by only a single isomer:

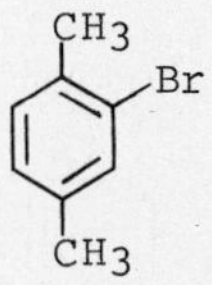

This method also serves to establish the structure of that bromoxylene that gave the unique p-xylene. Note how this method is simply a variation of the Körner absolute method.

9.   (a) $CH_3CHCH_2CH_2OH$ (b)   (c) $(CH_3)_2COCH_3$

      (d) $(CH_3)_2COH$ (e) CH_2CH_3 (f) $\overset{O}{\overset{\|}{C}}CH_3$

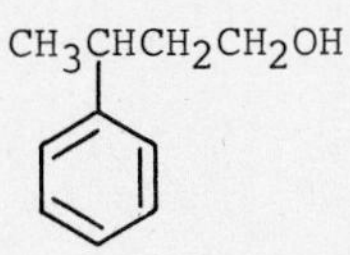

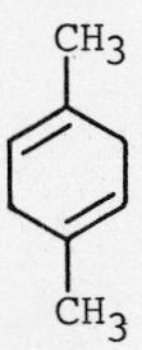

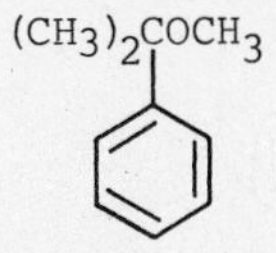

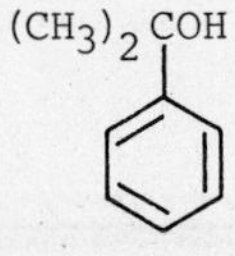

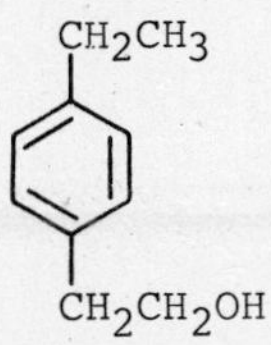

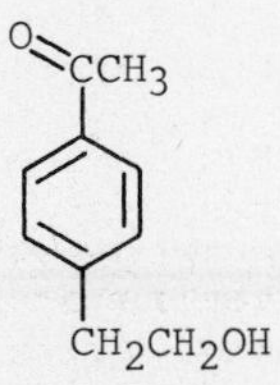

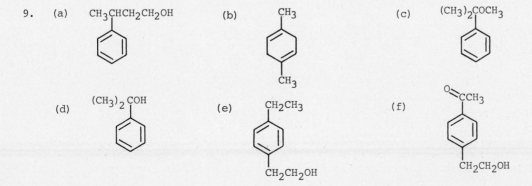

(g)   [cyclohexenone with CH$_3$]   and   [cyclohexenone with CH$_3$]

10.

(a) [benzene] $\xrightarrow[\text{AlBr}_3]{\text{Br}_2}$ [bromobenzene] $\xrightarrow{\text{Mg}}$ [ketone] $\rightarrow$ $CH_3CH_2\overset{\text{OH}}{C}CH_2CH_3$ (phenyl) $\xrightarrow[\text{HClO}_4]{\text{H}_2/\text{Pd}}$ $CH(CH_2CH_3)_2$ (phenyl)

(b) [toluene] $\xrightarrow[\text{liq. NH}_3]{\text{Na, C}_2\text{H}_5\text{OH}}$ [1-methyl-1,4-cyclohexadiene]

(c) CH_2CH_3 (phenyl) $\xrightarrow[h\nu]{\text{Br}_2}$ CBr_2CH_3 (phenyl) $\xrightarrow[\Delta]{\text{NaOH}}$ $C\equiv CH$ (phenyl)

(d) CH_3 (phenyl) $\xrightarrow[h\nu]{\text{Cl}_2}$ CH_2Cl (phenyl) $\xrightarrow{\text{Mg}\atop\text{ether}}$ CH_2MgCl (phenyl) $\xrightarrow{C_6H_5CH_2Cl}$ CH_2CH_2 (diphenyl)

(e) [p-xylene, CH$_3$...CH$_3$] $\xrightarrow[h\nu]{\text{Br}_2}$ [CH$_2$Br...CH$_3$] $\xrightarrow[\text{or}\atop\text{LiAlD}_4]{\text{D}_2/\text{Pt}}$ [CH$_2$D...CH$_3$]

(f) CH_2Cl (phenyl) *(from (d))* $\xrightarrow{\text{NaC}\equiv\text{CH}}$ $CH_2C\equiv CH$ (phenyl)

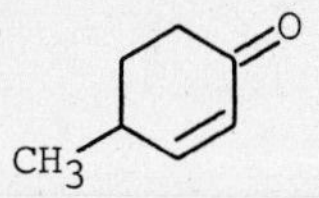

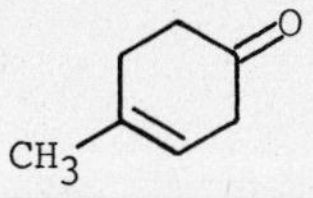

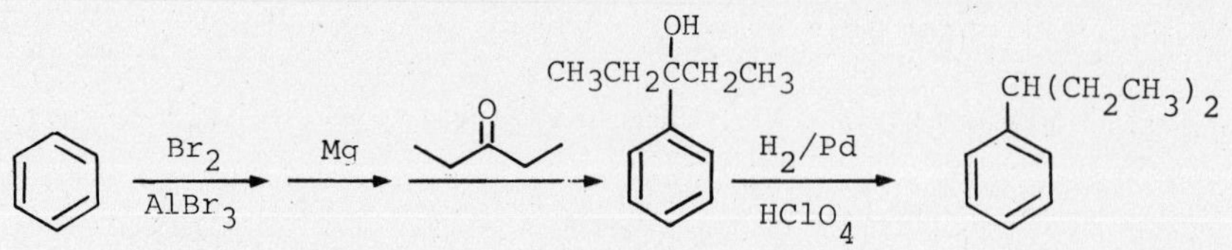

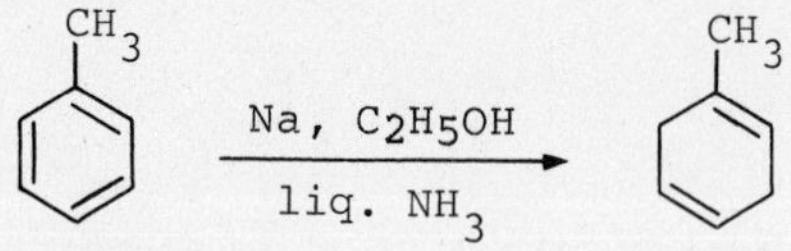

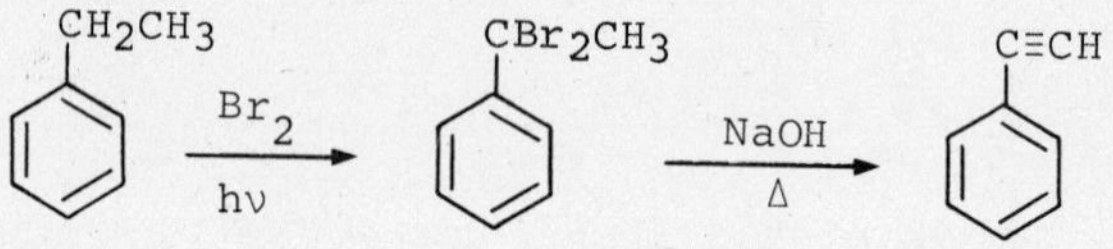

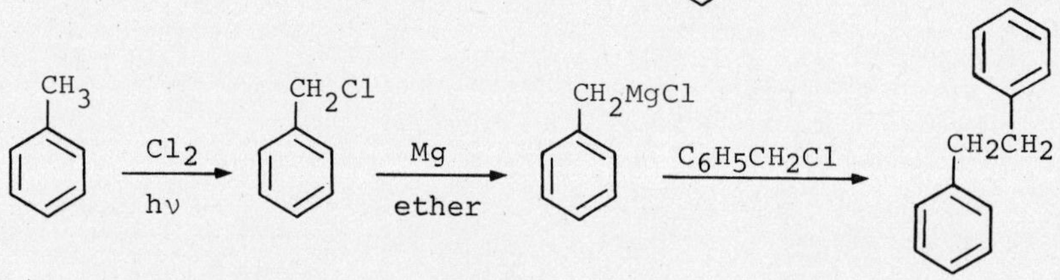

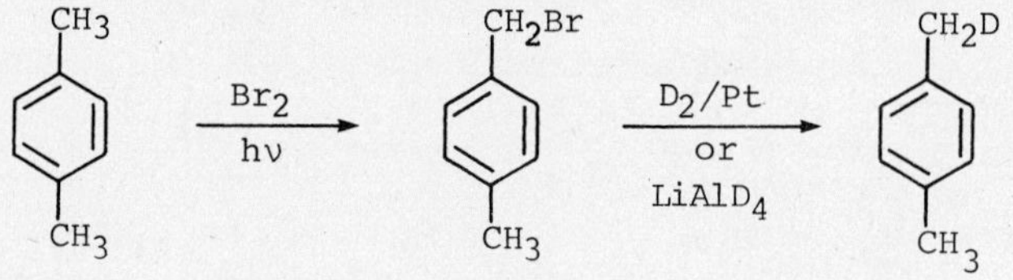

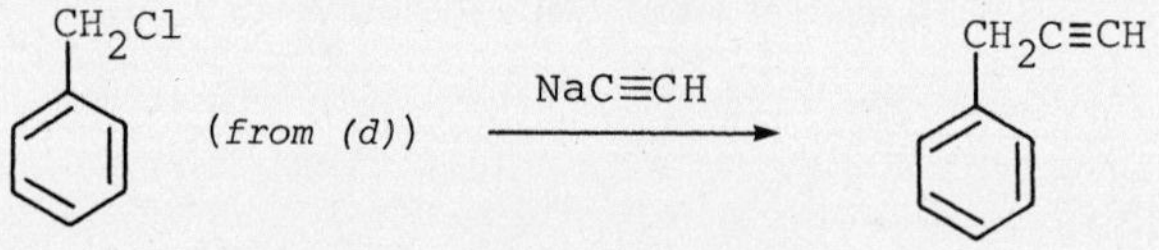

11. (a) and (b) $Br_2 \longrightarrow 2\ Br\cdot$ *(initiation)*

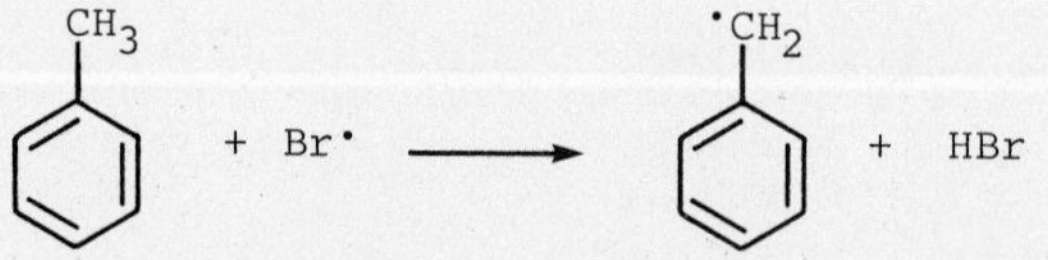

CH_3 (phenyl) $+ Br\cdot \longrightarrow$ $\cdot CH_2$ (phenyl) $+ HBr$

$\Delta H^\circ_f =$ 12.0   26.7   48   −8.7 $\Delta H^\circ = 1$ kcal mole^{-1}

$\cdot CH_2$ (phenyl) $+ Br_2 \longrightarrow$ CH_2Br (phenyl) $+ Br\cdot$

$\Delta H^\circ = -12^*$ kcal mole^{-1}

*Since Appendix I does not have ΔH°_f for benzyl bromide, the enthalpy change for the second step of the bromination procedure must be estimated as follows:

$- DH^\circ$ (benzyl-Br) + DH° (Br$_2$) = −58 (Appendix II) + 46 (Appendix III)

= −12 kcal mole^{-1}

The first step is barely endothermic and occurs readily; the second step is quite exothermic.

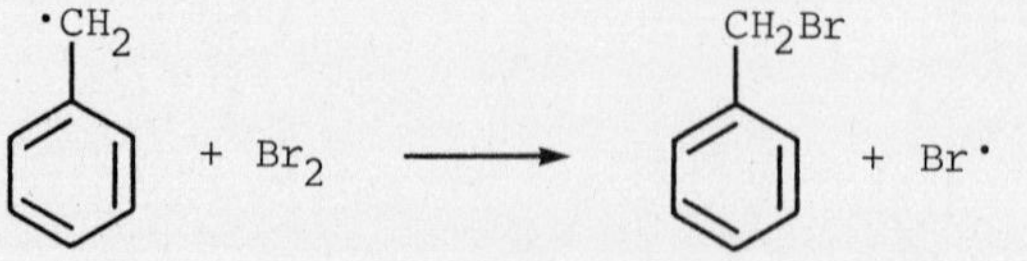

(c)   <u>For ethane</u>:   the first step is very endothermic and occurs slowly:

$$CH_3CH_3 + Br_2 \longrightarrow CH_3CH_2\cdot + HBr \qquad \Delta H° = 11 \text{ kcal mole}^{-1}$$

<u>For 2-methylpropane</u>:   this step is still endothermic, but much less so:

$$(CH_3)_2CH + Br_2 \longrightarrow (CH_3)_2C\cdot + HBr \qquad \Delta H° = 6 \text{ kcal mole}^{-1}$$

12.   [<u>Note</u>: in the drawings below, only Cl bonds are shown. Each position also has a hydrogen.]

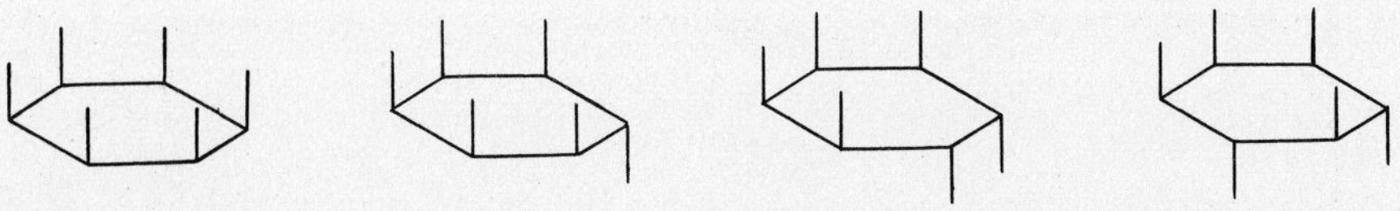

all <u>cis</u>

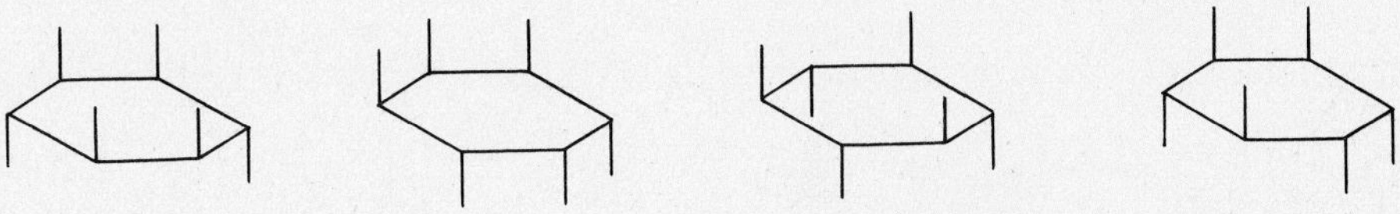

slowest in E₂ elimi-
nations, since there
are no H's anti to a Cl

chiral; all others
have a plane of
symmetry

13.

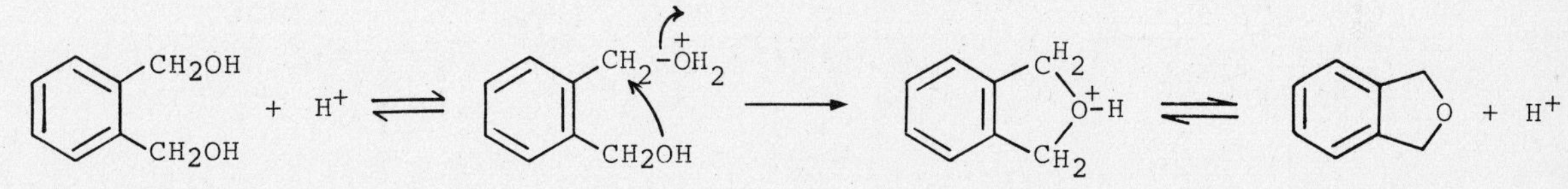

14.

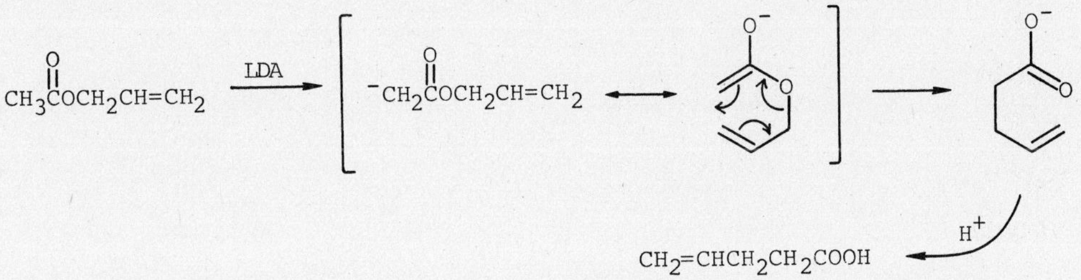

$$CH_2=CHCH_2CH_2COOH$$

15.

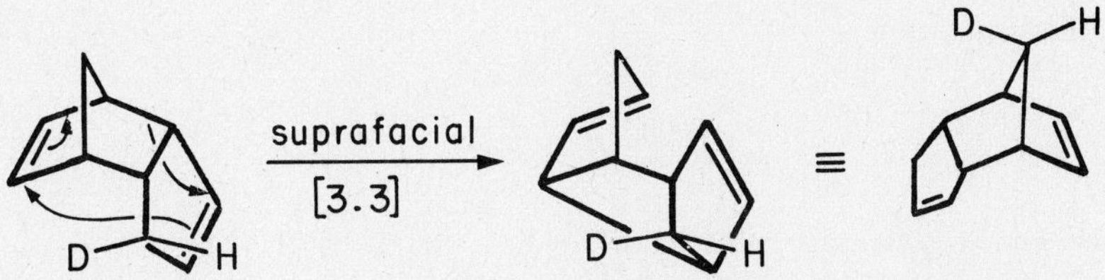

This is the product from an allowed
[3.3]sigmatropic rearrangement. The other
isomer cannot arise by an allowed pathway.

16.

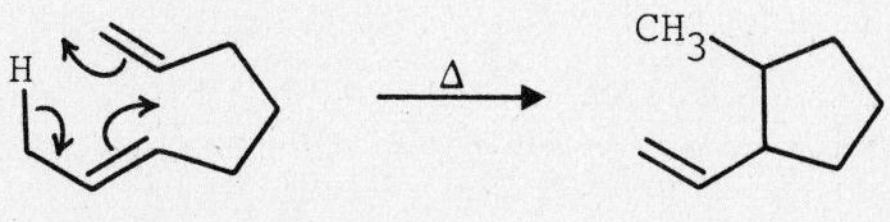

six electrons moving in a ring
= aromatic transition state

17. (a)

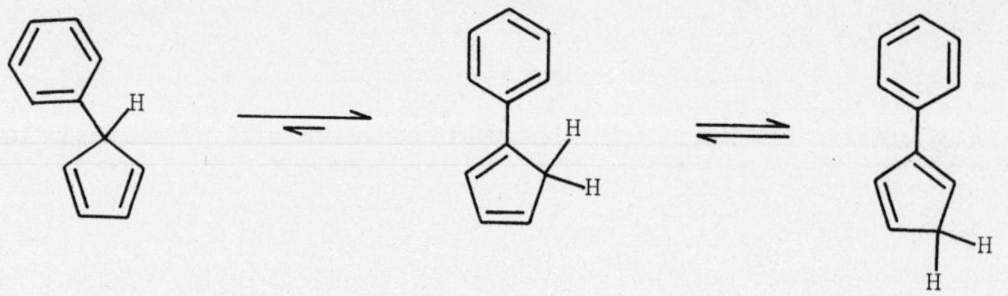

(b)

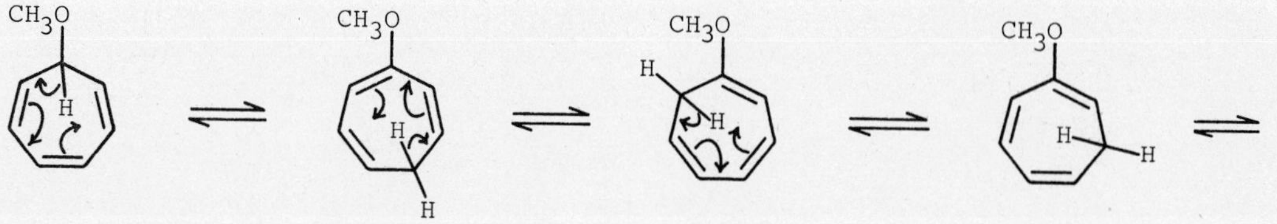

etc.

(c)

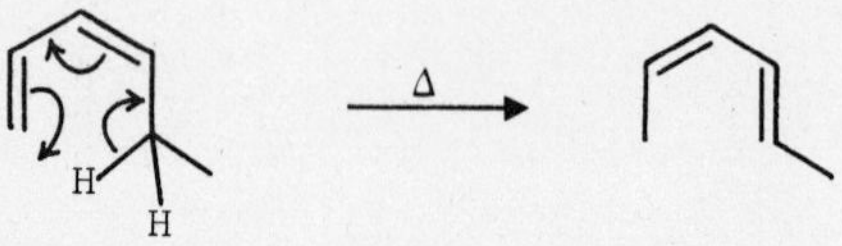

18.

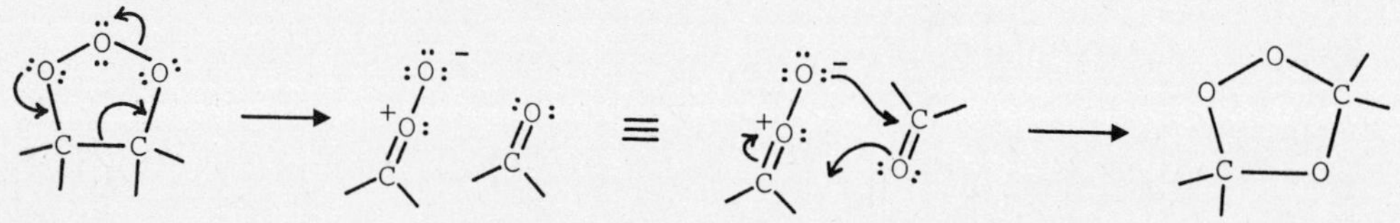

20.F Supplementary Problems

S1. Provide an acceptable name for each of the following compounds.

(a)

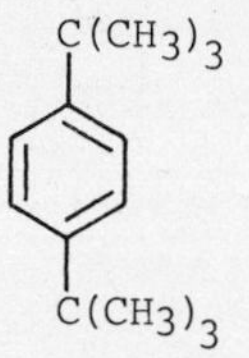

(b)

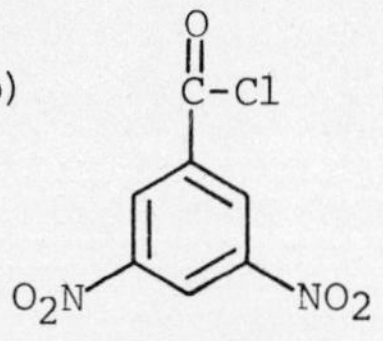

(c)

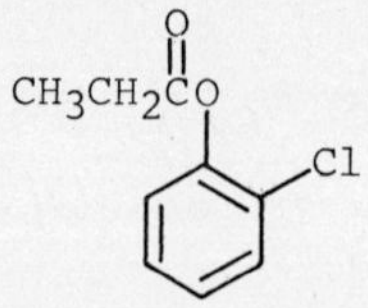

(d)

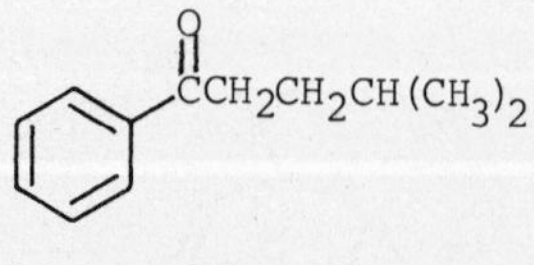

(e)

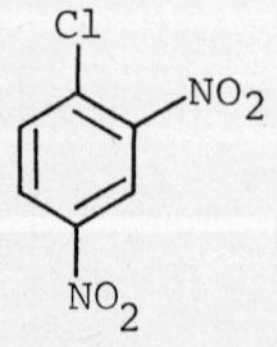

(f)

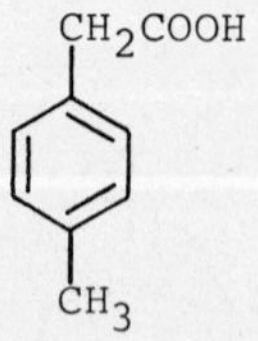

S2. Predict the major product from each of the following reaction sequences:

(a)

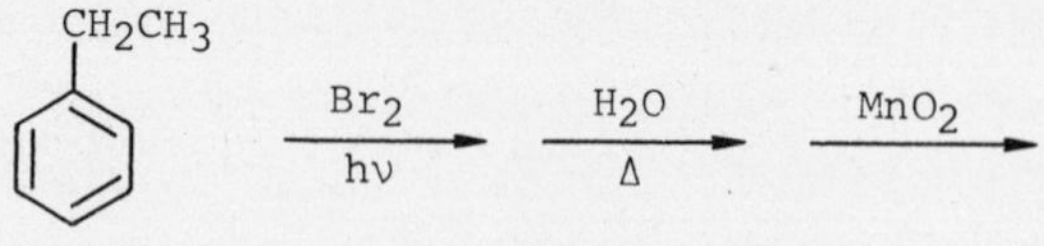

(b)

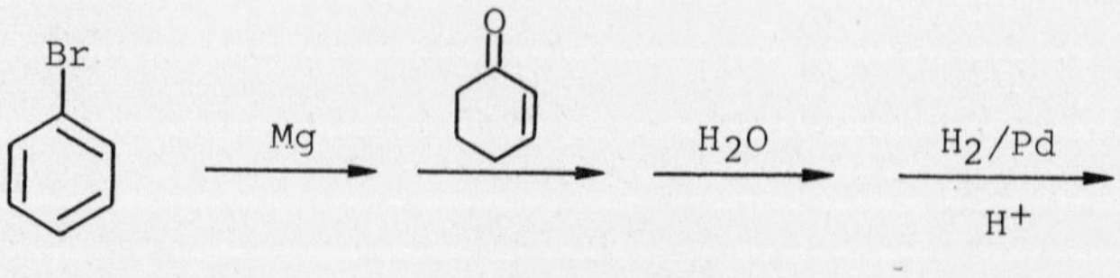

(c)

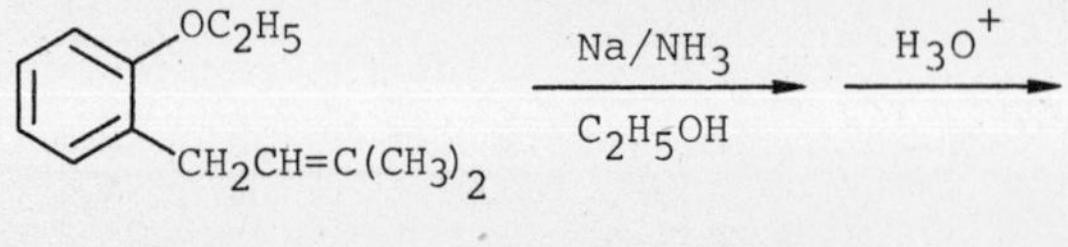

(d)

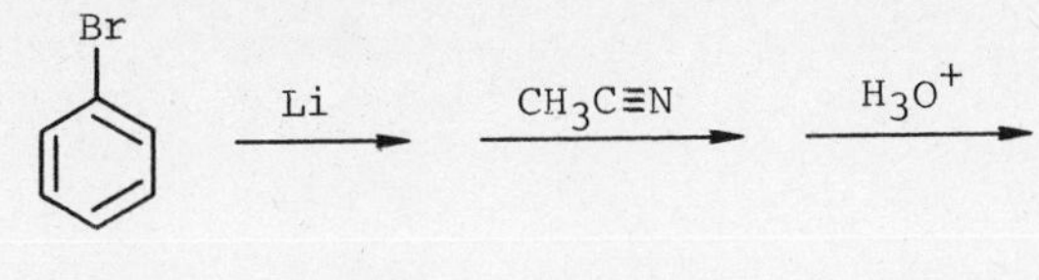

$$\xrightarrow{\text{Li}} \quad \xrightarrow{\text{CH}_3\text{C}\equiv\text{N}} \quad \xrightarrow{\text{H}_3\text{O}^+}$$

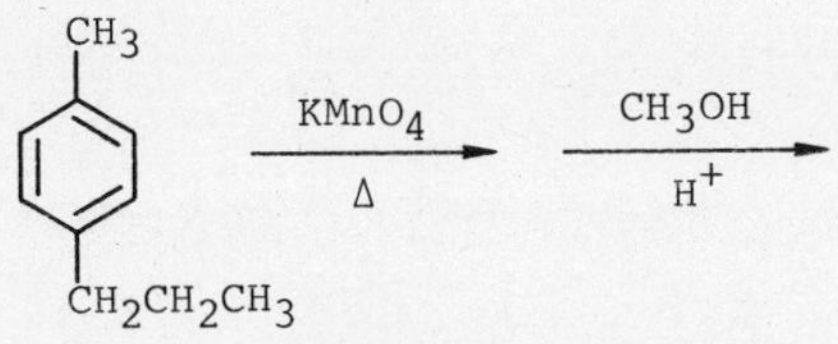

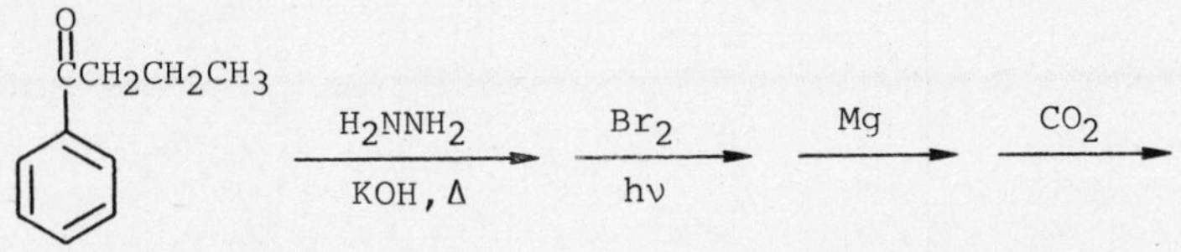

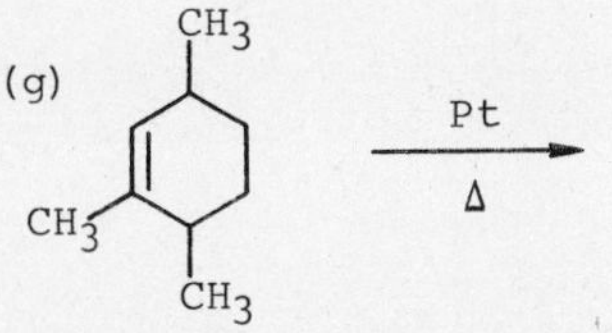

(e)

$$\xrightarrow[\Delta]{\text{KMnO}_4} \quad \xrightarrow[\text{H}^+]{\text{CH}_3\text{OH}}$$

(f)

$$\xrightarrow[\text{KOH}, \Delta]{\text{H}_2\text{NNH}_2} \quad \xrightarrow[\text{h}\nu]{\text{Br}_2} \quad \xrightarrow{\text{Mg}} \quad \xrightarrow{\text{CO}_2}$$

(g)

$$\xrightarrow[\Delta]{\text{Pt}}$$

(h)

$$\xrightarrow[\text{D}^+]{\text{D}_2/\text{Pd}}$$

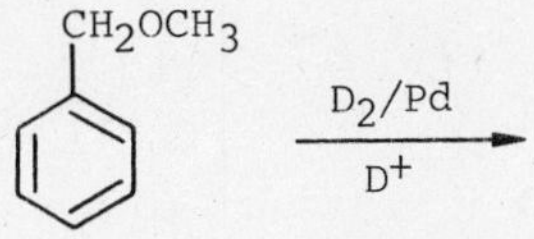

S3. Predict the major product from reaction of <u>cis</u>-1-phenylpropene with each of the following reagents, and explain your choice.

  (a) HCl

  (b) Br_2/CH_3OH

  (c) HBr, peroxides

  (d) $Hg(OAc)_2/CH_3OH$; then $NaBH_4$

S4. Which of the two compounds illustrated below is more acidic? Why?

S5. Which of the following retro-Diels-Alder reactions will take place most easily? Which one will be the most difficult?   Why?

(a)

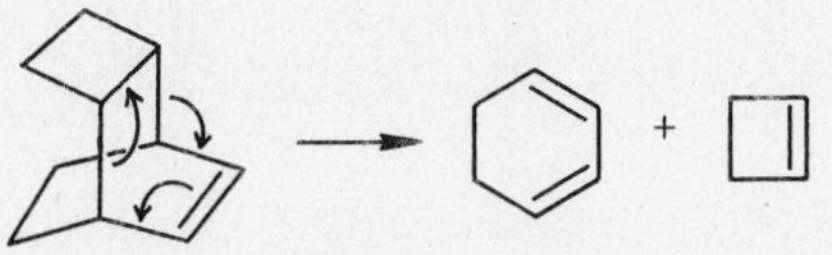

(b)

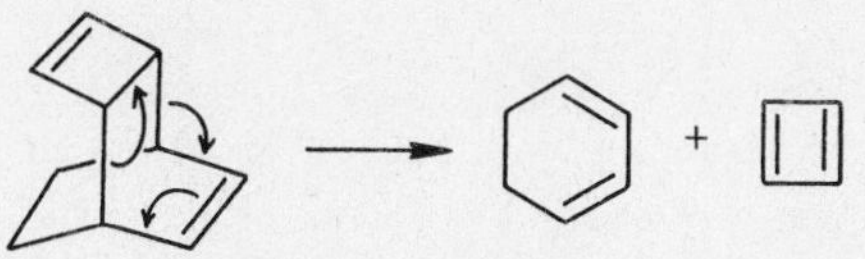

(c)

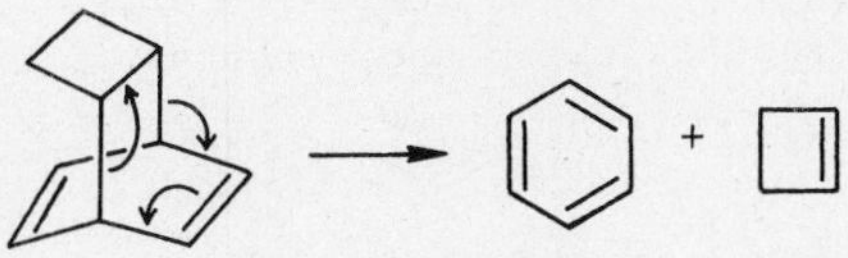

S6. The stabilization that a phenyl group provides to a radical center can be determined by comparing the bond dissociation energies of $C_6H_5CH_2$-H and CH_3-H bonds.

  (a) How does this stabilization compare with that provided by a vinyl group in the allyl radical?

  (b) Perform the same comparison for the cations *(see Sections 19.1.A and 20.5.B in the Text)*.

  (c) Explain any significant difference you see in radical vs. cation stabilization.

S7. Benzylic alcohols and ethers are cleaved under the conditions of the Birch reduction:

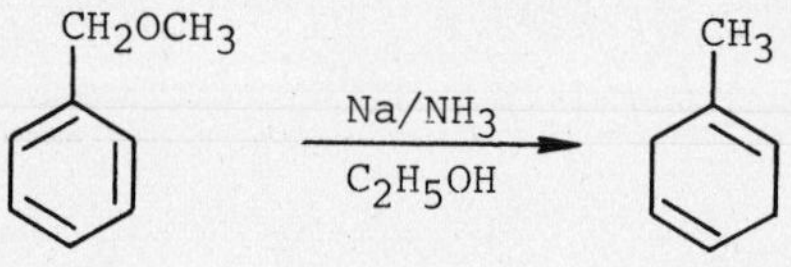

CH$_2$OCH$_3$ $\xrightarrow[\text{C}_2\text{H}_5\text{OH}]{\text{Na/NH}_3}$ CH$_3$

(a) Write a mechanism for this reaction.

(b) Explain why the following ether undergoes Birch reduction without cleavage:

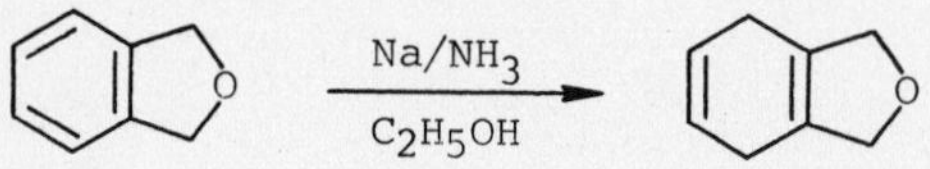

$\xrightarrow[\text{C}_2\text{H}_5\text{OH}]{\text{Na/NH}_3}$

S8. Rank the following compounds in order of acidity.

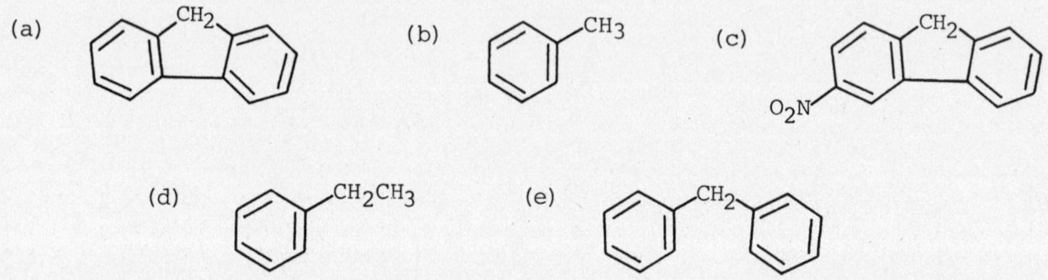

(a) CH$_2$

(b) CH$_3$

(c) CH$_2$ O$_2$N

(d) CH$_2$CH$_3$

(e) CH$_2$

S9. The aliphatic Claisen rearrangement involves a "chair-like" transition state, as depicted below.

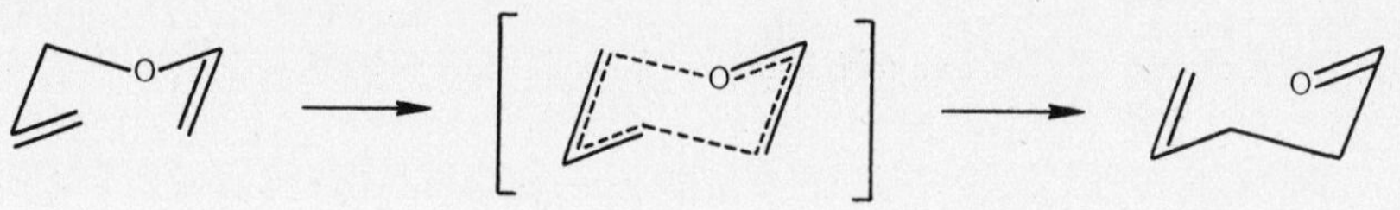

(a) If a secondary allylic vinyl ether is the substrate for the rearrangement, a *trans*-olefin is produced selectively.
Show how this observation is consistent with the transition state illustrated above.

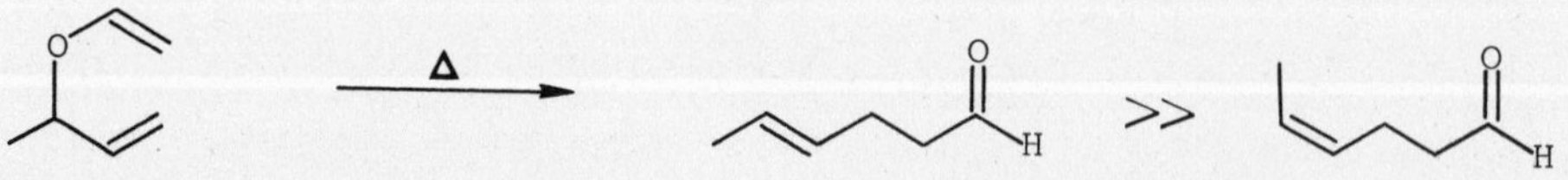

$\xrightarrow{\Delta}$ $\gg$

(b) What products would you expect from the Claisen rearrangement of the following enol ethers?

1)

2)

S10. *Para*-methoxybenzyl bromide, illustrated below, hydrolyzes in water many times faster than the *meta* isomer. Explain why this is so.

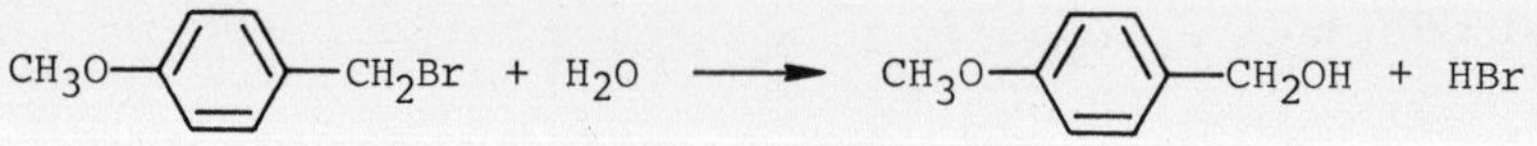

CH$_3$O—⟨ ⟩—CH$_2$Br + H$_2$O $\longrightarrow$ CH$_3$O—⟨ ⟩—CH$_2$OH + HBr

20.G   Answers to Supplementary Problems

S1. (a) <u>p</u>-di-<u>t</u>-butylbenzene   (d) 4-methyl-1-phenyl-1-pentanone

     (b) 3,5-dinitrobenzoyl chloride   (e) 1-chloro-2,4-dinitrobenzene

     (c) <u>o</u>-chlorophenyl propionate,   (f) <u>p</u>-methylphenylacetic acid
          or 2-chlorophenyl propanoate

S2.

(a)

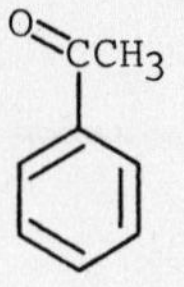

(b)

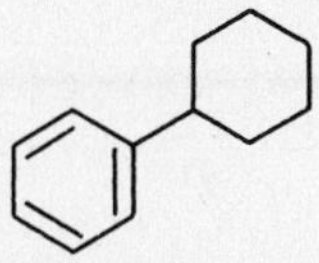

(c)

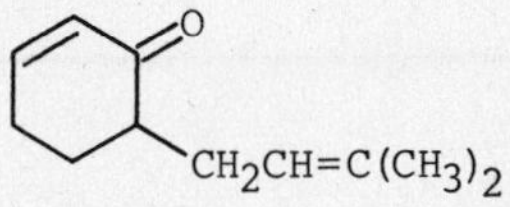

(d)

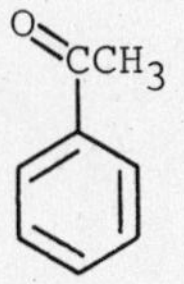

(e)

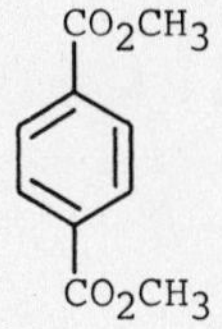

(f)

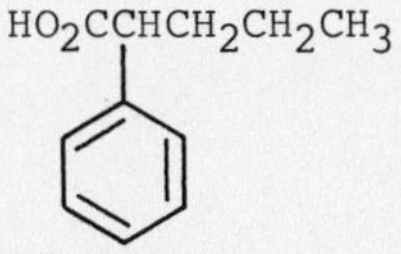

(g)

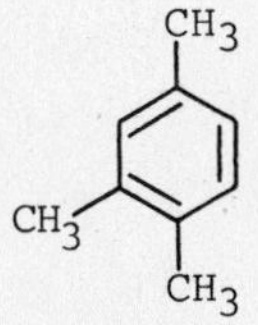

(h)

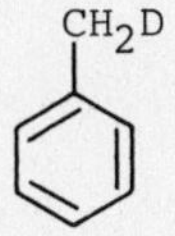

S3. (a)

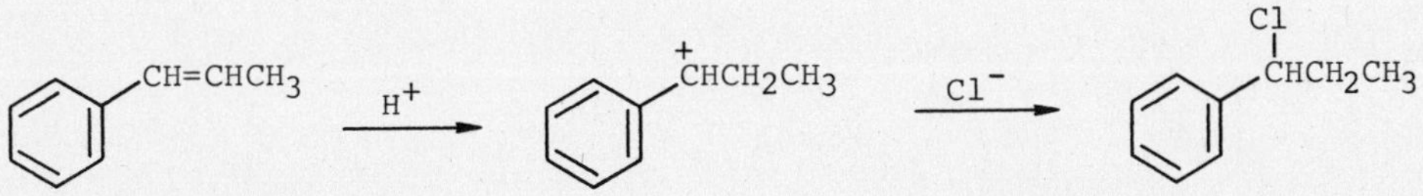

     (b)

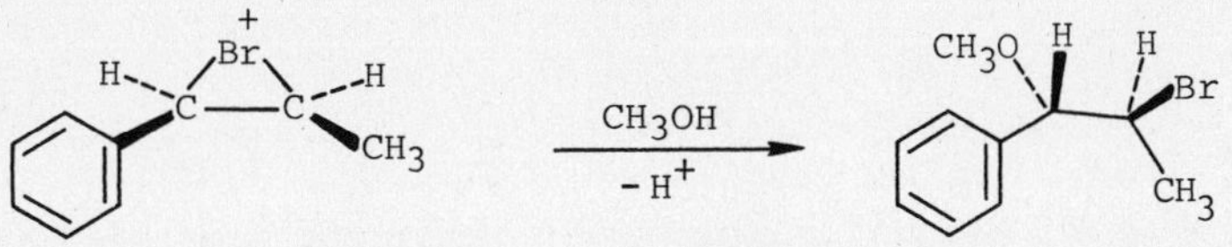

     (c)

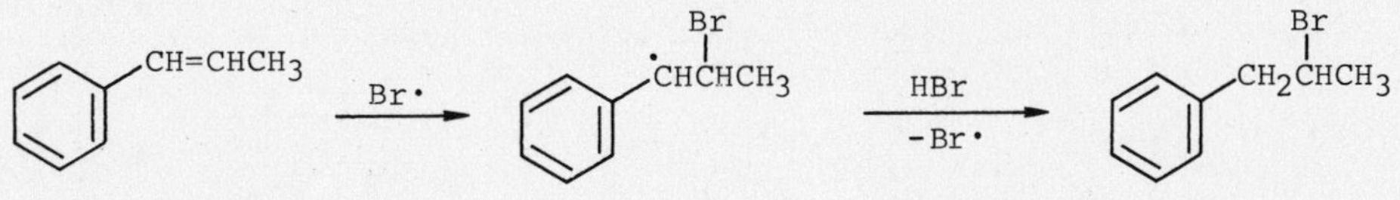

     (d)

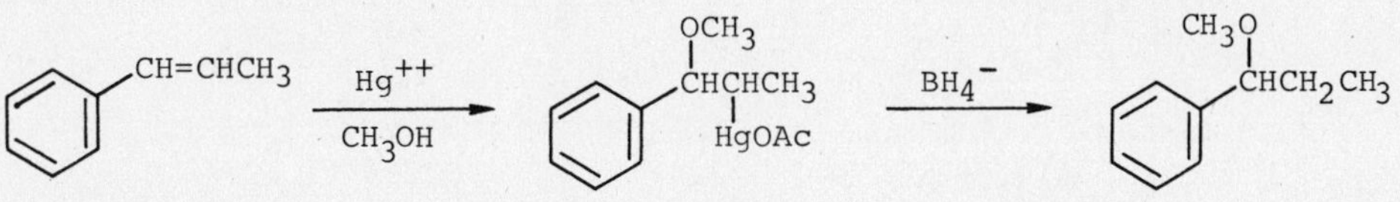

In (a), (b), and (d), the additions proceed in the Markovnikov sense (the most stable
carbocation is formed); in (c), Br· adds so as to afford the most stable radical.
Phenyl stabilizes radicals and carbocations better than a simple alkyl group does.

S4.

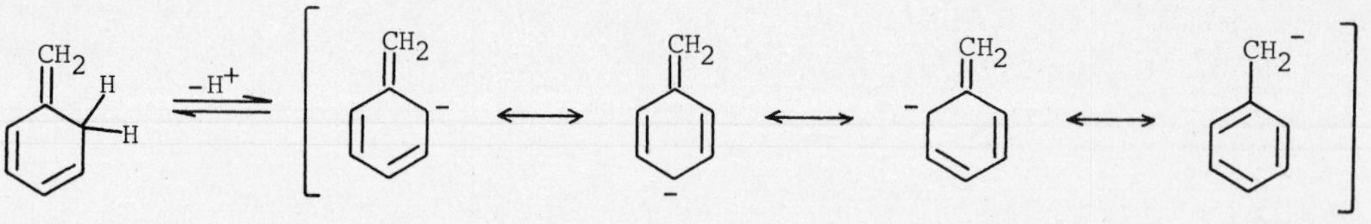

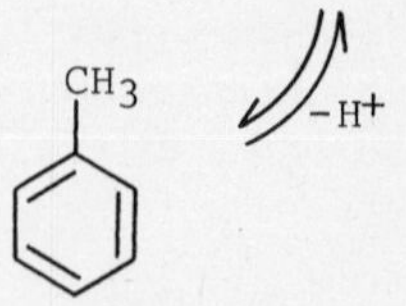

Both isomers ionize to give the same carbanion,
so the difference in equilibrium will depend
only on the difference in stability of the
starting materials. Toluene is more stable than
the methylenecyclohexadiene isomer, and therefore it will be less acidic.

S5.   Reaction (c) will occur most rapidly because the aromatic stabilization of
benzene is gained. Reaction (b) will be the most difficult because the very
unstable (high-energy) cyclobutadiene is being formed. In reaction (a), no
aromatic or antiaromatic compounds are being produced.

S6. (a)

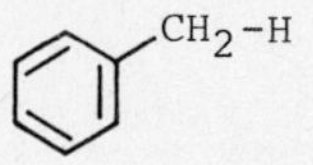

$$DH° = \quad 88 \qquad\qquad 105 \qquad\qquad 86 \qquad\qquad kcal\ mole^{-1}$$

Stabilization: $\quad$ 17 $\qquad\qquad$ 19 $\qquad\qquad$ kcal mole^{-1}

Stabilization of a radical is about the same for phenyl and vinyl.

(b)

	$\Delta H°$ (kcal mole^{-1})	
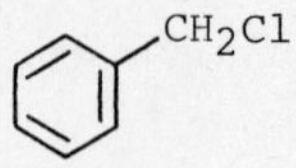 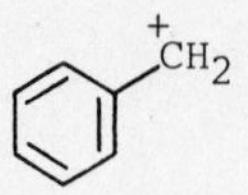	154	*Stabilization:* 36 kcal mole^{-1}
$CH_3CH_2Cl \rightarrow CH_3CH_2^+ + Cl^-$	190	
$CH_2=CHCH_2Cl \rightarrow CH_2=CHCH_2^+ + Cl^-$	172	18 kcal mole^{-1}

(c) The phenyl and vinyl groups provide essentially the same stabilization to
a radical center. (Although more carbons can share the radical in the
benzylic case, those resonance structures lack the cyclic valence bond
structure of an aromatic ring:

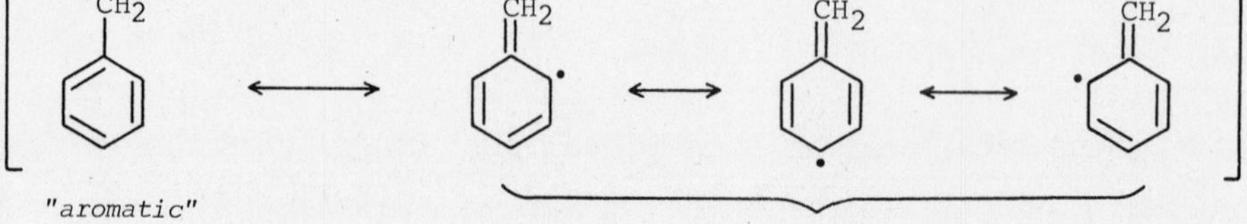

"aromatic" $\qquad\qquad\qquad$ *"non-aromatic"*

In the case of a cation, the ability to distribute the positive charge
over several atoms becomes more important, and the benzylic cation therefore becomes more stabilized than the allyl cation.

S7. (a)

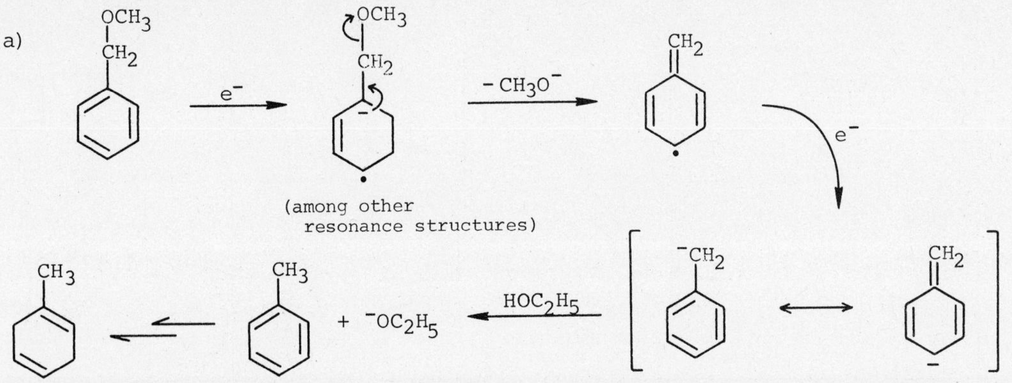

(among other
resonance structures)

(b)

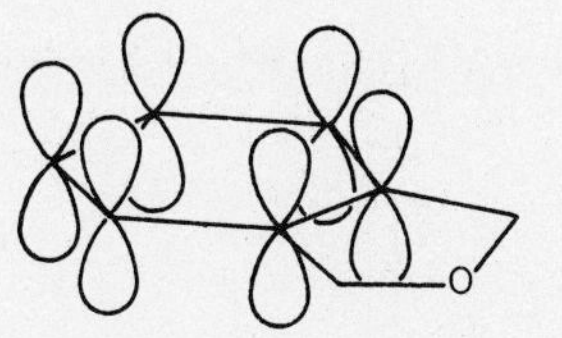

The C-O bonds are perpendicular to the
p-orbitals of the π-system. Therefore the
orbitals of the C-O bond cannot overlap with
the aromatic p-orbitals, and bond cleavage
cannot take place.

S8. *Most acidic*: (c), because of stabilization of the carbanion by both coplanar
rings and electron-withdrawing nitro group.

   (a) is more acidic than (e) because the tricyclic structure holds
   both rings coplanar for maximum overlap with the p-orbital of
   the benzylic carbanion.

   (e) is more acidic than (b) and (d) because it has two phenyl rings
   which stabilize the carbanion.

   (b) is more acidic than (d) because it does not have the electron-
   releasing methyl substituent on the carbanionic carbon.

   Least acidic: (d)

S9. (a) Since there is a chiral center in the molecule, there are two diastereomeric chair-like transition states possible:

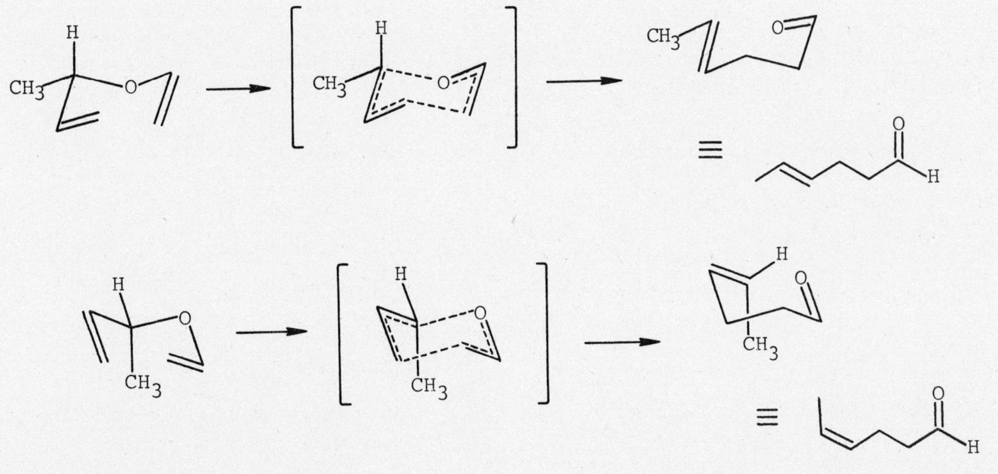

Rearrangement by the first transition state is preferred because the methyl
group is in an equatorial-like position, rather than the axial-like orientation in the transition state which leads to the *cis*-product.

(b)

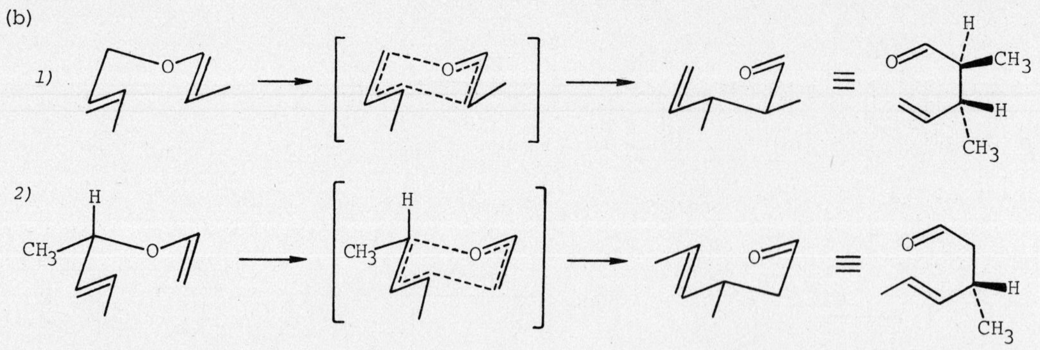

1)

2)

S10. The benzylic cation from S_N1-type cleavage of the *para*-isomer can be stabil-ized by the oxygen lone pair electrons by resonance:

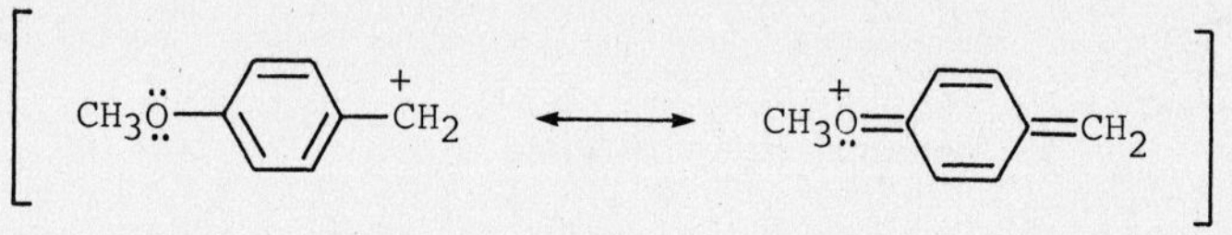

No such resonance structure is possible for the *meta*-isomer.

21. MOLECULAR ORBITAL THEORY

21.A   Chapter Outline and Important Terms Introduced

21.1   <u>Molecular Orbital Description of Allyl and Butadiene</u>
bonding, antibonding, non-bonding molecular orbitals

21.2   <u>Molecular Orbital Theory of Benzene</u>
degeneracy   shell

21.3   <u>Aromaticity</u>

    A. Cyclooctatetraene: The Hückel 4n + 2 Rule
aromatic vs. non-aromatic or antiaromatic
    B. Two-Electron Systems
cyclopropenyl cation
cyclopropenone
    C. Six-Electron Systems
not cyclobutadiene (antiaromatic)
cyclopentadienyl anion
cycloheptatrienyl cation
    D. Ten-Electron Systems
cyclononatetraenyl anion
    E. Larger Cyclic π-Systems
annulenes

21.4   <u>Hückel Transition States</u>

21.5   <u>Möbius Transition States</u>

    A. Electrocyclic Reactions
conrotatory vs. disrotatory motion
Woodward-Hoffmann Rules
Hückel vs. Möbius molecular orbital systems
    B. Cycloaddition Reactions
suprafacial vs. antarafacial

21.6   <u>Ultraviolet Spectroscopy</u>

    A. Electronic Transitions
excited state   ground state
    B. $\pi \longrightarrow \pi^*$ Transitions
longer conjugation $\Longrightarrow$ longer wavelength
    C. $n \longrightarrow \pi^*$ Transitions
extinction coefficient
    D. Alkyl Substituents
hyperconjugation
    E. Benzene
symmetry forbidden
    F. Other Functional Groups
    G. Photochemical Reactions

21.7   <u>Perturbational MO Approach to Reactivity</u>
donor vs. acceptor
<u>H</u>ighest <u>O</u>ccupied <u>M</u>olecular <u>O</u>rbital (HOMO)
<u>L</u>owest vacant (= <u>U</u>noccupied) <u>M</u>olecular <u>O</u>rbital (LUMO)
frontier orbitals

21.B   Important Reactions Introduced

Electrocyclic reactions (21.4)

Equation:

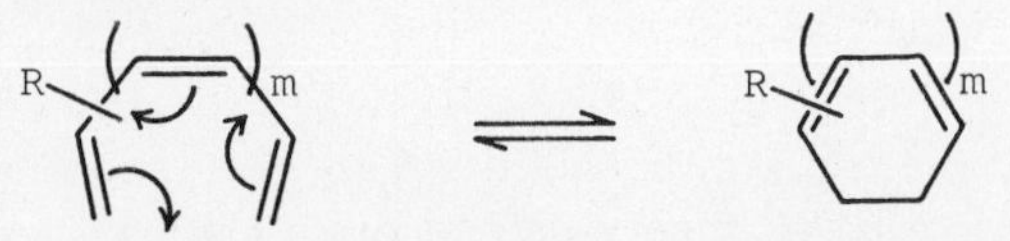

Generality: R = various substituents, ring systems, etc.
               m = 0, 1, 2, ...

Key features: m = even, i.e. 4n electron systems: Möbius transition state; conrotatory motion
               m = odd, i.e. 4n + 2 systems: Hückel transition state; disrotatory motion

Cycloaddition reactions (21.

Equation:

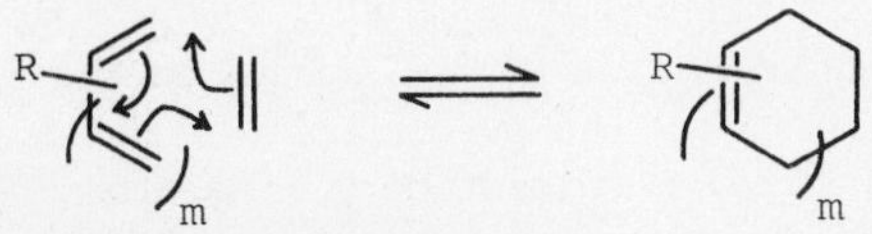

Generality: R = various substituents
               m = 0, 1, 2, ...

Key features: p + q cycloaddition reaction: p π-electrons in one part, q in the other
               if p + q = 4n: Möbius transition state, antarafacial stereochemistry
               if p + q = 4n + 2: Hückel transition state, suprafacial stereochemistry

Photochemical cis/trans isomerization of alkenes (21.5.G)

Equation:

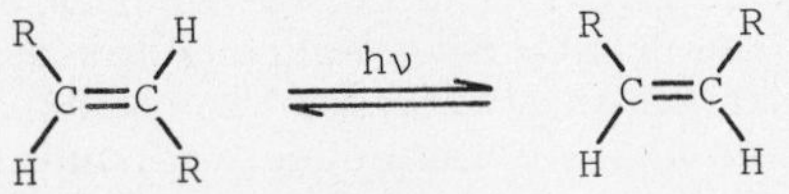

Generality: R = alkyl, aryl, etc.

Key features: reaction proceeds via $\pi \longrightarrow \pi^*$ electronic excitation
               equilibrium process

21.C   Important Concepts and Hints

For many years, the concept of a "reaction mechanism" in organic chemistry consisted of simply showing what fragments of the starting materials moved around and became attached to each other in the products. As our understanding and sophistication increased, so did the finesse with which we displayed reaction mechanisms. The "lasso" diagrams (Eq. 1) gave way to the convention of using curved arrows to represent the movement of electron pairs which are involved in bond cleavage and formation. This style is now universally used because it is helps us keep track of the crucial features in a reaction mechanism: the valence electrons. In the process of writing the reaction of sodium cyanide with methyl iodide as in Eq. 2, we can easily see why it is the cyanide ion that bonds to the methyl group, and why it becomes attached via the carbon and not the nitrogen.

(1) $Na\overbrace{CN + CH_3}I \longrightarrow CH_3CN + NaOH$

(2) $Na^+ \; \bar{:}C\equiv N\!: \; + CH_3\!-\!I \longrightarrow \; :N\equiv C\!-\!CH_3 + Na^+ \; I^-$

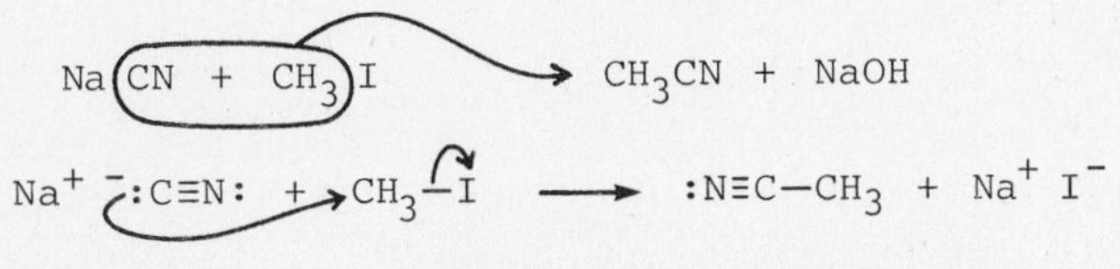

Nevertheless, for many reactions, our detailed understanding of the mechanism has now advanced beyond the level that can be described by curved arrows. For example, the cyclization of E,Z,E-2,4,6-octatriene to cis-5,6-dimethyl-1,3-cyclohexadiene can be written with curved arrows (Eq. 3), showing us the cyclic movement of electrons, but this diagram cannot let us see why the cis product is formed and not the trans. To adequately describe this type of reaction, an understanding of molecular orbital theory has become indispensable. Interestingly, the types of reactions for which MO theory is most applicable are in turn becoming increasingly important in modern organic chemistry. Which of these parallel developments has the greatest importance is a present-day version of the chicken-and-the-egg question.

(3)

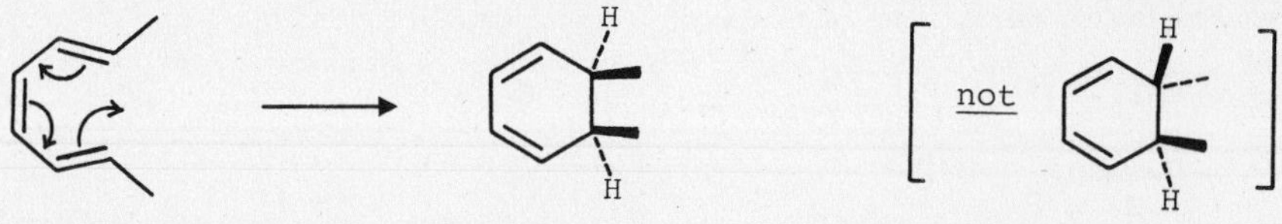

For many types of reactions, molecular orbital theory can be distilled down to some straight-forward rules. It is of course a good idea to understand the <u>derivation</u> of these rules, but at the least you should learn what they are:

(1) For cyclic π-systems:

   4n + 2 electrons involved in a ring = Hückel = aromatic = stabilized
   4n electrons in a ring = antiaromatic = destabilized

(2) For electrocyclic reactions

   4n + 2 electrons involved in a ring requires: a Hückel system in the transition state
                                                    an even number of nodes
                                                    disrotatory ring closure/opening
   4n electrons in a ring requires: a Möbius transition state
                                        an odd number of nodes
                                        conrotatory ring closure/opening

(3) For cycloaddition reactions

   4n + 2 = Hückel = suprafacial addition
   4n = Möbius = antarafacial addition

One other point can be made which may help to clear up a common confusion about molecular orbitals, their energies, and what effect their occupancy by electrons has on the energy of the molecule. Think of an orbital as a landlord thinks of an apartment: A vacant apartment (orbital) exists and has a defined price (energy level) even when it is unoccupied, but this rent (energy) only counts when a paying tenant (an electron) moves in. Of course, in any MO system there are an equal number of bonding and anti-bonding orbitals, so the apartment analogy isn't perfect. Whereas there is an unfavorable energy change when an electron moves into an antibonding orbital, it is unlikely that any apartments can be found where the landlord pays money to the tenants...

UV Spectroscopy

As a useful spectroscopic method, UV spectroscopy is limited to conjugated systems. There-fore, it is not as generally applicable as NMR or IR. Nevertheless it can provide important information on structure and conformation in such systems.

The process of electronic excitation, on which UV spectroscopy is based, is also important in photochemistry. Many reactions which do not occur thermally with a molecule in its ground state can be made to go when the molecule is in an excited state. For example, the cyclization of two olefins to give a cyclobutane can be made to occur under irradiation, but not thermally, as pointed out in Chapter 20.

21.D   Answers to Exercises

21.1 $\left[CH_2=CH-CH=CH-\bar{C}H_2 \longleftrightarrow CH_2=CH-\bar{C}H-CH=CH_2 \longleftrightarrow {}^-CH_2-CH=CH-CH=CH_2 \right]$

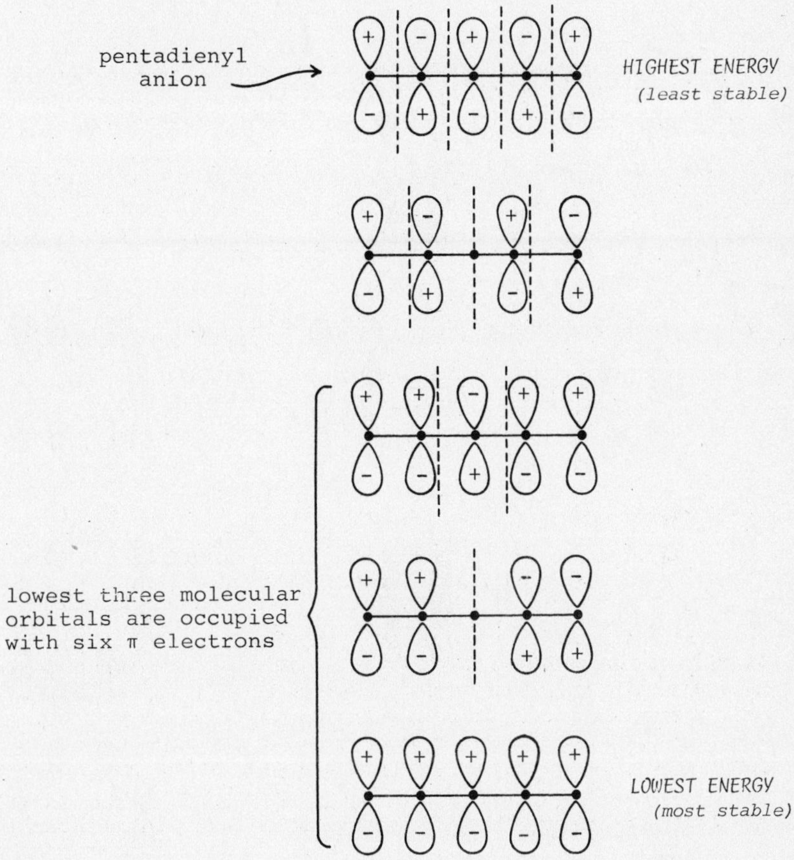

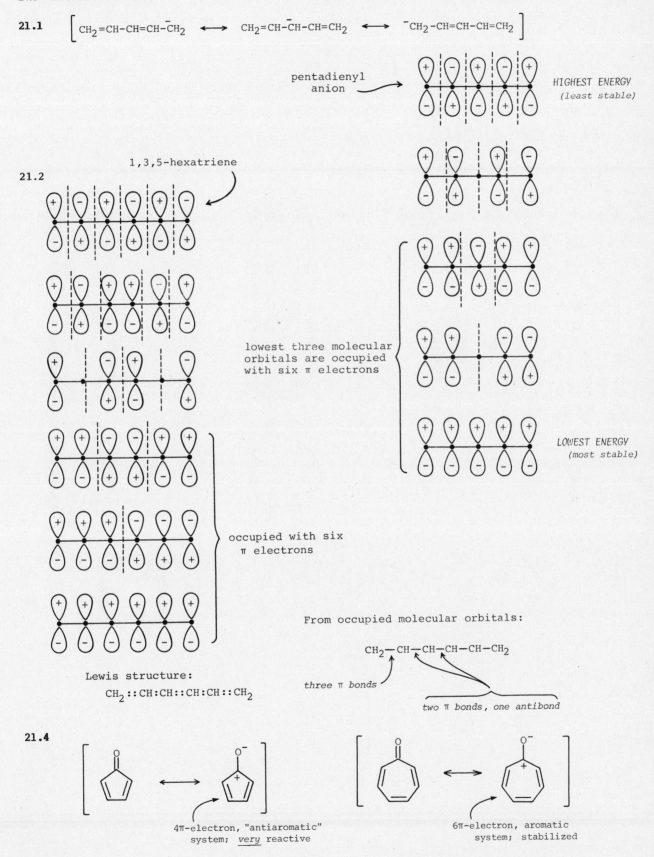

pentadienyl
anion

HIGHEST ENERGY
(least stable)

1,3,5-hexatriene

21.2

lowest three molecular
orbitals are occupied
with six π electrons

LOWEST ENERGY
(most stable)

occupied with six
π electrons

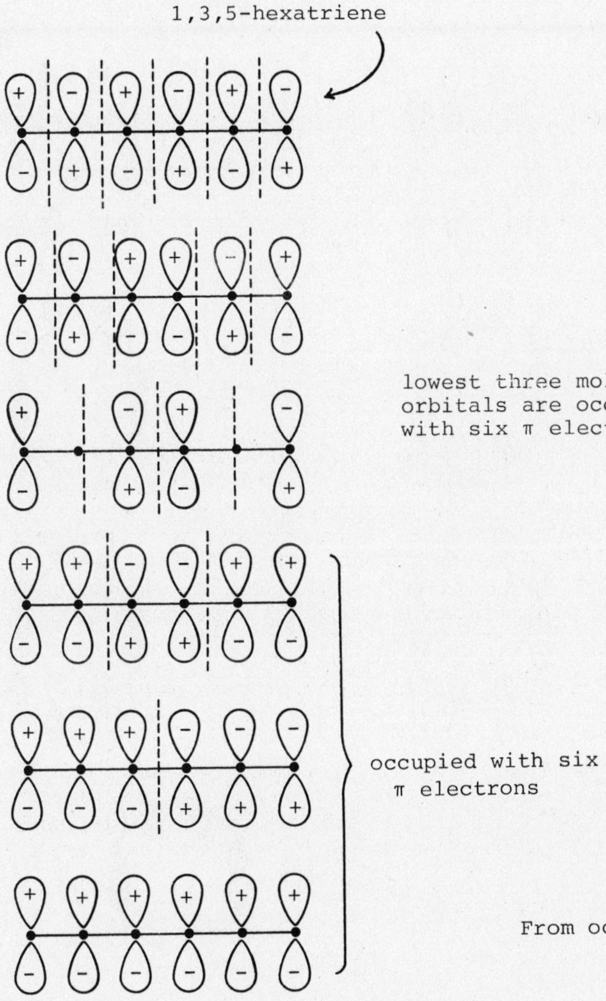

Lewis structure:

$CH_2::CH:CH::CH:CH::CH_2$

From occupied molecular orbitals:

$CH_2-CH-CH-CH-CH-CH_2$

three π bonds

two π bonds, one antibond

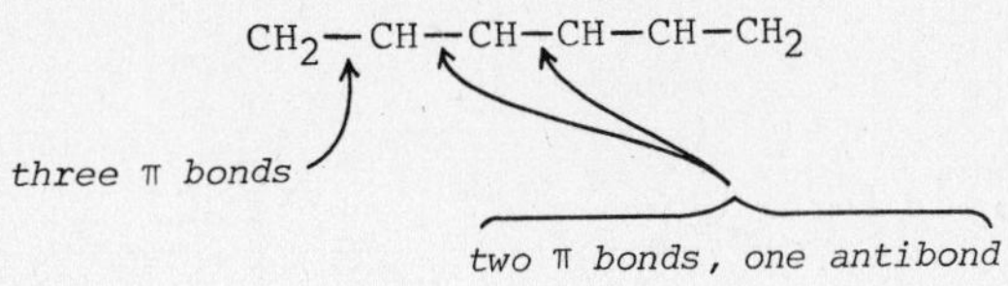

21.4

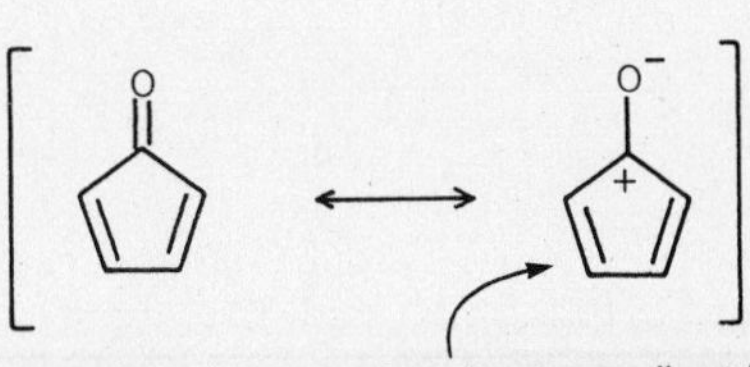

4π-electron, "antiaromatic"
system; *very* reactive

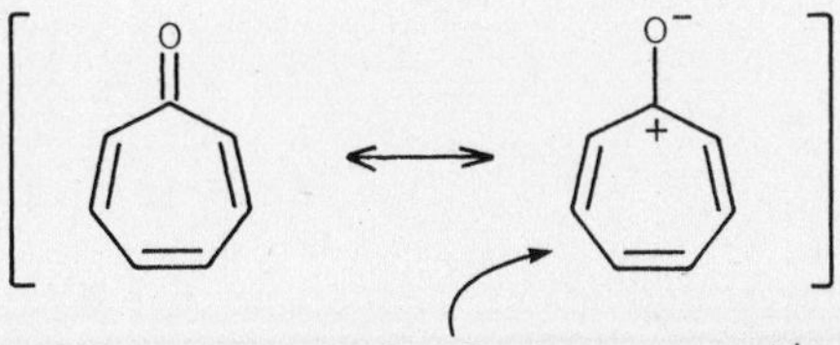

6π-electron, aromatic
system; stabilized

21.5 The following will show Hückel aromaticity:

(b) (22 π electrons)   **(d)** (6 π electrons)   **(e)** (26 π electrons)   **(f)** (10 π electrons)

21.6 **(a)**

2 + 2 :

4 + 4 :

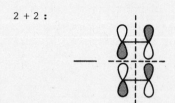
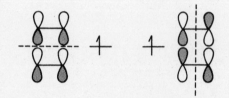

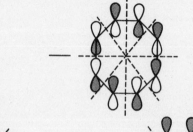
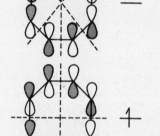
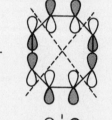
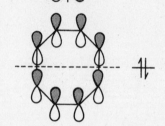
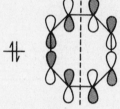
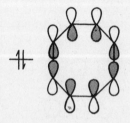

(NOTE: dashed lines indicate
nodes in the molecular
orbitals)

(b)

21.7 The transition states for the forward and reverse reactions are the same.

21.8

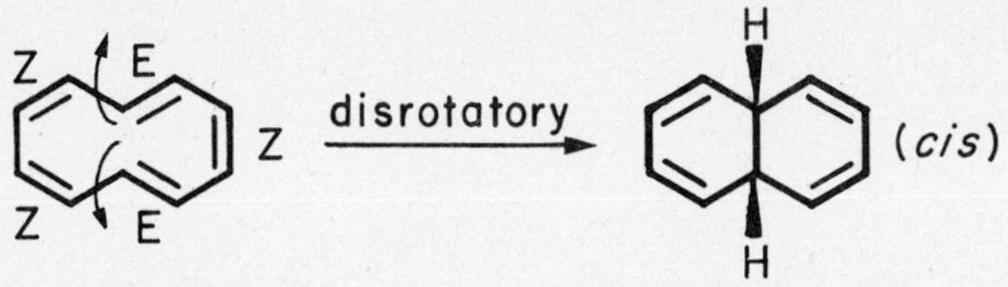

six = 4n + 2 electrons involved in the electrocyclization; therefore disrotatory

21.9

(a)

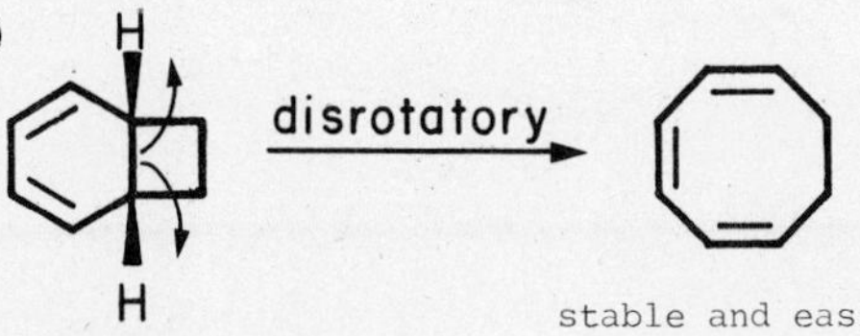

stable and easily formed

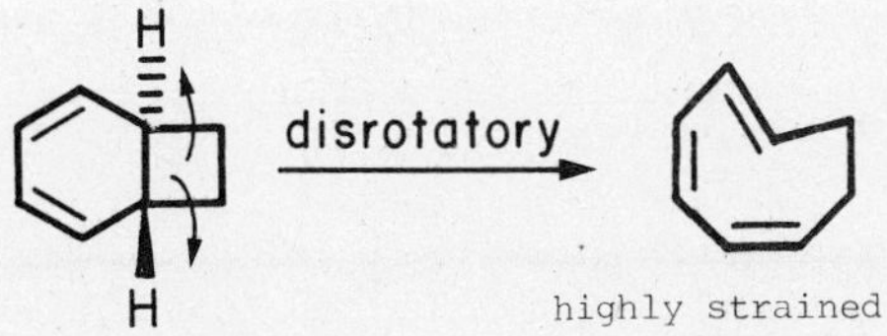

highly strained because of *trans* double bond, therefore formed with greater difficulty

(b)

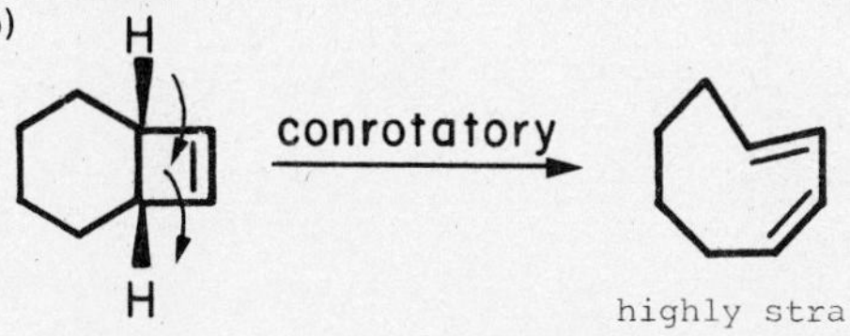

highly strained and hard to form

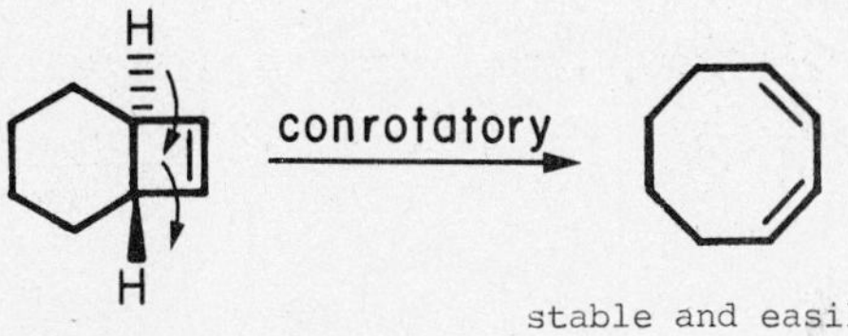

stable and easily formed

21.10

(a)

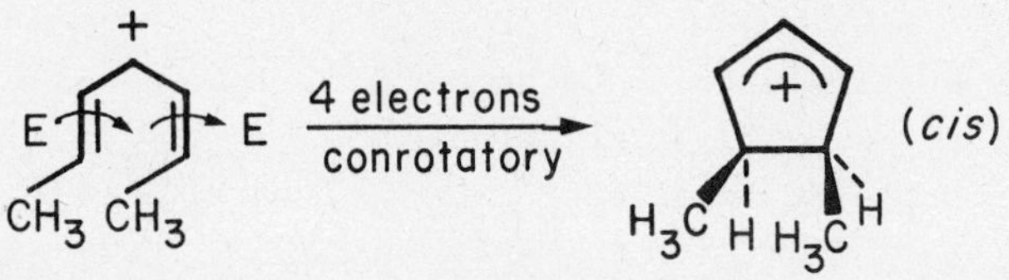

(b)

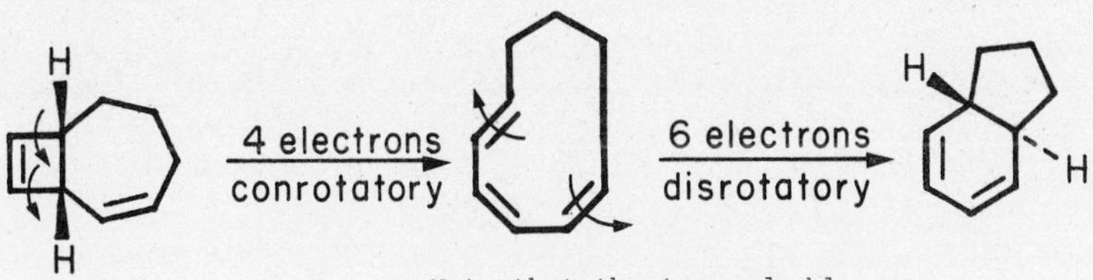

Note that the *trans* double bond is in a nine-membered ring and forms readily

(c)

$$\underset{CH_3 \quad CH_3}{\overset{C_6H_5}{\underset{E}{\overset{E}{\rule{0pt}{0pt}}}}} \xrightarrow[\text{conrotatory}]{8 \text{ electrons}} \quad (\textit{trans})$$

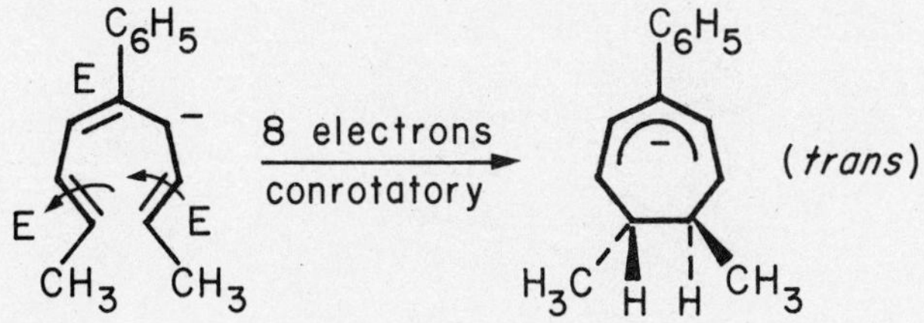

21.11   (i) $_4\pi_s + _4\pi_s$:disallowed   (the allowed $_4\pi_s + _4\pi_a$ is geometrically unlikely)

(ii) $_8\pi_s + _2\pi_s$: allowed

(iii) $_2\pi_s + _2\pi_s + _2\pi_s$: allowed

(iv) $_{12}\pi_s + _2\pi_s$: allowed

21.12   Allyl anion: Pentadienyl anion:

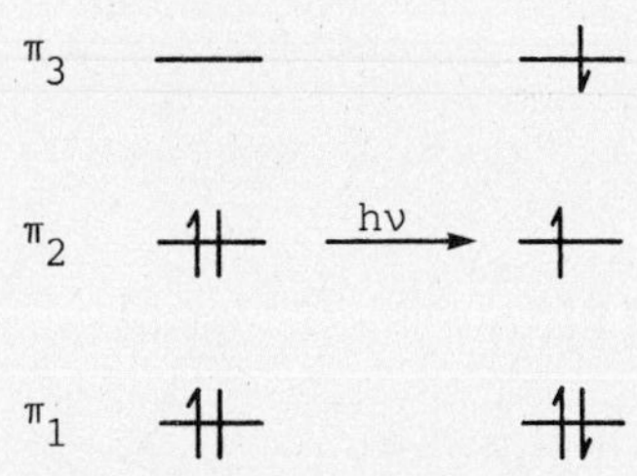

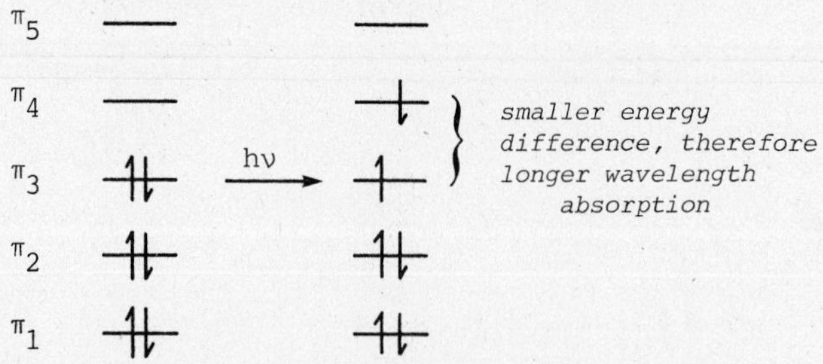

π_3 ———   —╀— π_5 ———   ———

                                     π_4 ———   —╀—   ⎫
                                                                ⎬ *smaller energy*
                                                                  difference, therefore
π_2 � $\xrightarrow{h\nu}$ —╀— π_3 ⥮ $\xrightarrow{h\nu}$ —╀—   ⎭ *longer wavelength*
                                                                     absorption

                                     π_2 ⥮   ⥮

π_1 ⥮   ⥮ π_1 ⥮   ⥮

21.13 $n \longrightarrow \pi^*$:   0.00731 g crotonic acid/10 mL = 8.5×10^{-3} M

$$\varepsilon_{250} = \frac{0.77}{(8.5 \times 10^{-3})(1)} = 91$$

$\pi \longrightarrow \pi^*$: 8.5×10^{-3} M diluted 100-fold = 8.5×10^{-5} M

$$\varepsilon_{200} = \frac{0.86}{(8.5 \times 10^{-5})(1)} = 10,120$$

21.14 $E = \dfrac{hc}{\lambda}$; $E\,(\text{kcal mole}^{-1}) = \dfrac{2.857 \times 10^{-5}}{500 \times 10^{-9}} = 57$ kcal mole^{-1}

21.15   There is a large lobe available for bonding
behind the carbon of the C–F bond. Overlap here
with an incoming nucleophile is involved
in S_N2 displacement.

(side view)

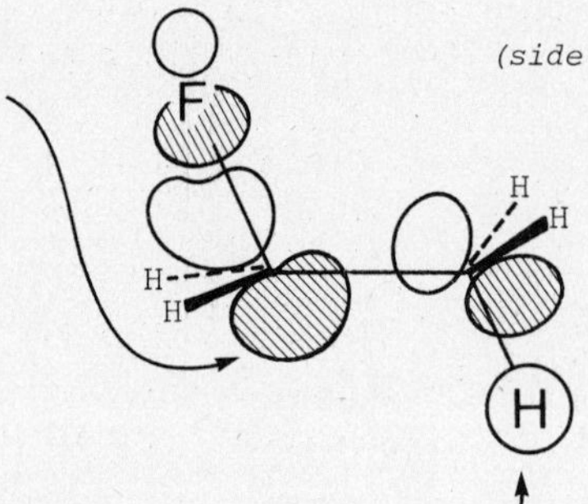

There is another lobe accessible for bonding at the <u>anti</u>-hydrogen.
Overlap there leads to E2 elimination, via the transition state:

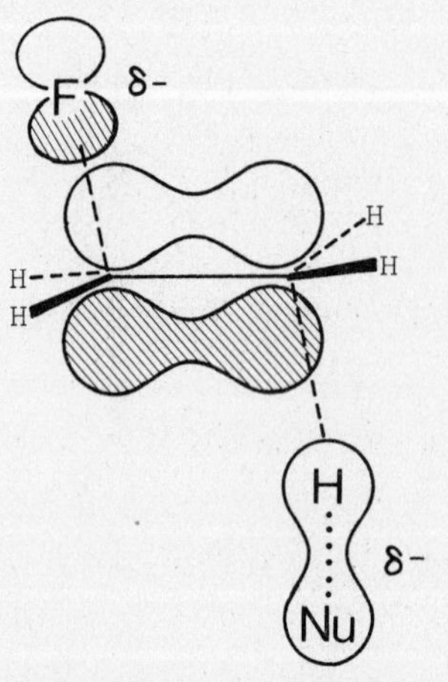

21.16   Reaction with a nucleophile involves the LUMO of the allyl cation. Since this
orbital has a node at the central carbon, attack occurs at the end.

21.17

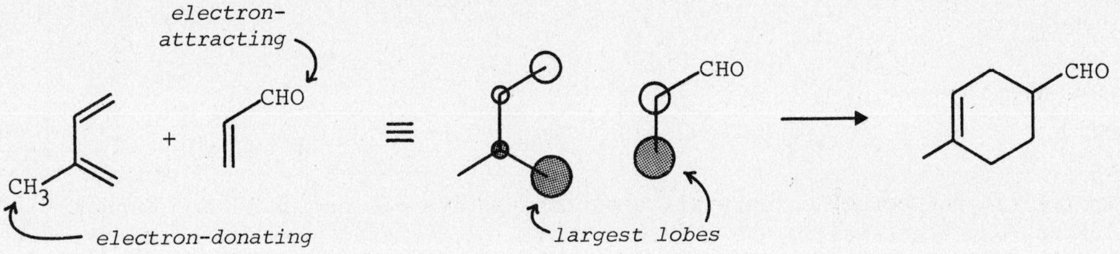

electron-attracting

CHO

CH_3

electron-donating

largest lobes

CHO

CHO

21.E   Answers and Explanations for Problems

1.

(a)

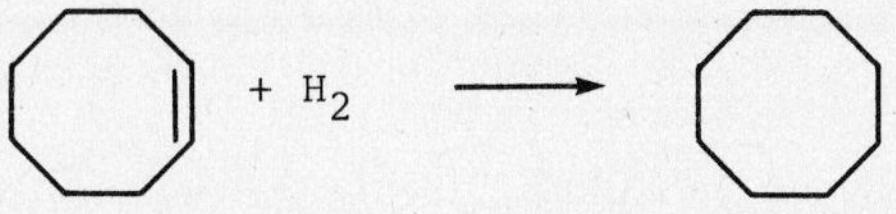

$+ H_2 \longrightarrow$

$\Delta H^\circ = -23.3$ kcal mole^{-1}

$+ 4 H_2 \longrightarrow$

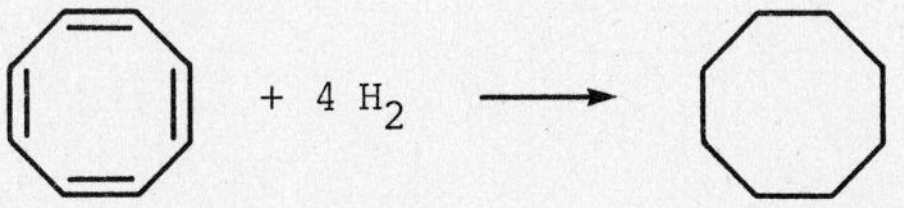

$\Delta H^\circ = -100.9$ kcal mole^{-1}

$4 \times (-23.3) - (-100.9) = +7.7$ kcal mole^{-1}

Empirical resonance energy: -7.7 kcal mole^{-1}.

The negative value implies that the four double bonds in cyclooctatetraene are less stable than 4×1 double bonds; i.e., this value represents a __destabilization__ energy or negative resonance energy. This means that not only is there no stabilization energy (resonance), but that cyclooctatetraene is probably more strained because of the four double bonds.

(b)

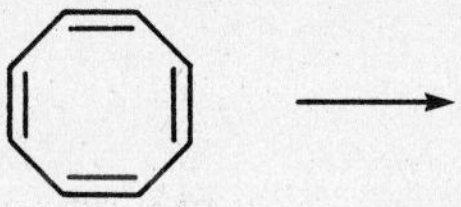

$\longrightarrow \quad 8 \cdot \ddot{C} \cdot \ + \ 8 \ H\cdot$

<u>Breaking</u>   four C–C: $4 \times 83 = 332$

four C=C: $4 \times 146 = 584$

eight C–H: $8 \times 99 = \underline{792}$

Sum: 1708 kcal mole^{-1}

Empirical resonance energy: $1713 - 1708 = 5$ kcal mole^{-1}

(c)

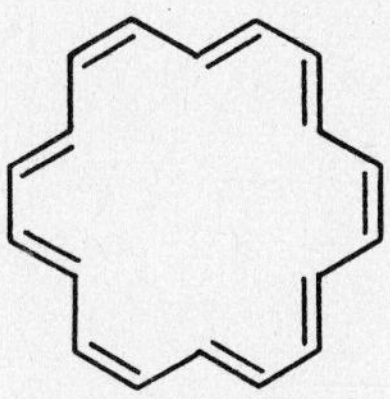

[18]annulene

Calculated empirical resonance energy:

$9 \times 83 = \ \ \ 747$

$9 \times 146 = 1314$

$18 \times 99 = \underline{1782}$

3843

$3890 - 3843 = 47$ kcal mole^{-1}

This resonance energy implies that [18]annulene is aromatic, as the Hückel $4n+2$ rule would suggest.

2. The anion which results from proton removal from the first isomer is the most stable.

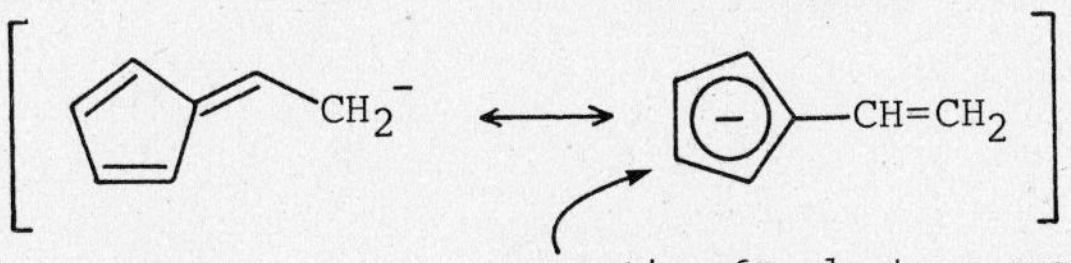

aromatic, 6π-electron cyclopentadienyl anion

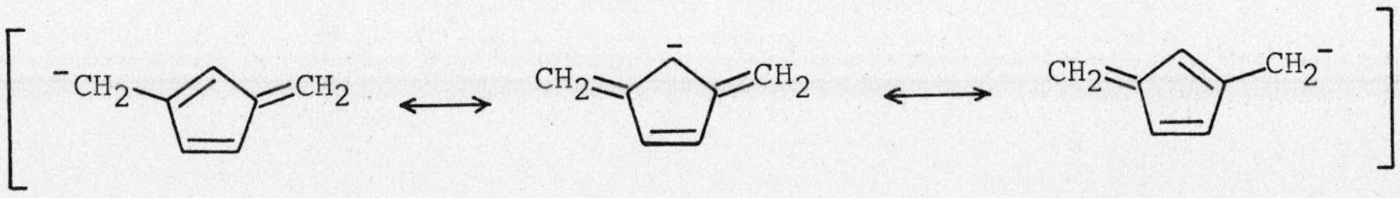

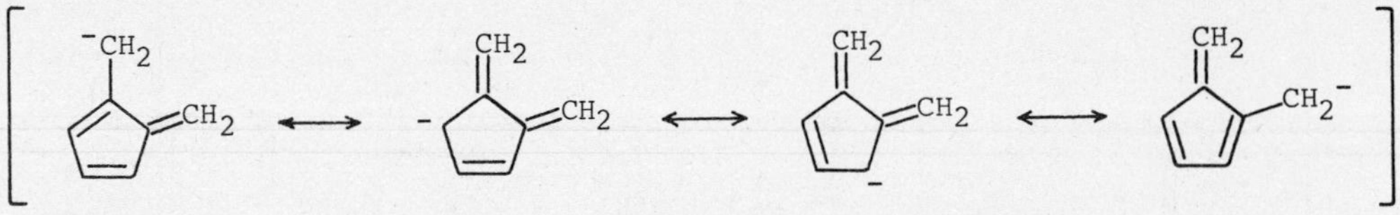

3. (a) Nonaromatic: the boron has only six electrons in its valence shell and cannot contribute any electrons to the π system (total of 4 π electrons in the ring).

   (b) Nonaromatic: each nitrogen has two lone pair electrons, which, combined with those from the double bonds, makes eight.

   (c) Aromatic: one of the oxygen lone pairs (not both!) can be delocalized into the ring to provide the third pair of π electrons (total = 6).

   (d) Aromatic: cyclo-$C_7H_7^{-3}$ has seven π orbitals, but the 3- charge indicates that there are three extra electrons, for a total of 10 π electrons in the ring.

   (e) Aromatic: cyclo-$C_8H_8^{++}$ has eight π orbitals and 2+ charge, therefore six π electrons.

   (f) Aromatic: eight π electrons from the double bonds and two from the nitrogen lone pair = 10 π electrons.

4.

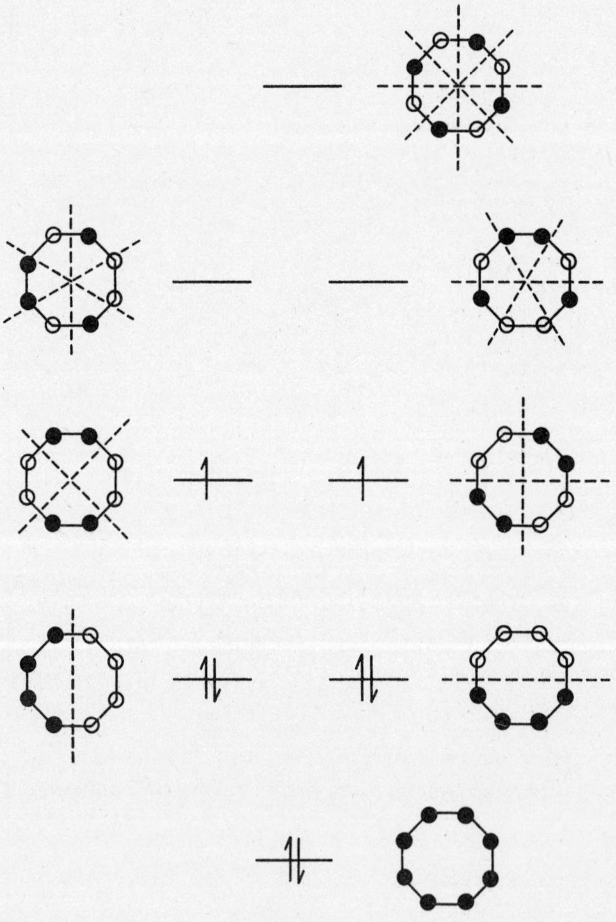

5. 4n + 2:   (b)   (c)

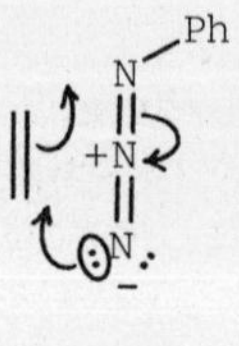

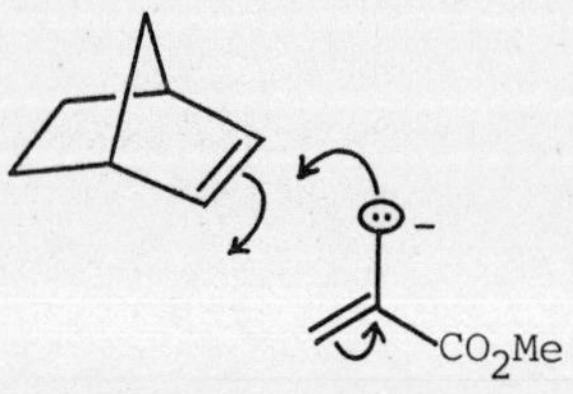

__Not__ 4n + 2 : (a) (4 electrons) (d) (8 electrons)

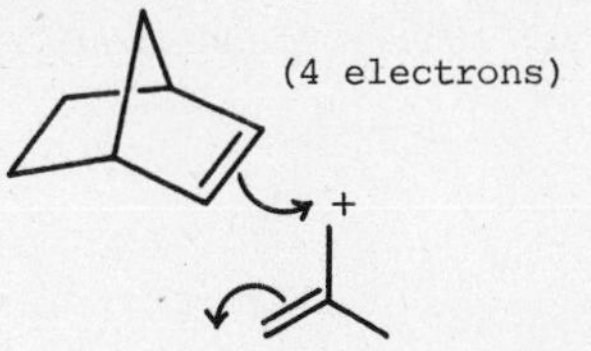

+

O

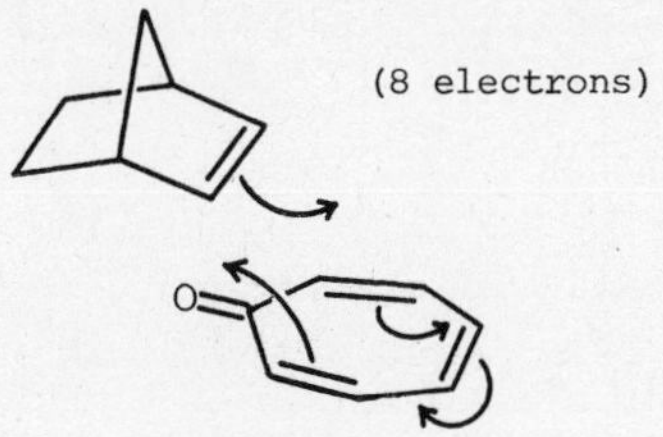

6. The anionic product is stabilized by aromatic resonance in the case of the five-membered ring product (six π electrons), whereas the corresponding seven-membered ring anion is not aromatic.

7. The reaction with butadiene is favored according to HOMO-LUMO interactions; it also has a 4n + 2 (Hückel aromatic) transition state:

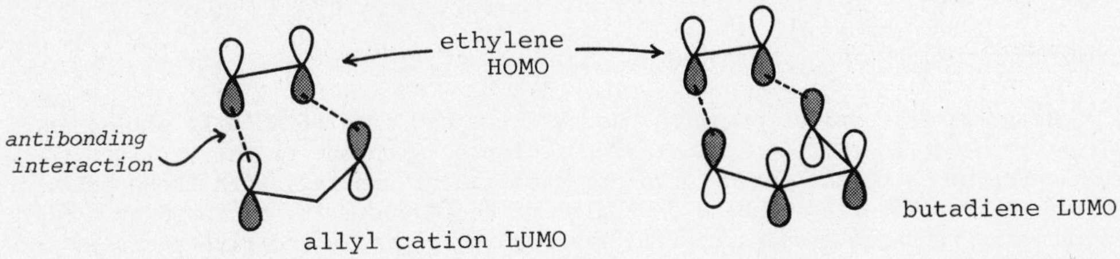

ethylene
HOMO

antibonding
interaction

allyl cation LUMO

butadiene LUMO

8.

(a) CO_2Et ≡ CO_2Et → CO_2Et

MeO   MeO   MeO

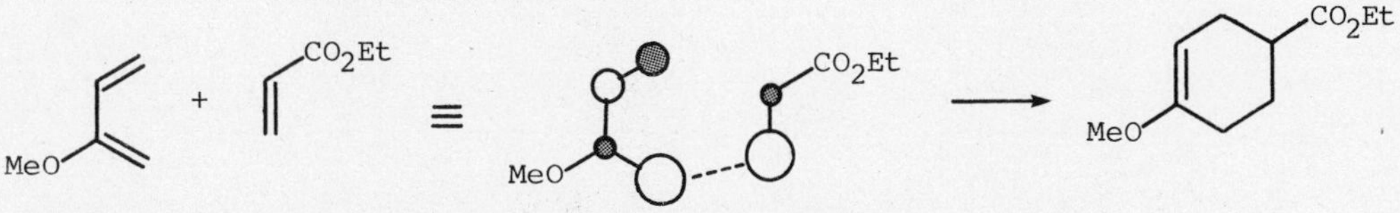

(b)   ≡   →

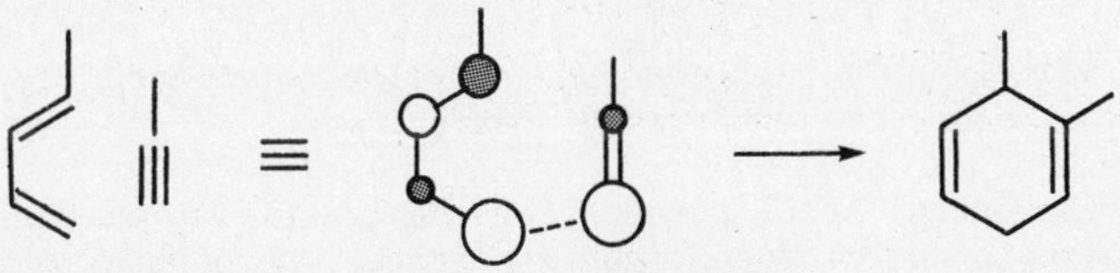

(c)   ≡   →

CO_2H CO_2H CO_2H

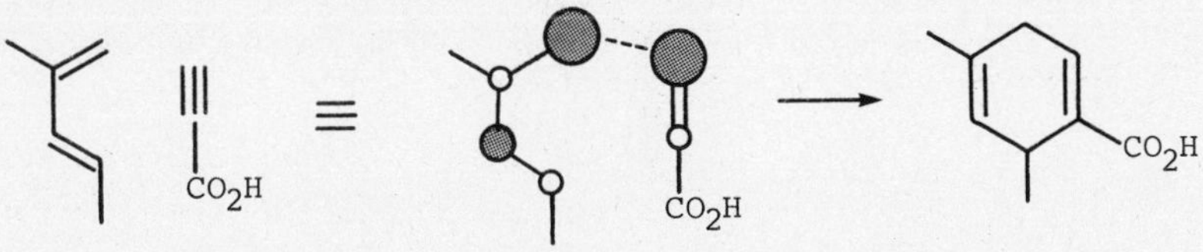

9. The first step is the photoinitiated reverse of the addition of HX to a double bond:

$$R-CH_2-\overset{X}{\underset{|}{CH}}-R' \xrightarrow{h\nu} R-CH_2-\overset{\bullet}{CH}-R' + X\cdot$$

$$X\cdot + R-CH_2-\overset{X}{\underset{|}{CH}}-R' \longrightarrow R-CH_2-\overset{\bullet}{CH}-R' + X_2$$

The color arises from the I_2 or Br_2 produced. Eventually the alkyl radicals combine or disproportionate:

$$2\ R-CH_2-\overset{\bullet}{CH}-R' \longrightarrow R-CH=CH-R' + R-CH_2-CH_2-R'$$

$$2\ R-CH_2-\overset{\bullet}{CH}-R' \longrightarrow R-CH_2-\underset{\underset{R'}{|}}{CH}-\underset{\underset{R'}{|}}{CH}-CH_2-R$$

10. Suitable solvents are those which do not have any significant UV absorption above 220 nm: methanol, perfluoropropane, 1-chlorobutane, ethyl ether, cyclohexane, and acetonitrile.

The alkyl bromides and iodides absorb in the region 250-260 nm (n → σ* transition); sulfides at 210 and 230 nm (n-d transitions); the benzene π-system absorbs strongly below 280 nm.

11. The linear correlation is especially good for $n \geq 3$. The interpolated value for N = 9 $(1/n = 0.111)$ is $1/\lambda = 0.00236$, or $\lambda = 424$ nm.

12. Molecular weight = 138; 1.486×10^{-5} g mL^{-1} = 1.08×10^{-4} M

$$\varepsilon = \frac{1}{1.08 \times 10^{-4}} = 9260 \qquad \lambda_{max} = 232 \text{ nm}$$

13. The UV spectrum of butadiene depends on the energy difference between the highest occupied (HOMO) and lowest unoccupied (LUMO) molecular orbitals. These orbitals are the π_2 and π_3 molecular orbitals, as depicted in Figure 21.5. As you can see, the magnitude of the wave function is largest at carbons 1 and 4 in these two orbitals (the π lobes are biggest at the ends), hence a substituent at these positions will have more of an influence than at the 2 and 3 positions.

21.F Supplementary Problems

S1. A popular mnemonic for determining the relative ordering of MO's in an [n]-annulene is to inscribe the appropriate polygon inside a circle, with one of the vertices down. Each vertex then corresponds to the energy level of a molecular orbital, with those below the center of the circle representing bonding orbitals and those above it, antibonding orbitals. When enough electrons are present to fill the bonding orbitals and give a closed shell, the molecule is aromatic. The mnemonic is illustrated below for benzene:

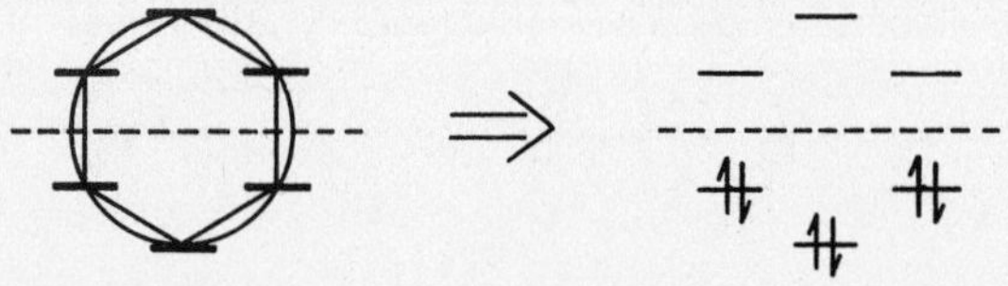

To convince yourself of its validity, apply this concept to cyclooctatetraene, cyclopentadienyl anion, cyclopropenyl anion, and cycloheptatrienyl cation.

S2. Figure 21.18 in the Text shows the energy level pattern for the transition states of alternative conrotation and disrotation in the closure of octatetraene. According to the perturbation approach to reactivity, the transition state is dominated by the HOMO of the reactant. Sketch the occupied molecular orbitals of octatetraene, and determine which mode of cyclization is predicted by the form of the HOMO.

S3. Show that each of the following reactions is allowed in terms of HOMO–LUMO interactions:

(a)

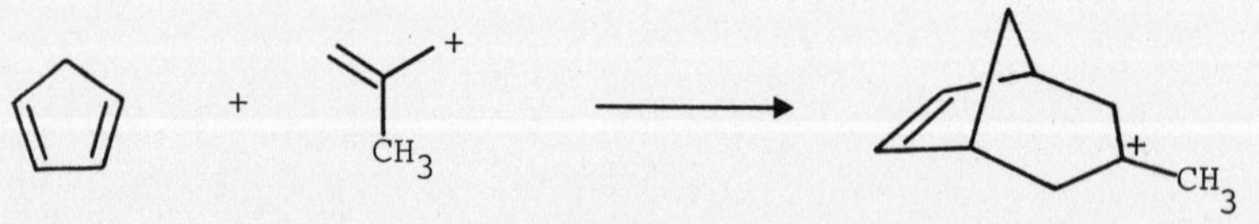

(b) $CH_2=CH_2$ + Br^+ ⟶

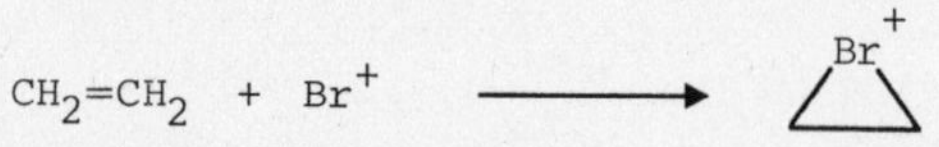

(c)

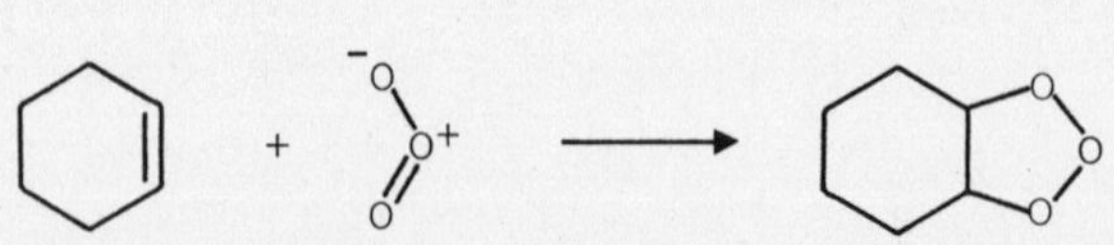

S4. During the course of a research project in organic synthesis, we attempted to hydrolyze the complex acetate ester **1** with NaOH. Instead of the desired product **2**, we isolated the tricyclic compound **3**. The mechanism of this unanticipated reaction involves enolate formation, followed by loss of methoxide ion to form intermediate **4**.

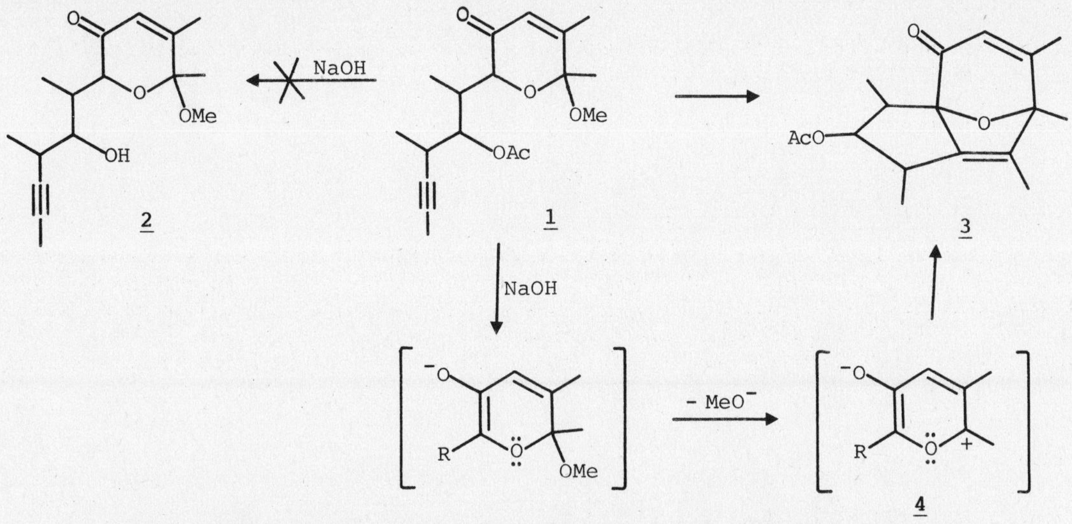

(a) Do you expect intermediate **4** to be aromatic or antiaromatic, or neither?

(b) Write a mechanism for the transformation of **4** to the observed product **3**. Is this a Hückel-allowed reaction?

S5. A phenyl substituent normally raises the energy of a HOMO and lowers the energy of a LUMO. What effect would you predict that a phenyl group has on an electronic transition corresponding to HOMO → LUMO?

S6. What are plausible structures for intermediate **A** and product **B**?

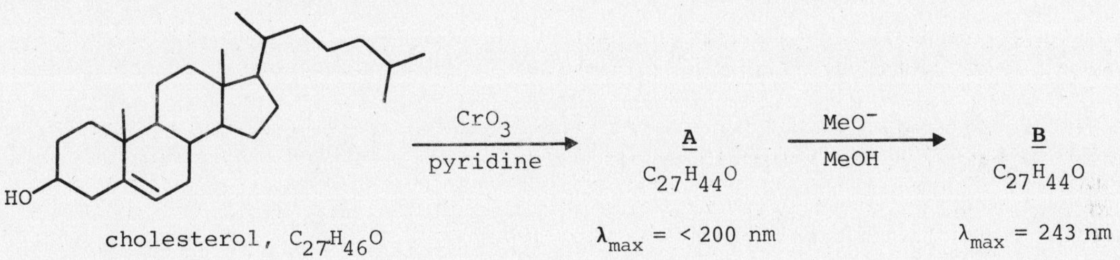

cholesterol, $C_{27}H_{46}O$

$\xrightarrow[\text{pyridine}]{CrO_3}$

A
$C_{27}H_{44}O$
$\lambda_{max} = < 200$ nm

$\xrightarrow[\text{MeOH}]{MeO^-}$

B
$C_{27}H_{44}O$
$\lambda_{max} = 243$ nm

21.G   Answers to Supplementary Problems

S1.

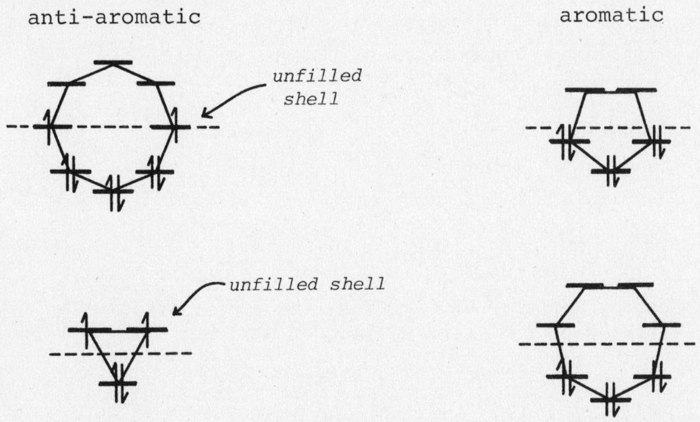

anti-aromatic   aromatic

unfilled shell

unfilled shell

S2. In an electrocyclic reaction, the ends of the π-system must interact; positive overlap between the end orbitals of the HOMO of octatetraene requires conrotation:

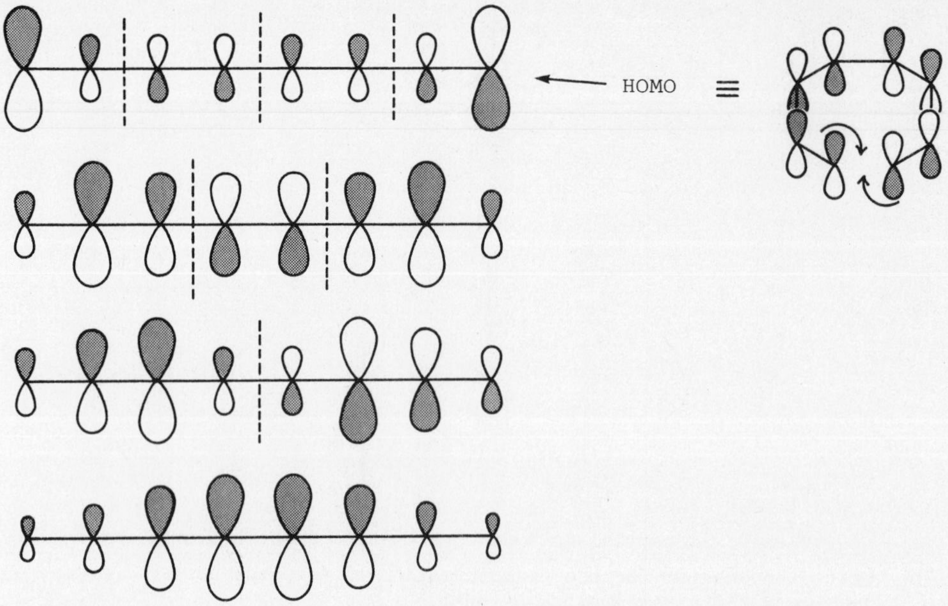

S3. (a)

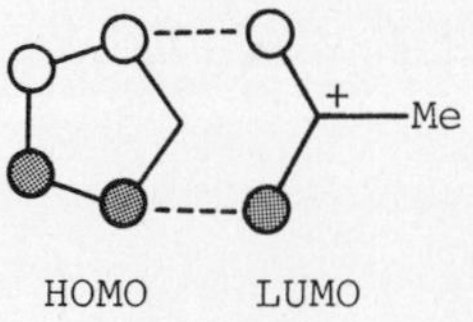

HOMO   LUMO

(b)

HOMO   LUMO

(c)

HOMO   LUMO

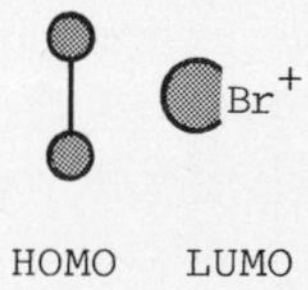

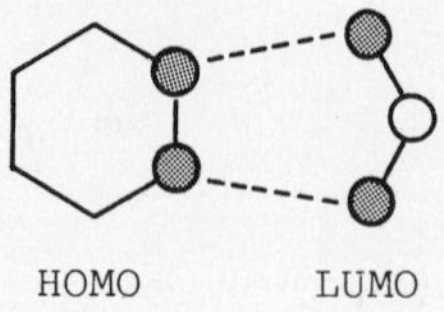

O_3 has four π-electrons in the "allyl MO's", with an electronic configuration similar to allyl anion. Hence the LUMO is ψ_3, as shown.

S4. (a) Intermediate **4** is a cyclic system of six π-electrons and hence is Hückel aromatic.

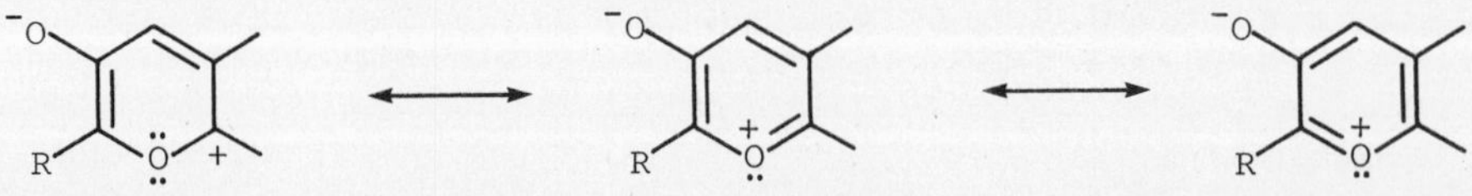

(b) Formation of product **3** involves a Hückel-allowed [4 + 2] cycloaddition reaction:

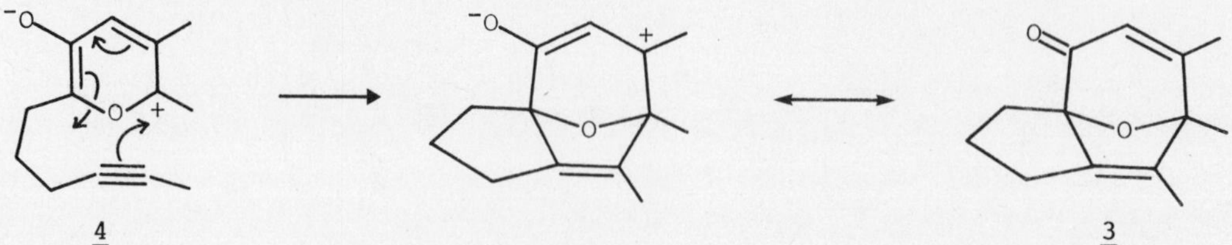

4   **3**

S5. If the HOMO is raised in energy and the LUMO lowered, the energy difference between them becomes smaller and the electronic transition will occur at lower energy = longer wavelength.

S6.

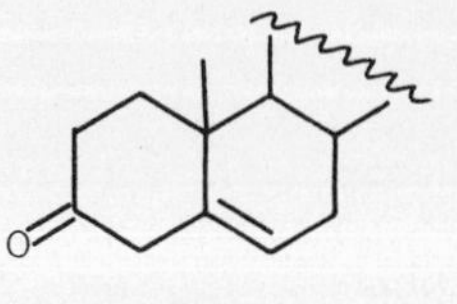

A   **B**

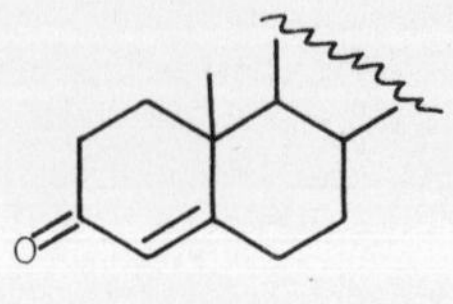

22. ELECTROPHILIC AROMATIC SUBSTITUTION

22.A   Chapter Outline and Important Terms Introduced

22.1 <u>Halogenation</u>

22.2 <u>Protonation</u>
        tracer isotope vs. macroscopic isotope
        liquid scintillation counter

22.3 <u>Nitration</u>

22.4 <u>Friedel-Crafts Reactions</u> (will not work on strongly deactivated rings)
        A. Acylations
        B. Alkylations
                with alkyl halides and olefins, chloromethylation

22.5 <u>Orientation in Electrophilic Aromatic Substitution</u>

        ortho,para- vs. <u>meta</u>-directors   activating vs. deactivating
           1. <u>o,p</u>- with activation
           2. <u>o,p</u>- with deactivation
           3. <u>m</u>- with deactivation

22.6 <u>Theory of Orientation in Electrophilic Aromatic Substitution</u>
        stabilization of resonance structures

22.7 <u>Quantitative Reactivities: Partial Rate Factors</u>

22.8 <u>Effects of Multiple Substituents</u>

22.9 <u>Synthetic Utility of Electrophilic Aromatic Substitution</u>
        acylation + deoxygenation = "alkylation"
        limitations of orientation and reactivity
        avoidance of inseparable isomers

22.10 <u>Perturbational MO Approach to Orientation</u>

22.B   Important Reactions Introduced

<u>Electrophilic aromatic substitution</u>

   <u>Halogenation</u> (22.1):

Equation: <u>o-, p-directors</u>   <u>m-directors</u>

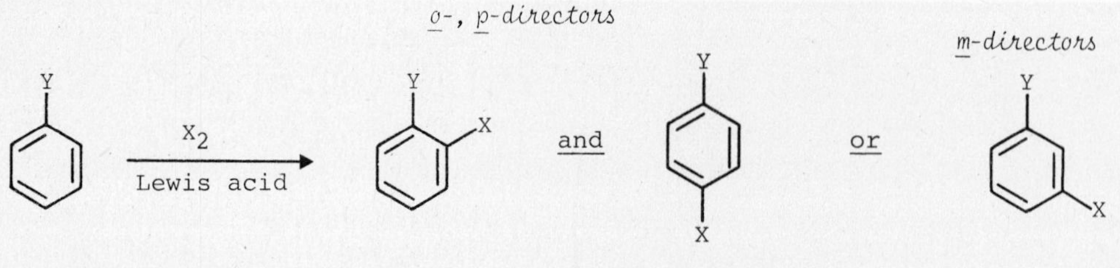

Generality: X = Cl, Br
               Lewis acid = FeX_3 or AlX_3
               (for X = I, use I_2/H_3AsO_4)
               Y = various substituents

Key features: X is a deactivating substituent, so stepwise formation of mono-, di-, or tri-
                      halogenated products is possible

Nitration (22.3):

Equation:

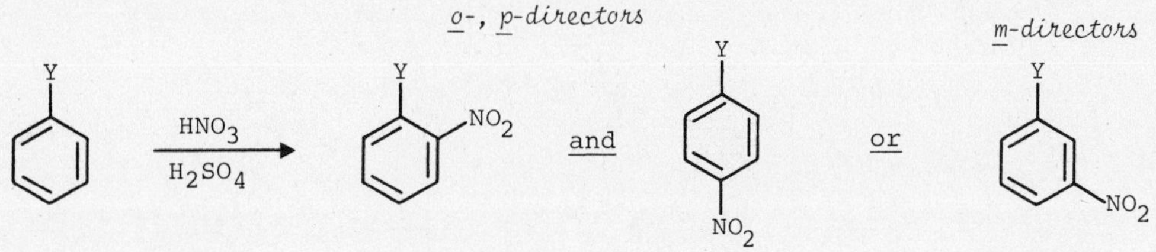

o-, p-directors   *m-directors*

Generality: Y = various substituents

Key features: NO_2 is a deactivating substituent, so stepwise formation of mono-, di-, or tri-halogenated products is possible

Friedel-Crafts acylation (22.4.A):

Equation:

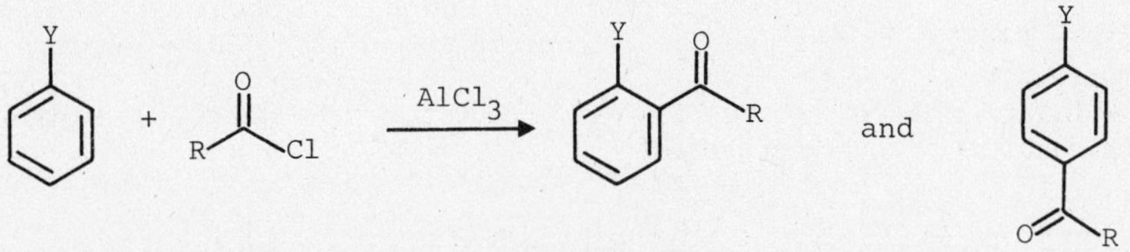

Generality: Y **cannot** be a <u>meta</u>-directing substituent

Key features: coupled with deoxygenation, acylation is a useful method for introduction of 1^O alkyl groups in aromatic rings (gives only mono-substitution, and is not susceptible to carbocation rearrangements)

intramolecular reaction useful for making cyclic aromatic compounds

Friedel-Crafts alkylation (22.4.B):

Equation:

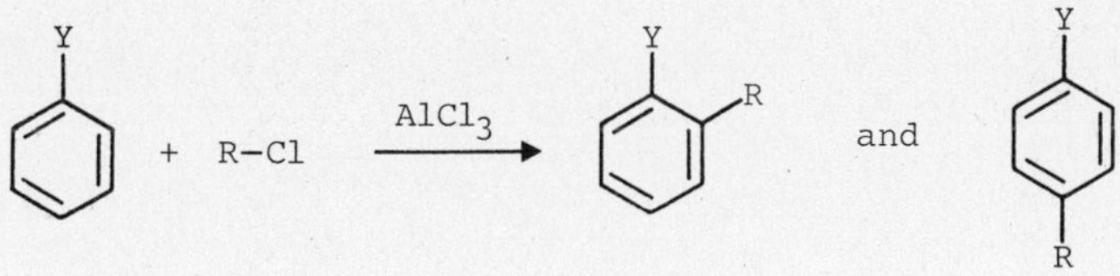

Generality: Y **cannot** be <u>meta</u>-directing substituent

R = 2^O or 3° alkyl

other reagents: alkene or alcohol + HF + BF_3

chloromethylation: CH_2O + HCl

Key features: an alkyl group is an activating substituent, therefore polyalkylation is a common side reaction

carbocation rearrangements also common

R ≠ 1^O alkyl

<u>Other</u> <u>things</u> <u>to</u> <u>keep</u> <u>in</u> <u>mind:</u>

Y = OR', NR'_2:   strong <u>ortho</u>-,<u>para</u>-directing, strongly activating

Y = alkyl: weak <u>ortho</u>-,<u>para</u>-directing, activating

Y = halide: <u>ortho</u>-,<u>para</u>-directing, deactivating

Y = COR', CO_2R', CN, NO_2:   strongly <u>meta</u>-directing, strongly deactivating

22.C   Important Concepts and Hints

This entire chapter is devoted to the reaction depicted below: electrophilic aromatic substitution. We have drawn it in such a way as to show how the p-orbitals and electron distribution of the ring change throughout the process:

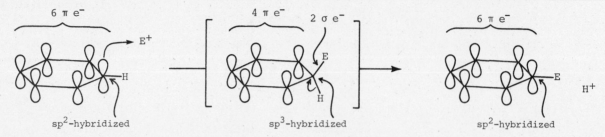

In the course of forming the intermediate, the π-system goes from neutral (six electrons/six orbitals) to positively charged (four electrons/five orbitals). Two electrons and one orbital are taken up in the new bond to the electrophile E^+. As pointed out in the text, instead of a nucleophile **adding** to the cationic intermediate, a proton is lost. This is simply the reverse of the initial attack, with the two electrons and the carbon orbital of the C-H bond going to reform the aromatic, 6π electron system.

A substituent which is attached to the ring can affect this process in two ways: by adding or withdrawing electron density through the σ-bond:

(this is usually called the "inductive effect")

or by adding or withdrawing electron density via a π-type interaction:

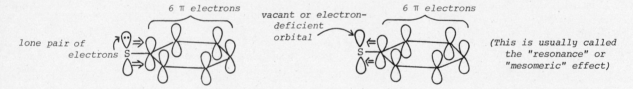

(This is usually called the "resonance" or "mesomeric" effect)

The effect through the σ-framework decreases in the order o > m > p, but it does not greatly influence the position of electrophilic attack. On the other hand, the effect through the π-system is only felt in the ortho and para positions, so it is the determining factor in orientation. The table below illustrates the influence of σ- and π-effects for a variety of substituent types:

Type of Substituent	Group	π-effect	σ-effect	*Substitution Rate, relative to benzene*	
				o-, p-positions	m-positions
$R\ddot{\text{O}}$, $R_2\ddot{\text{N}}$, $\underset{\ddot{\ddot{}}}{RC}NH$	I	strongly electron-releasing	electron-withdrawing	+++	–
Alkyl	II	electron-releasing (via hyperconjugation)	electron-releasing	++	+
Halogen	II	electron-releasing	electron-withdrawing	–	– –
NO_2, RC, RS	III	strongly electron-releasing	electron-withdrawing	– – –	– –

Notice how the meta reactivity (relative to benzene) parallels the σ-effect, because the resonance (π) effect can only influence the ortho and para positions. The π-effect combines with the σ-effect in influencing the ortho and para rates. For strongly activating substituents, the π-effect dominates the σ-effect and the ortho and para positions are strongly activated. For alkyl substituents, the two effects act together, and ortho,para substitution gets an extra boost relative to meta. For halogens, the σ- and π-effects work in opposite directions again, but this time the π-effect is weaker: substitution at all positions is deactivated, but the <u>ortho,para</u> ones are less so. Finally, for strongly deactivating groups, the σ- and π-effects combine to deactivate <u>ortho</u> and <u>para</u> the most, resulting in <u>meta</u>-direction.

    In predicting the results of competition between the directive effects of two substituents on the same ring, it is best to remember **three** groups of substituents (instead of the four above). Group I includes the strongly activating <u>ortho,para</u>-directors such as RÖ- and R₂N̈-; their influence dominates that of the other groups. Group II includes the "moderate" <u>ortho,para</u>-directors such as alkyl and halogen; these substituents will yield to Group I effects, and will win out only over those of Group III. Group III includes all the <u>meta</u>-directing substituents; they will control orientation only in the absence of Group I or II substituents. If the competition is between members of the same group, no "winner" is predictable, and you can expect to see mixtures of isomeric products.

22.D   Answers to Exercises

22.1

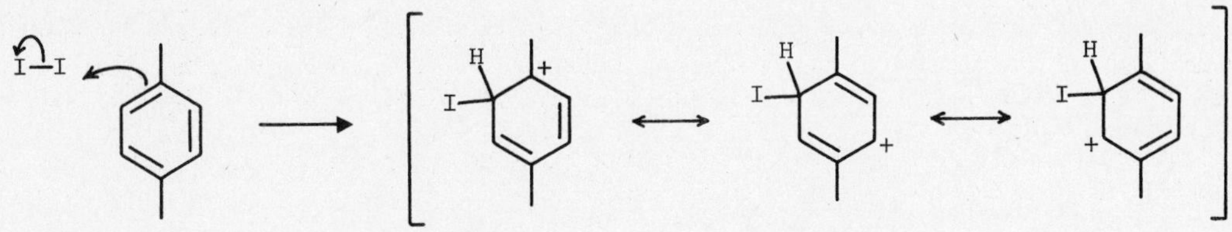

22.2

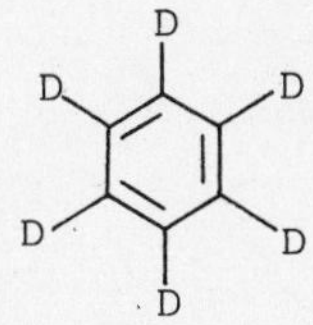

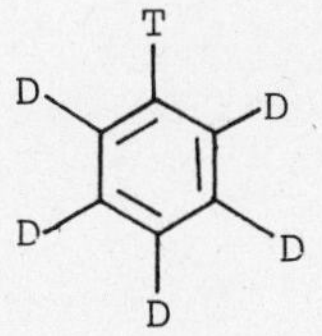

22.3

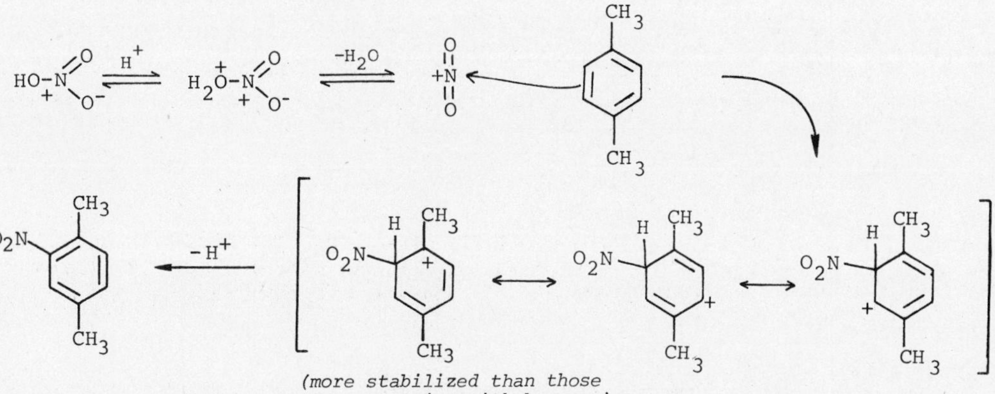

*(more stabilized than those
from reaction with benzene)*

22.4

(a) Benzene

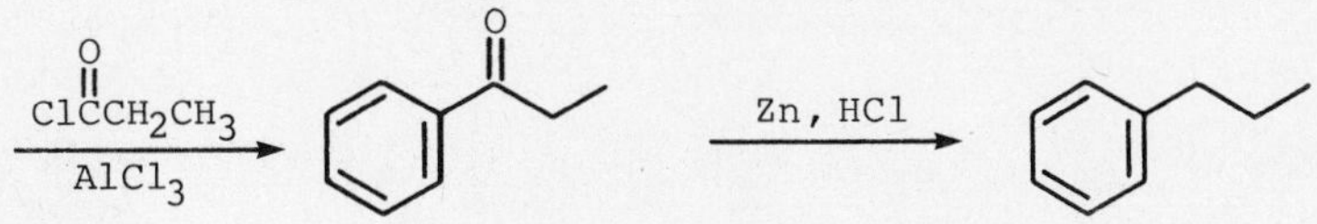

(b) Benzene

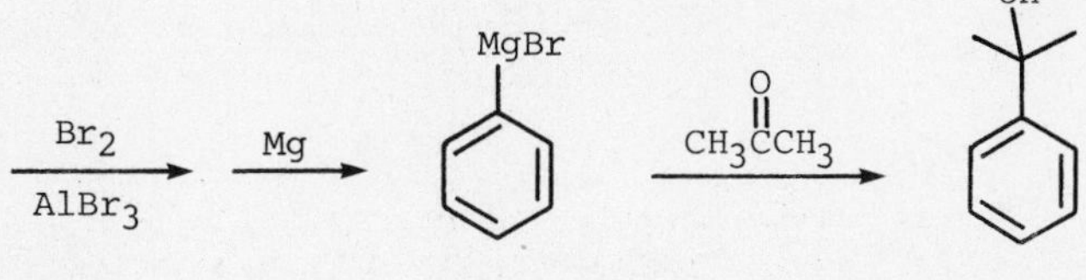

(c) Benzene

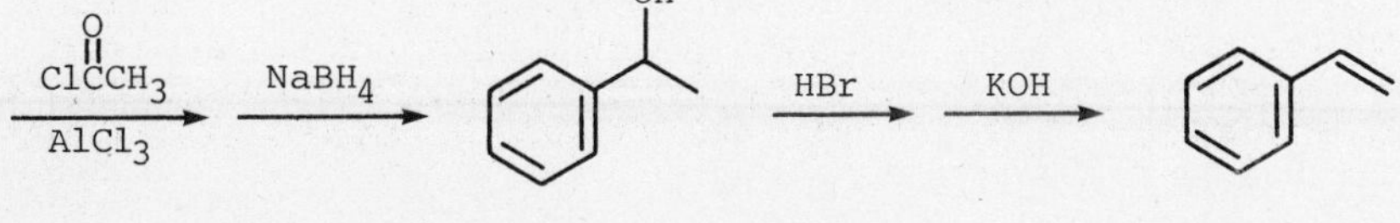

22.5 The carbocation that would be produced from 3-methyl-2-butanol rearranges to the tertiary cation faster than it undergoes Friedel-Crafts reaction:

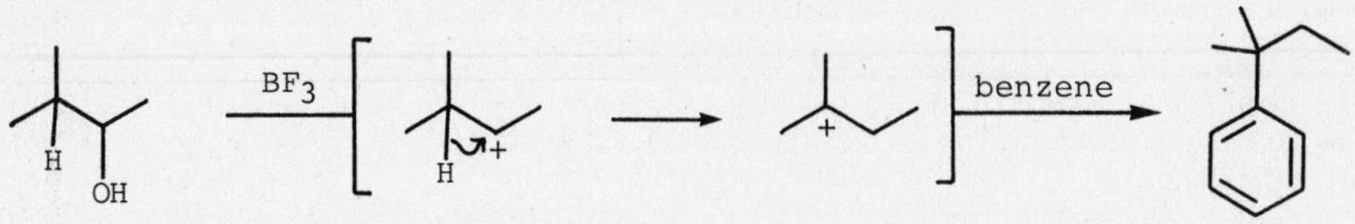

The desired product can be obtained from the following sequence:

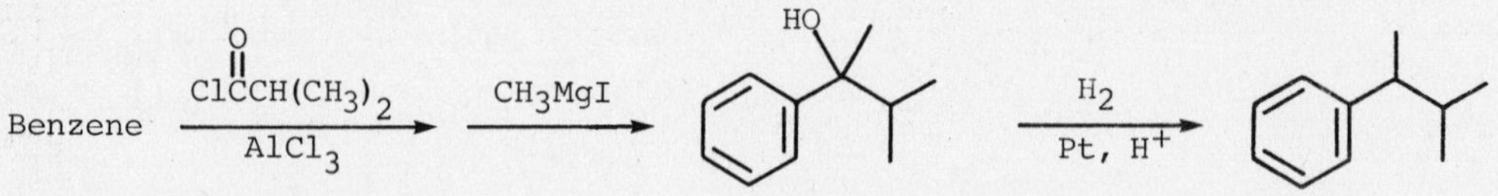

Benzene $\xrightarrow[\text{AlCl}_3]{\overset{\overset{\text{O}}{\|}}{\text{ClCCH(CH}_3)_2}}$ $\xrightarrow{\text{CH}_3\text{MgI}}$ $\xrightarrow[\text{Pt, H}^+]{\text{H}_2}$

22.6

(a) $\text{CH}_3\text{CH}_2\text{CH}_2\overset{\overset{\text{O}}{\|}}{\text{C}}\text{Cl} + \text{AlCl}_3 \rightleftharpoons {}^-\text{AlCl}_4 + \text{CH}_3\text{CH}_2\text{CH}_2\text{C}\equiv\overset{+}{\text{O}}$

$\text{CH}_3\text{CH}_2\text{CH}_2\overset{\overset{\text{O}}{\|}}{\text{C}}$ $\xleftarrow{-\text{H}^+}$ $\left[\text{CH}_3\text{CH}_2\text{CH}_2\overset{\overset{\text{O}}{\|}}{\text{C}}\text{–} \text{(ring cation)} + \text{other resonance structures} \right]$

(b) $\text{HF} + \text{BF}_3 \rightleftharpoons \text{BF}_4^- \, \text{H}^+ \xrightarrow{\text{CH}_2=\text{C(CH}_3)_2} (\text{CH}_3)_3\overset{+}{\text{C}}$

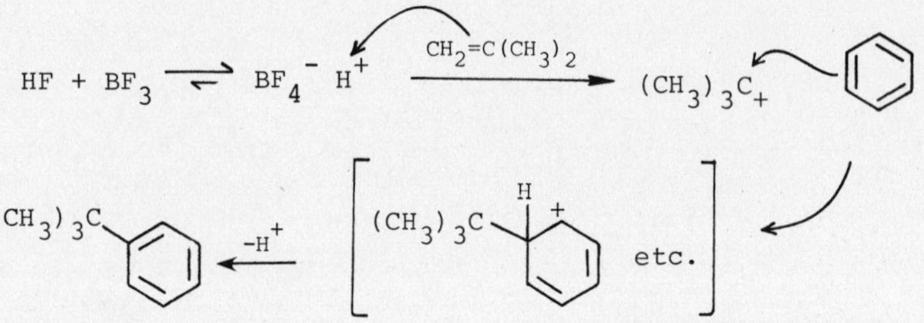

$(\text{CH}_3)_3\text{C}$ $\xleftarrow{-\text{H}^+}$ $\left[(\text{CH}_3)_3\text{C}\text{–} \text{(ring cation)} \quad \text{etc.} \right]$

(c) $\underset{\text{OH}}{\text{CH}_3\text{CH}_2\text{CHCH}_3} \xrightarrow{\text{H}_2\text{SO}_4} \underset{+\text{OH}_2}{\text{CH}_3\text{CH}_2\text{CHCH}_3} \xrightarrow[\text{−H}_2\text{O}]{} \text{CH}_3\text{CH}_2\overset{+}{\text{CHCH}_3}$

$\underset{\text{CH}_3}{\text{CH}_3\text{CH}_2\text{CH}}$ $\xleftarrow{-\text{H}^+}$ $\left[\text{CH}_3\text{CH}_2\underset{\text{CH}_3}{\text{CH}}\text{–} \text{(ring cation)} \quad \text{etc.} \right]$

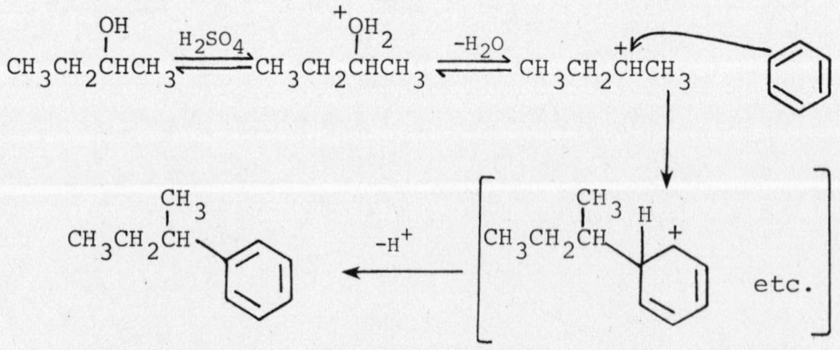

(d) $\text{H}_2\text{C}=\text{O} + \text{ZnCl}_2 \rightleftharpoons \text{Cl}_2\overset{-}{\text{Zn}}\text{–}\overset{+}{\text{O}}=\text{CH}_2$ $\left[\text{Cl}_2\overset{-}{\text{Zn}}\text{OCH}_2\text{–} \text{(ring cation)} \quad \text{etc.} \right]$

$\xdownarrow{-\text{H}^+}$

ClCH_2 $\underset{\text{Cl}^-}{\rightleftharpoons}$ ${}^+\text{CH}_2$ $\underset{-\text{H}_2\text{O}}{\rightleftharpoons}$ $\text{H}_2\overset{+}{\text{O}}\text{CH}_2$ $\underset{\text{H}^+}{\rightleftharpoons}$ HOCH_2

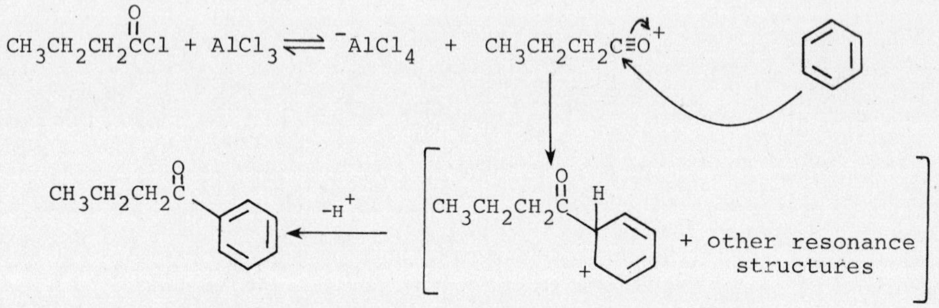

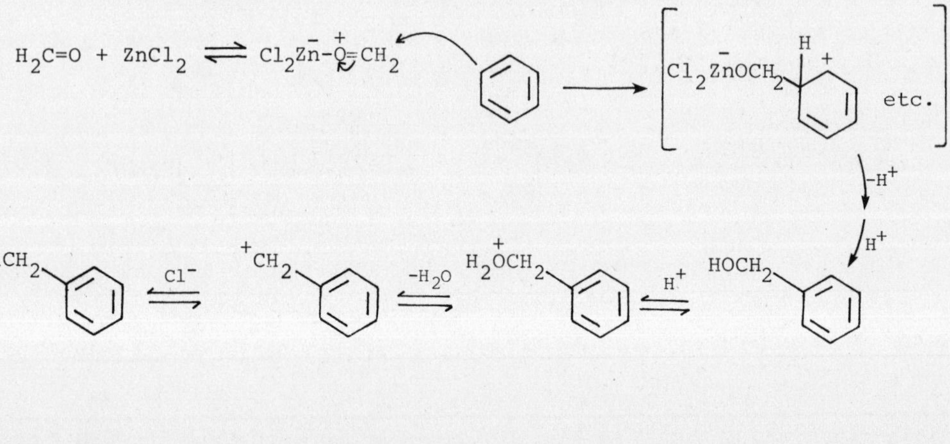

22.7

	$Br_2 + FeBr_3$	HNO_3, H_2SO_4	$(CH_3)_3CCl + AlCl_3$	$\overset{\overset{\text{O}}{\|}}{CH_3CCl} + AlCl_3$
$C_6H_5CH_3$	$o\text{-}BrC_6H_4CH_3$ and p-isomer; *faster*	$o\text{-}O_2NC_6H_4CH_3$ and p-isomer; *faster*	$o\text{-}(CH_3)_3CC_6H_4CH_3$ and p-isomer (plus rearr.); *faster*	$o\text{-}CH_3\overset{\overset{\text{O}}{\|}}{C}C_6H_4CH_3$ and p-isomer; *faster*
$C_6H_5\overset{\overset{\text{O}}{\|}}{C}CH_3$	$\left(C_6H_5\overset{\overset{\text{O}}{\|}}{C}CH_2Br \right)$	$m\text{-}O_2NC_6H_4\overset{\overset{\text{O}}{\|}}{C}CH_3$; *slower*	*no reaction*	*no reaction*
C_6H_5Br	$o\text{-}C_6H_4Br_2$ and p-isomer; *slower*	$o\text{-}O_2NC_6H_4Br$ and p-isomer; *slower*	$o\text{-}(CH_3)_3CC_6H_4Br$ and p-isomer; *slower*	$o\text{-}CH_3\overset{\overset{\text{O}}{\|}}{C}C_6H_4Br$ and p-isomer; *slower*
$C_6H_5OCH_3$	$o\text{-}BrC_6H_4OCH_3$ and p-isomer; *faster*	$o\text{-}O_2NC_6H_4OCH_3$ and p-isomer; *faster*	$o\text{-}(CH_3)_3CC_6H_4OCH_3$ and p-isomer; *faster*	$o\text{-}CH_3\overset{\overset{\text{O}}{\|}}{C}C_6H_4OCH_3$ and p-isomer; *faster*
$C_6H_5NO_2$	$m\text{-}BrC_6H_4NO_2$; *slower*	$m\text{-}C_6H_4(NO_2)_2$; *slower*	*no reaction*	*no reaction*
$C_6H_5\overset{\overset{\text{O}}{\|}}{NHCCH_3}$	$o\text{-}BrC_6H_4\overset{\overset{\text{O}}{\|}}{NHCCH_3}$ and p-isomer; *faster*	$o\text{-}O_2NC_6H_4\overset{\overset{\text{O}}{\|}}{NHCCH_3}$ and p-isomer; *faster*	$o\text{-}(CH_3)_3CC_6H_4\overset{\overset{\text{O}}{\|}}{NHCCH_3}$ and p-isomer; *faster*	$o\text{-}CH_3\overset{\overset{\text{O}}{\|}}{C}C_6H_4\overset{\overset{\text{O}}{\|}}{NHCCH_3}$ and p-isomer; *faster*

"faster" = reaction occurs faster than with benzene; *"slower"* = reaction occurs slower than with benzene

22.8

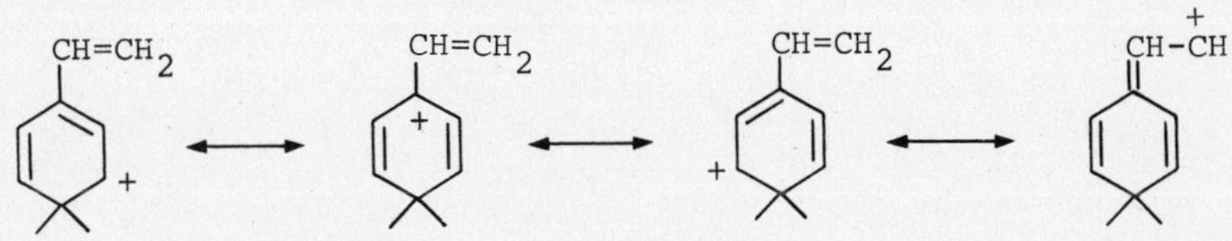

In the o- and p- positions, the vinyl group helps to distribute positive charge; thus, it is o,p-directing and activating. In the m-position, the vinyl group does not conjugate with the charge:

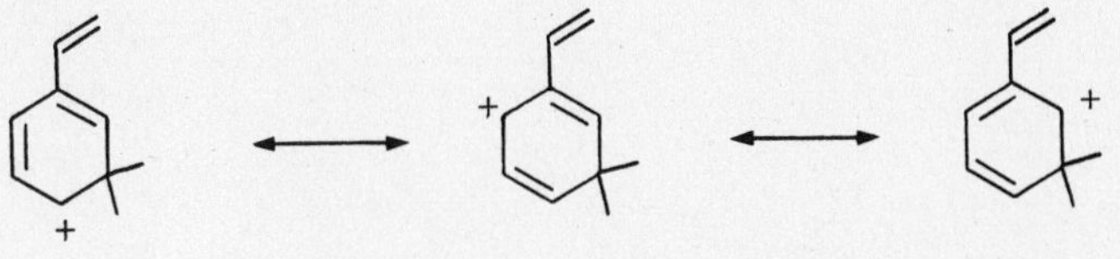

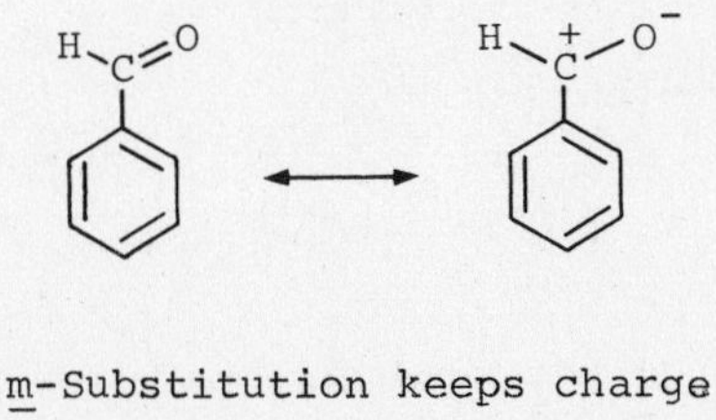

∴ large dipole directed away from ring:

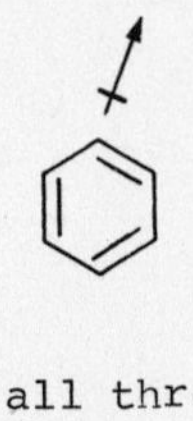

m-Substitution keeps charge away from dipole in all three structures:

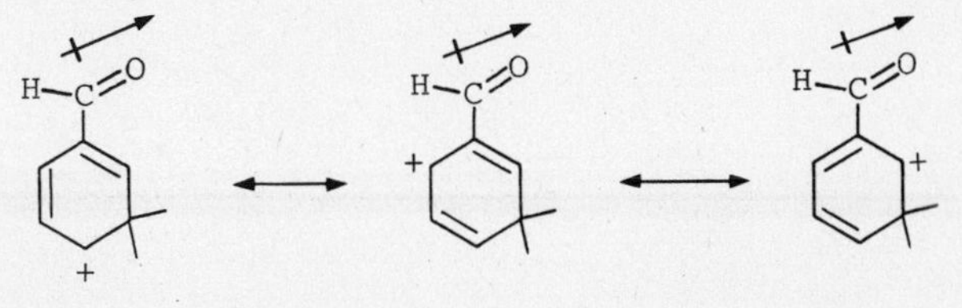

In o,p-substitution, one structure has (+) next to dipole:

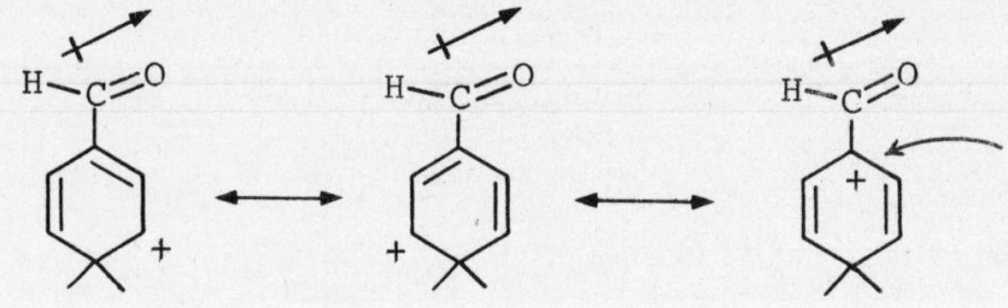

the positive charge is next to the positive carbon of the CO group, so that this structure contributes less; the resonance stabilization of intermediate and the transition state leading to it are reduced.

22.9

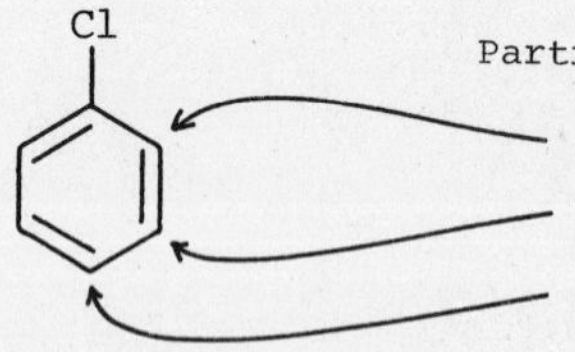

Partial rate factor × number of positions = relative amounts

0.03	×	2	= 0.06	= 30%
0.0009	×	2	= 0.0018	= 1%
0.14	×	1	= 0.14	= 69%

22.10

(a) (b) 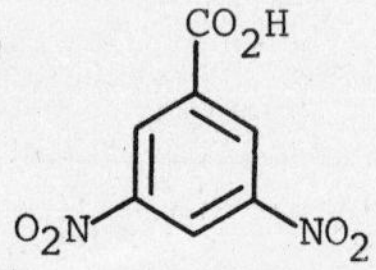 (c)

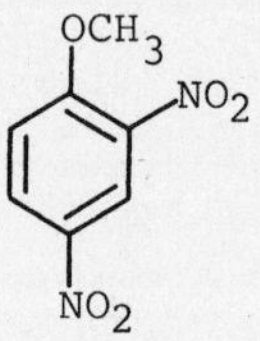

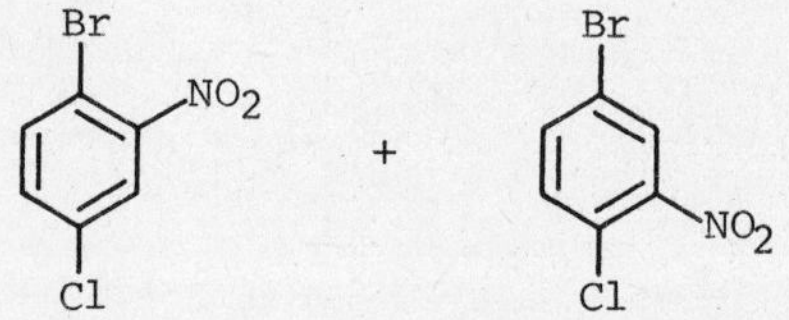

(d)

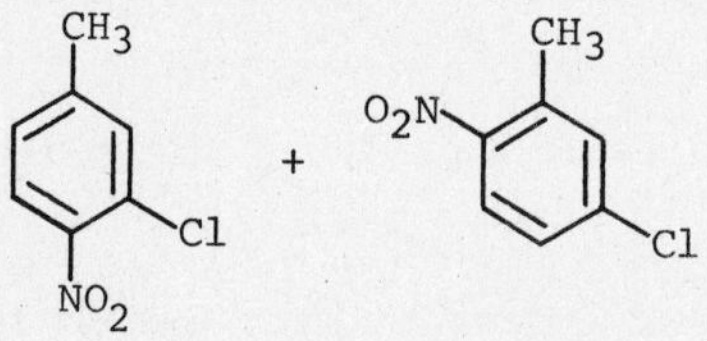

22.11 All of these transformations of Ar–Br require formation of a Grignard reagent, which cannot be generated in the presence of the –CH=O, –CO$_2$H, or –NO$_2$ functional groups. The mono-Grignard reagents can be prepared from m- and p-dibromobenzene, however.

22.12

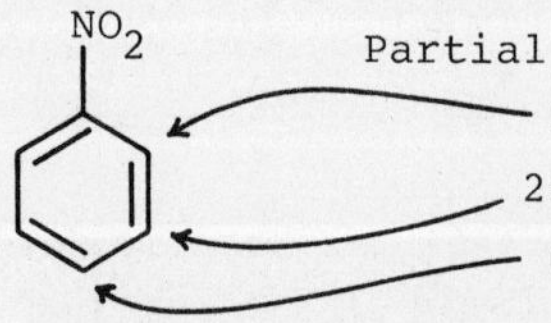

Partial rate factor × number of positions = relative amounts

1.8	×	2	= 3.6	= 6%
28	×	2	= 56	= 94%
0.2	×	1	= 0.2	= 0.3%

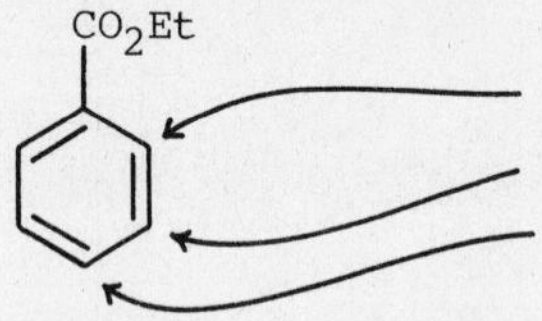

1	×	2	= 2	= 28%
2.5	×	2	= 5	= 69%
0.24	×	1	= 0.24	= 3.3%

22.13 The largest orbital of the HOMO is at the terminus of the vinyl group, which suggests that electrophilic attack will occur more readily there than on the ring itself.

22.E   Answers and Explanations for Problems

1. $I_2 + H_2O_2 \longrightarrow 2\ HOI \rightleftharpoons H_2\overset{+}{O}I + {}^-OI$

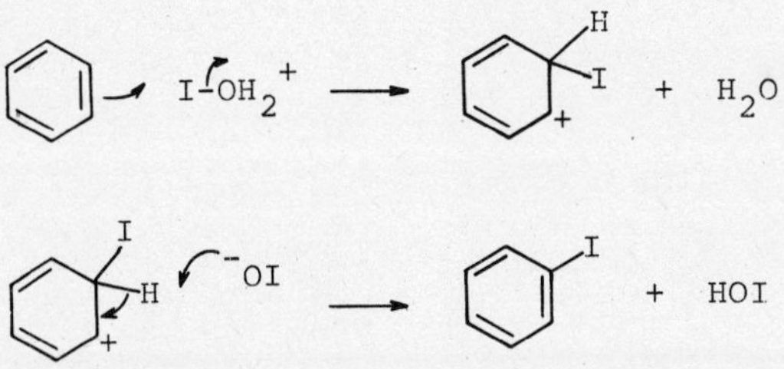

2. (a)   <u>Mechanism A</u>:

1) $CH_2{=}O + ZnCl_2 \rightleftharpoons CH_2{=}\overset{+}{O}{-}\overset{-}{Zn}Cl_2$

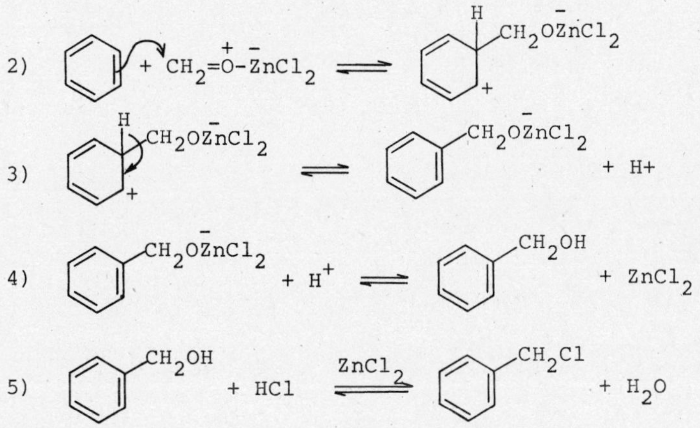

2)

3)

4)

5)

<u>Mechanism B</u>:

1) $CH_2{=}O + ZnCl_2 \rightleftharpoons CH_2{=}\overset{+}{O}{-}\overset{-}{Zn}Cl_2$

2) $CH_2{=}\overset{+}{O}{-}\overset{-}{Zn}Cl_2 + Cl^- \rightleftharpoons ClCH_2\overset{-}{O}ZnCl_2$

3) $ClCH_2\overset{-}{O}ZnCl_2 + H+ \rightleftharpoons ClCH_2\overset{H}{\underset{+}{O}}{}^-ZnCl_2$

4) $ClCH_2\overset{H}{\underset{+}{O}}{}^-ZnCl_2 \rightleftharpoons ClCH_2{}^+ + H\overset{-}{O}ZnCl_2$

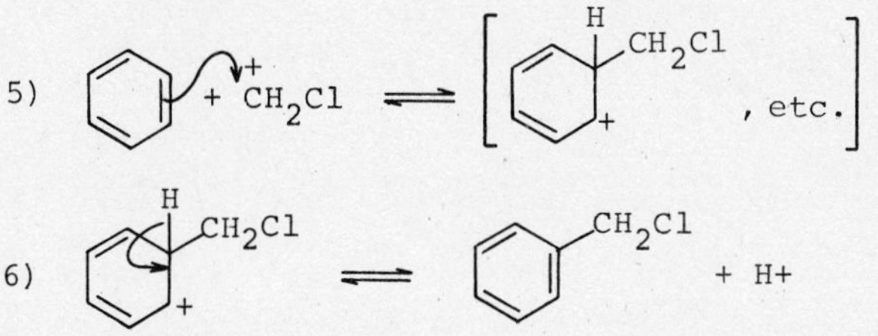

5)

6)

(b)   1) $CH_2{=}O + {}^+CH_2Cl \rightleftharpoons CH_2{=}\overset{+}{O}{-}CH_2Cl$

2) $Cl^- + CH_2{=}\overset{+}{O}CH_2Cl \longrightarrow ClCH_2OCH_2Cl$

<u>or</u>

1) $CH_2{=}O + CH_2{=}\overset{+}{O}{-}\overset{-}{Zn}Cl_2 \rightleftharpoons CH_2{=}\overset{+}{O}{-}CH_2{-}\overset{-}{O}ZnCl_2$

2) $Cl^- + CH_2{=}\overset{+}{O}CH_2\overset{-}{O}ZnCl_2 \rightleftharpoons ClCH_2OCH_2\overset{-}{O}ZnCl_2$

3) $\text{ClCH}_2\text{OCH}_2\overset{-}{\text{O}}\overset{..}{\text{Zn}}\text{Cl}_2$ $\xrightleftharpoons{\text{H}^+}$ $\text{ClCH}_2\text{OCH}_2\overset{\text{H}}{\underset{+}{\text{O}}}\overset{-}{\text{Zn}}\text{Cl}_2$

4) $\text{ClCH}_2\overset{..}{\overset{..}{\text{O}}}\!-\!\text{CH}_2\!-\!\overset{\text{H}}{\underset{+}{\text{O}}}\overset{-}{\text{Zn}}\text{Cl}_2$ $\rightleftharpoons$ $\text{ClCH}_2\overset{+}{\text{O}}\!=\!\text{CH}_2$ $\text{HO}\overset{-}{\text{Zn}}\text{Cl}_2$

5) $\text{ClCH}_2\overset{+}{\text{O}}\!=\!\text{CH}_2$ Cl^- $\longrightarrow$ $\text{ClCH}_2\text{OCH}_2\text{Cl}$

3.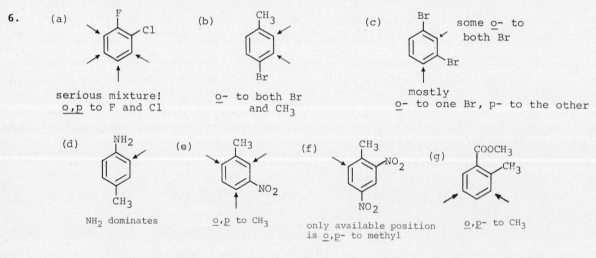

$$\underset{O}{\overset{O}{\text{CH}_3\text{C}}}\text{OHgO}\underset{O}{\overset{O}{\text{C}}}\text{CH}_3 + \text{H}^+ \rightleftharpoons \text{CH}_3\overset{+\text{OH}}{\text{C}}\text{OHgO}\underset{O}{\overset{O}{\text{C}}}\text{CH}_3$$

$$\text{CH}_3\overset{+\text{OH}}{\text{C}}\text{OHgO}\underset{O}{\overset{O}{\text{C}}}\text{CH}_3 \rightleftharpoons \text{CH}_3\overset{O}{\text{C}}\text{OH} + {}^+\text{HgOAc}$$

In the o- and p-positions, the charge is distributed to the second benzene ring.

5. The carboxy group is <u>meta</u>-directing and deactivating for the same reason that the formyl group is (see answer to Exercise at the end of Section 22.8)

6. (a) serious mixture!
        <u>o,p</u> to F and Cl

    (b) <u>o</u>- to both Br
        and CH₃

    (c) some <u>o</u>- to
        both Br

        mostly
        <u>o</u>- to one Br, p- to the other

    (d) NH₂ dominates

    (e) <u>o,p</u> to CH₃

    (f) only available position
        is <u>o,p</u>- to methyl

    (g) <u>o,p</u>- to CH₃

    (h)

    (i) <u>o,p</u>- to OCH₃ and to OH

    (j)

7. (a) Rate/toluene molecule = 605 × rate/benzene molecule
        Rate/toluene <u>ortho</u> position = f_o = 0.329/2 × 605 × 6 × rate/benzene position
        $f_o = 597$, $f_m = 0.003/2 \times 605 \times 6 = 5.4$, $f_p = 0.668/1 \times 605 \times 6 = 2425$

(b)

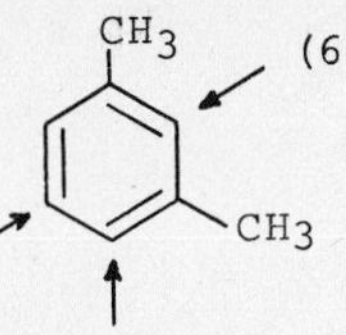

$$2 \times 820 \times 620 = 10.17 \times 10^5 \quad \text{[2 because 4- and 6-positions are equivalent]}$$

2-position: $(3.84 \times 10^5)/[(3.84 \times 10^5) + (10.17 \times 10^5) + 25] = 27.4\%$

4-position: $(10.17 \times 10^5)/[\quad " \quad + \quad " \quad + 25] = 72.6\%$

5-position: $25 \quad /[\qquad\qquad " \qquad\qquad\qquad] = 0.0018\%$

(c)

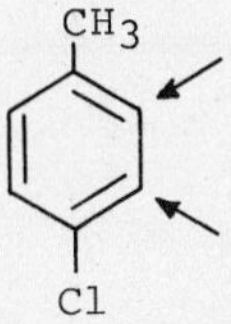

8. (a) No; both Cl and Br are o,p-directors.

(b) No; Friedel-Crafts acylation cannot be applied to a ketone.

The sequence

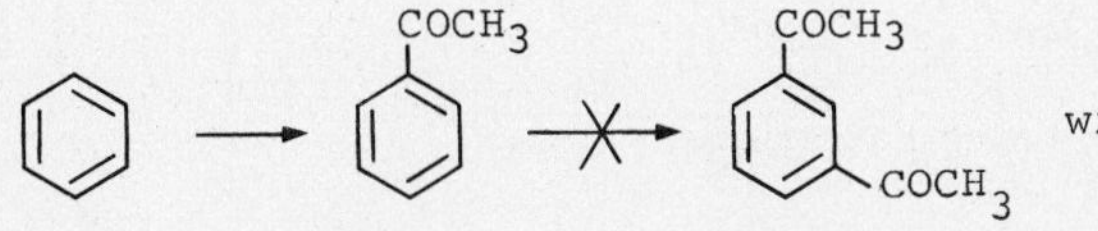

will not work.

(c) OK;

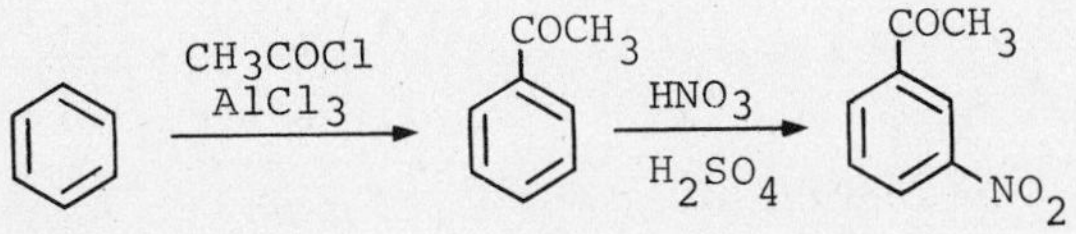

Note that nitration first, followed by Friedel-Crafts acylation, will not work. Acylation cannot be applied to $ArNO_2$ compounds.

(d) No; the sequence

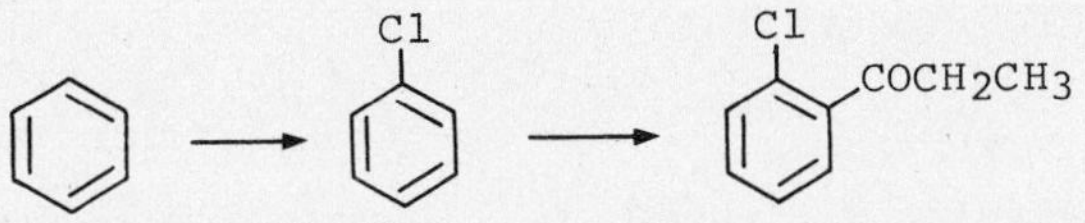

gives mostly para. The ortho-isomer is difficult to isolate pure. This method is okay for the para-isomer, since it is higher-melting and less soluble and can be separated pure from the ortho-isomer by crystallization.

(e) OK;

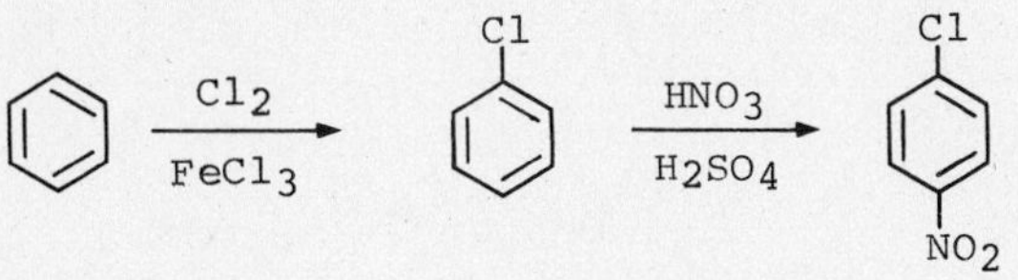

can be separated from ortho-isomer by crystal-lization (see Table 22.4)

(f) OK; nitration of t-butylbenzene strongly favors para-substitution.

9. (a) OK:

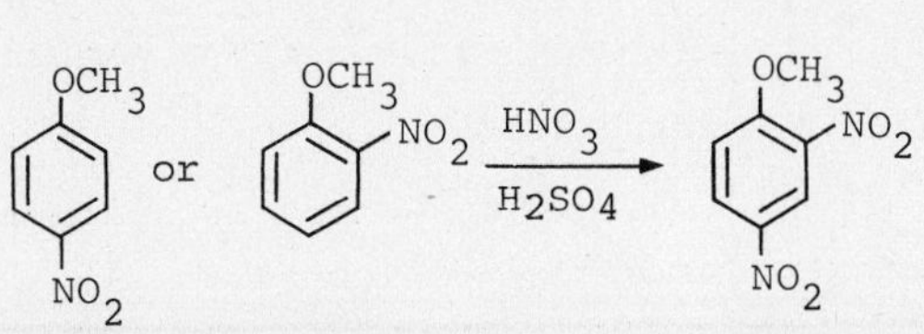

(b) OK;

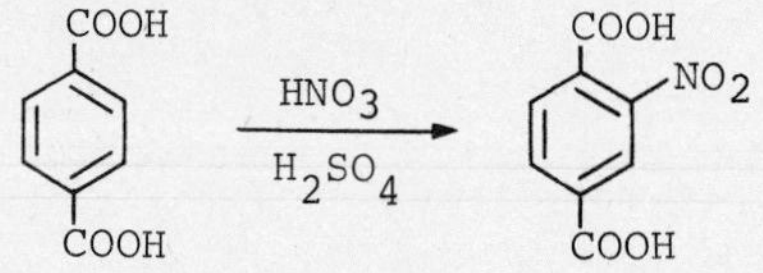

$\xrightarrow[\text{H}_2\text{SO}_4]{\text{HNO}_3}$

(no isomers possible)

(c) OK;

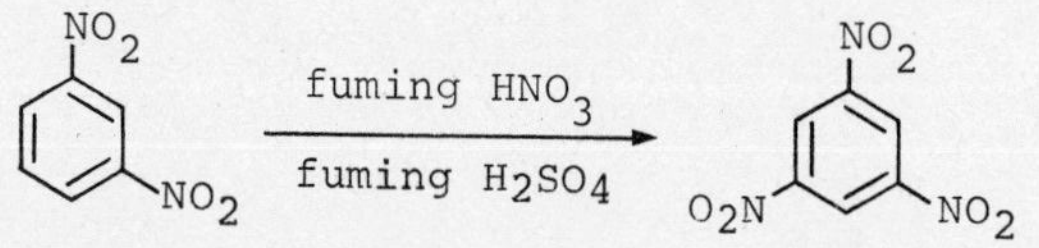

$\xrightarrow[\text{fuming H}_2\text{SO}_4]{\text{fuming HNO}_3}$

(both NO$_2$ groups direct *meta*-)

(d) OK;

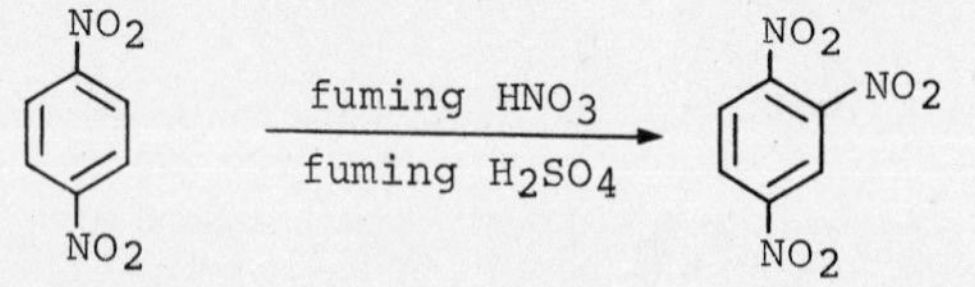

$\xrightarrow[\text{fuming H}_2\text{SO}_4]{\text{fuming HNO}_3}$

(no isomers possible)

(e) No; nitration of o-dichlorobenzene gives mostly 4-nitro; chlorination of o- or m-chloronitrobenzene would give a mixture of isomers.

(f) OK;

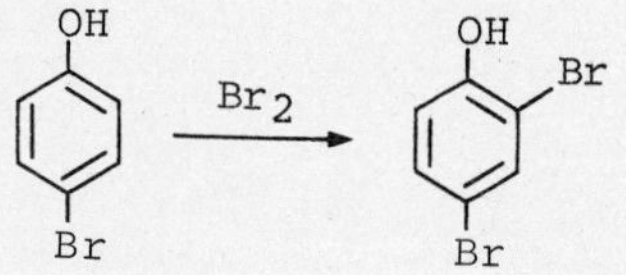

$\xrightarrow{\text{Br}_2}$

(OH dominates)

(g) No. Chlorination of

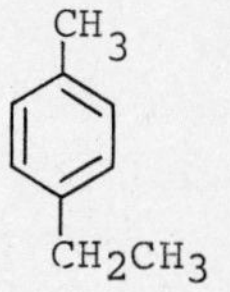

goes ortho to both CH$_3$ and CH$_2$CH$_3$ and gives a mixture.

(h) No.

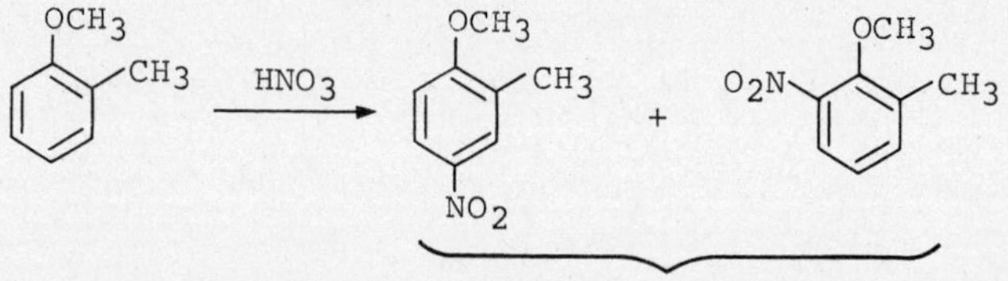

$\xrightarrow{\text{HNO}_3}$

difficult to separate
(compare O$_2$NC$_6$H$_5$OCH$_3$ isomers in Table 22.6)

(i) OK;

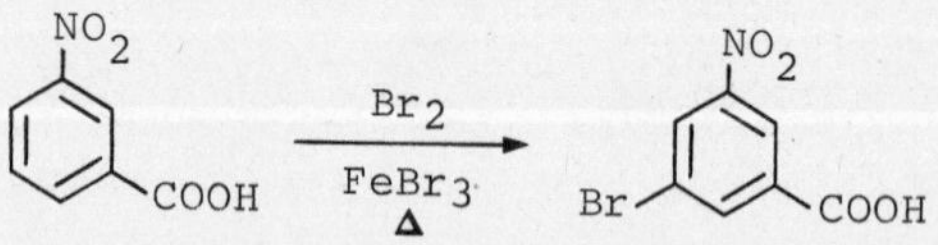

$\xrightarrow[\Delta]{\substack{\text{Br}_2 \\ \text{FeBr}_3}}$

both groups orient *meta*-

(j) No. Nitration of

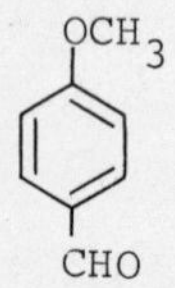

gives

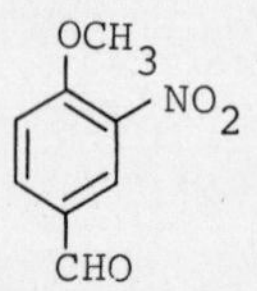

Friedel-Crafts acylation reactions cannot be applied to nitro compounds, so *m*-nitroanisole cannot be formylated.

10. The trifluoromethyl group is electron-withdrawing because of the C-F bond dipole $\left(\underset{-\text{CF}_3}{\xrightarrow{\quad}} \right)$. The explanation is analogous to that given for the COOH group in the answer to problem #5.

11.

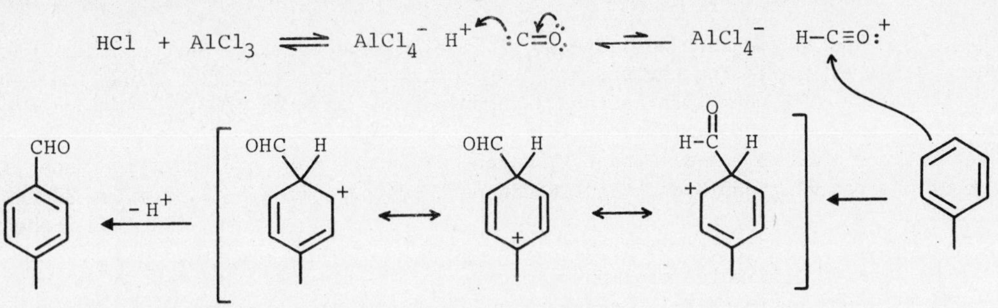

$$HCl + AlCl_3 \rightleftharpoons AlCl_4^- \; H^+ \; :C\!\!=\!\!O: \rightleftharpoons AlCl_4^- \; H-C\!\equiv\!O:^+$$

12. (a)

$$\longrightarrow \quad (CH_3)_3C^+ \; HOBF_3^-$$

rearrangement of primary carbocation to tertiary

(b) $CH_3CDOHCH_2CH_3 + BF_3 \rightleftharpoons$

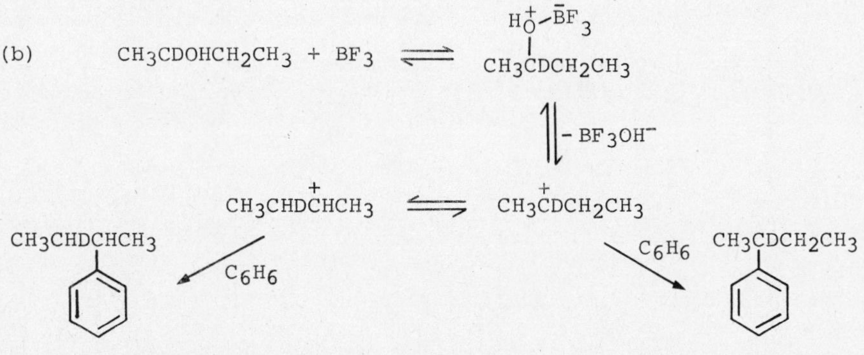

(c) Scrambling would require a primary carbocation:

$$CD_3\overset{+}{C}HCH_3 \rightleftharpoons {}^+CD_2CHDCH_3 \rightleftharpoons CD_2H\overset{+}{C}DCH_3$$

Primary carbocations are so unstable relative to secondary ones that the reaction does not occur.

(d) Carbocations have a planar central carbon which is achiral. Consequently, a racemic reaction product is anticipated. In practice, the reaction product is 99% racemized.

13.   Aluminum chloride, unless specially purified and handled on a vacuum line, always has traces of H_2O and HCl.

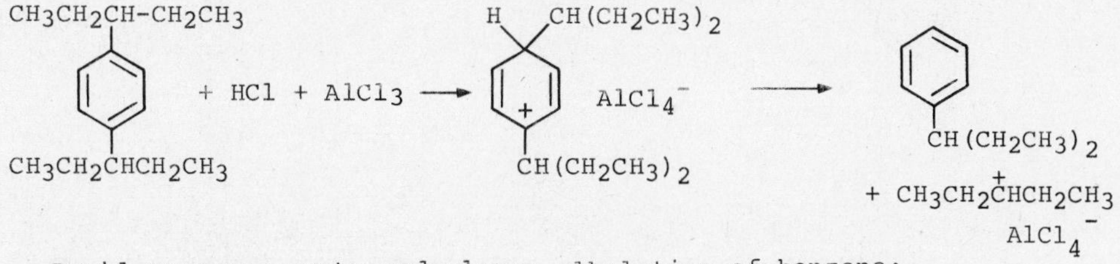

Rapid rearrangements and slower alkylation of benzene:

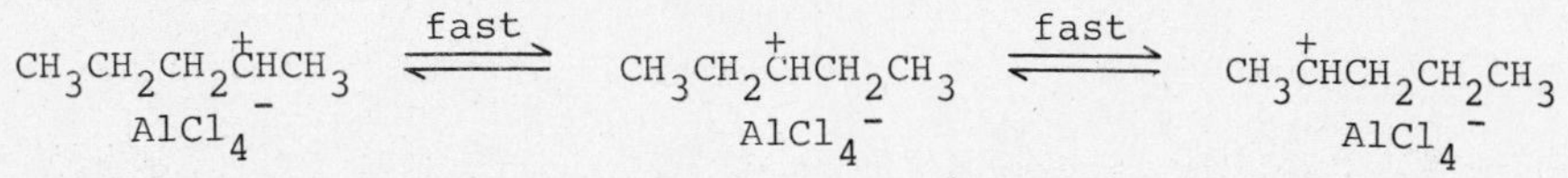

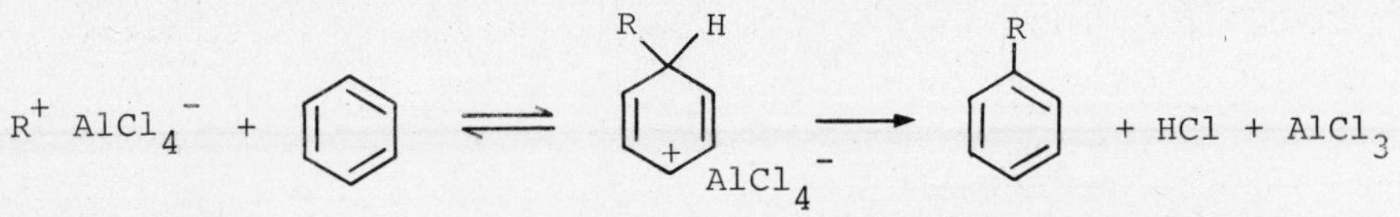

$CH_3\overset{+}{C}HCH_2CH_2CH_3$ and $CH_3CH_2\overset{+}{C}HCH_2CH_3$ are so similar in structure, we may confidently expect that their rates of alkylating benzene will be closely similar as well. Thus, the relative rates of formation of 2-phenylpentane and 3-phenylpentane will be the same as the relative populations of the two carbocations, or 2:1.

Consequently, one mole of 1,4-di(3-pentyl)benzene gives one mole of 3-phenylpentane (after cleavage of one pentyl group), and the cleaved pentyl group gives: 0.33 moles 3-phenylpentane
0.67 moles 2-phenylpentane

<u>Total</u>: 1.33 moles of 3-phenylpentane
and 0.67 moles of 2-phenylpentane,
or a ratio of 2:1 for 3-isomer/2-isomer.

14.

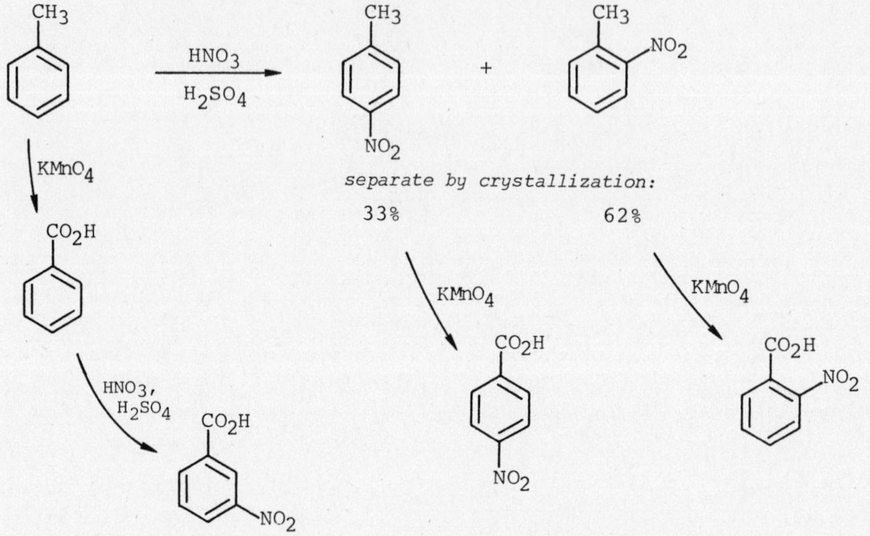

$\xrightarrow[H_2SO_4]{HNO_3}$

separate by crystallization:

33% 62%

$\downarrow$ KMnO₄

$\xrightarrow{KMnO_4}$ $\xrightarrow{KMnO_4}$

$\xrightarrow[H_2SO_4]{HNO_3,}$

15.

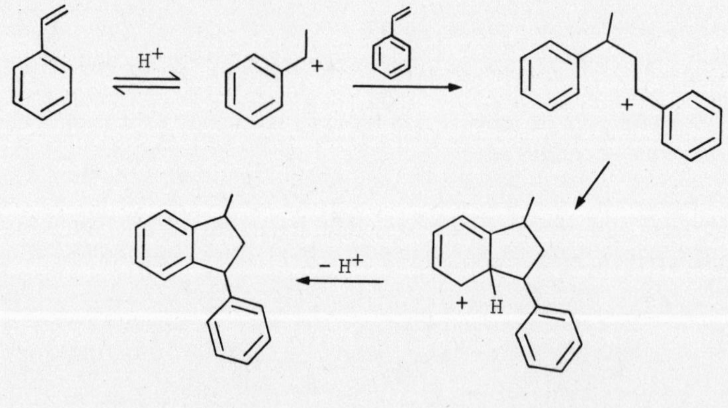

$\underset{H^+}{\rightleftharpoons}$

$- H^+$

16. (a)

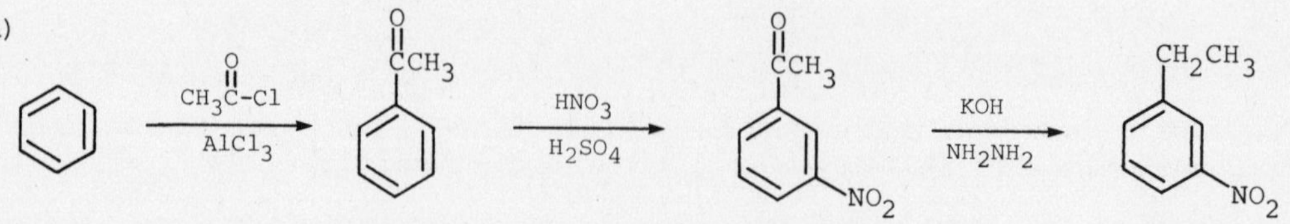

$\xrightarrow[AlCl_3]{CH_3\overset{O}{\overset{\|}{C}}-Cl}$ $\xrightarrow[H_2SO_4]{HNO_3}$ $\xrightarrow[NH_2NH_2]{KOH}$

(b)

$\xrightarrow[FeBr_3]{Br_2}$ $\xrightarrow{Mg}$ $\xrightarrow[2.\ H_2O]{1.\ (CH_3CH_2)_2C=O}$ $\xrightarrow[H^+]{H_2/Pd}$

$\underset{===}{or:}$ $\xrightarrow[AlCl_3]{CH_3CH_2\overset{O}{\overset{\|}{C}}Cl}$ $\xrightarrow{CH_3CH_2MgBr}$ $\xrightarrow{H_2O}$

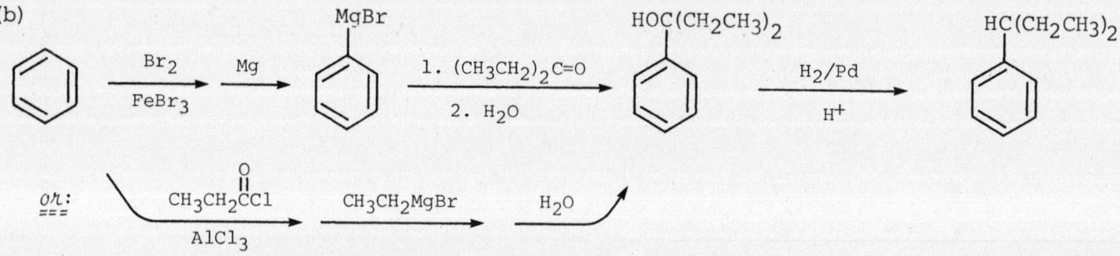

(c)

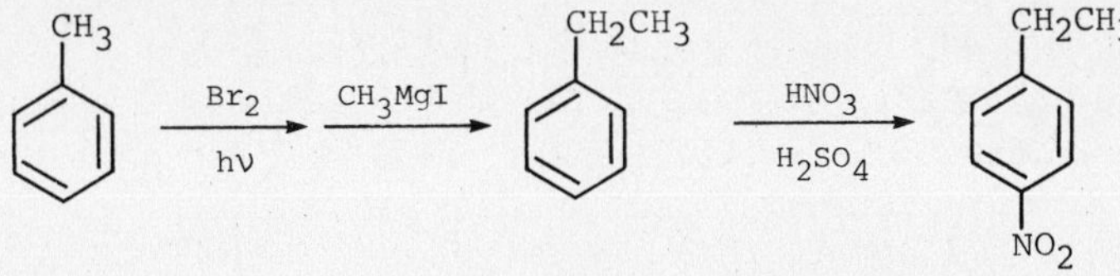

CH_3 benzene $\xrightarrow[h\nu]{Br_2}$ $\xrightarrow{CH_3MgI}$ CH_2CH_3 benzene $\xrightarrow[H_2SO_4]{HNO_3}$ CH_2CH_3 / NO_2 benzene (plus *ortho*-isomer)

(d)

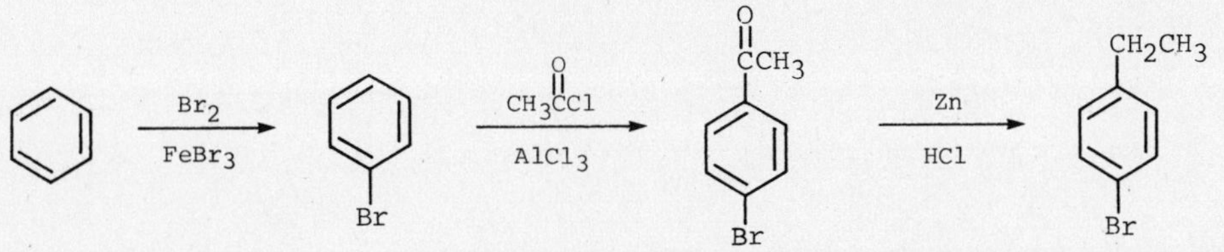

benzene $\xrightarrow{Br_2}{FeBr_3}$ Br-benzene $\xrightarrow[AlCl_3]{CH_3CCl \text{ (O)}}$ $\overset{O}{\overset{\|}{C}}CH_3$ / Br benzene $\xrightarrow[HCl]{Zn}$ CH_2CH_3 / Br benzene

(e)

benzene $\xrightarrow[FeBr_3]{Br_2}$ Br-benzene $\xrightarrow[AlCl_3]{CH_3C-Cl \text{ (O)}}$ Br / $O=CCH_3$ benzene $\xrightarrow[HCl]{Zn}$ Br / CH_2CH_3 benzene $\xrightarrow{Li}$ $CH_2-CHCH_2CH_3 \text{ (O epoxide)}$

$\rightarrow$ OH / $CH_2CHCH_2CH_3$ — CH_2CH_3 benzene

(f)

CH_3 toluene $\xrightarrow{KMnO_4}$ CO_2H benzene $\xrightarrow[FeBr_3]{Br_2}$ CO_2H / Br benzene $\xrightarrow[H^+]{CH_3OH}$ CO_2CH_3 / Br benzene

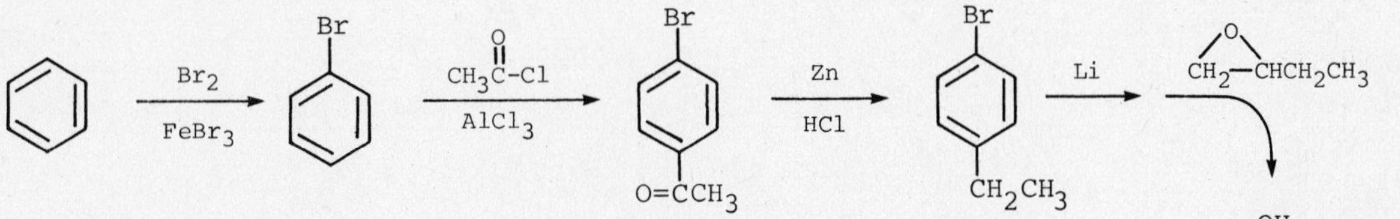

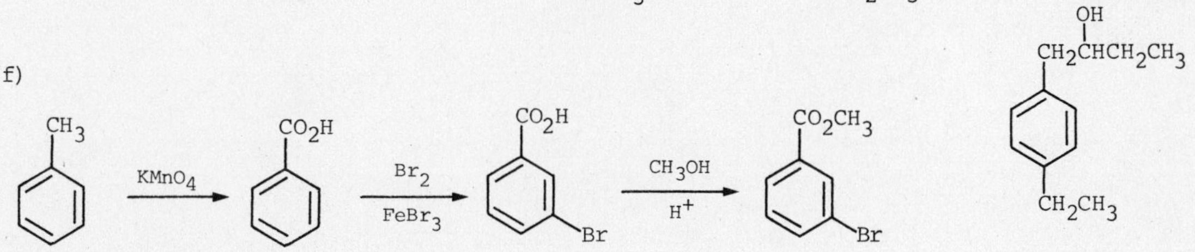

17. (a)

$$C_6H_5C(CH_3)_2Cl \xrightarrow{slow} C_6H_5\overset{+}{C}(CH_3)_2 + Cl^-$$

$$C_6H_5\overset{+}{C}(CH_3)_2 + H_2O \xrightarrow{fast} C_6H_5\overset{CH_3}{\underset{CH_3}{C}}-\overset{+}{O}H_2 \rightleftharpoons C_6H_5C(CH_3)_2OH + H^+$$

(b) *p*-CH_3 stabilizes carbocation intermediate and the transition state lead-ing to it because one of the contributing resonance structures is that of a tertiary carbocation. *p*-CH_3O stabilizes still more because of an oxonium ion structure:

$$CH_3\overset{+}{\underset{}{C}}CH_3 \leftrightarrow CH_3\overset{}{\underset{}{C}}CH_3 \quad\quad CH_3\underset{CH_3}{C}CH_3 \leftrightarrow CH_3\underset{OCH_3}{C}CH_3 \leftrightarrow CH_3\underset{+OCH_3}{C}CH_3$$

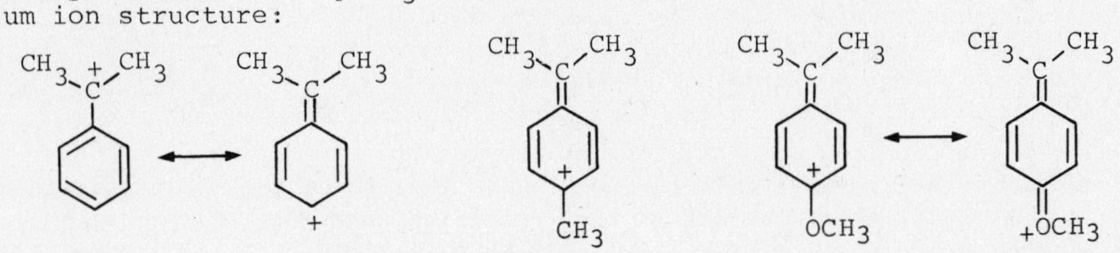

unsubstituted   *tertiary*   *oxonium ion*

The *p*-NO_2 group destabilizes the carbocation by electrostatic repulsion:

$$CH_3\underset{}{C}CH_3 \leftrightarrow CH_3\underset{}{C}CH_3$$

substituent dipole → ... $\overset{+}{N}$, $O=\overset{}{}$ O^- ... *repulsion* ... $-O-\overset{+}{N}-O$

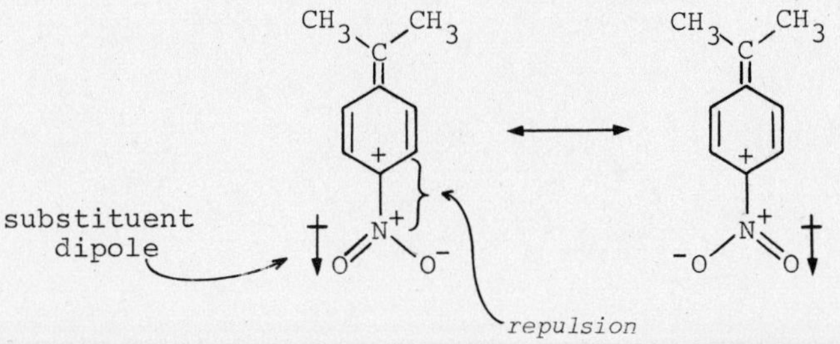

18.   *Lowest dissociation constant:* $(p\text{-}O_2NC_6H_4)_3CCl$

                                           $(m\text{-}ClC_6H_4)_3CCl$

                                             $(C_6H_5)_3CCl$

                                         $(m\text{-}CH_3C_6H_4)_3CCl$

                                         $(p\text{-}CH_3C_6H_4)_3CCl$

        Highest dissociation constant: $(p\text{-}CH_3OC_6H_4)_3CCl$

Substituents which activate the ring toward electrophilic substitution will also stabilize the carbocation. The influence of these substituents is greatest in the *para* position because of resonance.

19.   (a)

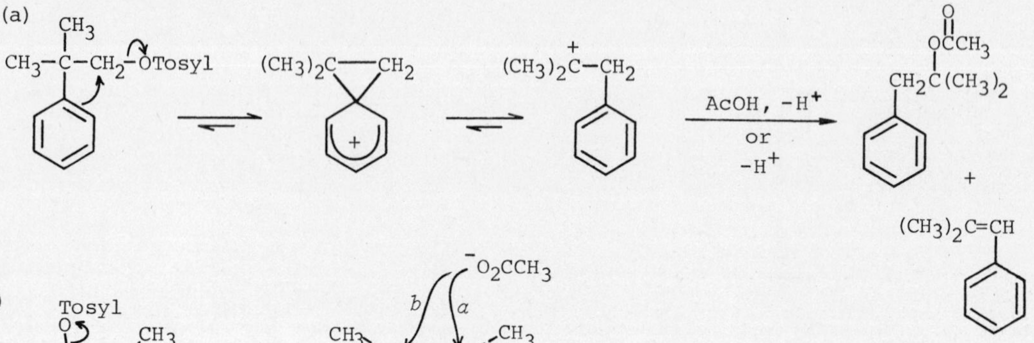

    (b)

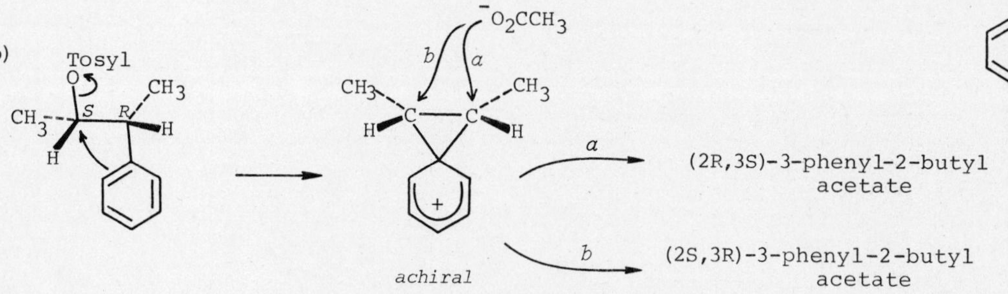

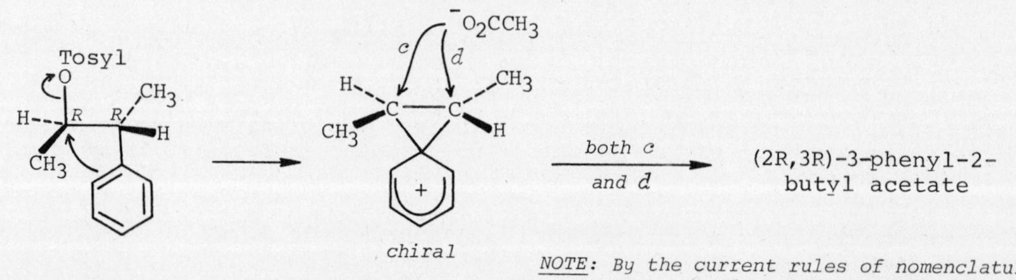

NOTE: *By the current rules of nomenclature, the correct names are 1-methyl-2-phenylpropyl tosylate, etc.*

20.   Substitution occurs predominantly at the 1-position, where the orbital is the largest. The minor product results from attack at the 2-position, and there is no reaction at the 9-position.

22.F   Supplementary Problems

S1.   Predict the products from the following reactions. If more than one product is anticipated, indicate which (if any) will predominate.

(a)

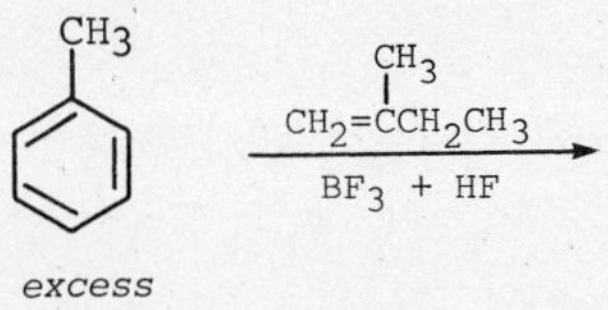

(b)

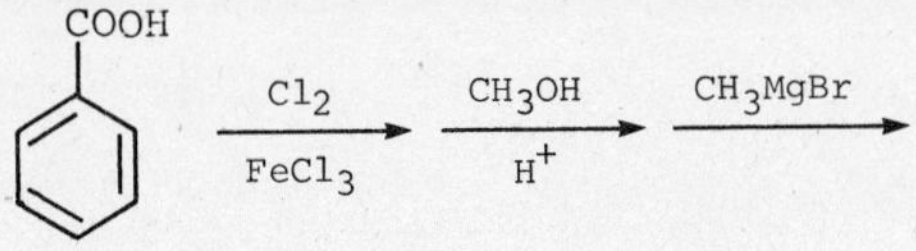

(c)

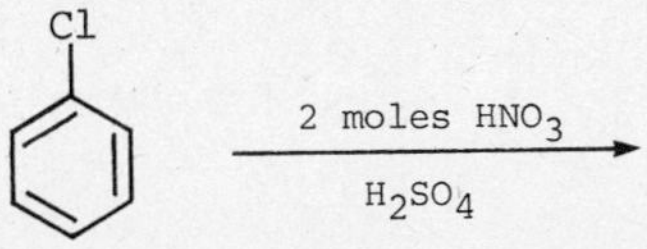

(d)

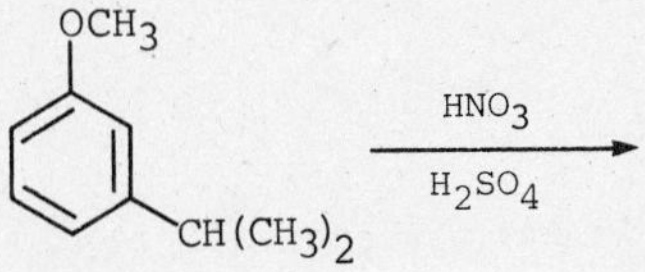

(e)

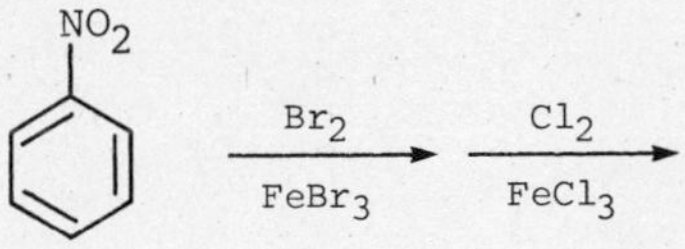

(f)

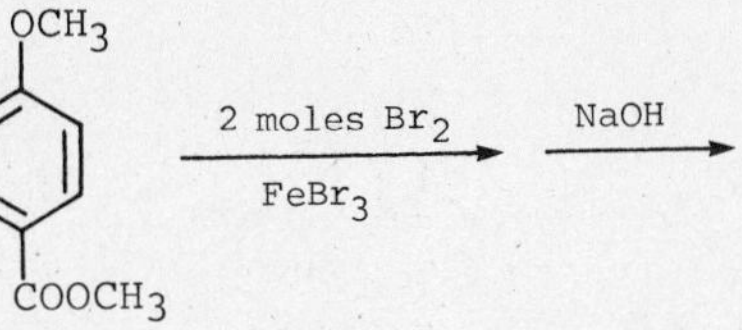

(g)

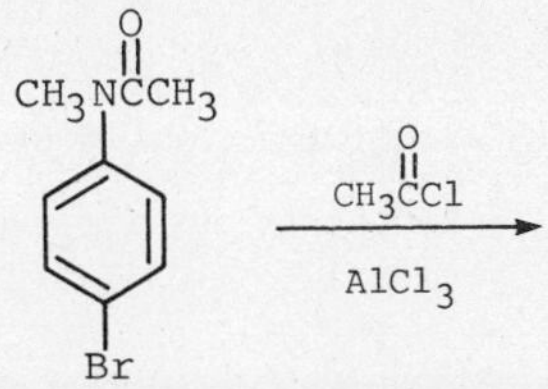

(h)

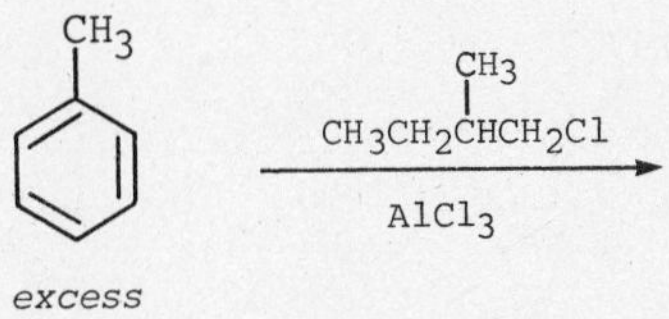

(i)

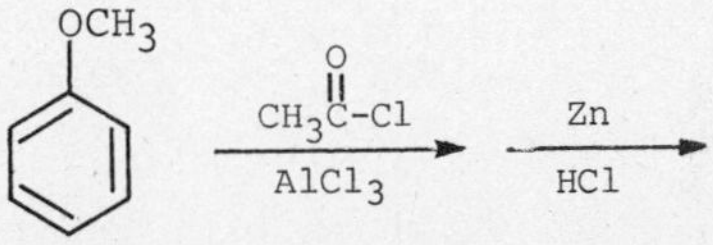

(j)

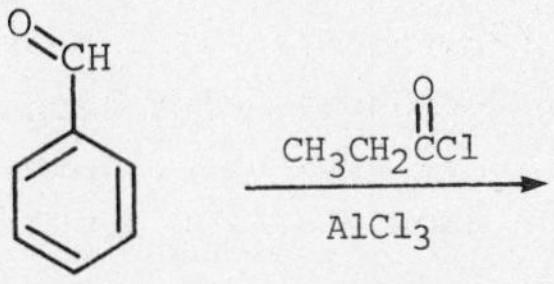

(k)

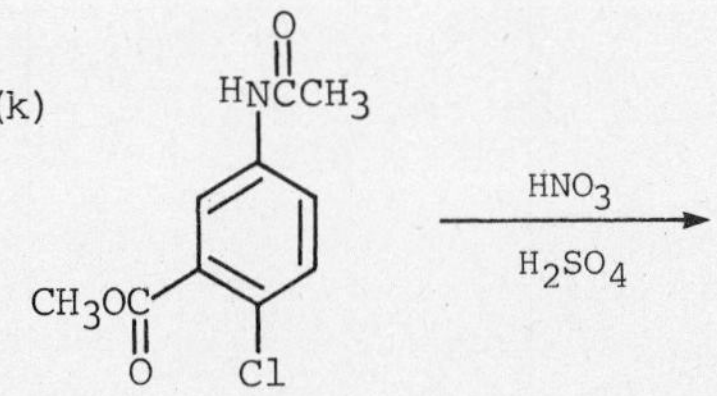

(ℓ)

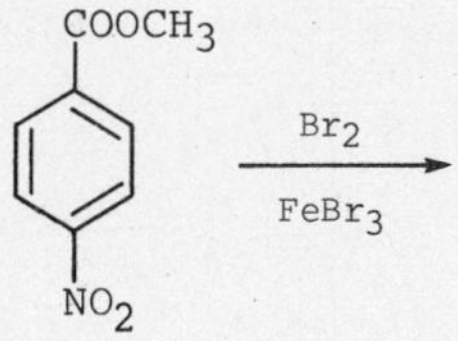

S2.   Show how to make each of the following compounds (as free of isomers as possible), starting with benzene or toluene and any other reagents.

(a)

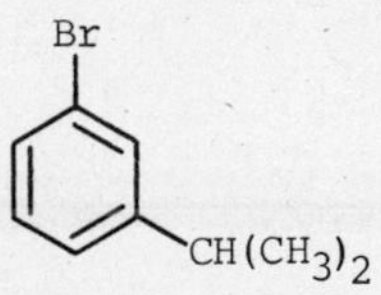

(b)

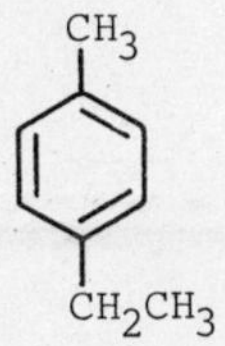

(c)

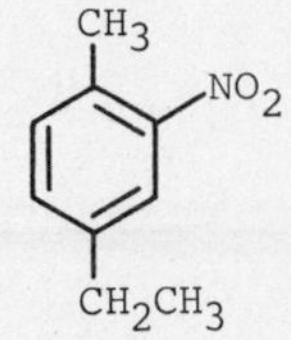

(d)

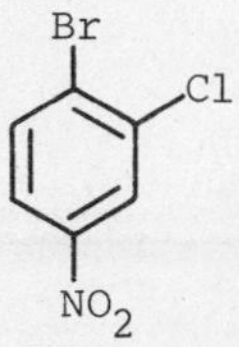

(e)

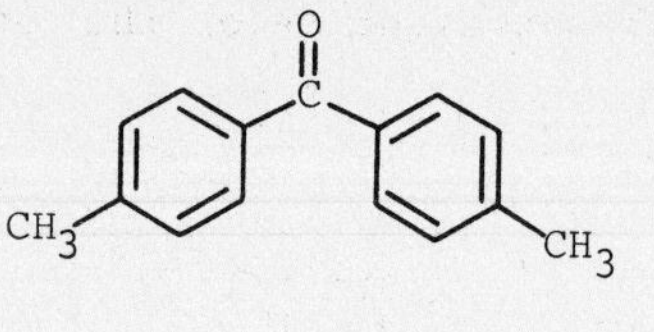

(f)

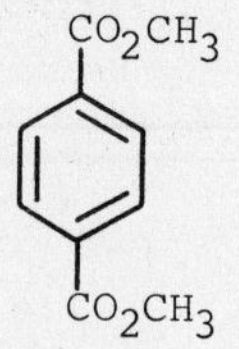

(g)

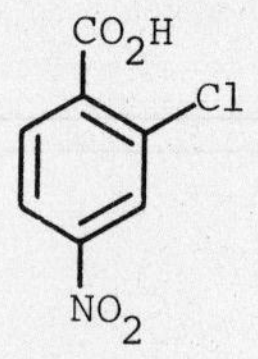

(h)

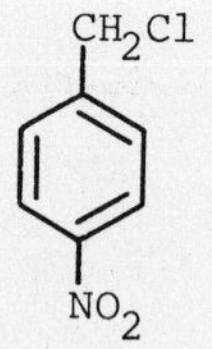

(i)

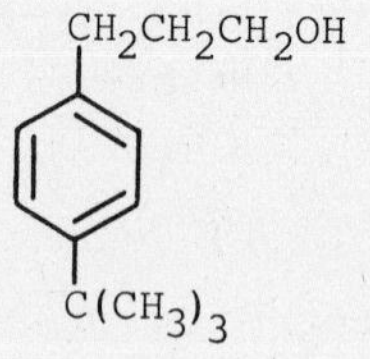

(j)

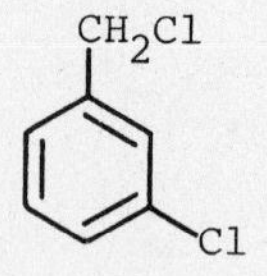

S3. Write a reasonable mechanism for the cyclization illustrated below, showing all of the intermediates involved. Do you expect to see any other compound(s) as products of this reaction?

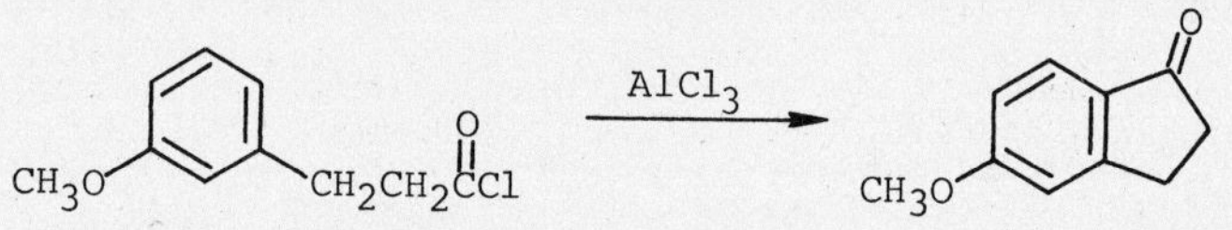

S4. Treatment of phenol with sodium nitrite and HCl results in the formation of p-nitrosophenol. Write a reasonable mechanism for the formation of the active electrophilic species and its reaction with phenol.

S5. None of the reaction sequences outlined below will lead to the compounds that are shown as the major products. For each case, show what the main product(s) actually would be, and provide an alternative seqence that will produce the desired compound as the major isomer, **using the same starting materials.**

(a)

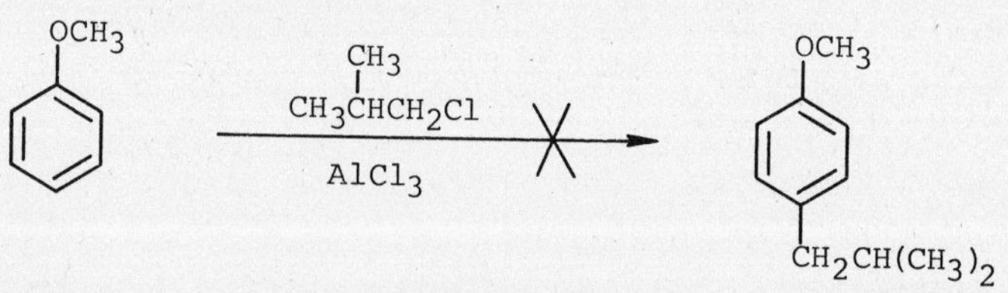

(b)

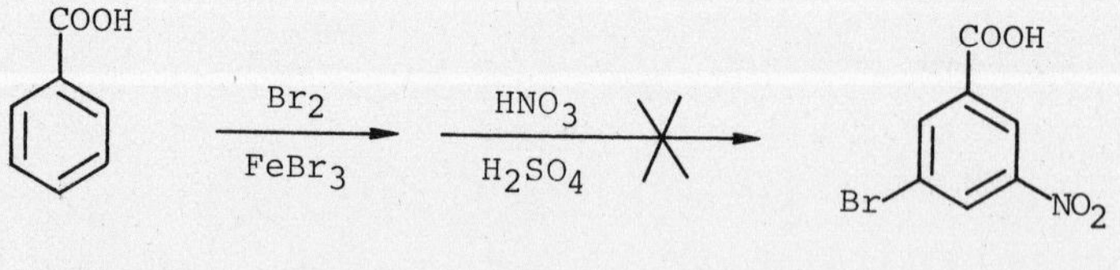

(c)

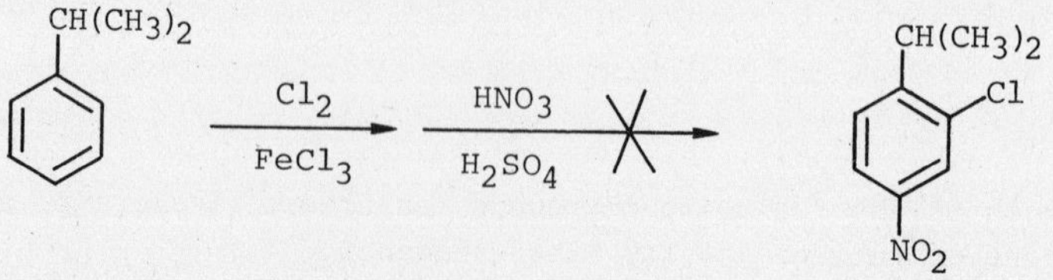

(d)

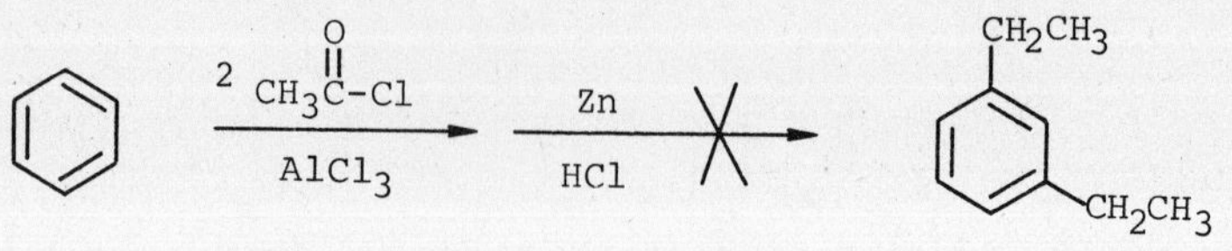

S6.   Predict the favored position of electrophilic aromatic substitution of the
      following compounds, and justify your answer.

(a) 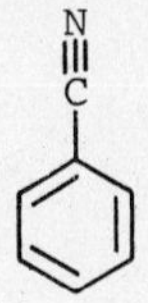   (b) 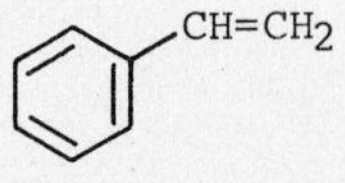   (c) 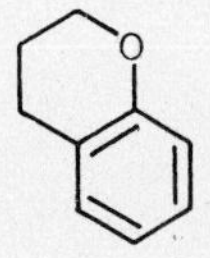   (d)

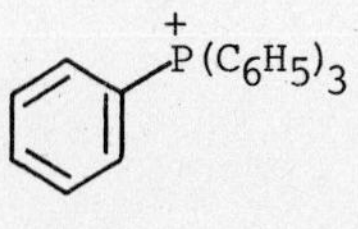

S7.   If sodium triethylphenylborate is treated with D_2SO_4/D_2O, it undergoes cleav-
      age to give deuteriobenzene and a triethylboron compound:

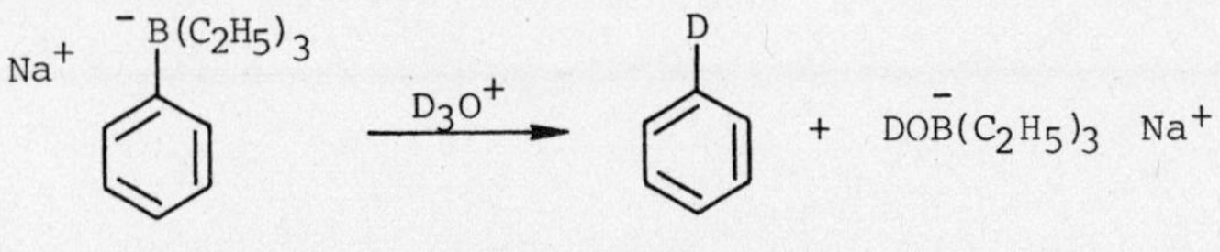

$$Na^+ \quad ^-B(C_2H_5)_3 \qquad \xrightarrow{D_3O^+} \qquad + \quad D\bar{O}B(C_2H_5)_3 \quad Na^+$$

(a) Write a mechanism for this transformation.

(b) What product would you expect if you treated the same compound with Br_2?
     Write a mechanism for the reaction you predict.

S8.   Write a mechanism for the following transformation:

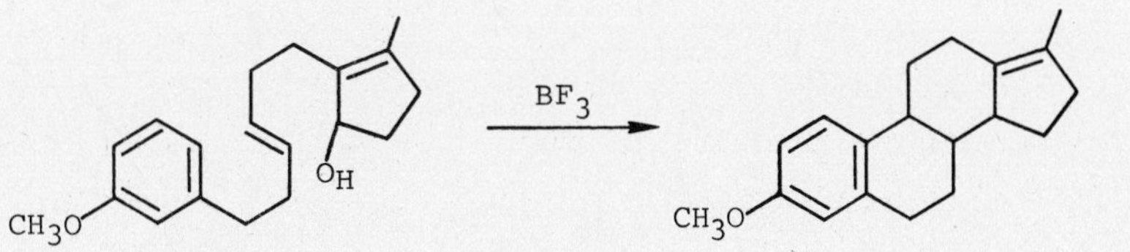

$$\xrightarrow{BF_3}$$

22.G   Answers to Supplementary Problems

S1.   (a) 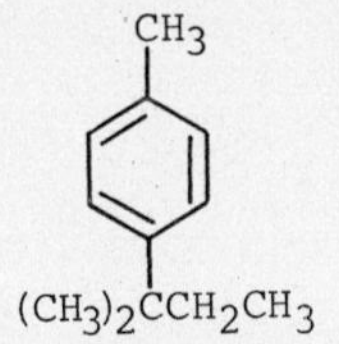 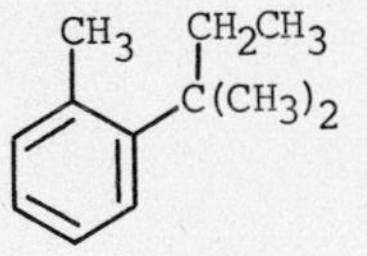   (e)

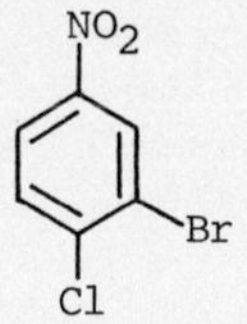

      $(CH_3)_2CCH_2CH_3$ (less)   and   ;

                                                                                   (less)

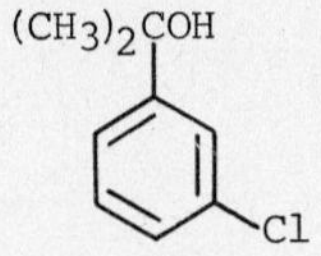

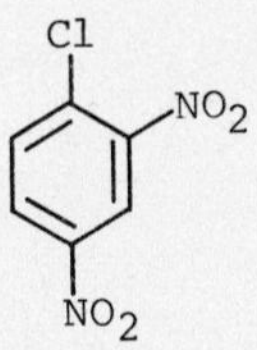

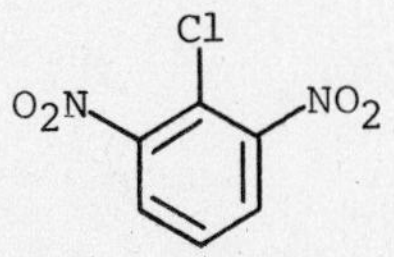

      (b) $(CH_3)_2COH$

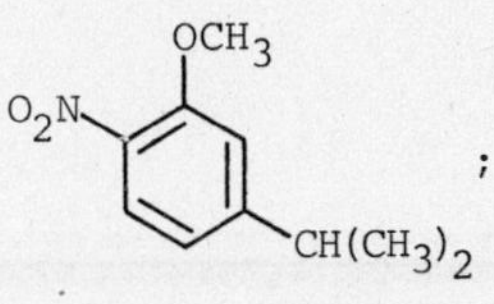

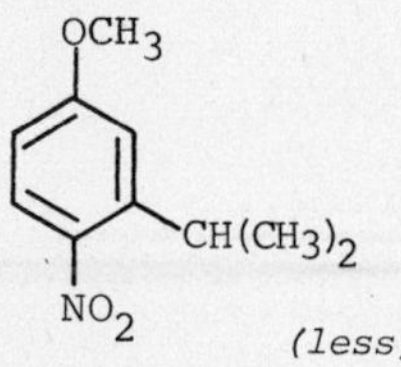

      (c)   ;   (f)

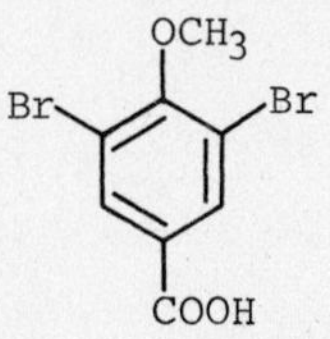

                              (less)

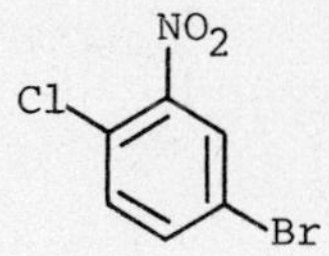

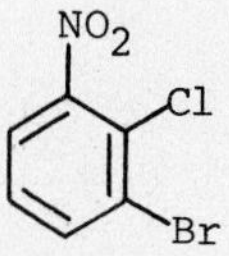

      (d)   ;   (g)

                              (less)

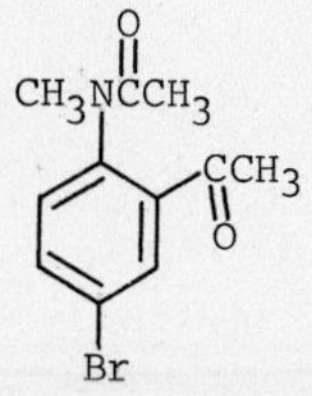

(h) CH_3 ... $(CH_3)_2CHCH_2CH_3$; CH_3 CH_2CH_3 / $CH(CH_3)_2$ *(less)*

(k) $HNCCH_3$ (=O), NO_2, CH_3OOC, Cl ; $HNCCH_3$ (=O), O_2N, CH_3OOC, Cl *(less)*

(i) OCH_3 / CH_2CH_3 and OCH_3 CH_2CH_3

(ℓ) $COOCH_3$ Br / NO_2 and $COOCH_3$ / Br NO_2

(j)   no reaction

S2. (a) CH_3 $\xrightarrow{KMnO_4}$ $\xrightarrow[H^+]{CH_3OH}$ $COOCH_3$ $\xrightarrow[FeBr_3]{Br_2}$ $\xrightarrow{CH_3MgBr}$ Br, $C(CH_3)_2$ OH $\xdownarrow{H_2/Pd}$ Br, $CH(CH_3)_2$

(b) CH_3 $\xrightarrow[AlCl_3]{CH_3CCl\ (=O)}$ CH_3, $COCH_3$ $\xrightarrow[HCl]{Zn}$ CH_3, CH_2CH_3

(c) CH_3 $\xrightarrow[AlCl_3]{CH_3CCl\ (=O)}$ CH_3, $COCH_3$ $\xrightarrow[H_2SO_4]{HNO_3}$ CH_3, NO_2, $COCH_3$ $\xrightarrow[NH_2NH_2]{KOH}$ CH_3, NO_2, CH_2CH_3

(d) $\xrightarrow[FeBr_3]{Br_2}$ $\xrightarrow[H_2SO_4]{HNO_3}$ Br, NO_2 $\xrightarrow[FeCl_3]{Cl_2}$ Br, Cl, NO_2

(e) CH_3 *(excess)* $\xrightarrow[HCl, ZnCl_2]{CH_2=O}$ CH_3—CH_2—CH_3 $\xrightarrow{CrO_3}$ CH_3—$C(=O)$—CH_3

(f) CH_3, $COCH_3$ *[from (c)]* $\xrightarrow{KMnO_4}$ $\xrightarrow[H^+]{CH_3OH}$ $COOCH_3$, $COOCH_3$

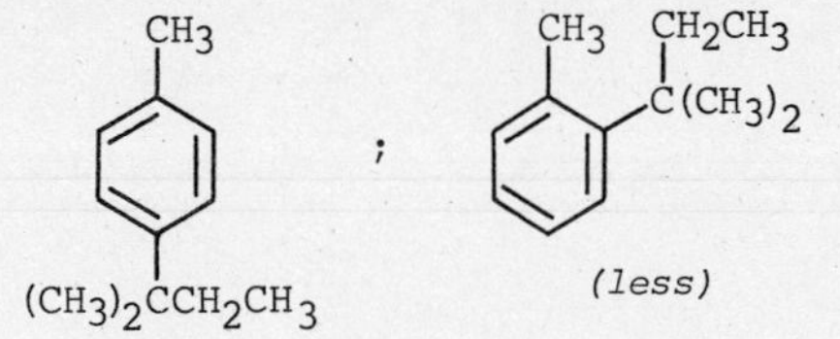

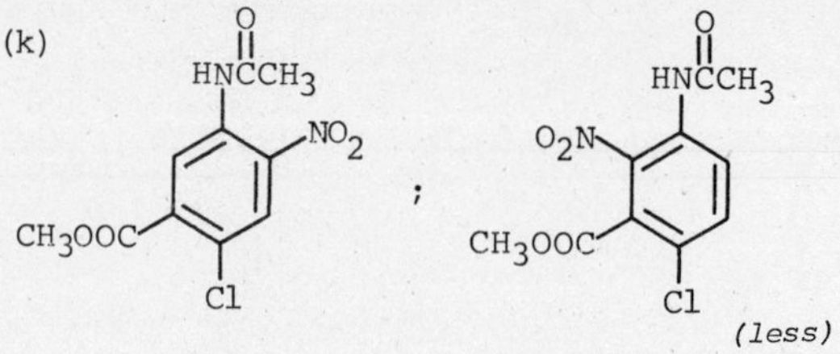

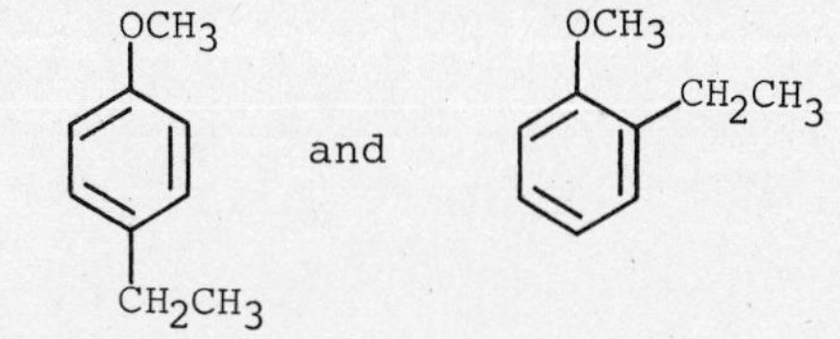

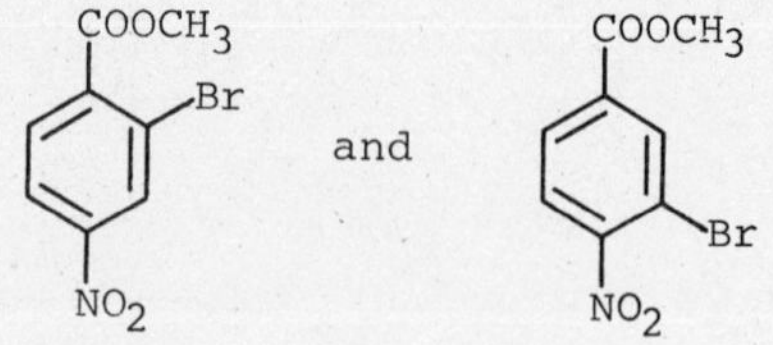

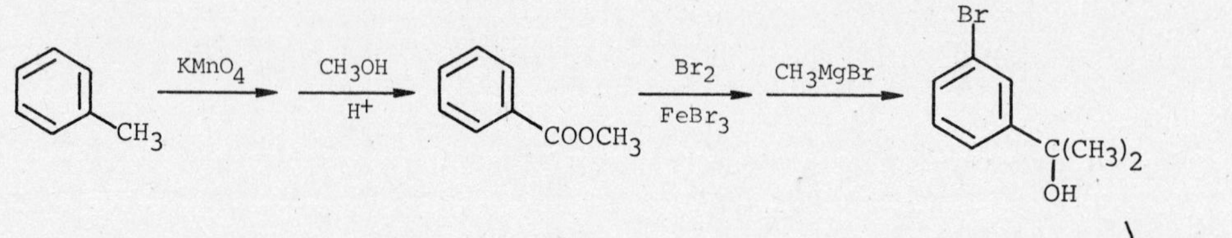

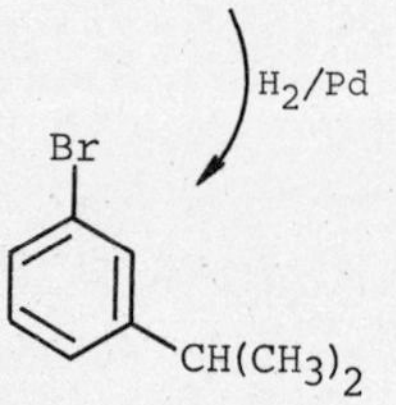

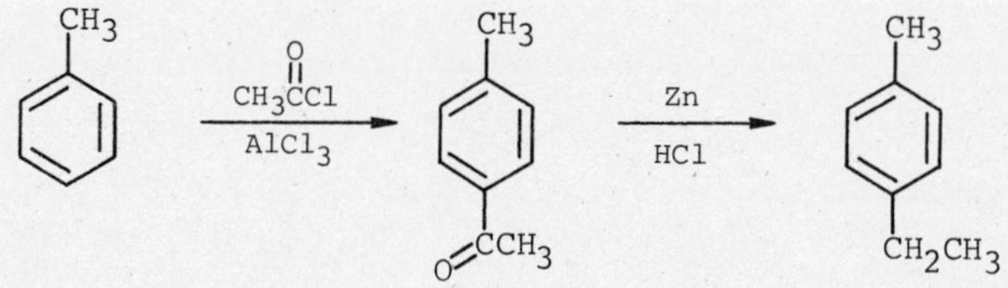

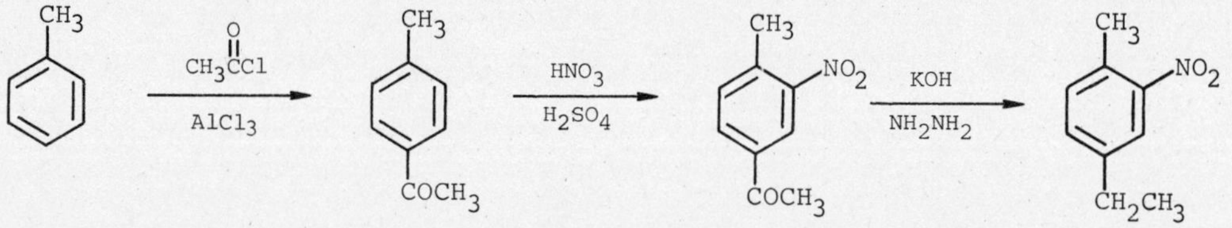

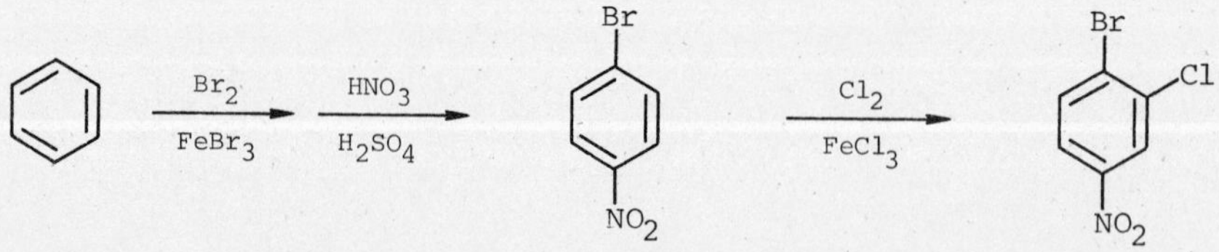

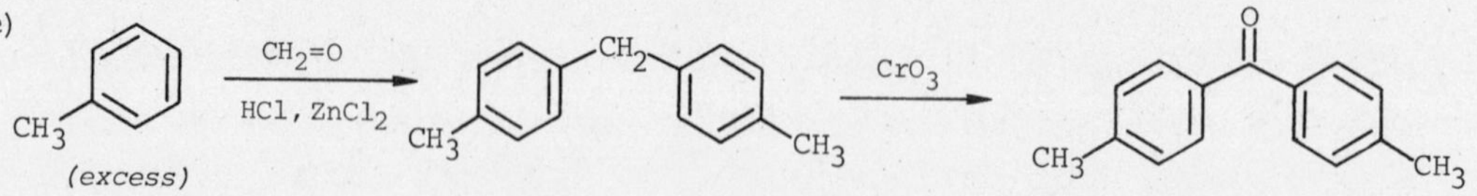

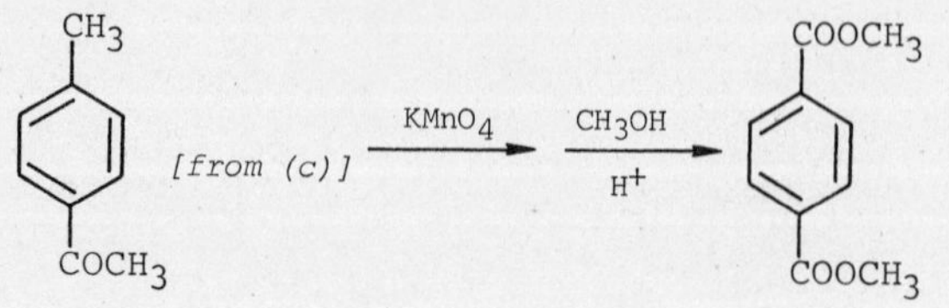

(g)

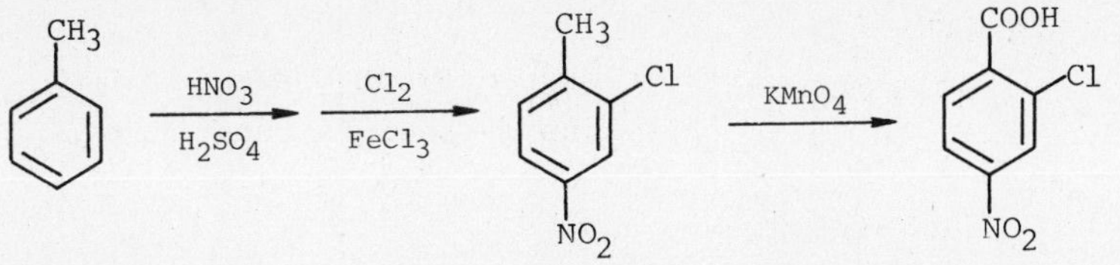

(h)

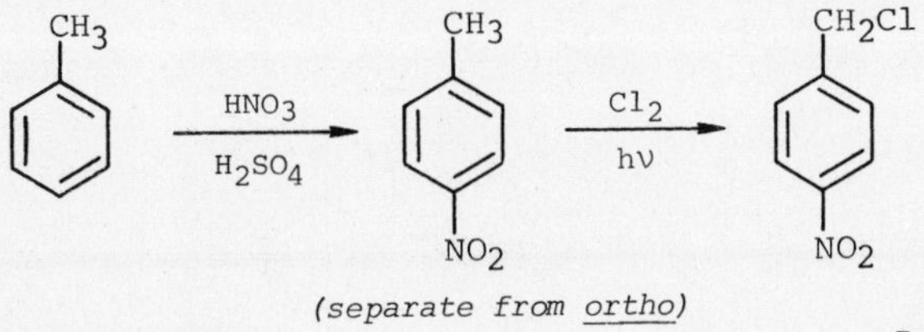

(separate from ortho)

(i)

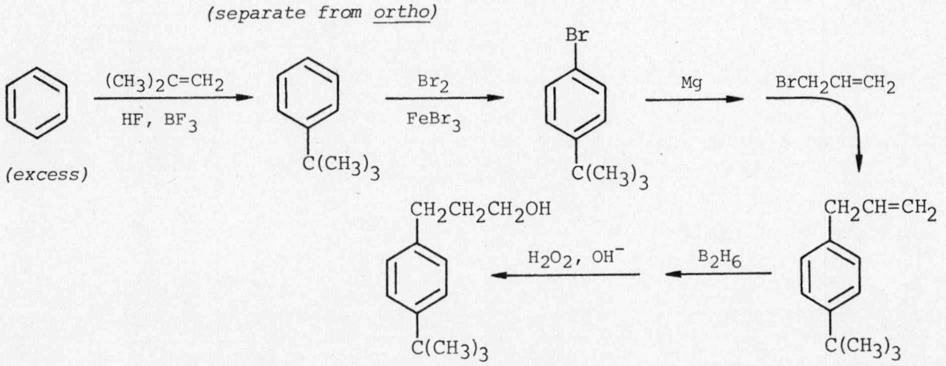

(excess)

(j)

(see Problem #11)

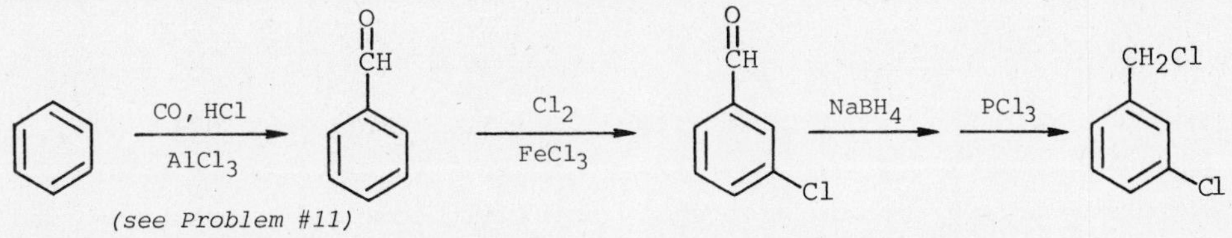

S3.

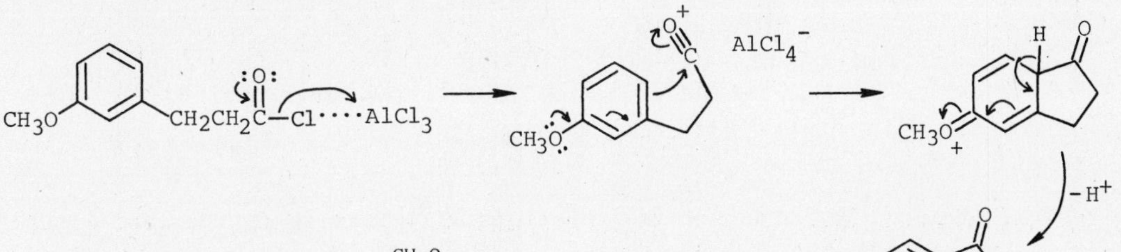

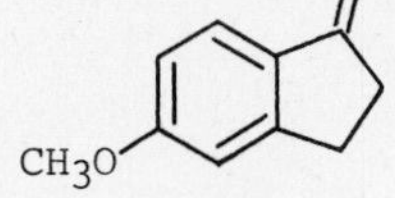

Some product from *ortho* attack will also be seen:

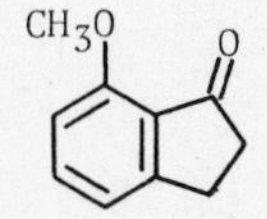

S4.

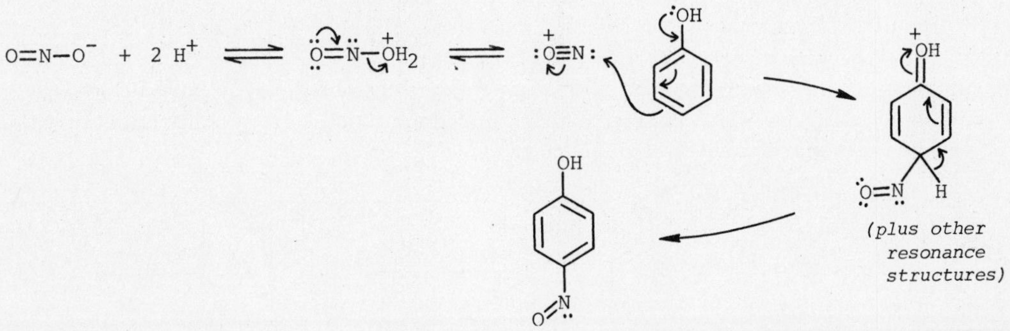

(plus other resonance structures)

S5. (a) The main product would be

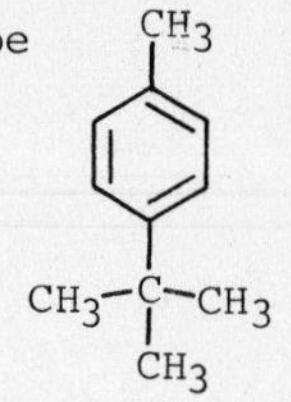

from rearrangement of the primary alkyl halide before substitution.

To make the desired compound, employ an acylation/deoxygenation sequence:

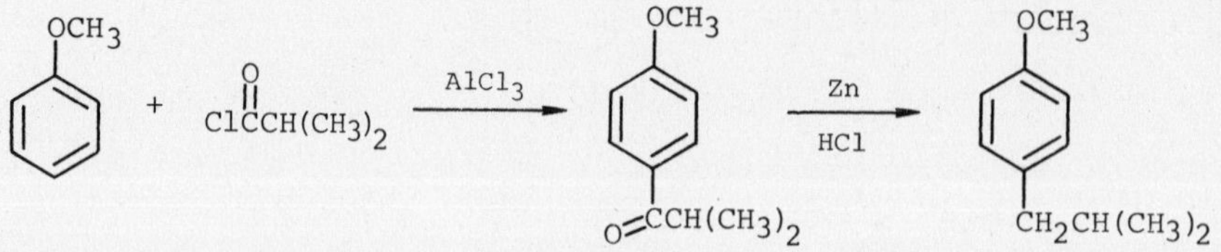

(b)

Main products would be

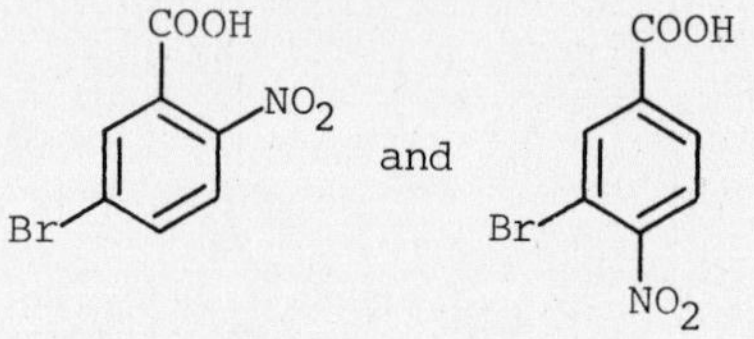

and

because Br (Group II) dominates COOH (Group III) in directing power.

To obtain the desired product, reverse the sequence of steps:

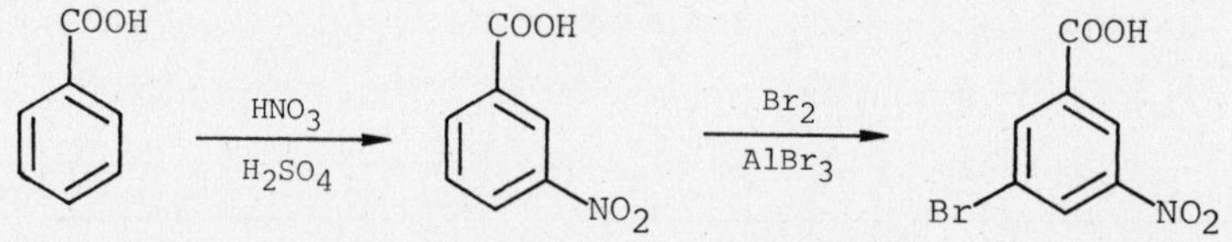

(c) The chlorine will go preferentially *para* (with some *ortho*), and then will compete with the isopropyl group to give a mixture of isomers:

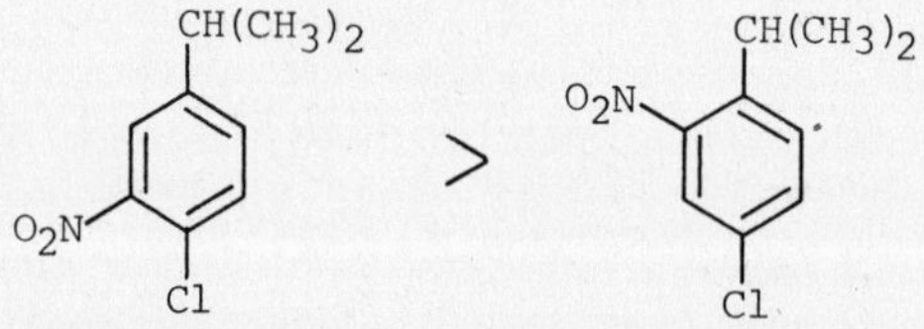

>

(for steric reasons)

Again, reversing the order of the reactions will furnish the correct product

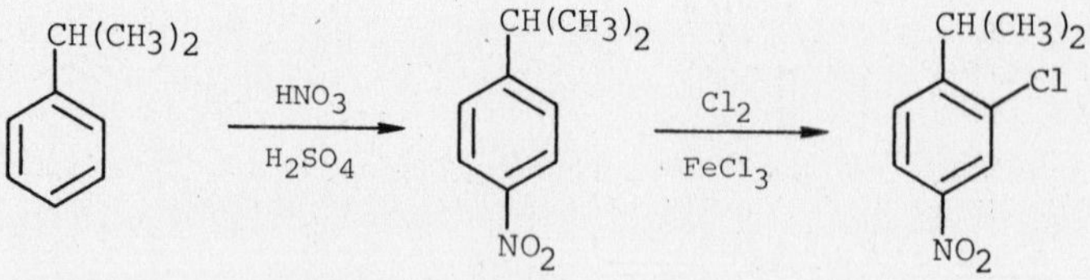

(d) Only one acyl group can be attached in a Friedel–Crafts acylation reaction, so ethylbenzene will be the overall product. To get around this involves a somewhat more involved sequence:

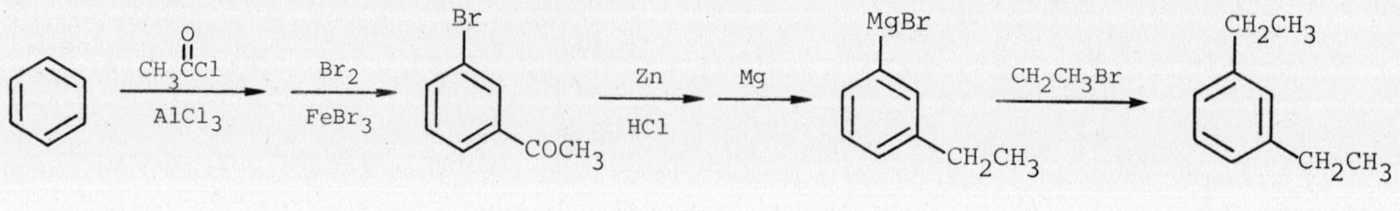

S6. (a)

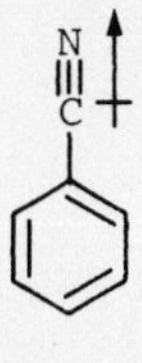

Dipole moment and resonance 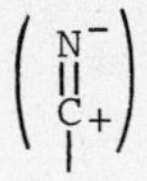 both disfavor adjacent positive charge, so this $\left(\begin{array}{c} N^- \\ \| \\ C^+ \\ | \end{array}\right)$ group will be deactivating, *meta*-directing.

(b) A vinyl group is o,p-directing because conjugation with the double bond helps to stabilize the positive charge:

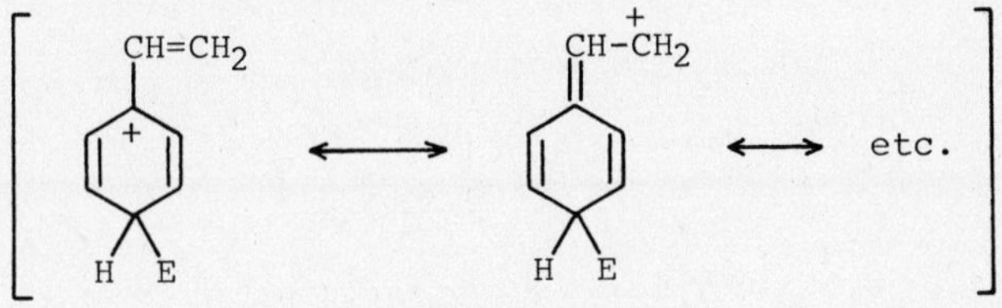

etc.

NOTE: electrophilic attack on the vinyl group itself is preferred:

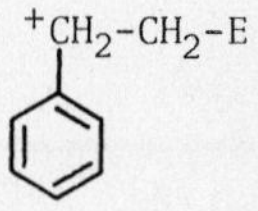

(c) 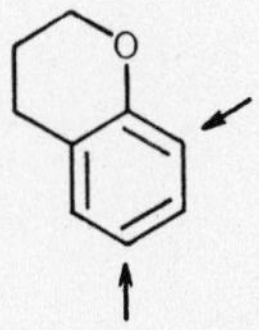 This is simply an aryl ether, and substitution will occur ortho and para to the oxygen.

(d) 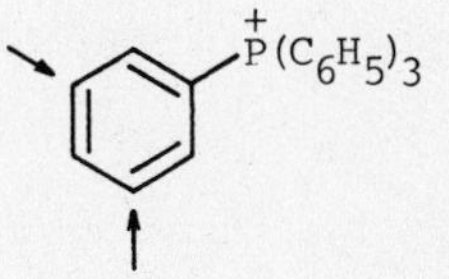 Because of the cationic phosphorus, the ring is deactivated, with the greatest effect at the ortho and para positions;

this substituent is deactivating, meta-directing.

S7. (a)

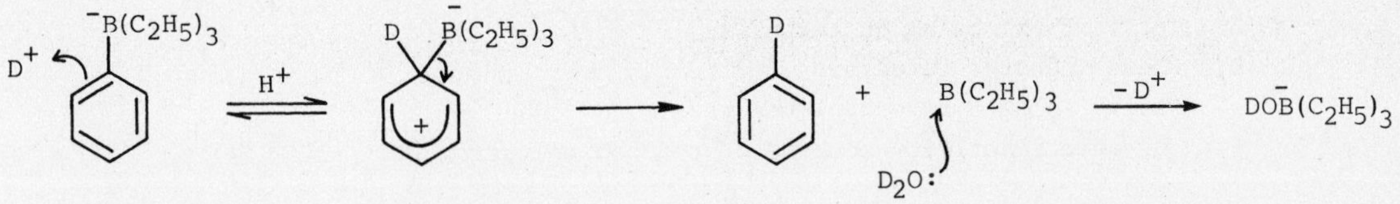

$$D^+ \quad H^+ \qquad \longrightarrow \qquad + \quad B(C_2H_5)_3 \quad \xrightarrow{-D^+} \quad DO\bar{B}(C_2H_5)_3$$

$D_2O:$

(This is simply the reverse of the electrophilic aromatic substitution reactions which we have been focussing on.)

(b)

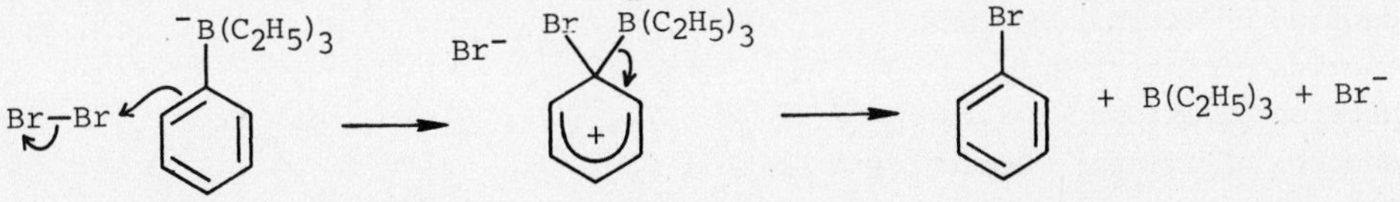

$$Br-Br \qquad Br^- \qquad \longrightarrow \qquad + \quad B(C_2H_5)_3 + Br^-$$

S8.

$$CH_3O \qquad \xrightarrow{\quad} \qquad [\qquad \longleftrightarrow \qquad]$$

$$\xrightarrow{-H^+} \qquad CH_3O$$

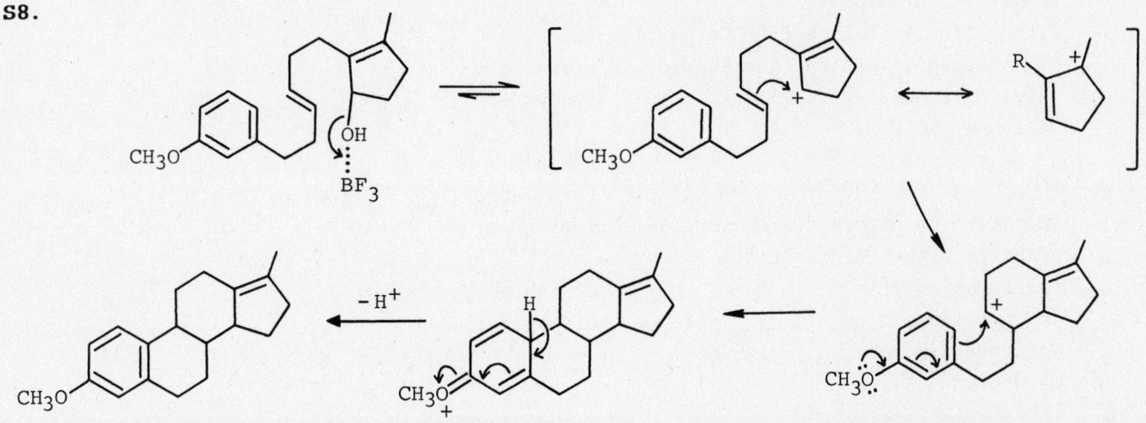

23. AMINES

23.A Chapter Outline and Important Terms Introduced

23.1 Structure

- primary, secondary, and tertiary amines
- quaternary ammonium compounds
- nonbonding electron pair
- nitrogen inversion

23.2 Nomenclature

- -amine
- amino-, alkylamino-
- aniline, benzeneamine
- N-

23.3 Physical Properties

A. Colligative Properties

B. Infrared Spectra (weak N-H stretch)

C. Nuclear Magnetic Resonance Spectra

CH_3NR_2: 2.2 ppm   NH: 0.6-3.0 ppm

23.4 Basicity

$R_3N: + H \rightleftharpoons R_3\overset{+}{N}H$ pK_a of alkylammonium compounds: 9-11

pK_a of anilinium ion: 4.6

resolution of racemic carboxylic acids via formation of diastereomeric salts

23.5 Quaternary Ammonium Compounds

A. Tertiary Amines as Nucleophiles

B. Phase-Transfer Catalysis

- salts soluble in organic synthesis
- greater reactivity because of reduced solvation

23.6 Synthesis

A. Direct Alkylation of Ammonia or other Amines (polyalkylation problems)

B. Indirect Alkylation: The Gabriel Synthesis

C. Reduction of Nitro Compounds

D. Reduction of Nitriles

E. Reduction of Oximes

F. Reduction of Imines: Reductive Amination

- Eschwieler-Clarke reaction
- Leuckart reaction
- immonium ion

G. Reduction of Amides

H. Preparation of Amines from Carboxylic Acids: The Hofmann, Curtius, and Schmidt Rearrangements

- acyl nitrene
- carbamic acid
- isocyanate

23.7 Reactions (see Sections 23.4, 23.5, and 23.6, as well)

A. Formation of Amides (see Section 18.7.B)

B. Reaction with Nitrous Acid

- nitrosation
- nitrosamines
- nitrosonium ion
- diazonium compound
- diazotization

C. Oxidation

- hydroxylamines
- amine oxides

    D. Electrophilic Aromatic Substitution
        (strong <u>ortho,para</u>-directing)
        Vilsmeier reaction
    E. Elimination of the Amino Group: the Cope and Hofmann elimination reactions)

23.8 <u>Enamines, Immonium Ions</u>
      Mannich reaction

23.B   Important Reactions Introduced

<u>Direct</u> <u>alkylation</u> <u>of</u> <u>ammonia</u> <u>and</u> <u>other</u> <u>amines</u> (23.6.A)

Equation:

$$H_3N: \ + \ RX \ \longrightarrow \ H_3\overset{+}{N}R \ X^- \ \underset{\longleftarrow}{\overset{:NH_3}{\rightleftharpoons}} \ H_2\overset{..}{N}R \ \overset{RX}{\longrightarrow} \ H_2\overset{+}{N}R_2 \ , \ etc.$$

Generality: $R \neq 3^\circ$ alkyl (E2 occurs instead)

Key features: because of equilibria between ammonium species, polyalkylation is a problem

<u>Gabriel</u> <u>synthesis</u> <u>of</u> <u>amines</u> (23.6.B)

Equation:

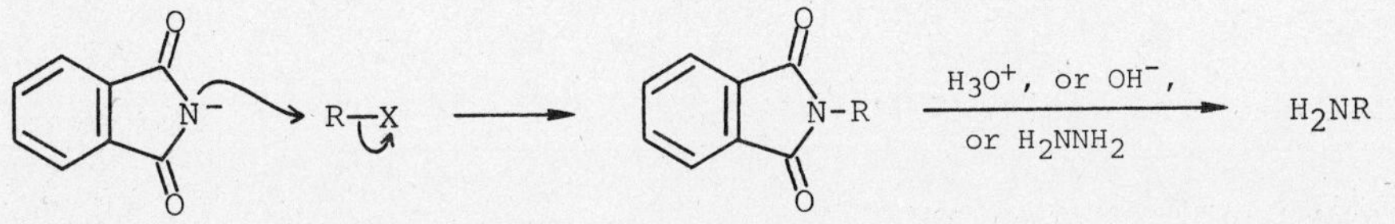

phthalimide anion

Generality: $R \neq 3^\circ$ alkyl (E2 occurs instead)

Key features: method for the synthesis of 1° amines without problems of overalkylation
               substitution reaction is an S_N2 displacement

<u>Reduction</u> <u>of</u> <u>nitro</u> <u>compounds</u> (23.6.C)

Equation:
$$Ar-NO_2 \ \xrightarrow{[H]} \ Ar-NH_2$$

Generality: Ar = aryl group
           [H] = H_2/Ni, Fe/HCl, $SnCl_2$/HCl, Zn/HCl, Sn/HCl, or NaSH

Key features: this is the best method for the formation of aryl amines
              with polynitro compounds, selective reduction is sometimes possible

<u>Reduction</u> <u>of</u> <u>nitriles</u> (23.6.D)

Equation:
$$RC{\equiv}N \ \xrightarrow{[H]} \ RCH_2NH_2$$

Generality: R = alkyl or aryl
           [H] = H_2/Ni or $LiAlH_4$

Key features: in combination with displacement of RX with $^-$CN, useful method for synthesis of 1°
                                                        amines

              hydrogenation method sometimes leads to secondary amines; this can be minimized by
                  conducting reaction in presence of excess NH_3

<u>Reduction</u> <u>of</u> <u>oximes</u> (23.6.E)

Equation:
$$\underset{R-C-R'}{\overset{NOH}{\overset{||}{}}} \ \xrightarrow{[H]} \ \underset{R-CH-R'}{\overset{NH_2}{\overset{|}{}}}$$

Generality: R, R' = H, alkyl, or aryl
           [H] = H_2/Ni or $LiAlH_4$

Reductive amination (23.6.F)

Equation:

$$\underset{\text{O}}{\overset{\parallel}{\text{R-C-R'}}} + H_2NR'' \rightleftharpoons \underset{\text{H}\overset{+}{N}R''}{\overset{\parallel}{\text{R-C-R'}}} \xrightarrow{[H]} \underset{\text{H}NR''}{\overset{\mid}{\text{R-CH-R'}}}$$

Generality: R, R', R'' = H, alkyl, or aryl

[H] = H_2/Ni; CH_2O/HCO_2H (Eschwieler-Clarke reaction); $HCONR_2$, heat (Leuckart reaction)

Key features: general method for the synthesis of a wide range of 1^O, 2^O, and 3° amines
proceeds via immonium ion intermediate

Reduction of amides (23.6.G)

Equation:

$$\underset{\text{O}}{\overset{\parallel}{\text{R-C-NR'}_2}} \xrightarrow{[H]} RCH_2NR'_2$$

Generality: R, R' = H, alkyl, or aryl

[H] = $LiAlH_4$ or B_2H_6

Key features: useful for the preparation of 1^O, 2^O, or 3° amines

Degradation of carboxylic acid derivatives to primary amines (23.6.H)

Equation:

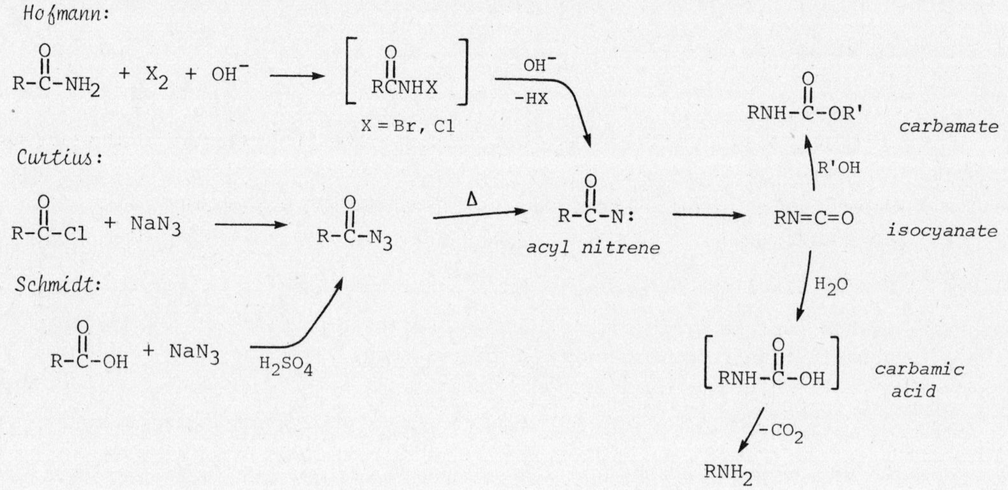

Hofmann:

$$\underset{\text{O}}{\overset{\parallel}{\text{R-C-NH}_2}} + X_2 + OH^- \longrightarrow \left[\underset{X = Br, Cl}{\overset{\overset{\text{O}}{\parallel}}{RCNHX}}\right] \underset{-HX}{\overset{OH^-}{\searrow}}$$

Curtius:

$$\underset{\text{O}}{\overset{\parallel}{\text{R-C-Cl}}} + NaN_3 \longrightarrow \underset{\text{O}}{\overset{\parallel}{\text{R-C-N}_3}} \xrightarrow{\Delta} \underset{\text{acyl nitrene}}{\overset{\overset{\text{O}}{\parallel}}{\text{R-C-N:}}} \longrightarrow RN=C=O \quad \text{isocyanate}$$

Schmidt:

$$\underset{\text{O}}{\overset{\parallel}{\text{R-C-OH}}} + NaN_3 \xrightarrow{H_2SO_4}$$

$$\underset{\text{carbamate}}{\overset{\overset{\text{O}}{\parallel}}{RNH-C-OR'}} \xleftarrow{R'OH}$$

$$\left[\underset{\text{carbamic acid}}{\overset{\overset{\text{O}}{\parallel}}{RNH-C-OH}}\right] \xleftarrow{H_2O}$$

$$\xrightarrow{-CO_2} RNH_2$$

Generality: R = alkyl, aryl

Key features: mechanism involves rearrangement of acyl nitrene intermediate

Reactions of amines with nitrous acid (23.7.B)

Secondary amines:

Equation: $R_2NH + HONO \longrightarrow R_2N-N=O + H_2O$

Generality: R = alkyl, aryl

Key features: compounds with R = methyl can be carcinogenic

Primary amines; diazotization:

Equation: $RNH_2 + HONO \longrightarrow \underset{\text{diazonium ion}}{R-\overset{+}{N}\equiv N} \longrightarrow \text{"R}^+\text{"} \longrightarrow$ carbocation reactions

Generality: if R = alkyl, diazonium ion loses N_2 and products arising from R^+ are obtained
if R = aryl, diazonium ion can be isolated

Key features: diazonium ions are important intermediates in chemistry of aromatic compounds
3° amines generally don't react with nitrosating agents, unless one of the
substituents is an aryl group (ring nitrosation then occurs)

Oxidation of amines (23.7.C)

Equation:

2^O amines: $R_2NH \xrightarrow{[Ox]} R_2N-OH$ (hydroxylamines)

3° amines: $R_3N: \xrightarrow{\text{[Ox]}} R_3N\!-\!O^-$ (amine oxides)

Generality: R = alkyl
$\quad\quad\quad\quad\quad$ [Ox] = H_2O_2 or $R'CO_3H$

Key features: oxidation to hydroxylamines usually occurs in poor yield

Vilsmeier reaction (23.7.D)

Equation:

$$\underset{\text{O}}{\overset{\text{O}}{\underset{\|}{H\!C\!N(CH_3)_2}}} \xrightarrow{POCl_3} \underset{\textit{Vilsmeier reagent}}{\overset{Cl}{\underset{\|}{H\!C\!=\!N(CH_3)_2}}} \xrightarrow{} \xrightarrow{H_2O}$$

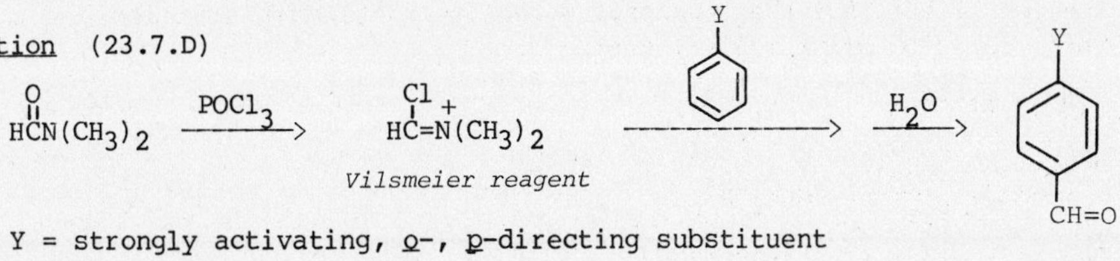

Generality: Y = strongly activating, o-, p-directing substituent

Elimination of amines (23.7.E)

Hofmann degradation:

Equation:

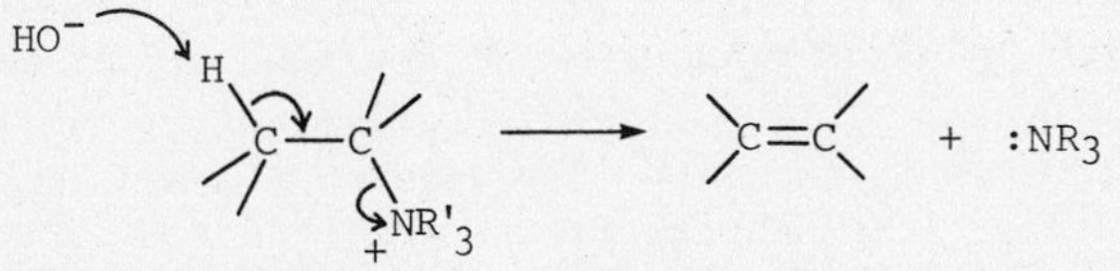

$$\xrightarrow{} \quad \overset{}{C\!=\!C} \quad + \quad :NR_3$$

Generality: $R' \neq H$, usually CH_3
$\quad\quad\quad\quad\quad$ elimination usually involves pyrolysis of quaternary ammonium hydroxide salt

Key features: mechanism involves **anti**-elimination
$\quad\quad\quad\quad\quad$ Hofmann rule: least-substituted alkene is the major product
$\quad\quad\quad\quad\quad$ S_N2 displacement of CH_3 group common side reaction when $R' = CH_3$

Cope elimination:

Equation:

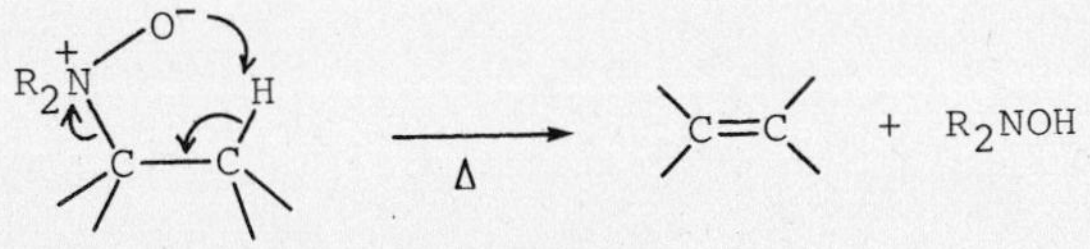

$$\xrightarrow{\Delta} \quad \overset{}{C\!=\!C} \quad + \quad R_2NOH$$

Generality: $R \neq H$
$\quad\quad\quad\quad\quad$ elimination proceeds at $150\text{-}200^{\circ}$

Key features: mechanism involves **syn**-elimination

Enamine formation and alkylation (23.8)

Equation:

$$-\overset{O}{\underset{\|}{C}}-CH \;+\; R_2NH \;\rightleftharpoons\; -\overset{NR_2}{\underset{\|}{C}}=C \xrightarrow{R'X} -\overset{+NR_2}{\underset{\|}{C}}-\overset{}{\underset{\|}{C}}-R' \xrightarrow{H_2O} -\overset{O}{\underset{\|}{C}}-\overset{}{\underset{\|}{C}}-R'$$

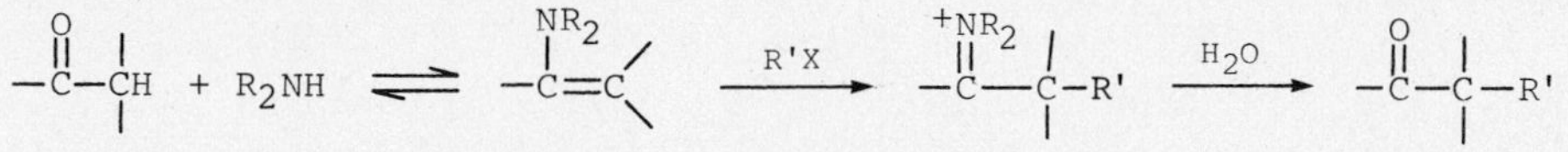

Generality: R' must be reactive toward S_N2 displacement

Key features: useful method for mono-alkylation of ketones

Mannich reaction (23.8)

Equation:

$$-\overset{OH}{\underset{\|}{C}}=C \;+\; C\!=\!\overset{+}{N}R_2 \xrightarrow{-H^+} -\overset{O}{\underset{\|}{C}}-\overset{}{\underset{\|}{C}}-\overset{}{\underset{\|}{C}}-NR_2$$

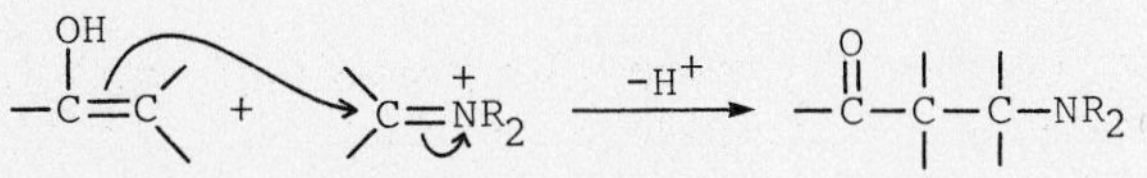

Generality: acid-catalyzed reaction
$\quad\quad\quad\quad\quad$ immonium ion usually derived from an aldehyde and 2° amine

Key features: useful carbon-carbon bond-forming reaction

23.C   Important Concepts and Hints

The amino group is different from the other functional groups you have encountered because, in its neutral form, it is basic and appreciably nucleophilic. Other functional groups require strong acid to be completely protonated, and usually it is only when they are in a deprotonated, anionic form that they are good nucleophiles (for instance: acetylide anions from acetylenes, enolates from ketones, etc.). As you know, acidity and basicity are commonly indicated by referring to the "pK_a" of a compound. The pK_a value indicates the position of the following equilibrium:

$$H-Y \xrightleftharpoons{K_a} Y^- + H^+ \; ; \qquad K_a = \frac{[H^+][Y^-]}{[HY]} \; ; \qquad pK_a = -\log K_a$$

It is clearly convenient to use the same term to indicate both how acidic H-Y is and how basic Y^- is, since they are related. But confusion can arise if you forget that pK_a literally refers to a compound functioning as an acid; i.e., losing a proton. This has not been a problem when discussing the functional groups presented in the text previously, but it can arise in the chemistry of amines. In Chapter 4 of this Study Guide, we pointed out what was wrong with the common statement: "The pK_a of ammonia is 9." Two correct statements are: "The pK_a of ammonium ion is 9", or "The pK_a of ammonia is 34." Because acid-base chemistry plays such an important role in the reactions of amines, it would be a good idea for you to review Chapter 4 of the text and of this Study Guide.

Much of the chemistry of amines involves the formation and reactions of imines and immonium ions. These reactions are analogous to those of carbonyl compounds to a great extent, as you can see from the list below. In general, imines (the neutral forms) are less reactive toward nucleophilic attack than are their carbonyl counterparts, and immonium ions (the cationic forms) are more reactive than their carbonyl analogs.

Starting Material	Reaction	Product
	reduction (H_2/catalyst; $LiAlH_4$; $NaBH_4$; (i-PrO)$_3$Al; etc.)	
	reduction (H_2/catalyst; $LiAlH_4$; $NaBH_4$ or $NaBH_3CN$; Eschweiler-Clarke and Leuckart)	
	aldol condensation	
	Mannich reaction	
	enol formation (acid- or base-catalyzed)	
	enamine formation	

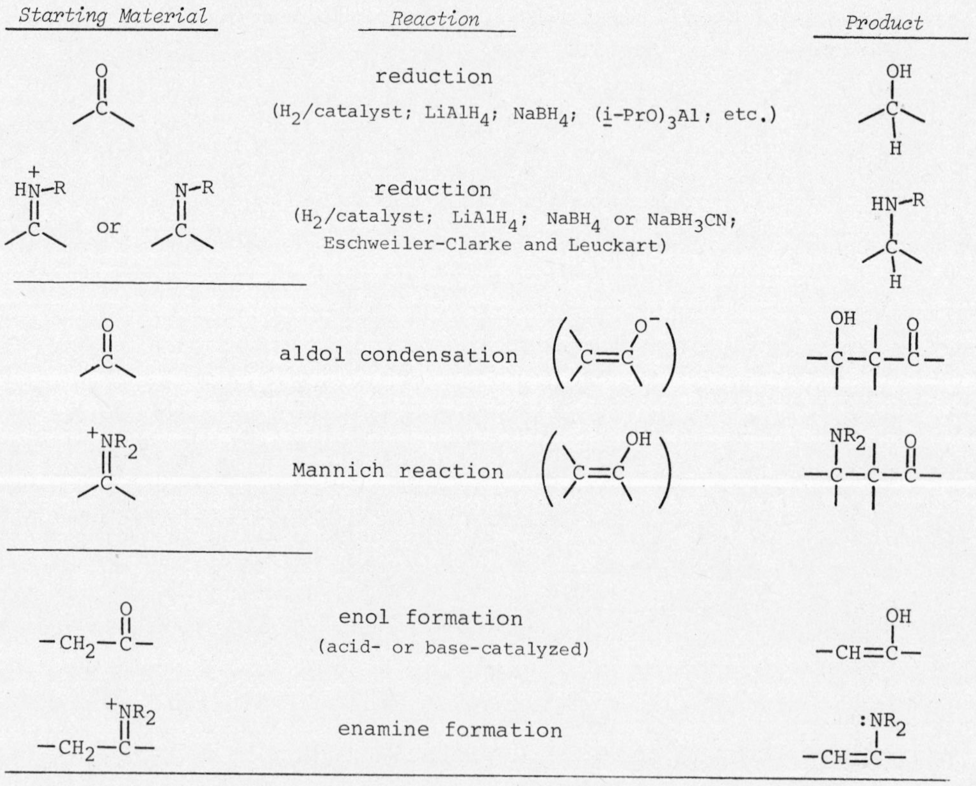

23.D   **Answers to Exercises**

23.1 $R_1R_2R_3R_4N^+ + X^- \rightleftharpoons R_1X + R_2R_3R_4N$ (inverts)

In this specific case, the most reactive group for S_N2 reaction by X^- is allyl:

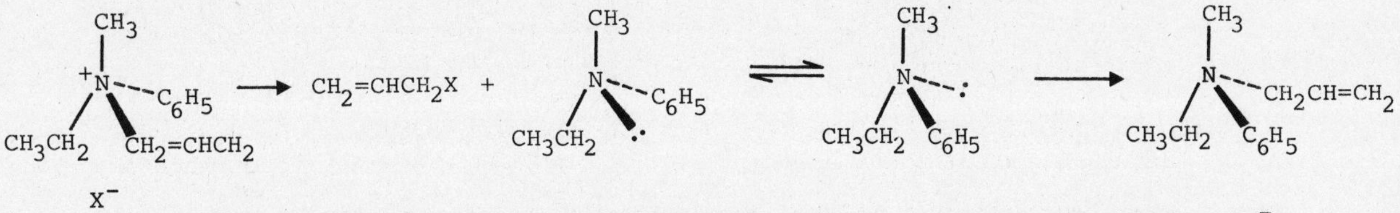

I^- is generally more nucleophilic and faster in S_N2 reactions than Br^-.

23.2   methanamine   N-ethylethanamine   N,N-dipropylpropanamine

N-methylethanamine   N-ethyl-N-methylethanamine   N-ethyl-N-methylcyclopropanamine

1-methylpropanamine   1-ethyl-3-methylbutanamine

N,N-dimethylethanamine   N,N-diethyl-1,3-dimethylbutanamine

N-ethyl-N,1-dimethylpropanamine   N,3-dimethylpentanamine

benzenamine   3-bromobenzenamine   4-nitrobenzenamine   N,N-dimethylbenzenamine

4-methylaminobutanoic acid   4-aminobenzoic acid

4-methylbenzenamine   3-methoxybenzenamine   2-ethoxybenzenamine

23.3   IR: no N-H

NMR: δ 1.0, d } overlapped, { 4 CH$\underline{C}$H$_3$

       1.0, t } 15H total { 1 -CH$_2$C$\underline{H}_3$

    2.5, q, 2H: -C$\underline{H}_2$CH$_3$

    3.0, septet, 2H: -C$\underline{H}$(CH$_3$)$_2$

CMR: four different resonances

<u>Structure</u>: diethylpropylamine, $(CH_3CH_2)_2NCH_2CH_2CH_3$

23.4 $\underline{K}_a = \dfrac{[H^+][RNH_2]}{[RNH_3^+]}$ $\underline{K}_a \times \underline{K}_b = \dfrac{[H^+][RNH_2]}{[RNH_3^+]} \times \dfrac{[RNH_3^+][OH^-]}{[RNH_2]}$

$= [H^+][OH^-] = \underline{K}_w = 10^{-14}$ M^2

$pK_a(NH_2^-) = 14 - pK_a(NH_3)$

    $14 - 34 = -20$ $-\log(\underline{K}_a \times \underline{K}_b) = pK_a + pK_b = -\log(10^{-14}) = 14$

23.5

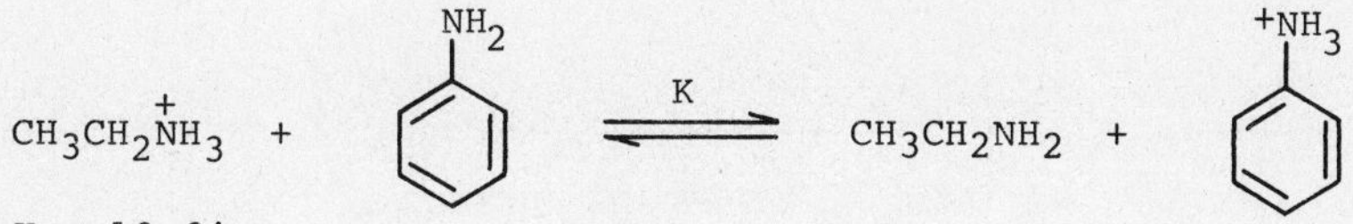

$CH_3CH_2\overset{+}{N}H_3$ + ⟷ $CH_3CH_2NH_2$ +

$pK_a = 10.64$ $pK_a = 4.60$

$K = \dfrac{10^{4.60}}{10^{10.64}} = 10^{-6.04} = 9.1 \times 10^{-7}$

$pK_a = 2.75$ $pK_a = 4.60$

$K = \dfrac{10^{4.60}}{10^{2.75}} = 10^{1.85} = 71$

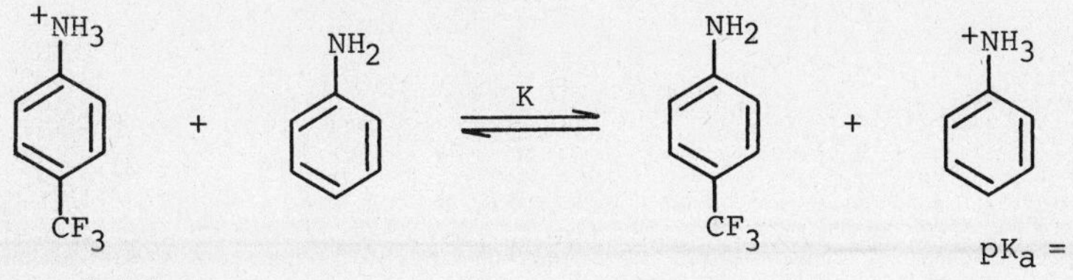

23.6 If you make the ester of racemic 2-octanol with (S)-1-methoxy-1-phenylacetic acid, two diastereomers will be obtained:

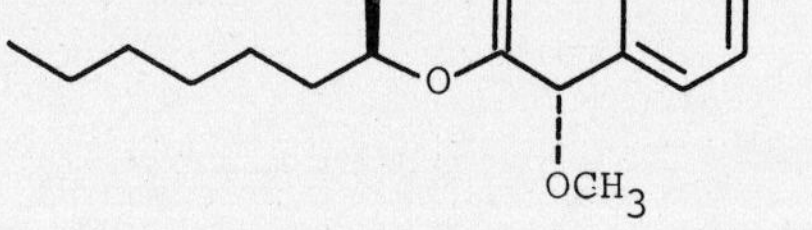

(R)-1-methylheptyl
(S)-1-methoxy-1-phenylacetate

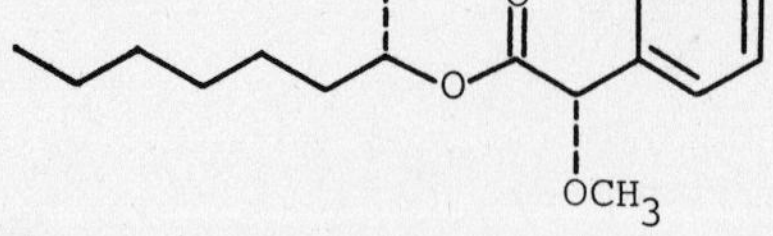

(S)-1-methylheptyl
(S)-1-methoxy-1-phenylacetate

These isomers have different physical properties and can be separated by crystallization, chromatography, etc. After separation of the isomers, hydrolysis of each ester separately will release the optically active alcohols.

23.7

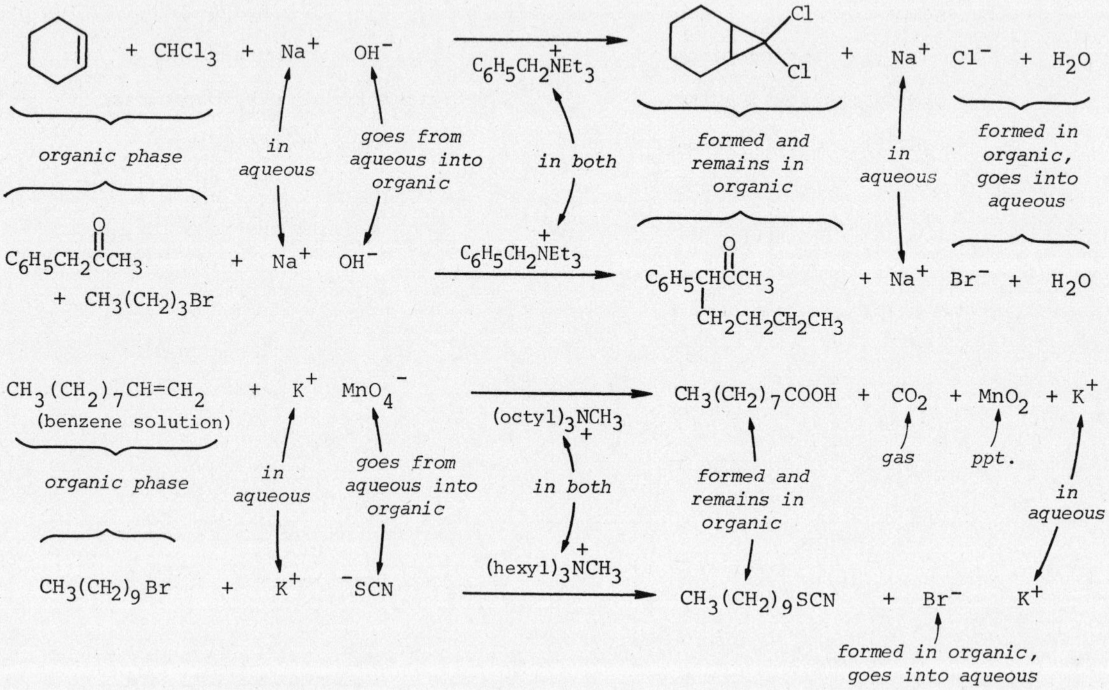

23.8 Alkylation of the phthalimide ion involves S$_N$2 displacement, which will not occur with a neopentyl halide (too sterically hindered) or a t-butyl halide (E2 elimination instead). In addition, the sequence can only give primary amines, and cannot provide di-n-propylamine.

23.9

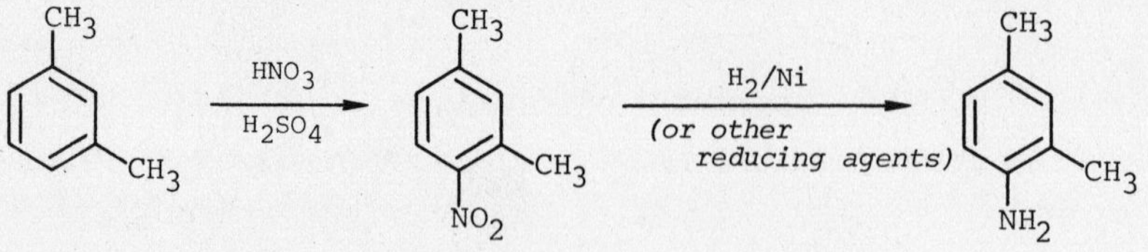

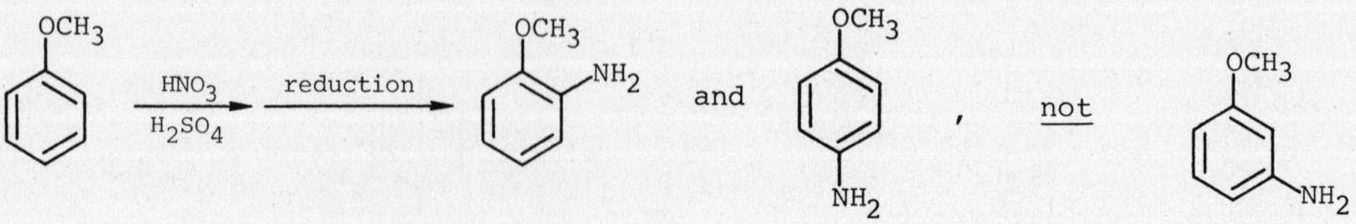

$$\text{(benzaldehyde)} \xrightarrow[\text{H}_2\text{SO}_4]{\text{HNO}_3} \xrightarrow[\text{HCl}]{\text{SnCl}_2} \text{(3-aminobenzaldehyde)} \quad (\text{not } ortho)$$

23.10 (a) $(CH_3)_2CHCH_2CH_2Br \xrightarrow{NaCN} (CH_3)_2CHCH_2CH_2C\equiv N \xrightarrow{LiAlH_4} (CH_3)_2CHCH_2CH_2CH_2NH_2$

(b) $(CH_3)_2CHCH=O \xrightarrow{HCN} (CH_3)_2CHCHC\equiv N \xrightarrow{H_2/Ni} (CH_3)_2CHCHCH_2NH_2$

with OH on the central carbons

23.11

(a) 4-methylbenzylamine (CH_2NH_2 / CH_3)

(b) cyclopentyl—$NHCH_2CH_2CH_3$

(c) $C_6H_5CH_2CH(CH_3)HN(CH_3)_2$

(d) 1,2-dimethylpyrrolidine

23.12 (a) $CH_3CH_2CH_2CH_2NH_2 \xrightarrow[Et_3N]{ClCCH(CH_3)_2} CH_3CH_2CH_2CH_2NHCCH(CH_3)_2 \xrightarrow{LiAlH_4} CH_3CH_2CH_2CH_2NHCH_2CH(CH_3)_2$

(b) $(CH_3)_2CHNH_2 \xrightarrow{CH_3CCl} \xrightarrow{LiAlH_4} (CH_3)_2CHNH(CH_2CH_3) \xrightarrow[\text{2. LiAlH}_4]{\text{1. ClCCH}_2\text{CH}_2\text{CH}_3} (CH_3)_2CHNCH_2CH_2CH_2CH_3$ with CH_2CH_3

23.13

$CH_3CH_2CH-CH_2CH_2COOH$ (with CH_3 branch)

or 2-bromobenzoic acid ($C_6H_4(Br)COOH$)

$\xrightarrow{SOCl_2} R-CCl \xrightarrow{NH_3} R-CNH_2 \xrightarrow{NaOH, Cl_2}$

$\xrightarrow{NaN_3}$

$\xrightarrow[H_2SO_4]{NaN_3} R-C-N_3 \xrightarrow{\Delta} \xrightarrow{H_2O} R-NH_2$

23.14 (a) $CH_3CH_2CH_2NH_2 \xrightarrow[HCl]{NaNO_2} CH_3CH_2CH_2Cl + CH_3CH_2CH_2OH + CH_3CHCH_3$ with OH

(b) $(CH_3CH_2CH_2)_2NH \xrightarrow[HCl]{NaNO_2} (CH_3CH_2CH_2)_2NN=O$

(c) $(CH_3CH_2CH_2)_3N \xrightarrow[HCl]{NaNO_2} \left[(CH_3CH_2CH_2)_3\overset{+}{N}H \quad Cl^- \right]$ *only product*

(d) aniline (NH_2) $\xrightarrow[HCl]{NaNO_2}$ benzenediazonium chloride ($\overset{+}{N_2}$ Cl^-)

(e) CH_3CH_2NH—C$_6$H$_5$ $\xrightarrow[HCl]{NaNO_2}$ $CH_3CH_2NN=O$—C$_6$H$_5$

(f) $(CH_3CH_2)_2N$—C$_6$H$_5$ $\xrightarrow[HCl]{NaNO_2}$ $(CH_3CH_2)_2N$—C$_6$H$_4$—N=O

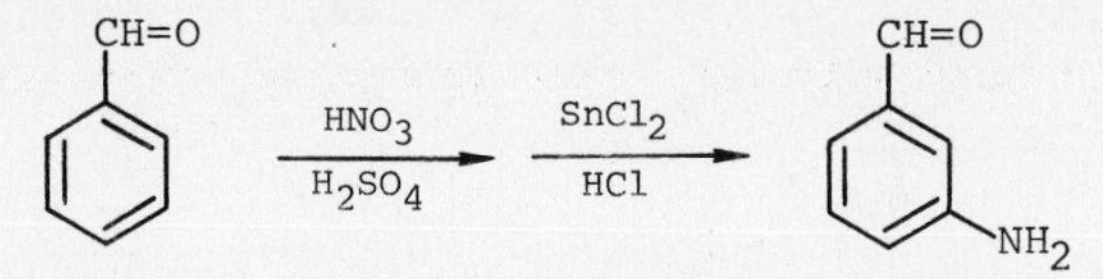

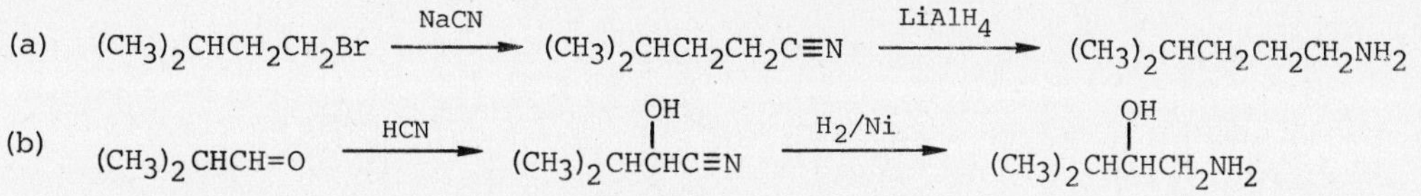

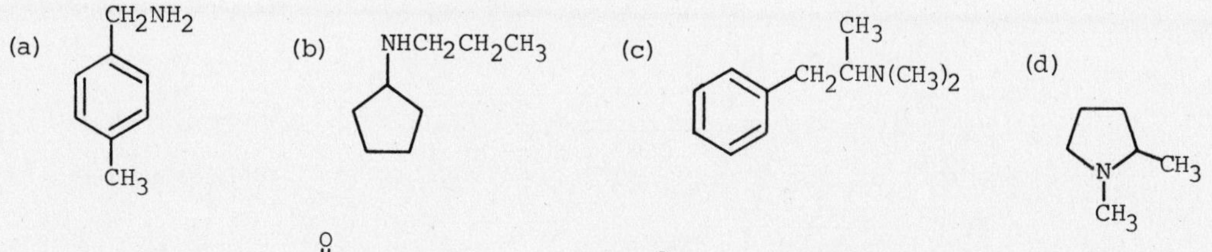

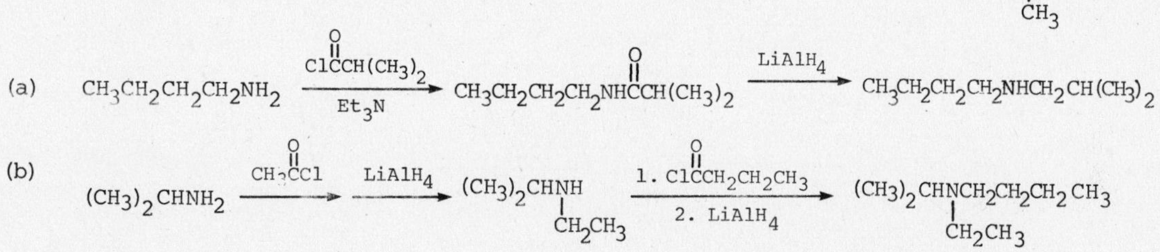

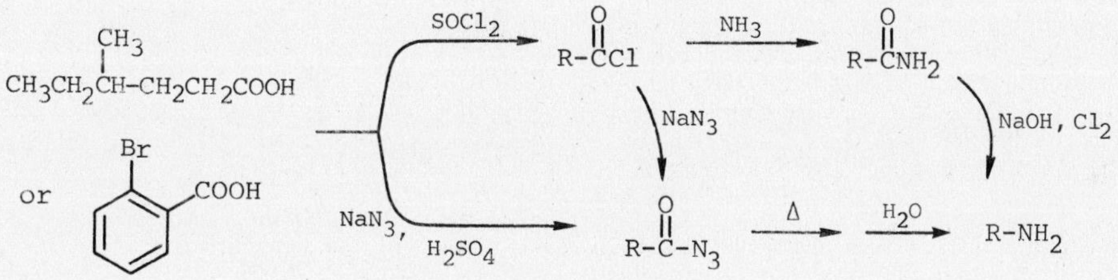

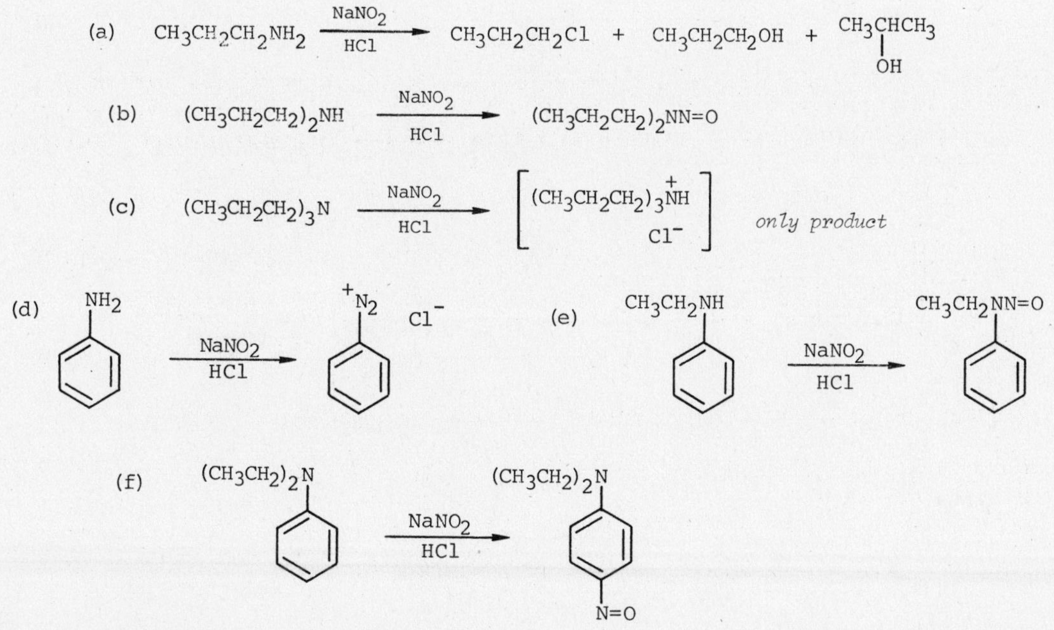

23.15 (a)

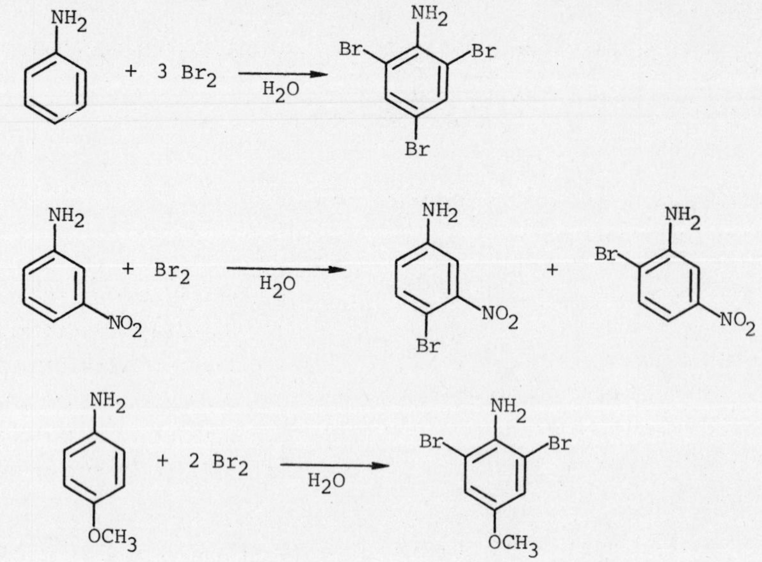

NH$_2$ + 3 Br$_2$ $\xrightarrow{H_2O}$ (2,4,6-tribromoaniline)

NH$_2$ (with NO$_2$) + Br$_2$ $\xrightarrow{H_2O}$ product + product

NH$_2$ (with OCH$_3$) + 2 Br$_2$ $\xrightarrow{H_2O}$ product

(b)

NH$_2$ $\xrightarrow[\text{pyridine}]{Ac_2O}$ HN$\overset{O}{\overset{\|}{C}}CH_3$ $\xrightarrow[\text{CH}_3\text{COOH}]{HNO_3}$ HN$\overset{O}{\overset{\|}{C}}CH_3$ (with NO$_2$) + HN$\overset{O}{\overset{\|}{C}}CH_3$ (with NO$_2$)

1. H$^+$
2. OH$^-$

NH$_2$ (with NO$_2$)

(mixture of ortho and para)

NH$_2$ (with NO$_2$) $\xrightarrow{\text{same sequence}}$ O$_2$N—NH$_2$—NO$_2$ + NH$_2$ (with two NO$_2$)

NH$_2$ (with OCH$_3$) $\xrightarrow{\text{same sequence}}$ NH$_2$, NO$_2$ (with OCH$_3$)

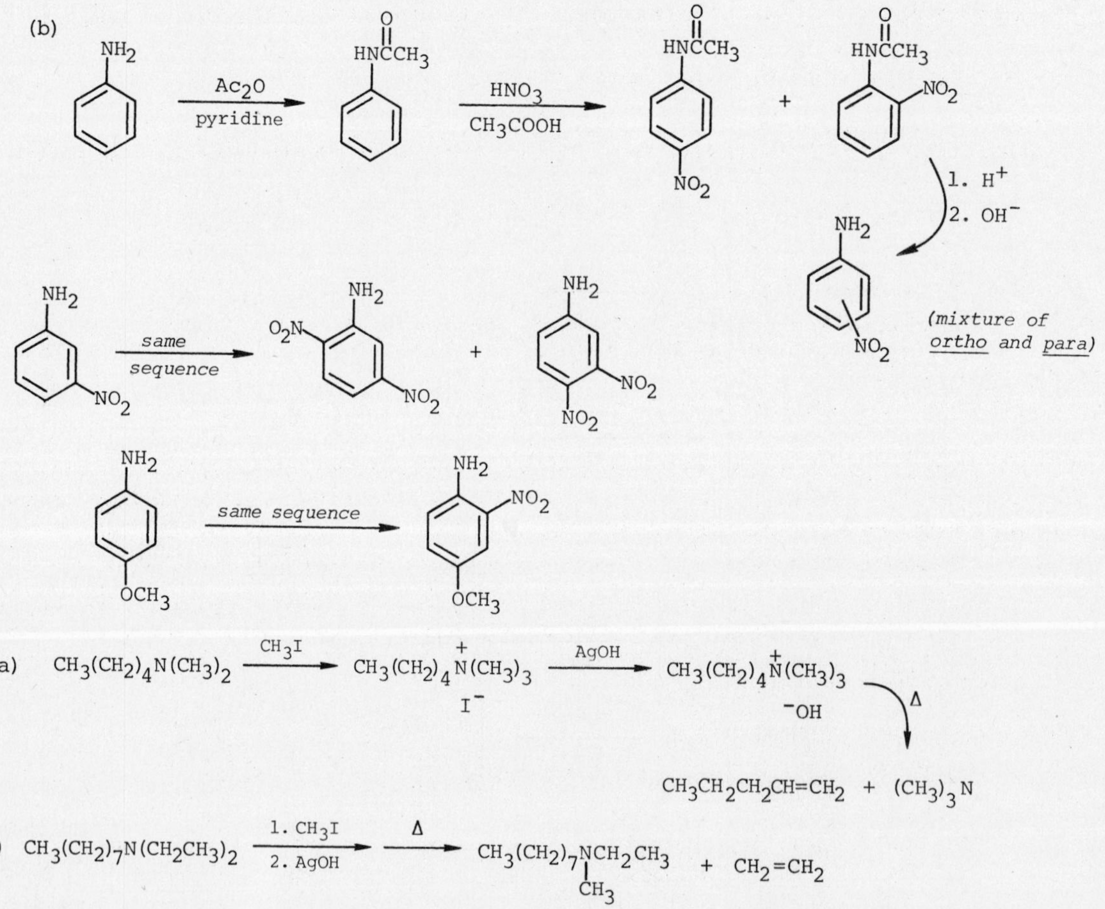

23.16 (a) CH$_3$(CH$_2$)$_4$N(CH$_3$)$_2$ $\xrightarrow{CH_3I}$ CH$_3$(CH$_2$)$_4$$\overset{+}{N}$(CH$_3$)$_3$ I$^-$ $\xrightarrow{AgOH}$ CH$_3$(CH$_2$)$_4$$\overset{+}{N}$(CH$_3$)$_3$ $^-$OH $\xrightarrow{\Delta}$

CH$_3$CH$_2$CH$_2$CH=CH$_2$ + (CH$_3$)$_3$N

(b) CH$_3$(CH$_2$)$_7$N(CH$_2$CH$_3$)$_2$ $\xrightarrow[\text{2. AgOH}]{\text{1. CH}_3\text{I} \quad \Delta}$ CH$_3$(CH$_2$)$_7$$\underset{CH_3}{N}CH_2CH_3$ + CH$_2$=CH$_2$

(c) (CH$_3$CH$_2$)$_3$N $\xrightarrow{H_2O_2}$ (CH$_3$CH$_2$)$_3$$\overset{+}{N}$—O$^-$ $\xrightarrow{\Delta}$ (CH$_3$CH$_2$)$_2$NOH + CH$_2$=CH$_2$

(d) CH$_3$CH$_2$—C—C—N(CH$_3$)$_2$ $\xrightarrow{H_2O_2}$ [intermediate] $\xrightarrow{\Delta}$ CH$_3$CH$_2$ / CH$_3$ \,C=C\, H / D + (CH$_3$)$_2$NOH

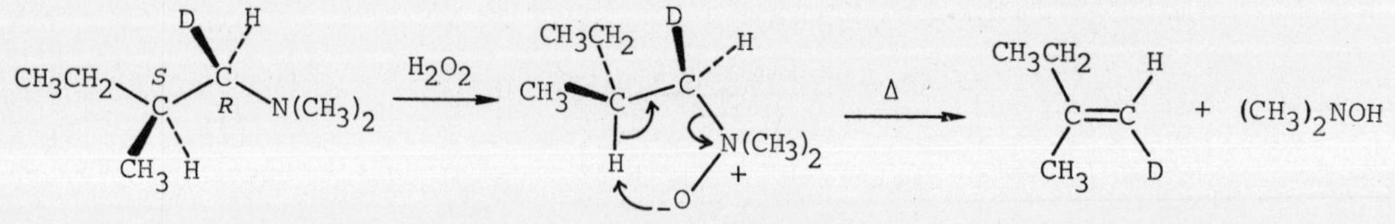

23.17

$$CH_3CH_2\overset{\overset{\displaystyle O}{\|}}{C}CH_2CH_3 \; + \; CH_2{=}O \; + \; (CH_3)_2\overset{+}{N}H_2 \; Cl^- \; \longrightarrow \; CH_3CH_2\overset{\overset{\displaystyle O}{\|}}{C}\underset{\underset{\displaystyle CH_3}{|}}{C}HCH_2N(CH_3)_2$$

23.E   Answers and Explanations for Problems

1. (a) 2-methylbutanamine

    (b) trimethylamine
            (N,N-dimethylmethanamine)

    (c) N-ethyl-N-methyl-2-propenamine

    (d) p-bromophenyltrimethylammonium chloride

    (e) N-ethyl-N-nitrosobenzenamine

    (f) N-ethyl-4-nitrosobenzenamine

    (g) ethyltrimethylammonium iodide

    (h) N,N-dimethylpropanamine oxide

    (i) 1-ethyl-N,N-dimethylpropanamine

    (j) N-ethyl-3-methylbenzenamine

    (k) N,4-diisopropyl-N-methylbenzenamine

    (l) 2,4,6-trichloroaniline

2. IR: doublet at 3290 and 3370 cm^{-1} and bands at 1600, 1160, and 850 cm^{-1} suggest $R{-}NH_2$

    NMR: δ 2.8, sextuplet, 1H: hydrogen with 5 adjacent H's, perhaps: $RCH_2{-}\underset{\underset{\displaystyle N}{|}}{C}H{-}CH_3$

    The 10:1 ratio of other hydrogens suggests: $CH_3CH_2{-}\underset{\underset{\displaystyle NH_2}{|}}{C}H{-}CH_3$

    CMR: four different carbons, and chemical shifts, are consistent with this structure.

3. IR: 3300 cm^{-1}, weak: R_2NH
          700 cm^{-1}:   NH wag

    NMR: δ 0.4, very broad, 1: NH
         1.0, d, 12: four equivalent CH_3's next to one hydrogen
         2.8, septet, 2: $(CH_3)_2CH$

    Structure: diisopropylamine, $(CH_3)_2CHNHCH(CH_3)_2$

4. In a planar amine, the bonding orbitals from nitrogen are sp^2 hybrids which have a natural angle of 120°. The ring strain compared to a three-membered ring is greater than the difference between the angle in the aziridine ring and the 107° angle in the open amine.

    An alternative but equivalent explanation focuses on the lone pair. In an ordinary amine, this lone pair is in an orbital having some s-character; in the planar amine the lone pair is in a pure p-orbital. Removing s-character from the lone pair electrons takes some energy. In aziridine, the narrow bond angle of the three-membered ring requires more p-character and leaves more s-character for the lone pair. This greater degree of s-character requires more energy to form the planar system with a p-lone pair.

5. (a) $$K_a = \frac{[RNH_2][H^+]}{[RNH_3{}^+]} \qquad -\log K_a = -\log[H^+] - \log\frac{[RNH_2]}{[RNH_3{}^+]}$$

    At equal $[RNH_2]$ and $[RNH_3{}^+]$, the last term = 0, so that pK_a = pH
              for CH_3NH_2, pK_a = pH = 10.62

    (b) $\log[RNH_2]/[RNH_3{}^+]$ = $-pK_a$ + pH

	pH	$\log[RNH_2]/[RNH_3{}^+]$	$[RNH_2]/[RNH_3{}^+]$
for CH_3NH_2:	6	-4.62	2.4×10^{-5}
	8	-2.62	2.4×10^{-3}
	10	-0.62	0.24
	12	1.38	24

6.   (a) $CH_3NH_2 + H^+ \rightleftharpoons CH_3NH_3^+$

$$\underline{CH_3COOH \rightleftharpoons CH_3CO_2^- + H^+}$$

$$CH_3NH_2 + CH_3COOH \rightleftharpoons CH_3NH_3^+ + CH_3CO_2^-$$

$$K = \frac{[CH_3NH_3^+][CH_3CO_2^-]}{[CH_3NH_2][CH_3COOH]} = \frac{[CH_3NH_3^+]}{[CH_3NH_2][H^+]} \cdot \frac{[H^+][CH_3CO_2^-]}{[CH_3COOH]}$$

$$= \frac{K_a(CH_3COOH)}{K_a(CH_3NH_3^+)} = \frac{1.75 \times 10^{-5}}{2.40 \times 10^{-11}} = 7.29 \times 10^5$$

(b) Assume equal concentrations of amine and acid to start, then $7.29 \times 10^5 = \dfrac{x^2}{(a-x)^2}$

$$\frac{x}{a-x} = 854 \qquad \text{(from Problem \#5(b):)}$$

$$-\log 854 = -pK_a + pH$$

$$pH = 10.62 - \log 854 = 7.69$$

7.   (a)   Extract with dilute HCl to remove amine; extract with dilute NaOH or Na_2CO_3 to remove the carboxylic acid. Hydrocarbon remains.

(b) A mixture of both enantiomers of the hydrogen phthalate results. Reaction with an optically pure amine such as naturally-occurring brucine or strychnine gives two diastereomeric salts, e.g.,

$$(-)\text{brucine-H}^+ \quad (+) \text{ [COOR / CO}_2^-\text{]} \qquad \text{and} \qquad (-)\text{brucine-H}^+ \quad (-) \text{ [COOR / CO}_2^-\text{]}$$

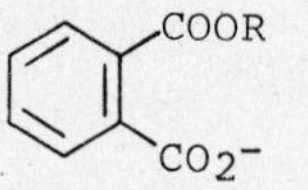

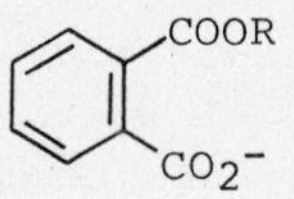

These salts are separated by crystallization. Actually, the brucine (-)(+) salt is usually less soluble in acetone. The individual salts are treated with dilute HCl (which removes the alkaloid as the soluble hydrochloride). Heating each hydrogen phthalate with aqueous NaOH hydrolyzes the ester and gives each enantiomer of the alcohol.

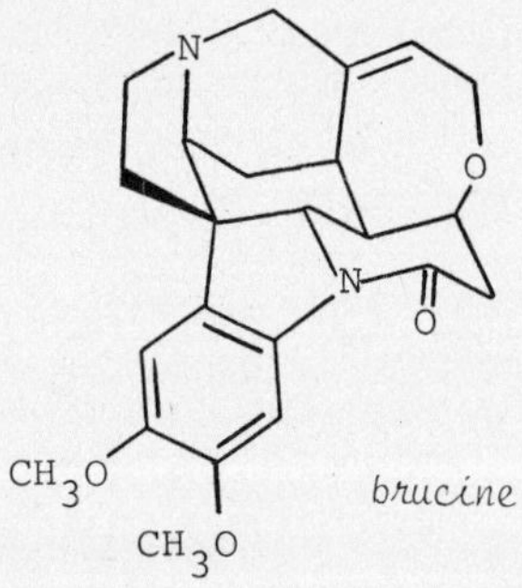

brucine

8.   (a)   [structure: HNCOCH$_3$, NO$_2$, CH$_3$ substituted benzene]

(b) [structure: CH$_3$, NH$_2$ substituted benzene]

(c) [structure: HNCOCH$_3$, Cl, Cl, NH$_2$ substituted benzene]

(d) [structure: NH$_2$, COOH substituted benzene]

(e) [structure: CH$_3$ branched, $N(CH_3)_2$, C=O, phenyl]

(f) [structure: CH$_3$, NH$_2$, CH$_3$, NO$_2$ substituted benzene]

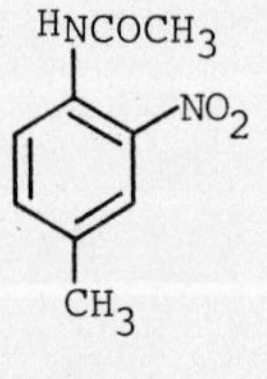

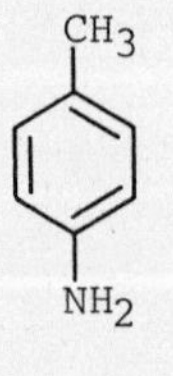

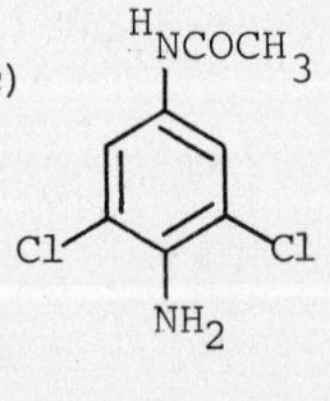

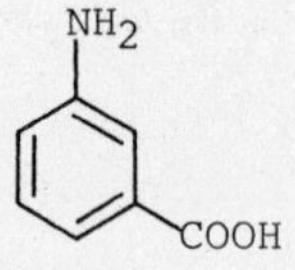

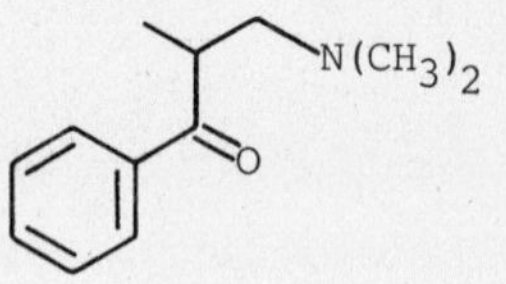

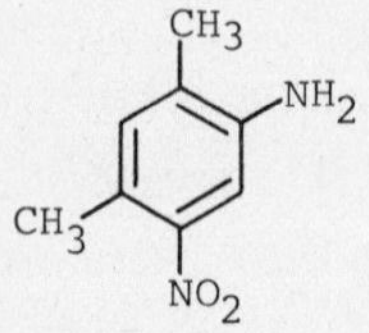

9. $CH_3\overset{O}{\overset{\|}{C}}CH_3 + CH_2{=}O + (CH_3)_2\overset{+}{N}H_2\ Cl^- \longrightarrow CH_3\overset{O}{\overset{\|}{C}}CH_2CH_2N(CH_3)_2 \xrightarrow{CH_3I}$

$$CH_3\overset{O}{\overset{\|}{C}}CH{=}CH_2 + (CH_3)_3N \xleftarrow[\Delta]{Ag_2O} CH_3\overset{O}{\overset{\|}{C}}CH_2CH_2\overset{+}{N}(CH_3)_2\ I^-$$

10.   (a)   primary arylamine $\longrightarrow$ diazonium ion: $C_6H_5N_2^+$

(b)   secondary amine $\longrightarrow$ N-nitrosamine: $C_6H_5N\overset{NO}{\underset{CH_3}{}}$

(c)   substituted amide $\longrightarrow$ N-nitroso amide: $C_6H_5N\overset{NO}{\underset{COCH_3}{}}$

     N-nitroso amides are best prepared by reaction of
the amide with NOCl. They rearrange readily to provide diazoesters, $RN{=}NO\overset{O}{\overset{\|}{C}}R'$, which
then undergo further radical or carbocation reactions involving $R^\bullet$ or R^+.

(d)   tertiary arylamine $\longrightarrow$ electrophilic substitution: $ON{-}\langle\!\bigcirc\!\rangle{-}N(CH_3)_2$

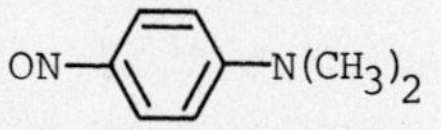

(e)   primary alkylamine $\longrightarrow$ diazonium ion which decomposes: $C_6H_5CH_2OH$

(f) $C_6H_5{-}HN{-}NH_2$ $\xrightarrow{HONO}$ $C_6H_5{-}HN{-}\overset{+}{N}{\equiv}N$ $\xrightarrow{-H^+}$ $[\; C_6H_5{-}{}^-N{-}\overset{+}{N}{\equiv}N \;\longleftrightarrow\; C_6H_5{-}N{=}\overset{+}{N}{=}N^- \;]$

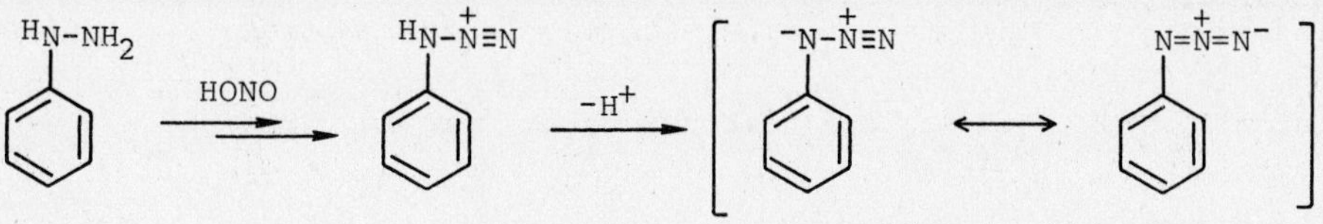

                                               (phenyl azide)

(g)   secondary amine $\longrightarrow$ N-nitrosamine: $C_6H_5CH_2N\underset{N=O}{CH_3}$

(h)   tertiary alkylamine $\longrightarrow$ no reaction (except salt formation: $C_6H_5CH_2\overset{H}{\underset{+}{N}}(CH_3)_2$ Cl^-)

(i)   same answer as for part (c): $C_6H_5CH_2\underset{N=O}{N}COCH_3$

11.   Dipole moments are oriented because of the conjugation effects indicated:

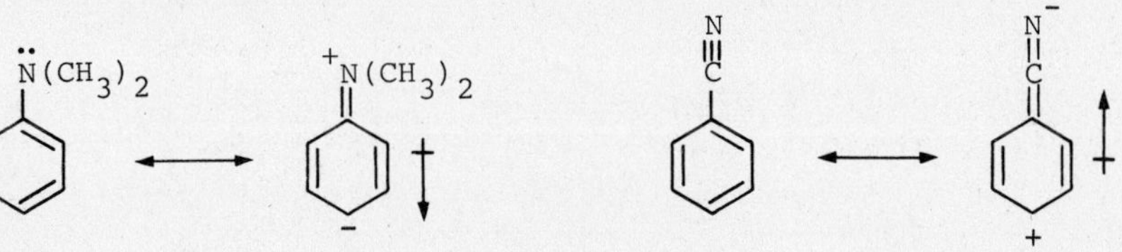

     $\ddot{N}(CH_3)_2 \;\longleftrightarrow\; {}^+N(CH_3)_2$ $N{\equiv}C \;\longleftrightarrow\; {}^-N{=}C$

When the functional groups are conjugated in the
same molecule, the dipolar effects are enhanced
by the structure drawn at the right. Since the
charges are now far apart, even a small contribution by this structure has an important effect
on the dipole moment.

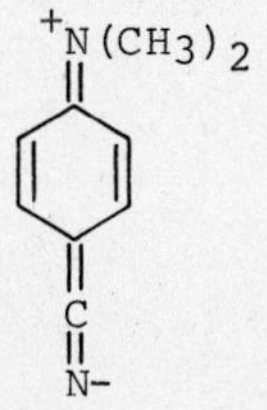

                            ${}^+N(CH_3)_2 \cdots C{=}N^-$

12. $N(CH_3)_2$ $+ Br_2 \longrightarrow$ (cyclohexadienyl cation with H Br, $+$) $+ Br^-$ $\xrightarrow{-H^+}$ $N(CH_3)_2{-}\langle\!\bigcirc\!\rangle{-}Br$

The resonance structures: $N(CH_3)_2 \;\longleftrightarrow\; N(CH_3)_2 \;\longleftrightarrow\; {}^+N(CH_3)_2$ (with H Br) *stable immonium ion*

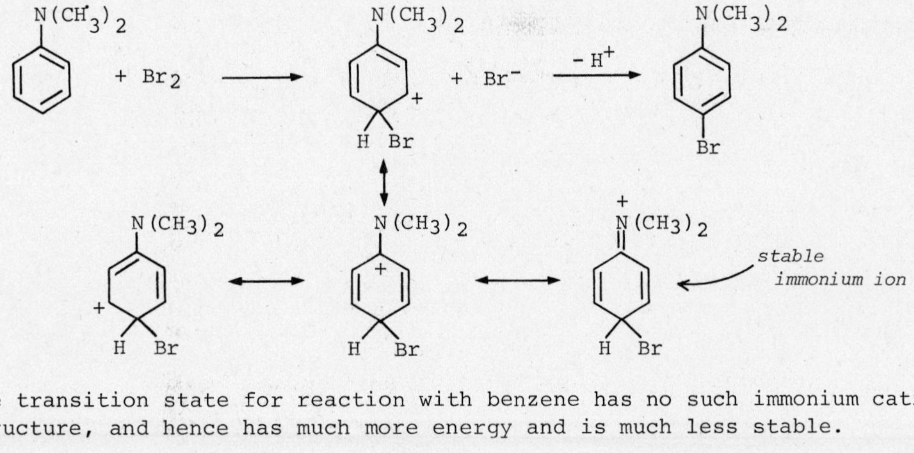

The transition state for reaction with benzene has no such immonium cation
structure, and hence has much more energy and is much less stable.

13. Aniline is a weaker base than aliphatic amines, in part because of conjugation of the nitrogen lone pair electrons with the aromatic π-system:

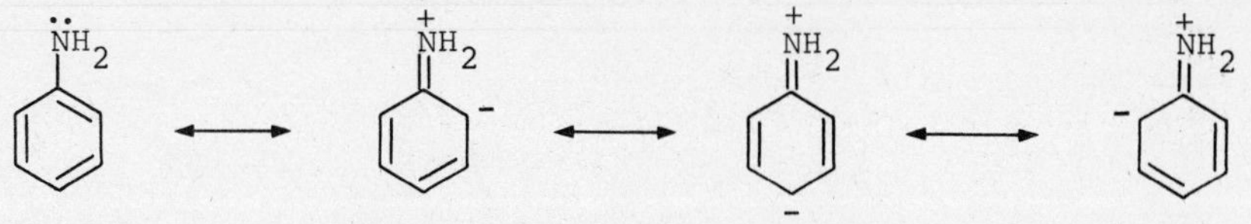

This conjugation is not present in the ammonium ion; hence, the amine has additional stabilization and the equilibrium, $RNH_3^+ \rightleftharpoons H^+ + RNH_2$ is displaced more to the right for R = aromatic ring compared to R = alkyl. However, in o-methyl-N,N-dimethylaniline, steric hindrance prevents effective conjugation (see (I) below). The $(CH_3)_2N$ group must twist at right angles to the ring (see (II) below). The nitrogen lone pair now cannot overlap with the π-system. This

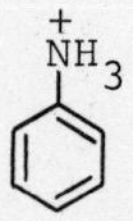

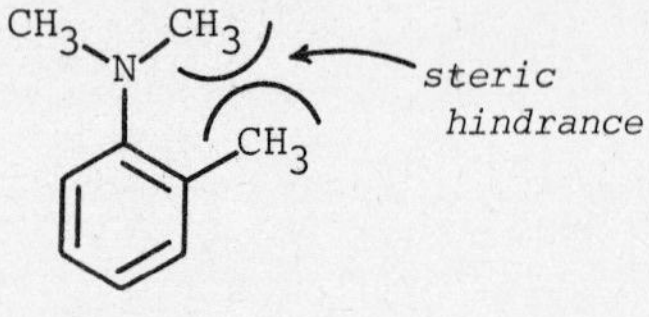

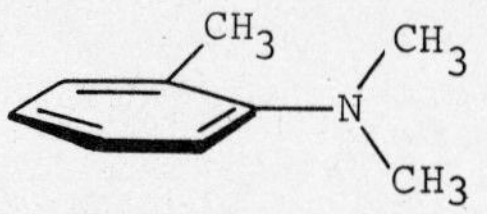

amine does not have additional conjugation stabilization, so it is more basic than the primary amine, in which the smaller hydrogens are not as involved in steric hindrance.

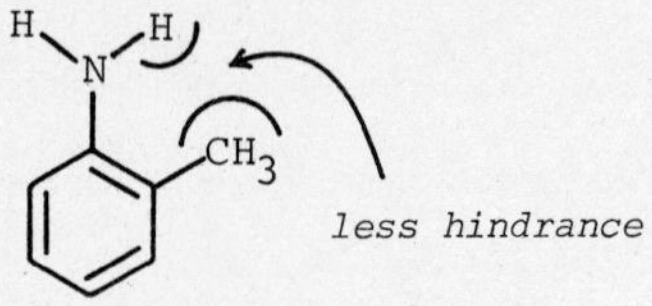

14. (a)

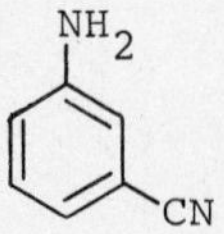

The basicity of p-cyanoaniline is reduced by

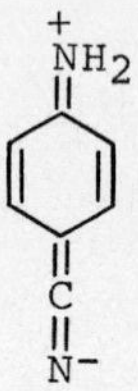

(b)

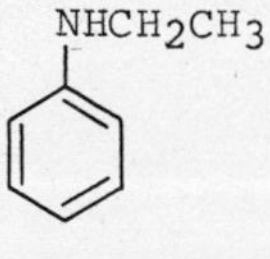

The basicity of the amide is reduced by

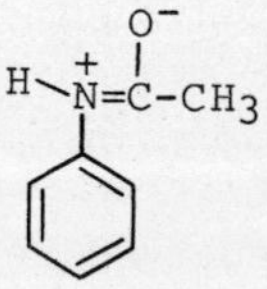

(c)

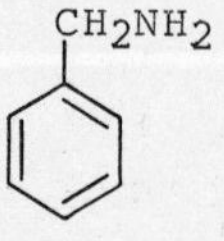

The basicity of the aromatic amine is reduced by

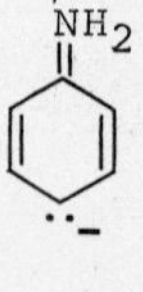

, etc.

(d)

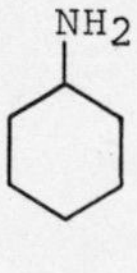

Same reason as for part (c) above.

(e)

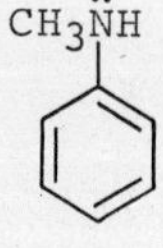

The lone pair of the imine is more sp^2 in character; more s-character = more stable electrons = less basic.

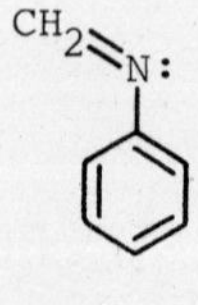

(f)

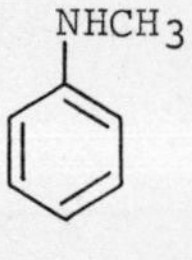

The Cl group is more electron-withdrawing than CH_3, because Cl is more electronegative than carbon.
Therefore, the structure illustrated at the right is less stable.

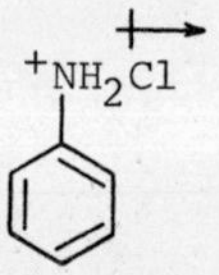

(g)

NH$_2$ / Cl (2-chloroaniline structure)

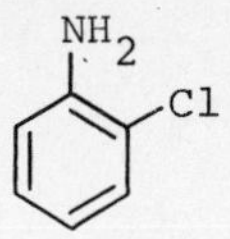

The effect of the electronegative Cl substituent is
much greater when it is attached directly to the nitrogen.

15. (a) $CH_3(CH_2)_3CH_2OH$ $\xrightarrow[H_2SO_4]{HBr}$ $CH_3(CH_2)_3CH_2Br$ $\xrightarrow[\text{(large excess)}]{NH_3}$ $CH_3(CH_2)_3CH_2NH_2$

or $\searrow$ Gabriel synthesis $\nearrow$

(b) $CH_3(CH_2)_3CH_2NH_2$ *[from (a)]* $\xrightarrow[\substack{HCO_2H \\ 100°}]{CH_2=O}$ $CH_3(CH_2)_3CH_2N(CH_3)_2$

(c) $CH_3CH_2CH_2OH$ $\xrightarrow{PCC}$ CH_3CH_2CHO $\xrightarrow[H_2/Pt]{\substack{NH_3 \\ C_2H_5OH}}$ $[\,CH_3CH_2CH_2NH_2\,]$ $\searrow$

$(CH_3CH_2CH_2)_2NCH_3$ $\xleftarrow[\substack{HCOOH \\ \Delta}]{CH_2=O}$ $(CH_3CH_2CH_2)_2NH$

(d) $(CH_3)_2CHCH_2CH_2OH$ $\xrightarrow[H_2SO_4]{HBr}$ $(CH_3)_2CHCH_2CH_2Br$ $\xrightarrow[\substack{\text{Gabriel} \\ \text{synthesis}}]{NH_3 \text{ or}}$ $(CH_3)_2CHCH_2CH_2NH_2$ $\searrow$

$\xrightarrow[\substack{(CH_3CO)_2O}]{CH_3COOH, \Delta \text{ or}}$

$(CH_3)_2CHCH_2CH_2NHCH_2CH_3$ $\xleftarrow{LiAlH_4}$ $(CH_3)_2CHCH_2CH_2NHCOCH_3$

16. (a) Requires a single inversion of configuration:

[structure (R) alcohol with OH] $\xrightarrow[\text{pyridine}]{TsCl}$ [structure (R) with OTs] $\xrightarrow{\text{= "FtN}^-\text{"}}$ [structure (S) with NFt] $\xrightarrow{H_2NNH_2}$ [structure (S) with NH$_2$]

(R)   *(R)*   *(S)*   *(S)*

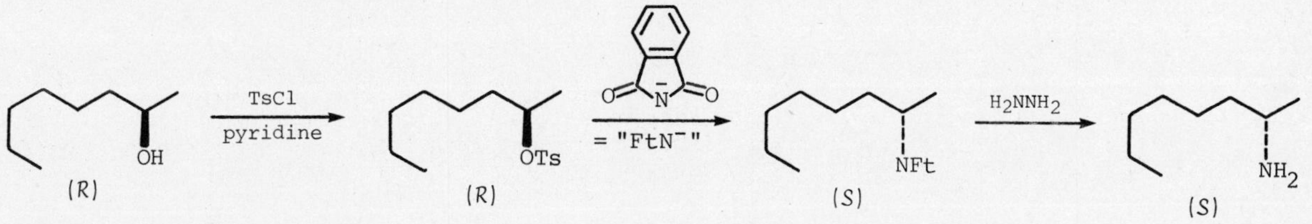

(b) Requires two inversions, to give overall retention:

[structure (R) with OH] $\xrightarrow[\text{pyridine}]{SOCl_2}$ [structure (S) with Cl] $\xrightarrow{\text{"FtN}^-\text{"}}$ [structure (R) with NFt] $\xrightarrow{H_2NNH_2}$ [structure (R) with NH$_2$]

(R)   *(S)*   *(R)*   *(R)*

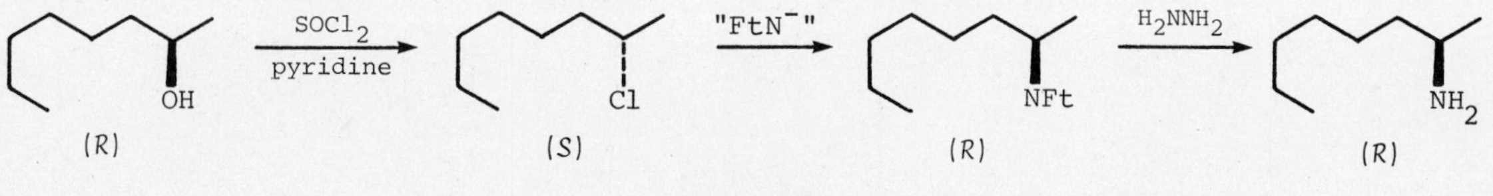

17. (a)

$2\ CH_3CH_2CHO$ $\xrightarrow{OH^-}$ $\underset{\underset{OH}{|}}{OHCCHCHCH_2CH_3}$ (with CH$_3$) $\xrightarrow[\Delta]{Ag_2O \quad HN_3}$ $\underset{\underset{OH}{|}}{H_2NCHCHCH_2CH_3}$ (with CH$_3$)

*mixture of
diastereomers*

(b) Best method is by epoxide opening:

[cis-2-butene structure] $\xrightarrow{C_6H_5CO_3H}$ [epoxide structure] $\xrightarrow{\text{= "FtN}^-\text{"}}$ [FtN / CH$_3$ / OH structure] $\xrightarrow{H_2NNH_2}$ [NH$_2$ / CH$_3$ / OH structure]

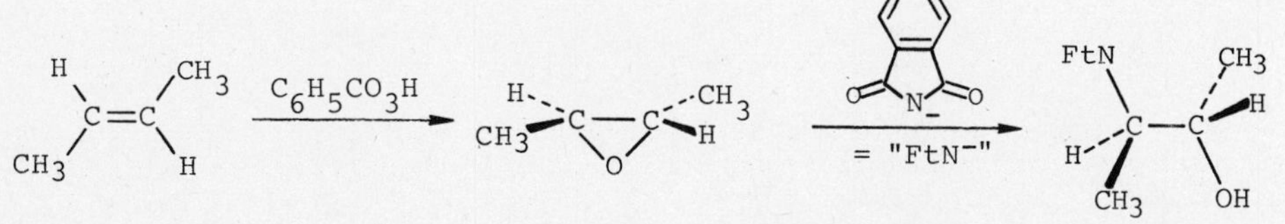

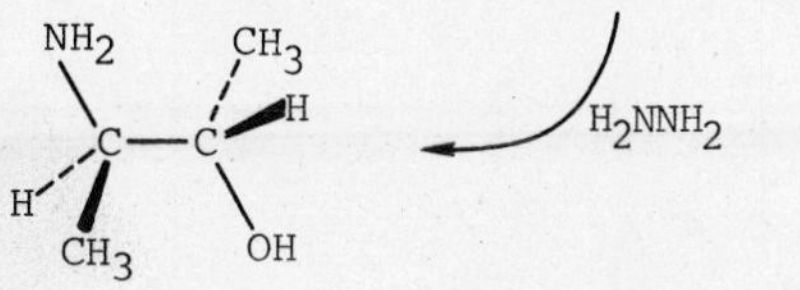

<u>NOTE</u>: what happens if phthalimide
attacks the other epoxide carbon?

(c)

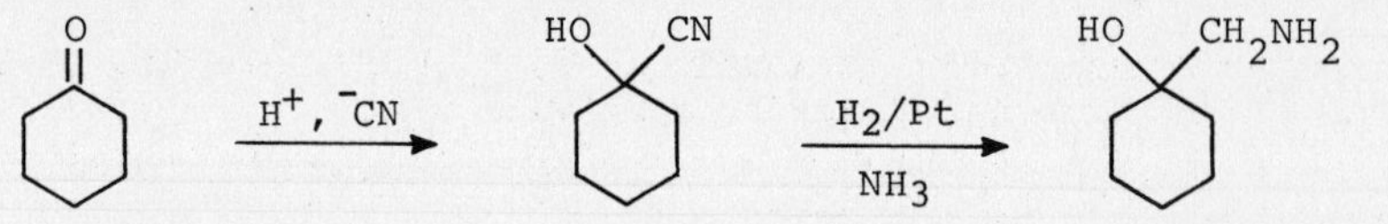

(d)

(e)

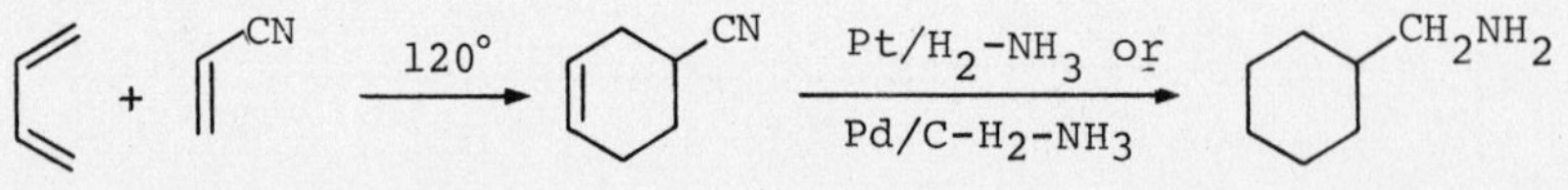

Catalytic hydrogenation reduces both the double bond and C≡N.

(Alternatively, use LiAlH$_4$ first *(to reduce CN)*, then Pt/H$_2$ *(to reduce double bond))*.

(f)

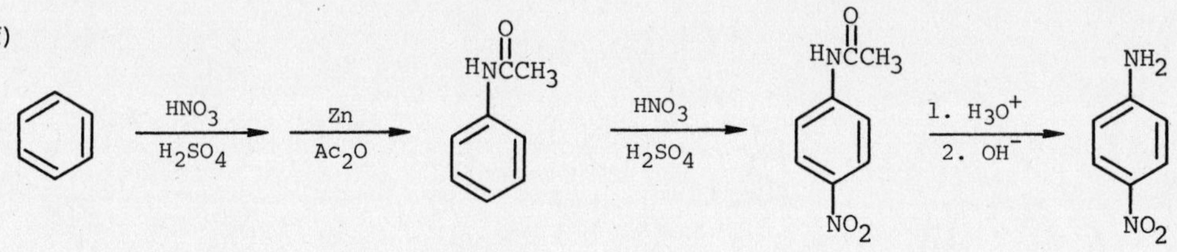

(g)

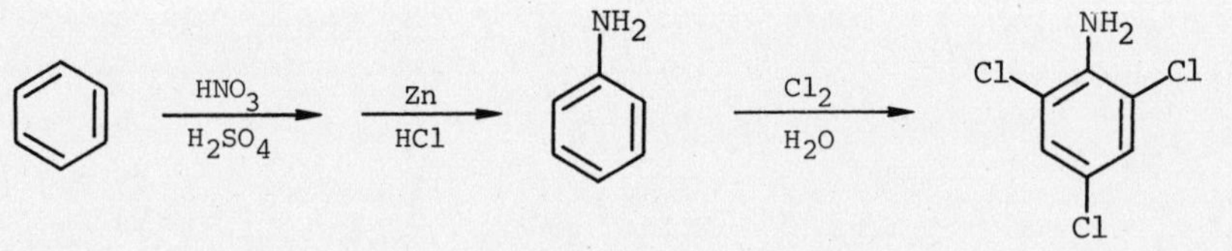

18. The basicity of aniline is lower than that of aliphatic amines because of conjugation of the nitrogen lone pair with the benzene ring. In diphenylamine, the lone pair can conjugate with two rings; hence, the basicity is still lower.

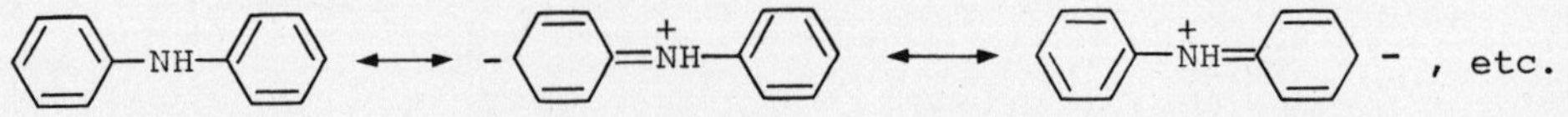

19. *ortho-*

adjacent positive charges, resulting in high electrostatic repulsion. These structures are of high energy and contribute little to the resonance hybrid.

para-

meta-

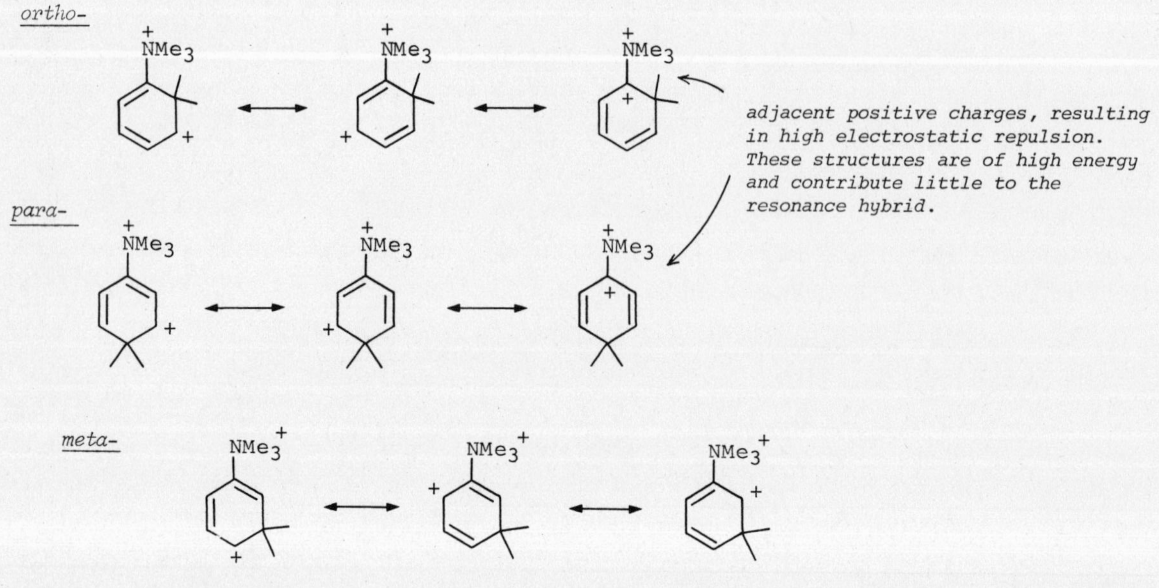

The positive charges in the meta-isomer are separated by at least one atom; thus, the meta transition state is of lowest energy. However, two positive charges in the same molecule represent substantial electrostatic repulsion. For this reason the trimethylammonium group is highly deactivating, but m-directing.

20. Addition of N-C is best accomplished by a Michael reaction:

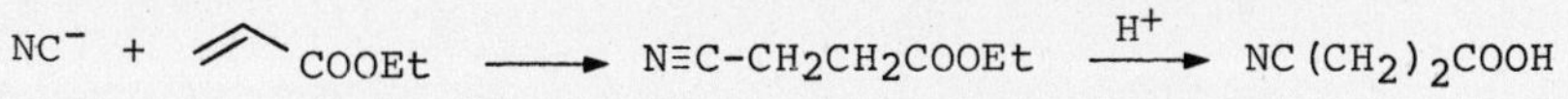

$$NC^- + \; \diagdown\!\!\!=\!\!\!\diagup\!\!COOEt \longrightarrow N\equiv C-CH_2CH_2COOEt \xrightarrow{H^+} NC(CH_2)_2COOH$$

$$RCOOH \xrightarrow{SOCl_2} RCOCl \xrightarrow{(CH_3)_2NH} RCON(CH_3)_2$$

$$NC(CH_2)_3\overset{O}{\overset{\|}{C}}-N(CH_3)_2 \xrightarrow[\substack{(reduces\ both \\ -CN\ and\ amide)}]{LiAlH_4} H_2N(CH_2)_4N(CH_3)_2$$

(b)

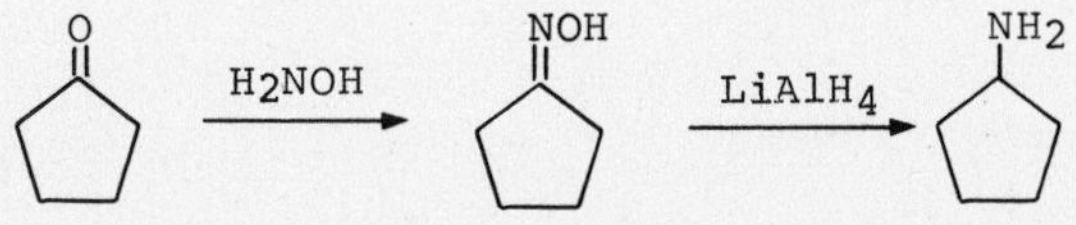

an oxime

(c)

excess

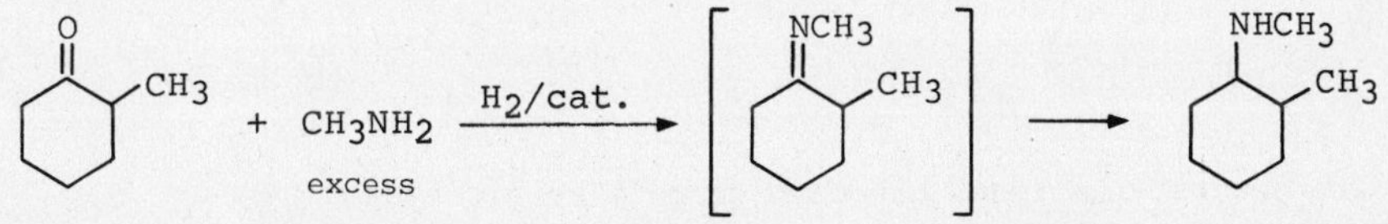

(d)

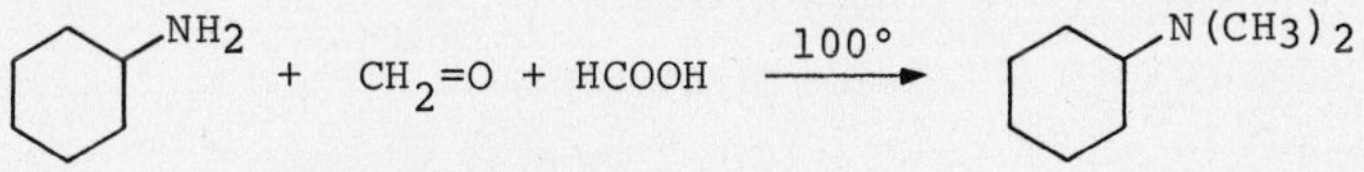

(Eschweiler-Clarke)

(e)

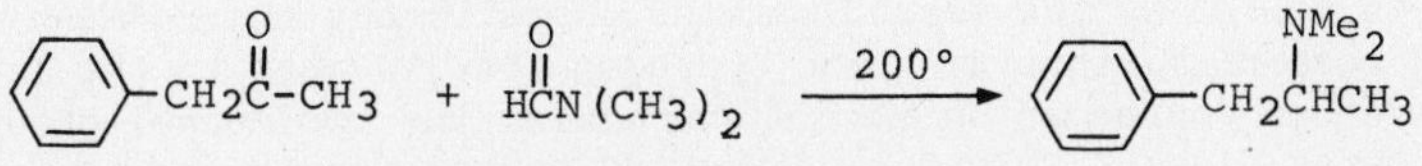

(Leuckart)

21.

(a)

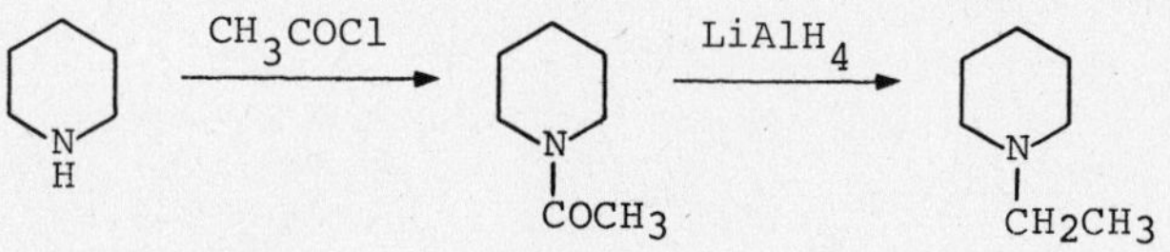

(b)

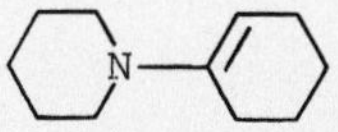

an enamine

(c)

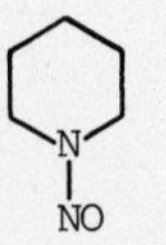

(d)

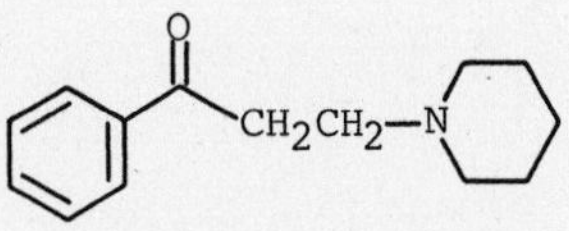

(e)

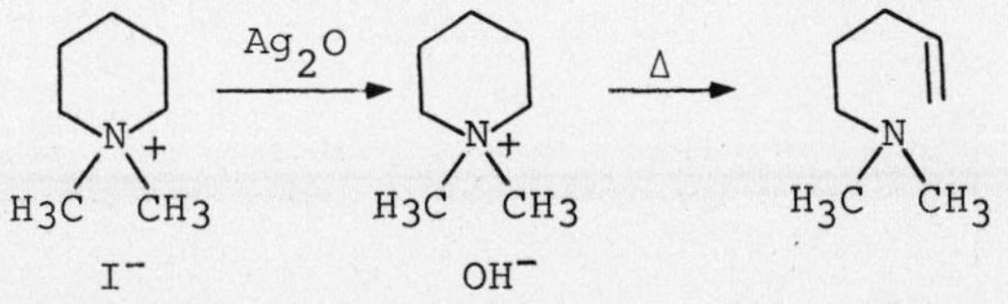

(f)

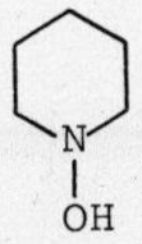

22.

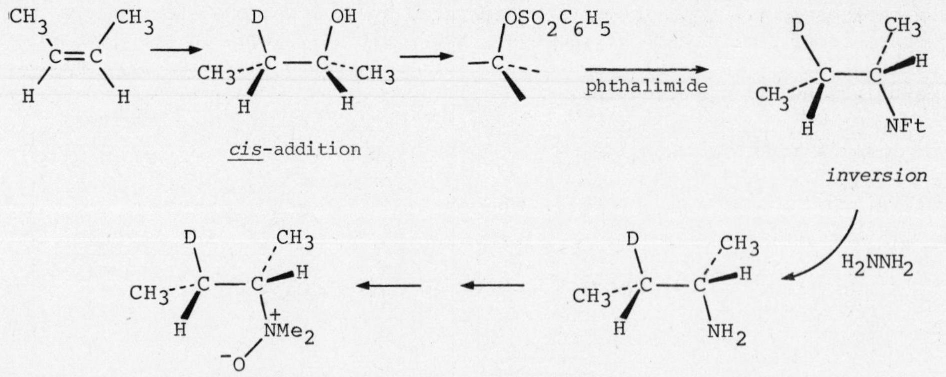

cis-addition

phthalimide

inversion

H_2NNH_2

There are three possible pathways for elimination. Loss of H from CH_3 gives $CH_3CHDCH=CH_2$ (one deuterium).

From methylene group, the molecule may lose H or D by *syn*-elimination:

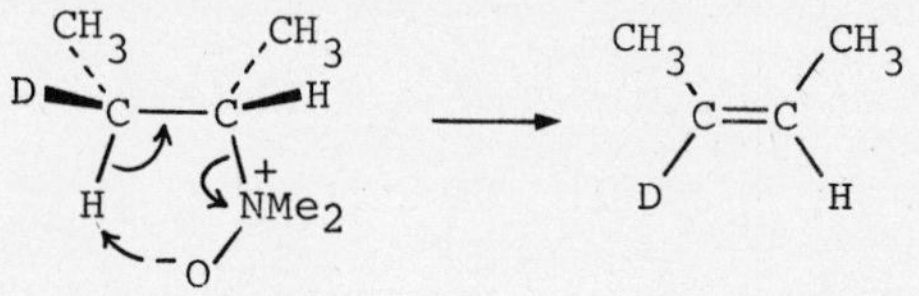

cis-2-butene has one deuterium

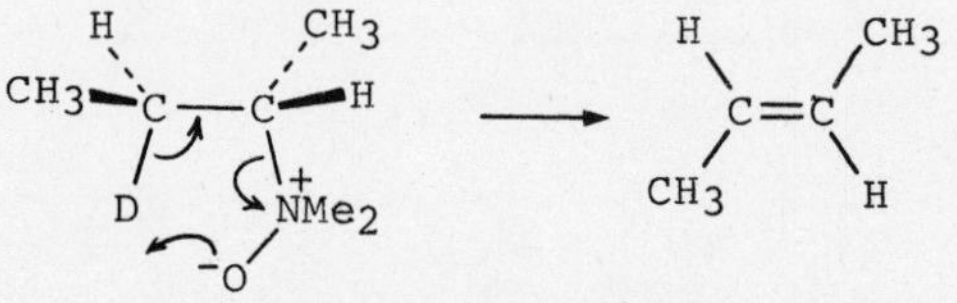

trans-2-butene has no deuterium

23. This elimination occurs with least hindered or most acidic hydrogen:

(a) $CH_2=CH_2$ + $Me_2NCH_2CH(CH_3)_2$ (least hindered)

(b) $(CH_3)_3N$ + $(CH_3)_2CHCH=CH_2$ (least hindered)

(c)   The hydrogen α to the CO group is most acidic; it eliminates rather than the less hindered hydrogen on CH_3 of the ethyl group: $(CH_3CH_2)_2N$ + $CH_2=CHCOCH_3$

(d)   This problem is best solved by the use of models. Recall that the Hofmann elimination proceeds by the E2 mechanism, involving the hydrogen that is <u>anti</u> to the leaving nitrogen. The preferred conformation is the one having the two methyl groups equatorial to the six-membered rings. Only the bridgehead proton has the necessary <u>anti</u>-coplanar relationship to the C-N bond which is being broken:

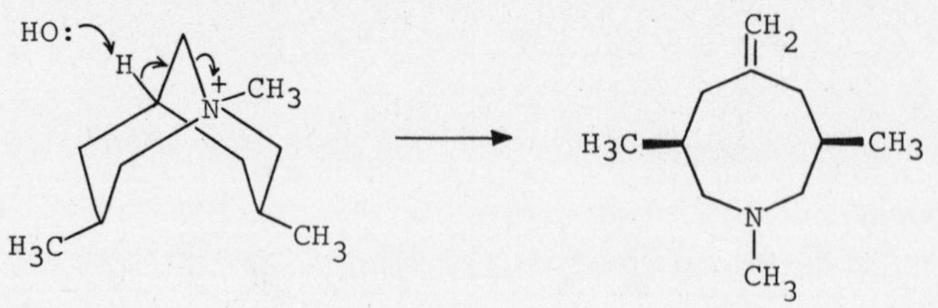

(e)   *syn*-elimination:

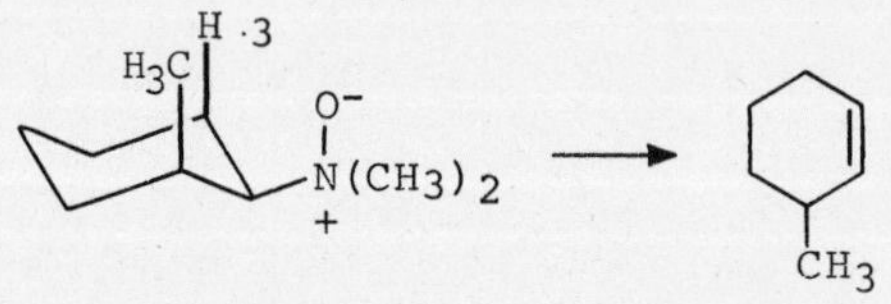

24. (a) requires *syn*-elimination; ∴ use amine oxide

$$\xrightarrow{\text{H}_2\text{O}_2} \quad \xrightarrow{\Delta}$$

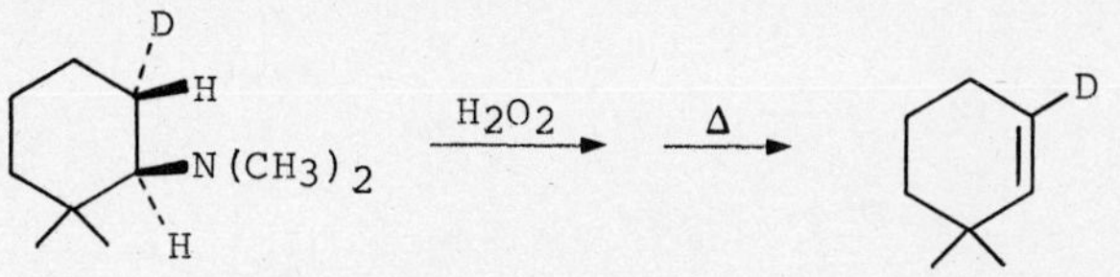

(b) requires *anti*-elimination; use Hofmann reaction

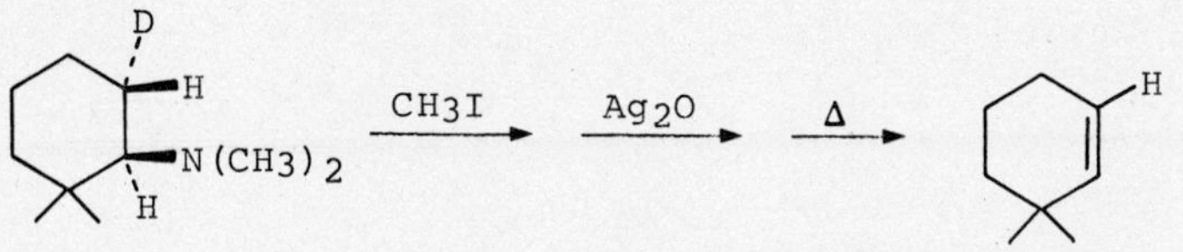

$$\xrightarrow{\text{CH}_3\text{I}} \quad \xrightarrow{\text{Ag}_2\text{O}} \quad \xrightarrow{\Delta}$$

25.

$$\text{—CH}_2\text{NH}_2 \xrightarrow{\text{HONO}} \text{—CH}_2\text{-N}_2^+ \xrightarrow[\text{by H}_2\text{O}]{\text{S}_\text{N}2} \text{—CH}_2\text{-OH}$$

elimination of β-H ⟶ =CH$_2$

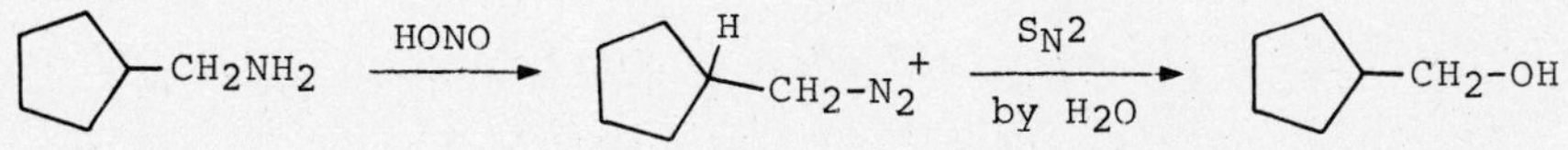

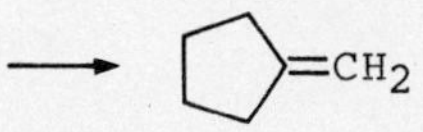

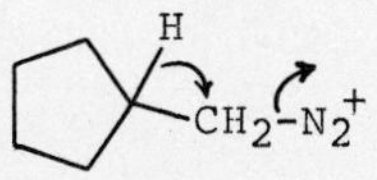

rearrangement of β-H gives:

$$\overset{+}{}\text{—CH}_3 \longrightarrow =\text{CH}_2 + \text{—CH}_3$$

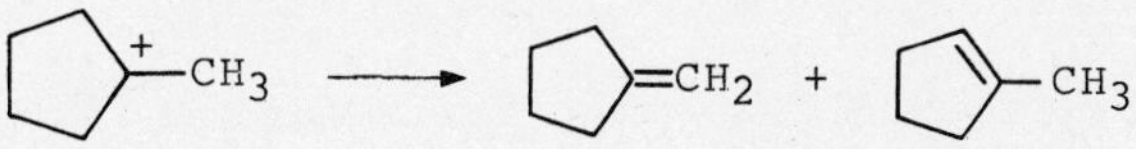

Rearrangement of ring:

$$\text{—CH}_2\text{—N}_2^+ \longrightarrow \text{—CH}_2 \quad \xrightarrow{\text{elimination}}$$

$$\xrightarrow{\text{H}_2\text{O}} \text{—OH}$$

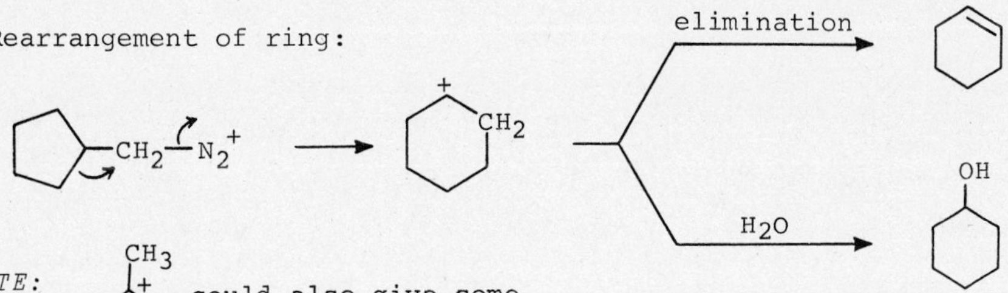

NOTE: could also give some   and a small amount is probably present.

26. (a) $\underline{n}\text{-C}_{10}\text{H}_{21}\text{Br} \xrightarrow[\text{aq. NaOOCCH}_3]{\text{C}_6\text{H}_5\text{CH}_2\overset{+}{\text{N}}\text{Et}_3\ \text{Cl}^-} \underline{n}\text{-C}_{10}\text{H}_{21}\overset{\text{O}}{\overset{\|}{\text{OCCH}_3}}$

(CH_3CO_2^- solubilized in organic phase)

(b) $3,4\text{-(CH}_3)_2\text{C}_6\text{H}_3\overset{\text{O}}{\overset{\|}{\text{CCH}_3}} \xrightarrow[\text{NaOD, D}_2\text{O}]{\text{C}_6\text{H}_5\text{CH}_2\overset{+}{\text{N}}\text{Et}_3\ \text{Cl}^-} 3,4\text{-(CH}_3)_2\text{C}_6\text{H}_4\overset{\text{O}}{\overset{\|}{\text{CCD}_3}}$

$\left(\overset{\text{O}}{\overset{\|}{\text{RCCH}_3}} + \text{OD}^- \rightleftharpoons \overset{\text{O}^-}{\overset{|}{\text{RC=CH}_2}} + \text{HOD}\ \text{ in organic phase}\right)$

(c) $(\text{CH}_3)_2\text{CH(CH}_2)_4\text{OH} + (\text{CH}_3)_2\text{SO}_4 \xrightarrow[\text{50\% NaOH}]{\text{C}_6\text{H}_5\text{CH}_2\overset{+}{\text{N}}\text{Et}_3\ \text{Cl}^-} (\text{CH}_3)_2\text{CH(CH}_2)_4\text{OCH}_3 + \text{Na}^+\ {}^-\text{O}_3\text{SOCH}_3$

($\text{ROH} + \text{OH}^- \rightleftharpoons \text{RO}^- + \text{H}_2\text{O}\ $ in organic phase)

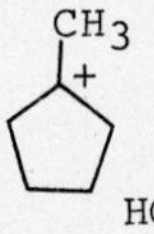

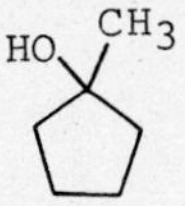

(d) $(CH_3)_2CHCH$ (with O above) $+ C_6H_5CH_2Cl$ $\xrightarrow[\text{50\% NaOH}]{C_6H_5CH_2\overset{+}{N}Et_3\ Cl^-}$ $(CH_3)_2CCH$ (with O above) $+ NaCl$
                                                                                                                        $CH_2C_6H_5$

$\left((CH_3)_2CHCH \text{ (with O above)} + OH^- \rightleftharpoons (CH_3)_2C=CH \text{ (with O}^-\text{ above)} + H_2O \quad \text{in organic phase} \right)$

(e) $C_6H_5CH=CH_2 + CHCl_3$ $\xrightarrow[\text{50\% NaOH}]{C_6H_5CH_2\overset{+}{N}Et_3\ Cl^-}$ (cyclopropane with Cl, Cl and C_6H_5) $+ NaCl$

$(CHCl_3 + OH^- \longrightarrow :CCl_2 + H_2O + Cl^- \quad \text{in organic phase})$

27. (a) $ClCH_2CH_2\overset{+}{N}H_3$;   inductive effect of Cl

(b) $CH_3O\overset{+}{N}H_3$;   inductive effect of oxygen

(c) $CH_3\overset{O}{\overset{\|}{C}}\overset{+}{N}H_3$;   electron-withdrawing inductive effect of carbonyl; in addition, the
                        product amide is resonance-stabilized by $R-C=\overset{+}{N}H_2$
                                                                                          $\overset{|}{O^-}$

(d) $CH_2=\overset{+}{N}H_2$;   lone pair in $CH_2=\overset{..}{N}H$ has more s-character than that in $CH_2CH_2\overset{..}{N}H_2$

(e) $CH_3OOCCH_2\overset{+}{N}H_3$;   inductive effect of COOR group

(f) $CH_2=CHNH_3^+$;   amine is resonance-stabilized: $\left[CH_2=CH-\overset{..}{N}H_2 \longleftrightarrow {}^-CH_2-CH=\overset{+}{N}H_2 \right]$

28. Since the mixture of cyclooctadienes contains no 1,3-isomer, it must consist of a mixture of
the 1,4- and 1,5-isomers. Hence, the starting $C_9H_{17}N$ amine must have the symmetrical
bicyclic structure:

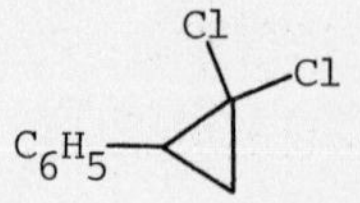

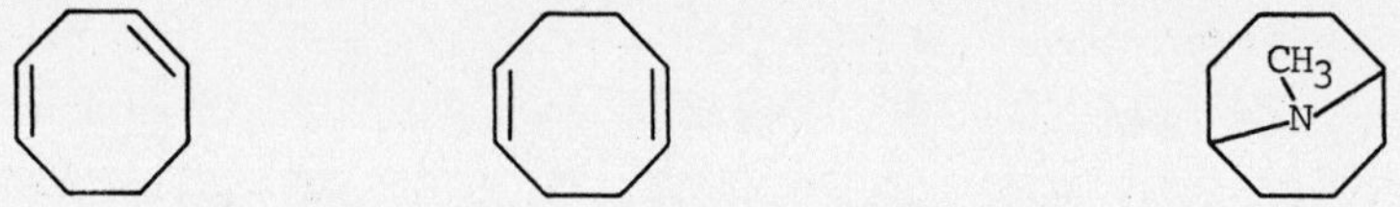

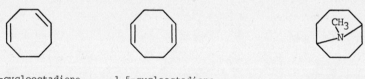

1,4-cyclooctadiene   1,5-cyclooctadiene

granatine

29.

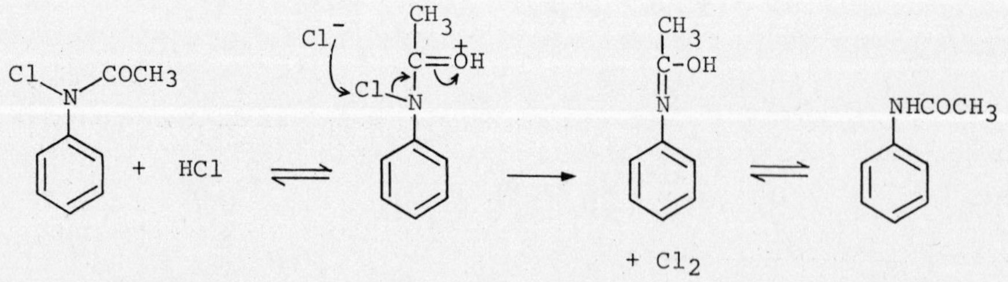

(reaction scheme showing Cl–N–COCH₃ on benzene ring + HCl ⇌ intermediate with CH₃ C=ÖH, then → imine with CH₃ C–OH, ⇌ NHCOCH₃ on ring + Cl₂)

(NHCOCH₃ on benzene ring) + Cl₂ ⟶ mixture of o- and p-chloroacetanilide

30.

(cyclohexane with NH₂ and HO substituents) $\xrightarrow{HNO_2}$ (intermediate with $\overset{+}{N_2}$ and migrating H-O) $\xrightarrow[-H^+]{-N_2}$ (cycloheptanone, O)

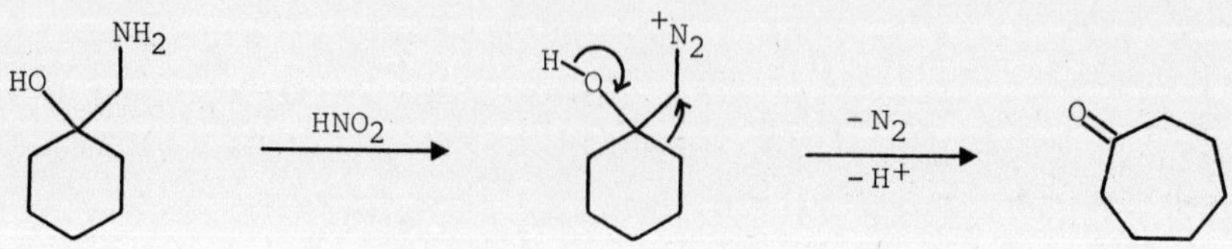

23.F   Supplementary Problems

S1.   Draw the structure of each of the following compounds.

(a) triisobutylamine

(b) <u>cis</u>-1,4-diaminocyclohexane

(c) 3-(aminomethyl)aniline

(d) N,3-dimethylbutanamine

(e) ethyltripropylammonium chloride

(f) ethyldiisopropylamine oxide

(g) N,O-diethylhydroxylamine

(h) anilinium bromide

S2.   For each pair of compounds below, explain how you would distinguish between the two without using NMR.

(a) $(CH_3)_2N-CH_2CH(CH_3)_2$ and $(CH_3)_2CHNHCH(CH_3)_2$

(b) $(CH_3CH_2CH_2)_2NH$ and $CH_3CH_2CHCH_2CH_2CH_3$ with NH_2 substituent

(c) $(CH_3)_3CCH_2NH_2$ and $CH_3CH_2CHCH_2NH_2$ with CH_3 substituent

(d)

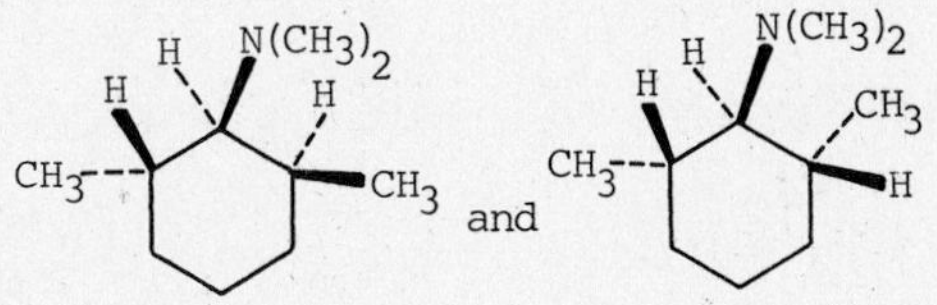

S3.   Rank the following compounds in order of increasing basicity.

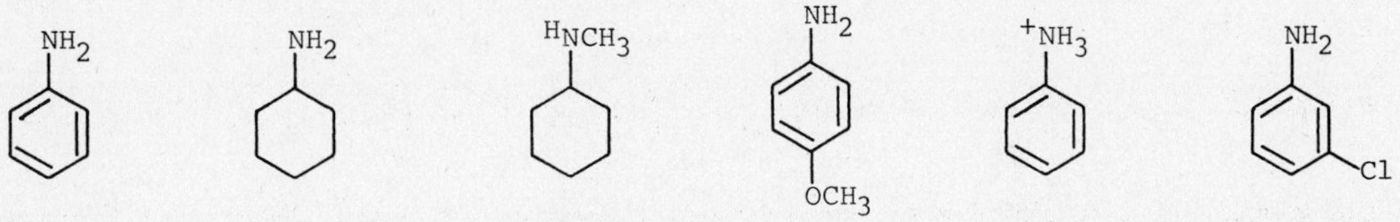

I   II   III   IV   V   VI

S4.   Do you expect p-aminoacetophenone ($H_2NC_6H_4\overset{O}{\overset{\|}{C}}CH_3$) to be a stronger or weaker base than aniline itself? Justify your answer with resonance structures.

S5.   What is the principal organic product to result from each of the following reaction sequences?

(a)

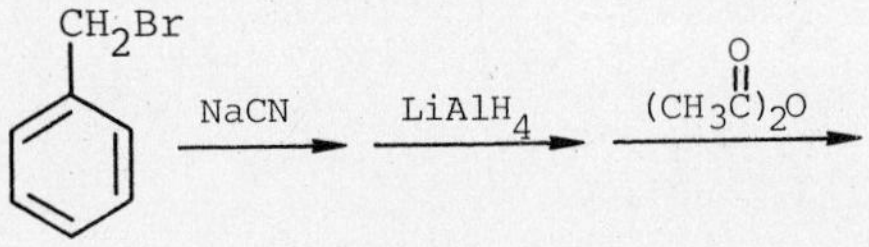

(b)

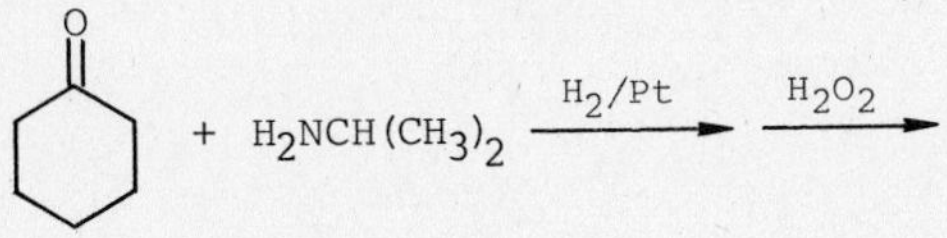

(c)

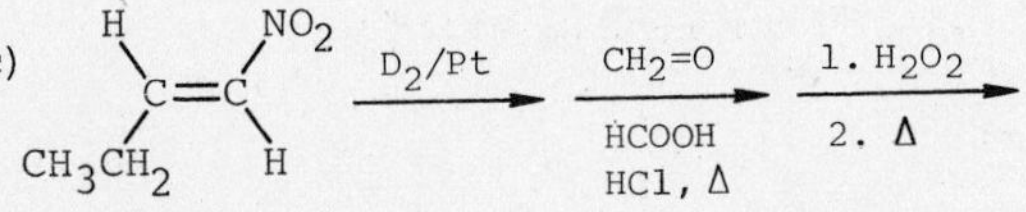

(d)

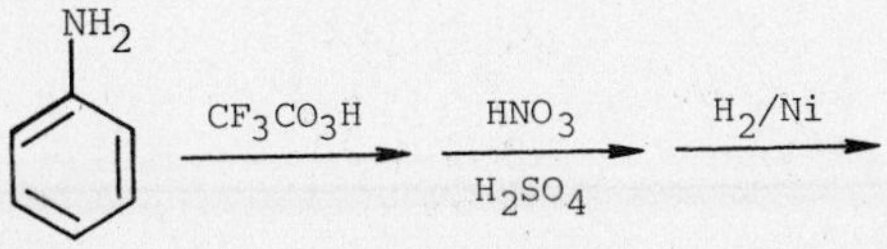

(e)

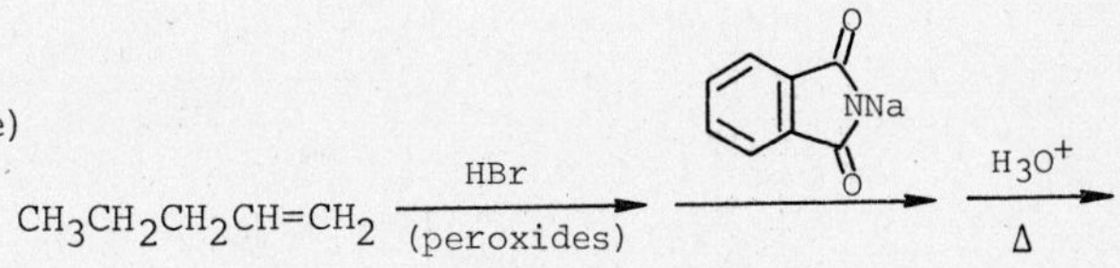

$CH_3CH_2CH_2CH=CH_2 \xrightarrow[\text{(peroxides)}]{HBr} \longrightarrow \xrightarrow[\Delta]{H_3O^+}$

(f) $CH_3CH_2CH_2CH=O \xrightarrow{H_2NOH} \xrightarrow{H_2/Ni} \xrightarrow{HCl}$

(g)

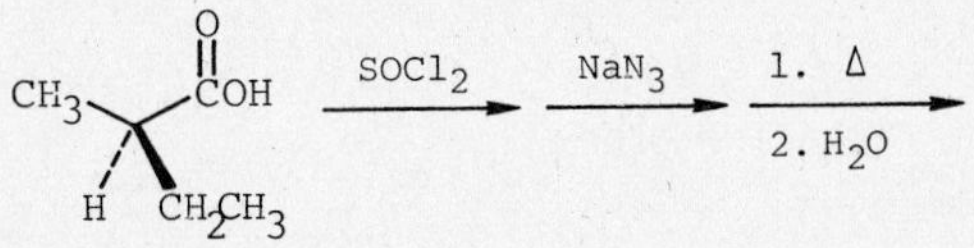

(h) $(CH_3)_3CCH_2CH_2\overset{O}{\overset{\|}{C}}CH_3 \xrightarrow[\Delta]{H\overset{O}{\overset{\|}{C}}N(CH_3)_2} \xrightarrow{CH_3I} \xrightarrow[2.\ \Delta]{1.\ Ag_2O}$

(i)

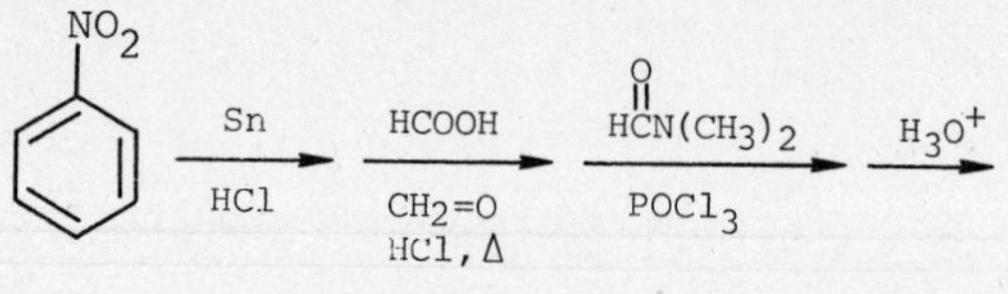

$$\underset{\text{HCl}}{\overset{\text{Sn}}{\longrightarrow}} \quad \underset{\substack{\text{CH}_2=\text{O} \\ \text{HCl}, \Delta}}{\overset{\text{HCOOH}}{\longrightarrow}} \quad \underset{\text{POCl}_3}{\overset{\text{HCN(CH}_3)_2}{\longrightarrow}} \quad \overset{\text{H}_3\text{O}^+}{\longrightarrow}$$

(ℓ)

$$\underset{\substack{\text{CH}_2=\text{O, HCl} \\ \Delta}}{\overset{\text{CH}_3\text{CCH}_3}{\longrightarrow}}$$

(j)

$$(\text{CH}_3)_2\text{CHCH}_2\text{NH}_2 \overset{(\text{CH}_3)_2\text{CHCCl}}{\longrightarrow} \overset{\text{LiAlH}_4}{\longrightarrow} \underset{\text{HCl}}{\overset{\text{NaNO}_2}{\longrightarrow}}$$

(m)

$$\overset{\text{COOH}}{} \quad \overset{\text{SOCl}_2}{\longrightarrow} \quad \overset{\text{NH}_3}{\longrightarrow} \quad \underset{\text{NaOH}}{\overset{\text{Br}_2}{\longrightarrow}}$$

(k)

$$\underset{\text{H}}{\overset{\text{N}}{\bigcirc}} \quad + \quad \text{CH}_3\text{CH}_2\text{CCH}_2\text{CH}_3 \quad \underset{-\text{H}_2\text{O}}{\overset{\Delta}{\longrightarrow}} \quad \underset{2.\ \text{H}_3\text{O}^+}{\overset{1.\ \text{CH}_3\text{I}}{\longrightarrow}}$$

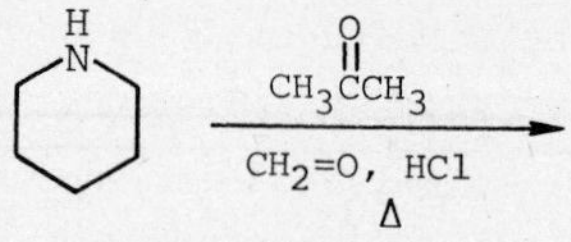

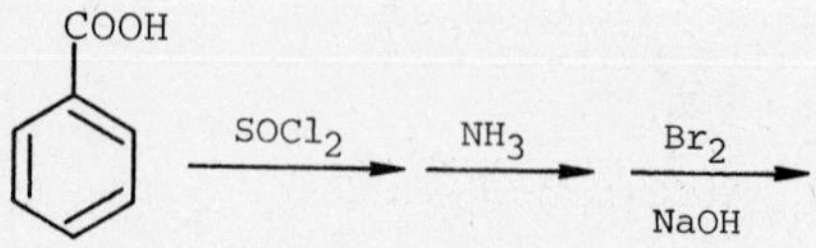

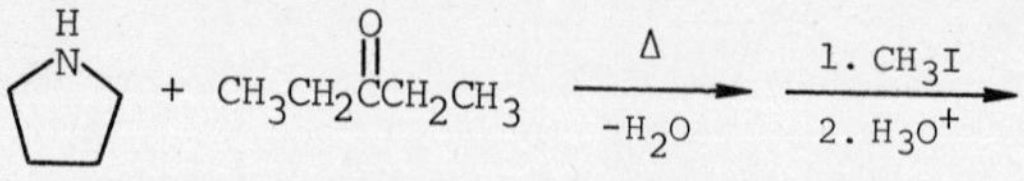

S6. Outline syntheses of the following compounds, using 3-methylbutanoic acid as starting material.

(a) $(\text{CH}_3)_2\text{CHCH}_2\text{NH}_2$ (b) $(\text{CH}_3)_2\text{CHCH}_2\text{CH}_2\text{NH}_2$ (c) $(\text{CH}_3)_2\text{CHCH}_2\text{CH}_2\text{CH}_2\text{NH}_2$

S7. Write the intermediates formed during the following reaction sequence, as well as a mechanism for the last step.

$$\text{CH}_3\text{CH}_2\text{CH}_2\text{CH} \overset{\text{HCN}}{\longrightarrow} \overset{\text{H}_2/\text{Ni}}{\longrightarrow} \underset{\text{K}_2\text{CO}_3, \Delta}{\overset{\text{excess CH}_3\text{I}}{\longrightarrow}} \text{CH}_3\text{CH}_2\text{CH}_2\text{CH}\text{---}\text{CH}_2$$

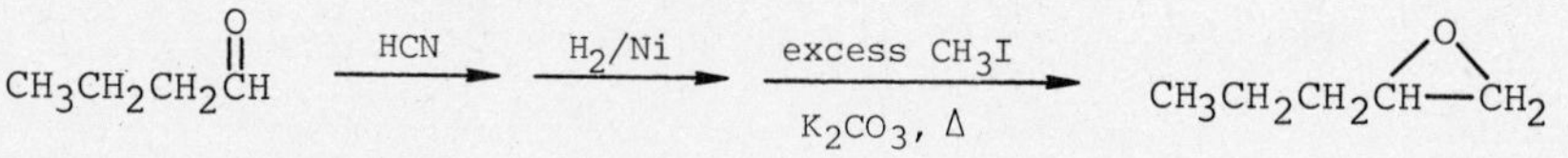

S8. Provide an explanation for the following behavior, and write a detailed mechanism for the conversion of B to A.

$$\text{HOCH}_2\text{CH}_2\text{NH}_2 \Bigg\langle \begin{array}{l} \underset{\text{K}_2\text{CO}_3}{\overset{\text{one mole } (\text{CH}_3\text{C})_2\text{O}}{\longrightarrow}} \quad \text{HOCH}_2\text{CH}_2\text{NHCCH}_3 \\ \qquad\qquad\qquad\qquad\qquad\qquad A \\ \\ \underset{\text{HCl}}{\overset{\text{one mole } (\text{CH}_3\text{C})_2\text{O}}{\longrightarrow}} \quad \text{CH}_3\text{COCH}_2\text{CH}_2\overset{+}{\text{NH}}_3\ \text{Cl}^- \\ \qquad\qquad\qquad\qquad\qquad\qquad B \end{array}$$

$$\overset{\text{K}_2\text{CO}_3}{\curvearrowleft}$$

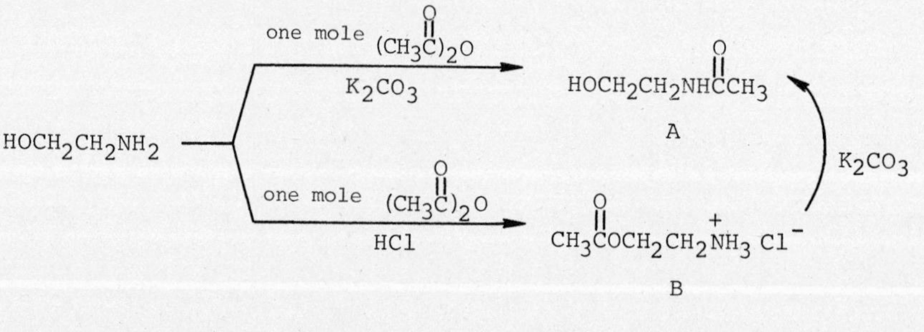

S9. Show how to synthesize the following compounds, using only inorganic compounds (e.g., NaNO_2, NH_3, NaCN, etc.) as a source of nitrogen.

(a) $\overset{\text{HNCH}_2\text{CH}_3}{\bigcirc}$

(b) $\overset{\text{NH}_2}{\underset{\text{CH}_3}{\bigcirc}}$

(c) $\overset{\overset{\text{O}}{\parallel}}{\bigcirc\text{CH}_2\text{NHCCH}_2\text{CH}_2\text{COOH}}$

(d) $\text{CH}_3\text{CH}_2\text{CH}_2\text{CH}_2\overset{\text{CH}_3}{\underset{}{\text{NCH}_2\text{CH}_2\text{CH}_3}}$

(e) $(\text{CH}_3)_2\text{CHCH}_2\text{CH}_2\text{N}\overset{\bigcirc}{}$

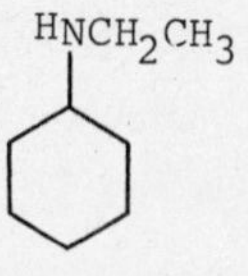

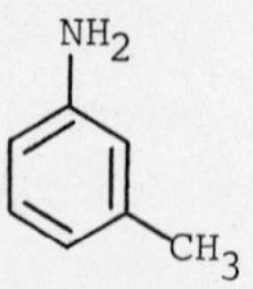

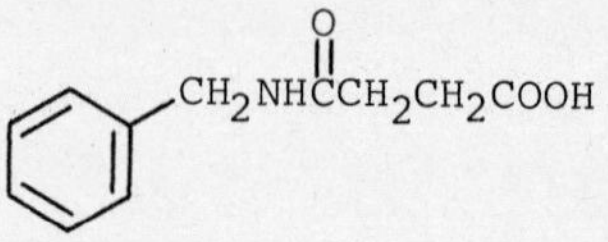

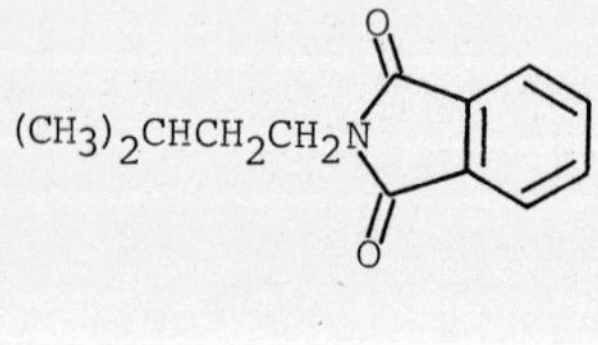

(f)

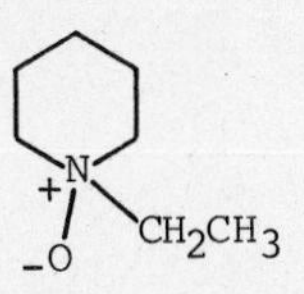

(g)

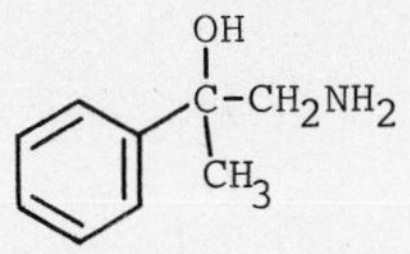

(h) $(CH_3CH_2)_2N-N=O$

S10.   Write a step-by-step mechanism for the following transformations:

(a)

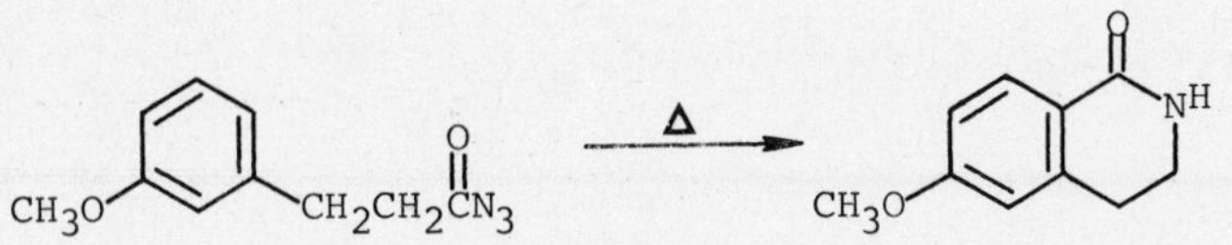

$$CH_3O \qquad CH_2CH_2CN_3 \xrightarrow{\Delta} CH_3O$$

(b)

$$+ HN_3 \longrightarrow$$

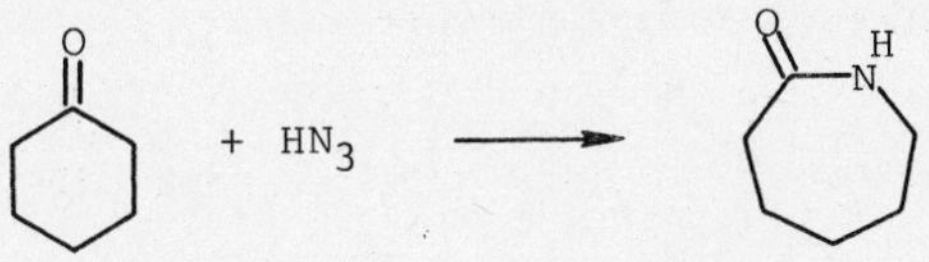

S11.   Offer an explanation for the degree of reactivity of immonium ions, carbonyl compounds, and imines toward nucleophilic attack:

$$Y = \overset{+}{N}R_2 > O > NR$$

S12.   Write a mechanism for the following transformation:

$$\xrightarrow[CH_3OH]{HCl}$$

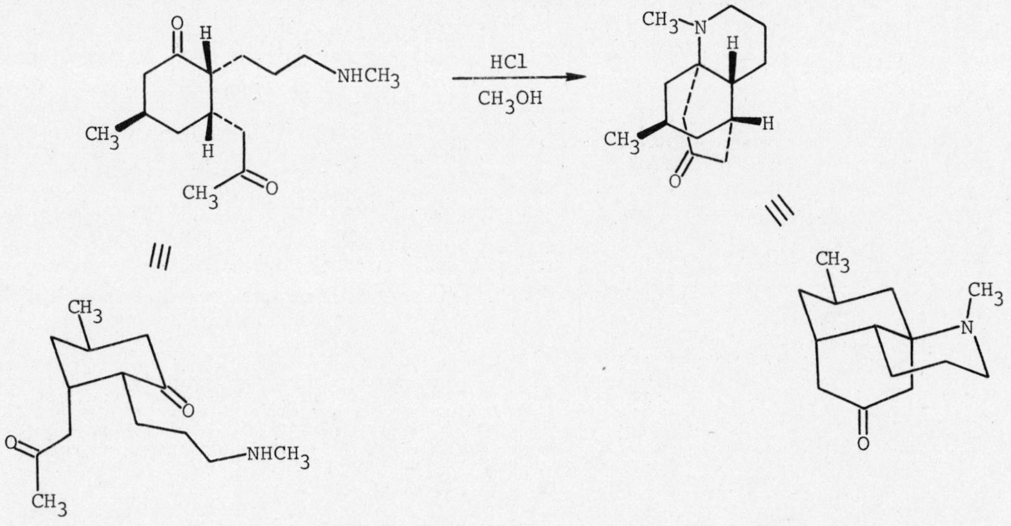

23.G   Answers to Supplementary Problems

S1.

(a) $((CH_3)_2CHCH_2)_3N$

(b)   [structure: cyclohexane ring with H and NH_2 at top, H and NH_2 at bottom]

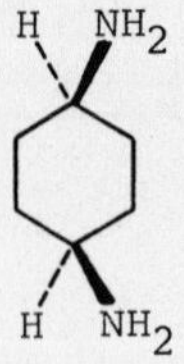

(c)   [benzene ring with NH_2 and CH_2NH_2 substituents]

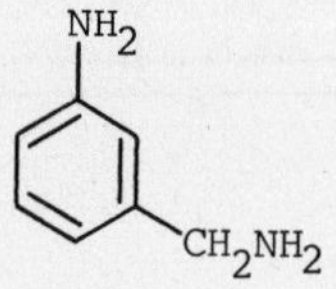

(d) $(CH_3)_2CHCH_2CH_2NHCH_3$

(e) $(CH_3CH_2CH_2)_3\overset{+}{N}CH_2CH_3$

(f) $CH_3CH_2\overset{+}{N}(CH(CH_3)_2)_2$ with $\overset{|}{O^-}$

(g) $CH_3CH_2NHOCH_2CH_3$

(h)   [benzene ring with $\overset{+}{N}H_3\ Br^-$]

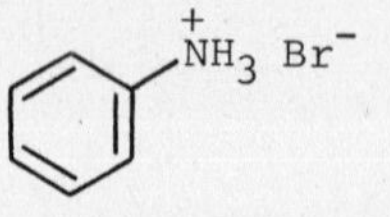

S2.

(a)   Only diisopropylamine will react with nitrous acid:

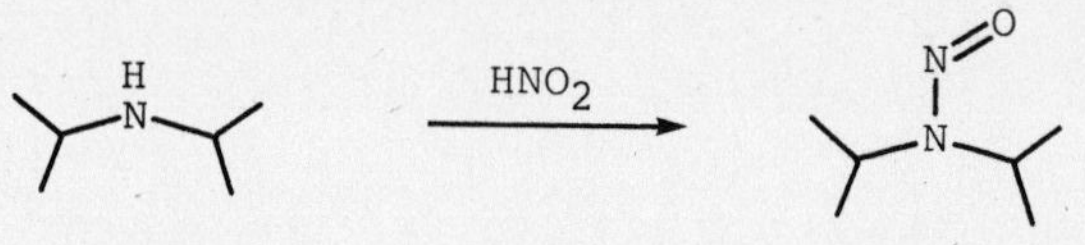

[structure: diisopropylamine with N–H] $\xrightarrow{HNO_2}$ [N-nitroso diisopropylamine, N–N=O]

(b) $(CH_3CH_2CH_2)_2NH$

very weak N–H stretch:
  3310–3350 cm^{-1}

[structure: $\overset{NH_2}{CH_3CH_2CHCH_2CH_2CH_3}$]

weak N–H stretch: doublet 3400, 3500 cm^{-1}

N–H band: 1580–1650 cm^{-1}

(c) RNH_2 $\xrightarrow[CH_2=O,\ HCl]{HCOOH}$ $RN(CH_3)_2$ $\xrightarrow{H_2O_2}$ $R-\overset{+}{\underset{}{N}}(CH_3)_2$ with O^- $\xrightarrow{\Delta}$

$R = (CH_3)_3CCH_2-$: no elimination takes place

$R = CH_3CH_2\overset{\overset{\displaystyle CH_3}{|}}{C}HCH_2-$: products are $CH_3CH_2\overset{\overset{\displaystyle CH_3}{|}}{C}=CH_2$ + $(CH_3)_2NOH$

(d) $RN(CH_3)_2$ $\xrightarrow[Ag_2O]{CH_3I}$ $R\overset{+}{N}(CH_3)_3\ OH^-$ $\xrightarrow{\Delta}$

[cyclohexane structure with $\overset{+}{N}(CH_3)_3$]   gives   [cyclohexene with CH_3 groups]   (resulting from *anti* elimination)

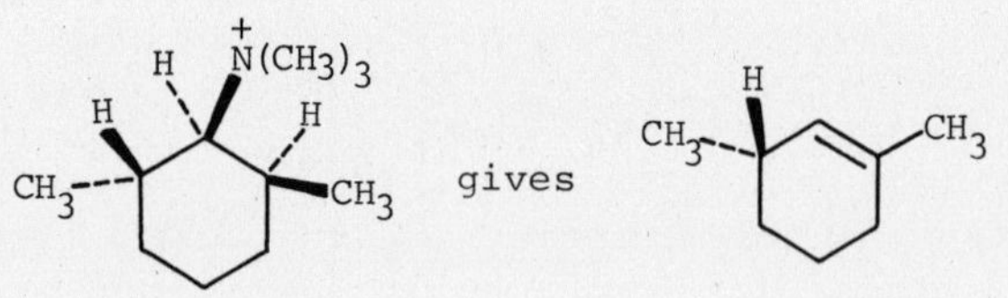

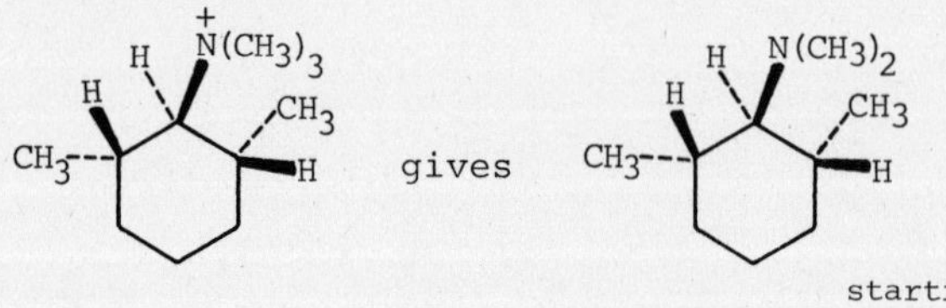

[cyclohexane structure with $\overset{+}{N}(CH_3)_3$]   gives   [cyclohexane structure with $N(CH_3)_2$]   (Demethylation occurs because there is no hydrogen *anti* to the nitrogen)

starting material

S3. *Weakest base:* V (to act as a base, it must gain a proton, and an *additional* positive charge)

VI (Cl is electron-withdrawing)

I

IV (CH$_3$O is electron-releasing, through conjugation of the lone pair electrons)

II (alkylamines are stronger bases than arylamines)

Strongest base: III (dialkylamines are even better than alkylamines)

S4.

$$\left[\text{H}_2\ddot{\text{N}}\text{—}\bigcirc\text{—}\overset{\text{O}}{\overset{\|}{\text{C}}}\text{—CH}_3 \longleftrightarrow \text{H}_2\overset{+}{\text{N}}\text{=}\bigcirc\text{=}\overset{\text{O}^-}{\overset{|}{\text{C}}}\text{—CH}_3 \right]$$

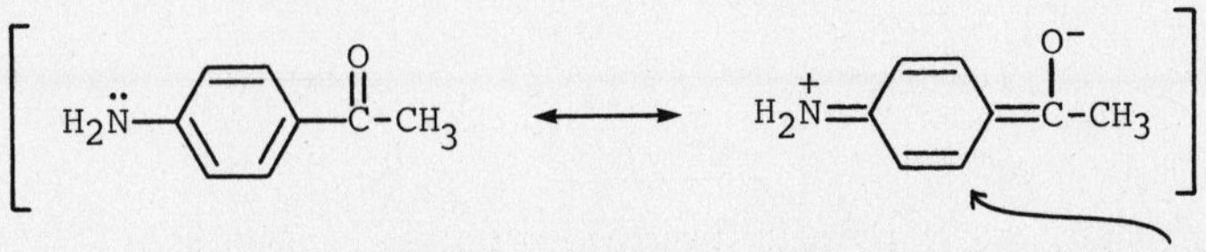

Because of some contribution from this resonance structure, the nitrogen already has positive character and will be a weaker base.

S5. (a) $\text{CH}_2\text{CH}_2\text{NHCCH}_3$ (phenyl, with C=O)

(b) HO—NCH(CH$_3$)$_2$ (cyclohexyl)

(c) $\text{CH}_3\text{CH}_2\text{—}\overset{\text{H}\ \text{D}}{\underset{\text{H}\ \text{D}}{\text{C}}}\text{—N(CH}_3)_2\ \text{O}^-$

→

$\underset{\text{CH}_3\text{CH}_2}{\overset{\text{H}}{}}\text{C=C}\overset{\text{H}}{\underset{\text{D}}{}}$ + (CH$_3$)$_2$NOD

$\underset{\text{CH}_3\text{CH}_2}{\overset{\text{D}}{}}\text{C=C}\overset{\text{D}}{\underset{\text{H}}{}}$ + (CH$_3$)$_2$NOH

(d) benzene with NH$_2$ (1,3)

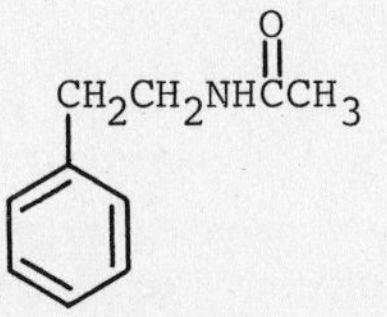

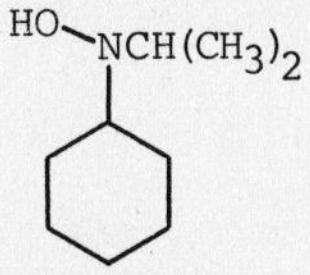

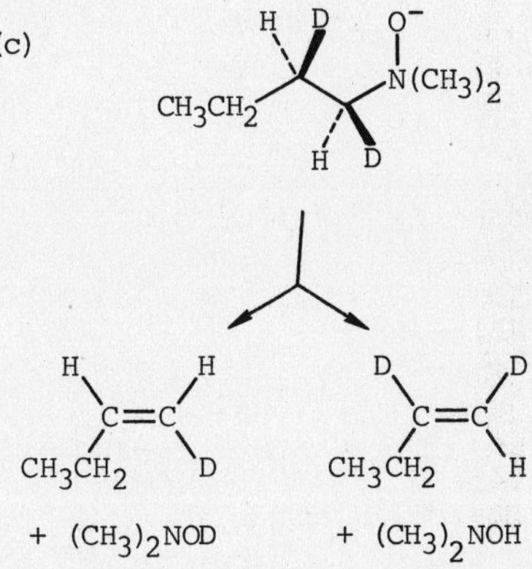

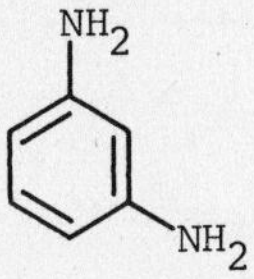

(e) CH$_3$CH$_2$CH$_2$CH$_2$CH$_2$NH$_2$

(f) $\text{CH}_3\text{CH}_2\text{CH}_2\text{CH}_2\overset{+}{\text{NH}}_3$ Cl$^-$

(g) $\text{CH}_3\text{—}\overset{\text{NH}_2}{\underset{\text{H}}{\text{C}}}\text{—CH}_2\text{CH}_3$

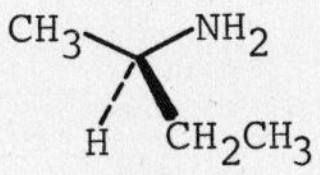

(h) (CH$_3$)$_3$CCH$_2$CH$_2$CH=CH$_2$ + (CH$_3$)$_3$N:

(i) N(CH$_3$)$_2$ benzene CH=O

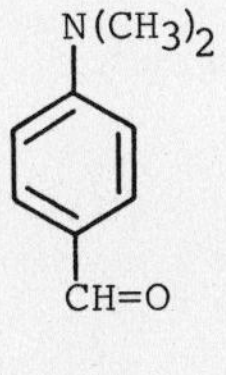

(j) (CH$_3$)$_2$CHCH$_2$NCH$_2$CH(CH$_3$)$_2$ N=O

(k) pyrrolidinium $^+\overset{\text{H}_2}{\text{N}}$ + (CH$_3$)$_2$CHCCH$_2$CH$_3$ (C=O)

(ℓ) $\text{CH}_3\overset{\text{O}}{\overset{\|}{\text{C}}}\text{CH}_2\text{CH}_2\text{N}$ piperidine

(m) aniline NH$_2$

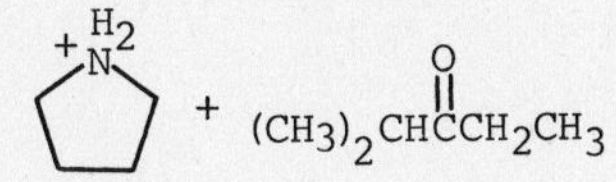

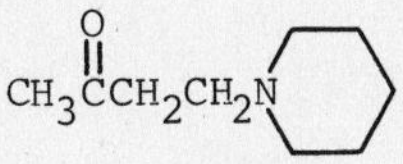

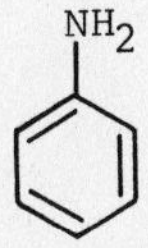

S6. (a) (CH$_3$)$_2$CHCH$_2$COOH $\xrightarrow[\text{H}_2\text{SO}_4]{\text{NaN}_3}$ [(CH$_3$)$_2$CHCH$_2$CN$_3$ (C=O)] → (CH$_3$)$_2$CHCH$_2$CN: (C=O)

→ [(CH$_3$)$_2$CHCH$_2$N=C=O]

(CH$_3$)$_2$CHCH$_2$NH$_2$ ←

(b) (CH$_3$)$_2$CHCH$_2$COOH $\xrightarrow[\Delta]{\text{NH}_3}$ (CH$_3$)$_2$CHCH$_2$CONH$_2$ $\xrightarrow{\text{LiAlH}_4}$ (CH$_3$)$_2$CHCH$_2$CH$_2$NH$_2$

or $\xrightarrow{\text{SOCl}_2}$ $\xrightarrow{\text{NH}_3}$

(c) $(CH_3)_2CHCH_2COOH$ $\xrightarrow[\text{2. PBr}_3]{\text{1. LiAlH}_4}$ $(CH_3)_2CHCH_2CH_2Br$ $\xrightarrow[\text{2. LiAlH}_4]{\text{1. NaCN}}$ $(CH_3)_2CHCH_2CH_2CH_2NH_2$

S7.

$$CH_3CH_2CH_2\overset{\overset{O}{\parallel}}{C}H + HCN \longrightarrow CH_3CH_2CH_2\overset{\overset{OH}{|}}{C}H-C\equiv N \xrightarrow{H_2/Ni} CH_3CH_2CH_2\overset{\overset{OH}{|}}{C}HCH_2NH_2 \xrightarrow{CH_3I}$$

$$KI, KHCO_3 \xleftarrow{K_2CO_3} \overset{+}{R}NH(CH_3)_2 \ I^- \xleftarrow{CH_3I} RNHCH_3 \xleftarrow{K_2CO_3} \overset{+}{R}NH_2CH_3 \ I^- \Big]$$

$$KI, KHCO_3$$

$$RN(CH_3)_2 \xrightarrow{CH_3I} CH_3CH_2CH_2\overset{\overset{OH}{|}}{C}H-CH_2-\overset{+}{N}(CH_3)_3 \Big] \xrightarrow{K_2CO_3} CH_3CH_2CH_2\overset{\overset{O^-}{|}}{C}H-CH_2 \\ \overset{+}{N}(CH_3)_3$$

$$\overset{I^-}{(CH_3)_4N^+} \xleftarrow{CH_3I} N(CH_3)_3 \ + \ CH_3CH_2CH_2\overset{O}{CH-CH_2}$$

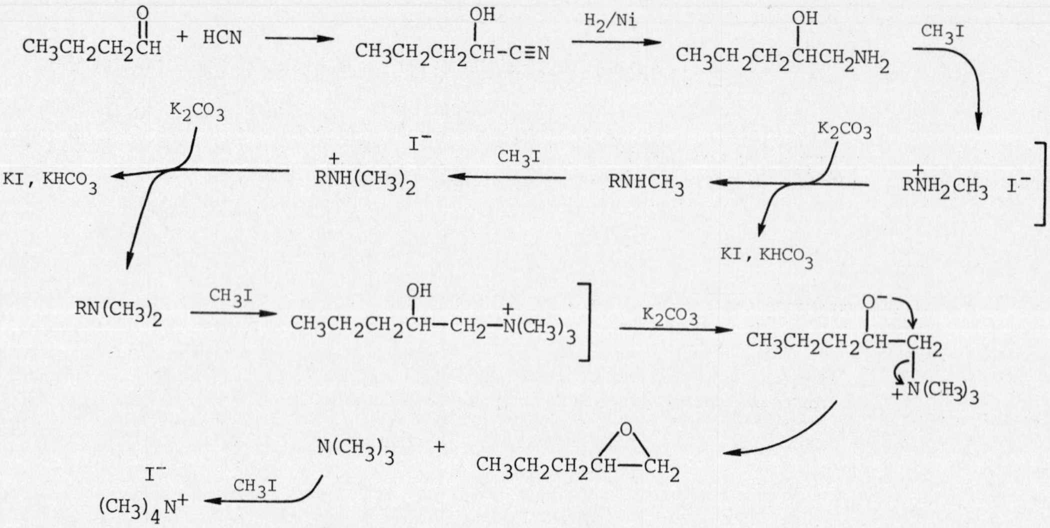

S8. Under basic conditions, the amine is more nucleophilic than the hydroxy group, and acylation takes place preferentially on nitrogen to give the amide. In acid, the amine is unreactive because it is protonated, and acylation occurs on oxygen to furnish the ester. However, on deprotonation of the amine again, a transacylation reaction takes place to provide the more stable amide:

$$CH_3\overset{\overset{O}{\parallel}}{C}OCH_2CH_2\overset{+}{N}H_3 \ \underset{}{\overset{CO_3^=}{\rightleftharpoons}} \ CH_3\overset{\overset{O}{\parallel}}{C}OCH_2CH_2\overset{..}{N}H_2 \ \rightleftharpoons \ \begin{matrix} O^- \\ | \\ CH_3-C-O \\ | \quad \ \ | \\ H_2N^+ \end{matrix}$$

$$\Big\Updownarrow CO_3^=$$

$$CH_3\overset{\overset{O}{\parallel}}{C}NHCH_2CH_2OH \ \underset{}{\overset{HCO_3^-}{\rightleftharpoons}} \ CH_3\overset{\overset{O}{\parallel}}{C}NHCH_2CH_2O^- \ \longleftarrow \ \begin{matrix} ^-O \\ | \\ CH_3-C-O \\ | \ \ \\ HN \end{matrix}$$

S9. (a)

cyclohexanone $\xrightarrow[\text{H}_2/\text{Pt}]{\text{excess NH}_3}$ cyclohexylamine $\xrightarrow{(CH_3C)_2O}$ $\xrightarrow{LiAlH_4}$ N-ethylcyclohexylamine

Alternatively,

phthalic anhydride $+ NH_3 \longrightarrow$ phthalimide $\xrightarrow[\text{CH}_3\text{CH}_2\text{Br}]{\text{NaOEt}}$ N-ethylphthalimide $\xrightarrow{H_3O^+} CH_3CH_2NH_2$

$\xrightarrow{H_2/Pt}$ CH_3CH_2NH—cyclohexyl

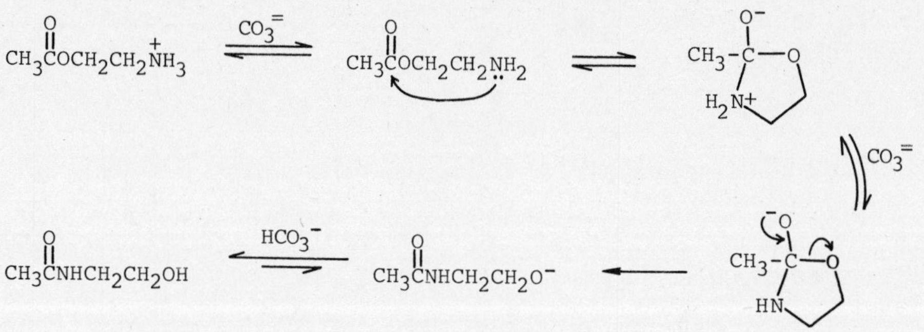

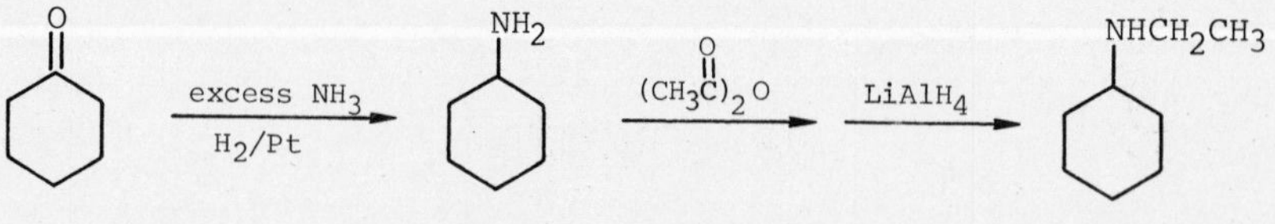

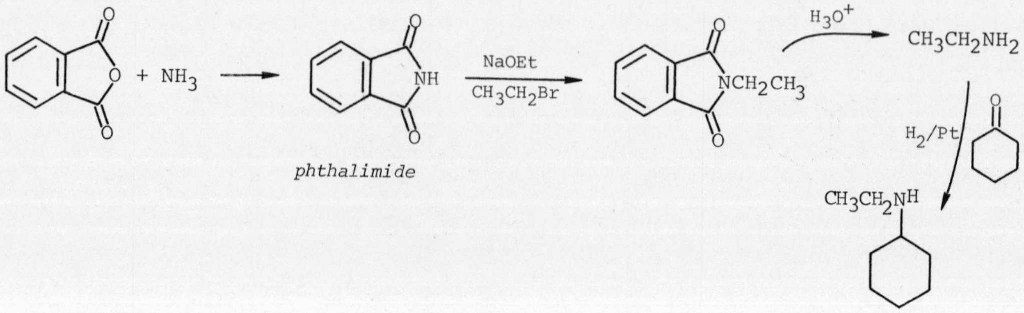

(b)

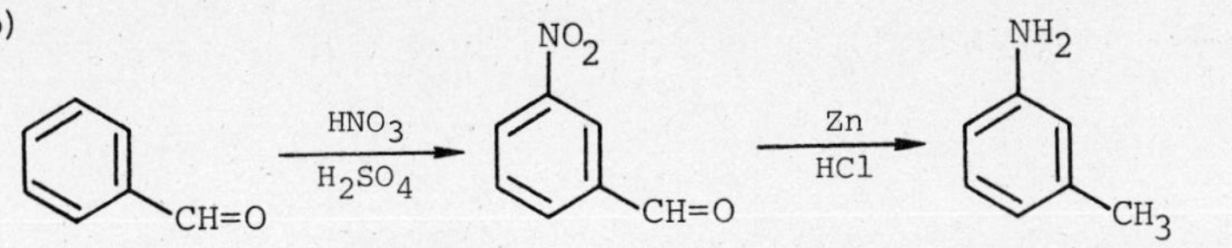

(Note that both reductions can be accomplished in one step.)

(c) phthalimide $\xrightarrow[\text{C}_6\text{H}_5\text{CH}_2\text{Br}]{\text{NaOEt}}$ $\xrightarrow{\text{H}_3\text{O}^+}$

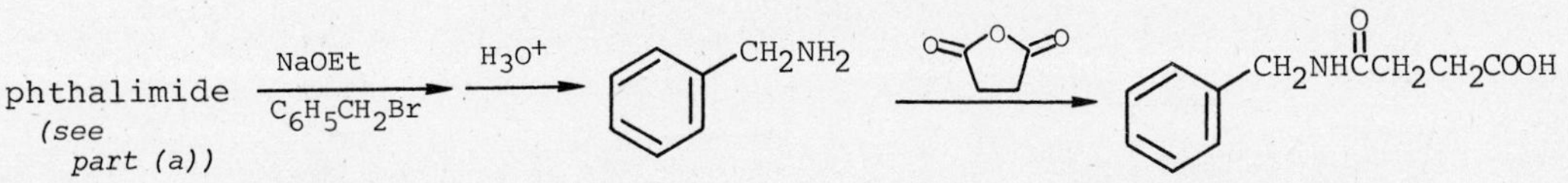

(d) phthalimide $\xrightarrow[\text{CH}_3\text{CH}_2\text{CH}_2\text{CH}_2\text{Br}]{\text{NaOEt}}$ $\xrightarrow{\text{H}_3\text{O}^+}$ $\text{CH}_3\text{CH}_2\text{CH}_2\text{CH}_2\text{NH}_2$ $\xrightarrow[\text{Et}_3\text{N}]{\text{CH}_3\text{CH}_2\overset{\text{O}}{\overset{\|}{\text{C}}}\text{Cl}}$

(e) phthalimide $\xrightarrow[\text{(CH}_3)_2\text{CHCH}_2\text{CH}_2\text{Br}]{\text{NaOEt}}$

(f) $\text{CH}_3\text{CH}_2\text{NH}_2$
(see part (a)) $\xrightarrow[\text{K}_2\text{CO}_3]{\text{BrCH}_2\text{CH}_2\text{CH}_2\text{CH}_2\text{CH}_2\text{Br}}$

(g) $\text{C}_6\text{H}_5\overset{\text{O}}{\overset{\|}{\text{C}}}\text{CH}_3$ $\xrightarrow{\text{HCN}}$

(h) $\text{CH}_3\text{CH}_2\text{NH}_2$ $\xrightarrow{\text{(CH}_3\overset{\text{O}}{\overset{\|}{\text{C}}})_2\text{O}}$ $\xrightarrow{\text{LiAlH}_4}$ $\text{(CH}_3\text{CH}_2)_2\text{NH}$ $\xrightarrow[\text{HCl}]{\text{NaNO}_2}$ $\text{(CH}_3\text{CH}_2)_2\text{N-N=O}$

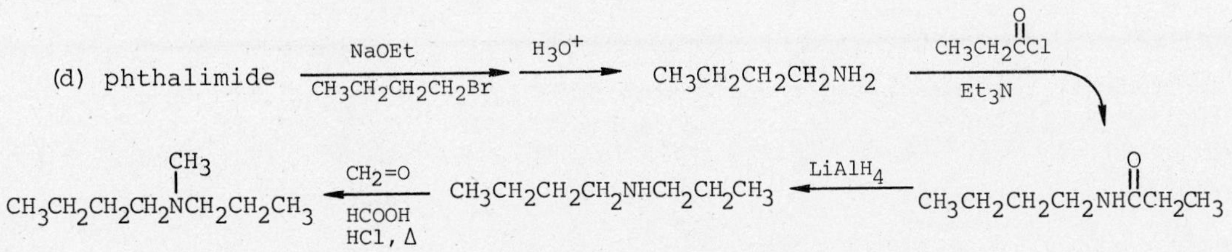

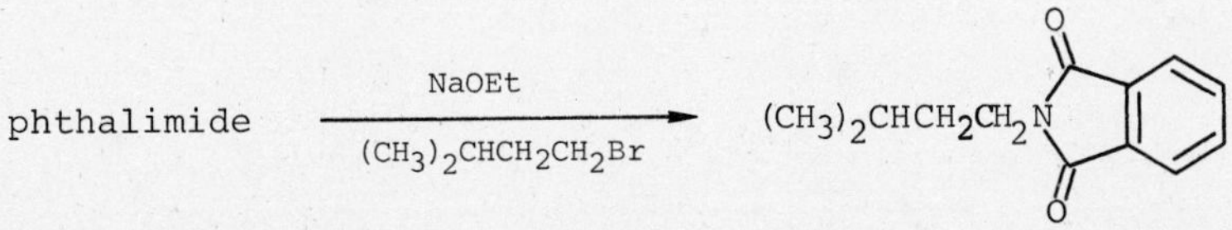

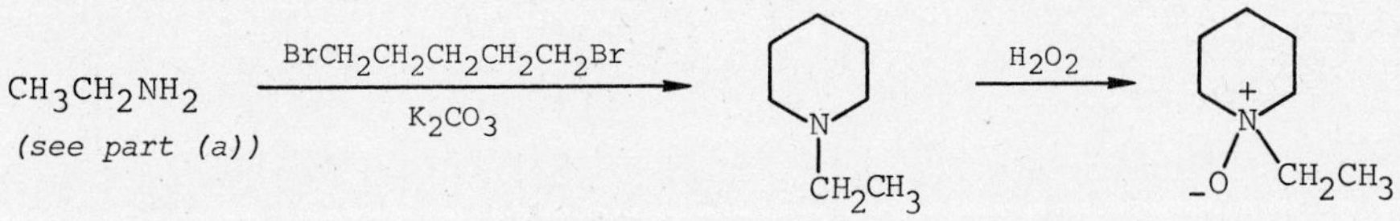

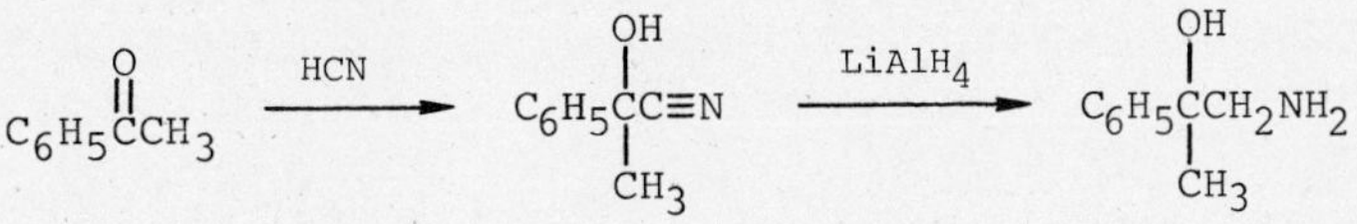

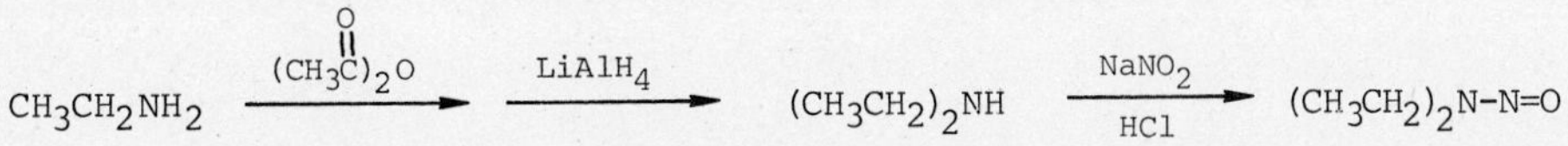

S10. (a)

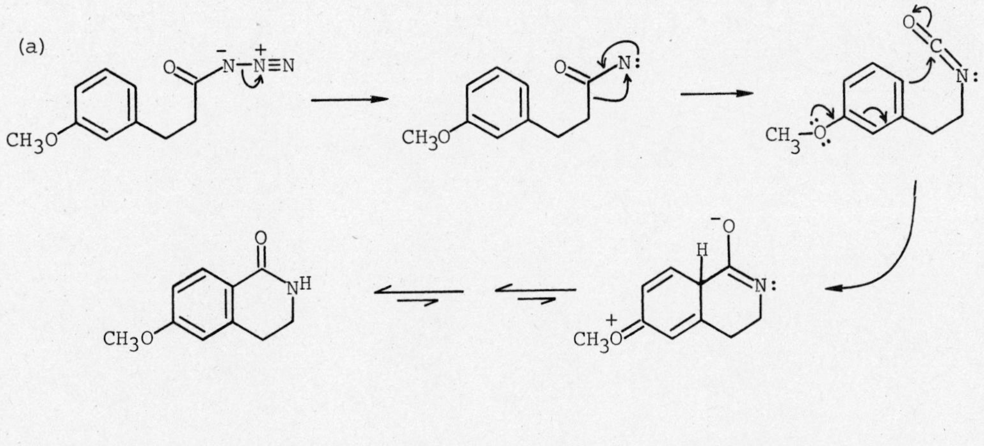

(b)

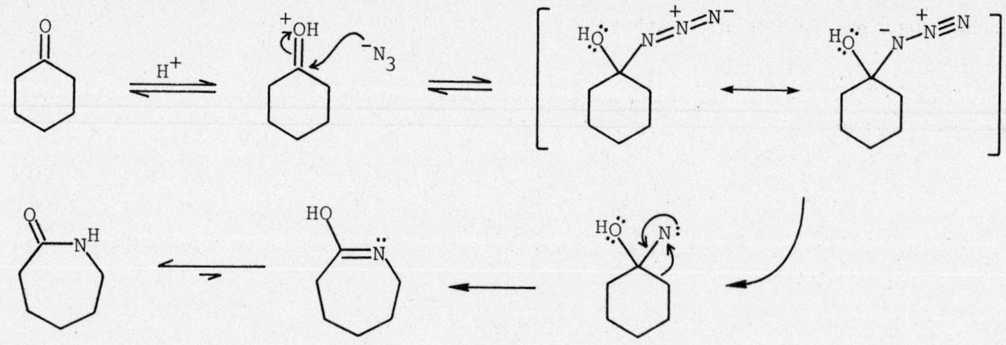

S11. The ability of Y to stabilize the electron pair it gains during the reaction is indicated by the pK_a of the conjugate acid:

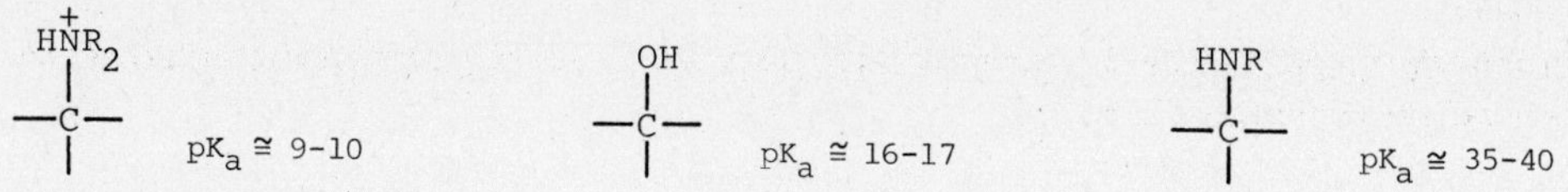

$pK_a \cong 9\text{-}10$

$pK_a \cong 16\text{-}17$

$pK_a \cong 35\text{-}40$

S12.

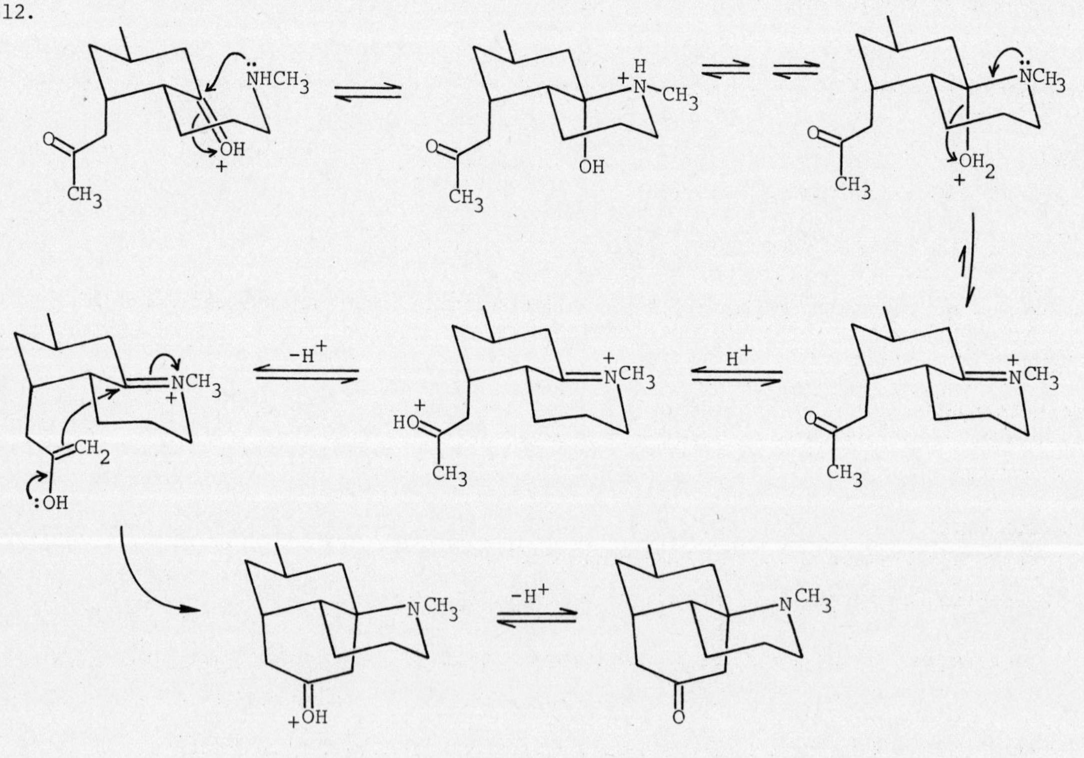

24. OTHER NITROGEN FUNCTIONS

24.A   Chapter Outline and Important Terms Introduced

24.1 Nitro Compounds
    A. Nitroalkanes
        from free radical nitration:

$$RH + HNO_3 \longrightarrow RNO_2 + H_2O$$

        from displacement by nitrite:

$$RX + NO_2^- \longrightarrow RNO_2 + X^-$$

        reduction of $-NO_2$ to $-NH_2$: see Section 23.6.C
        Henry reaction
    B. Nitroarenes (preparation covered in Chapters 22 and 23)
        TNT
    C. Reactions of Nitroarenes
        reduction
        hydroxylamines, azoxy compounds, azo compound, hydrazo compounds, nitroso compounds
        benzidine rearrangement

24.2 Isocyanates, Carbamates, and Ureas
    isocyanates from Hofmann rearrangement: see Section 23.6.H
    isocyanates from displacement:

$$RX + {}^-:\ddot{N}=C=O \longrightarrow RN=C=O + X^-$$

    carbamates (urethanes) and ureas from isocyanates

24.3 Azides
    alkyl and acyl azides by displacement:

$$RX + N_3^- \longrightarrow RN_3 + X^-$$

$$\overset{O}{\overset{||}{R-C-Cl}} + N_3^- \longrightarrow \overset{O}{\overset{||}{R-C-N_3}} + Cl^- \qquad \text{(see Curtius rearrangement, Section 23.6.H)}$$

    reduction of alkyl azides

24.4 Diazo Compounds
    preparation of esters with diazomethane: see Section 17.7.A
    diazoketones

24.5 Diazonium Salts
    preparation from aryl amines: see Section 23.7.B

    A. Acid-Base Equilibria of Arenediazonium Ions

$$Ar-\overset{+}{N}{\equiv}N + H_2O \underset{K_1}{\overset{-H^+}{\rightleftharpoons}} \underset{\textit{arenediazohydroxide}}{Ar-N=N-OH} \underset{K_2}{\overset{OH^-}{\rightleftharpoons}} \underset{\textit{arenediazotate}}{Ar-N=N-O^-} \qquad (K_2 > K_1)$$

    synthesis of substituted benzene derivatives via diazonium displacement

    B. Thermal Decomposition of Diazonium Salts; Formation of ArOH, ArI, and ArSH
    C. The Sandmeyer Reaction: Preparation of ArCl, ArBr, and ArCN
    D. Preparation of Fluoro- and Nitroarenes
        Gatterman reaction   Schiemann reaction
    E. Replacement of the Diazonium Group by Hydrogen
    F. Arylation Reactions
        Gomberg-Bachmann reaction
    G. Diazonium Ions as Electrophiles: Azo Compounds
    H. Synthetic Utility of Arenediazonium Salts

24.B   Important Reactions Introduced

<u>Carbanion reactions of nitroalkanes</u>   (24.1.A)

Equation:

$$CH_3NO_2 \underset{\text{base}}{\rightleftharpoons} {}^-CH_2NO_2 \xrightarrow{RCH=O} RCHCH_2NO_2 \xrightarrow{-H_2O} RCH=CHNO_2$$

(with OH above the carbon in $RCHCH_2NO_2$)

Key features: similar to aldol addition reaction

<u>Reduction of nitroarenes</u>   (24.1.B and C)

Equations and generality:

    to amine
$$ArNO_2 \xrightarrow{[H]} ArNH_2 \ ; \quad [H] = Zn, \ Sn, \ or \ SnCl_2 \ in \ HCl; \ H_2/catalyst$$

    to hydroxylamine
$$ArNO_2 \xrightarrow{[H]} ArNHOH \ ; \quad [H] = Zn, \ NH_4Cl$$

    to azoxy compound
$$2 \ ArNO_2 \xrightarrow{[H]} Ar-\overset{+}{N}=N-Ar \ ; \quad [H] = As_2O_3, \ aq. \ NaOH \ (via \ Ar-N=O + ArNH_2)$$

(with O^- on the first N)

    to azo compound
$$2 \ ArNO_2 \xrightarrow{[H]} Ar-N=N-Ar \ ; \quad [H] = Zn, \ alcoholic \ NaOH$$

    to hydrazo compound
$$2 \ ArNO_2 \xrightarrow{[H]} Ar-NHNH-Ar \ ; \quad [H] = H_2NNH_2, \ Ru/C, \ alcoholic \ KOH$$

<u>Interconversions of aromatic nitrogen compounds</u>   (24.1.C)

Equations and generality:

    hydroxylamines and nitroso compounds
$$ArNHOH \xrightarrow{[Ox]} Ar-N=O \ ; \quad [Ox] = Na_2Cr_2O_7, \ H_2SO_4$$

    azoxy compounds and azo compounds
$$Ar\overset{+}{N}=NAr \underset{[Ox]}{\overset{[H]}{\rightleftharpoons}} ArN=NAr \ ; \quad [H] = (EtO)_3P: ; \ [Ox] = H_2O_2, \ HOAc$$

(with O^- on the first N)

    azo compounds and hydrazo compounds
$$ArN=NAr \underset{[Ox]}{\overset{[H]}{\rightleftharpoons}} ArNHNHAr \ ; \quad [H] = H_2NNH_2, \ Pd/C; \ [Ox] = O_2 \ or \ NaOBr$$

    azo compounds and amines

$$ArN=NAr \xrightarrow{[H]} 2 \ ArNH_2 \ ; \quad [H] = Na_2S_2O_4, \ or \ any \ reagents \ which \ take \ ArNO_2 \ to \ ArNH_2$$

<u>Benzidine rearrangement</u>   (24.1.C)

Equation:
$$Ar-NH-NH-Ar \xrightarrow{H^+} H_2N-Ar-Ar-NH_2$$

Key feature: Benzidine and related compounds are carcinogenic

<u>Reaction of isocyanates with nucleophiles</u>   (24.2)

Equation:
$$R-N=C=O \ + \ H-Y \longrightarrow R-NH-\overset{O}{\overset{\|}{C}}-Y$$

Generality: Y = OH : product is a carbamic acid, which decomposes to give RNH_2 and CO_2
              Y = OR': product is a carbamate ester = a urethane
              Y = NR'$_2$: product is a urea

Key features: isocyanates are key intermediates in Hofmann, Schmidt, and Curtius rearrangements

Reduction of alkyl azides (24.3)

Equation:

$$R-N_3 \xrightarrow{[H]} R-NH_2$$

Generality: R = alkyl or aryl

[H] = LiAlH$_4$ or H$_2$/catalyst

Key features: coupled with displacement of RX with N$_3^-$, this is an alternative to the Gabriel synthesis of 1° amines

Preparation of diazomethane from N-nitroso amides (24.4)

Equation:

$$R-\overset{\overset{\displaystyle O}{\|}}{C}-\underset{\underset{\displaystyle N=O}{|}}{N}-CH_3 \xrightarrow{NaOH} RCO_2^- + CH_2=N=N$$

Generality: R = alkyl or aryl

applicable to preparation of other diazoalkanes

Formation and reaction of diazoketones (24.4)

Equation:

$$R-\overset{\overset{\displaystyle O}{\|}}{C}-Cl + 2\ CH_2N_2 \longrightarrow R-\overset{\overset{\displaystyle O}{\|}}{C}-CHN_2 + CH_3Cl + N_2$$

HX ↙   ↘ Δ or hυ   → dimer

$$R-\overset{\overset{\displaystyle O}{\|}}{C}-CH_2X + N_2$$

$$\left[R-\overset{\overset{\displaystyle O}{\|}}{C}-CH: \right] \longrightarrow R-CH=C=O \xrightarrow{R'OH} R-CH_2-\overset{\overset{\displaystyle O}{\|}}{C}-OR'$$

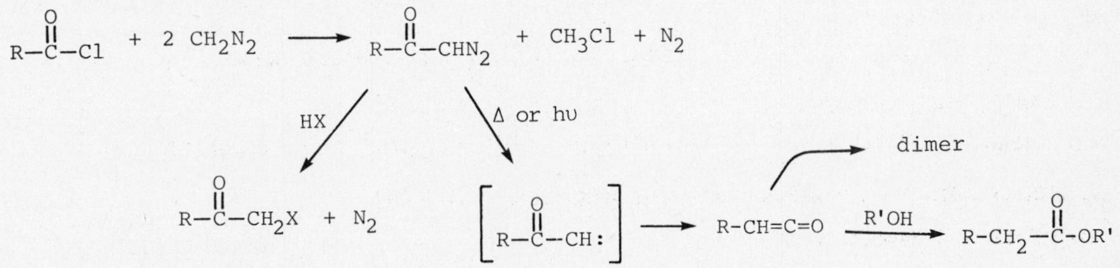

Carbene addition from α-diazoesters (24.4)

Equation:

$$N_2=CHCO_2Et \longrightarrow :CHCO_2Et \longrightarrow \text{(bicyclic)}-CO_2Et$$

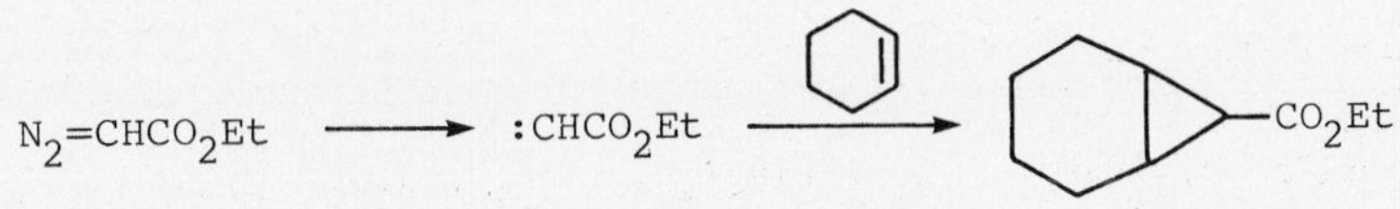

Generality: carbene formation induced either by heat or metal catalysis

Substitution of arenediazonium salts (24.5)

Equation:

$$Ar-N_2^+ + M^+Nu^- \longrightarrow Ar-Nu + M^+ + N_2$$

Generality: M$^+$Nu$^-$ = H—OH, H—I, H—SH (better alternative for formation of Ar—SH is EtOCS$_2^-$K$^+$, followed by hydrolysis of xanthate product)

= CuX (X = Cl, Br, CN; Sandmeyer reaction)

= NaNO$_2$/copper powder (Gatterman reaction)

= H$_3$PO$_2$ to give Ar—H

thermal decomposition of BF$_4^-$ or PF$_6^-$ salts gives Ar—F (Schiemann reaction)

Key features: substitution reactions proceed via complexed aryl cations or radical intermediates

Gomberg-Bachmann arylation reaction (24.5.F)

Equation:

$$Ar-N_2^+ + Ar'H \longrightarrow Ar-Ar' + H^+ + N_2$$

Generality: isomer mixtures produced if Ar'H is substituted

works best with Ar'H in excess

Key features: radical mechanism

low yield, but often the only way to form biphenyls

Formation of azo compounds (24.5.G)

Equation:

$$Ar{-}N_2^+ \; + \; Ar'{-}Y \longrightarrow Ar{-}N{=}N{-}Ar'{-}Y$$

Generality: Y = strongly activating, o-, p-directing group

Key features: reaction proceeds via triazene intermediate if Y = NH_2
azo compounds are important dyes and colorings

24.C Important Concepts and Hints

This chapter covers a true potpourri of reactions, with the common factor that each transformation concerns a nitrogen compound in which the nitrogen is not an amine. Much of this chemistry involves arene derivatives, including all of the intermediates along the way as an aryl nitro compound is reduced to the aryl amine. This topic is full of detail, and is difficult to learn in a way that doesn't ultimately rely on memorization. On the other hand, the reactions of arenediazonium salts involve the common goal of replacing the diazonium group with something else. This is an important group of reactions because it allows the introduction of a wide range of substituents onto an aromatic ring, by a method different from electrophilic aromatic substitution. This can be useful when normal directive effects in electrophilic substitution make it impossible to obtain a specific isomer. Keep in mind the fact that RS, HS, RO, HO, F, Cl, Br, CN, CH=O (from CN), CO_2H (from CN), and even H can be represented by amino or nitro substituents at various stages of a synthesis.

24.D Answers to Exercises

24.1 (a)

$$CH_3CH_2CH_2\overset{O}{\overset{\|}{C}}CH_3 \xrightarrow{NaBH_4} \xrightarrow{PBr_3} \xrightarrow{NaCN} \xrightarrow{LiAlH_4} CH_3CH_2CH_2\overset{CH_3}{\overset{|}{C}H}CH_2NH_2$$

(b)

$$CH_3CH_2CH_2\overset{O}{\overset{\|}{C}}CH_3 + CH_3NO_2 \xrightarrow{NaOH} \xrightarrow{H_2/Pt} CH_3CH_2CH_2\overset{OH}{\overset{|}{\underset{CH_3}{\underset{|}{C}}}}{-}CH_2NH_2$$

24.2 The negative charge can be delocalized via resonance onto the strongly electron-withdrawing nitro groups:

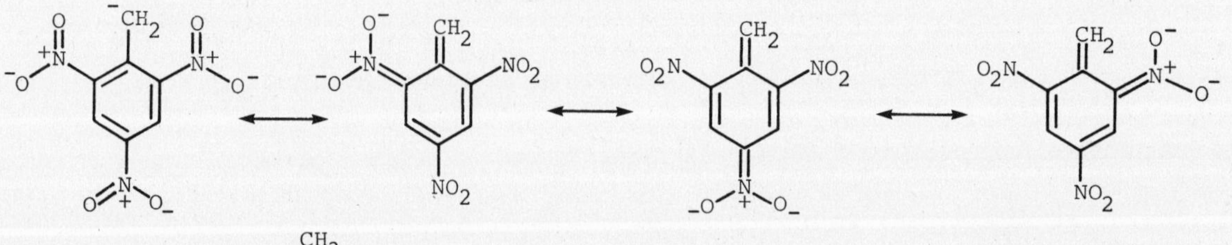

24.3

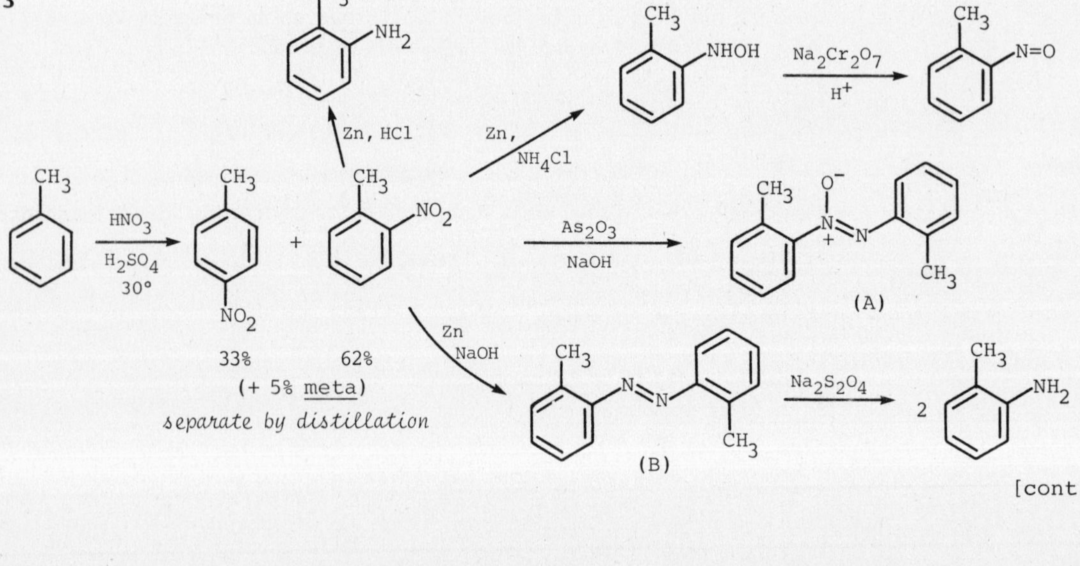

[cont'd]

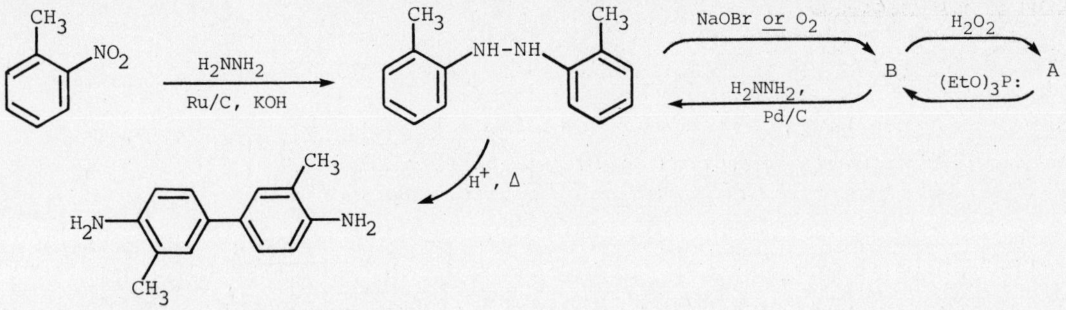

24.4 $R:\overset{..}{N}::C::\overset{..}{O}:$ $R:\overset{..}{N}::\overset{..}{\underset{..}{N}}::\overset{+}{N}:$

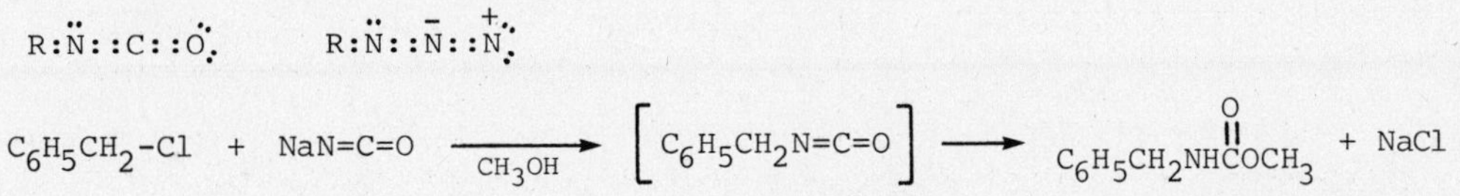

24.5

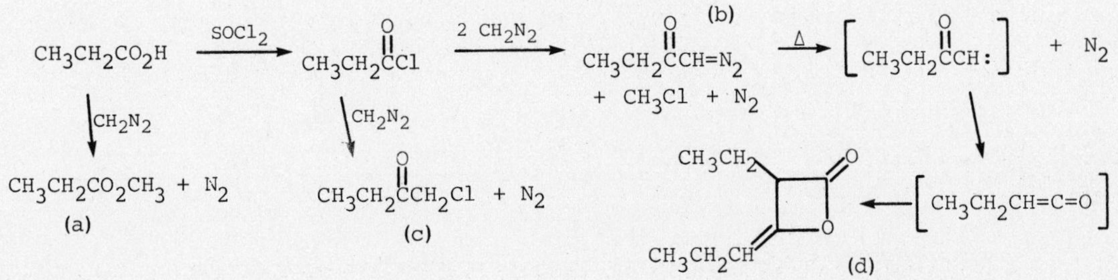

(a)

(b)

(c)

(d)

24.6

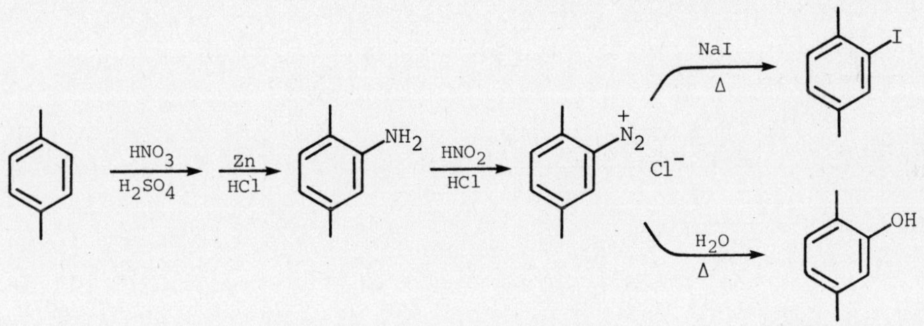

24.7

(a)

(b)

(c)

(d)   (e)

(Note the use of HBr for this
diazotization so that no
C_6H_5Cl is formed in the
CuBr reaction.)

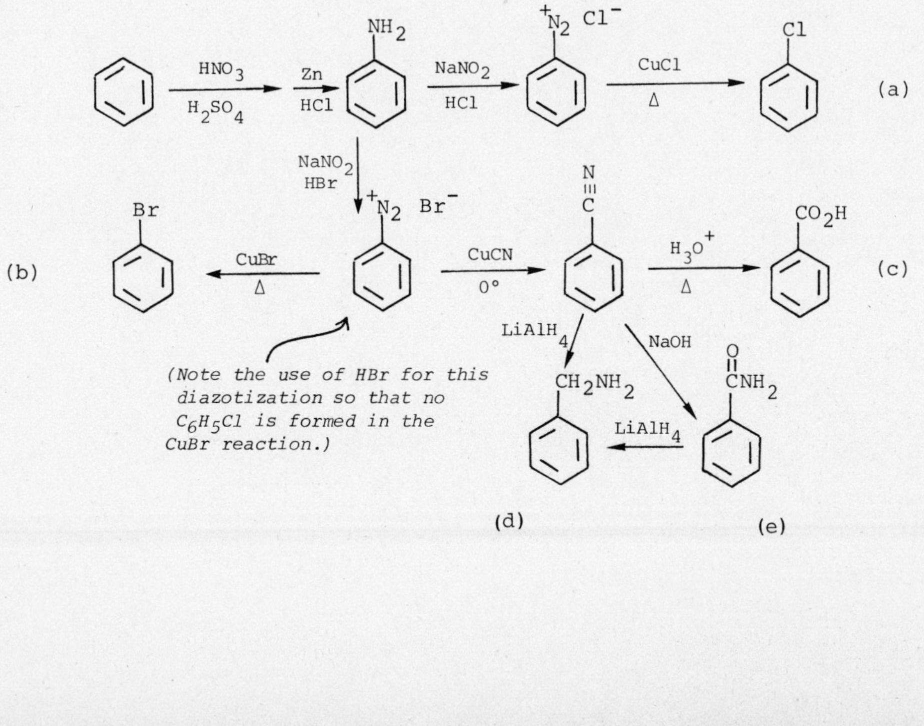

24.8

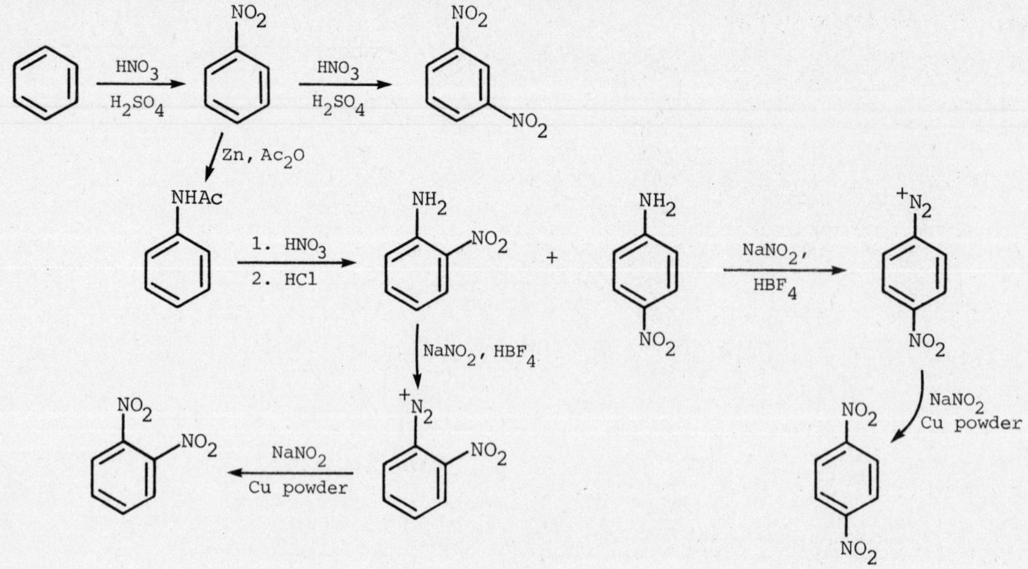

24.9

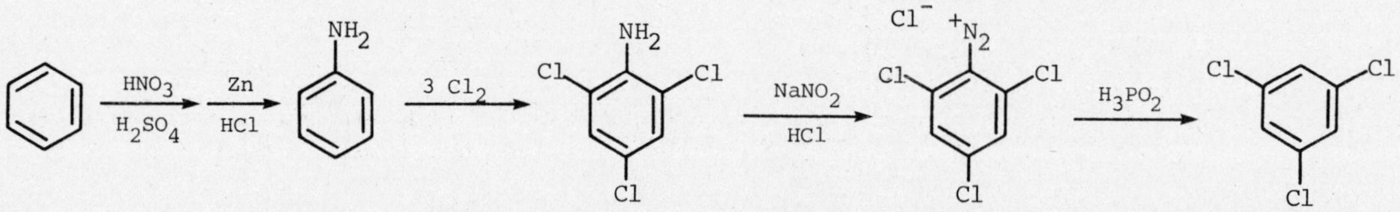

24.10

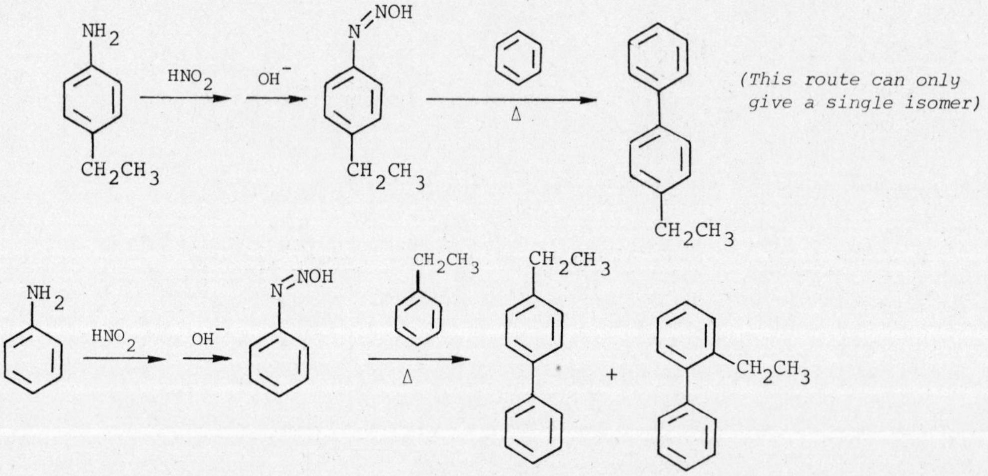

(This route can only give a single isomer)

24.11

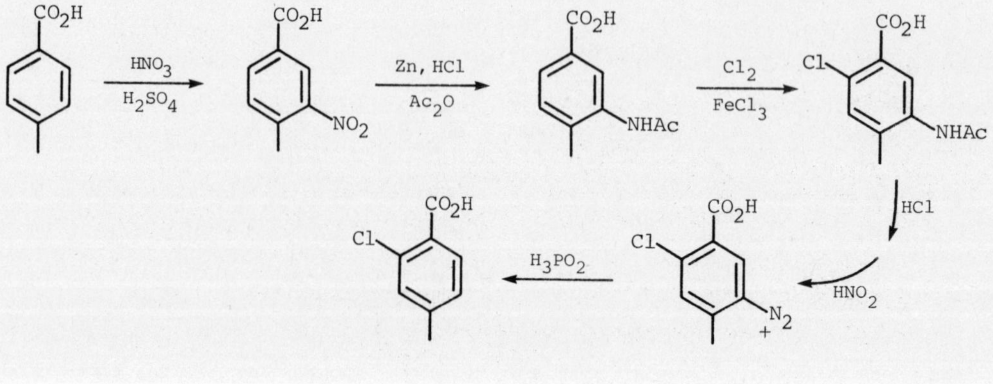

24.E   Answers and Explanations for Problems

1. (a)   (b)   (c)   (d)

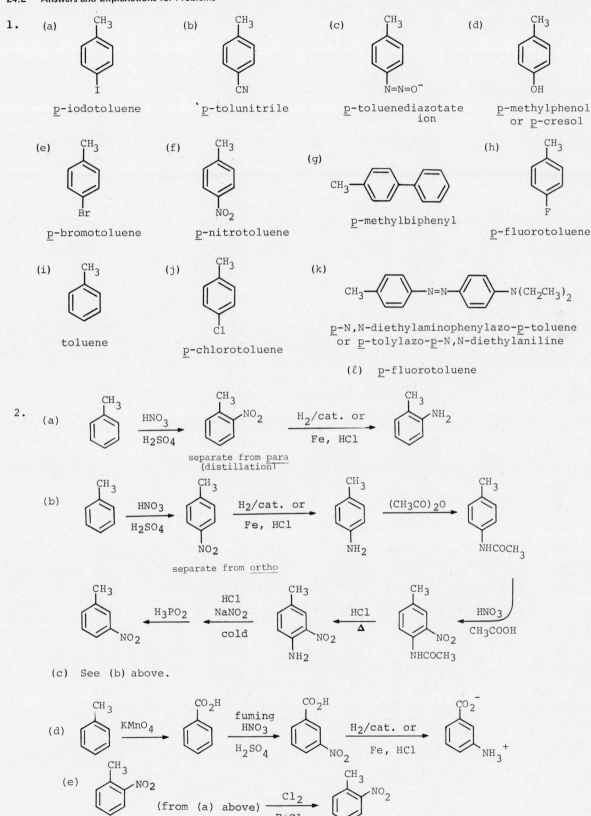

p-iodotoluene   p-tolunitrile   p-toluenediazotate   p-methylphenol
                                        ion   or p-cresol

(e)   (f)   (g)   (h)

p-bromotoluene   p-nitrotoluene   p-methylbiphenyl   p-fluorotoluene

(i)   (j)   (k)

toluene   p-chlorotoluene   p-N,N-diethylaminophenylazo-p-toluene
                                   or p-tolylazo-p-N,N-diethylaniline

                                        (ℓ)   p-fluorotoluene

2. (a)

        separate from para
        (distillation)

    (b)

        separate from ortho

(c) See (b) above.

    (d)

    (e)   (from (a) above)

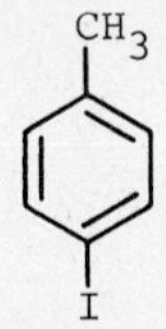

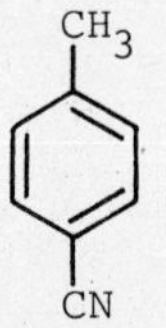

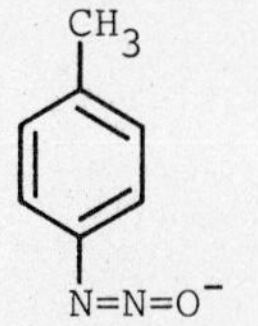

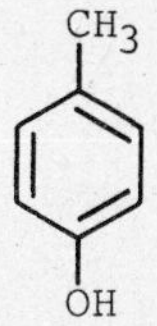

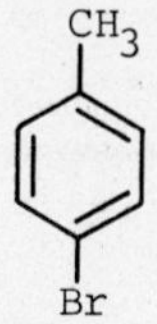

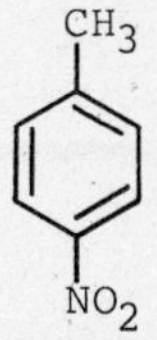

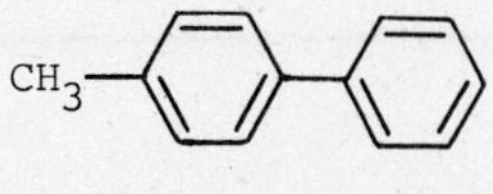

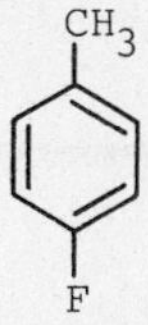

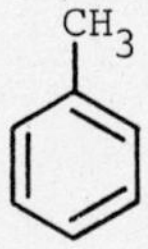

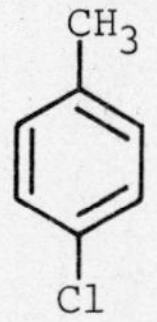

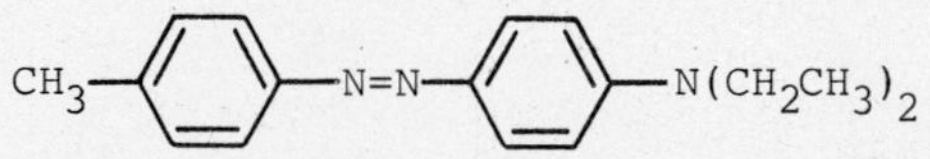

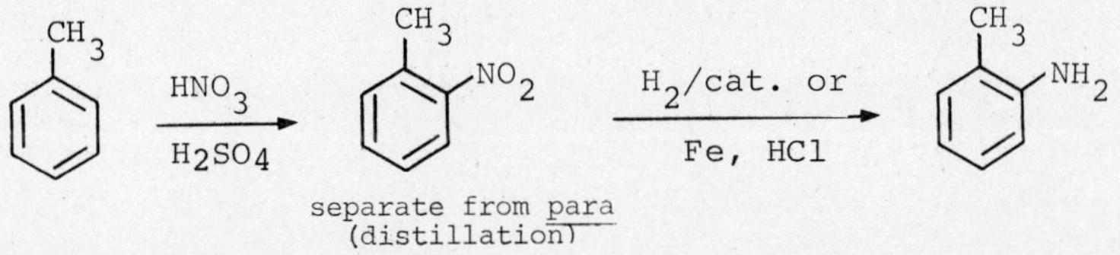

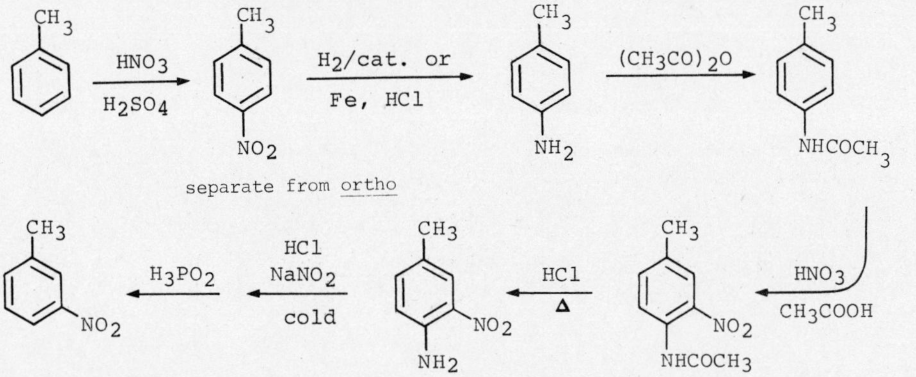

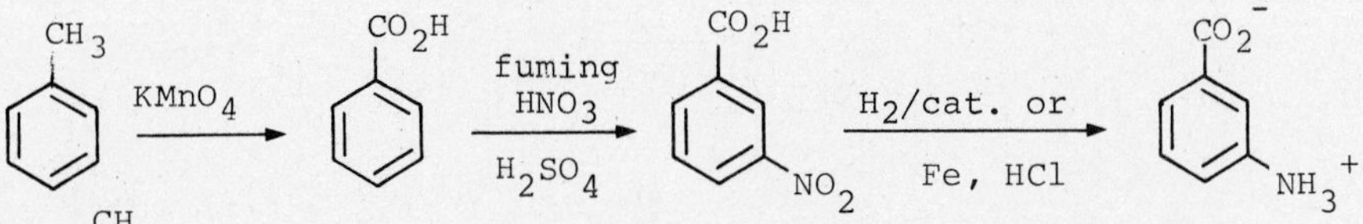

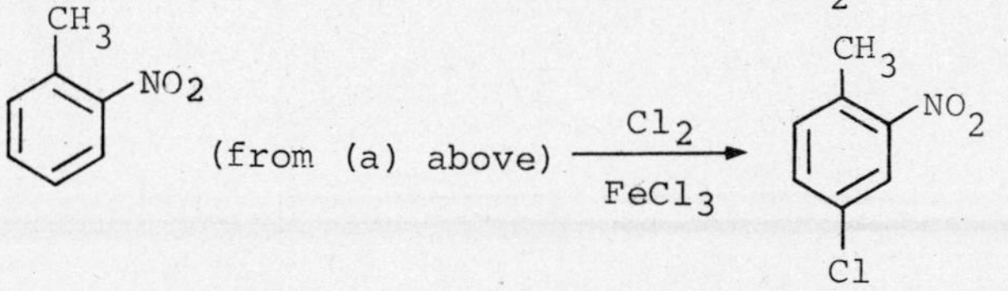

(f)

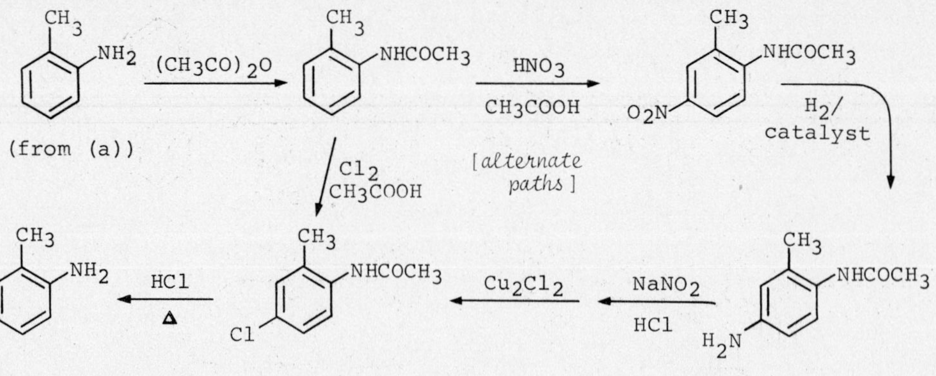

(from (a))

$(CH_3CO)_2O$

$\xrightarrow{HNO_3}{CH_3COOH}$

[alternate paths]

$\xrightarrow{H_2/}{catalyst}$

$\downarrow \begin{array}{c} Cl_2 \\ CH_3COOH \end{array}$

$\xleftarrow[\Delta]{HCl}$

$\xleftarrow{Cu_2Cl_2}$

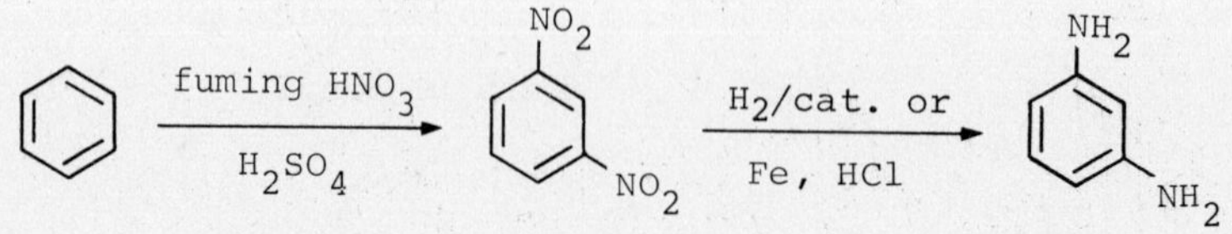

$\xleftarrow[HCl]{NaNO_2}$

(g)

$\xrightarrow[H_2SO_4]{fuming\ HNO_3}$

$\xrightarrow{H_2/cat.\ or}{Fe,\ HCl}$

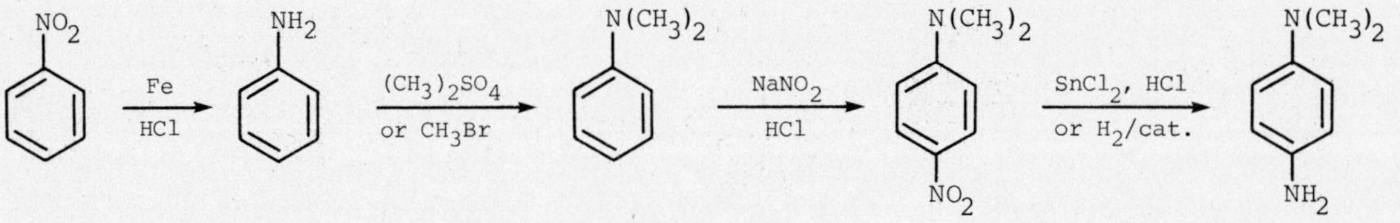

(h)

$\xrightarrow[HCl]{Fe}$

$\xrightarrow{(CH_3)_2SO_4}{or\ CH_3Br}$

$\xrightarrow[HCl]{NaNO_2}$

$\xrightarrow{SnCl_2,\ HCl}{or\ H_2/cat.}$

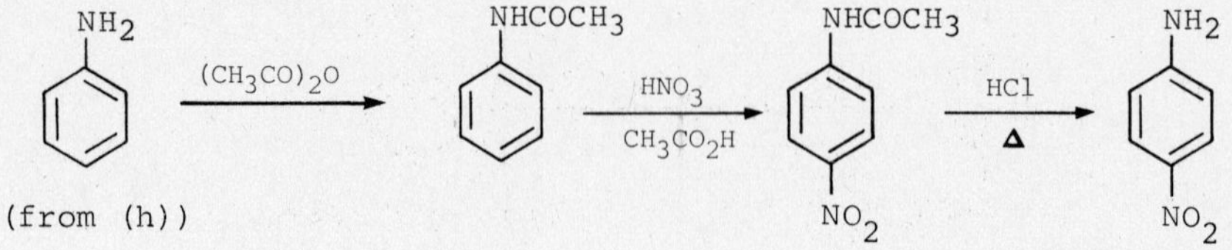

(i)

(from (h))

$(CH_3CO)_2O$

$\xrightarrow{HNO_3}{CH_3CO_2H}$

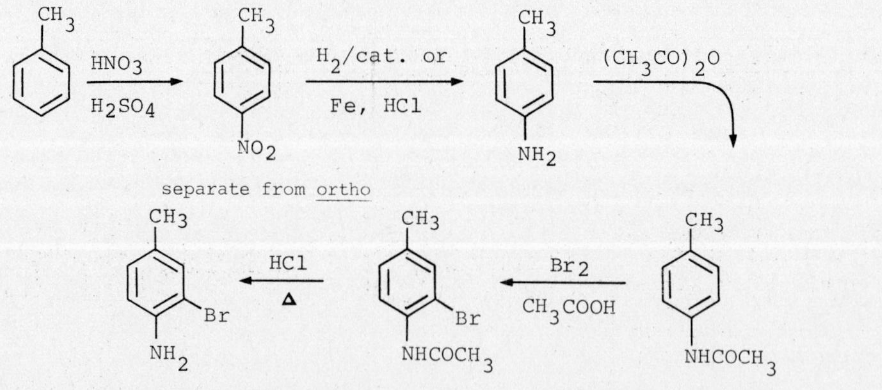

$\xrightarrow[\Delta]{HCl}$

3. (a)

$\xrightarrow[H_2SO_4]{HNO_3}$

$\xrightarrow{H_2/cat.\ or}{Fe,\ HCl}$

$(CH_3CO)_2O$

separate from ortho

$\xleftarrow[\Delta]{HCl}$

$\xleftarrow[CH_3COOH]{Br_2}$

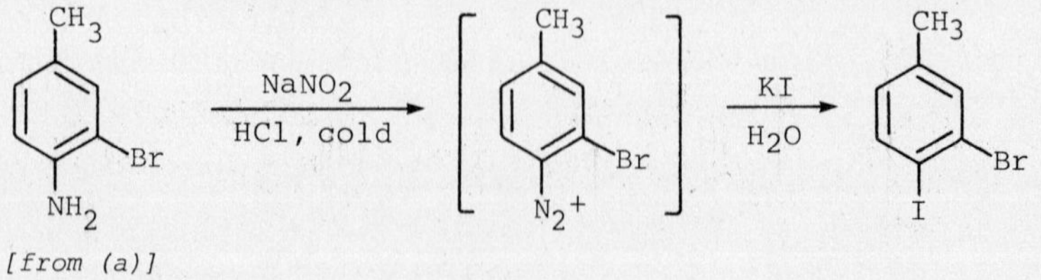

(b)

[from (a)]

$\xrightarrow{NaNO_2}{HCl,\ cold}$

$\xrightarrow{KI}{H_2O}$

(c)

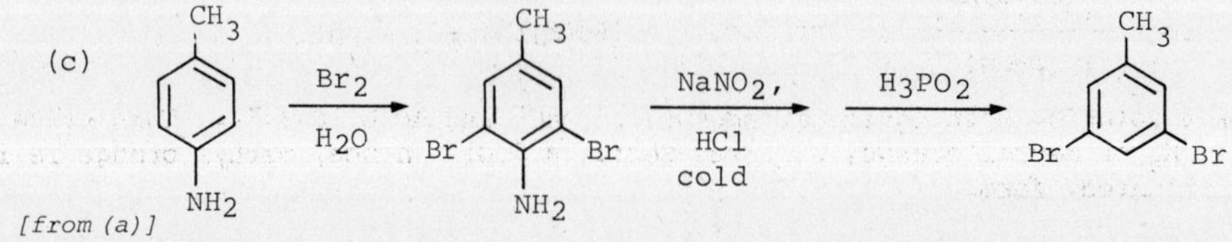

[from (a)]

$\xrightarrow{Br_2}{H_2O}$

$\xrightarrow{NaNO_2,}{HCl\ cold}$

$\xrightarrow{H_3PO_2}$

(d)

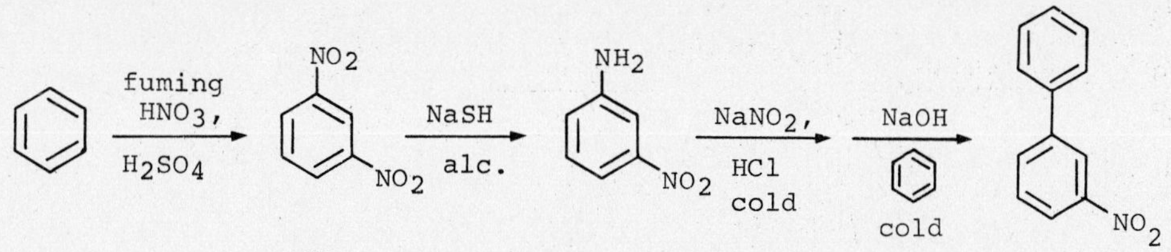

(e)

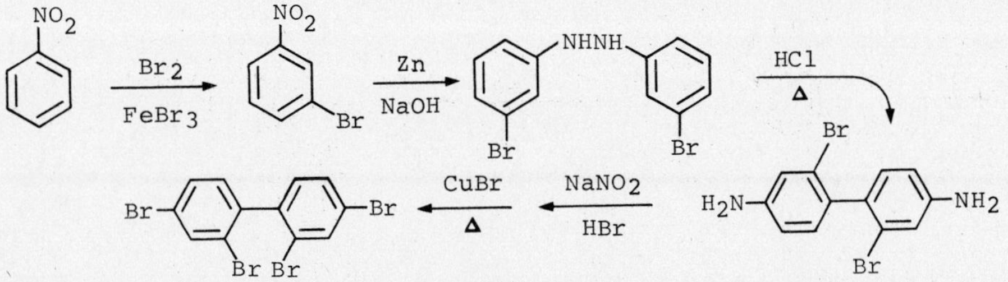

(f)

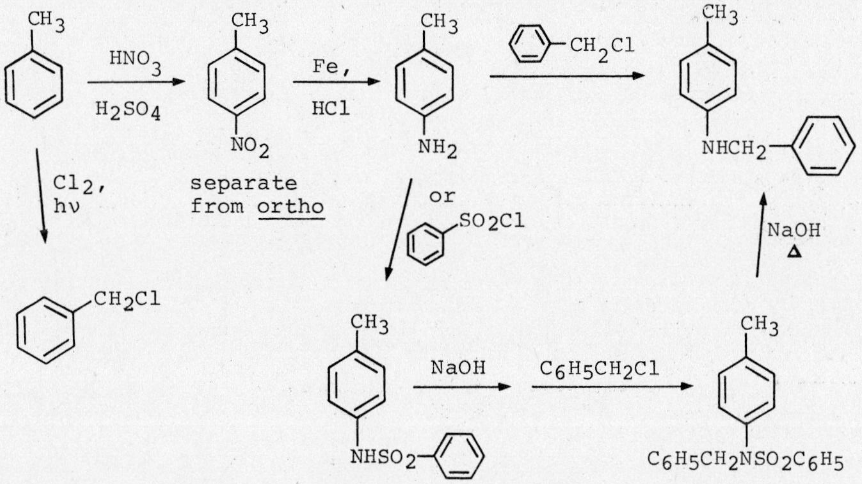

(g)

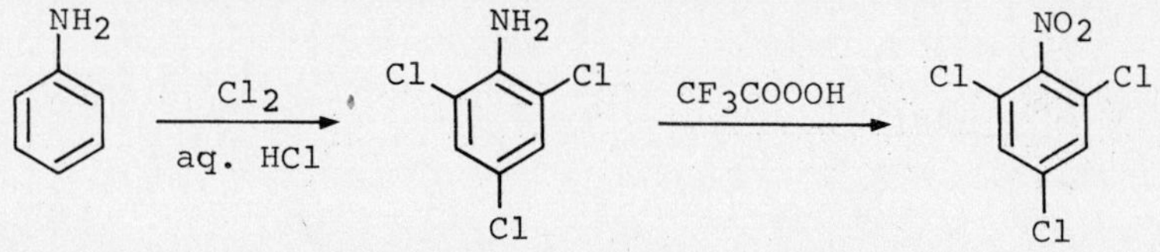

(h)

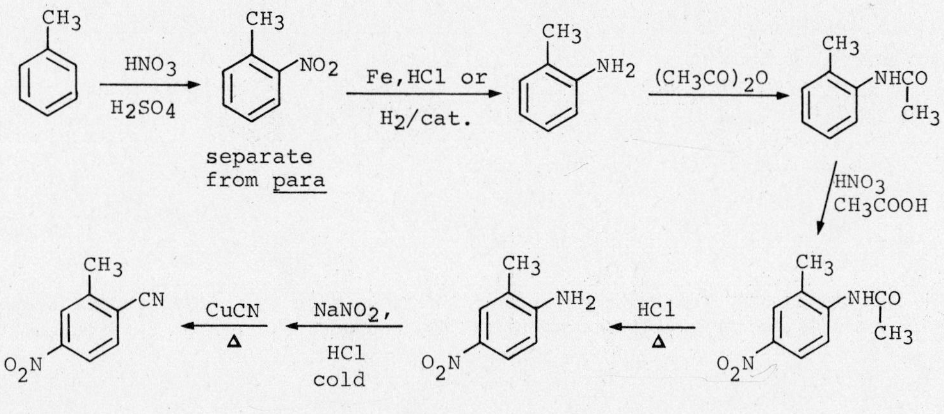

separate
from para

4.

$$pK_a = \log \frac{[H^+][AcO^-]}{[AcOH]}, \quad \text{for } [AcO^-] = [AcOH], \quad pK_a = pH$$

Hence, the pH of a solution with equimolar amounts of AcO⁻ and AcOH is 4.74. This value is greater than the pK_a of methyl orange, 3.5 (see Sect. 24.5.G); hence, methyl orange is in the yellow, unprotonated, form.

5. On reaction at the p-position, the odd electron can conjugate with the nitro group:

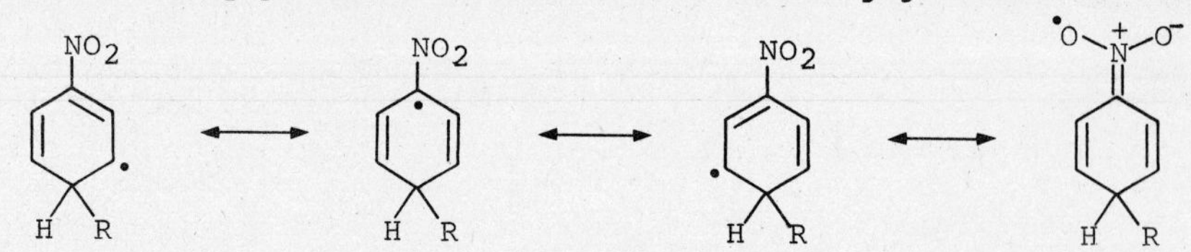

The nitro group helps to stabilize the odd electron and directs o, p-, just as in nucleophilic aromatic substitution.

6. (a)

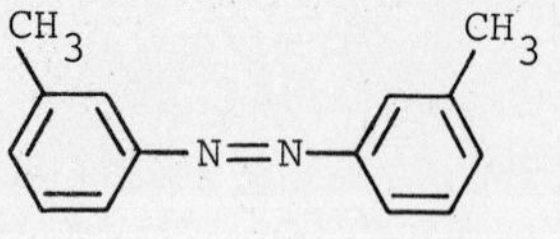

(b)

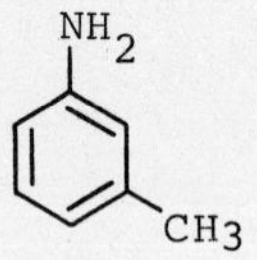

(c)

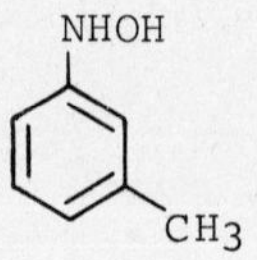

(d)

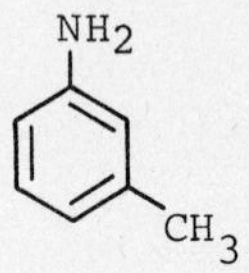

(e)

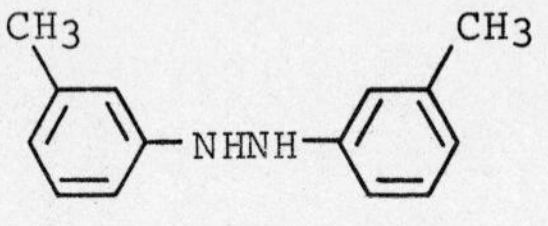

(f)

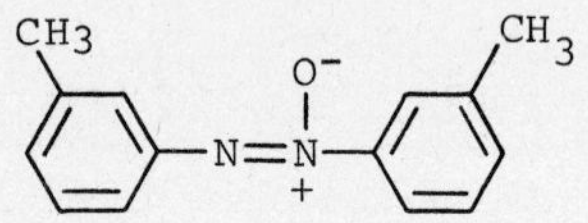

7. (a) Loss of N_2 gives a carbene which rearranges to a ketene:

$$\text{R-}\overset{\text{O}}{\overset{\|}{\text{C}}}\text{-CHNH}_2 \xrightarrow{-N_2} \text{R-}\overset{\text{O}}{\overset{\|}{\text{C}}}\text{-}\ddot{\text{C}}\text{-H} \longrightarrow \text{R-CH=C=O}$$

This rearrangement is similar to that which leads to a nitrene in the Curtius reaction. The ketene rapidly adds water to give a carboxylic acid.

$$\text{R-CH=C=O} + H_2O \longrightarrow \text{R-CH=}\underset{{}^{+}OH_2}{\text{C}}\text{-O}^- \longrightarrow RCH_2CO_2H$$

(b) $$CH_3COCHNH_2 \xrightarrow[-N_2]{h\nu} CH_3CO\ddot{C}H \longrightarrow CH_3CH{=}C{=}O \xrightarrow{CH_3OH} CH_3CH_2CO_2CH_3$$

8.

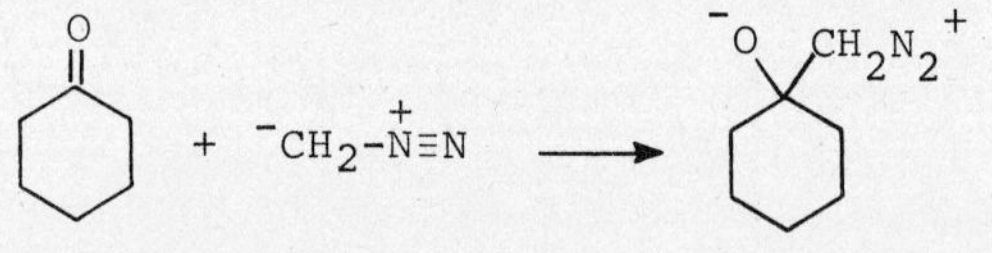

Two modes of further reaction:

Displacement of $-N_2$ by $-O^-$

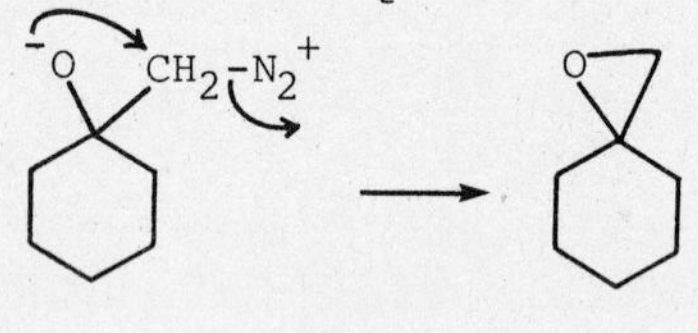

Rearrangement:

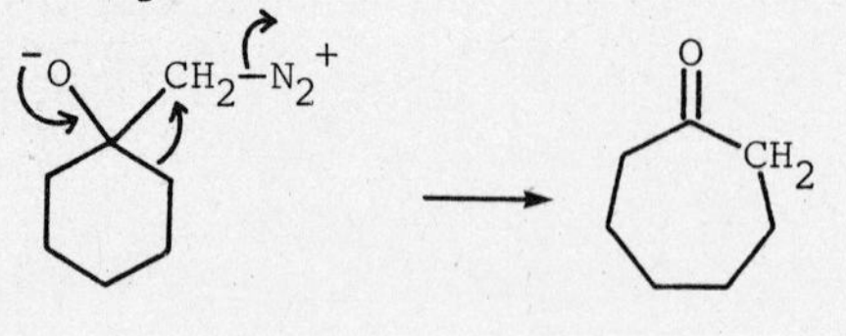

9. This is an example of the Hofmann degradation. When one gets to the isocyanate stage, the nucleophilic species now present is methanol. The product, a carbamic acid ester, is stable.

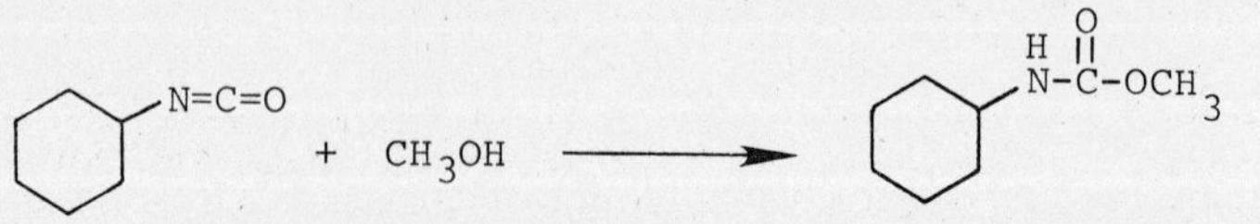

10. The predominant base in methanolic potassium hydroxide is actually methoxide ion, because of the equilibrium:

$$HO^- + \underset{\text{large excess}}{CH_3OH} \rightleftharpoons CH_3O^- + H_2O$$

The reaction is slow, since the ethyl carbamate is also an amide. The main reaction observed is **transesterification**:

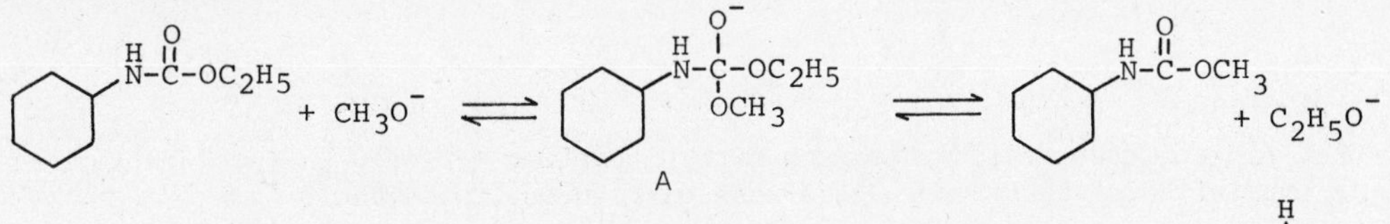

The alternative path (elimination of amide from A) is not observed, since 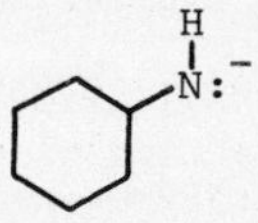 is such a poor leaving group. After a long time, of course, cyclohexyl-amine will be produced, since occasionally a hydroxide ion will attack to give an irreversible hydrolysis:

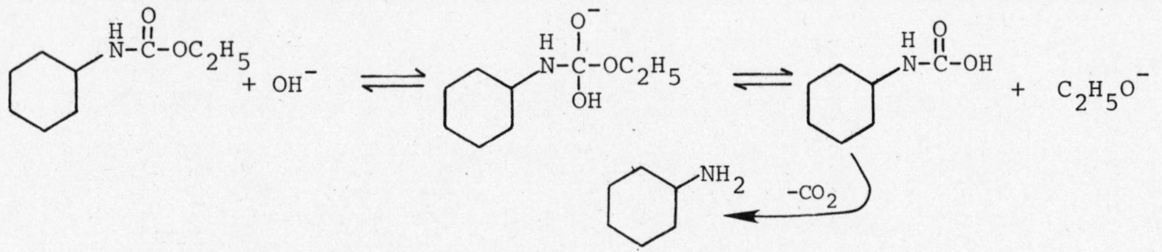

11. $CuBr + Cl^- \rightleftharpoons CuCl + Br^-$

The use of CuBr + HCl gives a mixture of bromocumene and chlorocumene.

12. The diazonium group is strongly electron-withdrawing and facilitates the nucleophilic aromatic substitution of groups in o- and p-positions:

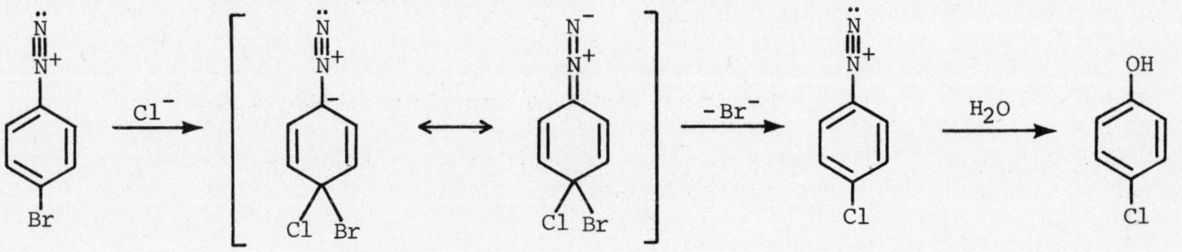

24.F   **Supplementary Problems**

S1. (a) Nitroethylene can be prepared from 2-nitroethanol by distillation from phthalic anhydride. Write a mechanism for this reaction.

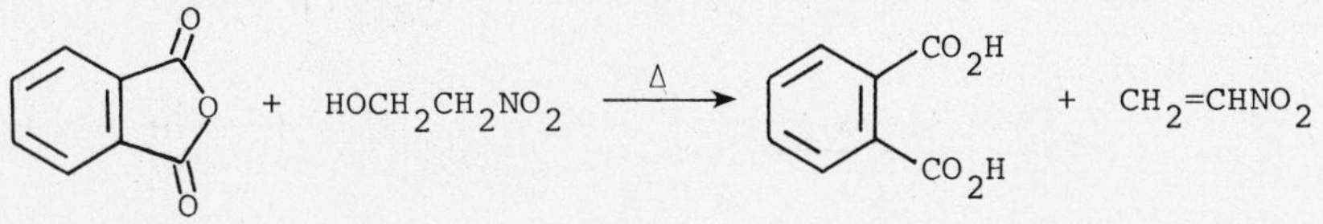

   (b) Nitroethylene is a powerful electrophile and reacts rapidly with dimethylamine to give N,N-dimethyl-2-nitroethanamine, for example. Write a reasonable mechanism for this reaction.

S2. (a) If nitrocyclohexane is treated with a strong base to form the anion, and then proton-ated with acid and isolated rapidly, the so-called <u>aci</u> tautomer is isolated. Propose a structure for this compound.

   (b) If the <u>aci</u> form of nitrocyclohexane is kept in the presence of aqueous acid, it undergoes hydrolysis to give cyclohexanone (the Nef reaction). Write a reasonable mechanism for this transformation.

(top reaction scheme)

NO$_2$-cyclohexane $\xrightarrow{\text{NaOH}}$ $\xrightarrow{\text{H}^+}$ $\underset{\text{tautomer}}{\text{aci}}$ $\xrightarrow{\text{H}_3\text{O}^+}$ (cyclohexanone) + "HNO" $\longrightarrow$ ½(N$_2$O + H$_2$O)

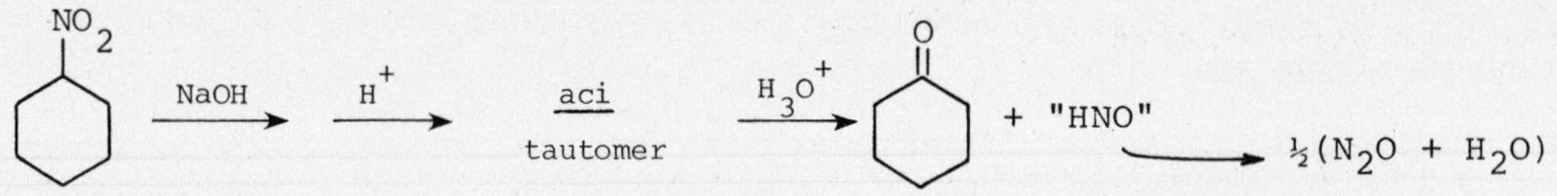

S3. What side product would you expect if the reaction depicted in Supplementary Problem #**S10** (a) in Chapter 23 of this Study Guide were carried out in ethanol?

S4. Phenyl azide can be prepared by treatment of benzenediazonium ion with sodium azide or by reaction of phenylhydrazine with nitrous acid. What intermediates are involved in this latter method?

S5. Show how to synthesize the following compounds from benzene or any monosubstituted derivative.

(a) [structure: 3-bromo-5-chlorobenzoic acid, HO$_2$C, Br, Cl]

(b) [structure: 2,4,6-trichlorothiophenol, SH, Cl, Cl, Cl]

(c) [structure: anisole derivative, OCH$_3$, Cl, Cl, D, D, H]

(d) [structure: 4-fluoro-2-chlorobenzaldehyde, F, Cl, CH=O]

(e) HO$_2$C— biphenyl —CO$_2$H

(f) (CH$_3$)$_3$C— biphenyl —Cl

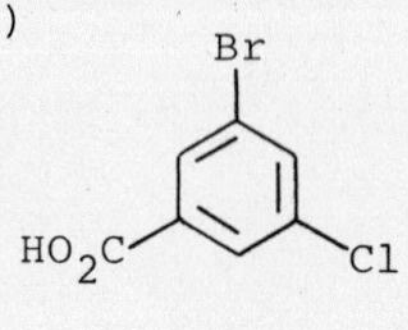

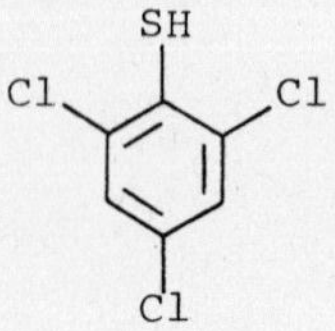

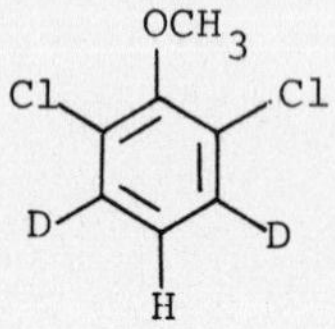

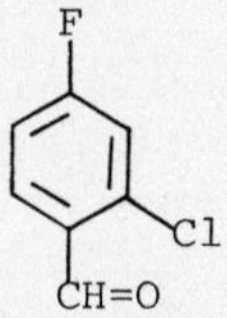

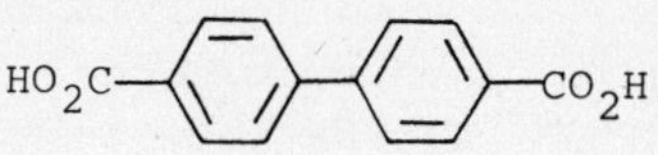

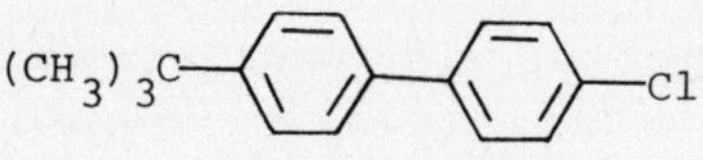

S6. Write a reasonable mechanism for the formation of diazomethane on treatment of N-methyl-N-nitrosoacetamide with sodium hydroxide.

S7. In contrast to ethyl diazoacetate, the diazoacetate anion is very unstable, decomposing in aqueous solution to give diazomethane and CO$_2$. Propose a mechanism for this transformation. *(NOTE: the diazomethane anion N$_2$CH$^-$ is not involved.)*

$$\text{N}_2\text{CHCO}_2^- \xrightarrow{\text{H}_2\text{O}} \text{N}_2\text{CH}_2 + \text{CO}_2 + \text{OH}^-$$

S8. What is the major product from each of the following reactions?

(a) [structure: 3-nitrotoluene (NO$_2$, CH$_3$)] $\xrightarrow[\text{HCl}]{\text{Zn}}$ $\xrightarrow[\text{HBF}_4]{\text{NaNO}_2}$ $\xrightarrow{\Delta}$

(d) CH$_3$— [structure azoxy: N$^+$(O$^-$)=N]— phenyl $\xrightarrow{\text{(EtO)}_3\text{P:}}$

(b) [structure: 3,5-dinitrotoluene (NO$_2$, O$_2$N, CH$_3$)] $\xrightarrow[\text{CH}_3\text{OH}]{\text{NaSH}}$ $\xrightarrow{\text{Ac}_2\text{O}}$

(e) [structure: 3-nitrobenzoic acid (NO$_2$, HO$_2$C)] $\xrightarrow[\text{aq. NH}_4\text{Cl}]{\text{Zn}}$ $\xrightarrow[\text{H}^+]{\text{K}_2\text{Cr}_2\text{O}_7}$

(c) [structure: 4-chloronitrobenzene (NO$_2$, Cl)] $\xrightarrow[\text{alc. NaOH}]{\text{Zn}}$ $\xrightarrow{\text{H}_2\text{O}_2}$

(f) [structure: acetanilide (NHCCH$_3$ with C=O)] $\xrightarrow{\text{Br}_2}$ $\xrightarrow{\text{H}_3\text{O}^+}$ $\xrightarrow{\text{CF}_3\text{CO}_3\text{H}}$

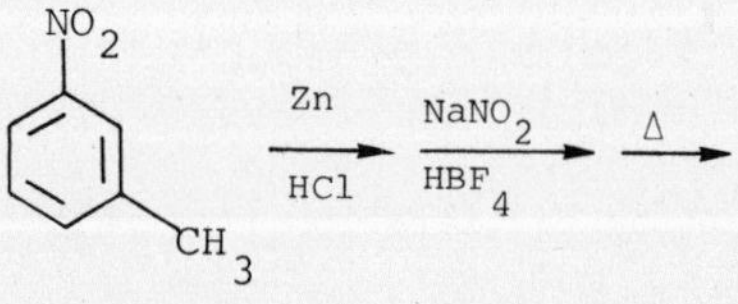

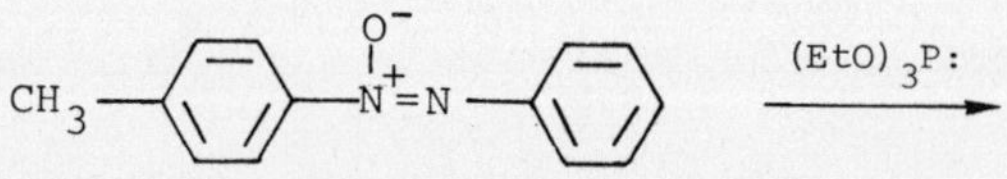

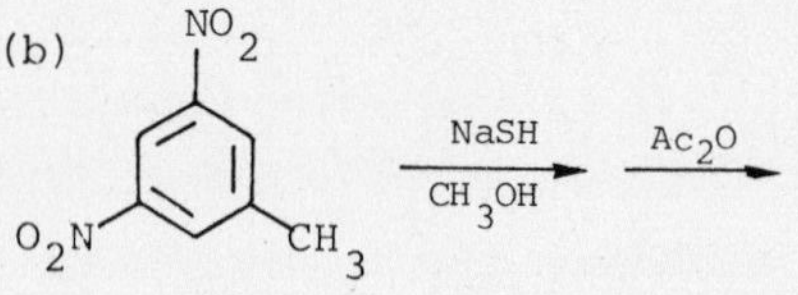

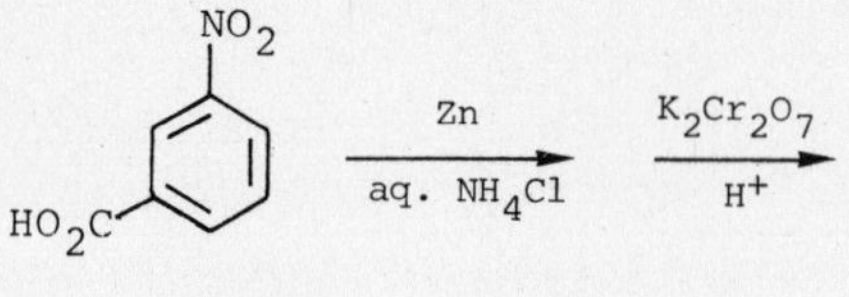

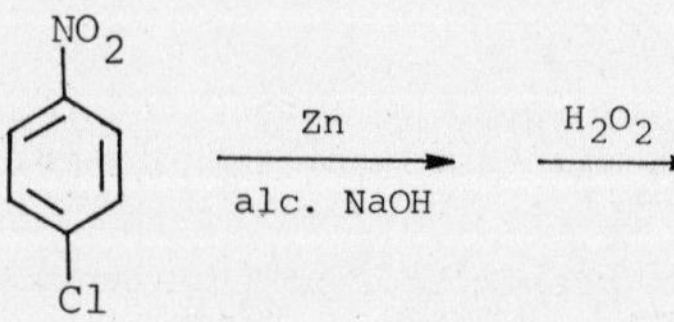

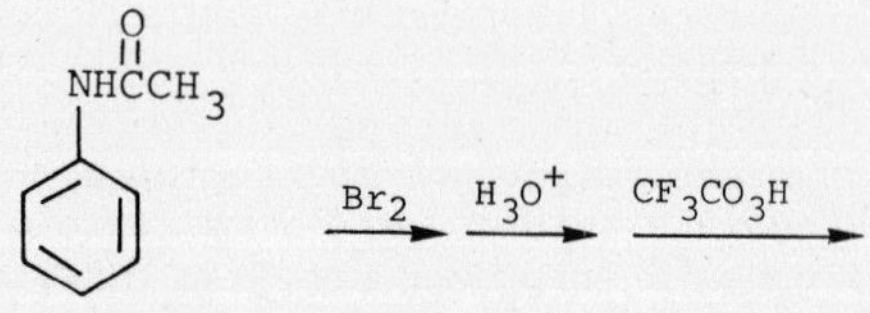

24.G Answers to Supplementary Problems

S1.

(a)

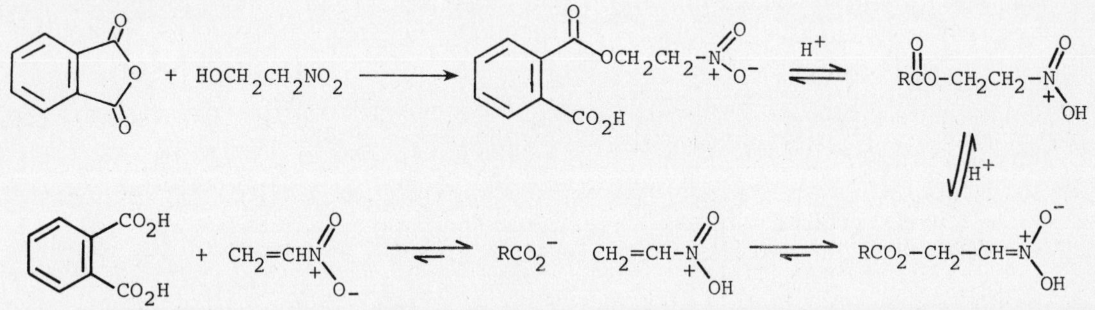

(b) $(CH_3)_2\ddot{N}H + CH_2=CH-NO_2 \longrightarrow \left[(CH_3)_2\overset{+}{\underset{H}{N}}CH_2\overset{-}{C}H-\overset{+}{N}\overset{O}{\underset{O^-}{}} \longleftrightarrow (CH_3)_2\overset{+}{\underset{H}{N}}CH_2CH=\overset{+}{N}\overset{O^-}{\underset{O^-}{}} \right]$

$(CH_3)_2NCH_2CH_2NO_2 \underset{H^+}{\overset{H^+}{\rightleftharpoons}} (CH_3)_2NCH_2CH=\overset{+}{N}\overset{O^-}{\underset{O^-}{}}$

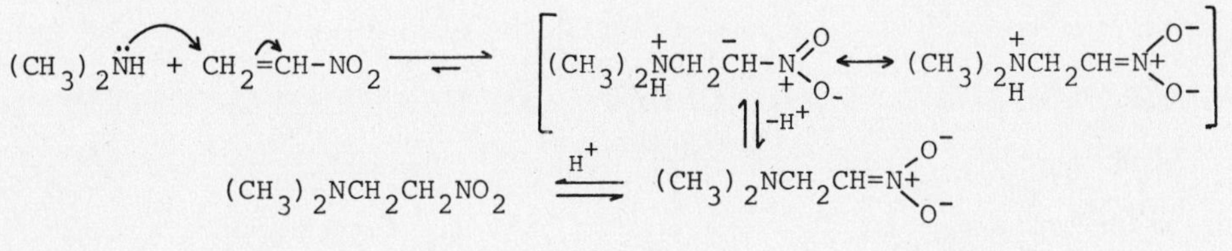

S2.

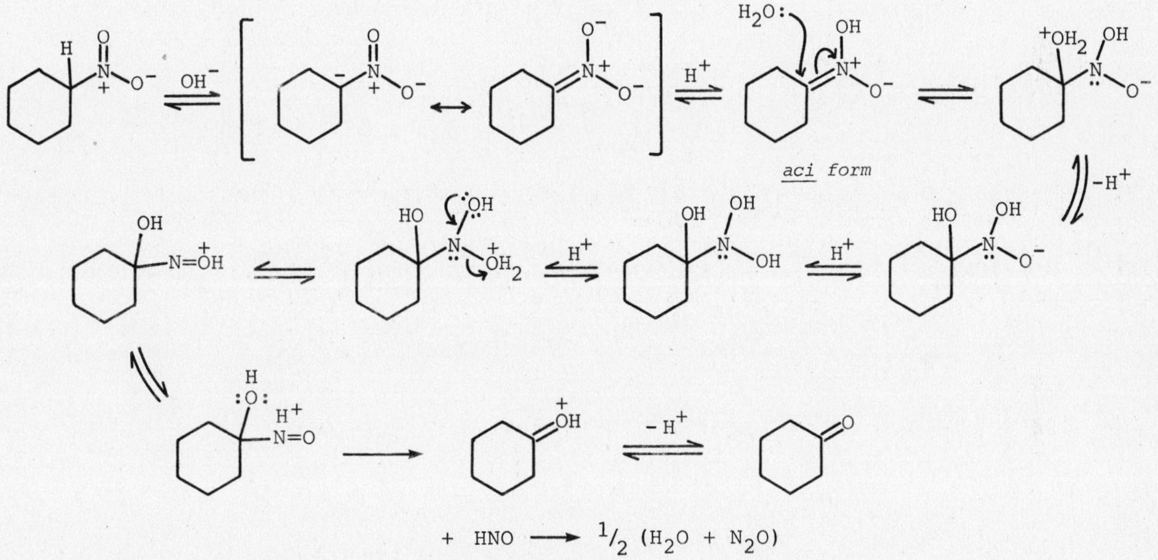

$+ \quad HNO \longrightarrow \tfrac{1}{2} (H_2O + N_2O)$

S3.

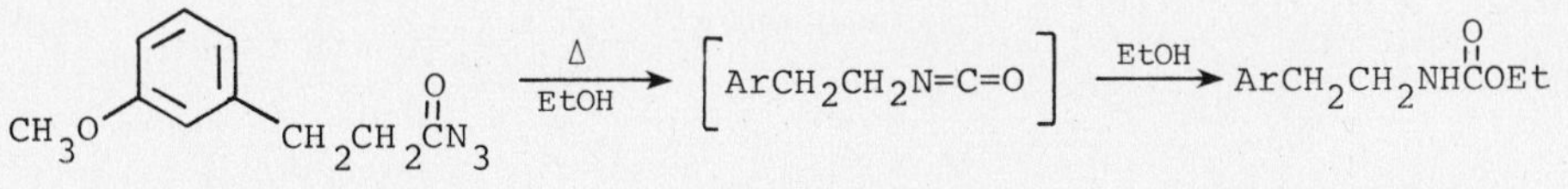

CH_3O-Ar-$CH_2CH_2\overset{O}{\overset{\|}{C}}N_3 \xrightarrow[EtOH]{\Delta} \left[ArCH_2CH_2N=C=O \right] \xrightarrow{EtOH} ArCH_2CH_2\overset{O}{\overset{\|}{NHC}}OEt$

S4.

$\phi\ddot{N}H\ddot{N}H_2 + \overset{+}{N}O \longrightarrow \phi\ddot{N}H\underset{H}{N}-\overset{..}{N}=O \underset{-H^+}{\overset{H^+}{\rightleftharpoons}} \phi\ddot{N}H\underset{H}{\overset{..}{N}}-\ddot{N}=O \rightleftharpoons \phi\ddot{N}H\ddot{N}=\ddot{N}-OH$

$\phi\ddot{N}=\overset{+}{N}=\ddot{N}: \longleftarrow \quad \phi\ddot{N}-\underset{H}{\overset{+}{N}}\equiv N: \underset{-H_2O}{\rightleftharpoons} \phi\ddot{N}H\ddot{N}=\overset{+}{N}-\overset{+}{O}H_2 \quad \Big\Uparrow H^+$

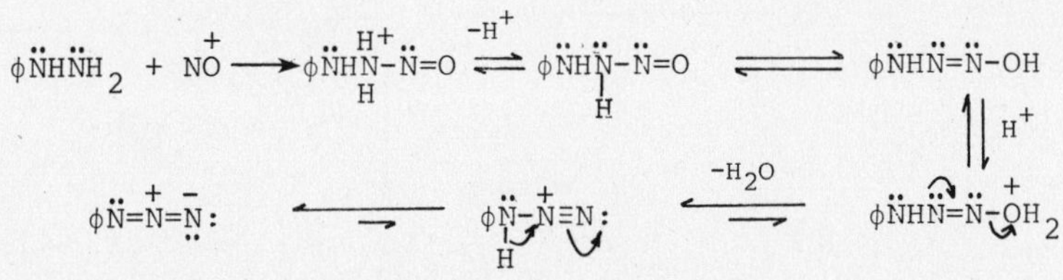

S5. (a)

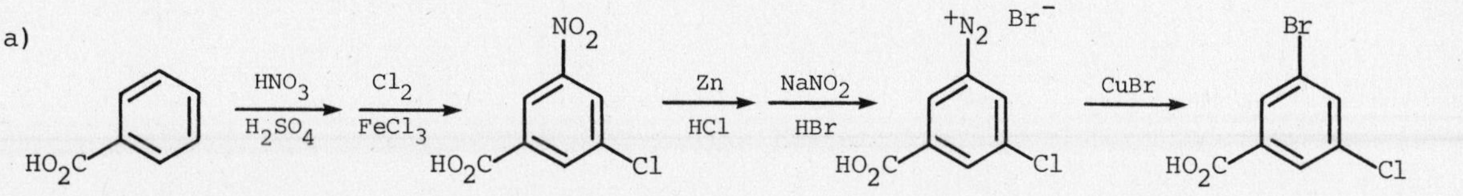

(b)

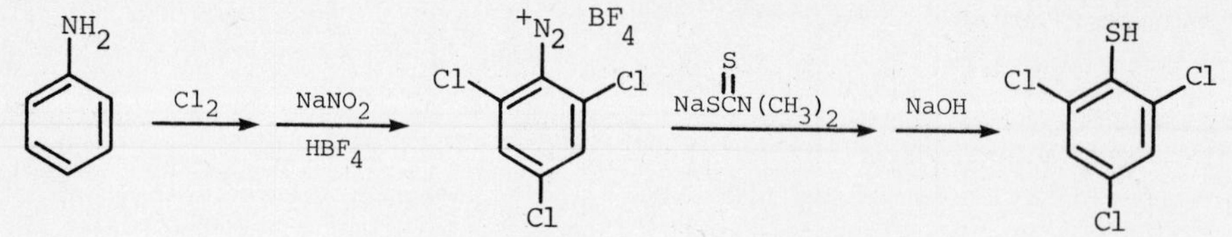

NH$_2$ → (Cl$_2$) → (NaNO$_2$ / HBF$_4$) → $^+$N$_2$ BF$_4^-$ (2,4,6-trichloro) → (NaSCN(CH$_3$)$_2$ / S) → (NaOH) → SH (2,4,6-trichlorothiophenol)

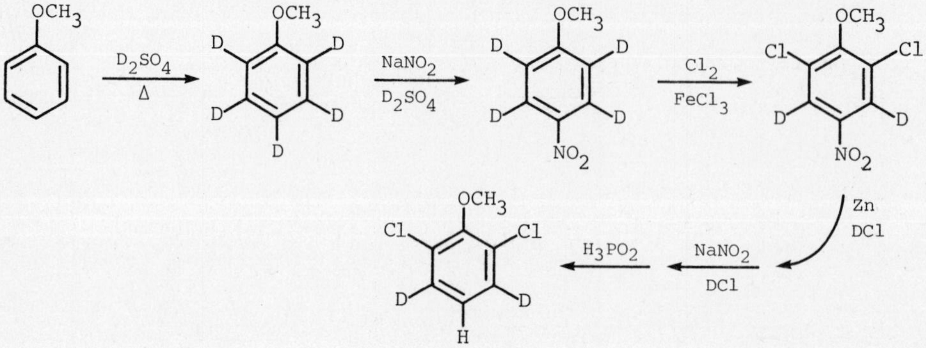

(c)

OCH$_3$ → (D$_2$SO$_4$ / Δ) → (pentadeutero anisole) → (NaNO$_2$ / D$_2$SO$_4$) → NO$_2$ → (Cl$_2$ / FeCl$_3$) → (dichloro nitro) NO$_2$ → (Zn / DCl)

→ (NaNO$_2$ / DCl) → (H$_3$PO$_2$) → OCH$_3$ with Cl, Cl, D, D, H

(d)

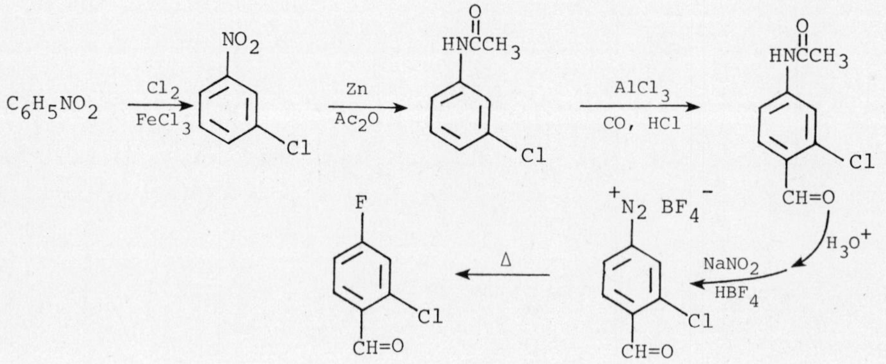

C$_6$H$_5$NO$_2$ → (Cl$_2$ / FeCl$_3$) → NO$_2$ ... Cl → (Zn / Ac$_2$O) → HNCCH$_3$ (O) ... Cl → (AlCl$_3$ / CO, HCl) → HNCCH$_3$ (O) ... Cl, CH=O → (H$_3$O$^+$) → $^+$N$_2$ BF$_4^-$ ... Cl, CH=O → (NaNO$_2$ / HBF$_4$) → (Δ) → F ... Cl, CH=O

(e)

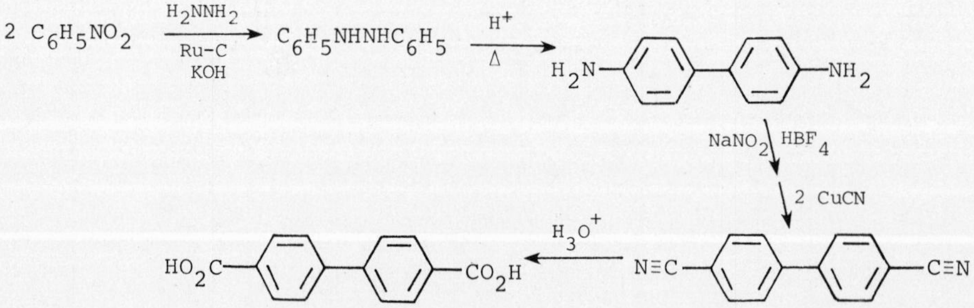

2 C$_6$H$_5$NO$_2$ → (H$_2$NNH$_2$ / Ru-C / KOH) → C$_6$H$_5$NHNHC$_6$H$_5$ → (H$^+$ / Δ) → H$_2$N— —NH$_2$

→ (NaNO$_2$ / HBF$_4$) → (2 CuCN) → N≡C— —C≡N → (H$_3$O$^+$) → HO$_2$C— —CO$_2$H

(f)

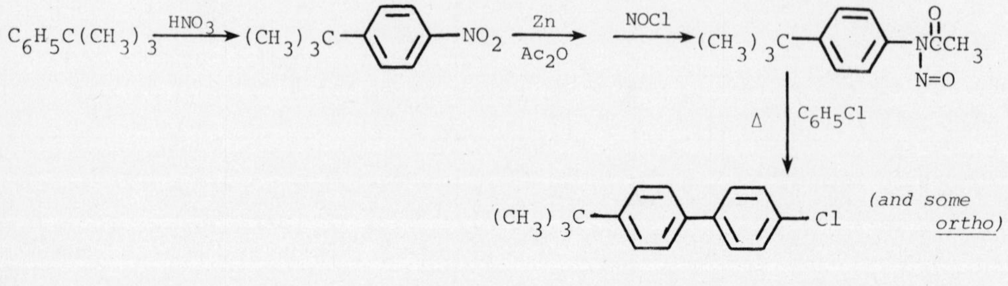

C$_6$H$_5$C(CH$_3$)$_3$ → (HNO$_3$) → (CH$_3$)$_3$C— —NO$_2$ → (Zn / Ac$_2$O) → (NOCl) → (CH$_3$)$_3$C— —N(O)CCH$_3$, N=O

→ (Δ / C$_6$H$_5$Cl) → (CH$_3$)$_3$C— —Cl   *(and some ortho)*

S6.

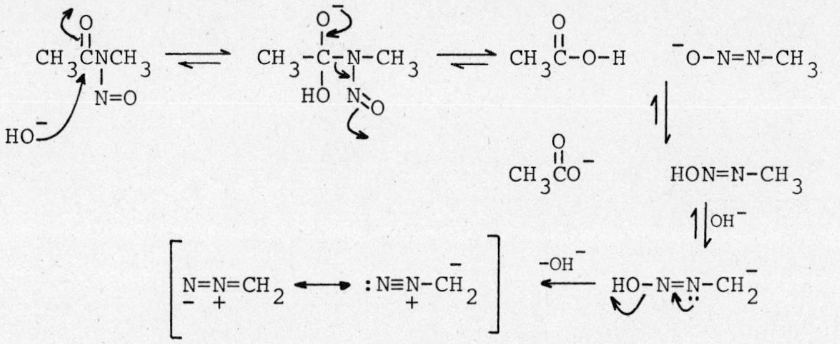

S7.

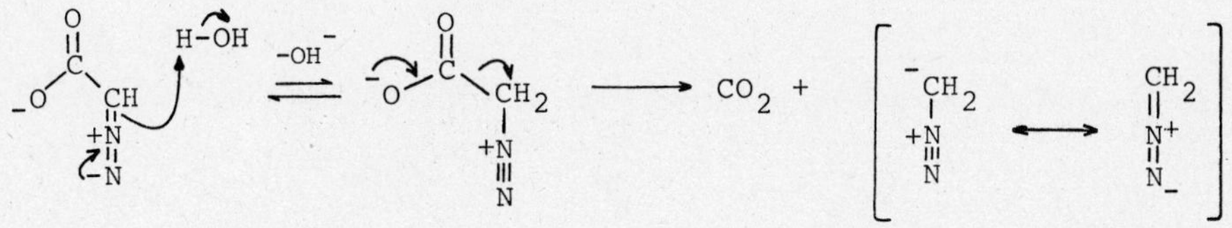

S8. a)

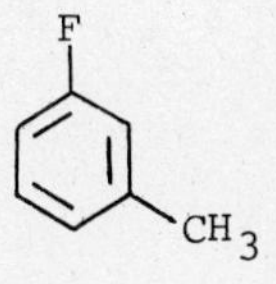

b)

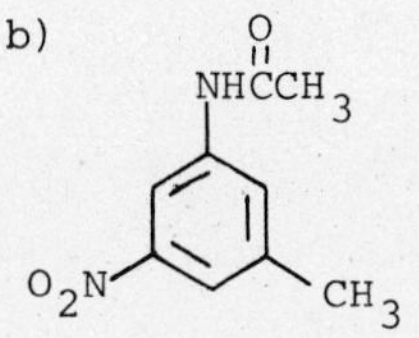

c)

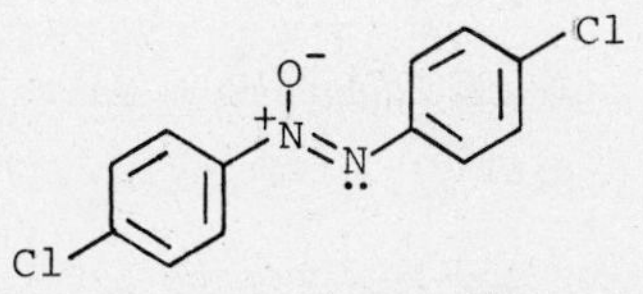

d)

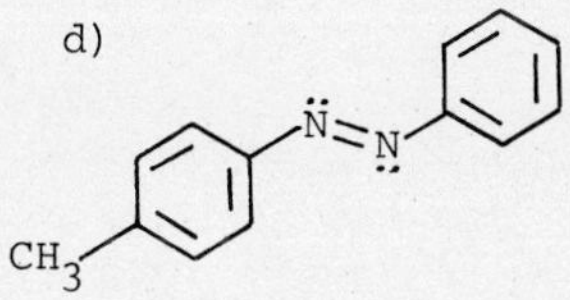

e)

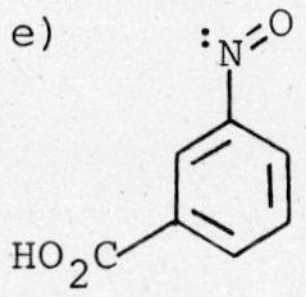

f)

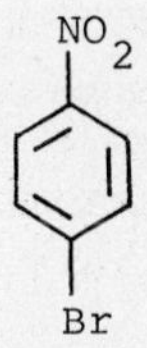

25. SULFUR, PHOSPHORUS, AND SILICON COMPOUNDS

25.A   Chapter Outline and Important Terms Introduced

25.1 <u>Thiols</u> <u>and</u> <u>Sulfides</u> (stink!)

      alkanethiol   dialkyl sulfide   alkylthio-

25.2 <u>Preparation</u> <u>of</u> <u>Thiols</u> <u>and</u> <u>Sulfides</u>

25.3 <u>Reactions</u> <u>of</u> <u>Thiols</u> <u>and</u> <u>Sulfides</u>

      pK_a of RSH = 10.5

sulfide	sulfenic acid
sulfoxide	sulfinic acid
sulfone	trialkylsulfonium salt

25.4 <u>Sulfate</u> <u>Esters</u>

      alkylsulfuric acid, $ROSO_3H$ dialkyl sulfate, $RO\overset{\overset{O}{\|}}{\underset{\underset{O}{\|}}{S}}OR$

25.5 <u>Sulfonic</u> <u>Acids</u>

      A. Alkanesulfonic Acids
      B. Arenesulfonic Acids
            nucleophilic aromatic substitution   sulfonyl halides

25.6 <u>Phosphines</u> <u>and</u> <u>Phosphonium</u> <u>Salts</u>

      alkyl-, dialkyl-, trialkylphosphines

25.7 <u>Phosphates</u> <u>and</u> <u>Phosphonate</u> <u>Esters</u>

      phosphoric acid and esters pK_a's of H_3PO_4: 2.15, 7.2, 12.4
      phosphorous acid and esters
      alkylphosphonic acids and esters
      Arbuzov-Michaelis reaction

25.8 <u>Sulfur-</u> <u>and</u> <u>Phosphorus-Stabilized</u> <u>Carbanions</u>

      phosphorus ylids, the Wittig reagent (phosphonium ion pK_a = 15-18)
      phosphonate carbanions, Horner-Emmons reaction
      sulfur-stabilized carbanions
      sulfonium ylids, epoxide formation
      anions of sulfones (pK_a = 31) and sulfoxides (pK_a = 35)

25.9 <u>Organosilicon</u> <u>Compounds:</u> <u>Structure</u> <u>and</u> <u>Properties</u>

25.10 <u>Organosilicon</u> <u>Compounds:</u> <u>Preparation</u>

25.11 <u>Organosilicon</u> <u>Compounds:</u> <u>Reactions</u>

      A. Nucleophilic Substitution at Silicon
          siliconate ions   pseudorotation
      B. Electrophilic Cleavage of the Carbon-Silicon Bond
          electrophilic substitution
      C. Silyl Ethers as Protecting Groups

25.B   Important Reactions Introduced

<u>Formation</u> <u>of</u> <u>thiols</u> <u>and</u> <u>sulfides</u> <u>by</u> <u>nucleophilic</u> <u>substitution</u> (25.2)

Equation: $RX + R'S^-M^+ \longrightarrow RSR' + MX$

Generality: R = 1° or 2° alkyl; R' = H, alkyl, or aryl

Key features: S_N2 displacement reaction (not for 3° RSH)
with R' = H, sulfide formation (RSR) is often observed
thiourea, followed by hydrolysis of thiuronium salt, used in place of NaSH to avoid
    sulfide formation

Reaction of Grignard reagents with sulfur (25.2)

Equation:
$$RMgX + S_8 \longrightarrow RSMgX \longrightarrow RSH$$

Key features: useful method for making 3° RSH or ArSH

Oxidation of thiols (25.3)

Equation:
$$2\ RSH \xrightarrow{\text{mild oxidation}} RS\text{—}SR \xrightarrow[\text{oxidation}]{\text{strong}} 2\ RSO_3H$$

Generality: R = alkyl or aryl
mild oxidation = I_2 or air
strong oxidation = $KMnO_4$ or HNO_3 (Cl_2/HNO_3 gives RSO_3Cl)

Reactions of sulfides as electrophiles (25.3)

Reduction

Equation:
$$RS\text{—}SR \xrightarrow{[H]} 2\ RSH$$

Generality: [H] = Na or Li in liquid NH_3

Sulfenylation of enolates

Equation:

$$RS\text{—}SR + \underset{}{\overset{O^-}{\underset{}{C=C}}} \longrightarrow RS\text{—}\overset{O}{\underset{}{C}}\text{—}C\text{—} + RS^-$$

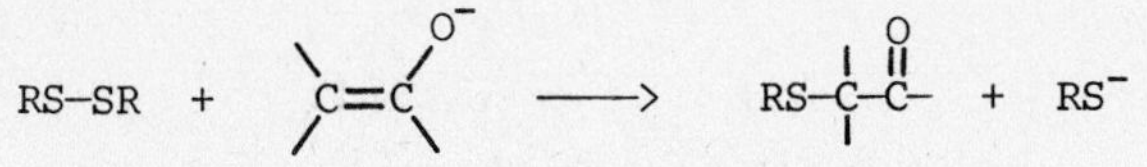

Generality: enolate = ester or ketone enolate

Oxidation of sulfides (25.3)

Equation:

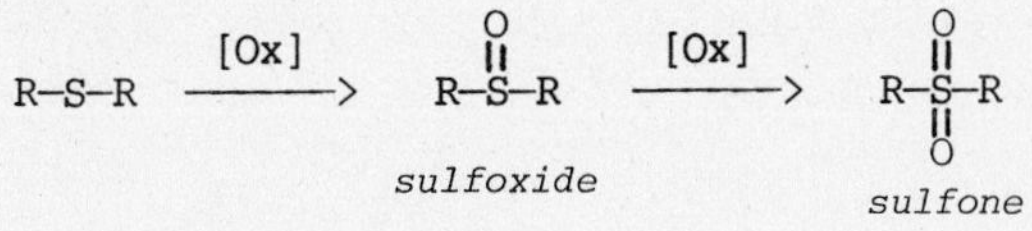

$$R\text{—}S\text{—}R \xrightarrow{[Ox]} \underset{\text{sulfoxide}}{R\overset{O}{\text{—}S\text{—}}R} \xrightarrow{[Ox]} \underset{\text{sulfone}}{R\overset{O}{\underset{O}{\text{—}S\text{—}}}R}$$

Generality: R = alkyl or aryl; [Ox] = H_2O_2, RCO_3H, $NaIO_4$
Key feature: $NaIO_4$ best reagent for stopping oxidation at sulfoxide level

Thermal elimination of sulfoxides (25.3)

Equation:

$$R\text{—}S\underset{}{\overset{O}{\big|}}\overset{H}{\underset{}{C}}\text{—}C\text{—} \longrightarrow R\text{—}S\text{—}OH + \underset{}{C=C}$$

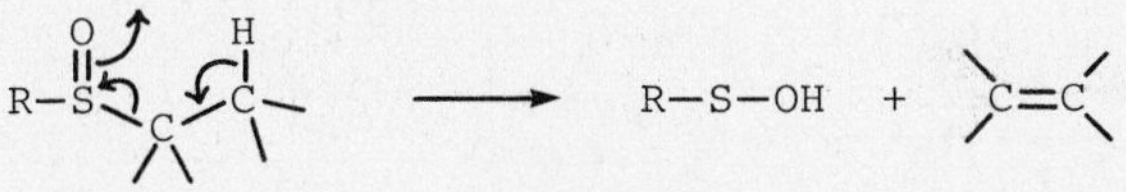

Key features: mechanism is syn elimination
initial product is sulfenic acid, which disproportionates to sulfinic acid and sulfide

Formation of sulfonium salts (25.3)

Equation: $RSR + R'X \longrightarrow R_2\overset{+}{S}R'\ X^-$

Generality: R, R' = alkyl: X = good leaving group (e.g. I)

Formation and reductive cleavage of dithioacetals (25.3)

Equation:

$$\underset{R\ \ \ R'}{\overset{O}{C}} + HS(CH_2)_3SH \xrightarrow{BF_3} \underset{R\ \ \ R'}{\overset{S\ \ \ S}{C}} \xrightarrow{H_2/Ni} \underset{R\ \ \ R'}{\overset{H\ \ \ H}{C}}$$

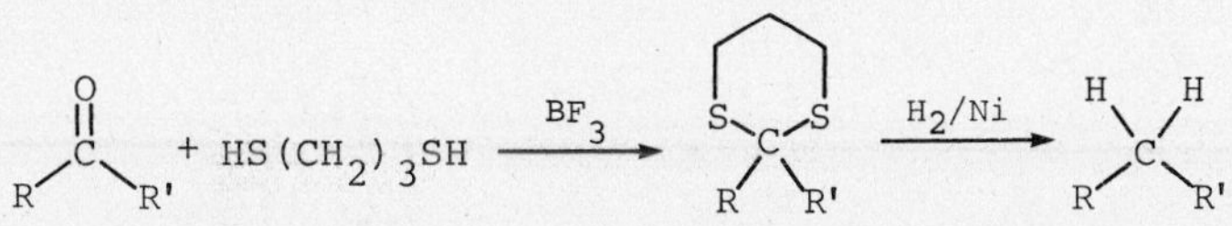

Generality: R, R' = H, alkyl, or aryl

Key features: useful method for deoxygenation of ketones and aldehydes under neutral conditions

Formation of alkylsulfonic acids (25.5)

Equation: $R-X + Na^+HSO_3^- \longrightarrow R-SO_3H + NaX$

Generality: $R = 1°$ or $2°$ alkyl; X = good leaving group

Formation of α-hydroxysulfonic acids (25.5)

Equation:

$$\underset{R'}{\overset{\overset{\displaystyle O}{\parallel}}{R-C-R'}} \xrightarrow{NaHSO_3} \underset{R'}{\overset{\overset{\displaystyle OH}{|}}{R-C-SO_3^-Na^+}}$$

Generality: R, R' = H or alkyl

Key features: seldom works for ketones
              reaction is reversible with acid or base

Formation of sulfonate esters (25.5)

Equation: $RSO_3H + PCl_5 \longrightarrow RSO_2Cl \xrightarrow[\text{pyridine}]{R'OH} RSO_3R'$

Generality: R = alkyl or aryl
              $SOCl_2$ can be used in place of PCl_5 as well

Electrophilic aromatic sulfonation (25.5)

Equation: $Ar-H + SO_3 \longrightarrow Ar-SO_3H$ *arenesulfonic acid*

                 $Ar-H + ClSO_3H \longrightarrow Ar-SO_2Cl$ *arenesulfonyl chloride*

Generality: reagent is "fuming sulfuric acid" (SO_3 in conc. H_2SO_4) or chlorosulfonic acid (HSO_3Cl)

Key features: mechanism is electrophilic aromatic substitution
              reaction can be reversed: heating $ArSO_3H$ in dilute H_2SO_4 gives ArH

Nucleophilic aromatic subsitution of arenesulfonic acids (25.5)

Equation: $Ar-SO_3H + Na^+X^- \xrightarrow{\Delta} Ar-X + NaHSO_3$

Generality: $X^- = OH^-$ or CN^-

Key features: requires vigorous temperatures (300 °C)
              sulfonate group useful as a blocking group in synthesis of substituted aromatic
                compounds

Reactions of arenesulfonyl halides (25.5)

Equation: $ArSO_2-Cl + Nu: \longrightarrow ArSO_2-Nu$

Generality: Nu: = Ar'H: Friedel-Crafts reaction, $AlCl_3$ as catalyst, to give sulfone as product
                = HNR_2: amide formation, to give sulfonamide as product
                = HOR': ester formation, to give sulfonate ester as product (see above)
              Reduction (Zn, H_2O) gives $ArSO_2H$, an arenesulfinic acid

Alkylation of sulfinic acid salts (25.5)

Equation:

$$R-SO_2^-Na^+ + R'X \longrightarrow \underset{\overset{\displaystyle \parallel}{O}}{\overset{\overset{\displaystyle O}{\parallel}}{R-S-R'}} + NaX$$

Generality: R = alkyl or aryl; R' = $1°$ or $2°$ alkyl

Key features: byproduct is sulfinate ester, $\overset{\overset{\displaystyle O}{\parallel}}{R-S-OR'}$

Formation of phosphines from Grignard reaction (25.6)

Equation: $3\ RMgX\ +\ PX_3\ \longrightarrow\ R_3P:\ +\ 3\ MgX_2$

Generality: R = alkyl or aryl; X = halogen
other organometallic reagents can be used (e.g. RLi)

Formation of phosphate esters (25.7)

Equation:

$$POCl_3\ +\ 3\ ROH\ \longrightarrow\ RO\!-\!\overset{\displaystyle O}{\underset{\displaystyle OR}{\overset{\|}{\underset{|}{P}}}}\!-\!OR$$

Generality: R = H, alkyl, or aryl
with less than 3 equivalents of ROH, can stop at $ROPCl_2$ or $(RO)_2PCl$
hydrolysis of phosphate esters occurs with C-O bond cleavage in acid, with P-O bond
cleavage in base (mostly)

Arbuzov-Michaelis reaction (25.7)

Equation:

$$R\!-\!X\ +\ (R'O)_3P:\ \longrightarrow\ R\!-\!\overset{\displaystyle O}{\underset{\displaystyle OR'}{\overset{\|}{\underset{|}{P}}}}\!-\!OR'\ +\ R'X$$

Generality: R, R' = alkyl; X = halogen
Key features: reaction proceeds via S_N2 displacement and trialkoxyphosphonium salt intermediate

Formation and reactions of sulfur- and phosphorus-stabilized carbanions (25.8)

Equation:

$$RCH_2\!-\!Y\ \xrightarrow{\text{[base]}}\ {}^-\!\underset{R}{C}H\!-\!Y\ \xrightarrow{\text{["E"]}}\ E\!-\!\underset{R}{C}H\!-\!Y\ \Longrightarrow$$

Generality: [base] = LDA or nBuLi
R = H, alkyl, or aryl
Y = $^+PR'_3$: phosphorus ylide = Wittig reagent; E = ketone or aldehyde;
   product = alkene
Y = $PO_3R'_2$: phosphonate anions = Horner-Emmons reagent; E = ketone or aldehyde;
   product = alkene
Y = SR', SOR', SO_2R' (or dithiane): sulfide, sulfoxide, or sulfone α-anions;
   can be alkylated with R'X, carbonyl compounds, etc.
Y = $^+SR'_2$: sulfonium ylide; E = aldehyde or ketone; product is epoxide

Nucleophilic substitution reactions at silicon (25.11.A)

Equation: $R_3Si\!-\!X\ +\ Nu{:}^-\ \longrightarrow\ Nu\!-\!SiR_3\ +\ X^-$

Generality: X = good leaving group; Nu: = good nucleophile

Key features: reaction involves addition/elimination process, with intermediacy of pentavalent
      "siliconate" ion
reaction usually proceeds with inversion of configuration, but retention via
      "pseudorotation" is also possible
S_N1-type mechanism **not** observed

Electrophilic cleavage of carbon-silicon bonds (25.11.B)

Equation: $R\!-\!SiR_3\ +\ E^+X^-\ \longrightarrow\ R\!-\!E\ +\ R_3SiX$

Generality: R = aryl, vinyl, or allyl group; E^+ = H^+ or other electrophile

Key features: for R = allyl, allylic rearrangement occurs during substitution reaction
useful method for formation of a wide variety of carbon-carbon bonds

<u>Formation</u> <u>and</u> <u>hydrolysis</u> <u>of</u> <u>silyl</u> <u>ethers</u> (25.11.C)

Equation: $\quad$ ROH + R'$_3$SiX $\longrightarrow$ ROSiR'$_3$ + HX

$\qquad\qquad\qquad$ ROSiR'$_3$ + H$_2$O $\longrightarrow$ ROH + HOSiR'$_3$

Generality: $\quad$ R, R' = alkyl (usually); X = Cl or O$_3$SCF$_3$
$\qquad\qquad\qquad$ formation of silyl ether by reaction of RO$^-$ or with 3° amine catalysis
$\qquad\qquad\qquad$ hydrolysis of silyl ether catalyzed with H$^+$ or F$^-$

Key feature: $\quad$ because of stability of silyl ethers to basic reagents, they are useful as alcohol
$\qquad\qquad\qquad\qquad$ protecting groups

25.C Important Concepts and Hints

The chemistry of sulfur, phosphorus, and silicon compounds is becoming increasingly important because of the invention of many functional group interconversions and carbon-carbon bond-forming reactions which involve these intermediates. In many respects, analogies can be drawn between thiols/sulfides/disulfides and alcohols/ethers/peroxides, and between tetravalent silicon compounds and tetrahedral carbon compounds. However, there are no oxygen counterparts to the more highly oxidized sulfur compounds: sulfoxides, sulfones, and sulfinic and sulfonic acids. In a similar manner, the organic chemistry of phosphorus ranges from the reduced derivatives (phosphines) to the higher oxidation states (phosphonic and phosphoric acids). Silicon derivatives have a less varied chemical behavior, undergoing primarily substitution reactions.

The major utility of sulfur- and phosphorus-containing compounds as carbon-carbon bond-forming reagents lies in the diverse ways that these functional groups can stabilize adjacent carbanions. With strong base (n-butyllithium or LDA) a proton can be removed from carbons that are adjacent to sulfide, sulfoxide, sulfone, sulfonium ion, phosphonium ion, and phosphonate groups (among others!). These carbanionic reagents react with alkyl halides or carbonyl derivatives to form new carbon-carbon bonds. Particularly important examples are the Wittig reaction, and the use of dithioacetal anions as synthetic equivalents to acyl anions (" $\overset{\overset{\text{O}}{\|}}{\underset{\text{C-C-}}{}}$ "). In contrast, for carbon-carbon bond formation, silane derivatives derive their reactivity from silicon's ability to stabilize adjacent positive charge.

More "synthetic methods" which use sulfur, phosphorus, and silicon functional groups are being invented all the time -- perhaps you can think of some new ones yourself!

25.D Answers to Exercises

25.1

(a) CH$_3$CH$_2$SCH(CH$_3$)$_2$ $\quad$ (b) CH$_3$CH$_2$CH$_2$CH$_2$SH $\quad$ (c) CH$_3$(CH$_2$)$_4\overset{\overset{\text{SCH}_3}{|}}{\text{CH}}CH_2CH_3$

(d) C$_6$H$_5$SC$_6$H$_5$ $\quad$ (e) CH$_3$CH$_2\overset{\overset{\text{SH}}{|}}{\text{CH}}CH_2CH_3$ $\quad$ (f) CH$_3\overset{\overset{\text{S}}{\|}}{\text{C}}$H $\quad$ (g) CH$_3\overset{\overset{\text{O}}{\|}}{\text{C}}SC_2H_5$

25.2

(a) (CH$_3$)$_3$CCH$_2$Br $\xrightarrow{\text{Mg}}$ $\xrightarrow{\text{S}_8}$ $\xrightarrow{\text{H}^+}$ (CH$_3$)$_3$CCH$_2$SH $\qquad$ *(neopentyl bromide is*
$\qquad\qquad\qquad\qquad\qquad\qquad\qquad\qquad\qquad\qquad\qquad\qquad$ *too hindered to undergo*
$\qquad\qquad\qquad\qquad\qquad\qquad\qquad\qquad\qquad\qquad\qquad\qquad$ *displacement reaction)*

(b) 2 CH$_3$CH$_2$CH$_2$OH $\xrightarrow{\text{PBr}_3}$ 2 CH$_3$CH$_2$CH$_2$Br $\xrightarrow{\text{Na}_2\text{S}}$ (CH$_3$CH$_2$CH$_2$)$_2$S

25.3

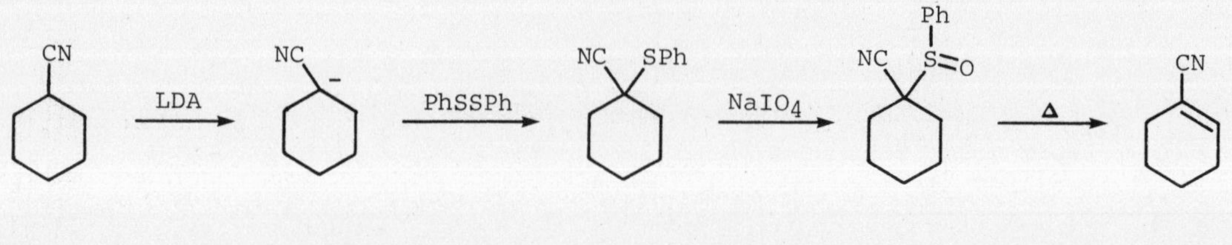

25.4

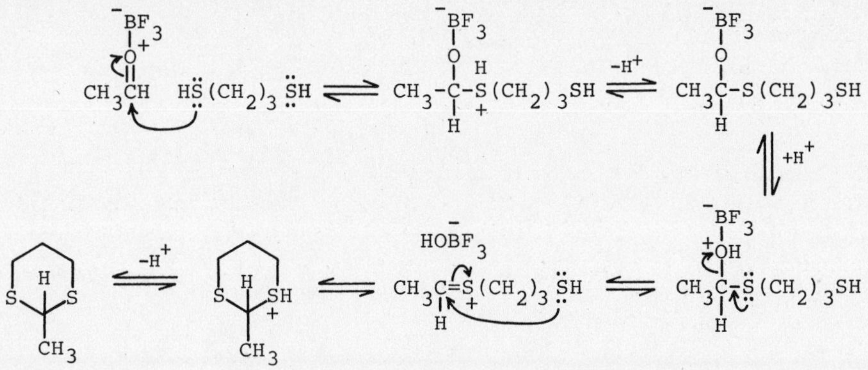

25.5

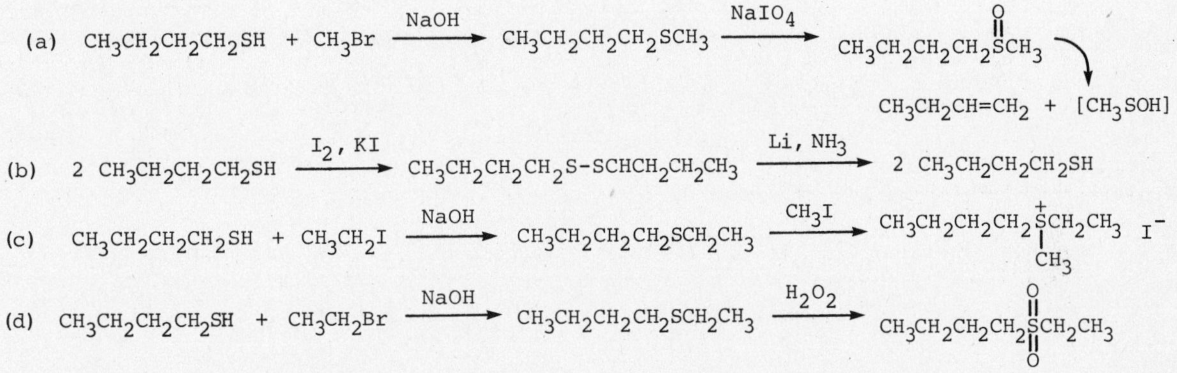

(a) $CH_3CH_2CH_2CH_2SH + CH_3Br \xrightarrow{NaOH} CH_3CH_2CH_2CH_2SCH_3 \xrightarrow{NaIO_4} CH_3CH_2CH_2CH_2\overset{O}{\overset{\|}{S}}CH_3$

$\longrightarrow CH_3CH_2CH=CH_2 + [CH_3SOH]$

(b) $2\ CH_3CH_2CH_2CH_2SH \xrightarrow{I_2,\ KI} CH_3CH_2CH_2CH_2S\text{-}SCHCH_2CH_2CH_3 \xrightarrow{Li,\ NH_3} 2\ CH_3CH_2CH_2CH_2SH$

(c) $CH_3CH_2CH_2CH_2SH + CH_3CH_2I \xrightarrow{NaOH} CH_3CH_2CH_2CH_2SCH_2CH_3 \xrightarrow{CH_3I} CH_3CH_2CH_2CH_2\overset{+}{\underset{CH_3}{S}}CH_2CH_3\ \ I^-$

(d) $CH_3CH_2CH_2CH_2SH + CH_3CH_2Br \xrightarrow{NaOH} CH_3CH_2CH_2CH_2SCH_2CH_3 \xrightarrow{H_2O_2} CH_3CH_2CH_2CH_2\overset{O}{\underset{O}{\overset{\|}{\underset{\|}{S}}}}CH_2CH_3$

25.6

$$HO\text{-}\overset{O}{\underset{O}{\overset{\|}{\underset{\|}{S}}}}\text{-}O\text{-}H \rightleftharpoons HO\text{-}\overset{O}{\underset{O}{\overset{\|}{\underset{\|}{S}}}}\text{-}O^-\ H^+\ ; \qquad F\text{-}\overset{O}{\underset{O}{\overset{\|}{\underset{\|}{S}}}}\text{-}O\text{-}H \rightleftharpoons F\text{-}\overset{O}{\underset{O}{\overset{\|}{\underset{\|}{S}}}}\text{-}O^-\ H^+$$

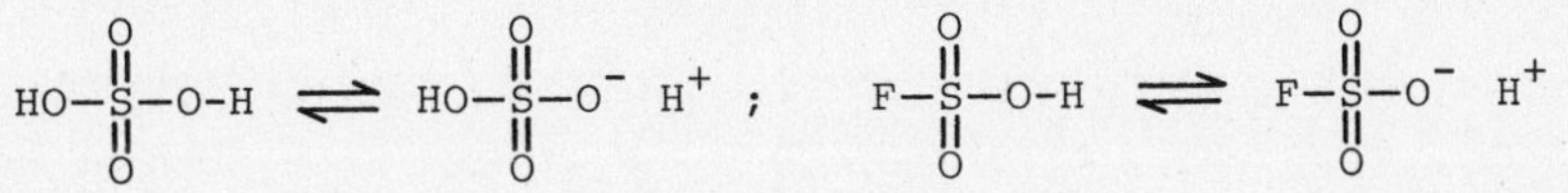

The OH group in sulfuric acid is replaced by the more strongly electron-withdrawing F substituent in fluorosulfonic acid.

25.7

$(CH_3)_2CHCH_2CH_2Cl + NaHSO_3 \longrightarrow (CH_3)_2CHCH_2CH_2SO_3H \xrightarrow{PCl_5} (CH_3)_2CHCH_2CH_2SO_2Cl + CH_3OH$

$(CH_3)_2CHCH_2CH_2SO_3CH_3 \xleftarrow{\text{pyridine}}$

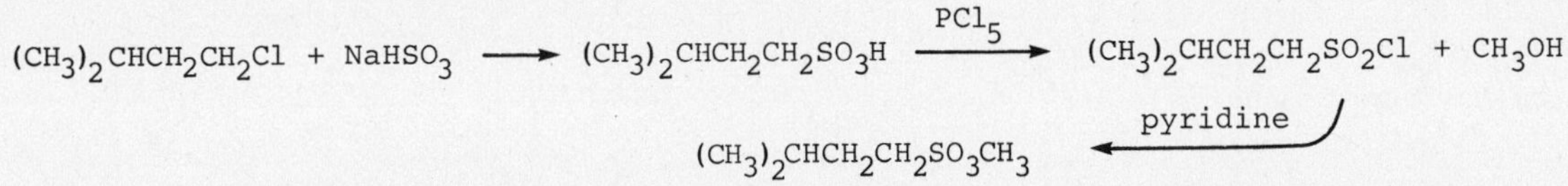

25.8 In the toluenesulfonic acids, you would expect that the o-isomer would be less stable than the others because of the steric interaction between the methyl and the sulfonate groups. On the other hand, it is unlikely that there would be much difference between the m- and p-isomers, neither of which has such a steric interaction. The fact that there is a significantly greater amount of p-isomer than m-isomer in the product of reaction at 100 °C suggests that the mixture still does not reflect the thermodynamic ratio.

25.9

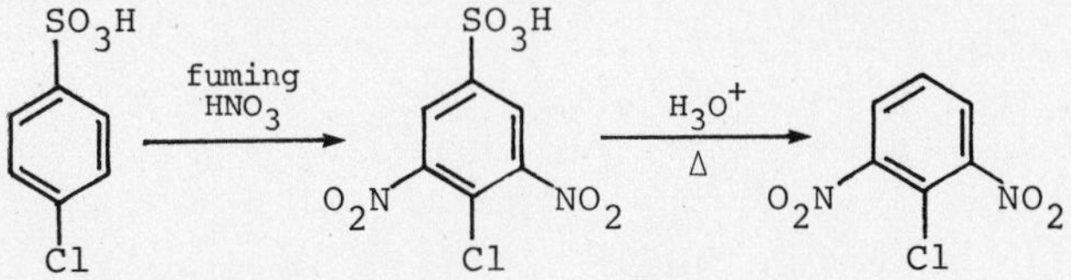

25.10

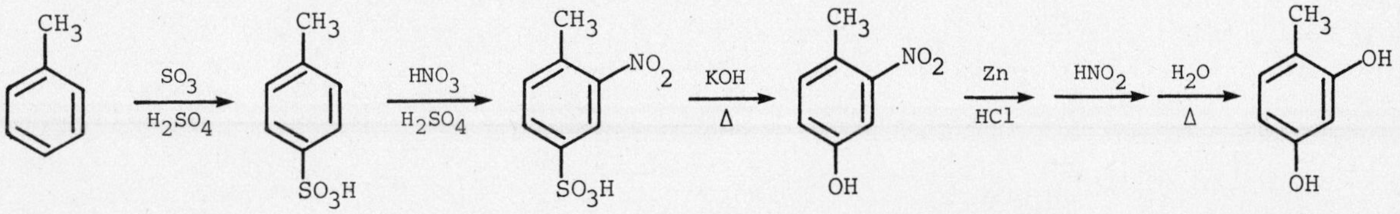

25.11 $Br\text{-}C_6H_4\text{-}SO_2Na \xrightarrow{PCl_5} Br\text{-}C_6H_4\text{-}SO_2Cl$

(a) $Br\text{-}C_6H_4\text{-}SO_2\text{-}O\text{-}CH_2CH_2CH_2CH_3$

(b) $Br\text{-}C_6H_4\text{-}SO_2\text{-}C_6H_4\text{-}CH_3$

(and ortho)

(c) $Br\text{-}C_6H_4\text{-}SO_2\text{-}CH_2\text{-}C_6H_5$

(d) $Br\text{-}C_6H_4\text{-}SH$

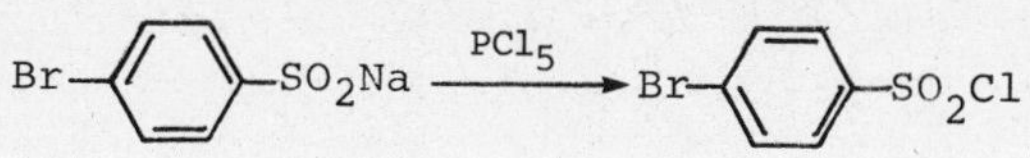

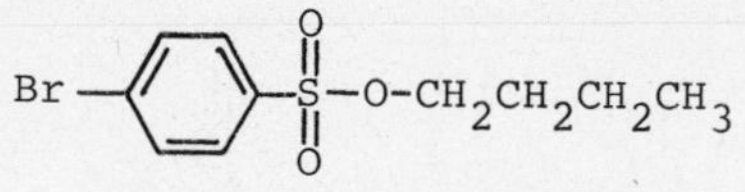

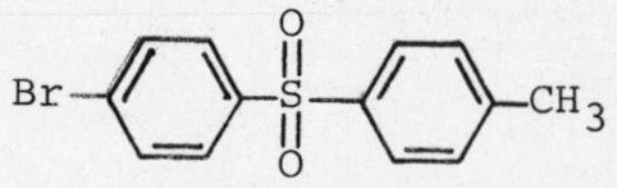

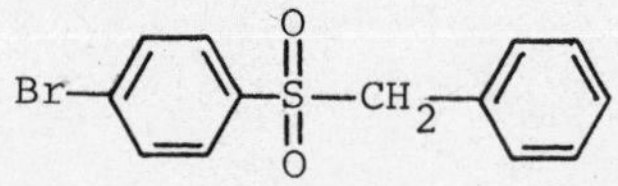

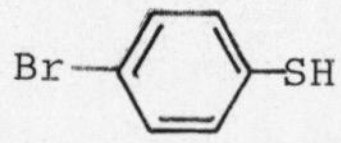

25.12 (b) and (e) are chiral: (c) and (d) could be chiral if the oxygens were istopically different:

$$Ph\text{---}\overset{O}{\underset{CH_3}{S}}:\quad Ph\text{---}\overset{O}{\underset{CH_3O}{S}}:\quad Ph\text{---}\overset{*O}{\underset{CH_3}{S}}\text{=}O\quad Ph\text{---}\overset{*O}{\underset{CH_3O}{S}}\text{=}O$$

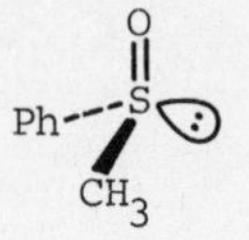

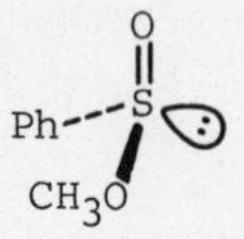

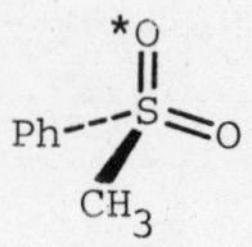

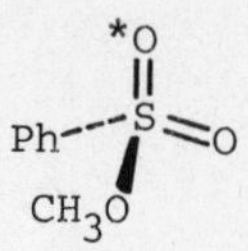

25.13 $C_6H_5MgCl + PCl_3 \longrightarrow (C_6H_5)_3P + BrCH_2C_6H_5 \longrightarrow (C_6H_5)_3\overset{+}{P}CH_2C_6H_5 \; Br^-$

$\xrightarrow{\text{n-BuLi}}$

$(C_6H_5)_3P{=}O + CH_3CH{=}CHC_6H_5 \xleftarrow{CH_3CHO} (C_6H_5)_3\overset{+}{P}\overset{-}{C}HC_6H_5$

25.14 $(CH_3CH_2O)_3P: + CH_3I \longrightarrow CH_3\overset{O}{P}(OCH_2CH_3)_2 + CH_3CH_2I \xrightarrow{(CH_3CH_2O)_3P:} CH_3CH_2\overset{O}{P}(OCH_2CH_3)_2$

(trace)   *(major product)*

$+ CH_3CH_2I$

25.15 (a) $2\, C_2H_5OH + POCl_3 \xrightarrow{\text{pyridine}} (C_2H_5O)_2\overset{O}{P}Cl \xrightarrow{CH_3ONa} (C_2H_5O)_2\overset{O}{P}OCH_3$

(b) $3\, \underline{i}\text{-}C_4H_9OH + POCl_3 \xrightarrow{\text{pyridine}} (\underline{i}\text{-}C_4H_9O)_3P{=}O$

(c) $3\, C_2H_5OH + PCl_3 \xrightarrow{\text{pyridine}} (C_2H_5O)_3P: \xrightarrow[\Delta]{CH_3CH_2CH_2I} CH_3CH_2CH_2\overset{O}{P}(OC_2H_5)_2 + C_2H_5I$

(d) $(C_2H_5O)_3P: \xrightarrow[\Delta]{C_2H_5I\ (catalytic)} C_2H_5\overset{O}{P}(OC_2H_5)_2 \xrightarrow[2.\ H^+]{1.\ NaOH} C_2H_5\overset{O}{P}OC_2H_5$

[from (c)] $\underset{OH}{\ }$

25.16 (a) $(CH_3O)_3P: \xrightarrow{CH_3I} CH_3\overset{O}{P}(OCH_3)_2 \xrightarrow{\text{n-BuLi}} LiCH_2\overset{O}{P}(OCH_3)_2 \xrightarrow{CH_3CCH_3} (CH_3)_2\overset{OH}{C}CH_2\overset{O}{P}(OCH_3)_2$

(b) $LiCH_2\overset{O}{P}(OCH_3)_2 \xrightarrow{(CH_3O)_2C{=}O} CH_3O_2CCH_2\overset{O}{P}(OCH_3)_2 \xrightarrow[NaOCH_3]{CH_3CH{=}O} CH_3CH{=}CHCO_2CH_3$

25.17 (a)

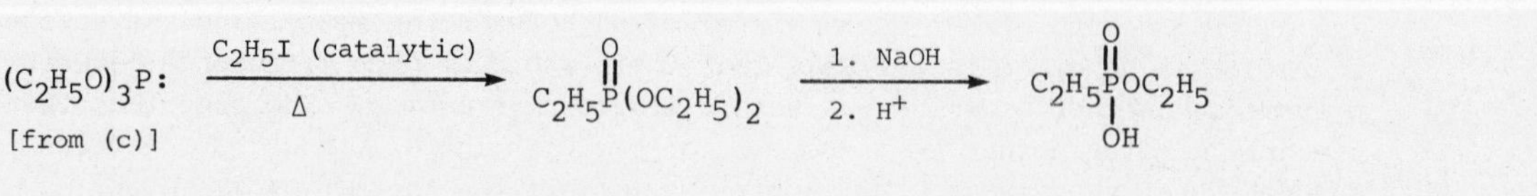

(b)

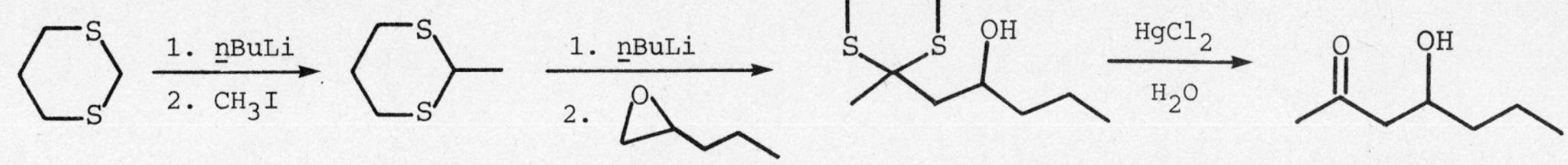

$$\text{[1,3-dithiane]} \xrightarrow[\text{2. } CH_3I]{\text{1. } \underline{n}BuLi} \text{[2-methyl-1,3-dithiane]} \xrightarrow[\text{2. } \triangle]{\text{1. } \underline{n}BuLi} \text{[dithiane-alcohol]} \xrightarrow[H_2O]{HgCl_2} \text{[hydroxy ketone]}$$

25.18 (a)

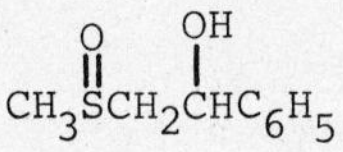

$$CH_3\overset{O}{\underset{\|}{S}}CH_2\overset{OH}{\underset{|}{C}}HC_6H_5$$

(b) 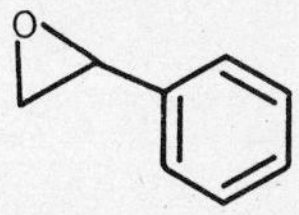 [phenyloxirane]

(c) 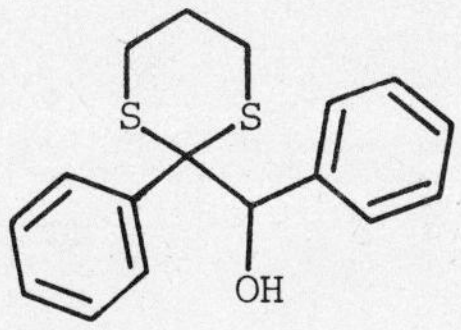 [2,2-diphenyl-1,3-dithiane with CH(OH)C₆H₅]

25.19 (a) $C_6H_5MgBr + (CH_3)_3SiCl \longrightarrow C_6H_5Si(CH_3)_3 + MgX_2$

(b) $2\ C_6H_5MgBr + SiCl_4 \longrightarrow (C_6H_5)_2SiCl_2 + MgX_2$

(c) $CH_2=CHCH_2MgCl + (CH_3)_3SiCl \longrightarrow CH_2=CHCH_2Si(CH_3)_3 + MgX_2$

(d) $CH_2=CHMgCl + (CH_3)_3SiCl \longrightarrow CH_2=CHSi(CH_3)_3 + MgX_2$

25.20 Two:

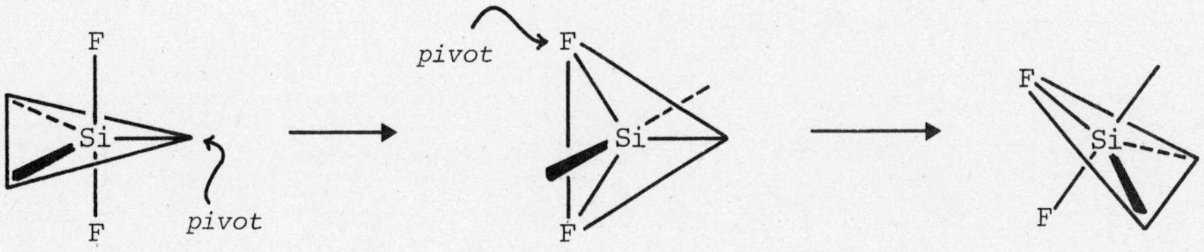

[trigonal bipyramidal Si structures showing pivot motion] *pivot* ⟶ *pivot*

25.21 No pseudorotation:

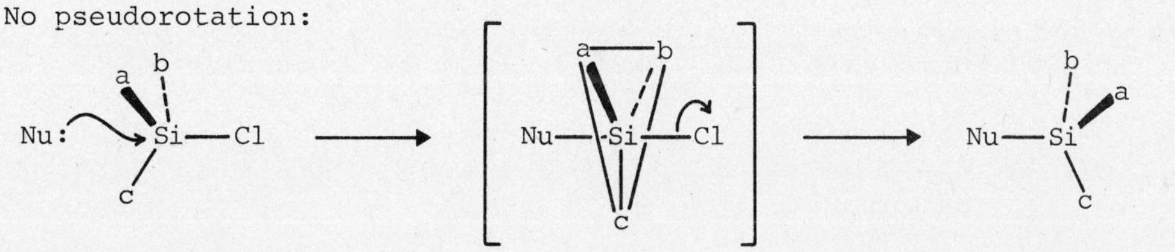

$Nu: \rightarrow$ [Si with a, b, c, Cl] $\longrightarrow$ $[Nu—Si—Cl]$ $\longrightarrow$ $Nu—Si$ (b, a, c)   *inversion*

One pseudorotation:

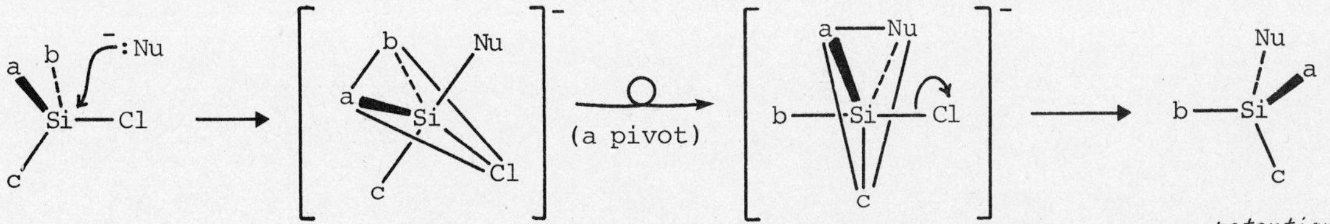

[Si structures] $\longrightarrow$ [trigonal bipyramid] $\xrightarrow{\text{(a pivot)}}$ [trigonal bipyramid] $\longrightarrow$ $b—Si$ (Nu, a, c)   *retention*

Two pseudorotations: (Cl pivot)

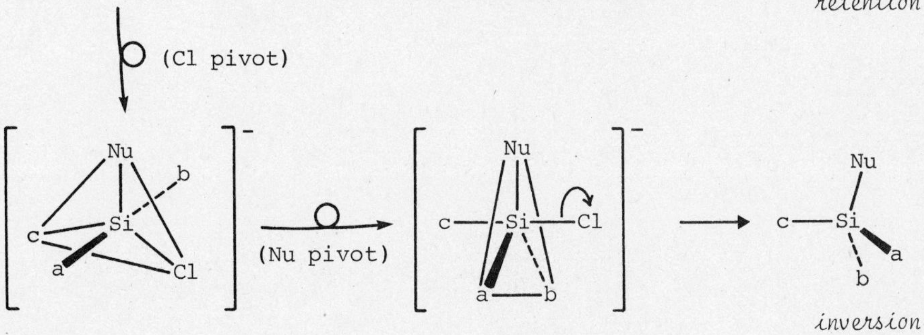

[trigonal bipyramid] $\xrightarrow{\text{(Nu pivot)}}$ [trigonal bipyramid] $\longrightarrow$ $c—Si$ (Nu, a, b)   *inversion*

25.22 (a)

[o-bromotoluene] $\xrightarrow{Li}$ $\xrightarrow{ClSiMe_3}$ [o-SiMe₃ toluene] $\xrightarrow{HNO_3}$ [o-nitrotoluene]

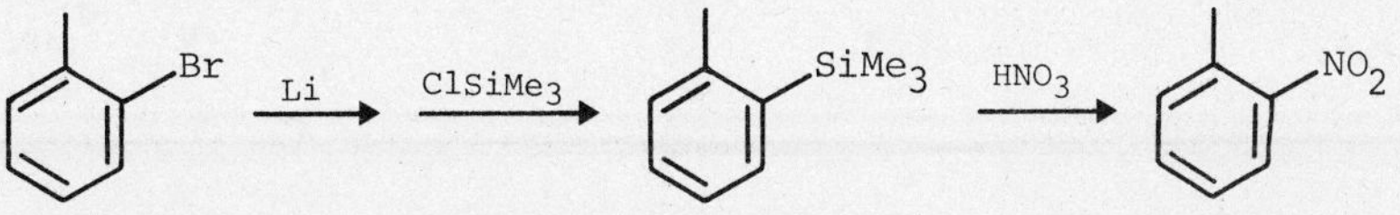

(b) Me_3Si ... Me ... $\xrightarrow{Br_2}$ ... Me_3Si ... Br ... Me ... H ... Br ... $\longrightarrow$ ... Br ... Me ... Me_3Si

RO⁻

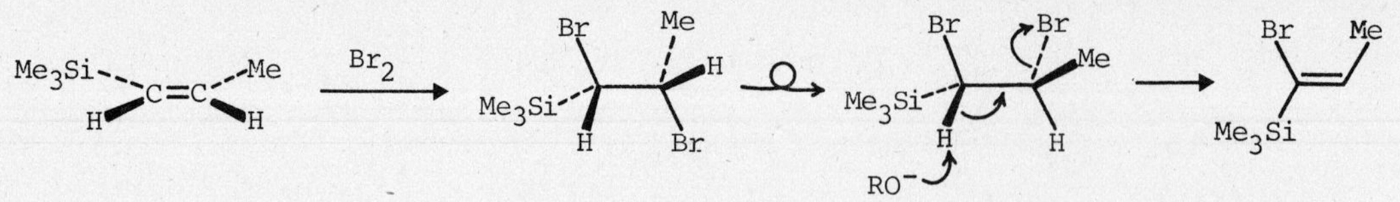

25.23 (a)

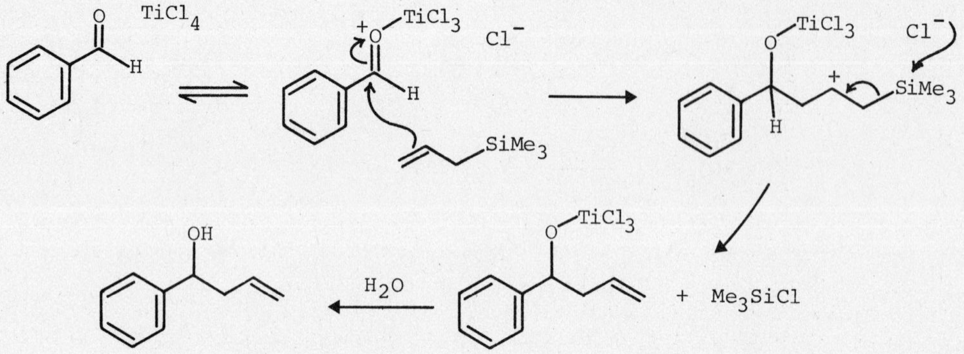

$\xrightarrow{TiCl_4}$ ... $^+$O—$TiCl_3$ ... Cl⁻ ... $SiMe_3$ ... $\longrightarrow$ ... O—$TiCl_3$ ... Cl⁻ ... $SiMe_3$

$\longrightarrow$

OH ... $\xleftarrow{H_2O}$ ... O—$TiCl_3$ ... $+ Me_3SiCl$

(b)

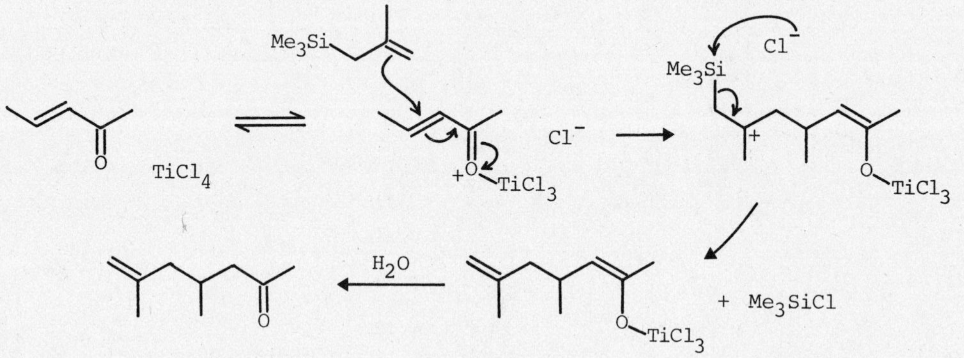

$\rightleftharpoons$ ... Me_3Si ... $^+$O—$TiCl_3$ ... Cl⁻ ... $\longrightarrow$ ... Me_3Si ... Cl⁻ ... O—$TiCl_3$

$TiCl_4$

$\xleftarrow{H_2O}$ ... O—$TiCl_3$ ... $+ Me_3SiCl$

25.24 (a)

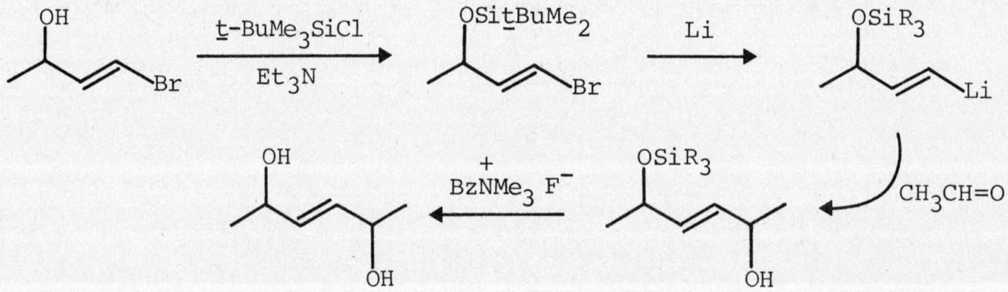

OH ... Br ... $\xrightarrow[Et_3N]{\underline{t}\text{-BuMe}_3SiCl}$ ... $OSi\underline{t}BuMe_2$ ... Br ... $\xrightarrow{Li}$ ... $OSiR_3$ ... Li

OH ... OH ... $\xleftarrow[BzNMe_3 \ F^-]{+}$ ... $OSiR_3$ ... OH ... $\xleftarrow{CH_3CH=O}$

(b)

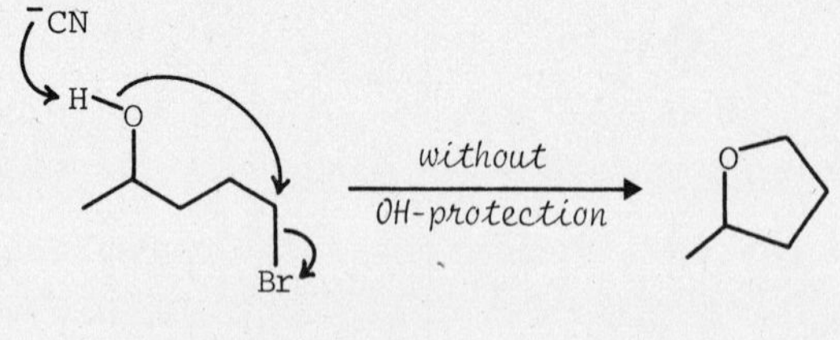

⁻CN ... H ... O ... Br ... $\xrightarrow[OH\text{-protection}]{without}$ ... O ... *(cyanide is a strong enough base to catalyze the intramolecular ether formation)*

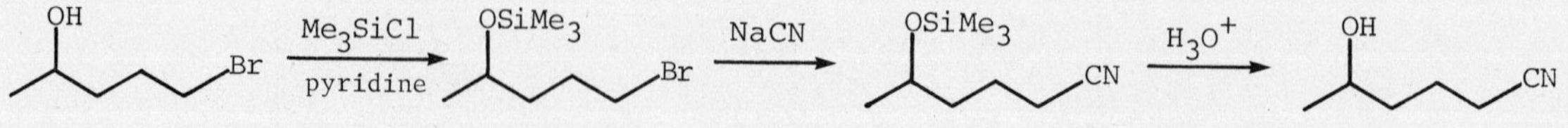

OH ... Br ... $\xrightarrow[pyridine]{Me_3SiCl}$ ... $OSiMe_3$ ... Br ... $\xrightarrow{NaCN}$ ... $OSiMe_3$ ... CN ... $\xrightarrow{H_3O^+}$ ... OH ... CN

25.E   Answers and Explanations for Problems

1. (a) $C_2H_5SCH_2C(CH_3)_3$ (b) $(CH_3)_2CHCH_2SH$ (c) [structure: cyclopentanone with SCH_3]   (d) $(CH_3CH_2CH_2CH_2)_2S_2$

(e) [structure: cyclohexane with SH]   (f) $(CH_3)_2CHCH_2OSO_3H$ (g) $C_2H_5OSO_2OC_2H_5$ (h) O_2N—[benzene ring]—SO_3CH_3

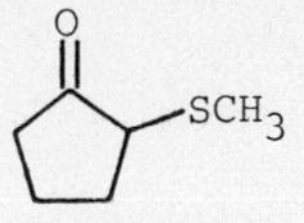

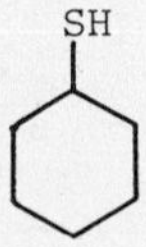

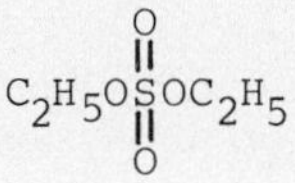

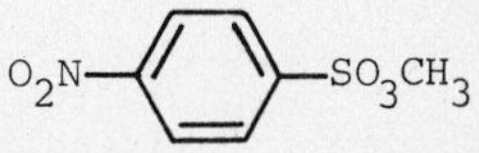

(i) $(CH_3CH_2CH_2CH_2O)_3P=O$ (j) $C_2H_5\overset{O}{\overset{\|}{P}}(OC_2H_5)_2$ (k) [structure: cyclohexane with OSO_2CH_3]

(l) $(C_6H_5O)_3P:$ (m) $CH_2=CH-CH_2O-\overset{O}{\overset{\|}{P}}-O-\overset{O}{\overset{\|}{P}}-O^-$ with O^- below each P   (n) $Me_3SiCH_2CH_2CH_3$ (o) [structure: benzene ring with $Si-Cl$ bearing two CH_3 groups]

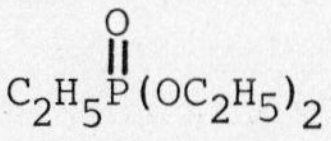

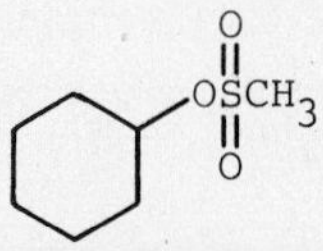

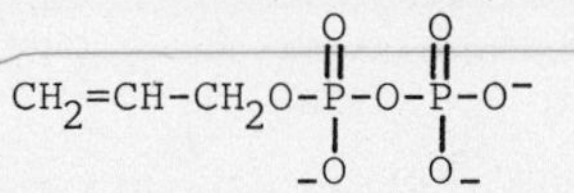

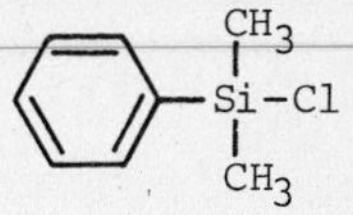

2.   (a) 4-methyl-2-pentanethiol   (f) p-nitrobenzenesulfonyl chloride
(b) 2-methyl-3-methylthiopentane   (g) methyl p-bromophenyl sulfone
(c) tetracyclopentylphosphonium bromide   (h) cyclopropyldisulfide
(d) N-methyl-4-isopropylbenzenesulfonamide   (i) diethyl ethylphosphonate
(e) 3-(2,2-dimethylpropyl)oxycarbonyl-   (j) cyclohexyltrimethylsilane
        4-bromobenzenesulfonic acid

In a complex case such as this, the sulfonic acid group can be expressed as a prefix, sulfo; hence: neopentyl 2-bromo-5-sulfobenzoate

3. (a) $\underline{t}$-BuOCH$_3$ + CH$_3$OSO$_3^-$ K$^+$

(b) $CH_3CH_2SCH_3$ + CH_3I

(c) $(CH_3)_3CCH_2SCH_2CH_3$ + CH_3CH_2Br

(d) [structure: cyclohexane with CH$_3$ and SCH_2CH_3] + CH_3CH_2Cl

(e) [structure: naphthalene with OH]

(f) $C_6H_5\overset{O}{\underset{O}{\overset{\|}{\underset{\|}{S}}}}CH_2C_6H_5$

(g) [structure: dithiane ring]

(h) C_6H_5CH [dithiane ring]

(i) [structure: dithiane ring with $CHCH(CH_3)_2$ and OH]

(j) $C_6H_5CH\overset{O}{-}CH_2$ + CH_3SCH_3

4. (a) $CH_3CH_2CH_2CH_2\overset{O}{\overset{\|}{P}}(OCH_2CH_2CH_2CH_3)_2$ (b) $CH_3CH_2CH_2\overset{O}{\overset{\|}{P}}OCH_3$ with OH below   (c) $(C_2H_5O)_2\overset{O}{\overset{\|}{P}}OCH_2CH_2CH(CH_3)_2$

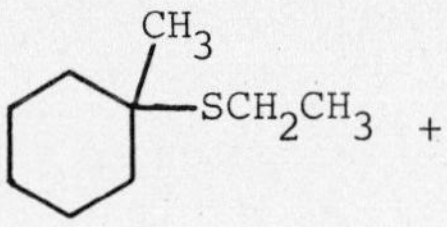

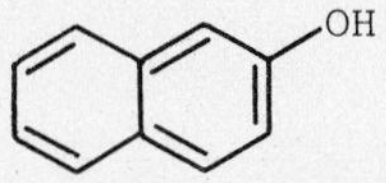

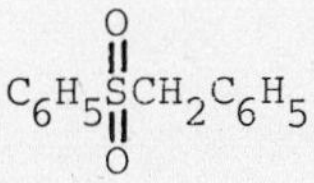

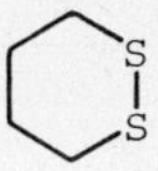

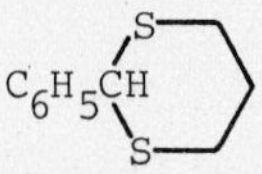

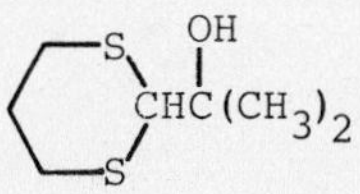

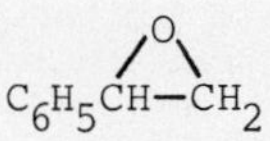

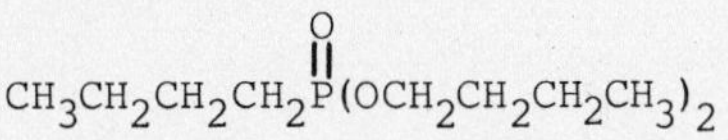

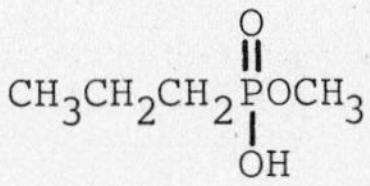

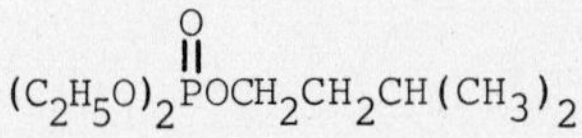

(d) $(CH_3O)_3P=O$ (e) $(C_6H_5)_3\overset{+}{P}CH_2CH=CH_2$ Br$^-$ (f) [structure: cyclohexane with OH and $CH_2\overset{O}{\overset{\|}{P}}(OCH_3)_2$]

(g) $CH_3-\overset{O}{\overset{\|}{C}}-CH-\overset{O}{\overset{\|}{P}}(OCH_3)_2$ with CH_3 below

5. (a) [structure: cyclohexane with Br and $=CH_2$]   (b) CH_3—CH(D)—CH=CH$_2$ drawn as CH$_3$ with CH=CH$_2$ and D   (c) [structure: benzene ring with two CH_3 and Cl]

(d) [structure: benzene ring with $Si-Cl$ bearing two CH_3 groups]   (e) [structure: phenyl ketone with CH=CH-CH$_3$]

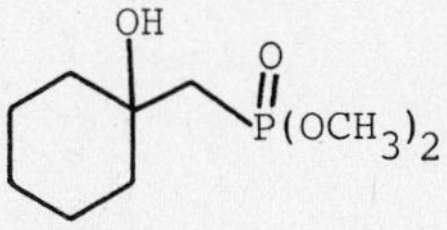

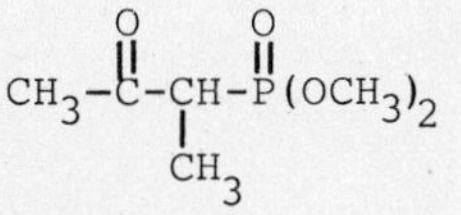

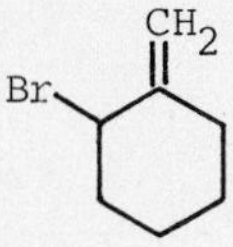

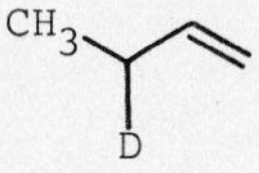

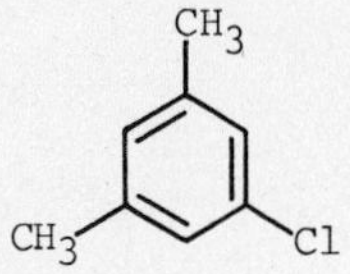

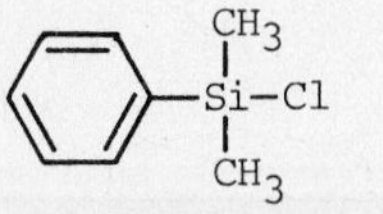

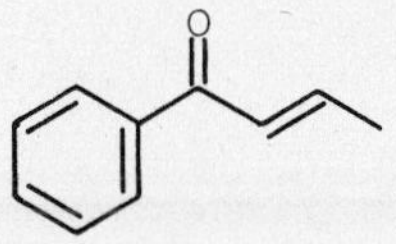

6. (a) $CH_3SH + 2 KMnO_4 \longrightarrow CH_3SO_3^- + OH^- + 2 K^+ + 2 MnO_2$

(b) $3 (CH_3)_2S + 4 KMnO_4 + 2 H_2O \longrightarrow 3 (CH_3)_2SO_2 + 4 MnO_2 + 4 KOH$

(c) $(CH_3)_2S + 4 HNO_3 \longrightarrow (CH_3)_2SO_2 + 4 NO_2 + 2 H_2O$

7. (a)   E2 elimination would occur during either step to give isobutylene rather than the desired phosphite triester or alkylphosphonate.

(b)   Friedel-Crafts reactions do not apply with <u>meta</u>-directing groups such as $-SO_3H$.

(c)   The ketone group is sensitive to strong base. Hydroxide promotes aldol condensation reactions; hence the final step with fused KOH will give a mess.

(d)   The trimethylsilyl group would be replaced in the chlorination step, to give 4-chlorotoluene.

8. (a) $(CH_3)_3CBr \xrightarrow{Mg} \xrightarrow{S_8} \xrightarrow{CH_3I} (CH_3)_3CSCH_3$

(*NOTE*: $(CH_3)_3CBr + NaSCH_3 \longrightarrow (CH_3)_2C=CH_2 + HSCH_3 + NaBr$)

(b) $CH_3CH_2CH_2CH_2OH \xrightarrow{PBr_3} \xrightarrow[\text{2. OH}^-]{\text{1. } H_2N\overset{S}{\overset{\|}{C}}NH_2} CH_3CH_2CH_2CH_2SH \xrightarrow{I_2} (CH_3CH_2CH_2CH_2)_2S_2$

(c) $CH_3-\langle\text{benzene ring}\rangle \xrightarrow{HSO_3Cl} CH_3-\langle\text{ring}\rangle-SO_2Cl \xrightarrow[\text{AlCl}_3]{\text{toluene}} CH_3-\langle\text{ring}\rangle-\overset{O}{\underset{O}{S}}-\langle\text{ring}\rangle-CH_3$

(d)   aniline (NH_2) $\xrightarrow[\text{180-190 °C}]{H_2SO_4}$ $^+NH_3$ ... SO_3^- $\xrightarrow{CF_3CO_3H}$ NO_2 ... SO_3H

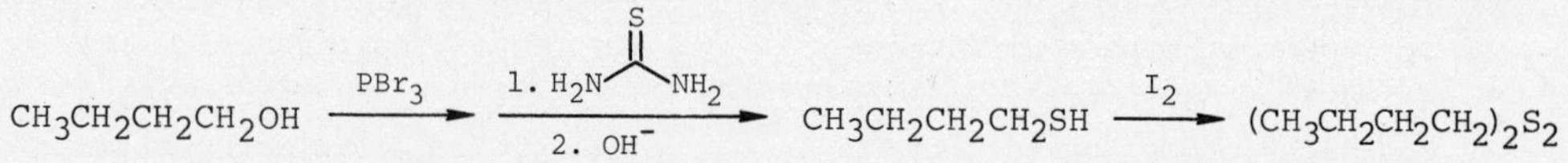

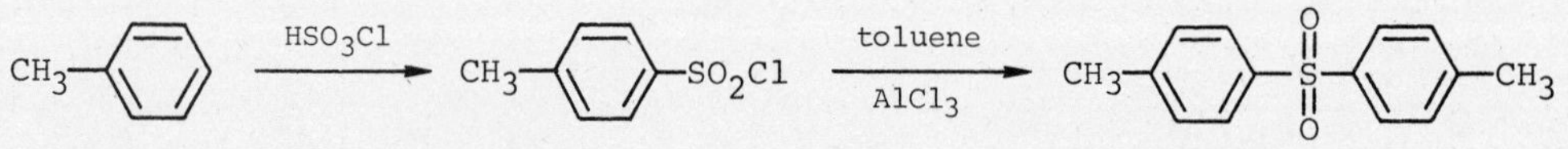

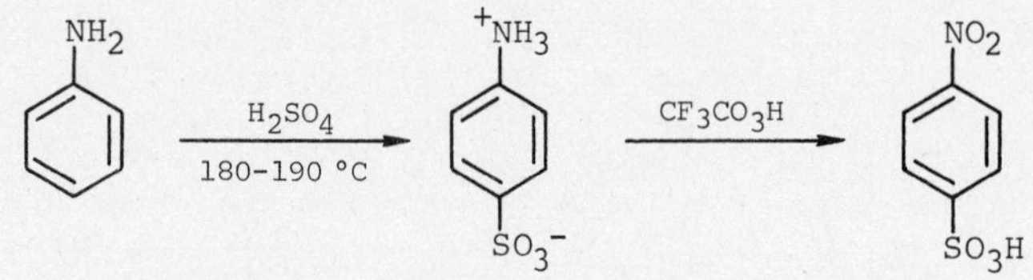

(e) $C_6H_5CH_3 \xrightarrow[\text{h}\nu]{Br_2} C_6H_5CH_2Br \xrightarrow{Na_2SO_3} C_6H_5CH_2SO_3^-\ Na^+ \xrightarrow{H^+} C_6H_5CH_2SO_3H$

(f) CH_3-ring-$SO_3H \xrightarrow[\text{350 °C}]{NaCN} CH_3$-ring-$CN \xrightarrow[\Delta]{H_3O^+} CH_3$-ring-$COOH$

(g)   cyclohexanone $\xrightarrow{(CH_3)_2\overset{+}{S}\overset{-}{C}H_2}$ epoxide $\xrightarrow[\text{or OH}^-]{H_3O^+}$ $\overset{OH}{\underset{CH_2OH}{C}}$ (cyclohexane)

(h)   sulfolane $\xrightarrow{n\text{-BuLi}} \xrightarrow{ICH_2CH_2CH_3}$ 2-propylsulfolane ($CH_2CH_2CH_3$)

9. (a) $3\ \langle\text{cyclopentanol, OH}\rangle + PCl_3 \xrightarrow{\text{pyridine}} \left(\langle\text{cyclopentyl}\rangle-O-\right)_3 P$

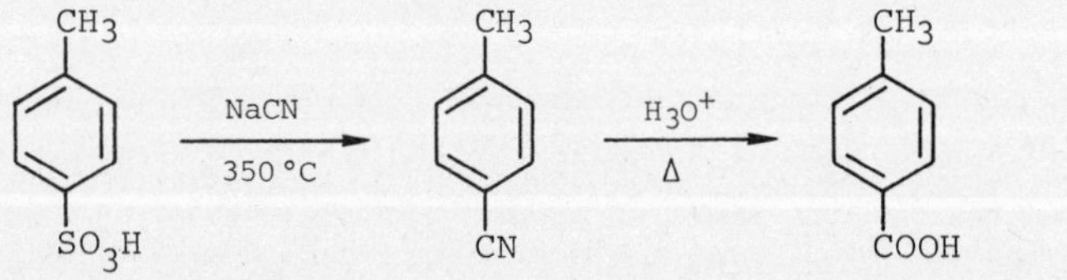

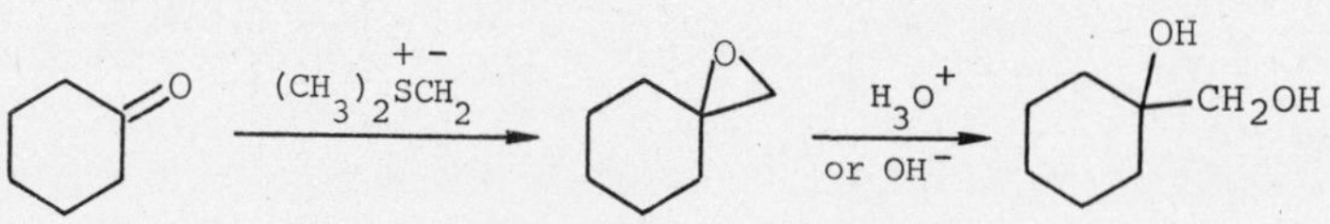

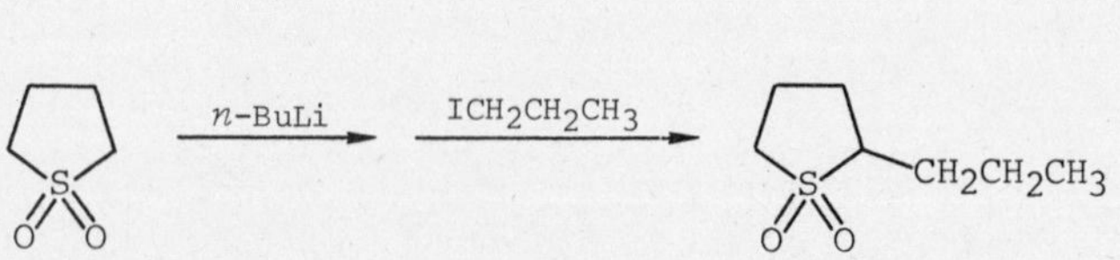

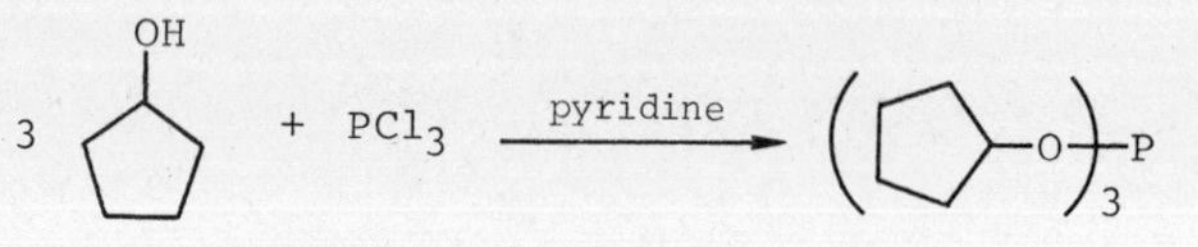

(b) $C_6H_5CH_2OH + PCl_3 \longrightarrow (C_6H_5CH_2O)_3P \xrightarrow{\Delta} C_6H_5CH_2\overset{\overset{O}{\|}}{P}(OCH_2C_6H_5)_2$

$\searrow$ HBr $\longrightarrow C_6H_5CH_2Br \xrightarrow{catalytic}$

(c) $C_6H_5\overset{\overset{O}{\|}}{C}H + HS(CH_2)_3SH \xrightarrow{HCl} C_6H_5\overset{S}{\underset{S}{C}}H \xrightarrow{n\text{-BuLi}} \overset{\overset{O}{\triangle}}{CH_2\text{-}CHCH_2CH_2CH_3}$

$\xleftarrow[\text{H}_2\text{O}]{\text{HgCl}_2}$

(d) $\xrightarrow[\Delta]{(C_6H_5O)_2\overset{\overset{O}{\|}}{P}CHCN}$ =CHCN

10. $ClCH_2CH_2\overset{..}{\underset{..}{S}}{\overset{CH_2}{\underset{CH_2\text{-}Cl}{<}}} \xrightarrow{-Cl^-} ClCH_2CH_2\text{-}\overset{+}{S}{\overset{CH_2}{\underset{CH_2}{<}}} \overset{:Nu}{\longleftarrow} \xrightarrow{+Nu^-} ClCH_2CH_2SCH_2CH_2Nu$

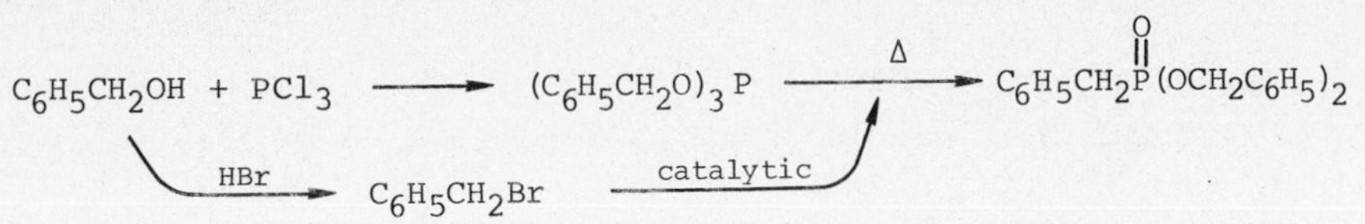

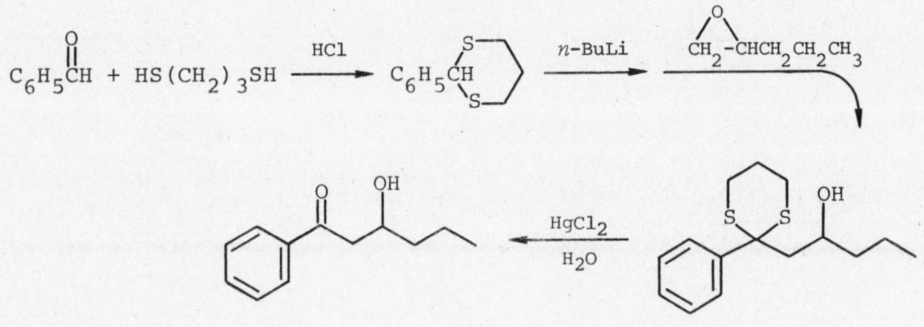

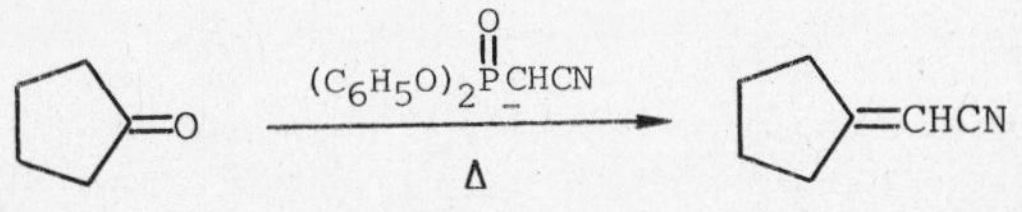

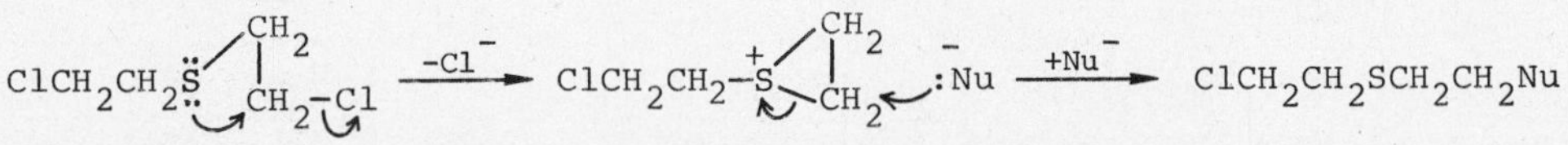

11.
$$CH_3S\cdot + H\cdot = CH_3SH \qquad\qquad \Delta H = -91$$
$$CH_4 = CH_3\cdot + H\cdot \qquad \Delta H° = DH° = 105$$
$$\rule{4cm}{0.4pt} \qquad\qquad \rule{4cm}{0.4pt}$$
$$CH_4 + CH_3S = CH_3SH + CH_3 \qquad \Delta H° = +14 \text{ kcal mole}^{-1}$$

$\Delta S°$ is probably about zero, therefore $\Delta G° \approx \Delta H°$, and the equilibrium lies far to the left. Hence, CH_3SH works as an inhibitor by reacting with alkyl radicals to stop propagation of the radical chains. The $CH_3S\cdot$ formed cannot abstract hydrogen atoms from carbon; hence nothing happens until two $CH_3S\cdot$ radicals come together to form the disulfide.

12. RSO_2OH are much more acidic than RCO_2H; the ΔpK_a is about 10. RSO_2NH_2 are more acidic than $RCONH_2$; the pK_a is about 5. With these analogies, we would expect RSO_2CH_3 to be more acidic than $RCOCH_3$; actually, RSO_2CH_3 are less acidic than $RCOCH_3$ in aqueous solution, but the difference is only a few pK_a units.

13. The shorter bond results from the increased coulombic attraction of the dipolar dative bond:

$\overset{\diagdown}{\underset{\diagup}{{}}}P{\rightarrow}O = \overset{\diagdown}{\underset{\diagup}{{}}}P^+{-}O^-$. This attraction also results in a stronger bond *(bond strengths:*
dative $P{\rightarrow}O$ bond ≈ 130 kcal mole^{-1}, single $P{-}O$ bond ≈ 90 kcal mole^{-1} *).*

The conversion of a $P{-}O$ single bond into a $P{\rightarrow}O$ dative bond provides most of the 47 kcal mole^{-1} which is the driving force of the rearrangement.

14. Because of the strain in the smaller five-membered ring, the P-O bonds in the ring do not both want to occupy equatorial positions simultaneously (O-P-O angle of 120°); instead, one of them is equatorial and one is apical (O-P-O) angle of 90°). A ring P-O bond (apical) is therefore cleaved in preference to the methoxy bond in the five-membered ring ester. For the six-membered ring ester, the larger ring can accommodate the pentacoordinate structure with apical methoxy, hence both types of cleavage are seen.

15.

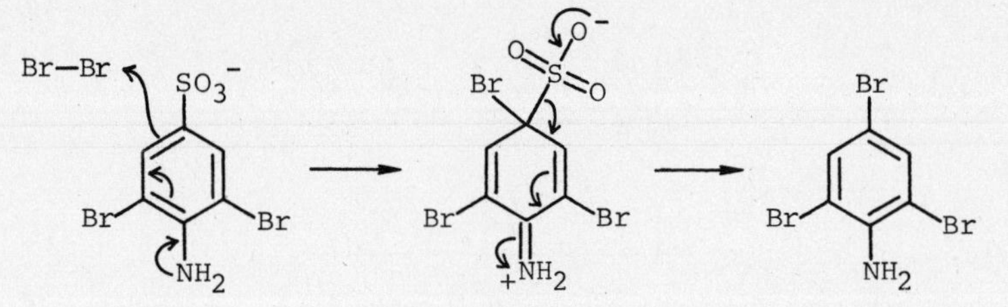

Ipso is the Latin word for "the same".

16.

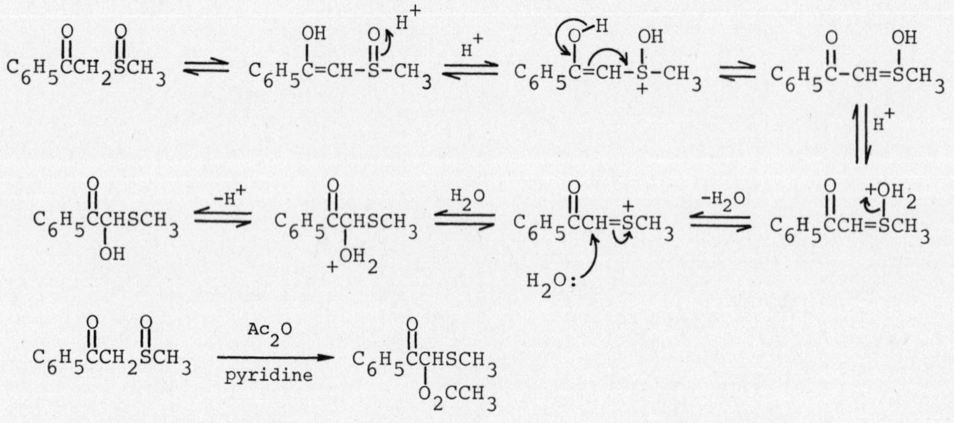

$$C_6H_5\overset{O}{\overset{\|}{C}}CH_2\overset{O}{\overset{\|}{S}}CH_3 \rightleftharpoons C_6H_5\overset{OH}{\overset{|}{C}}=CH-\overset{\overset{O}{\|}{H^+}}{S}-CH_3 \overset{H^+}{\rightleftharpoons} C_6H_5C=CH-\overset{OH}{\overset{|}{S}}-CH_3 \rightleftharpoons C_6H_5\overset{O}{\overset{\|}{C}}-CH=\overset{OH}{\overset{|}{S}}CH_3$$

$$\Big\Updownarrow H^+$$

$$C_6H_5\overset{O}{\overset{\|}{C}}\overset{}{C}HSCH_3 \overset{-H^+}{\rightleftharpoons} C_6H_5\overset{O}{\overset{\|}{C}}\overset{}{C}HSCH_3 \overset{H_2O}{\rightleftharpoons} C_6H_5\overset{O}{\overset{\|}{C}}CH=\overset{+}{S}CH_3 \overset{-H_2O}{\rightleftharpoons} C_6H_5\overset{O}{\overset{\|}{C}}CH=\overset{+OH_2}{S}CH_3$$

(OH) ... (+OH₂) ... H₂O:

$$C_6H_5\overset{O}{\overset{\|}{C}}CH_2\overset{O}{\overset{\|}{S}}CH_3 \xrightarrow[\text{pyridine}]{Ac_2O} C_6H_5\overset{O}{\overset{\|}{C}}\overset{}{C}HSCH_3 \quad (O_2CCH_3)$$

17.

$$+ (C_6H_5SOH)$$

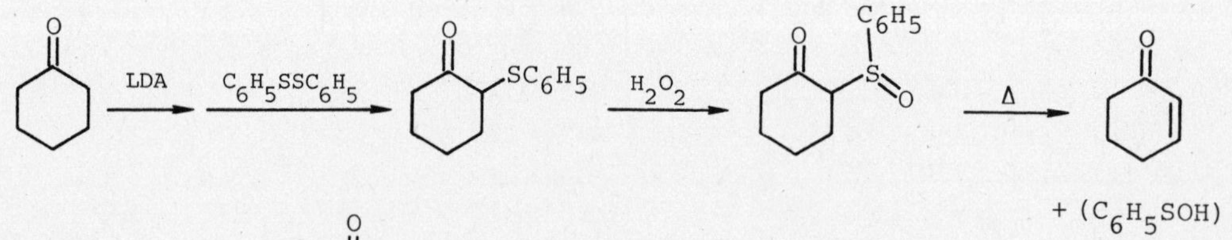

18.

$$CH_3SCH_3 + \tfrac{1}{2}O_2 \longrightarrow CH_3\overset{O}{\overset{\|}{S}}CH_3 \qquad \Delta H^\circ = -27.2 \text{ kcal mole}^{-1}$$

$$CH_3\overset{O}{\overset{\|}{S}}CH_3 + \tfrac{1}{2}O_2 \longrightarrow CH_3\overset{O}{\underset{O}{\overset{\|}{\underset{\|}{S}}}}CH_3 \qquad \Delta H^\circ = -53.0 \text{ kcal mole}^{-1}$$

The second oxidation step is much more exothermic than the first. Assuming that the analogy holds true for the disulfide systems, one would expect the thiosulfonic ester to be thermodynamically favored over the disulfoxide.

19.

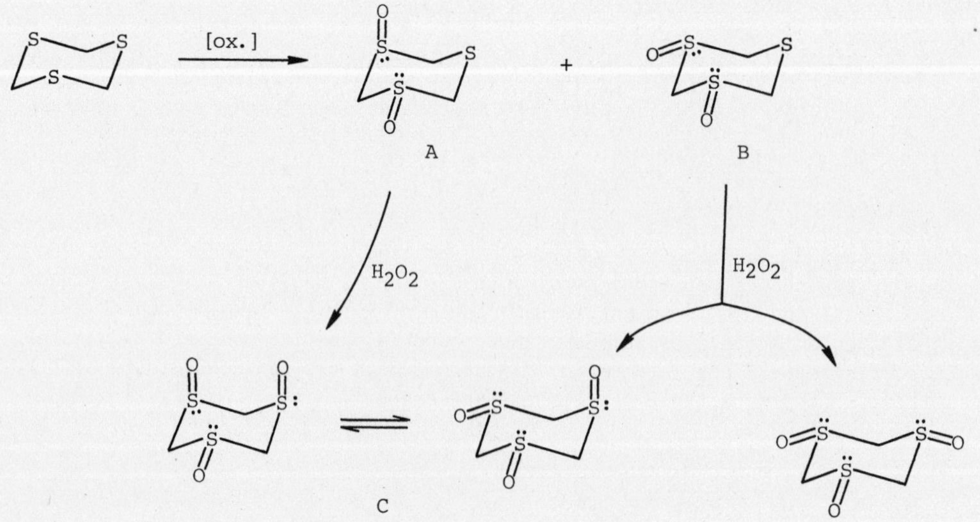

equivalent by chair ⇌ chair interconversion

20. (a)

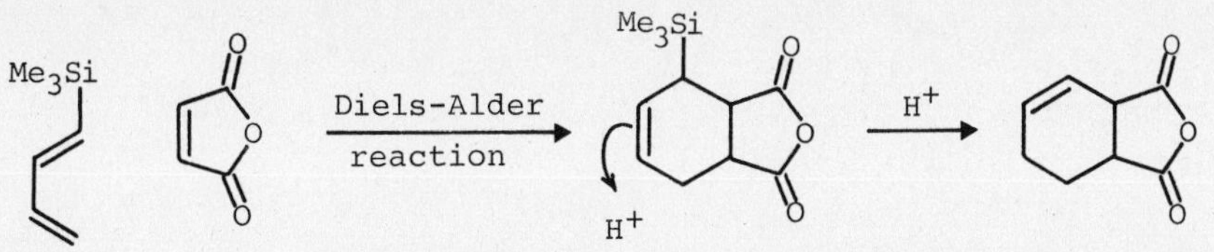

(b)

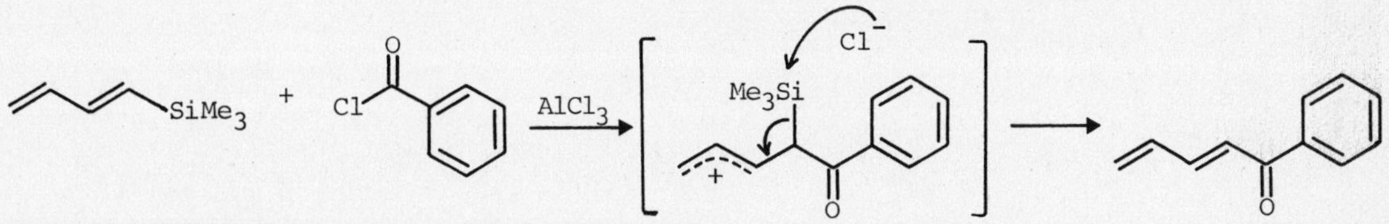

21.

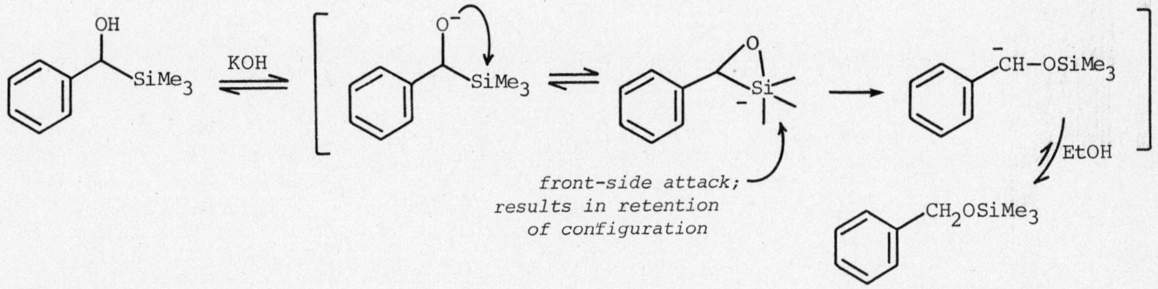

25.F Supplementary Problems

S1. Name the following compounds:

(a) $(CH_3O)_3P$

(b) 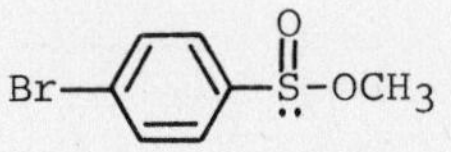

(c) 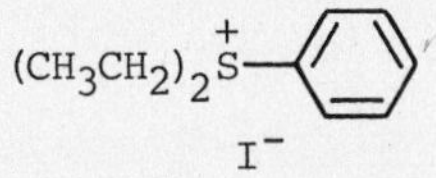

(d) $CH_3(CH_2)_{10}CH_2OSO_3^-\ Na^+$

(e) $(CH_3CH_2O)_2\overset{O}{\overset{\|}{P}}\text{-O-}\overset{O}{\overset{\|}{P}}(OCH_2CH_3)_2$

(f) $(CH_3CH_2CH_2CH_2)_3\overset{+}{P}CH_3\ Cl^-$

(g) 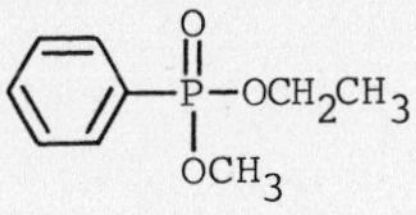

(h) $H_2NCH_2PO_3H_2$

(i) $CCl_3\text{-}SO_2\text{-}C_6H_5$

(j) $(CH_3CH_2CH_2)_2S{=}O$

(k) 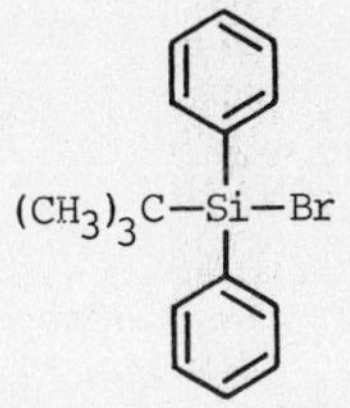

(l) 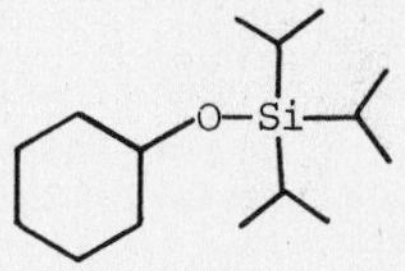

S2. What is the major product to result from each of the following reaction sequences?

(a) 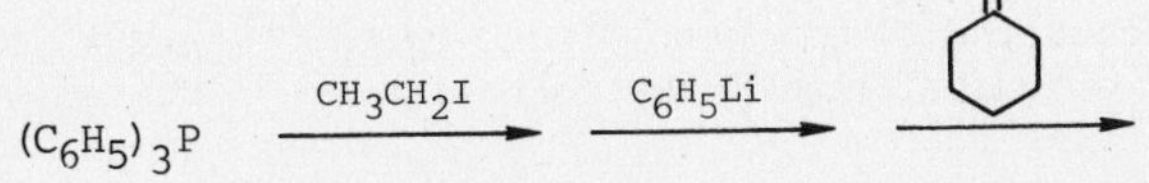

(b) $(CH_3)_2CHCH{=}O \xrightarrow[BF_3]{HS(CH_2)_3SH} \xrightarrow{n\text{-BuLi}} \xrightarrow{CH_3CH_2O\text{-}SO_2\text{-}C_6H_5} \xrightarrow[HgCl_2]{H_2O}$

(c) 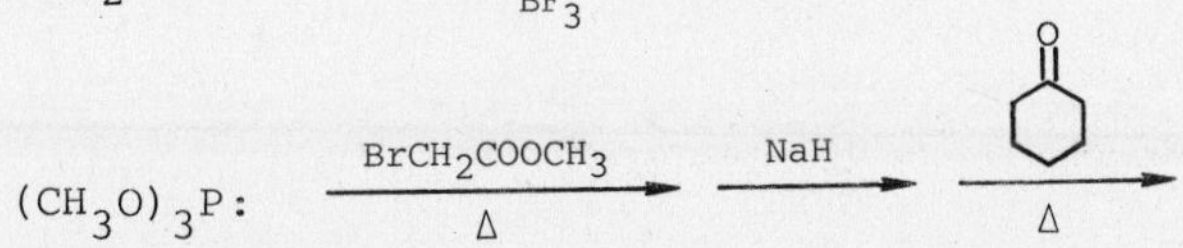

(d)

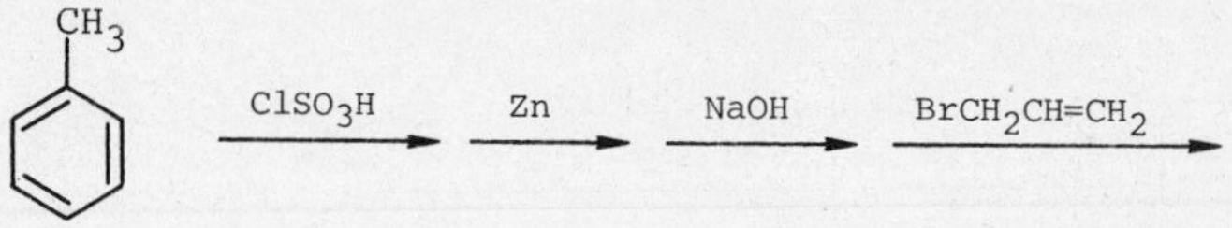

$$\text{toluene} \xrightarrow{\text{ClSO}_3\text{H}} \xrightarrow{\text{Zn}} \xrightarrow{\text{NaOH}} \xrightarrow{\text{BrCH}_2\text{CH}=\text{CH}_2}$$

(e) $\text{BrCH}_2\text{CH}_2\text{CH}_2\text{CH}_2\text{Br} \xrightarrow[\text{C}_2\text{H}_5\text{OH}]{\text{NaSH}}$

(f) $\text{BrCH}_2\text{CH}_2\text{CH}_2\text{CH}_2\text{Br} \xrightarrow{2\ (\text{NH}_2)_2\text{C}=\text{S}} \xrightarrow{\text{NaOH}}$

(g) $(\text{CH}_3\text{O})_2\overset{\text{O}}{\underset{}{\text{P}}}-\text{O}-\overset{\text{O}}{\underset{}{\text{P}}}(\text{OCH}_3)_2 \xrightarrow[\text{CH}_3\text{CH}_2\text{OH}]{\text{CH}_3\text{CH}_2\text{ONa}}$

(h) $\text{C}_6\text{H}_5\text{SCH}_3 \xrightarrow{n\text{-BuLi}} \xrightarrow[\text{2. 2 CH}_3\text{CO}_3\text{H}]{\text{1. (CH}_3)_2\text{C=O}}$

(i) $(\text{CH}_3)_2\text{SiCl}_2 + \underline{t}\text{-BuLi} \longrightarrow$

(j)

$$\xrightarrow{\text{TiCl}_4} \xrightarrow{\text{H}_2\text{O}}$$

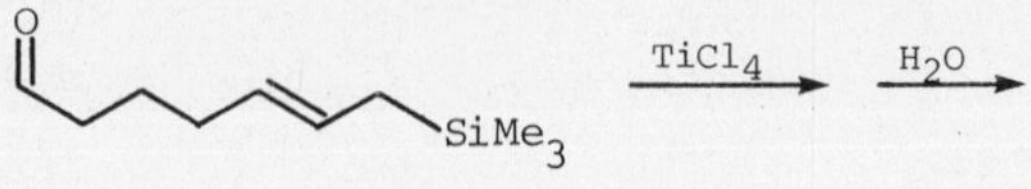

S3. Show how to accomplish the following transformations in a practical manner:

(a) $\text{CH}_3\text{CH}_2\text{CH}_2\overset{\text{O}}{\overset{\|}{\text{C}}}\text{CH}_2\text{CH}_3 \longrightarrow \text{CH}_3\text{CH}_2\text{CH}_2-\overset{\text{O}-\!-\!\text{CH}_2}{\underset{}{\text{C}}}-\text{CH}_2\text{CH}_3$

(b) $\text{CH}_3\text{CH}_2\text{CH}_2\overset{\text{O}}{\overset{\|}{\text{CH}}} \longrightarrow \text{CH}_3\text{CH}_2\text{CH}_2\overset{\text{O}}{\overset{\|}{\text{CD}}}$

(c) $(\text{CH}_3)_2\text{CHCH}_2\overset{\text{O}}{\overset{\|}{\text{C}}}\text{CH}_3 \longrightarrow (\text{CH}_3)_2\text{CHCH}_2\overset{\text{CH}_3}{\underset{}{\text{C}}}=\text{CHCOOCH}_2\text{CH}_3$

(d) $\text{C}_6\text{H}_5\text{CH}_3 \longrightarrow \text{C}_6\text{H}_5\text{CH}_2-\overset{\text{O}}{\underset{\text{O}}{\overset{\|}{\underset{\|}{\text{S}}}}}-\text{C}_6\text{H}_4\text{CH}_3$

(f)

(e)

$\longrightarrow (\text{C}_6\text{H}_5\text{O})_3\text{P}=\text{O}$

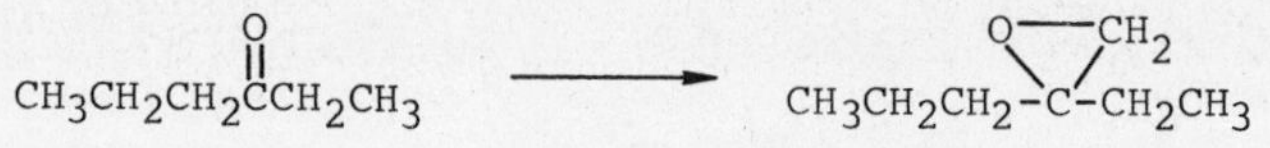

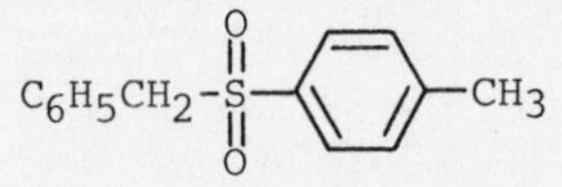

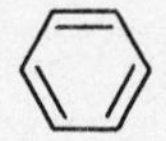

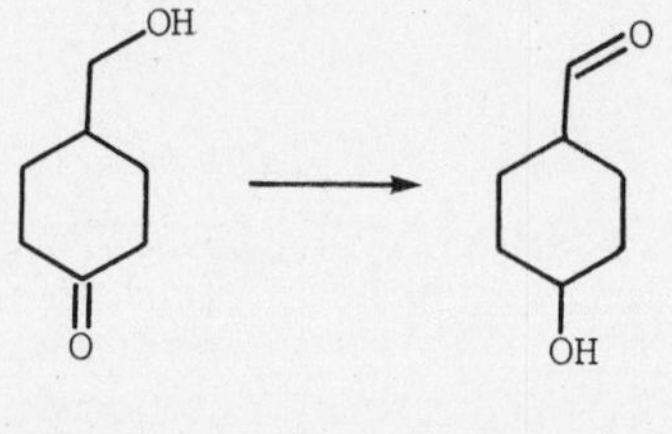

S4. The Arbuzov-Michaelis reaction is a very important one for the preparation of dialkyl alkyl-phosphonates from trialkylphosphites, but it fails if applied to the synthesis of diphenyl alkylphosphonates from triphenylphosphite. Why?
What products do you expect to see instead?

S5. A chemist tried to synthesize 1-methyl-2-(phenylthio)ethanamine from propylene oxide by sequential treatment with sodium benzothiolate, p-toluenesulfonyl chloride, and ammonia. However, 2-(phenylthio)propanamine was the actual product. Draw the intermediates involved in this transformation and explain why the unanticipated isomer was produced.

$$\text{CH}_3\overset{\text{O}}{\overset{}{\text{CH}}}\text{--CH}_2 \xrightarrow{\text{C}_6\text{H}_5\text{SNa}} \xrightarrow{\text{CH}_3\text{C}_6\text{H}_4\text{SO}_2\text{Cl}} \xrightarrow{\text{NH}_3} \overset{\text{SC}_6\text{H}_5}{\underset{}{\text{CH}_3\text{CHCH}_2\text{NH}_2}}$$

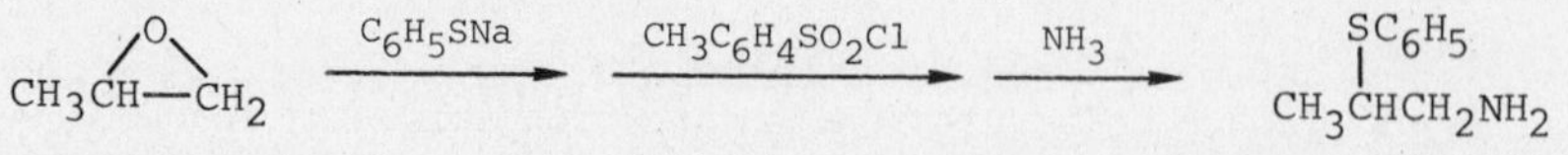

S6. If a carboxylic ester is to be converted to a β-ketosulfone by reaction with the carbanion derived from dimethyl sulfone, two equivalents of the carbanion are required; when one equivalent is used, only 50% of the ester reacts.

(a) Why are two equivalents necessary for complete conversion?

(b) β-Ketosulfones are "desulfonylated", to give the ketone itself, using aluminum amalgam in wet THF:

$$-\overset{\text{O}}{\overset{\|}{\text{C}}}-\overset{|}{\underset{|}{\text{C}}}-\text{SO}_2\text{R} \xrightarrow[\substack{\text{H}_2\text{O} \\ \text{THF}}]{\text{Al(Hg)}} -\overset{\text{O}}{\overset{\|}{\text{C}}}-\overset{|}{\text{CH}} + {}^-\text{O}_2\text{SR}$$

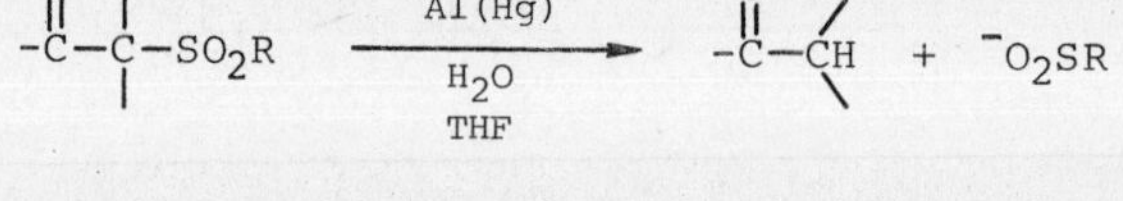

Using this reaction, devise a method for the conversion of a carboxylic ester into a ketone using dimethyl sulfone and an alkyl halide:

$$RCOOCH_3 + CH_3\overset{O}{\underset{O}{\overset{\|}{\underset{\|}{S}}}}CH_3 + BrR' \xrightarrow{?} R\overset{O}{\overset{\|}{C}}CH_2R'$$

S7. Dithioketals are often difficult to hydrolyze, even using mercuric chloride as catalyst, particularly if there is an acid-sensitive functional group in the molecule. A method for accomplishing this hydrolysis under neutral conditions using methyl iodide in aqueous acetone with sodium bicarbonate has been devised. Write a step-by-step mechanism to illustrate how this reaction occurs.

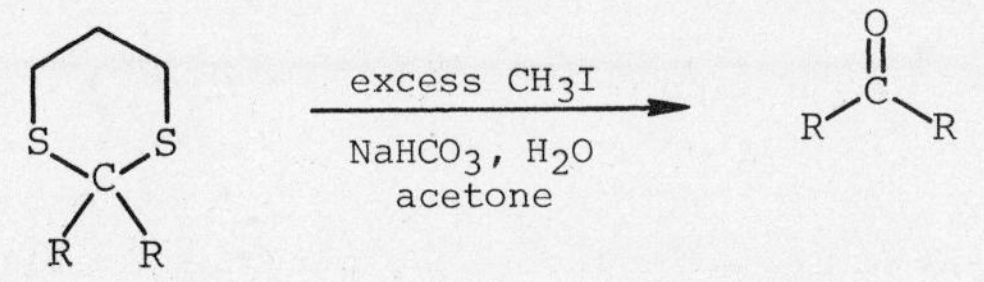

S8. Depending on the order in which substituents are introduced onto the bicyclic lactone illustrated below, the final sulfoxide elimination reaction produces one or the other double bond isomer. How do you account for this difference in behavior?

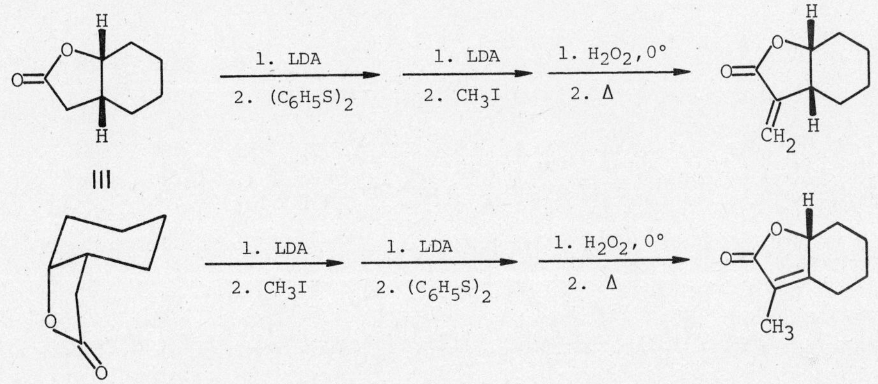

S9. β-Hydroxysilanes undergo elimination under either acidic or basic conditions to give olefins and a silanol. The elimination reactions are stereospecific, and opposite products are formed, depending on the conditions employed:

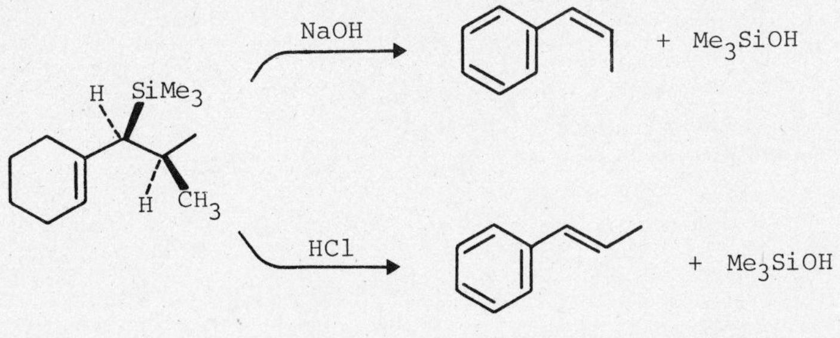

Write mechanisms that rationalize the stereochemical results of these two reactions.

25.G   Answers to Supplementary Problems

S1.   (a)   trimethyl phosphite

(b)   methyl p-bromobenzenesulfinate

(c)   diethylphenylsulfonium iodide

(d)   sodium dodecyl sulfate
      (an important detergent)

(e)   tetraethyl pyrophosphate

(f)   tributylmethylphosphonium chloride

(g)   ethyl methyl phenylphosphonate

(h)   aminomethylphosphonic acid

(i)   trichloromethyl phenyl sulfone

(j)   dipropyl sulfoxide

(k)   t-butyldiphenylsilyl bromide

(l)   cyclohexyl triisopropylsilyl ether

S2.

(a)   [cyclohexylidene structure with CHCH$_3$]   + $(C_6H_5)_3P=O$

(b) $(CH_3)_2CHCCH_2CH_3$ (with C=O)

(c)   [cyclohexylidene structure with CHCOOCH$_3$]

(d) CH_3—[benzene ring]—$S(=O)(=O)$—$CH_2CH=CH_2$

(e)   [tetrahydrothiophene ring with S]

($HSCH_2CH_2CH_2CH_2Br + HS^-$ ⇌ $H_2S + {}^-SCH_2CH_2CH_2CH_2Br$)

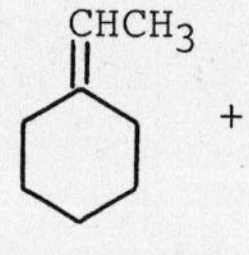

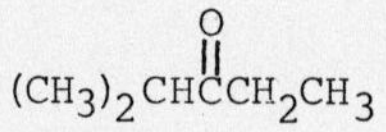

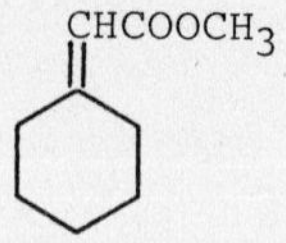

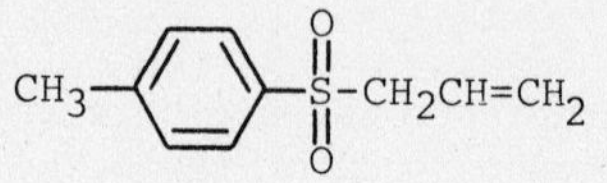

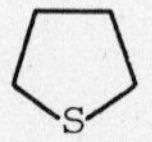

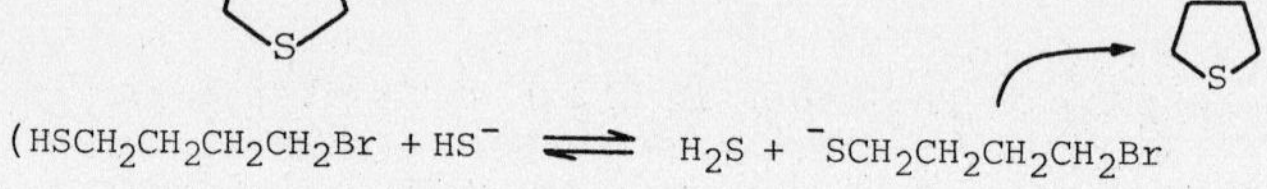

is faster than intermolecular
displacement by a second ^-SH group

→ [tetrahydrothiophene ring with S]

(f) $HSCH_2CH_2CH_2CH_2SH$

(g) $(CH_3O)_2PO_2{}^-$
      $+ CH_3CH_2OP(OCH_3)_2$ (with =O)

(h) $C_6H_5-S(=O)(=O)-CH_2C(OH)(CH_3)_2$

(i) $(CH_3)_3C-Si(CH_3)_2-Cl$

(j)   [cyclopentane ring with OH and vinyl group]

S3.

(a) $R-C(=O)-R'$ + $(CH_3)_2S^+$ $\bar{C}H_2$ ⟶   [epoxide: $R-C(R')$ with O—CH$_2$]   + $(CH_3)_2S$

(b) $CH_3CH_2CH_2CH(=O)$ $\xrightarrow[BF_3]{HS(CH_2)_3SH}$ [1,3-dithiane with $CH_3CH_2CH_2$, H] $\xrightarrow{n-BuLi}$ [1,3-dithiane with $CH_3CH_2CH_2$, Li] $\xrightarrow{D_2O}$ [1,3-dithiane with $CH_3CH_2CH_2$, D]

$CH_3CH_2CH_2CD(=O)$ $\xleftarrow[HgCl_2]{H_2O}$

(c) $R-C(=O)-R'$ + Et_2O_3P $\bar{C}HCOOC_2H_5$ $\xrightarrow{\Delta}$ [$R_2C=CHCOOC_2H_5$]   + $(EtO)_2PO_2{}^-$

(d) $C_6H_5CH_3$ $\xrightarrow{ClSO_3H}$ [toluene ring with CH_3 top, SO_2Cl bottom] $\xrightarrow[2.\ NaHCO_3]{1.\ Zn,\ H_2O}$ [toluene ring with CH_3, $SO_2{}^- Na^+$]   +   [benzene ring with CH_2Br] $\xleftarrow[h\nu]{Br_2}$ $C_6H_5CH_3$

CH_3—[benzene ring]—$S(=O)(=O)$—CH_2—[benzene ring]

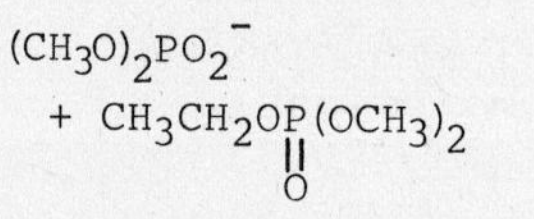

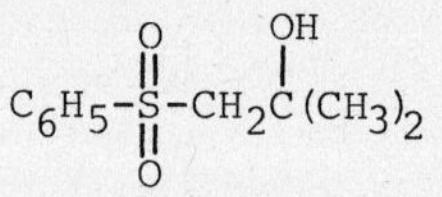

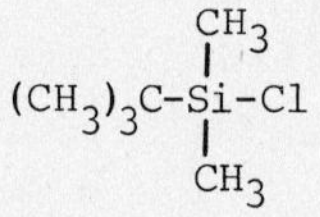

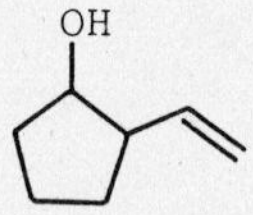

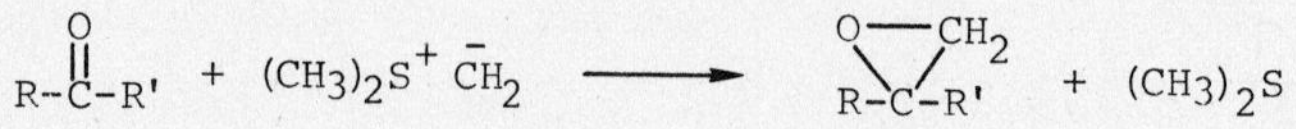

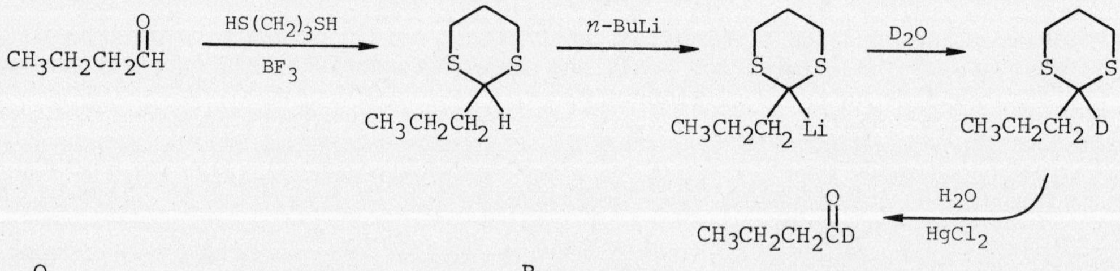

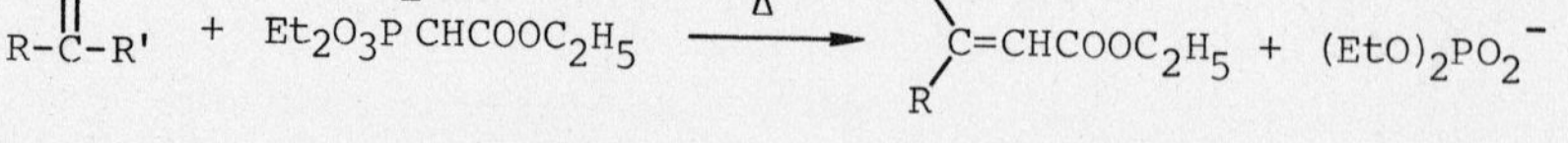

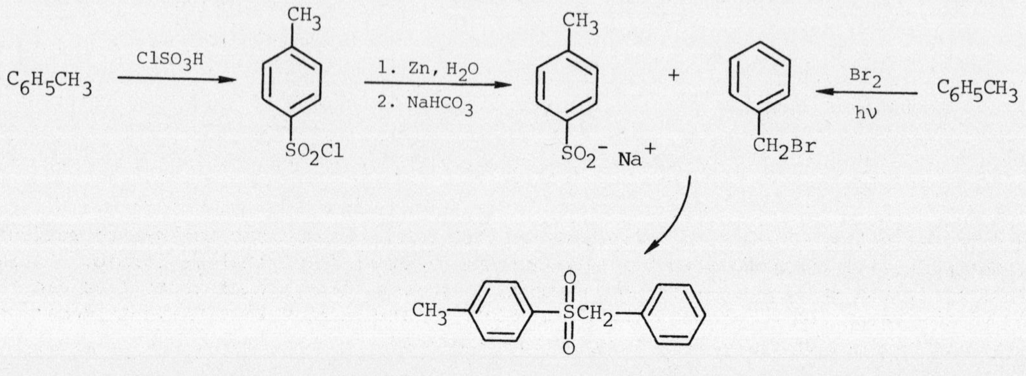

(e)

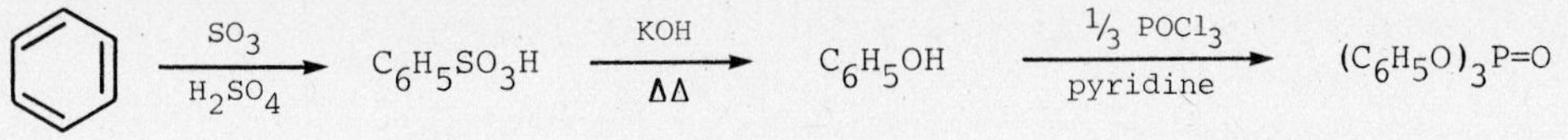

$$\text{[benzene]} \xrightarrow[\text{H}_2\text{SO}_4]{\text{SO}_3} \quad C_6H_5SO_3H \xrightarrow[\Delta\Delta]{\text{KOH}} \quad C_6H_5OH \xrightarrow[\text{pyridine}]{\frac{1}{3}\ POCl_3} \quad (C_6H_5O)_3P{=}O$$

(f)

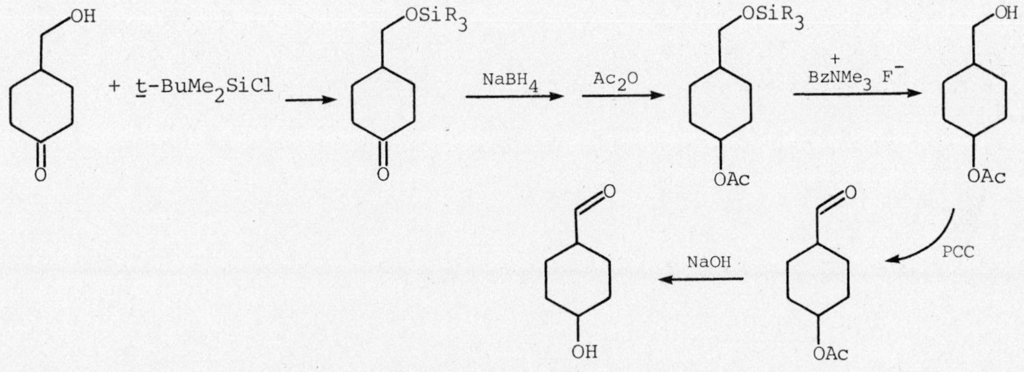

S4.

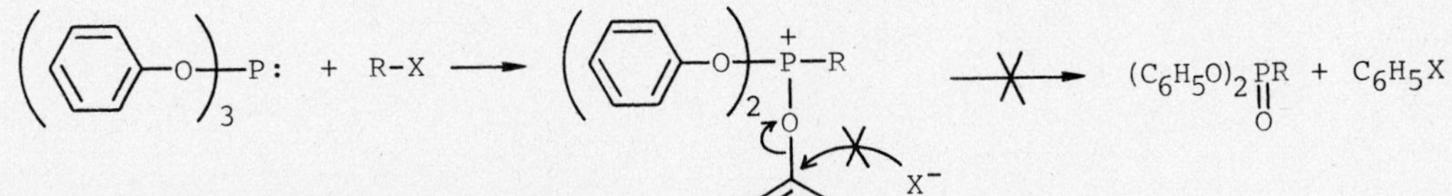

Alkylation of phosphorus occurs
readily, but cleavage of a phenyl-
oxygen bond to form the phosphonate is
not possible, due to the difficulty of nucleophilic substitution on the
benzene ring.

S5.

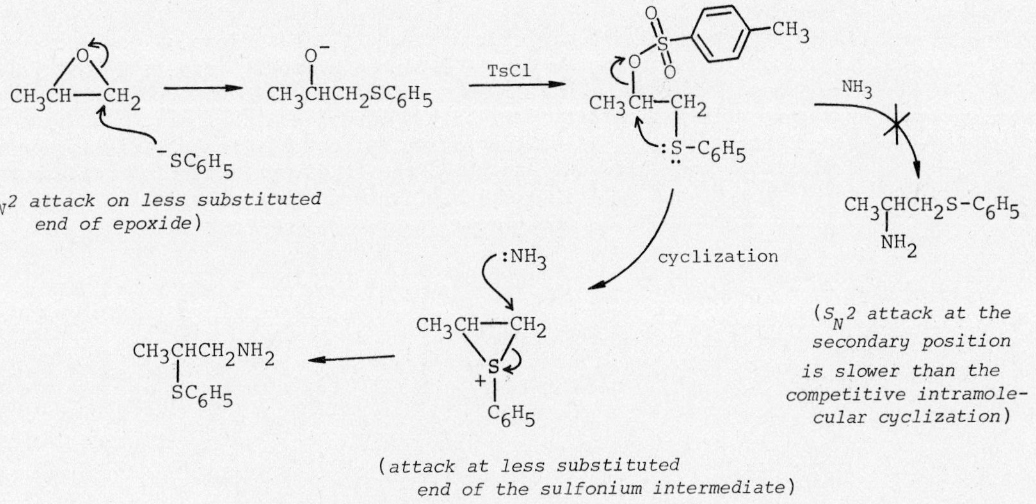

(S$_N$2 attack on less substituted
end of epoxide)

(S$_N$2 attack at the
secondary position
is slower than the
competitive intramole-
cular cyclization)

(attack at less substituted
end of the sulfonium intermediate)

S6.

(a)

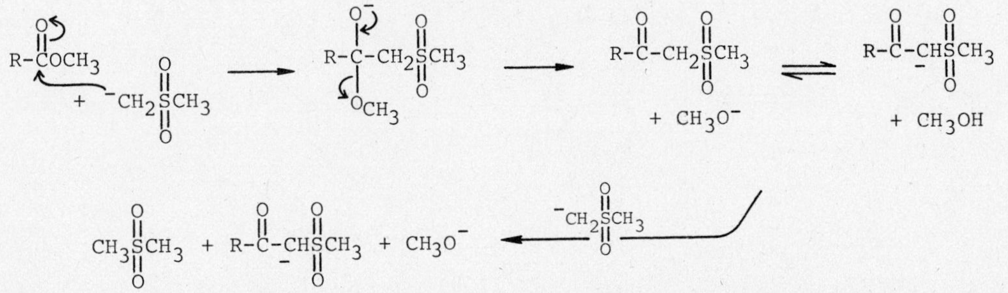

The dimethyl sulfone carbanion is more basic than both methanol and the β-keto sulfone product,
and one mole will be protonated for each mole of β-keto sulfone that is formed. It is commonly
necessary to use two equivalents of a carbanion whenever the product is more acidic than the
acid of the carbanion. Formation of the enolate of the product also prevents addition of
another equivalent of carbanion to the ketone carbonyl.

(b) $RCOOCH_3$ + 2 $NaCH_2SCH_3$ ⟶ R-C-CHSCH₃ $\xrightarrow{R'Br}$ R-C-CHSCH₃ $\xrightarrow{Al(Hg)}$

R-C-CH₂R'

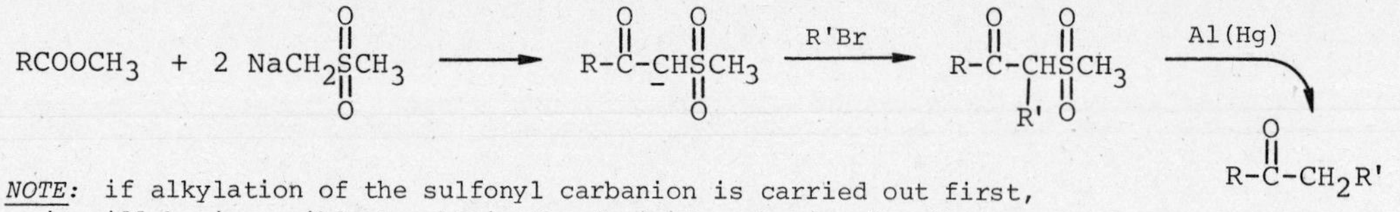

(*NOTE*: if alkylation of the sulfonyl carbanion is carried out first,
it will be impossible to obtain the desired carbanion for the
acylation reaction:

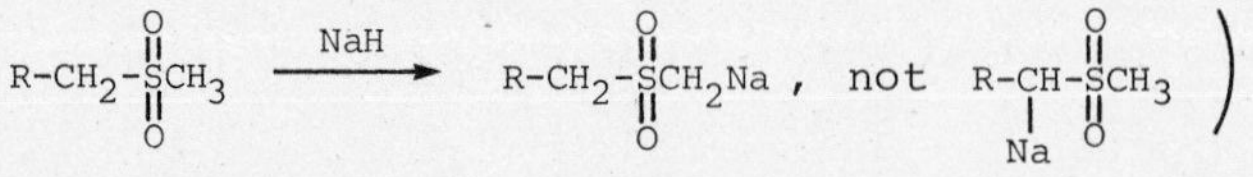

R-CH₂-SCH₃ $\xrightarrow{NaH}$ R-CH₂-SCH₂Na , not R-CH-SCH₃)

S7.

R-C-R
+
$CH_3SCH_2CH_2CH_2SH$

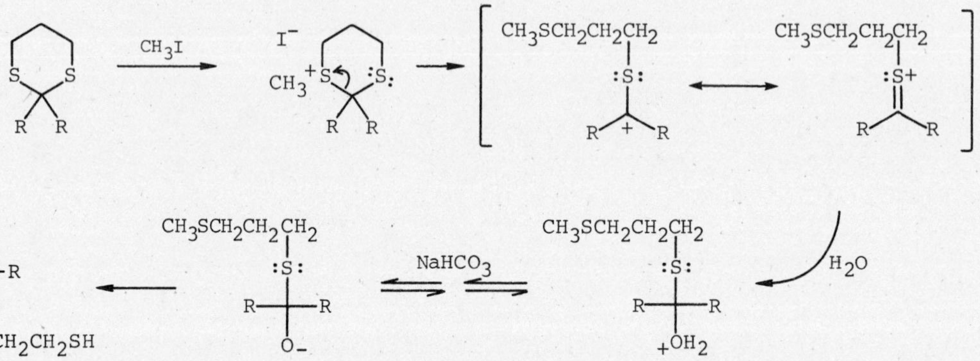

S8.   Because of the folded structure of the bicyclic lactone, all reactions of the enolates (alkylations and sulfenylations) occur from the top side of the molecule (_exo_ face), as illustrated
below, for steric reasons. If alkylation follows sulfenylation, compound A will result.
The subsequent sulfoxide elimination can occur only toward the methyl group, because the
bridgehead hydrogen is _trans_ to it. If sulfenylation follows alkylation, diastereomer B will
be produced. In this case, the sulfoxide can eliminate in either direction because the
bridgehead hydrogen is _cis_ to the sulfur group; as it turns out, elimination to give the
more highly substituted double bond is preferred.

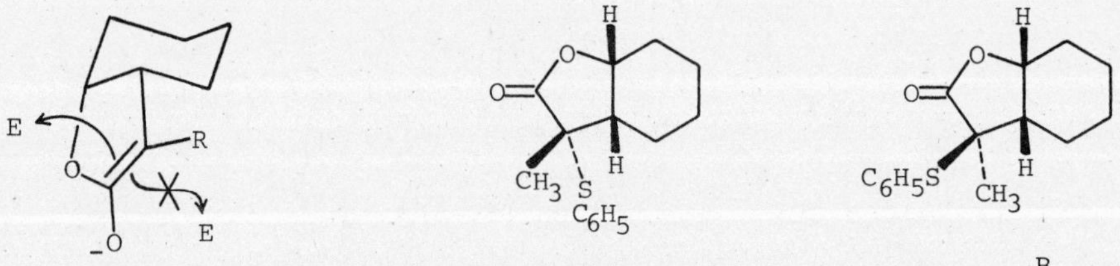

A   B

S9.

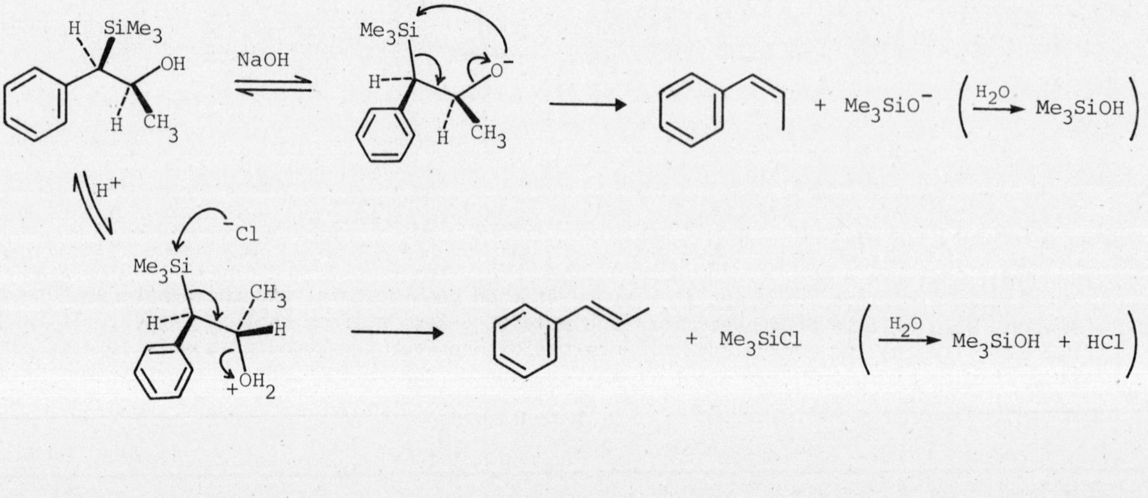

26. AROMATIC HALIDES, PHENOLS, PHENYL ETHERS, AND QUINONES

26.A   Chapter Outline and Important Terms Introduced

26.1   Introduction

benzyl vs. aryl halides

26.2   Preparation of Halobenzenes

electrophilic aromatic substitution   (see Section 22.1)
substitution of arenediazonium salts   (see Section 24.5)

26.3   Reactions of Halobenzenes

A.   Nucleophilic Aromatic Substitution: The Addition-Elimination Mechanism
          addition-elimination vs. elimination-addition
B.   Nucleophilic Aromatic Substitution: The Elimination-Addition Mechanism
          benzyne
C.   Metallation
          transmetallation   Ullmann reaction
          Wurtz-Fittig reaction   biaryl

26.4   Nomenclature of Phenols and Phenyl Ethers

phenol
                                        phenyl ethers
(benzenol)
                                        (alkoxyarenes)

26.5   Preparation and Properties of Phenols and Ethers

A.   Preparation of Phenols
B.   Acidity of Phenols (pKa = 10)
          effects of substitution
C.   Preparation of Ethers (Williamson ether synthesis)

26.6   Reactions of Phenolate Ions

A.   Halogenation
B.   Addition to Aldehyes
          Bakelite
C.   Kolbe synthesis
D.   Reimer-Tiemann Reaction
E.   Diazonium coupling

26.7   Reactions of Phenols and Ethers

A.   Esterification
          requires acid chloride or anhydride
B.   Electrophilic Substitutions on Phenols and Phenyl Ethers
          highly activated system   phthaleins
          chelation effects in orientation   Fries rearrangement
C.   Reactions of Ethers
          Claisen rearrangement   Cope rearrangement

26.7   Quinones

A.   Nomenclature
          benzoquinone, 1,2-naphthoquinone, etc.
B.   Preparation
C.   Reduction-Oxidation Equilibria
          reversibility of electron transfer
          dependence of reduction potentials on substituents
          radical anions, antioxidants

D. Charge–Transfer Complexes
      quinhydrone
E. Reactions of Quinones
      addition   Diels–Alder reaction

26.B   Important Reactions Introduced

<u>Nucleophilic</u> <u>aromatic</u> <u>substitution</u>

Addition-elimination mechanism (26.3.A)

Equation:

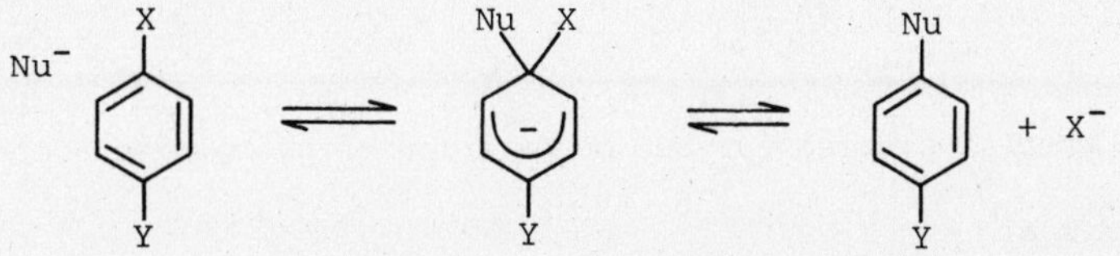

Generality: X = halogen, SO_3^-, or other good leaving group, Y = electron-withdrawing group in
                 <u>o</u>- or <u>p</u>-positions, such as NO_2, COR, CO_2R, etc.

               Nu:$^-$ = RO$^-$, other strong nucleophile

Key features: the more Y groups in <u>o</u>- and <u>p</u>-positions, the easier the reaction is

Elimination-addition mechanism (26.3.B)

Equation:

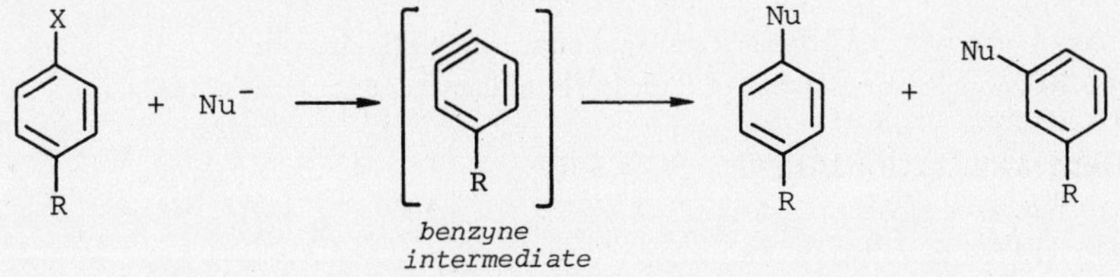

*benzyne
intermediate*

Generality: X = halogen; Nu:$^-$ = RO$^-$, $^-$:NH_2, or other strong base

Key features: strongly basic conditions

               mechanism involves benzyne intermediate, therefore mixtures of isomers possible with
                 substituted aromatic compounds

<u>Metallation</u> <u>of</u> <u>aryl</u> <u>halides</u>   (26.3.C)

Equation: Ar—X + M ———> Ar—MX or Ar—M

Generality: Ar must contain no easily reduced groups, such as NO_2, COR, SO_3R, CN, OH, NH_2, etc.
               X = Br, I (Cl possible in THF solvent)
               M = 2 Li, 2 Na, Mg, etc.

Key features: ordinary formation of Grignard reagent, aryllithium, etc.

<u>Transmetallation</u> <u>of</u> <u>aryl</u> <u>halides</u>   (26.3.C)

Equation: Ar—X + R—M ———> Ar—M + R—X

Generality: Ar must contain no easily reduced groups, such as NO_2, COR, SO_3R, CN, OH, NH_2, etc.
               X = Br, I; RM = alkyllithium

Key features: reaction is poor with X = Cl

<u>Aryl</u> <u>coupling</u> <u>reactions</u>   (26.3.C)

Equation:
               Ar—X + R—X' $\xrightarrow{[M]}$ Ar—R + MXX'

               2 Ar—Li $\xrightarrow{CuX}$ Ar$_2$CuLi $\xrightarrow{O_2}$ Ar—Ar

Generality: Wurtz-Fittig reaction: M = 2 Na; Ar contains no reactive groups; RX = 1° or 2° alkyl
                 bromide or iodide

Ullmann reaction: M = Cu powder; RX = **aryl**—Cl, -Br, or -I; reaction is better
    if Ar contains electron withdrawing groups (e.g. NO_2 or CN)

cuprate coupling: Ar contains no reactive groups

Key features: Ullmann coupling is the best way to make functionalized biaryls
               Ullmann coupling is probably a radical process

Oxidation of cumene (26.5.A)

Equation:

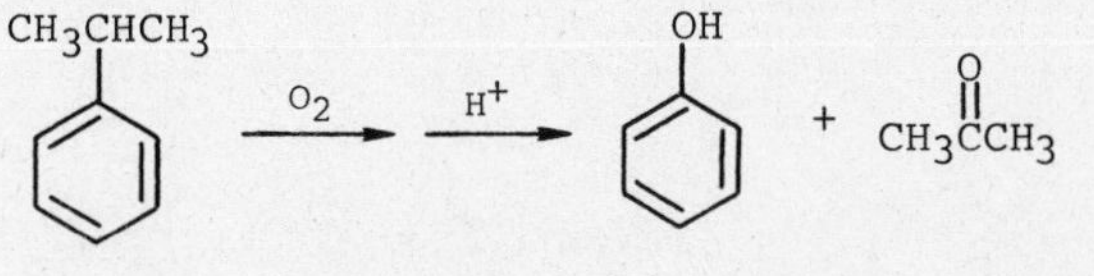

Key features: important industrial process for the preparation of phenol and acetone

Halogenation of phenols (26.6.A)

Equation:

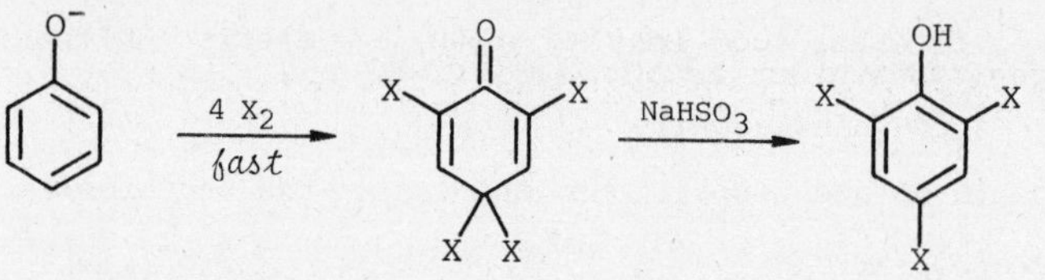

Generality: X = Cl, Br, or I

Key features: under basic conditions, form tetrahalocyclohexadienone
               stepwise halogenation is only possible under acidic conditions (26.7.B)

Condensation of phenolate ions with aldehydes (26.6.B)

Equation:

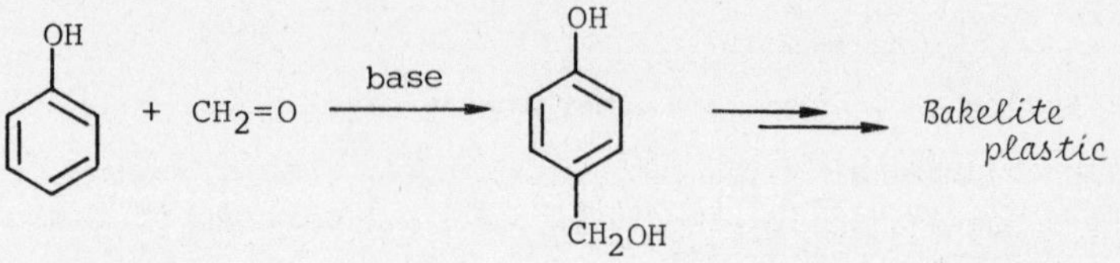

Key features: polymeric compound obtained is Bakelite, the first commmercial plastic

Kolbe synthesis (26.6.C)

Equation:

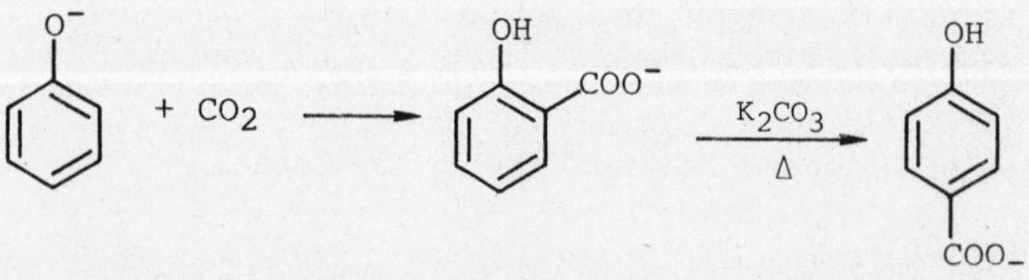

Key features: the product of kinetic control (first formed product) is the o-isomer; the product
               of thermodynamic control (more stable product) is the p-isomer
               o-hydroxybenzoic acid (salicylic acid) is starting material for aspirin

Reimer-Tiemann reaction (26.6.D)

Equation:

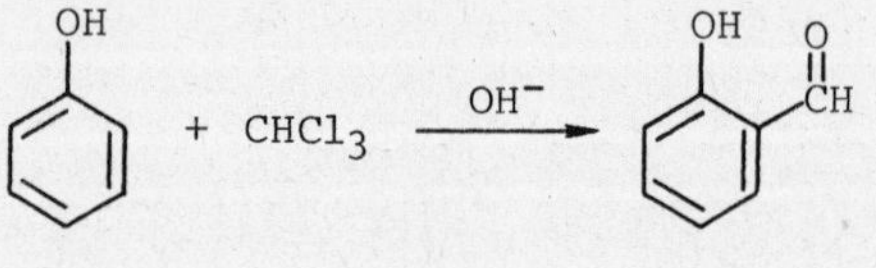

Key features: mechanism involves reaction of :CCl_2 to give dichloromethyl intermediate

Diazonium coupling (26.6.E)

Equation:

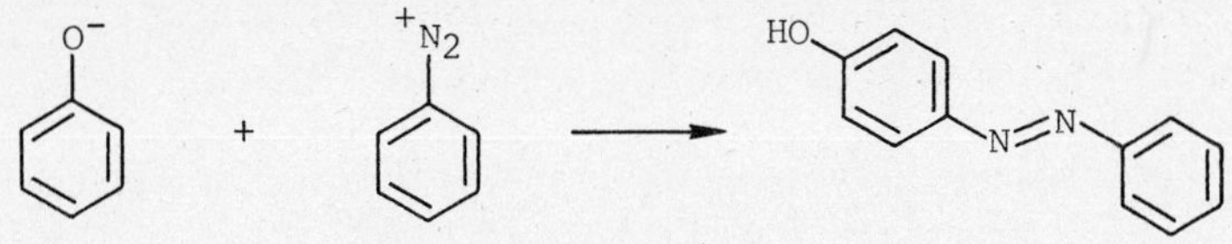

Key features: see also Section 24.5.G
              method for synthesis of azo dyes

Synthesis of phthaleins (26.7.B)

Equation:

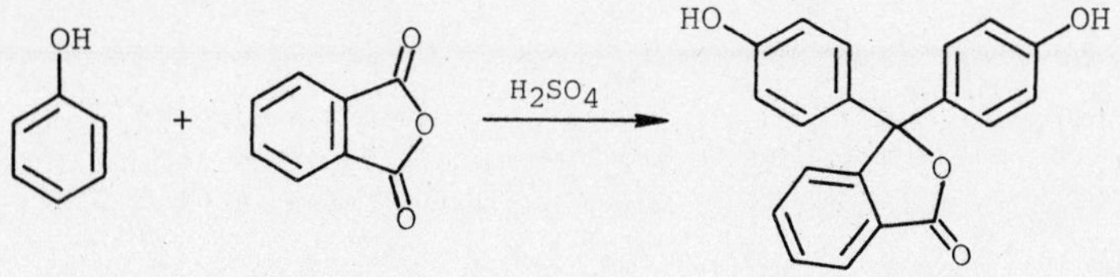

Key features: phthaleins are important dyes, pH indicators, and laxatives....

Synthesis of fluoresceins (26.7.B)

Equation:

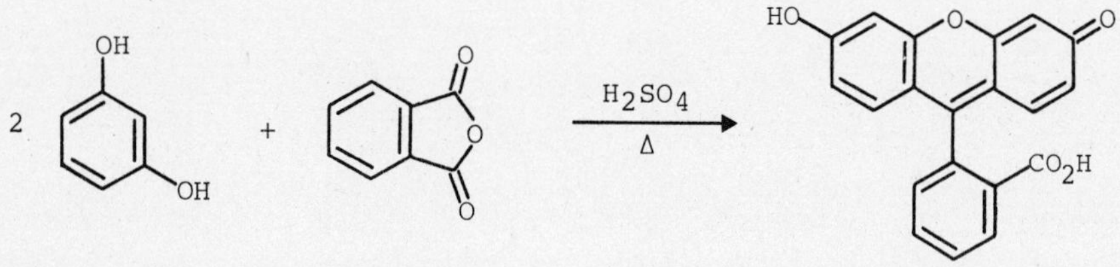

Fries rearrangement (26.7.B)

Equation:

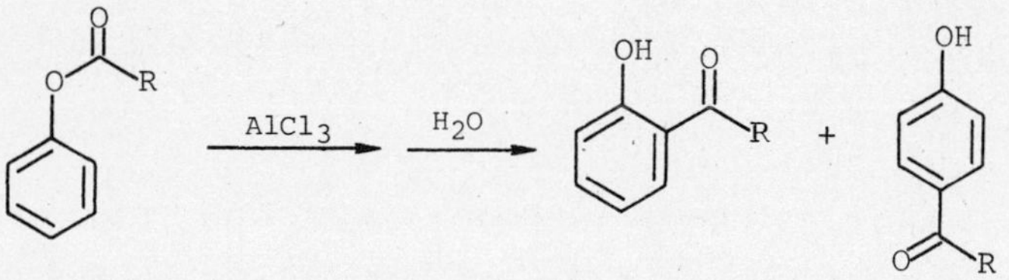

Key features: best method for Friedel-Crafts acylation of phenols

Aromatic Claisen rearrangement (26.7.C)

Equation:

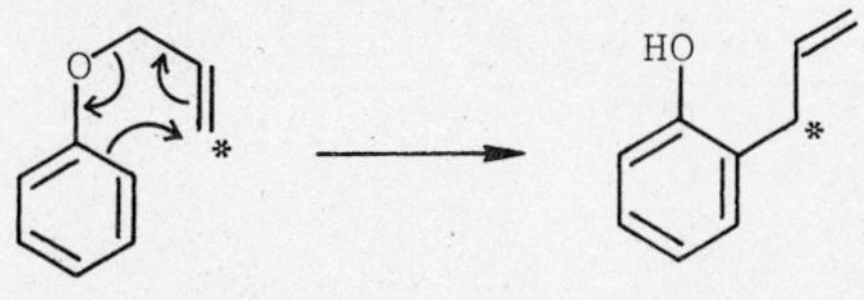

Key features: reaction proceeds with allylic rearrangement of allylic group
              if both o-positions are blocked, p-substituted products from
                  double rearrangement (Claisen plus Cope) are seen

Preparation of quinones by oxidation of hydroquinone derivatives (26.8.B)

Equation:

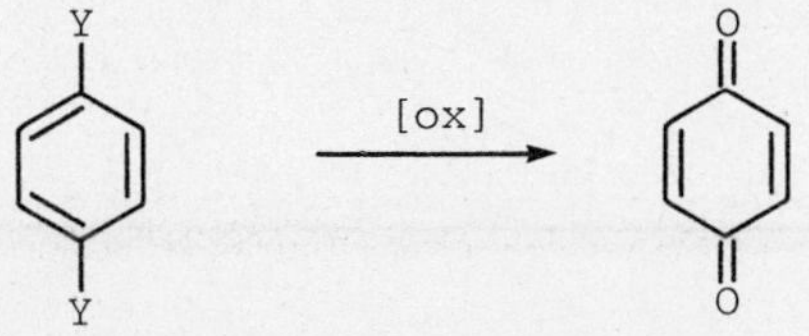

Generality: Y = combinations of OH, OR, NR$_2$, either o- or p-substituted

                [Ox] = air, HNO$_3$, Cr^{VI} salts, Fe^{+3}, N$_2$O$_4$, Na$_2$ClO$_3$/VO$_5$, etc.

Key features: redox couples involving quinone $\rightleftharpoons$ hydroquinone are important in biological systems
                and in photography

                quinones and hydroquinones also are important in forming charge-transfer complexes

Quinone addition reactions (26.8.E)

Equation:

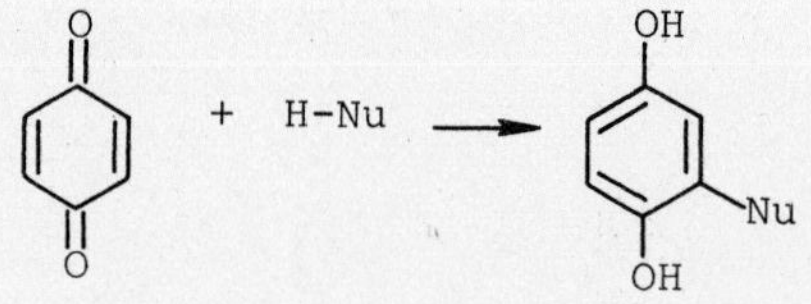

Key features: if Nu is electron-releasing, hydroquinone product is oxidized by quinone starting
               material

26.D   Answers to Exercises

26.1

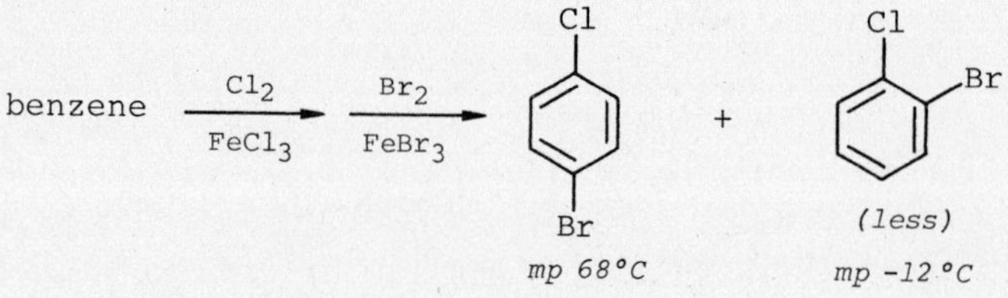

benzene $\xrightarrow[\text{FeCl}_3]{\text{Cl}_2}$ $\xrightarrow[\text{FeBr}_3]{\text{Br}_2}$ +   separate *para* by
                                                                                              crystallization

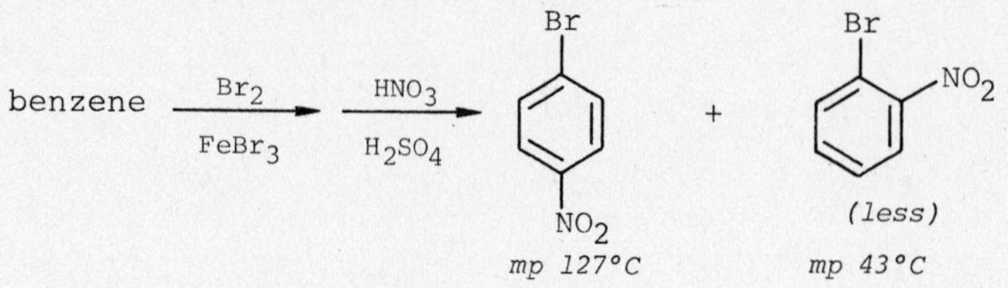

mp 68°C   (less)
                 mp –12°C

benzene $\xrightarrow[\text{FeBr}_3]{\text{Br}_2}$ $\xrightarrow[\text{H}_2\text{SO}_4]{\text{HNO}_3}$ +   separate *para* by
                                                                                                         crystallization

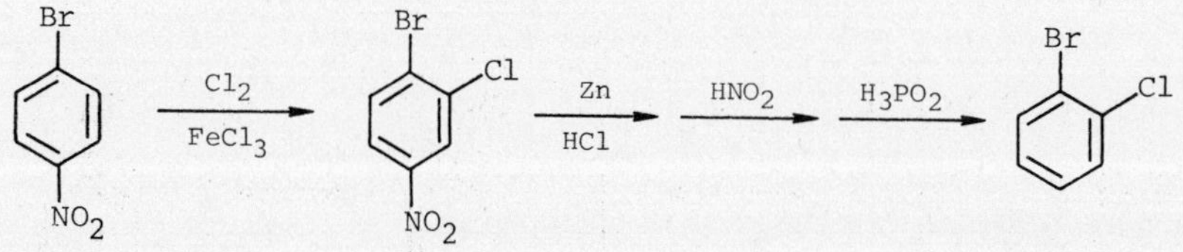

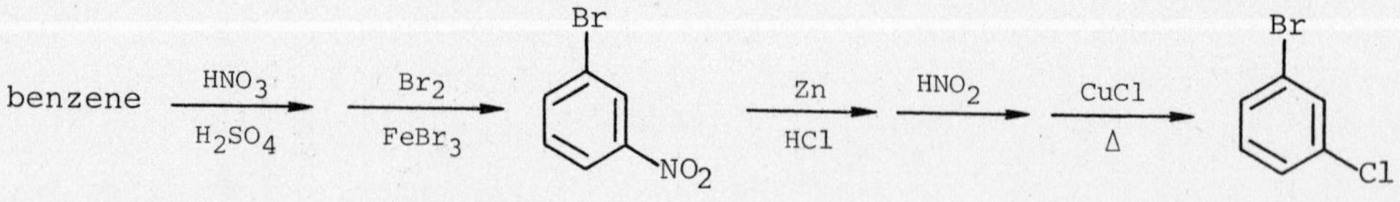

mp 127°C   (less)
                 mp 43°C

$\xrightarrow[\text{FeCl}_3]{\text{Cl}_2}$ $\xrightarrow[\text{HCl}]{\text{Zn}}$ $\xrightarrow{\text{HNO}_2}$ $\xrightarrow{\text{H}_3\text{PO}_2}$

benzene $\xrightarrow[\text{H}_2\text{SO}_4]{\text{HNO}_3}$ $\xrightarrow[\text{FeBr}_3]{\text{Br}_2}$ $\xrightarrow[\text{HCl}]{\text{Zn}}$ $\xrightarrow{\text{HNO}_2}$ $\xrightarrow[\Delta]{\text{CuCl}}$

26.2

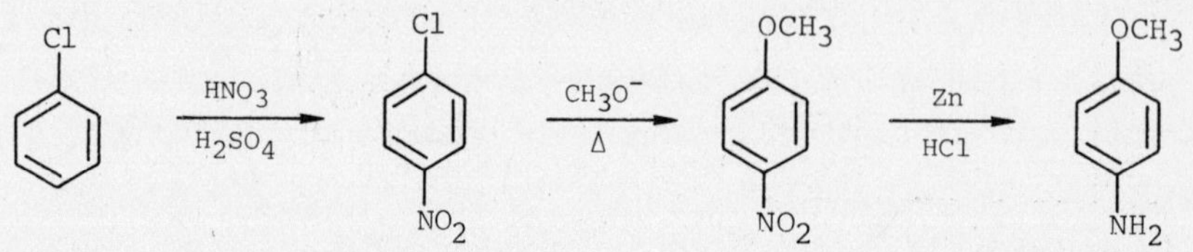

$\xrightarrow[\text{H}_2\text{SO}_4]{\text{HNO}_3}$ $\xrightarrow[\Delta]{\text{CH}_3\text{O}^-}$ $\xrightarrow[\text{HCl}]{\text{Zn}}$

26.3

$\xrightarrow[\text{NH}_3]{\text{KNH}_2}$ $\longrightarrow$ +

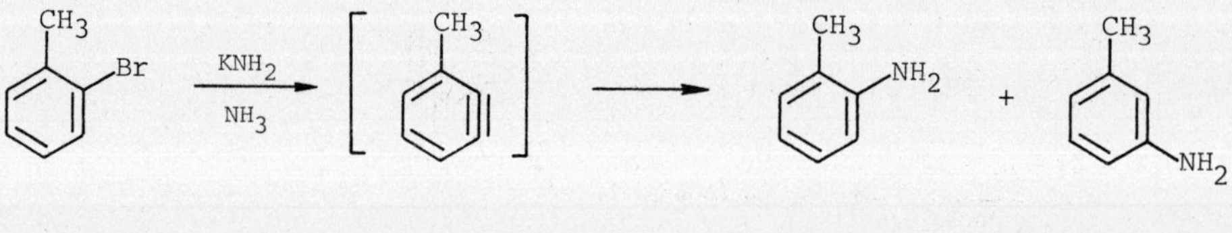

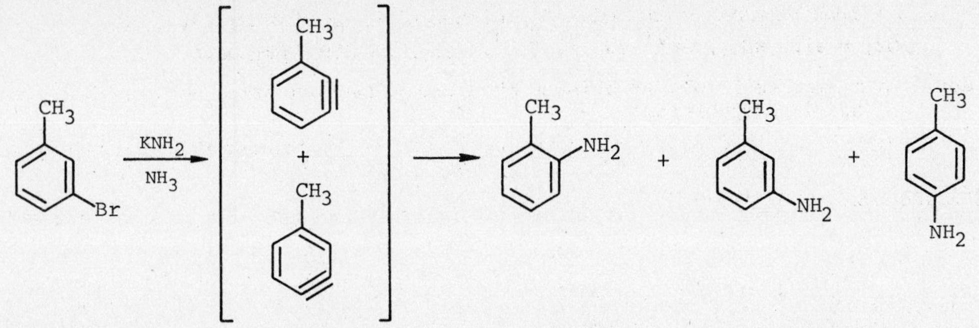

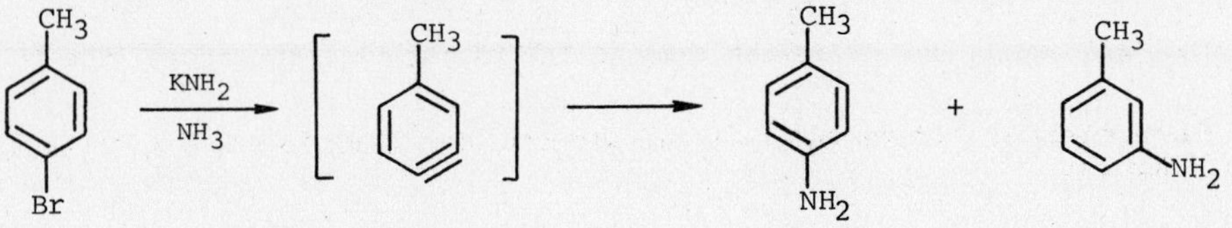

KNH_2 / NH_3

26.4

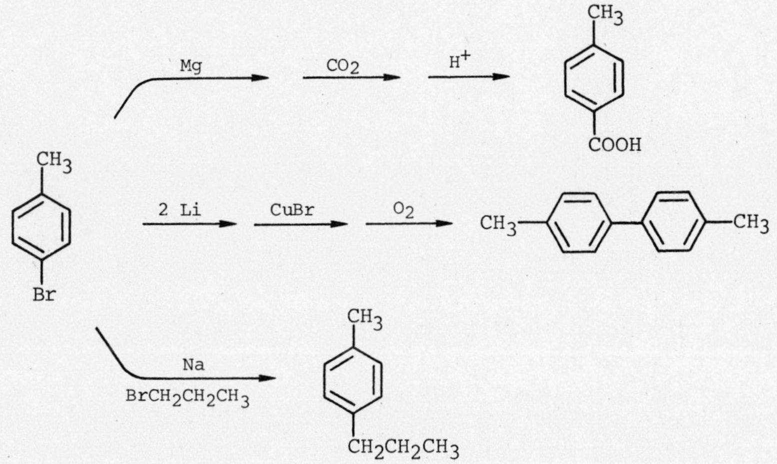

Mg CO_2 H^+

$2\ Li$ $CuBr$ O_2

Na / $BrCH_2CH_2CH_3$

26.5

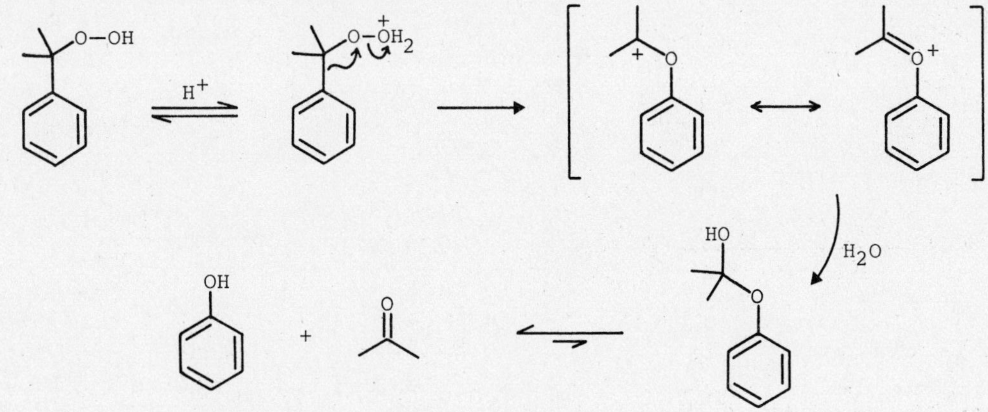

H^+

H_2O

26.6

benzene

HNO_3 Zn / HCl HNO_2 H_2O / Δ

Cl_2 / $FeCl_3$ $NaOH$ / Δ

H_2SO_4 $NaOH$ / Δ

$CH_3CH=CH_2$ / H_2SO_4 O_2 H_2SO_4

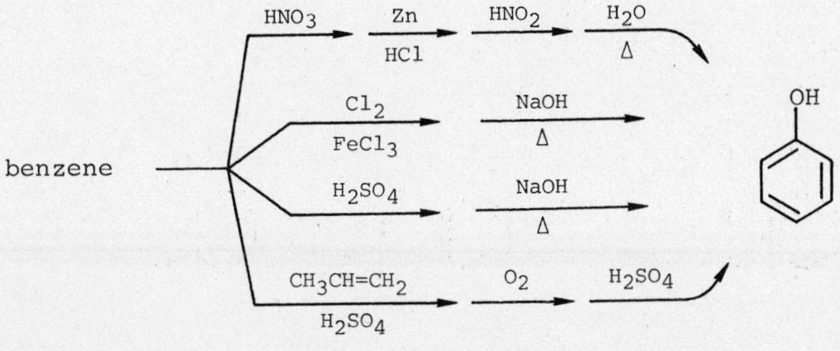

26.7 Because the acidity of phenols and anilinium ions is concerned with the loss of a proton from a hetero atom attached to an aromatic ring, similar substituent effects are seen in both cases.

26.8

$$pK_a \text{ of phenol} = 10.0 ; \quad \text{so that} \quad K = \frac{[C_6H_5O^-][H^+]}{[C_6H_5OH]} = 10^{-10}$$

Assuming that a negligible amount of the phenol ionizes, and that all protons arise from the ionization of phenol:

$$[C_6H_5O^-] = [H^+], \text{ and } [C_6H_5OH] = 0.1, \quad \text{so that} \quad K = \frac{[H^+]^2}{0.1} = 10^{-10}$$

Therefore $[H^+] = 3.16 \times 10^{-6}$ M ; $pK_a = 5.5$

When [HA] and [A⁻] are equal, the pH is the same as the pK_a of HA. Therefore, the pH is 10.0.

26.9 $C_6H_5OH + BrCH_2CH=CH_2 + NaOH \longrightarrow C_6H_5OCH_2CH=CH_2 + NaBr + H_2O$

26.10

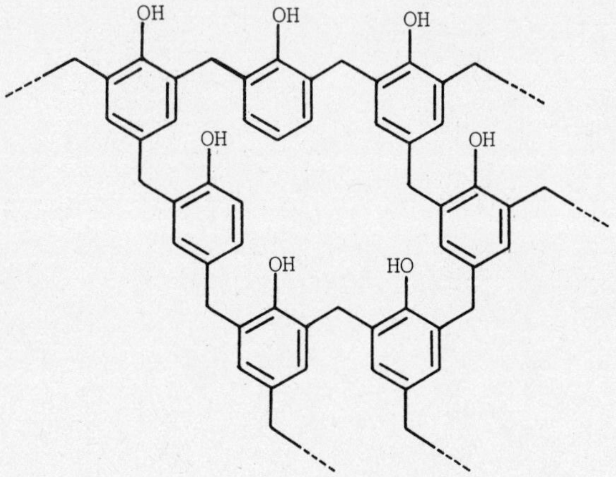

26.11 The hydrolysis reaction involves an elimination-addition mechanism which is not possible for the non-aromatic p-product:

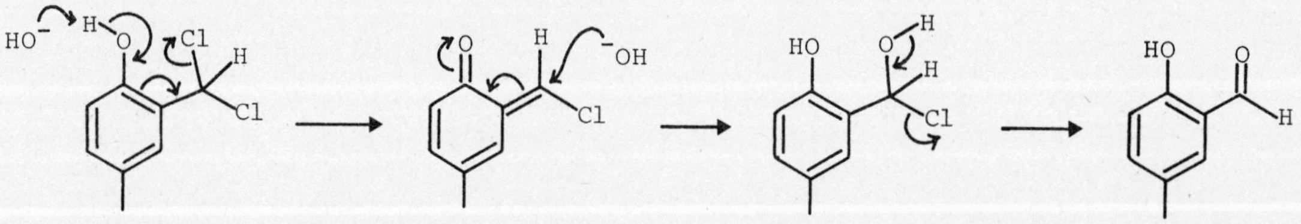

26.12

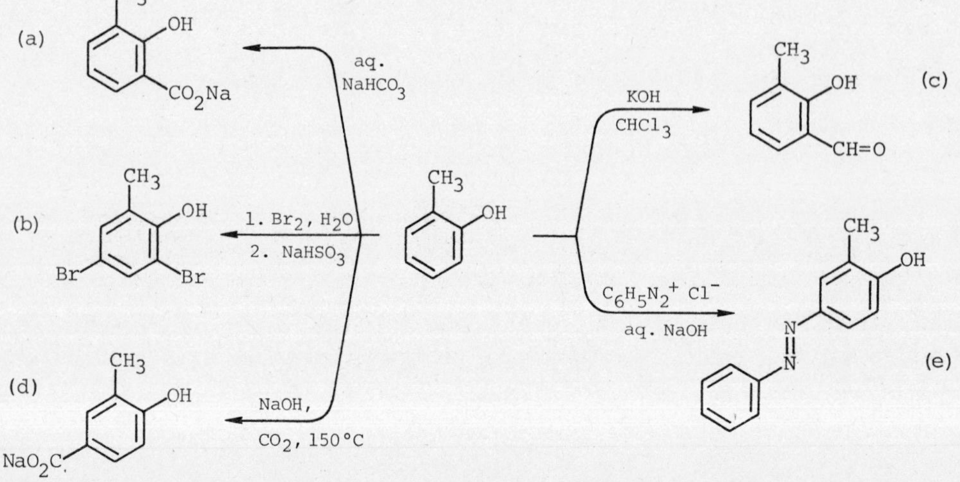

26.13 The p-isomer has hydrogen bonds between the hydroxyl group of one molecule and the ketone of another molecule. In contrast, the o-isomer can form intramolecular hydrogen bonds, and is therefore more volatile.

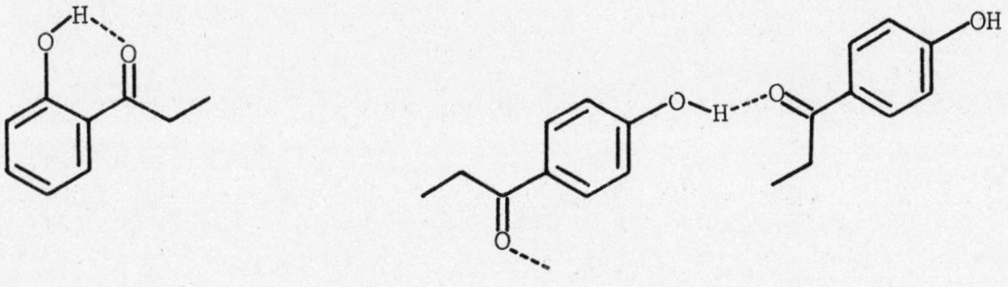

26.14

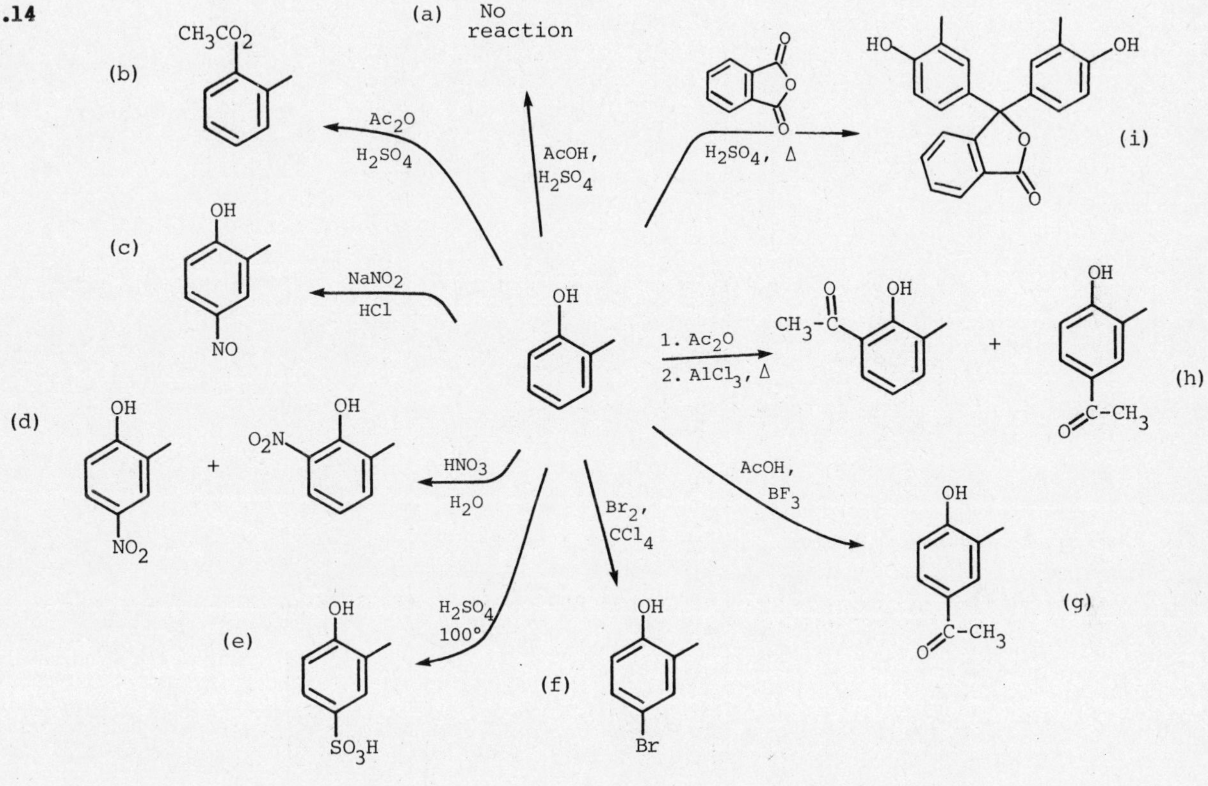

(a) No reaction

(b)

(c)

(d)

(e)

(f)

(g)

(h)

(i)

26.15

(a)

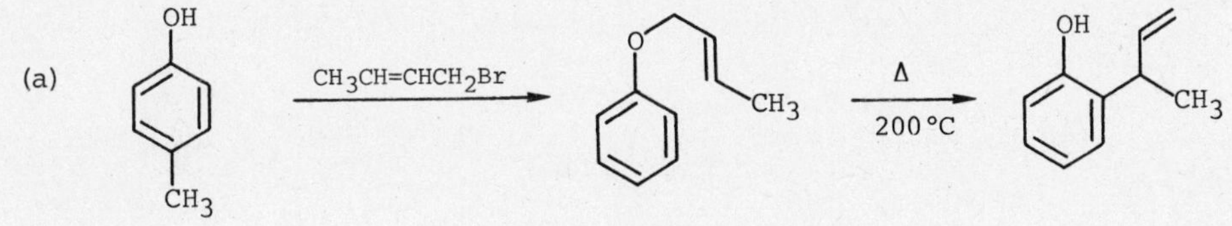

(b)

major product

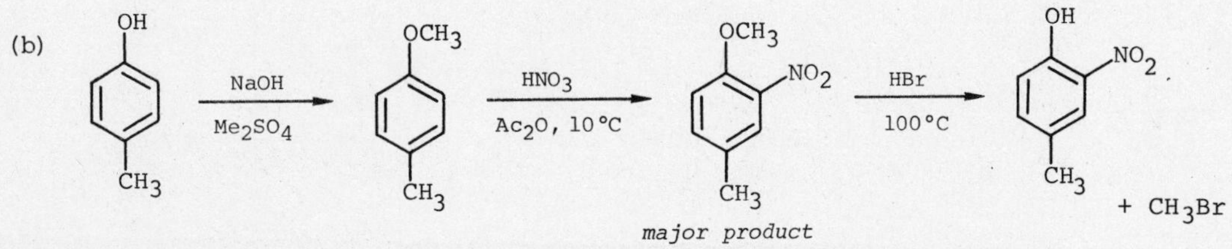

26.16

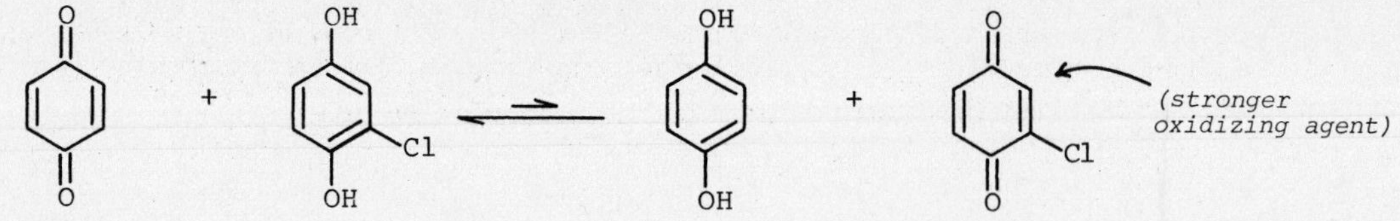

Reduction
potentials: 0.699   0.713

cell potential will be $E^{\circ}_1 - E^{\circ}_2$
= 0.014 volt

26.17

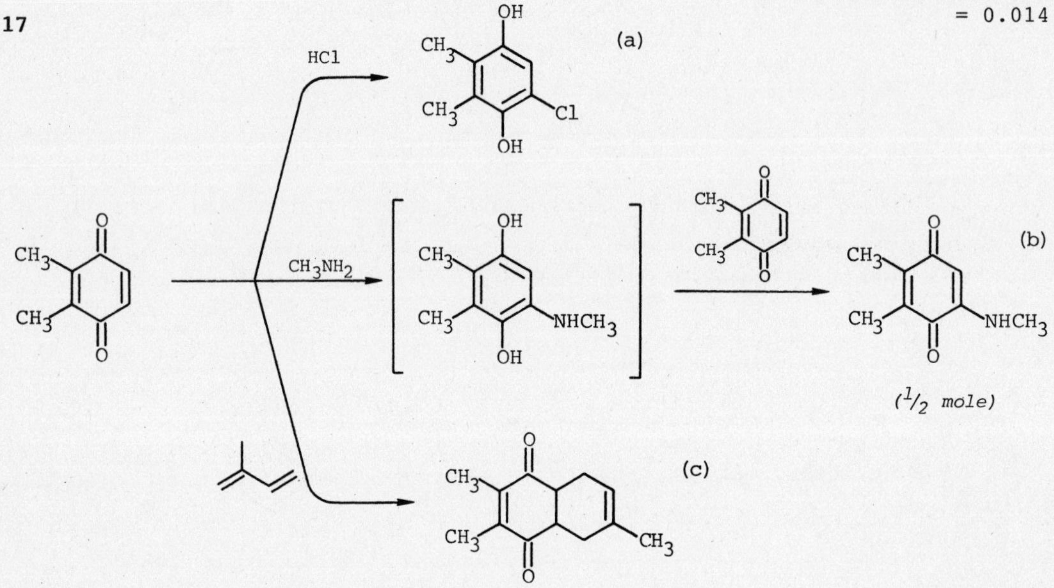

(a)

(b)

($1/2$ mole)

(c)

26.E   Answers and Explanations for Problems

1.   (a)   (b)   (c)   (d)

(e)   (f)   (g)

(h)   (i)   (j)

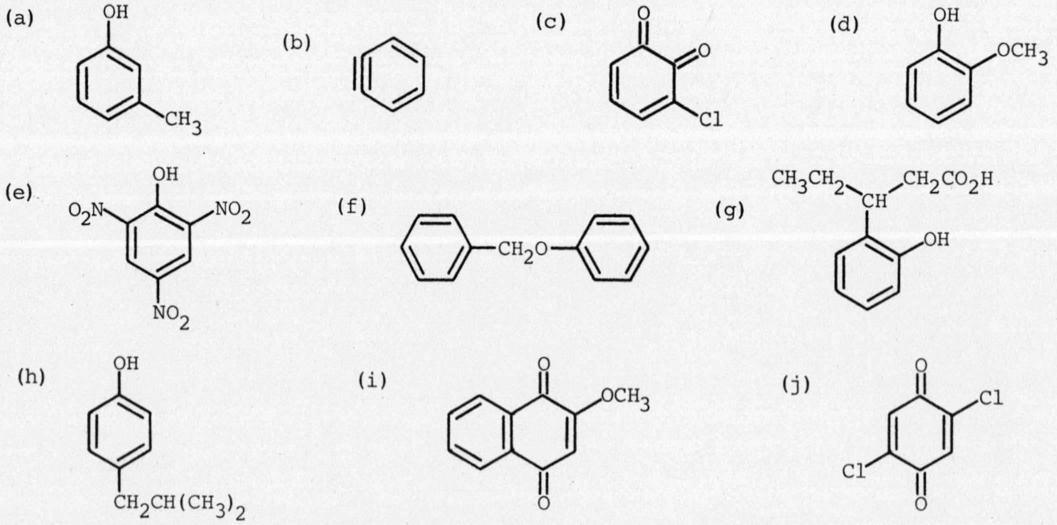

2.

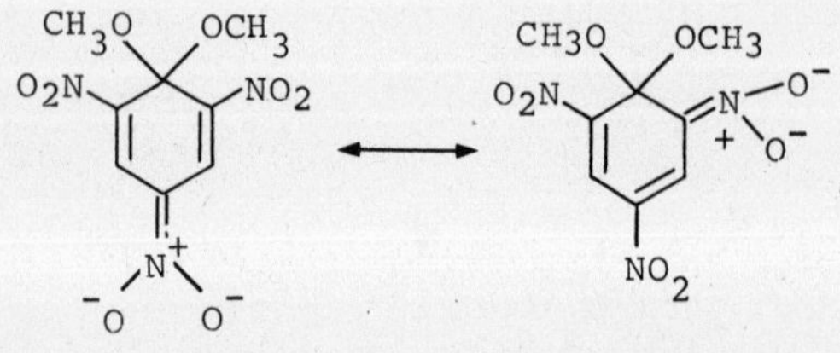

, etc.   *many structures
can be written*

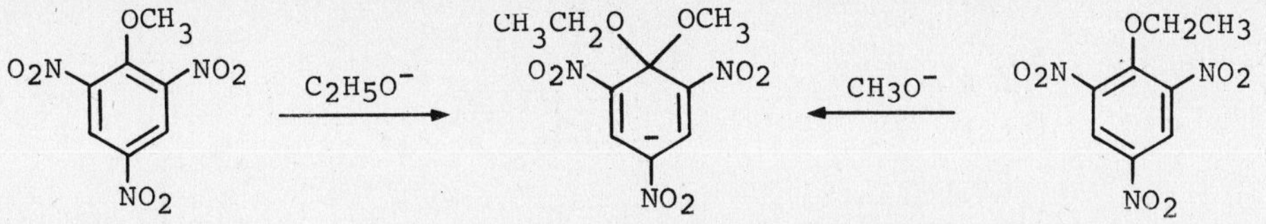

(same compound from either route)

3.

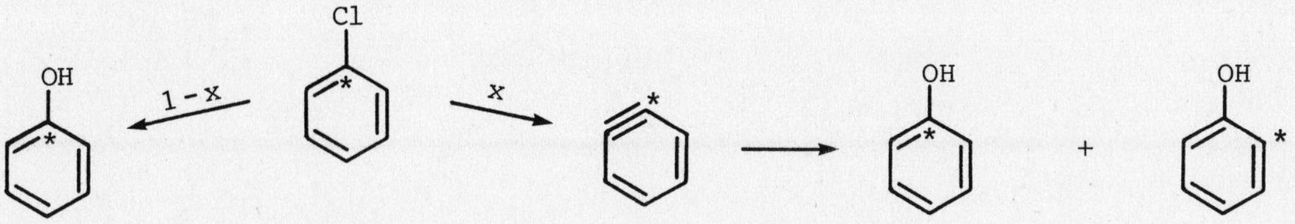

Let x = fraction that proceeds via the benzyne intermediate
Percent of label in the 2-position = 100(x/2) = 42% ; therefore, x = 0.84
Only 16% proceeds via normal nucleophilic substitution

4.   (a)   (b) 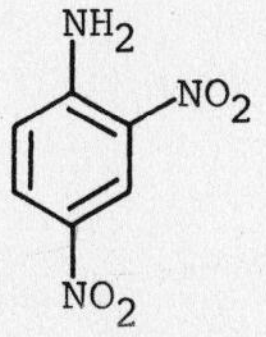   (c) 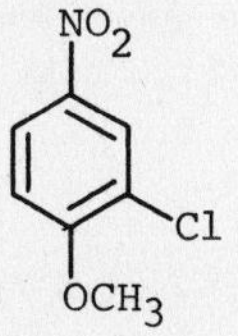   (d)

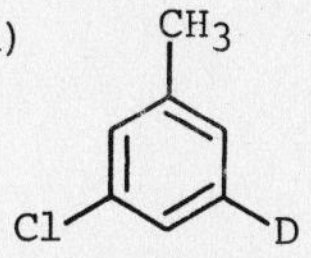

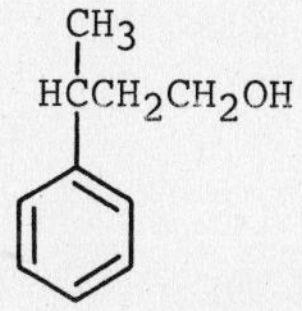

5.
(a)   (b) no reaction

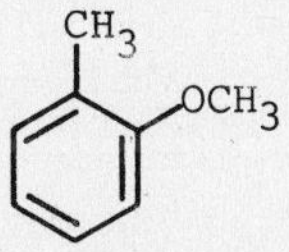

             (c) no reaction

             (d)   (e)

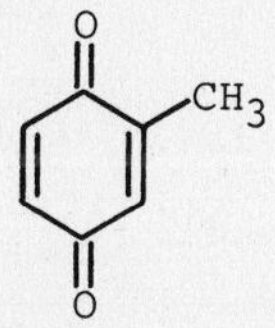

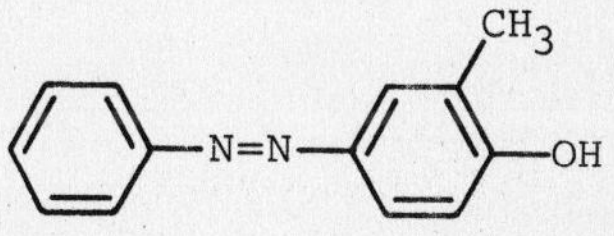

(f) no reaction

(h)

(g) no reaction   +   (i) CH_3CO_2H + CO_2 + H_2O

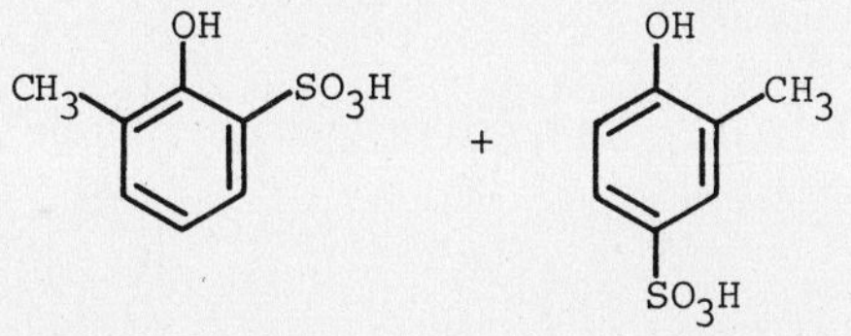

(j)   +   (k) 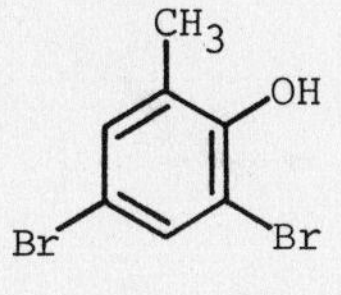   (l)

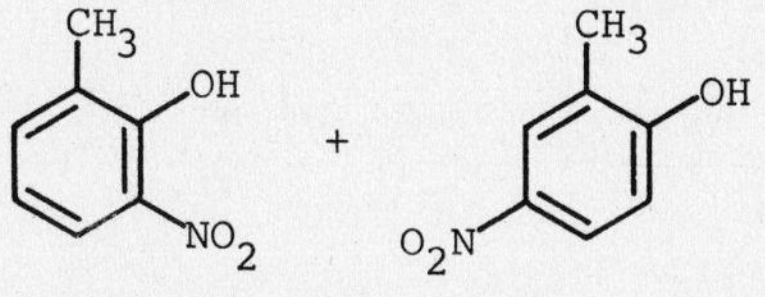

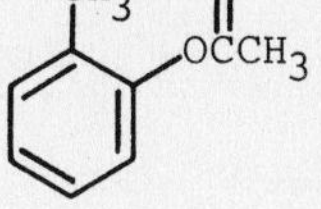

(m) 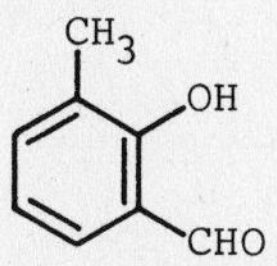   (n) 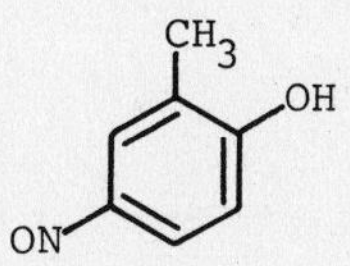   (o) 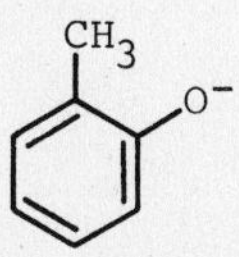   (p)

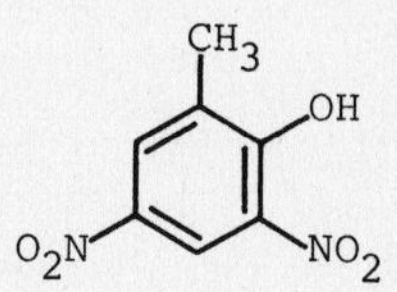

(q)   no reaction   (r)   (s)

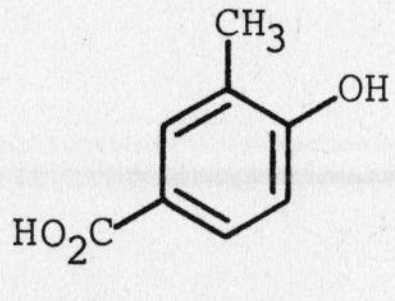

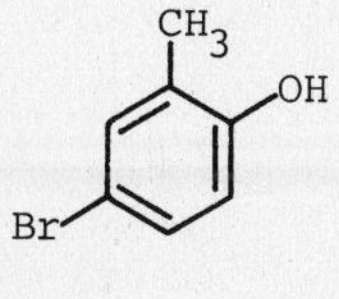

6.

(a) no reaction

(b) 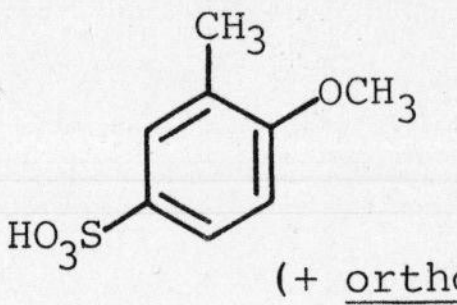

(+ ortho)

(c) 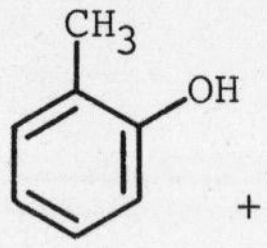

+ CH_3Br

(d) 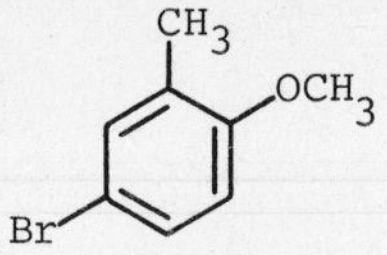

(e) 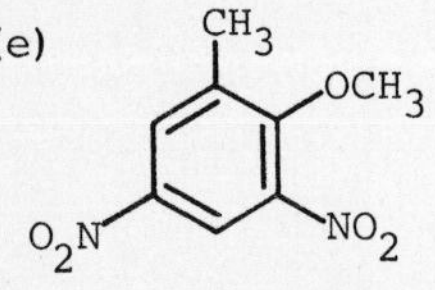

(f) no reaction

(g) no reaction

(h) 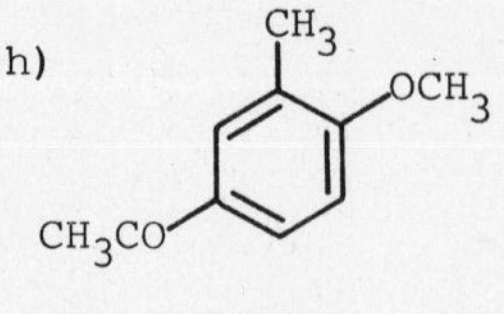

(i) 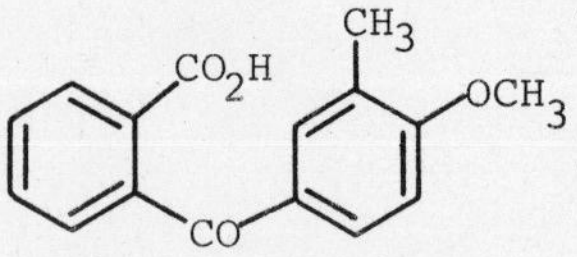

(j) From the following analogies:

the expected reaction would be:

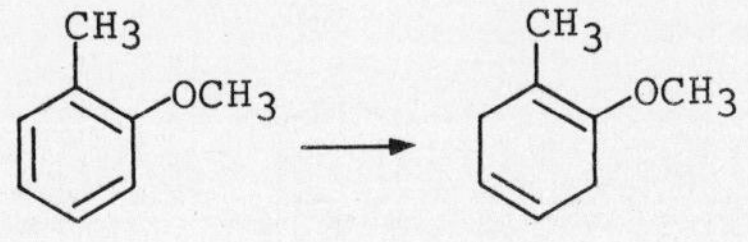

7.

(a) 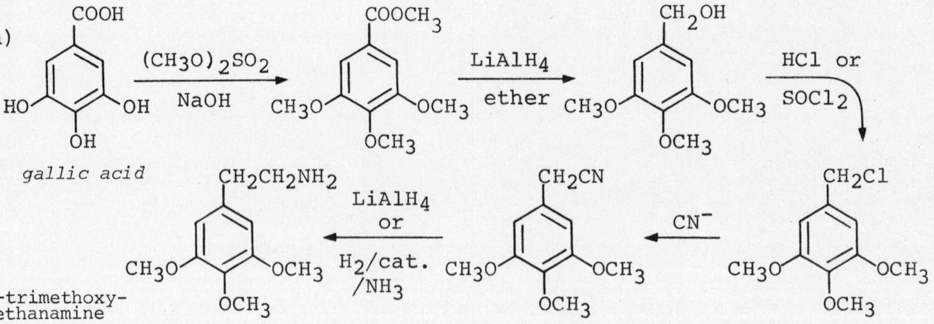

gallic acid

2-(3,4,5-trimethoxyphenyl)ethanamine

(b) 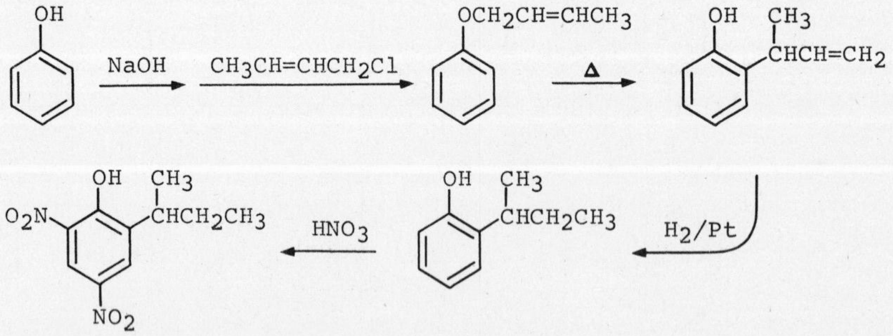

2-(1-methylpropyl)-4,6-dinitrophenol

(c) 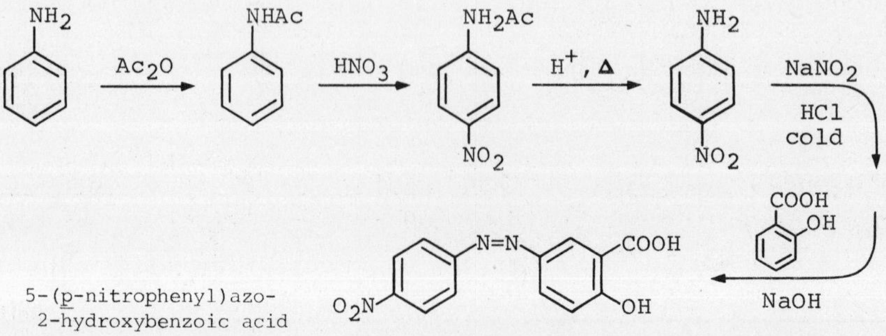

5-(p-nitrophenyl)azo-2-hydroxybenzoic acid

(d)

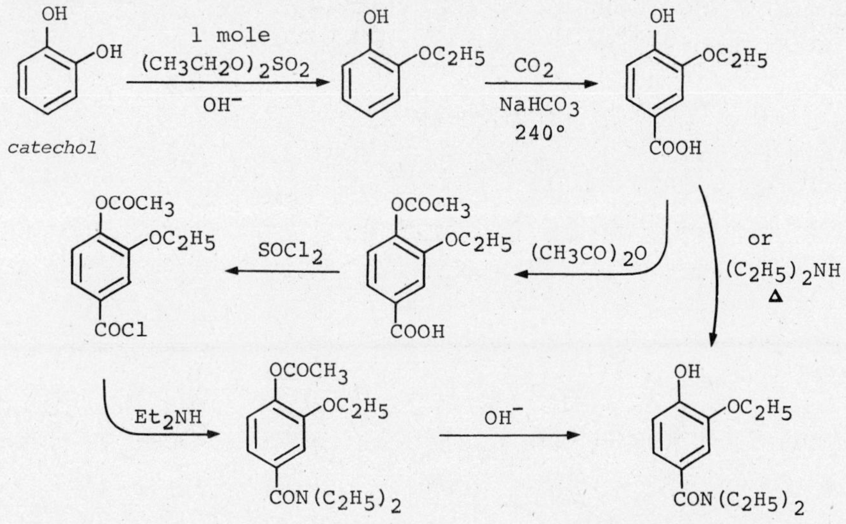

catechol

$\xrightarrow[\text{OH}^-]{\begin{array}{c}\text{1 mole}\\(CH_3CH_2O)_2SO_2\end{array}}$

$\xrightarrow[\begin{array}{c}NaHCO_3\\240°\end{array}]{CO_2}$

(3-ethoxy-4-hydroxybenzoic acid)

$\xrightarrow{(CH_3CO)_2O}$

$\xrightarrow{SOCl_2}$

$\xrightarrow{Et_2NH}$

$\xrightarrow{OH^-}$

or $\xrightarrow[\Delta]{(C_2H_5)_2NH}$

3-ethoxy-N,N-diethyl-
4-hydroxybenzamide

(e)

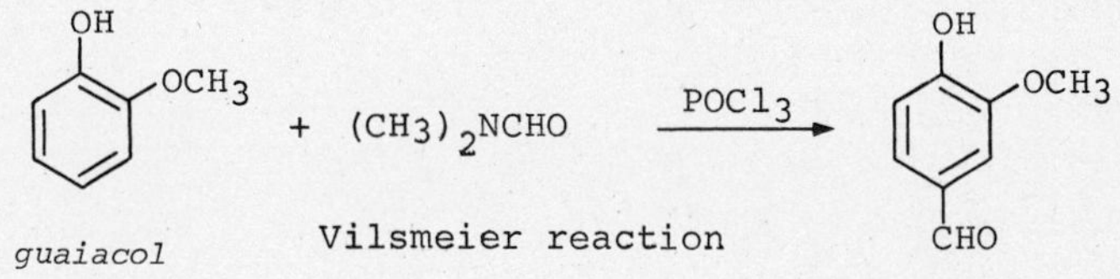

guaiacol + $(CH_3)_2NCHO$

Vilsmeier reaction

$\xrightarrow{POCl_3}$

4-hydroxy-3-methoxybenzaldehyde

(f)

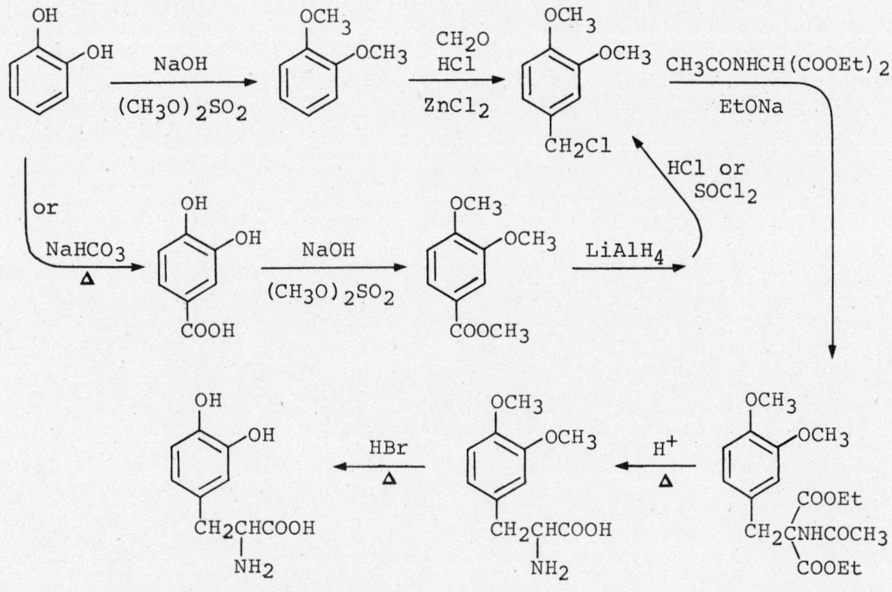

$\xrightarrow[(CH_3O)_2SO_2]{NaOH}$

$\xrightarrow[ZnCl_2]{\begin{array}{c}CH_2O\\HCl\end{array}}$

$\xrightarrow[EtONa]{CH_3CONHCH(COOEt)_2}$

or $\xrightarrow[\Delta]{NaHCO_3}$

$\xrightarrow[(CH_3O)_2SO_2]{NaOH}$

$\xrightarrow{LiAlH_4}$

$\xleftarrow{\begin{array}{c}HCl\ or\\SOCl_2\end{array}}$

$\xrightarrow[\Delta]{H^+}$

$\xrightarrow[\Delta]{HBr}$

2-amino-3-(3,4-dihydroxy-
phenyl)propanoic acid

(g)

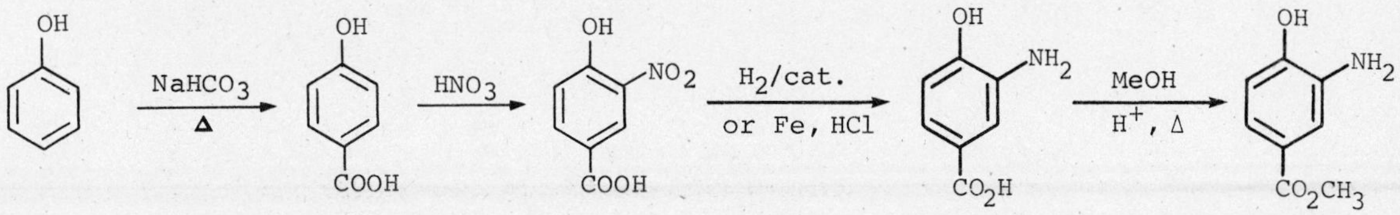

$\xrightarrow[\Delta]{NaHCO_3}$

$\xrightarrow{HNO_3}$

$\xrightarrow[\text{or Fe, HCl}]{H_2/cat.}$

$\xrightarrow[H^+, \Delta]{MeOH}$

methyl 3-amino-4-
hydroxybenzoate

8.

(a) OCH$_3$ / OCH$_3$ $\xrightarrow[\Delta]{HBr}$ OH / OH $\xrightarrow[\substack{ether \\ Na_2SO_4}]{Ag_2O}$ (o-benzoquinone)

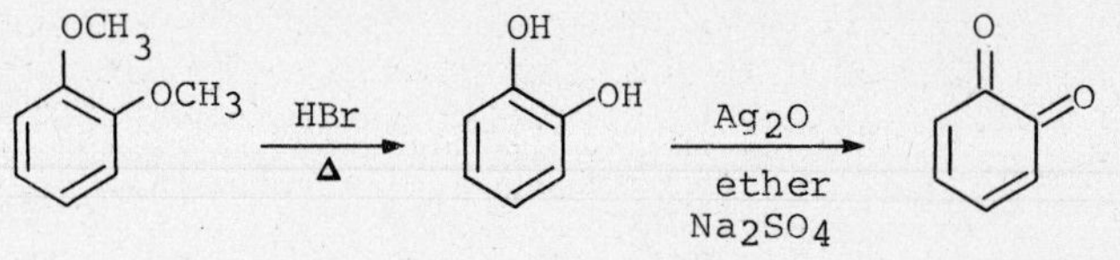

(b) phenol (CH$_3$) $\xrightarrow{NaOH \quad CH_3CH=CHCH_2Cl}$ OCH$_2$CH=CHCH$_3$ (CH$_3$) $\xrightarrow{\Delta}$ OH / CH=CH$_2$ CHCH$_3$ (CH$_3$) $\xrightarrow{H_2/Pt}$ OH / CH$_2$CH$_3$ CHCH$_3$ (CH$_3$)

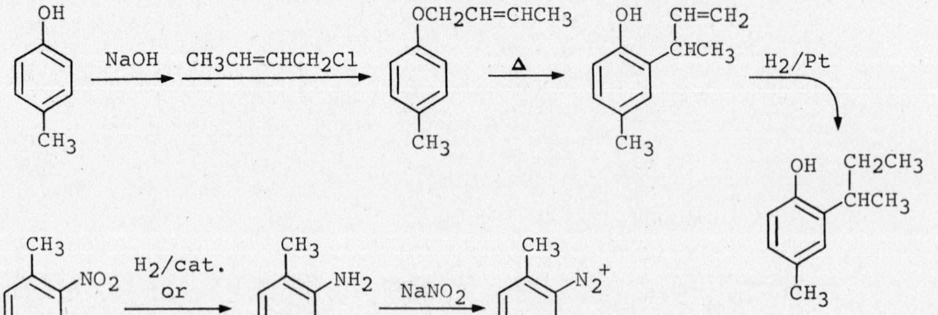

(c) CH$_3$ / NO$_2$ $\xrightarrow[Fe,HCl]{\substack{H_2/cat. \\ or}}$ CH$_3$ / NH$_2$ $\xrightarrow[\substack{H_2SO_4 \\ cold}]{NaNO_2}$ CH$_3$ / N$_2^+$ $\xrightarrow[H_2O]{\Delta}$ CH$_3$ / OH

CH$_3$ —N=N— CH$_3$ / OH $\xleftarrow{OH^-}$

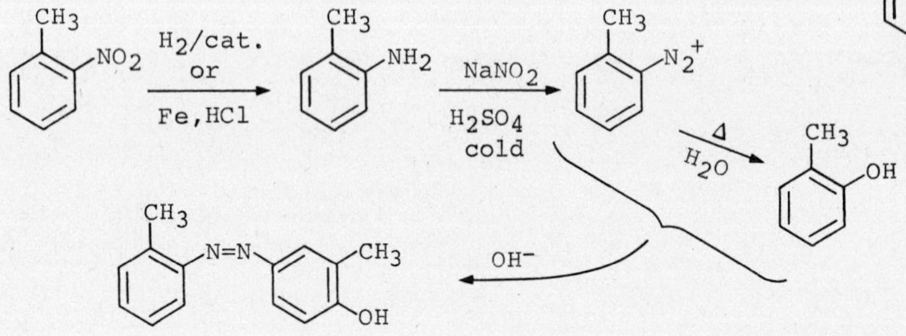

(d) CH$_3$ / CH$_3$ $\xrightarrow{H_2SO_4}$ CH$_3$ / CH$_3$ / SO$_3$H $\xrightarrow[fuse]{NaOH}$ CH$_3$ / CH$_3$ / OH $\xrightarrow[OH^-]{CHCl_3}$ CH$_3$ / CH$_3$ / OHC / OH

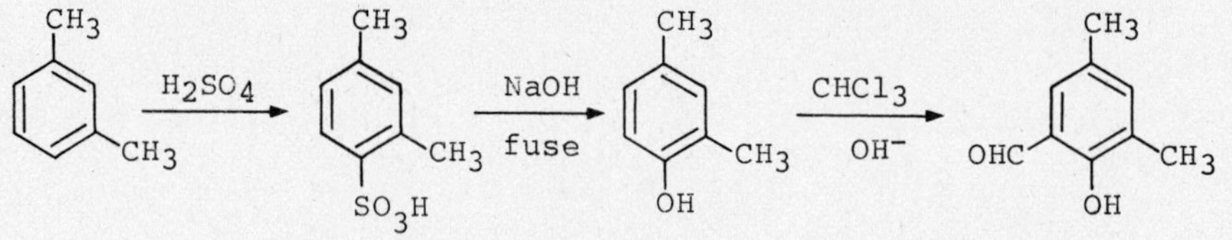

(e) OH $\xrightarrow{(CH_3CH_2CO)_2O}$ OCOCH$_2$CH$_3$ $\xrightarrow[\Delta]{AlCl_3}$ OH / COCH$_2$CH$_3$ $\xrightarrow[\substack{glycol \\ \Delta}]{\substack{H_2NNH_2 \\ KOH}}$ OH / CH$_2$CH$_2$CH$_3$ $\xrightarrow[(CH_3)_2SO_4]{NaOH}$ OCH$_3$ / CH$_2$CH$_2$CH$_3$

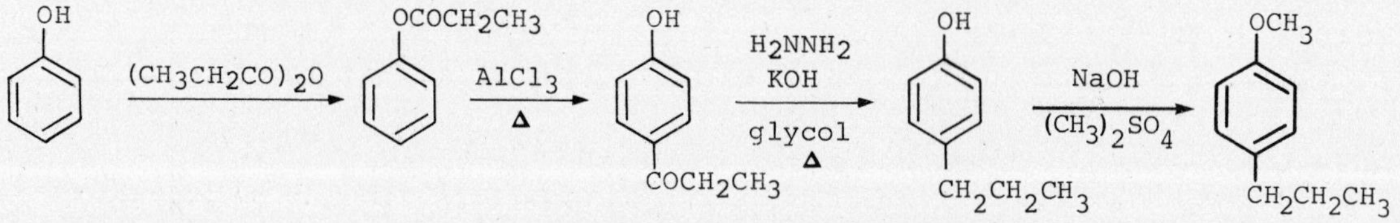

9.

(a) C$_6$H$_5$CH=CHCH$_2$Cl $\longrightarrow$ C$_6$H$_5$CH=CHCH$_2$O— $\longrightarrow$ OH / CH=CH$_2$ CH —phenyl

(b) OH / NH$_2$ (naphthalene) $\longrightarrow$ (naphthoquinone, O, O) $\longrightarrow$ OCOCH$_3$ / OCOCH$_3$ / OCOCH$_3$

(c) (structure with O) $\xrightarrow[rearrang.]{Claisen}$ (CH$_3$)$_2$C CH$_2$CHO / CH=CH$_2$ $\xrightarrow[rxn]{Wittig}$ (CH$_3$)$_2$C CH$_2$CH=CH$_2$ / CH=CH$_2$

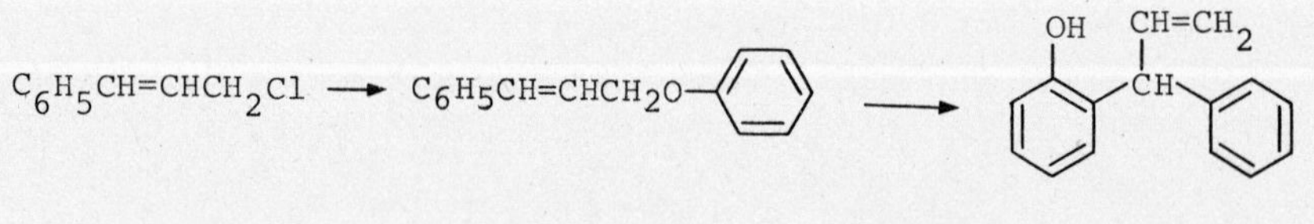

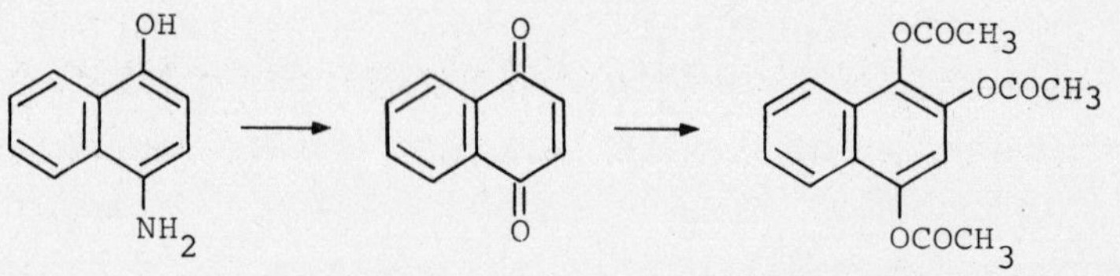

(CH$_3$)$_2$C=CHCH$_2$CH$_2$CH=CH$_2$ $\xleftarrow[rearrangement]{Cope}$

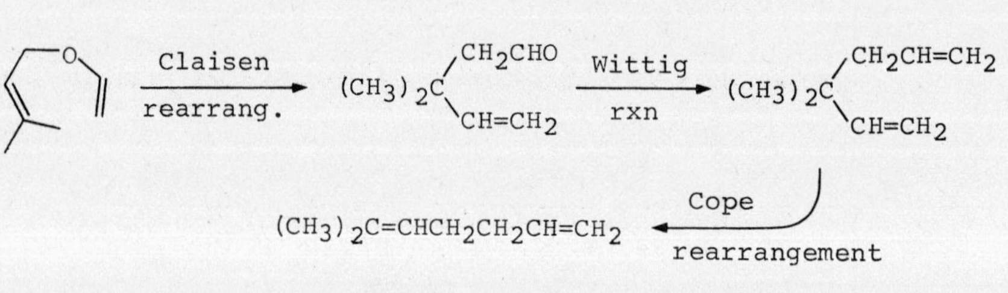

(d)

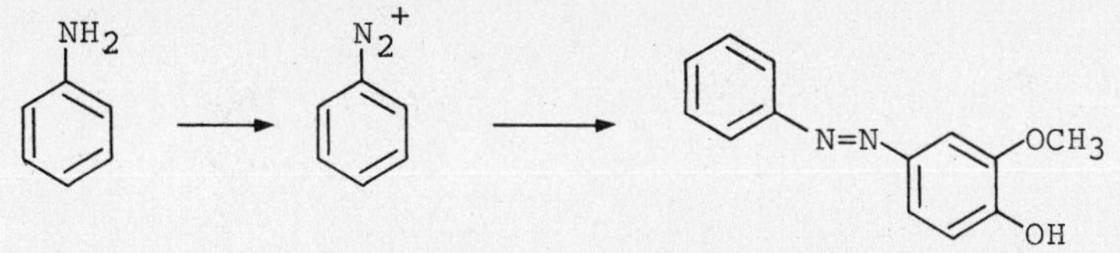

(e)

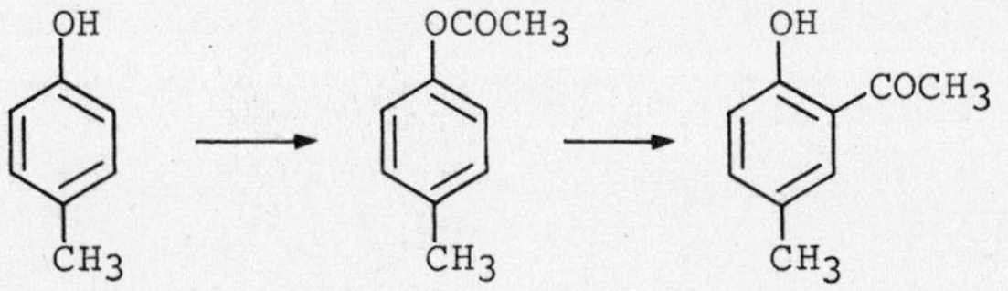

10.

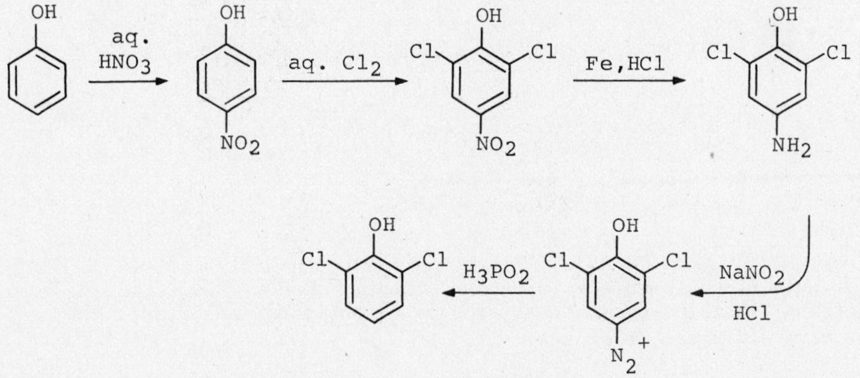

11.

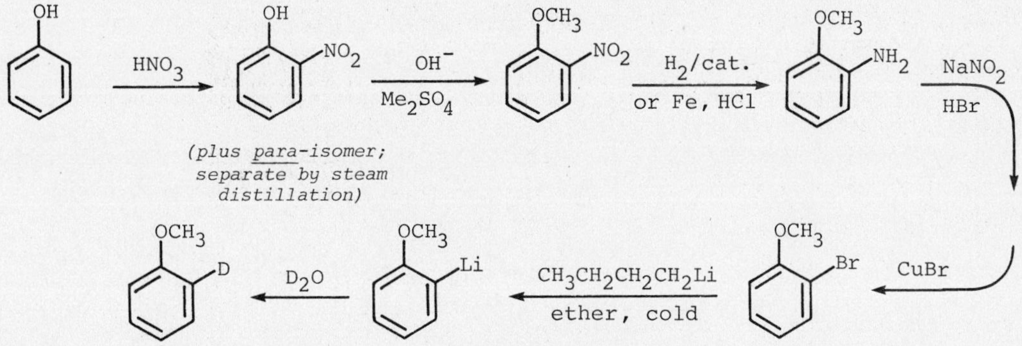

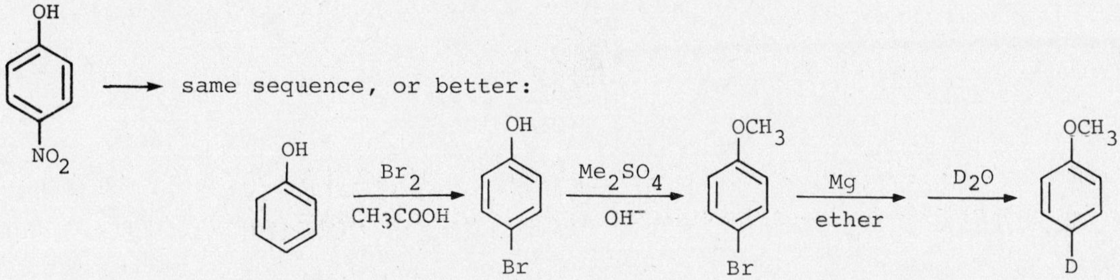

(plus *para*-isomer;
separate by steam
distillation)

$CH_3CH_2CH_2CH_2Li$
ether, cold

CuBr

same sequence, or better:

$\dfrac{Br_2}{CH_3COOH}$ $\dfrac{Me_2SO_4}{OH^-}$ $\dfrac{Mg}{ether}$ D_2O

Actually, anisole itself can be metallated to give a far simpler sequence for obtaining
the *ortho*-deuterated compound:

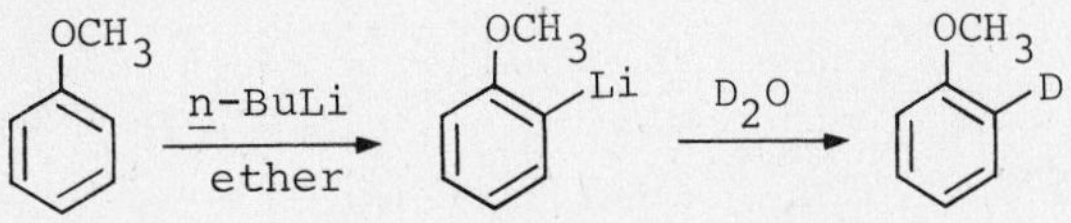

$\dfrac{n\text{-BuLi}}{ether}$ $\xrightarrow{D_2O}$

The only problem with this sequence is that it is difficult to accomplish complete metallation. Thus,
the final deuterioanisole is accompanied by undeuterated anisole which cannot be separated. For many
purposes, a partially deuterated compound will suffice. This procedure can be applied without problems
for tracer-labeled anisole-2-t.

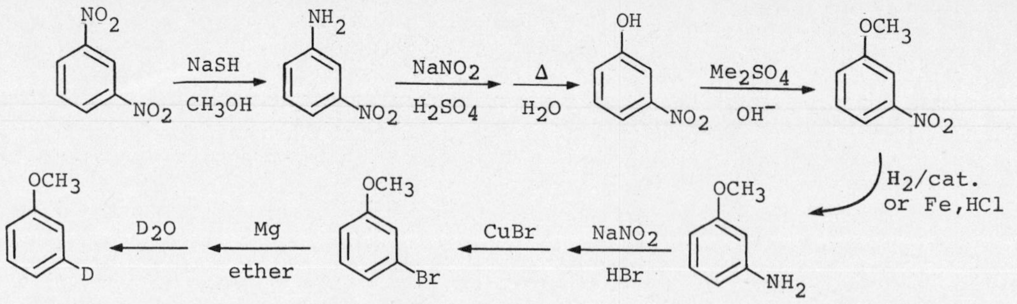

12.

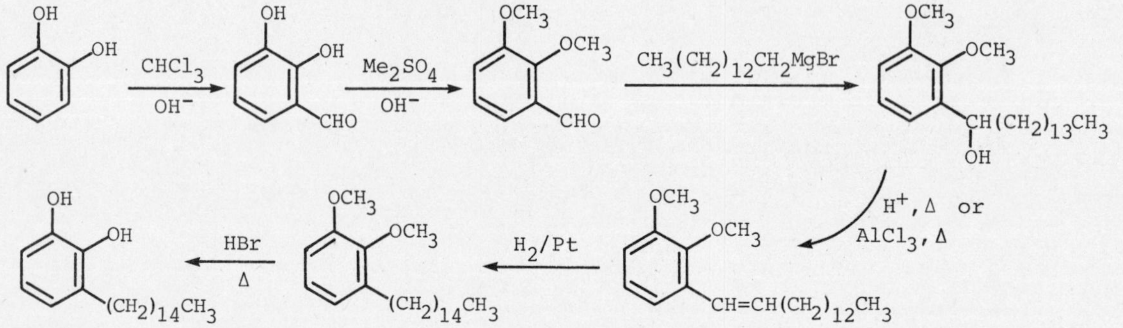

13. Benzyl alcohol is only slightly more acidic than ethanol; hence, a solution of potassium benzyloxide in ethanol contains substantial amounts of potassium ethoxide. Both can undergo S_N2 reactions to give a mixture of ethers:

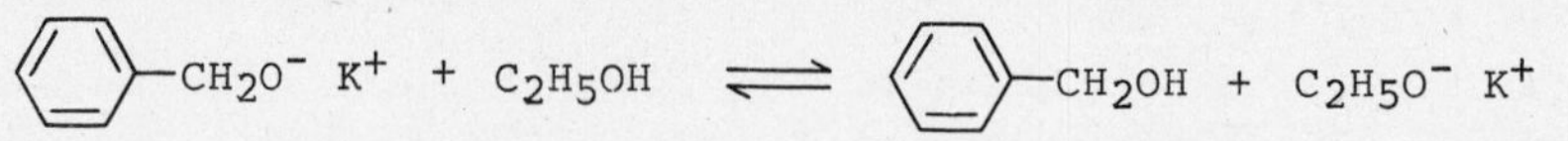

$$\text{C}_6\text{H}_5\text{—CH}_2\text{O}^-\ \text{K}^+ + \text{C}_2\text{H}_5\text{OH} \rightleftharpoons \text{C}_6\text{H}_5\text{—CH}_2\text{OH} + \text{C}_2\text{H}_5\text{O}^-\ \text{K}^+$$

p-Cresol, however, is much more acidic than ethanol. A solution of potassium p-methyl-phenolate in ethanol contains very little potassium ethoxide.

$$\text{CH}_3\text{—C}_6\text{H}_4\text{—O}^-\ \text{K}^+ + \text{C}_2\text{H}_5\text{OH} \longleftarrow \text{CH}_3\text{—C}_6\text{H}_4\text{—OH} + \text{C}_2\text{H}_5\text{O}^-\ \text{K}^+$$

14.

$$\underline{or} \qquad separate\ from\ \underline{ortho-}$$

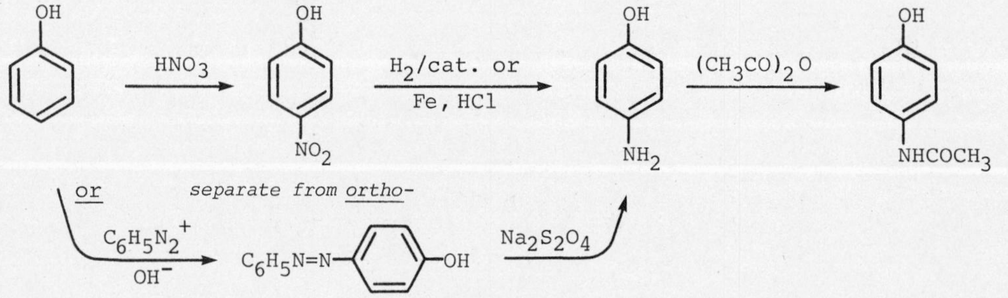

15.

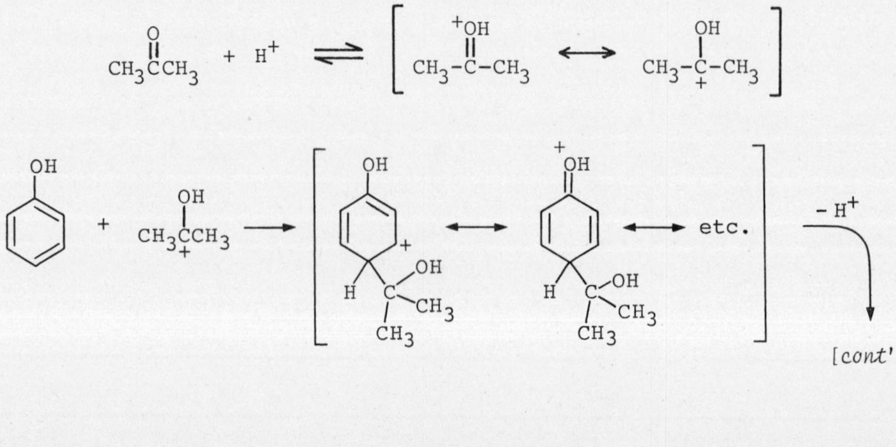

[cont'd on next page]

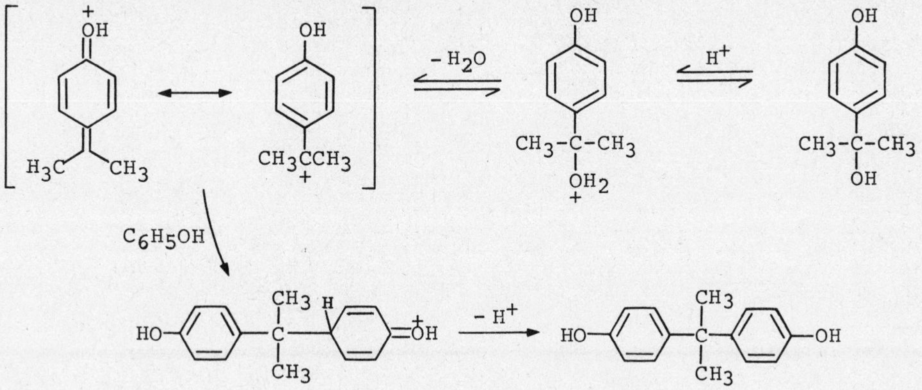

16. Yes. SO_3H is a bulky group and goes <u>ortho</u> to the smaller CH_3 group rather than to the larger $(CH_3)_2CH$ group.

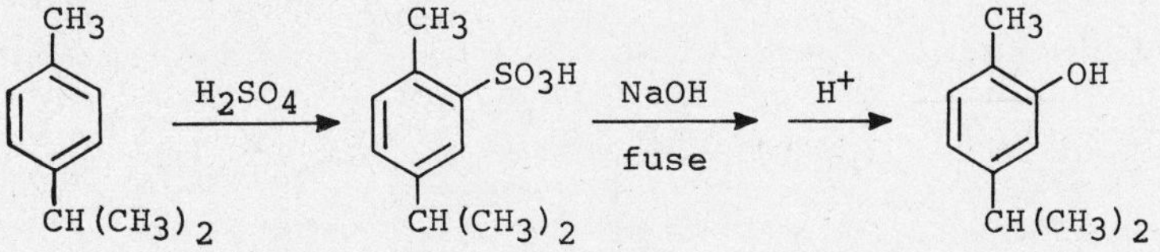

carvacrol

17. 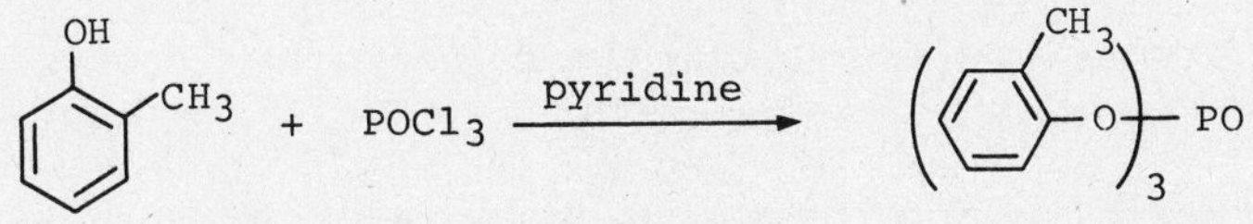

18. (a)

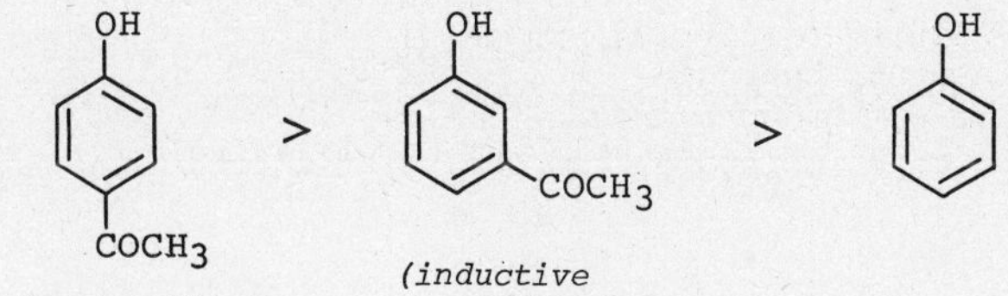

(conjugation) *(inductive effect)*

(b)

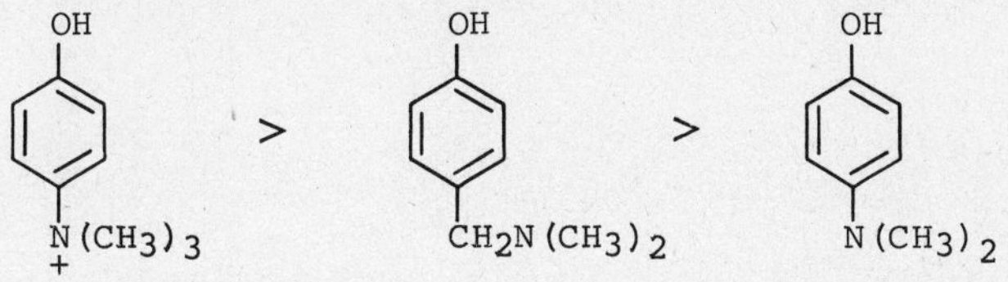

(inductive effect) *(electron-donating group)*

(c)

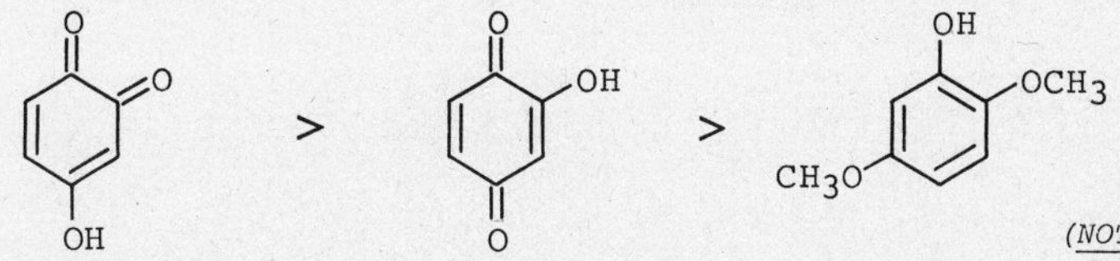

(*NOTE:* the two quinones give the same anion, but the *ortho*-quinone is less stable; thus, it is more acidic.)

19. Oxidation of a phenol gives the quinone.

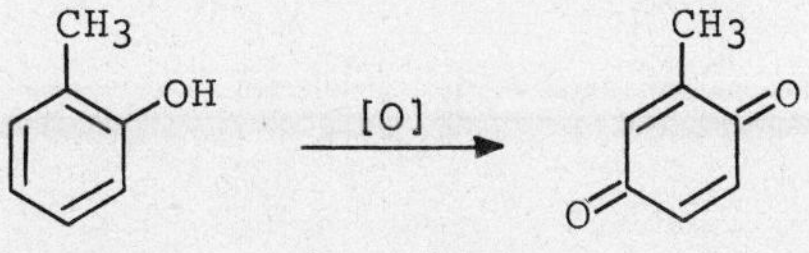

20.

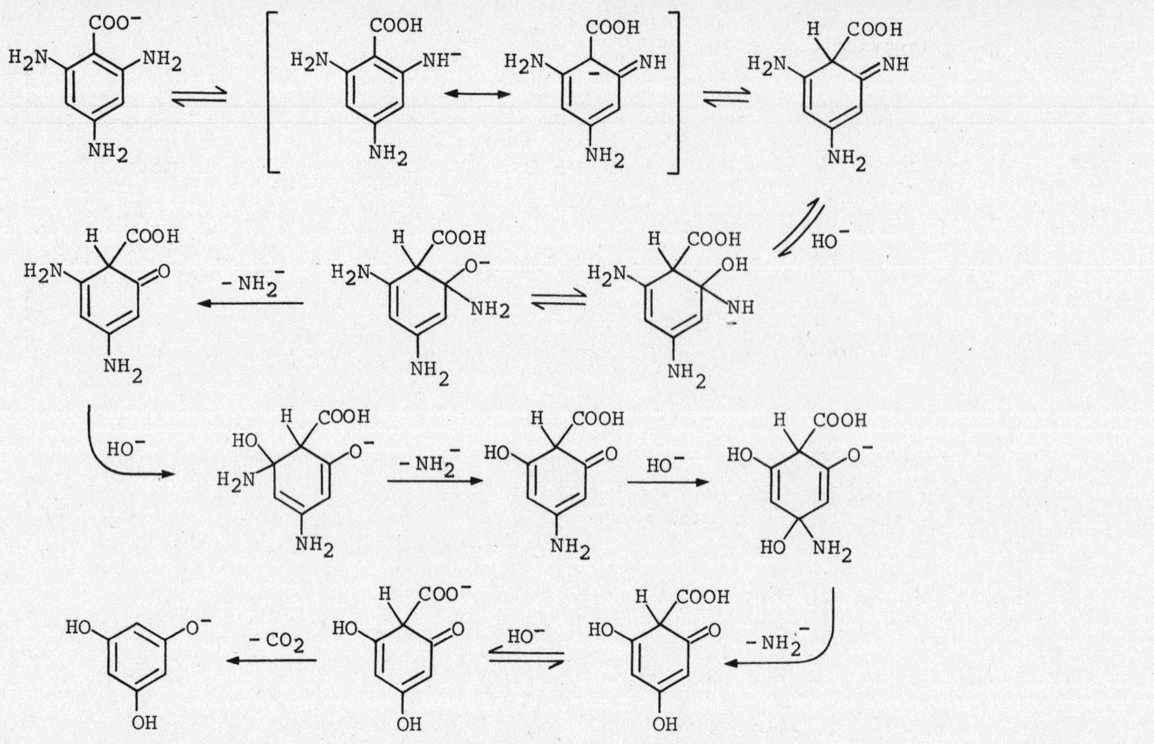

NOTE: this mechanism has many possibilities which depend on the timing of the steps for decarboxylation and hydrolysis of ammonia groups.

21.   Internal hydrogen-bonding:

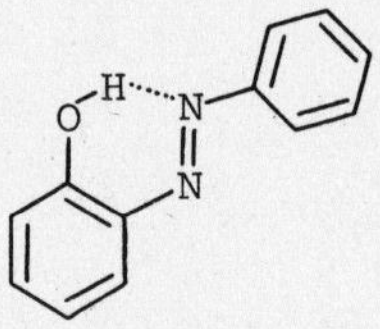

In the ortho case, the hydrogen-bonding is all
internal. In the para case, such internal hydrogen
bonding is not possible. Instead the -OH group hydrogen-
bonds to water or to -N=N- groups in other molecules and the volatility is decreased.

22.   (a)

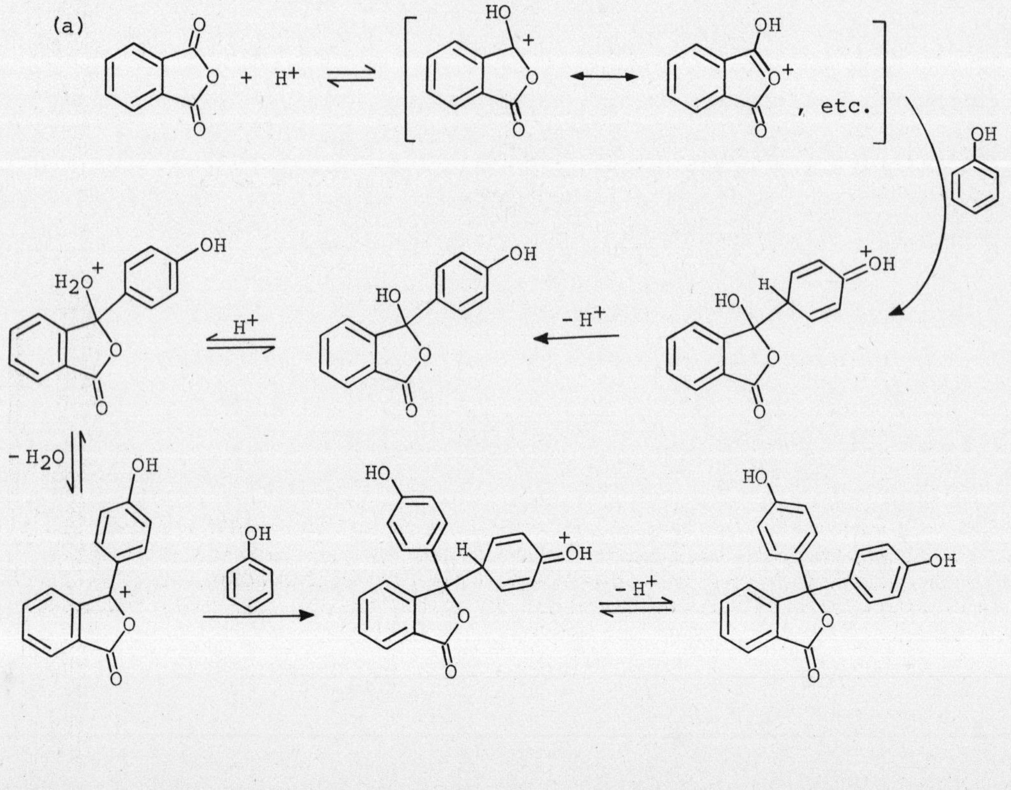

(b)   The immediate product is:

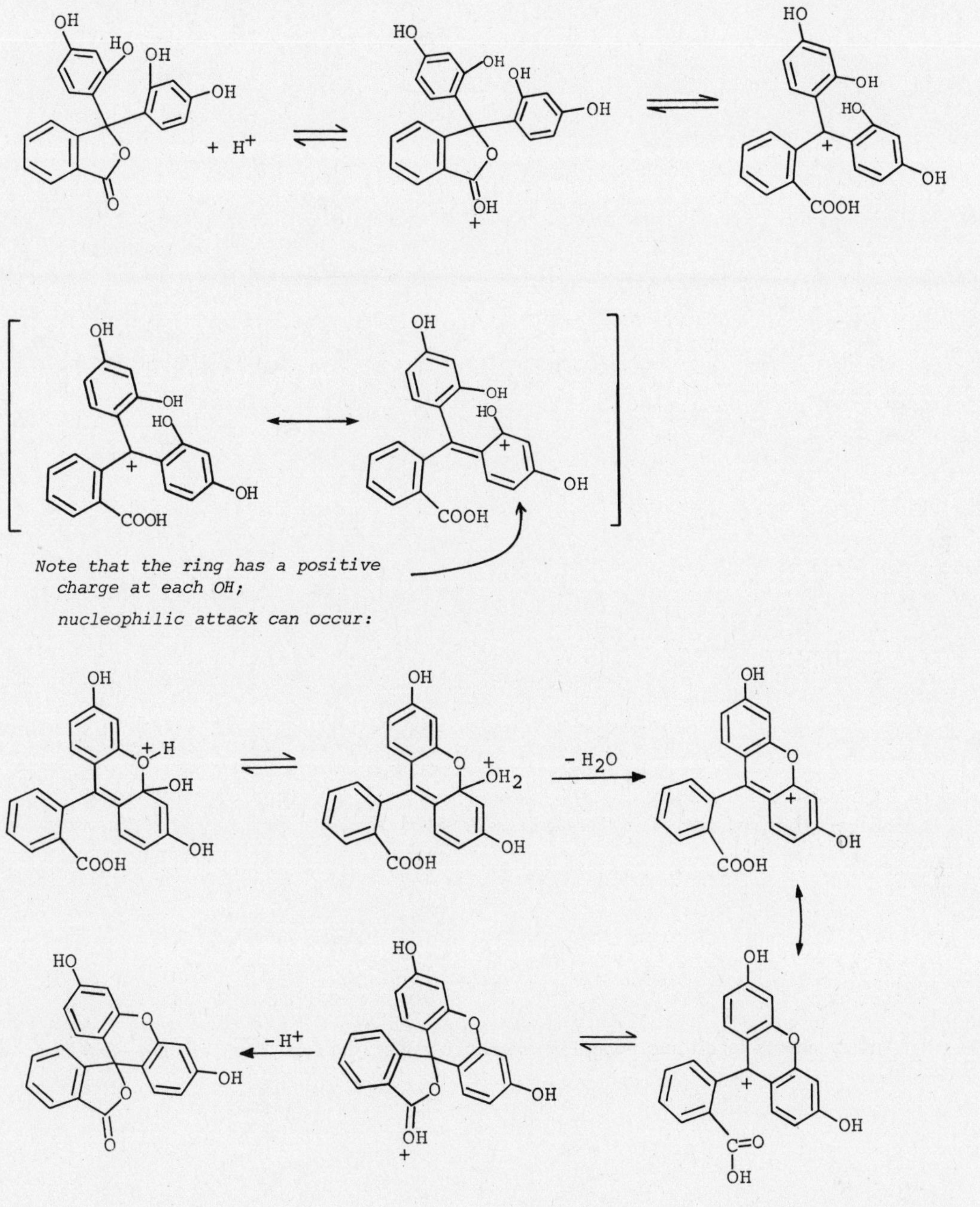

*Note that the ring has a positive
charge at each OH;*

nucleophilic attack can occur:

23.   The potential difference is given directly by Table 26.2   as 0.713 - 0.699 = 0.014 volts,
not a very powerful battery. When determining the signs, remember that the -Cl group
destabilizes the quinone; hence, this side needs protons and electrons to reach equilibrium.
Since it is drawing electrons, it must represent the anode, and the quinone-hydroquinone
side is the cathode.

24.

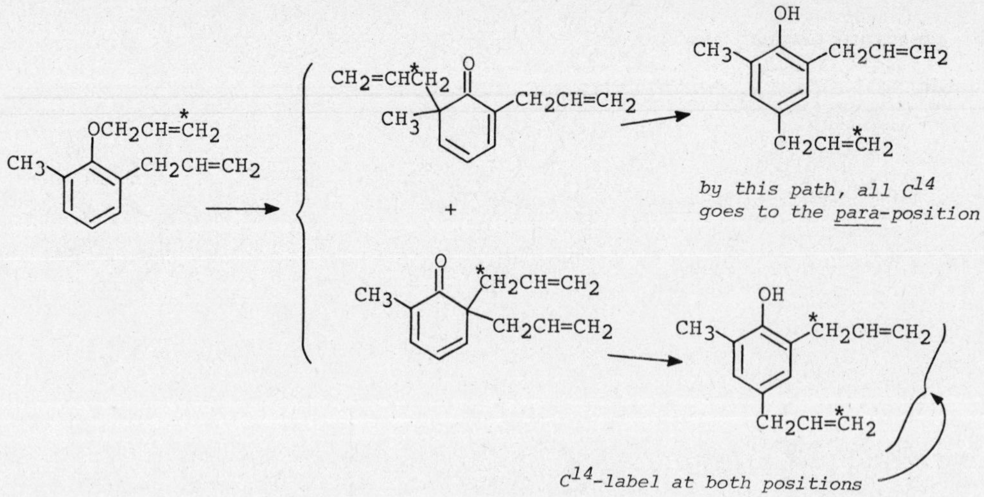

$CH_2=CH\overset{*}{C}H_2$

CH_3 ... $CH_2CH=CH_2$

+

by this path, all C^{14} goes to the _para-position_

C^{14}-label at both positions

25.

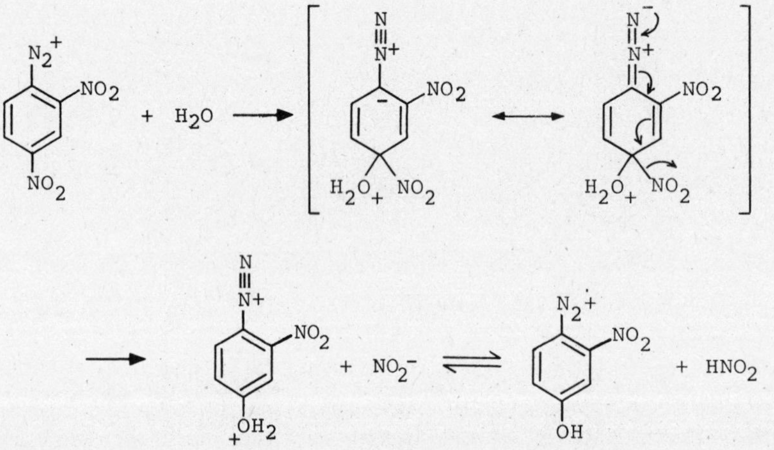

$+ H_2O \longrightarrow$

$\longrightarrow$ ... $+ NO_2^- \rightleftharpoons$ ... $+ HNO_2$

The $-N_2^+$ group deactivates nucleophilic aromatic substitution, much as the $-N=O$ and $-NO_2$ groups do.

26.

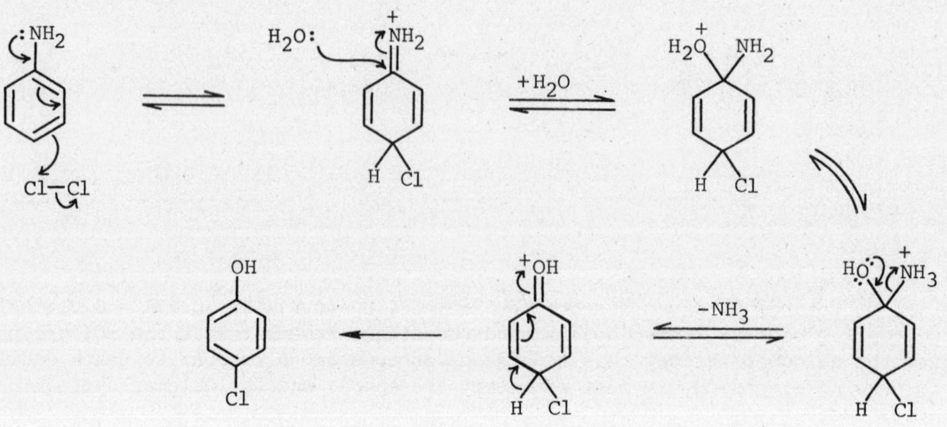

$Cl-Cl$ $\rightleftharpoons$ $H_2O:$ $\xrightarrow{+H_2O}$

$\xrightarrow{-NH_3}$

26.F   Supplementary Problems

S1.   Name the following compounds:

(a)

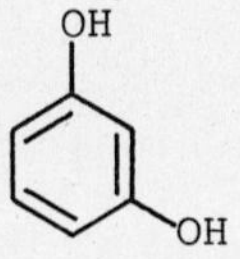

(c)

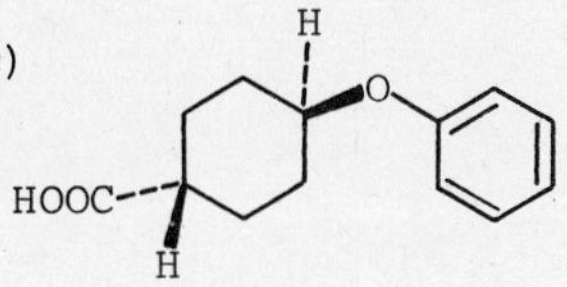

(e)

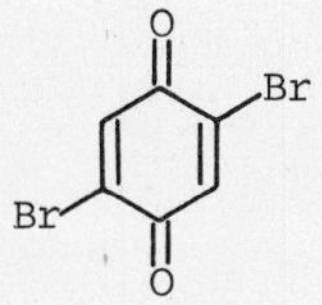

(b)

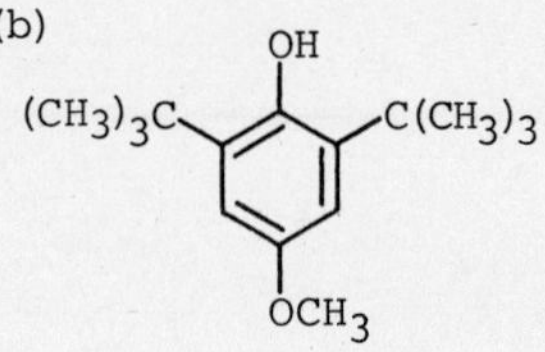

(d)

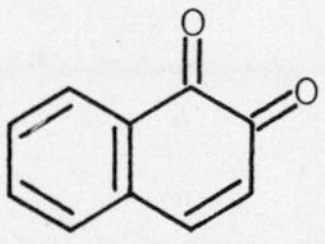

(f)

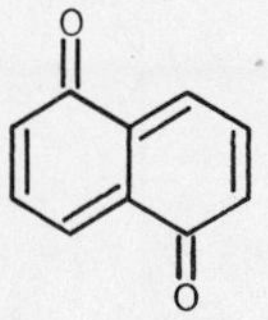

S2.   Predict the major product to result from each of the following reaction sequences.

(a)

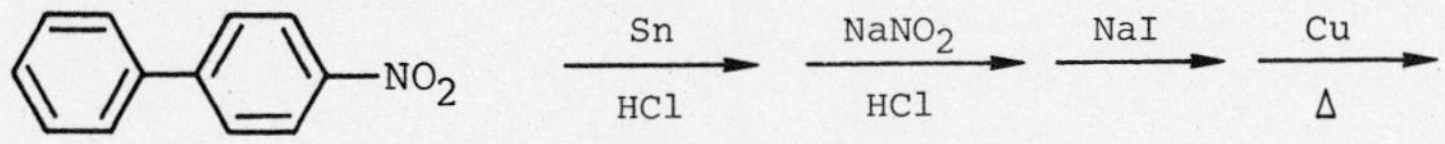

$$\xrightarrow[\text{HCl}]{\text{Sn}} \xrightarrow[\text{HCl}]{\text{NaNO}_2} \xrightarrow{\text{NaI}} \xrightarrow[\Delta]{\text{Cu}}$$

(b)

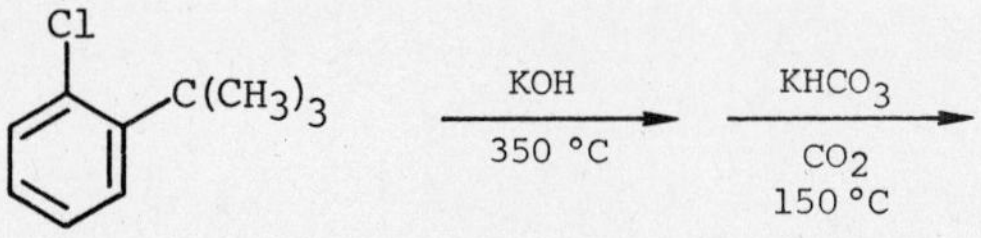

$$\xrightarrow[350\,^\circ\text{C}]{\text{KOH}} \xrightarrow[\substack{\text{CO}_2 \\ 150\,^\circ\text{C}}]{\text{KHCO}_3}$$

(c)

$$\xrightarrow[\text{aq. NaOH, }\Delta]{\text{C}_6\text{H}_5\text{N}_2{}^+} \xrightarrow{\text{Na}_2\text{S}_2\text{O}_4} \xrightarrow[\text{H}_2\text{SO}_4]{\text{K}_2\text{Cr}_2\text{O}_7}$$

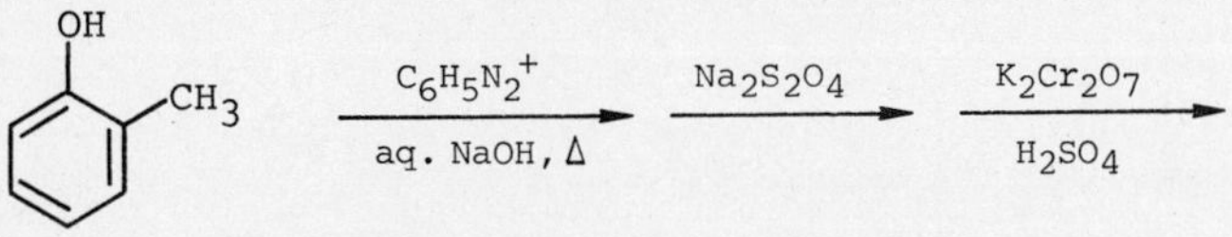

(d)   benzene
       (excess)

$$\xrightarrow[\text{BF}_3]{(\text{CH}_3)_3\text{COH}} \xrightarrow[\text{FeBr}_3]{\text{Br}_2} \xrightarrow[\text{ether}]{\underline{n}\text{-BuLi}} \xrightarrow{(\text{CH}_3)_2\text{C=O}} \xrightarrow{\text{H}_2\text{O}}$$

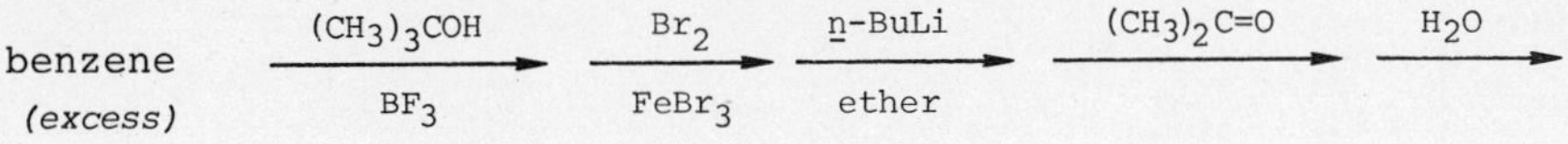

(e)

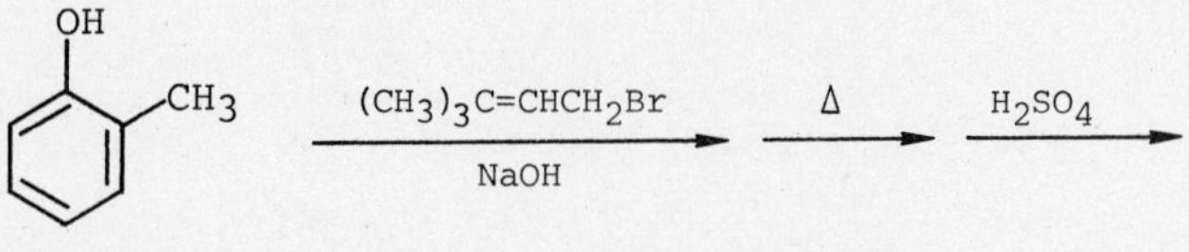

$$\xrightarrow[\text{NaOH}]{(\text{CH}_3)_3\text{C=CHCH}_2\text{Br}} \xrightarrow{\Delta} \xrightarrow{\text{H}_2\text{SO}_4}$$

(f)

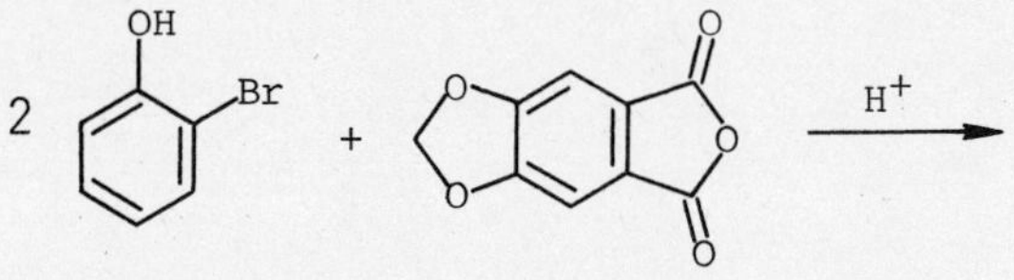

$$\xrightarrow{\text{H}^+}$$

(g)

$$\xrightarrow[\Delta]{\text{H}^+} \xrightarrow[\text{H}_2\text{SO}_4]{\text{H}_2\text{Cr}_2\text{O}_7}$$

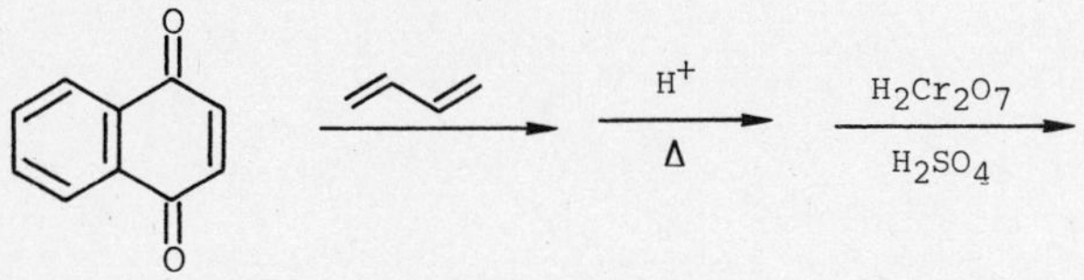

S3. Show how to synthesize the following compounds, starting with any monosubstituted benzene derivatives and any other non-aromatic compounds.

(a)

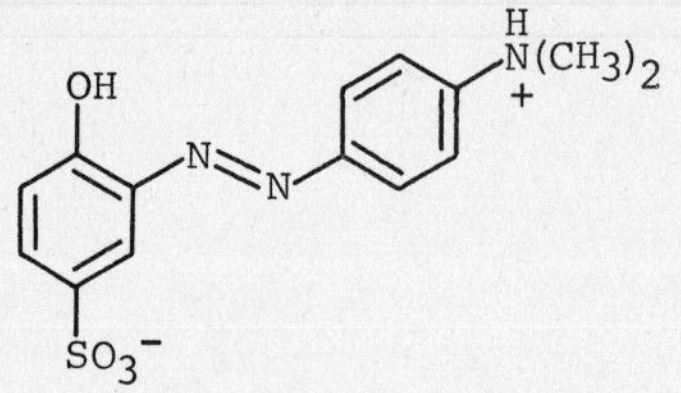

(c)

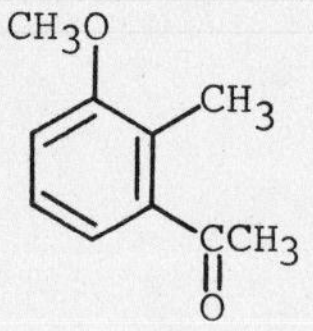

(e)

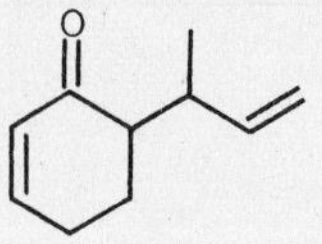

(b)

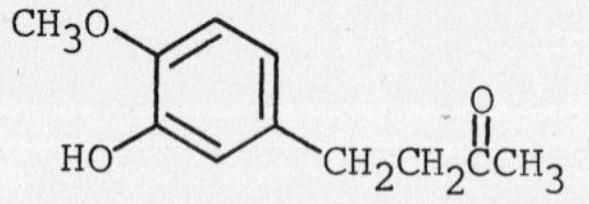

Zingerone (a constituent of ginger)

(d)

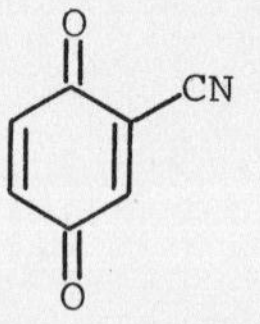

(f)

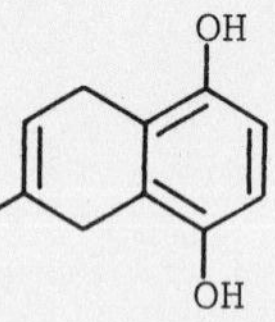

S4. Write the expected products from reaction of 2-hydroxy-5-(hydroxymethyl)benzoic acid with the following reagents:

    (a)   NaOH, CO_2, Δ

    (b)   excess CH_2N_2

    (c)   1 mole of CH_3COCH_3 (with two C=O)

    (d)   NaOH, $CHCl_3$

    (e)   HBr

S5. Write the expected products from reaction of 3-phenylpropanoic acid with the following reagents:

    (a) Cl_2, catalytic amount of PCl_3 (c) Cl_2, hν

    (b) Cl_2, $FeCl_3$ (d) $SOCl_2$

S6. Treatment of a protein with 2,4,6-trinitrobenzenesulfonic acid results in the attachment of 2,4,6-trinitrophenyl groups to the ε-amino groups of the lysine residues on the surface of the protein. Write a step-by-step mechanism for this reaction.

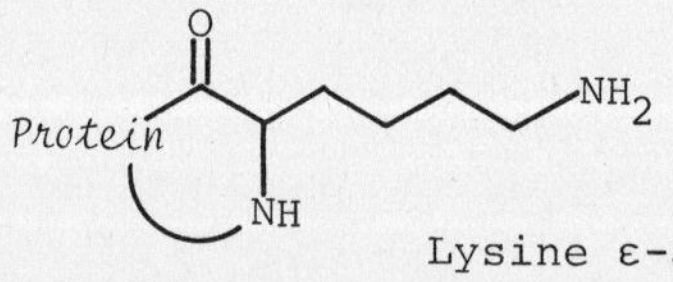

Lysine ε-amino group

S7. Hydroquinone, and molecules such as BHA and BHT, are used as antioxidants because they interrupt propagation of the radical chain involved in the usual autoxidation mechanism. Suggest a mechanism for this interruption.

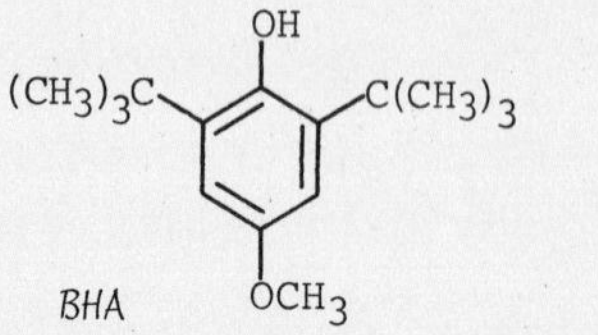

BHA 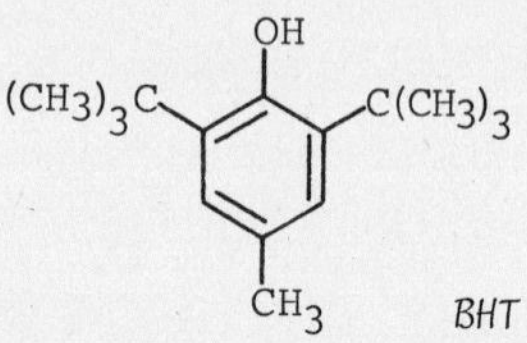   *BHT*

S8. Write a step-by-step mechanism for the following reaction:

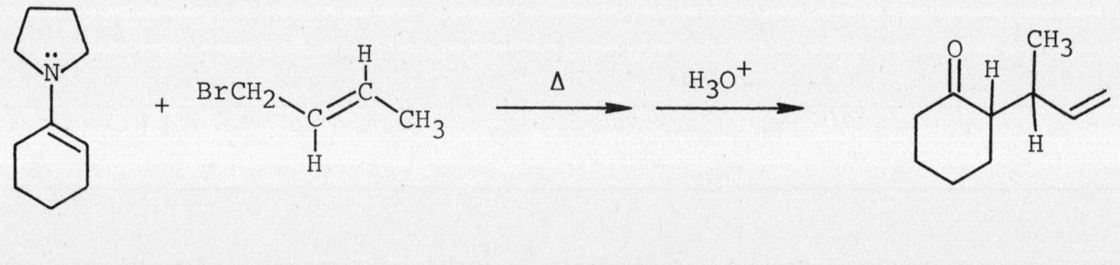

S9. (a) How do you account for the difference in the following reactions?

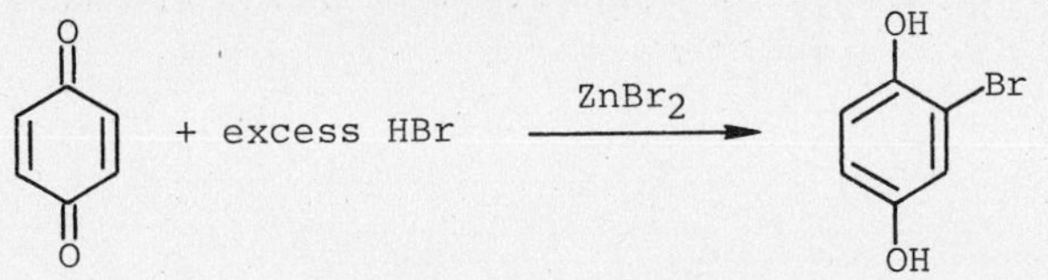

+ excess HBr $\xrightarrow{ZnBr_2}$

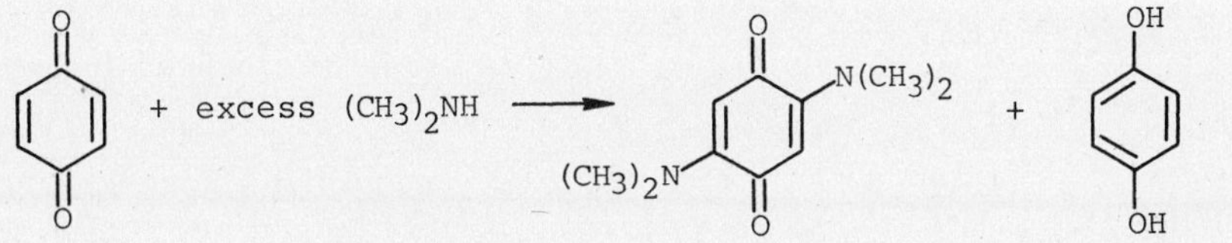

+ excess $(CH_3)_2NH$ →

one-third mole   two-thirds mole

(b) Why is the 2,5-di(dimethylamino) isomer produced in the second reaction above, rather than the 2,3- or 2,6-isomers?

26.G   Answers to Supplementary Problems

S1. (a) 1,3-dihydroxybenzene
(m-dihydroxybenzene, resorcinol)

(b) 2,6-di(t-butyl)-4-methoxyphenol
("butylated hydroxyanisole", BHA)

(c) trans-4-phenoxycyclohexanecarboxylic acid

(d) 1,2-naphthoquinone

(e) 2,5-dibromo-1,4-benzoquinone

(f) 1,5-naphthoquinone

S2.

(a)

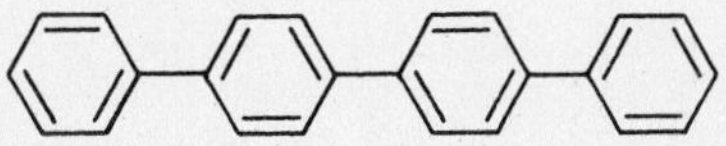

(b) 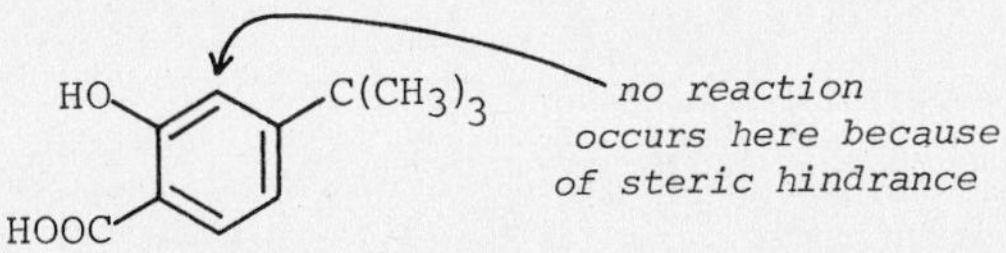   no reaction occurs here because of steric hindrance

(c)

(d)

(e) 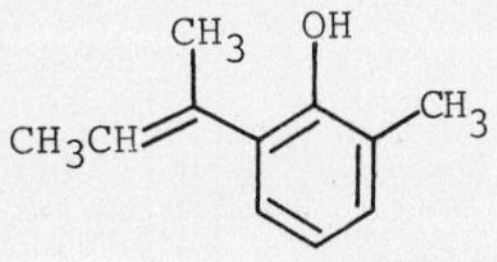   (from a carbocation rearrangement)

(f)

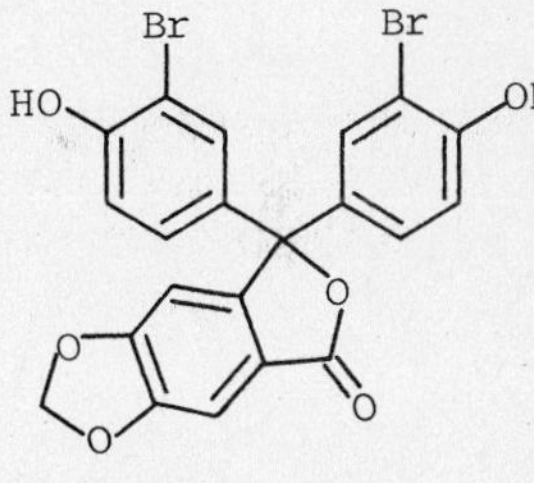

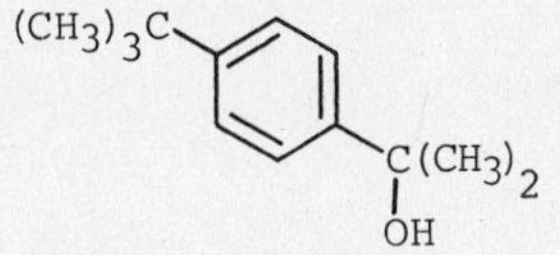

(g)

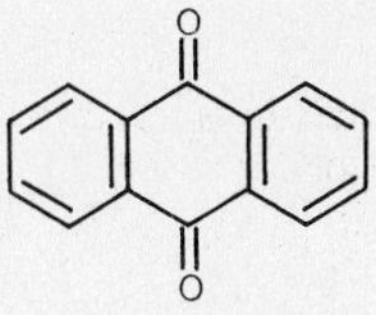

S3. (a)

$\xrightarrow[100\,°C]{98\%\ H_2SO_4}$

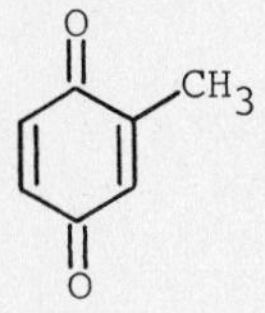

Base

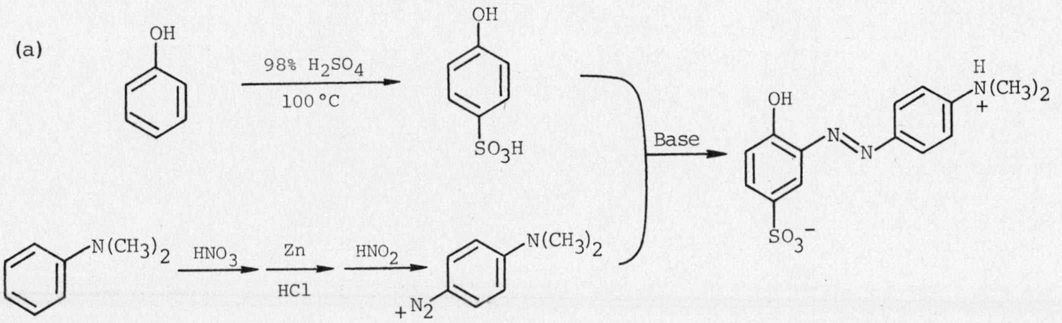

(b)

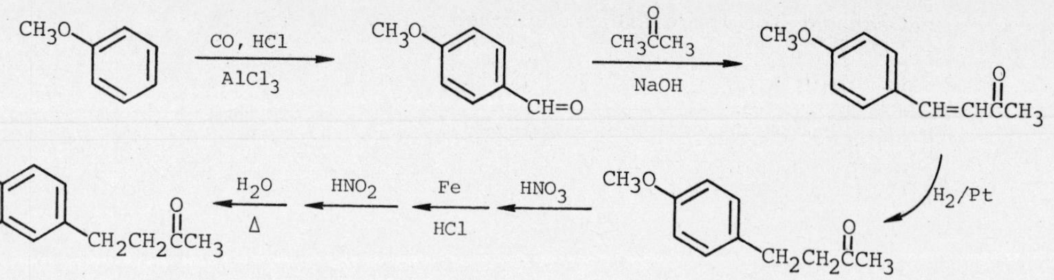

CH_3O—(benzene ring) $\xrightarrow[AlCl_3]{CO,\ HCl}$ CH_3O—(benzene ring)$CH=O$ $\xrightarrow[NaOH]{CH_3\overset{O}{\overset{\|}{C}}CH_3}$ CH_3O—(benzene ring)$CH=CHCCH_3$

$\xrightarrow{H_2/Pt}$ CH_3O—(benzene ring)$CH_2CH_2\overset{O}{\overset{\|}{C}}CH_3$ $\xleftarrow[HCl]{HNO_3\quad Fe}$ $\xleftarrow[\Delta]{HNO_2\quad H_2O}$ CH_3O—(benzene ring with HO)$CH_2CH_2\overset{O}{\overset{\|}{C}}CH_3$

(c)

(toluene) CH_3 $\xrightarrow[\Delta]{H_2SO_4}$ HO_3S—(ring)CH_3 $\xrightarrow{HNO_3}$ $\xrightarrow[FeBr_3]{Br_2}$ HO_3S—(ring with NO_2, CH_3, Br) $\xrightarrow{H_3O^+}$ $\xrightarrow[HCl]{Zn,}$

(ring with NH_2, CH_3, Br) $\xrightarrow{HNO_2}$ $\xrightarrow{CH_3OH}$ (ring with OCH_3, CH_3, Br) $\xrightarrow{Mg}$ $\xrightarrow{CH_3C\equiv N}$ $\xrightarrow{H_3O^+}$ (ring with CH_3O, CH_3, $\overset{O}{\overset{\|}{C}}CH_3$)

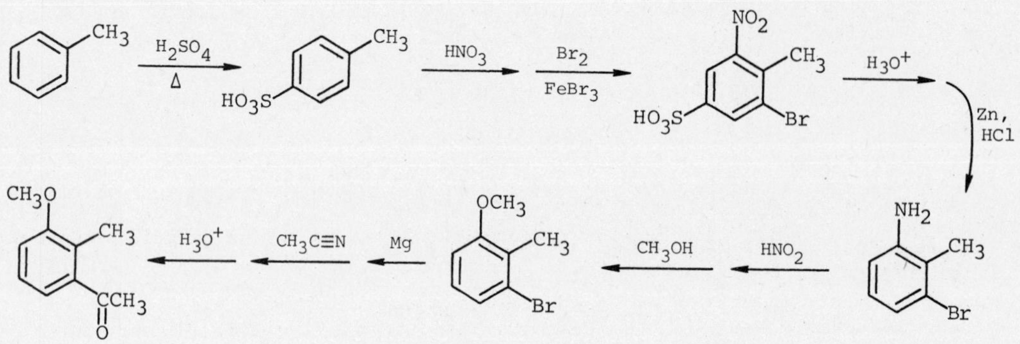

(d)

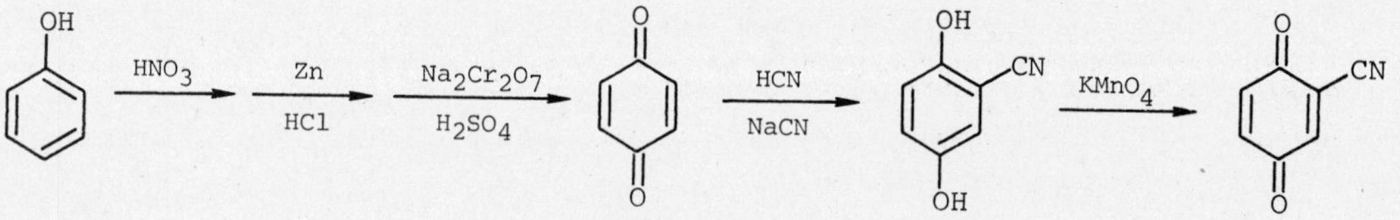

(phenol, OH) $\xrightarrow{HNO_3}$ $\xrightarrow[HCl]{Zn}$ $\xrightarrow[H_2SO_4]{Na_2Cr_2O_7}$ (benzoquinone) $\xrightarrow[NaCN]{HCN}$ (ring OH, CN, OH) $\xrightarrow{KMnO_4}$ (quinone, CN)

(e)

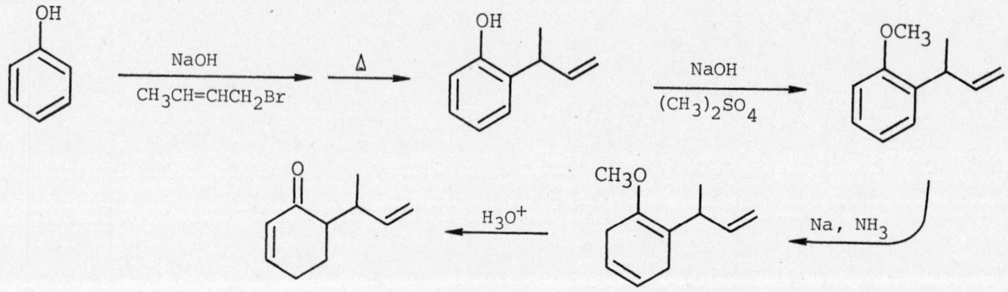

(phenol, OH) $\xrightarrow[CH_3CH=CHCH_2Br]{NaOH}$ $\xrightarrow{\Delta}$ (ring OH, CH—CH_3 with $=CH_2$) $\xrightarrow[(CH_3)_2SO_4]{NaOH}$ (ring OCH_3, CH—CH_3)

$\xleftarrow{Na,\ NH_3}$ (ring CH_3O) $\xrightarrow{H_3O^+}$ (cyclohexenone with CH—CH_3 group)

(f)

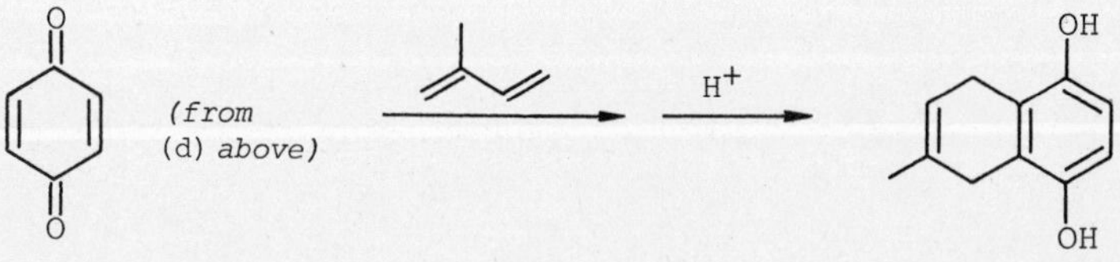

(benzoquinone, O=...=O) *(from (d) above)* $\xrightarrow{\text{(diene)}}$ $\xrightarrow{H^+}$ (naphthalenediol, OH, OH, CH_3)

S4.

(a) $HOOC$—(ring with OH, $COOH$, CH_2OH)

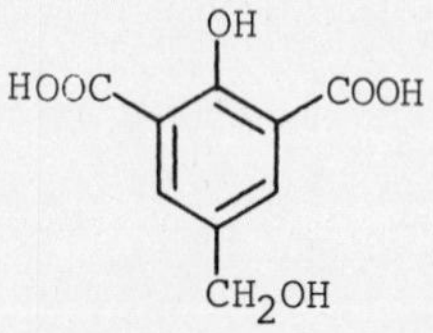

(b) CH_3O—(ring with $COOCH_3$, CH_2OH)

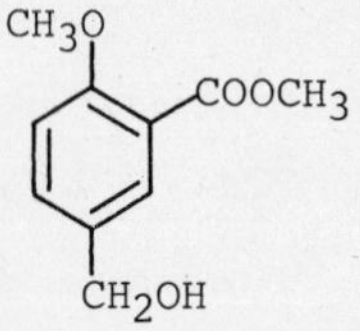

(c) (ring with OH, $COOH$, $CH_2O\overset{O}{\overset{\|}{C}}CH_3$)

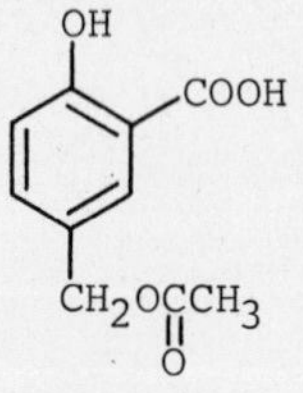

(d) $H\overset{O}{\overset{\|}{C}}$—(ring with OH, $COOH$, CH_2OH)

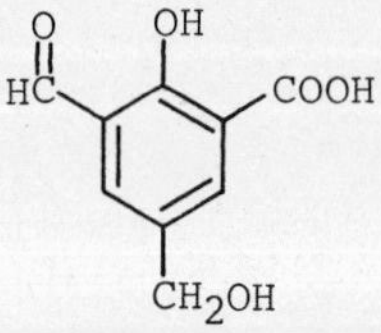

(e) (ring with OH, $COOH$, CH_2Br)

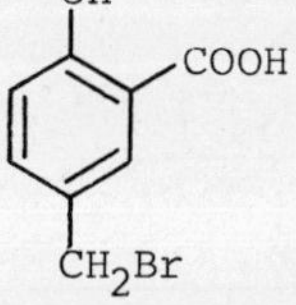

S5.   (a)

$$C_6H_5CH_2\overset{Cl}{\underset{}{C}HCOOH}$$

(b) 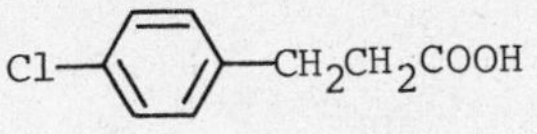 $Cl-\!\!\!\!\!\!\!\!\bigcirc\!\!\!\!\!\!\!\!-CH_2CH_2COOH$

(c)

$$C_6H_5\overset{Cl}{\underset{}{C}HCH_2COOH}$$

(d)

$$C_6H_5CH_2CH_2\overset{O}{\underset{}{C}}-Cl$$

S6.

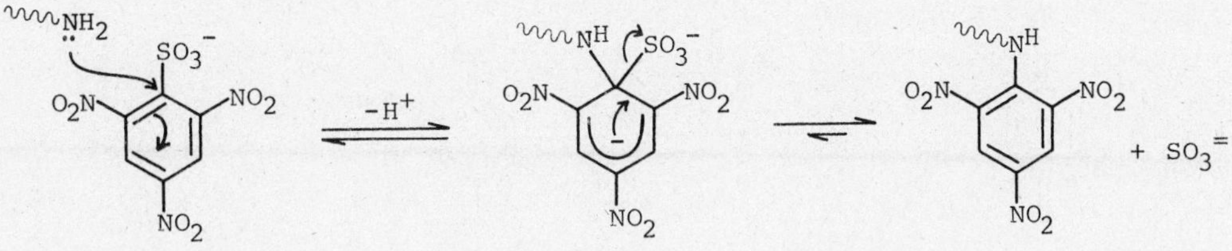

S7.   The propagation steps of a free radical oxidation process are the following:

$$R\cdot\ +\ O_2\ \longrightarrow\ ROO\cdot$$

$$ROO\cdot\ +\ RH\ \longrightarrow\ ROOH\ +\ R\cdot$$

Phenols such as hydroquinone, BHA, and BHT interrupt this chain because they lose a hydrogen atom more readily than RH. By doing so, they form a stable radical which is unable to continue the propagation chain.

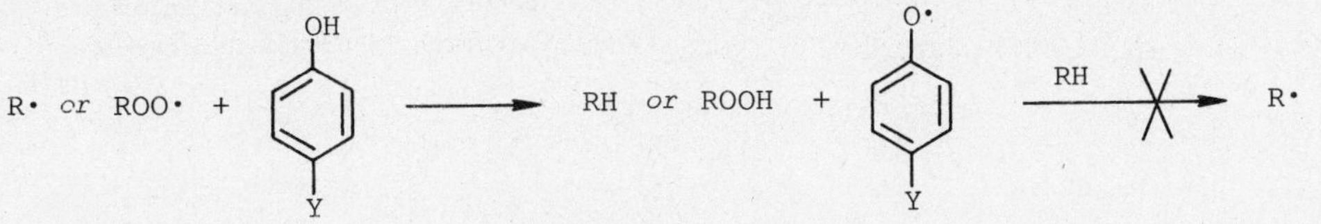

S8.   The clue is the fact that the enamine alkylation proceeds with allylic rearrangement:

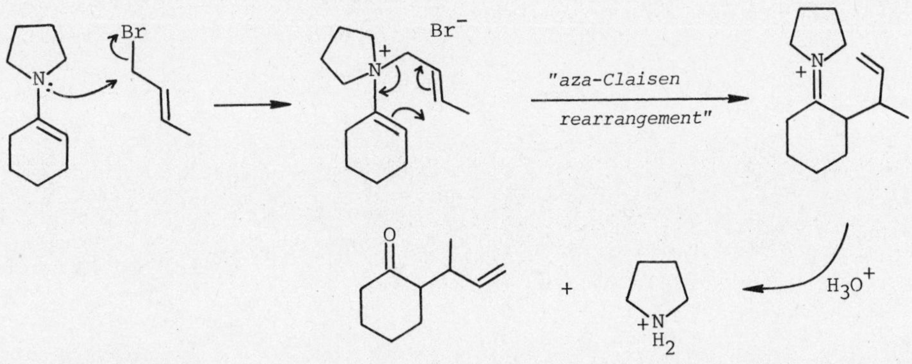

S9.   (a)   The product of HBr addition has a higher oxidation potential than hydroquinone itself, therefore only addition occurs:

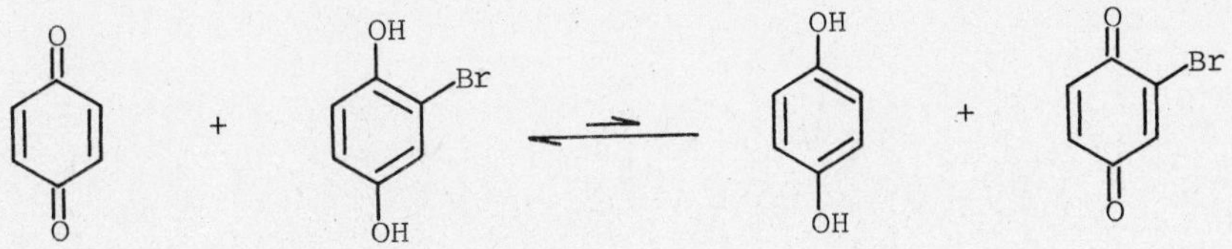

The opposite is true for the dimethylamine adduct. As soon as it is formed, it is oxidized by the starting material and another amine adds. This second product in turn undergoes oxidation as well:

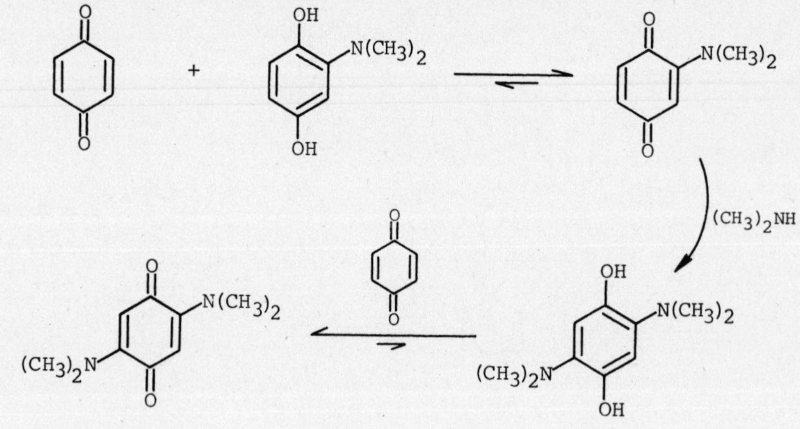

$(CH_3)_2NH$

(b)

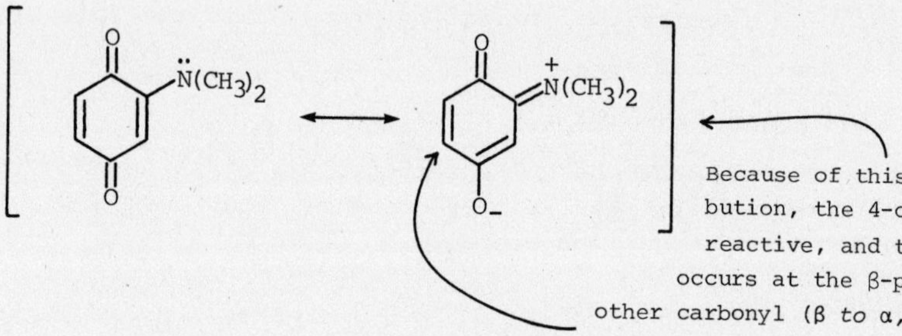

Because of this resonance contribution, the 4-carbonyl is much less
reactive, and the second Michael
occurs at the β-position of the
other carbonyl (β to α,β-*unsaturated*
carbonyl)

27. DIFUNCTIONAL COMPOUNDS

27.A Chapter Outline and Important Terms Introduced

27.1 Introduction

Scope of chapter: diols, dicarbonyl compounds, hydroxy carbonyl compounds

27.2 Nomenclature of Difunctional Compounds

diene, diyne, diol, dione, dicarboxylic acid

glycols   hydroxyalkanone

hydroxyalkanoic acid

27.3 Diols

A. Preparation (1,2-diols)

hydroxylation (see Sections 11.6.E and 10.11)

syn ($KMnO_4$ or OsO_4) or anti addition (via epoxide and hydrolysis)

erythro and threo

reductive dimerization (pinacol reaction)   ketyl radical anion

higher diols from same reactions as in monofunctional systems

B. Reactions of Diols

pinacol rearrangement   cyclic ethers from 1,4- and 1,5-diols

periodate cleavage   Lemieux-Johnson reaction

27.4 Hydroxy Aldehydes and Ketones

A. Synthesis

acyloin condensation   benzoin condensation

aldol condensation (see Section 14.8.C)

B. Reactions

dehydration of β-hydroxycarbonyl compounds

cyclic hemiacetals and hemiketals

periodate cleavage of α-hydroxyketones and α-aldehydes

27.5 Hydroxy Acids

A. Natural Occurrence (lactic, citric, malic, tartaric acids, etc.)

B. Synthesis

hydrolysis of α-halo acids   aldol-like additions

hydrolysis of cyanohydrins   Baeyer-Villiger reaction/lactone cleavage

C. Reactions

lactonization   lactones and lactides

polymerization   dehydration

27.6 Dicarboxylic Acids

A. Synthesis

chemistry of carbonic acid

B. Acidity

electrostatic effects

C. Reactions of Dicarboxylic Acids and Their Derivatives

decarboxylation of malonic acids   Dieckmann condensation

anhydride and imide formation from succinic and glutaric acids

27.7 Diketones, Keto Aldehydes, Keto Acids, and Keto Esters

A. Synthesis

1,2-diketones (α-diketones): oxidation of acyloins

SeO_2 oxidation of ketones

1,3-dicarbonyl compounds: Claisen condensation

B. Keto-Enol Equilibria in Dicarbonyl Compounds

vinylogy, vinylogs

    C. Decarboxylation of β-Keto Acids
    D. 1,3-Dicarbonyl Compounds as Carbon Acids
          2,4-pentanedione pK_a = 9
    E. The Malonic Ester and Acetoacetic Ester Syntheses
    F. The Knoevenagel Condensation
    G. The Michael Addition Reaction
          Robinson annelation

27.B   Important Reactions Introduced

Hydroxylation of alkenes to form 1,2-diols (27.3.A; see also Sections 11.6.E and 10.11.A)

Equation:

$$R_2C=CR_2 \xrightarrow{[Ox]} R-\underset{\underset{R}{|}}{\overset{\overset{HO}{|}}{C}}-\underset{\underset{R}{|}}{\overset{\overset{OH}{|}}{C}}-R$$

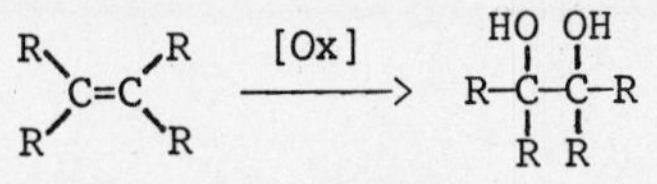

Generality: [Ox] = $KMnO_4$ or OsO_4 (syn) or 1. $R'CO_3H$ 2. H_3O^+ (anti)

Key features: see Sections 11.6.E and 10.11.A

Pinacol reaction (reductive dimerization) (27.3.A)

Equation:

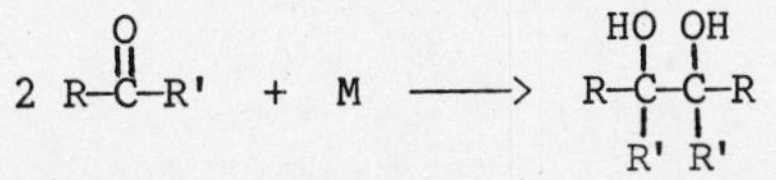

$$2\ R-\overset{\overset{\textstyle O}{\|}}{C}-R' \ +\ M \longrightarrow R-\underset{\underset{R'}{|}}{\overset{\overset{HO}{|}}{C}}-\underset{\underset{R'}{|}}{\overset{\overset{OH}{|}}{C}}-R$$

Generality: R, R' = H, alkyl, aryl; M = 2 Na or Mg

Key features: reaction proceeds via dimerization of ketyl radical anion

Pinacol rearrangement (27.3.B)

Equation:

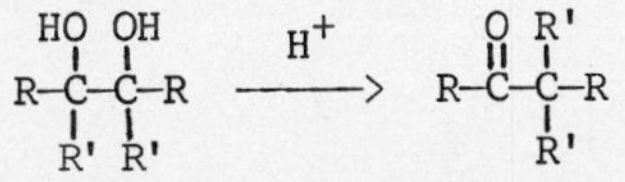

$$R-\underset{\underset{R'}{|}}{\overset{\overset{HO}{|}}{C}}-\underset{\underset{R'}{|}}{\overset{\overset{OH}{|}}{C}}-R \xrightarrow{H^+} R-\overset{\overset{\textstyle O}{\|}}{C}-\underset{\underset{R'}{|}}{\overset{\overset{R'}{|}}{C}}-R$$

Generality: R, R' = H, alkyl, aryl

Key features: carbocation rearrangement
               in unsymmmetrical diol, it is the more substituted carbon that loses the OH and
                  gains the migrating group

Dehydration of 1,4- and 1,5-diols to cyclic ethers (27.3.B)

Equation:

$$HO-(\quad)-OH \xrightarrow{H^+} \bigcirc_{O} + H_2O$$

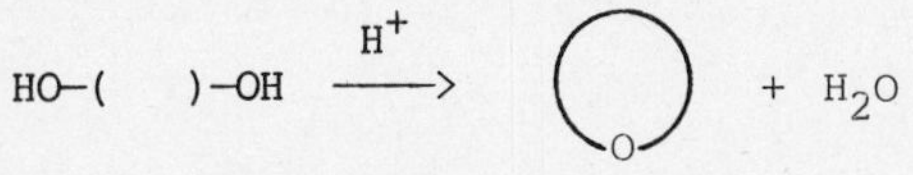

Generality: formation of 5- and 6-membered rings

Key features: intramolecular version of dehydration of alcohols to ethers: see Section 10.6.D

Periodate cleavage of 1,2-diols (27.3.B)

Equation:

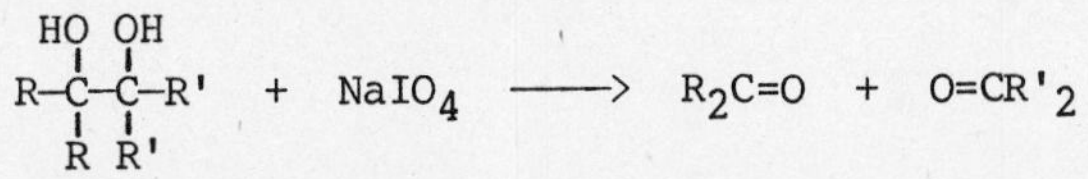

$$R-\underset{\underset{R}{|}}{\overset{\overset{HO}{|}}{C}}-\underset{\underset{R'}{|}}{\overset{\overset{OH}{|}}{C}}-R' \ +\ NaIO_4 \longrightarrow R_2C=O\ +\ O=CR'_2$$

Generality: R, R = H, alkyl, aryl
               reaction can also be applied to α-hydroxycarbonyl compounds
                  (product is a ketone or aldehyde and a carboxylic acid [section 27.4.B])

Key features: useful for structure elucidation in carbohydrate chemistry
               hydroxylation of an alkene (OsO_4) coupled with periodate cleavage (together called
                  the Lemieux-Johnson reaction) is an alternative to ozonolysis

Acyloin condensation (27.4.A)

Equation:

$$2 \text{ R}-\overset{\overset{\text{O}}{\|}}{\text{C}}-\text{OR}' \xrightarrow[\text{ether}]{2 \text{ Na}} \left[\text{R}-\overset{\overset{-\text{O}}{|}}{\text{C}}=\overset{\overset{\text{O}^-}{|}}{\text{C}}-\text{R} \right] \xrightarrow{\text{H}_2\text{O}} \text{R}-\overset{\overset{\text{O}}{\|}}{\text{C}}-\overset{\overset{\text{OH}}{|}}{\text{C}}\text{H}-\text{R}$$

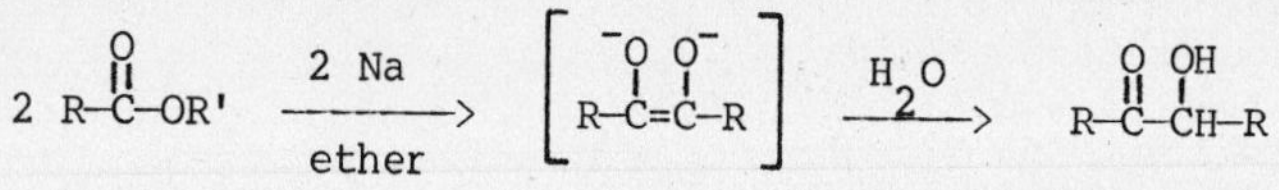

Generality: R, R' = alkyl

Key feature: useful for synthesizing large ring compounds from α,ω-diesters

Benzoin condensation (27.4.A)

Equation:

$$2 \text{ Ar}-\overset{\overset{\text{O}}{\|}}{\text{C}}\text{H} \xrightarrow{\text{NaCN}} \text{Ar}-\overset{\overset{\text{O}}{\|}}{\text{C}}-\overset{\overset{\text{OH}}{|}}{\text{C}}\text{H}-\text{Ar}$$

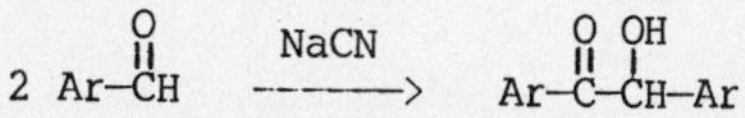

Generality: limited to aromatic aldehydes and cyanide catalysis

Key features: proceeds via benzylic anion of aldehyde cyanohydrin

Synthesis and dehydration of β-hydroxy carbonyl compounds by aldol and related addition-condensation reactions   (27.4.A and B; see also 14.8.C, 18.9, and 19.3.A)

Equation:

$$\text{R}-\overset{\overset{\text{O}}{\|}}{\text{C}}-\text{R} + \text{R}-\text{CH}_2-\overset{\overset{\text{O}}{\|}}{\text{C}}-\text{R}' \xrightarrow{\text{base}} \text{R}-\overset{\overset{\text{OH}}{|}}{\underset{\underset{\text{R}}{|}}{\text{C}}}-\overset{\overset{}{|}}{\underset{\underset{\text{R}}{|}}{\text{C}}}\text{H}-\overset{\overset{\text{O}}{\|}}{\text{C}}-\text{R}' \longrightarrow \overset{\text{R}}{\underset{\text{R}'}{}}\text{C}=\overset{}{\underset{\text{R}}{}}\text{C}-\overset{\overset{\text{O}}{\|}}{\text{C}}-\text{R}'$$

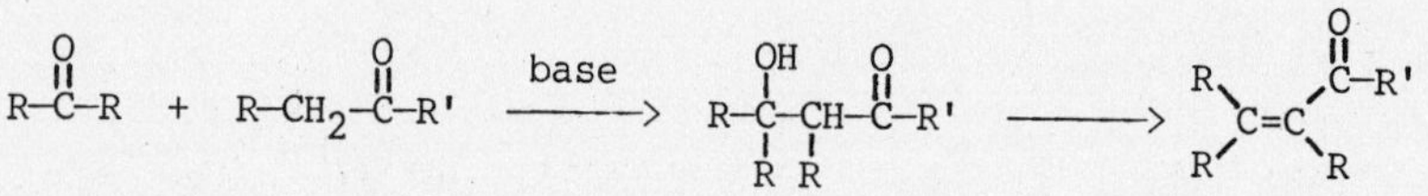

Generality: R = various combinations of H, alkyl, aryl; R' = alkyl, aryl, or OR
                dehydration step acid- or base-catalyzed

Key features: see Sections 14.8.C, 18.9, 19.3.A

Cyclic hemiacetals and hemiketals and acetals and ketals from hydroxy carbonyl compounds (27.4.B; see also 14.7.B)

Equation:

$$\text{HO}-(\quad)-\overset{\overset{\text{O}}{\|}}{\text{C}}-\text{R} \rightleftharpoons \text{(ring)}\overset{\text{R}}{\underset{\text{OH}}{}} \underset{\text{H}^+}{\overset{\text{R'OH}}{\rightleftharpoons}} \text{(ring)}\overset{\text{R}}{\underset{\text{OR}'}{}} + \text{H}_2\text{O}$$

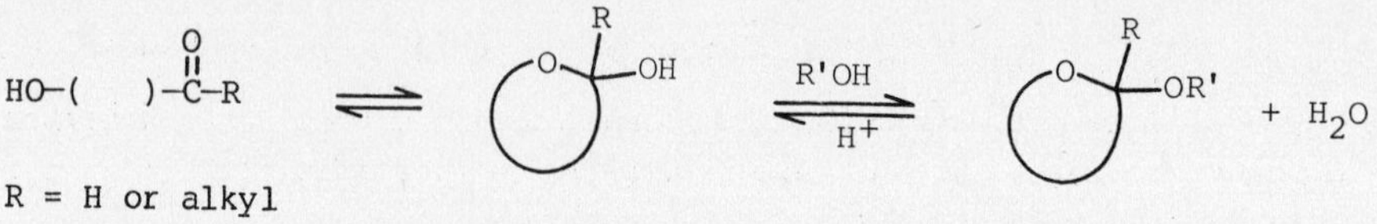

Generality: R = H or alkyl
                formation of 5- and 6-membered rings

Key features: simply the intramolecular version of hemiacetal and acetal formation (see Section 14.7.B)

Synthesis of α-hydroxyacids from α-haloacids (27.5.A)

Equation:

$$\text{R}-\overset{\overset{}{\underset{\underset{\text{X}}{|}}{\text{C}}}\text{H}}-\text{CO}_2\text{H} \xrightarrow{\text{NaOH}} \text{R}-\overset{\overset{}{\underset{\underset{\text{OH}}{|}}{\text{C}}}\text{H}}-\text{CO}_2\text{H}$$

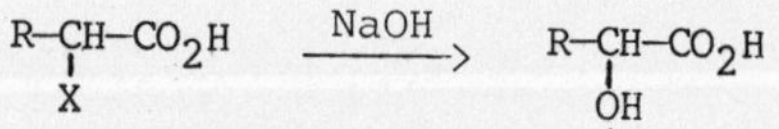

Generality: X = Br (also Cl or I)

Key features: S_N2 process
                useful combination with α-bromination of carboxylic acids (Section 17.7.B)

Synthesis of α-hydroxyacids from cyanohydrins (27.5.A)

Equation:

$$\text{R}-\overset{\overset{\text{OH}}{|}}{\underset{\underset{\text{R}}{|}}{\text{C}}}-\text{C}\equiv\text{N} \xrightarrow{\text{H}_3\text{O}^+} \text{R}-\overset{\overset{\text{OH}}{|}}{\underset{\underset{\text{R}}{|}}{\text{C}}}-\text{CO}_2\text{H}$$

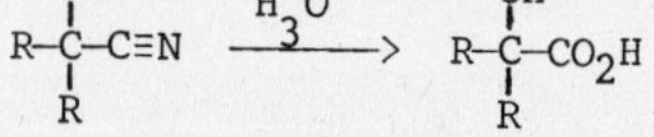

Key features: useful combination with formation of cyanohydrin (Section 13.8.B)
                process must be acid catalyzed; in presence of base, cyanohydrins decompose to NaCN and carbonyl compound

Lactonization   (27.5.B)

Equation:

$$HO-(\quad)-CO_2R \quad \rightleftharpoons \quad [\text{lactone ring}] \quad + \quad ROH$$

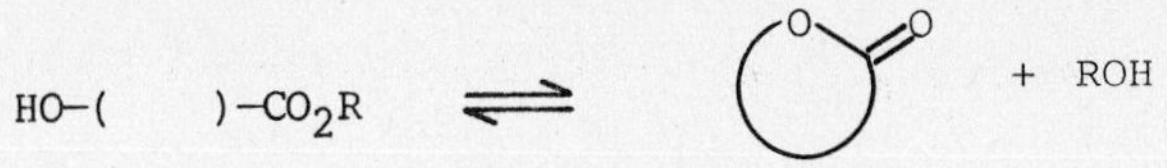

Generality: R = H: acid catalyzed equilibrium; R = alkyl: acid or base catalyzed equilibrium
for formation of five- and six-membered rings;
    longer-chain hydroxy acids tend to polymerize instead of lactonize

Key features: simply an intramolecular esterification or transesterification reaction

Lactide formation   (27.5.B)

Equation:

$$2\ R-CH-CO_2R' \quad \rightleftharpoons \quad [\text{lactide ring}] \quad + \quad 2\ R'OH$$
$$\quad\ \ |$$
$$\quad\ \ OH$$

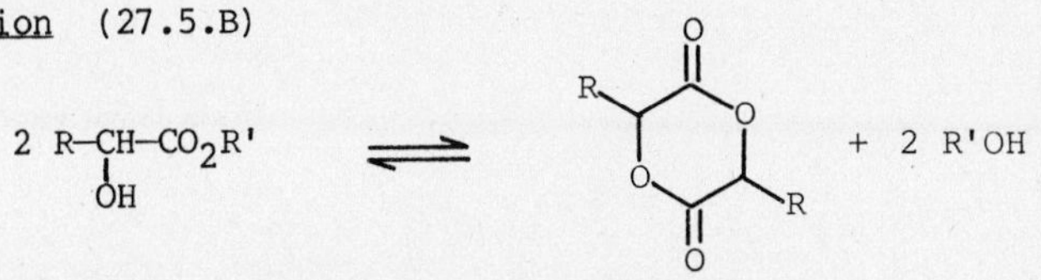

Generality: limited to α-hydroxy acids and esters

Synthesis of dicarboxylic acids by oxidative cleavage of cycloalkenes and cycloalkanones (27.6.A)

Equation:

$$[\text{cycloalkene}] \xrightarrow{KMnO_4} HO_2C-(\quad)-CO_2H \xleftarrow[\Delta]{HNO_3} [\text{cycloalkanone}]$$

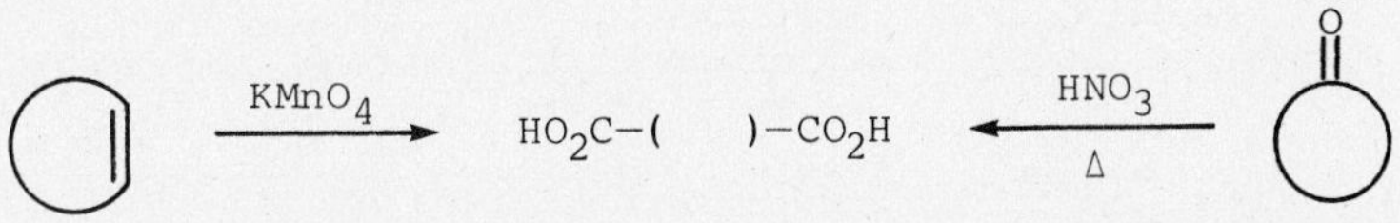

Decarboxylation of β-carbonyl carboxylic acid derivatives (27.6.C and 27.7.C)

Equation:

$$\underset{\ \ \ |}{\overset{O}{\underset{R'}{R-C-CH-CO_2H}}} \xrightarrow{\Delta} R-\overset{O}{\overset{||}{C}}-CH_2-R' \ + \ CO_2$$

Generality: R = H, alkyl, aryl, OR"; $R-\overset{O}{\overset{||}{C}}-$ group can be replaced by CN, too

Key features: reaction proceeds via cyclic transition state and enol form of carbonyl product
key step in malonic ester and acetoacetic ester syntheses

Cyclic anhydride and imide formation (27.6.C)

Equation:

$$HO-\overset{O}{\overset{||}{C}}-(\quad)-\overset{O}{\overset{||}{C}}-YH \quad \longrightarrow \quad [\text{cyclic anhydride/imide}] \quad + \quad H_2O$$

Generality: ring size = 5 or 6
Y = O (anhydride) or NR' (imide)
reaction is caused by heating or with a dehydrating agent such as PCl_5, $SOCl_2$, P_2O_5,
    $POCl_3$, etc.

Dieckmann condensation (27.6.C)

Equation:

$$RO_2C-CH_2-(\quad)-CO_2R \xrightarrow{RO^-} [\text{cyclic ketoester}] \ + \ ROH$$

Generality: ring size = 5 or 6
Key features: reaction is simply an intramolecular Claisen condensation

Oxidation of α-hydroxy ketones to α-diketones (27.7.A)

Equation:

$$\underset{}{\overset{OH\ O}{R-CH-C-R'}} \xrightarrow{Cu(OAc)_2} \underset{}{\overset{O\ \ O}{R-C-C-R'}}$$

Key features: α-hydroxy ketones are sensitive to oxidative cleavage, so cupric acetate is
       specific reagent

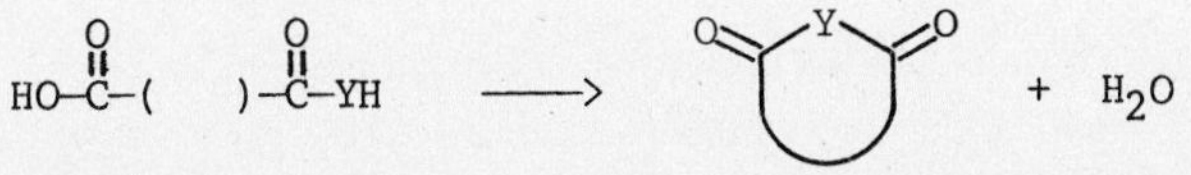

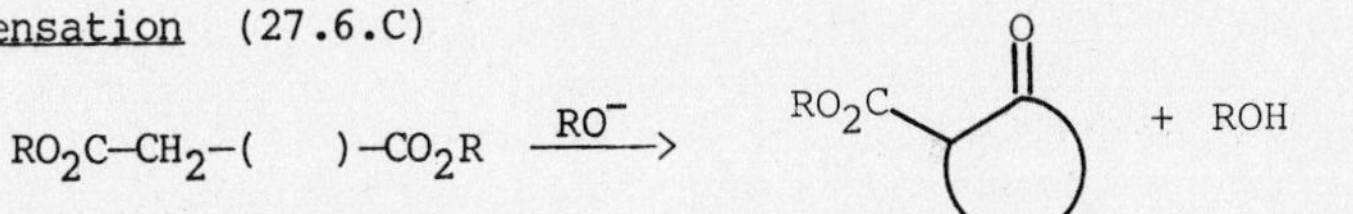

<u>Oxidation</u> <u>of</u> <u>ketones</u> <u>and</u> <u>aldehydes</u> <u>to</u> <u>α-dicarbonyl</u> <u>compounds</u>   (27.7.A)

Equation:

$$R-\overset{\overset{\displaystyle O}{\|}}{C}-CH_2-R' \xrightarrow{\ SeO_2\ } R-\overset{\overset{\displaystyle O}{\|}}{C}-\overset{\overset{\displaystyle O}{\|}}{C}-R'$$

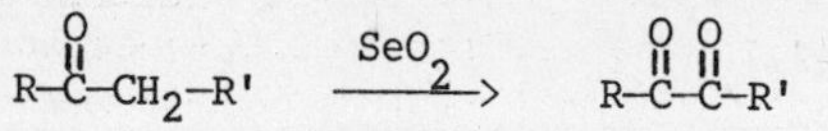

<u>Claisen</u> <u>condensation</u>   (27.7.A; see also 18.9)

Equation:

$$R-\overset{\overset{\displaystyle O}{\|}}{C}-OR'' \ + \ \underset{\underset{\displaystyle R'}{|}}{CH_2}-\overset{\overset{\displaystyle O}{\|}}{C}-Y \xrightarrow{\ R''O^-\ } R-\overset{\overset{\displaystyle O}{\|}}{C}-\underset{\underset{\displaystyle R'}{|}}{CH}-\overset{\overset{\displaystyle O}{\|}}{C}-Y$$

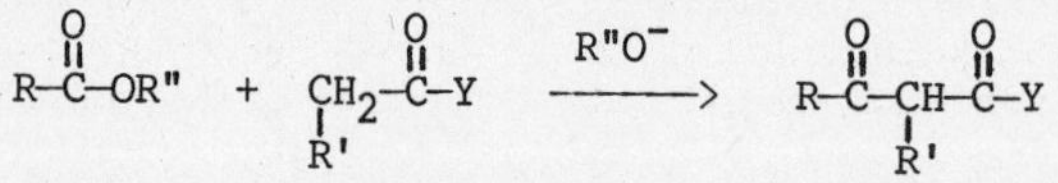

Generality: R, R' = H, alkyl, aryl; Y = alkyl, aryl, O-alkyl; R" = alkyl

Key features: see section 18.9

<u>Malonic</u> <u>ester</u> <u>and</u> <u>acetoacetic</u> <u>ester</u> <u>syntheses</u>   (27.7.E)

Equation:

$$R-\overset{\overset{\displaystyle O}{\|}}{C}-\underset{\underset{\displaystyle R'}{|}}{CH}-\overset{\overset{\displaystyle O}{\|}}{C}-OR''' \ + \ R''-X \xrightarrow{\ base\ } R-\overset{\overset{\displaystyle O}{\|}}{C}-\underset{\underset{\displaystyle R'}{|}}{\overset{\overset{\displaystyle R''O}{|}}{C}}-\overset{\overset{\displaystyle O}{\|}}{C}-OR''' \xrightarrow[\ 2.\ H^+,\ ]{\ 1.\ OH^-\ } R-\overset{\overset{\displaystyle O}{\|}}{C}-\underset{\underset{\displaystyle R'}{|}}{CH}-R'' \ + \ CO_2$$

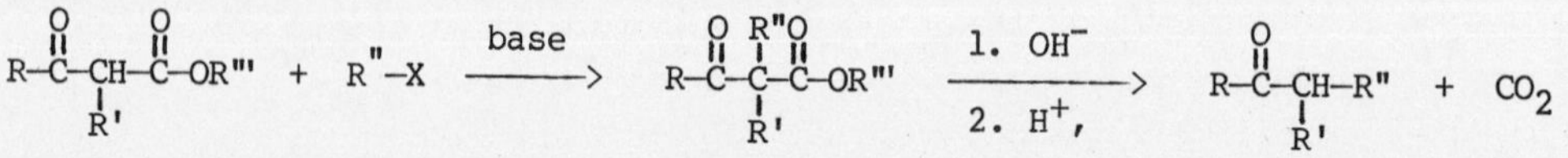

Generality: R = R'''O: malonic ester synthesis; R = H, alkyl, or aryl: acetoacetic ester synthesis
              R' = alkyl, aryl; R"X = good alkylating agent

Key features: important method for the synthesis of substituted ketones and carboxylic acids

<u>Knoevenagel</u> <u>condensation</u>   (22.7.F)

Equation: $RO_2C-CH_2-CO_2R \ + \ R'-CH=O \longrightarrow R'-CH=CH-CO_2R$

Generality: R, R' = H or alkyl; can be applied to ketones as well, although the yields are poor
              catalyzed by a weak base such as an amine

Key features: related to the aldol condensation (section 18.9)

<u>Michael</u> <u>addition</u> <u>reaction</u>   (27.7.G)

Equation:

$$R-\overset{\overset{\displaystyle O}{\|}}{C}-CH_2-\overset{\overset{\displaystyle O}{\|}}{C}-R \ + \ CH_2=CH-\overset{\overset{\displaystyle O}{\|}}{C}-R \xrightarrow{\ RO^-\ } (R-\overset{\overset{\displaystyle O}{\|}}{C})_2CH-CH_2-CH_2-\overset{\overset{\displaystyle O}{\|}}{C}-R$$

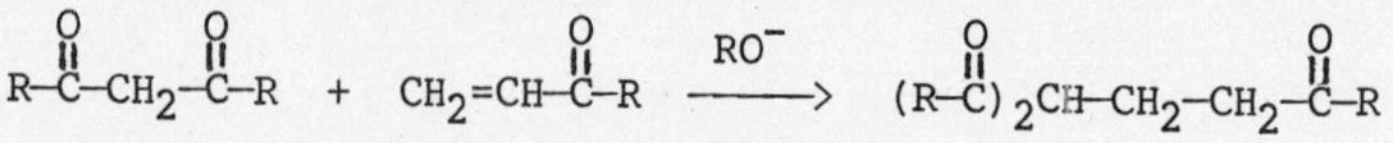

Generality: R = various combinations or H, alkyl, aryl, OR, etc.
              very general process
              RO⁻ used only in catalytic amounts

Key features: important method for the synthesis of 1,5-dicarbonyl compounds
              coupled with an intramolecular aldol condensation, this is an important component of
                  the **Robinson annelation**

27.C   Important Concepts and Hints

For the most part, previous chapters have focused on the chemistry of one functional group at a time. When two are present in a molecule, the reactions the compound undergoes often involve each group independently. However, in many cases the two functional groups interact, and together undergo reactions which are not typical of either group alone. In a sense, such a combination can be considered to be a new functional group, with its own set of reactions and ways to be synthesized. Some examples of this sort were presented in the chapter on conjugation (Chapter 19).

This chapter is organized in a logical fashion, presenting the various pairwise combinations of alcohol, aldehyde and ketone, and carboxylic acid functional groups, and outlining the special behavior which results when they are in 1,2- (adjacent), 1,3-, 1,4- or more remote relationships.

You may have seen many of the reactions in this chapter before; for instance, hydroxylation of olefins to give 1,2-diols and the cleavage of olefins to give dicarboxylic acids were both discussed in the chapter on alkenes (Chapter 11). Similarly, the synthesis of β-hydroxy ketones and their dehydration were discussed in Chapter 14 in connection with the aldol condensation. The reactions of difunctional compounds frequently involve the formation or cleavage of cyclic compounds, by reactions which you have previously learned for the intermolecular cases. For example, the hydrolysis or formation of a lactone is simply the hydrolysis or formation of an ester in which the hydroxy and carboxylic acid groups are part of the same molecule.

From the synthetic standpoint, the synthesis of β-keto esters by the Claisen condensation, its intramolecular counterpart the Dieckmann condensation, the alkylation of β-keto esters and malonic esters and their subsequent decarboxylation (the "acetoacetic ester synthesis" and the "malonic ester synthesis") are among the most important reactions in organic synthesis. (The decarboxylation of β-keto acids and malonic acids is another example of six electrons going around a circle -- see Section 19.B of this Study Guide.) The Robinson annelation is also a noteworthy sequence which involves a Michael addition and subsequent intramolecular aldol condensation, and it has been used extensively in the synthesis of natural products.

27.D   Answers to Exercises

27.1 For example:

HO(CH$_2$)$_6$OH

1,6-hexanediol

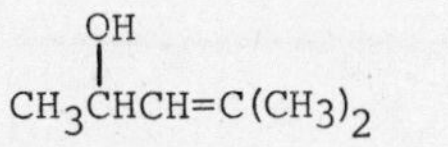

$\overset{\text{OH}}{\underset{}{\text{CH}_3\text{CHCH=C(CH}_3)_2}}$

4-methyl-3-penten-2-ol

$\overset{\text{OH}}{\underset{}{\text{(CH}_3\text{CH}_2)_2\text{CCH=O}}}$

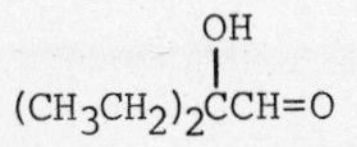

2-ethyl-2-hydroxybutanal

$\overset{\text{OH}}{\underset{\overset{\text{O}}{}}{\text{CH}_3\text{CH}_2\text{CHCCH}_2\text{CH}_3}}$

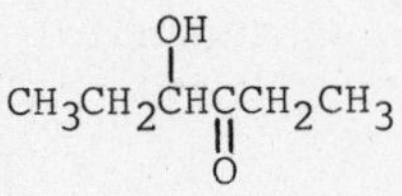

4-hydroxy-3-hexanone

$\overset{\text{OH}}{\underset{}{\text{(CH}_3)_2\text{CHCHCH}_2\text{COOH}}}$

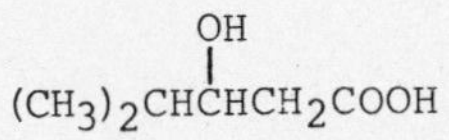

3-hydroxy-4-methyl-pentanoic acid

(CH$_3$)$_2$C=CHCH=CH$_2$

4-methyl-1,3-pentadiene

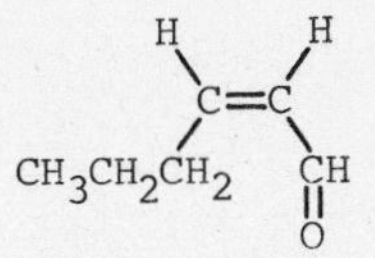

(Z)-2-hexenal

CH$_2$=CHCH$_2$CH$_2$CH$_2$COOH

5-hexenoic acid

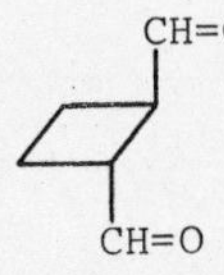

trans-1,2-cyclobutanedicarbaldehyde (or -dicarboxaldehyde)

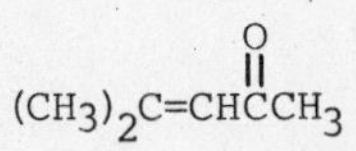

(CH$_3$)$_2$C=CHCCH$_3$

4-methyl-3-penten-2-one

$\overset{\text{O}}{\text{HCCH}_2}\overset{\text{CH}_3}{\underset{\overset{\text{O}}{}}{\text{CHCCH}_3}}$

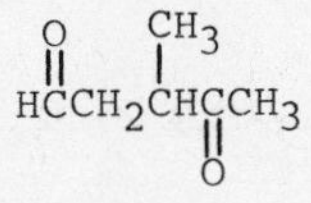

3-methyl-4-oxopentanal

$\overset{\text{O}}{\text{HCCH}_2}\overset{\text{CH}_3}{\underset{\text{CH}_3}{\text{CCOOH}}}$

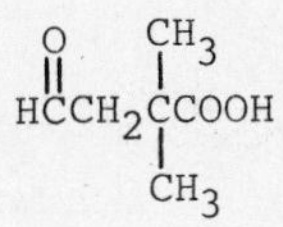

2,2-dimethyl-4-oxobutanoic acid

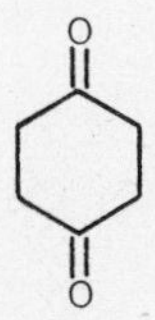

1,4-cyclohexanedione

$\text{CH}_3\text{CH}_2\text{CH}_2\overset{\text{O}}{\text{C}}\text{CH}_2\text{COOH}$

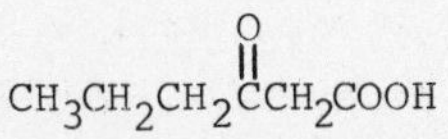

3-oxohexanoic acid

$\underset{\text{CH}_2\text{CH}_3}{\text{HOOCCHCH}_2\text{COOH}}$

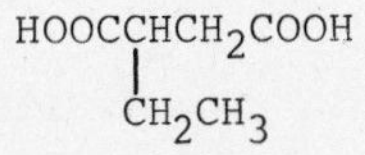

2-ethylbutanedioic acid

27.2

KMnO$_4$

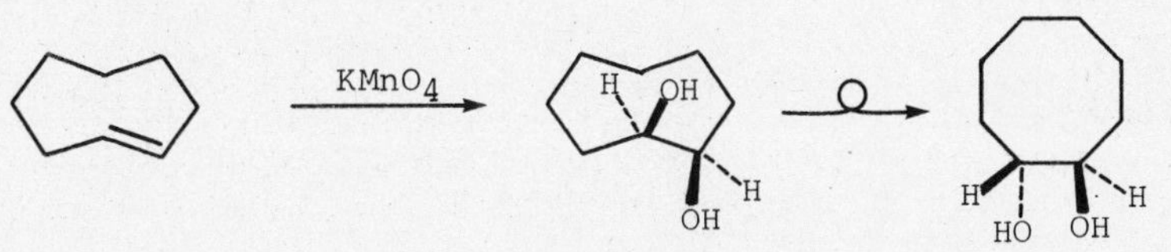

trans-1,2-cyclo-octanediol

27.3   (a)

2R,3R   2S,3S   2,3-butanediol

(*racemic mixture*)

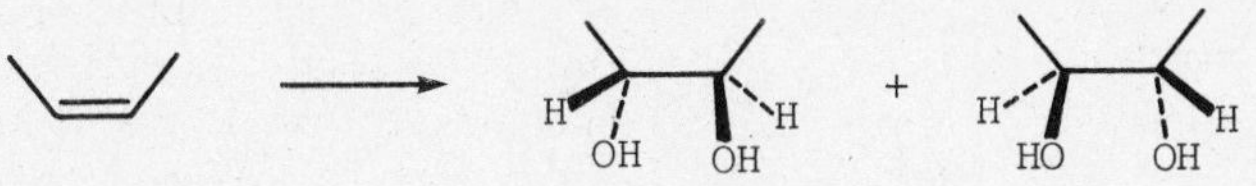

(b)

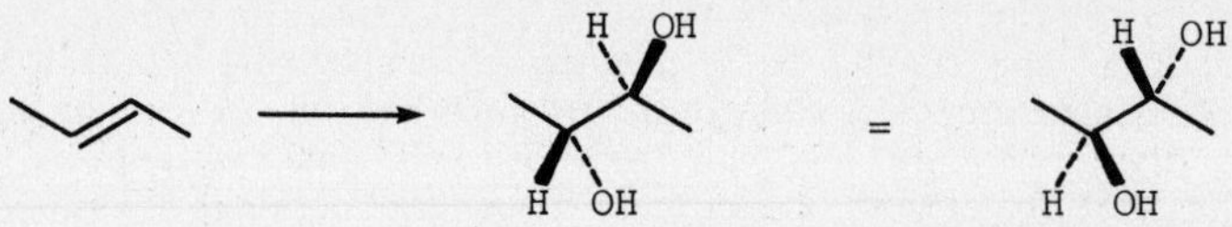

2R,3S-2,3-butanediol

meso compound

(c)

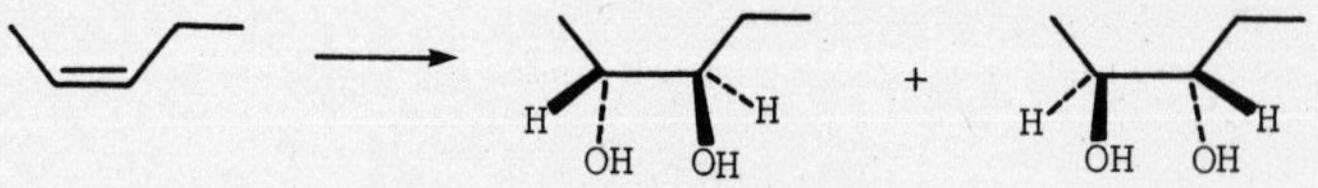

2R,3R   2S,3S   2,3-pentanediol

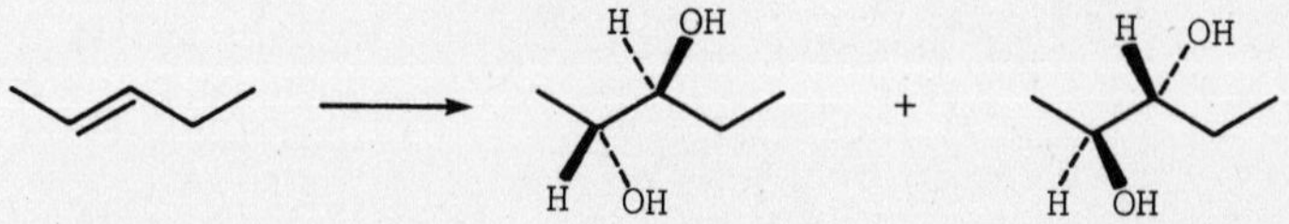

(racemic mixture)

(d)

2R,3S   2S,3R   2,3-pentanediol

(racemic mixture)

(e)

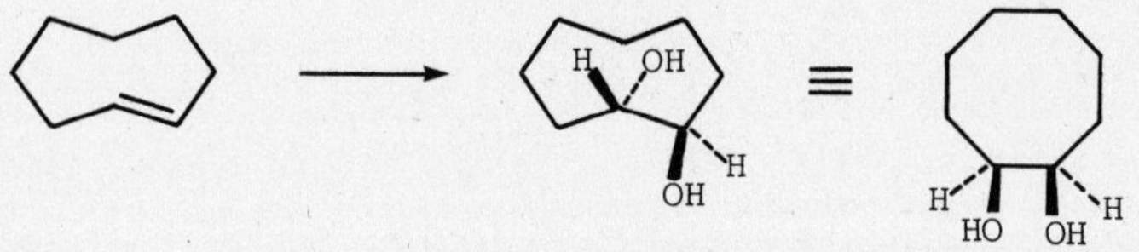

cis-1,2-cyclo-
        octanediol

27.4

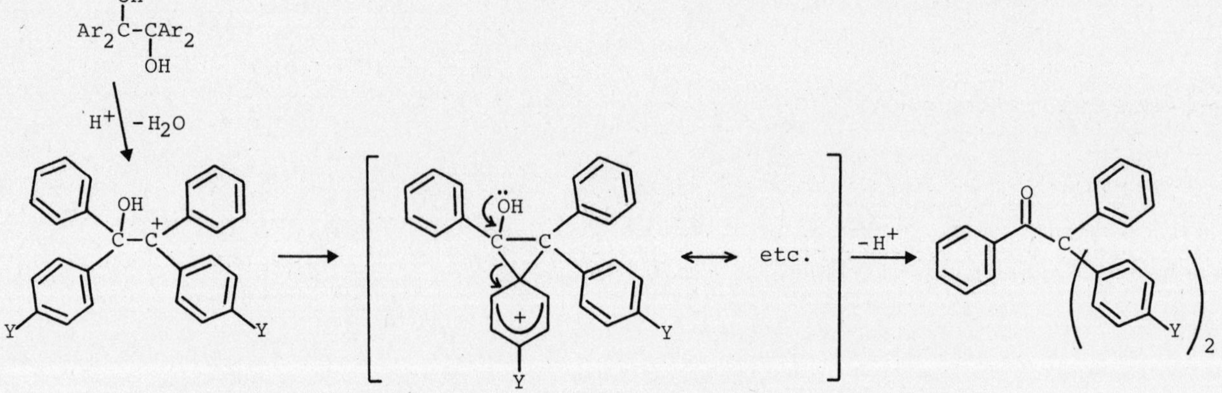

$$Ar_2C\text{--}CAr_2$$

with OH, OH groups

H^+, $-H_2O$

*favored relative to phenyl migration
when Y = CH₃, disfavored for Y = NO₂*

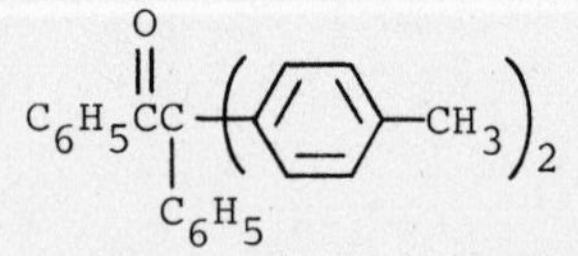

$$C_6H_5\overset{O}{C}\overset{}{C}\left(\text{--}\langle\text{--}\rangle\text{--}CH_3\right)_2 \quad \text{and} \quad O_2N\text{--}\langle\text{--}\rangle\text{--}\overset{O}{C}\text{--}C(C_6H_5)_2 \quad \text{are the major products.}$$

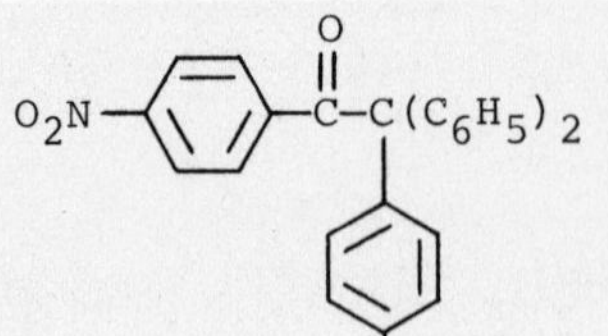

27.5

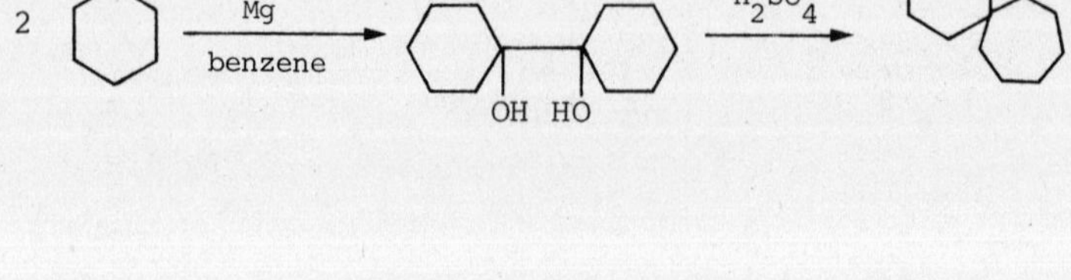

2 cyclohexanone $\xrightarrow[\text{benzene}]{\text{Mg}}$ bicyclohexyl diol $\xrightarrow{H_2SO_4}$ spiro ketone

27.6

(a)

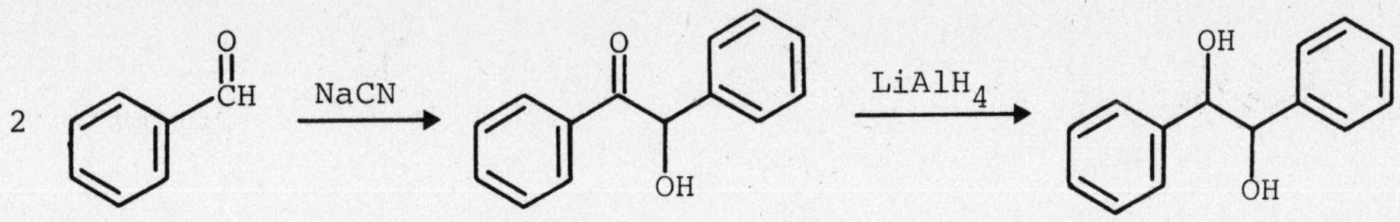

(b)

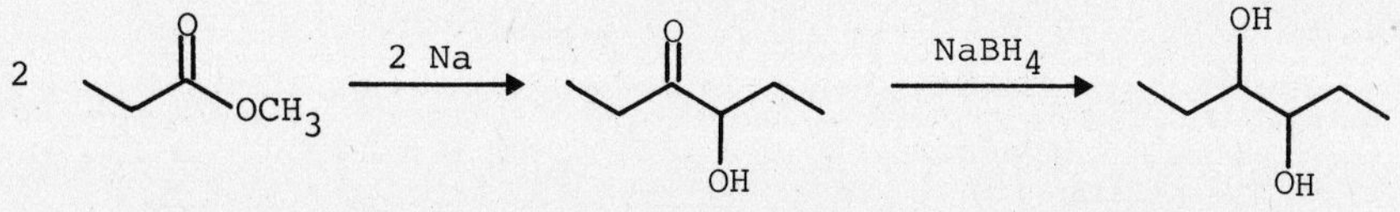

(c)

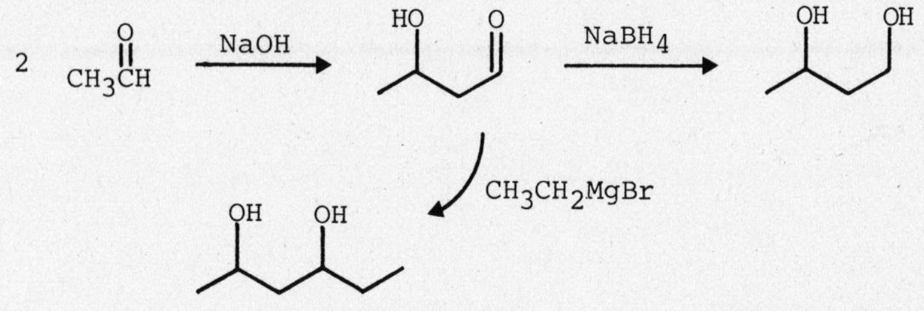

(d)

27.7 The intermediate cation is stabilized by resonance with the lone pair electrons on the ether oxygen:

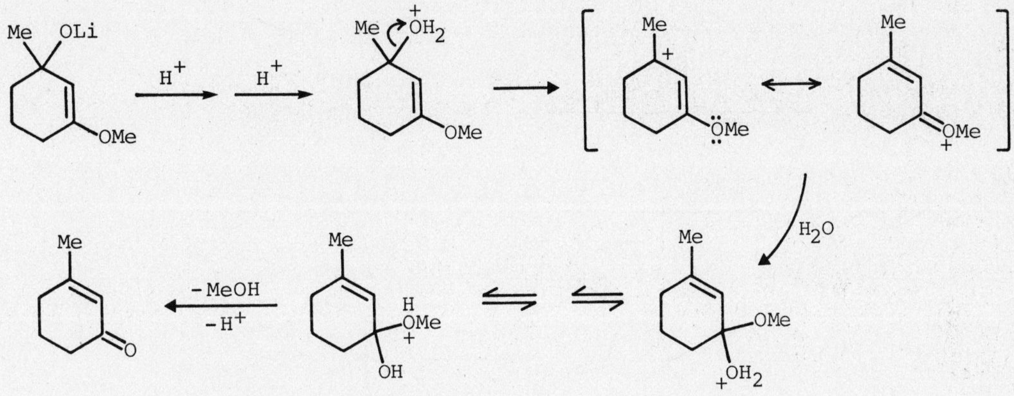

27.8

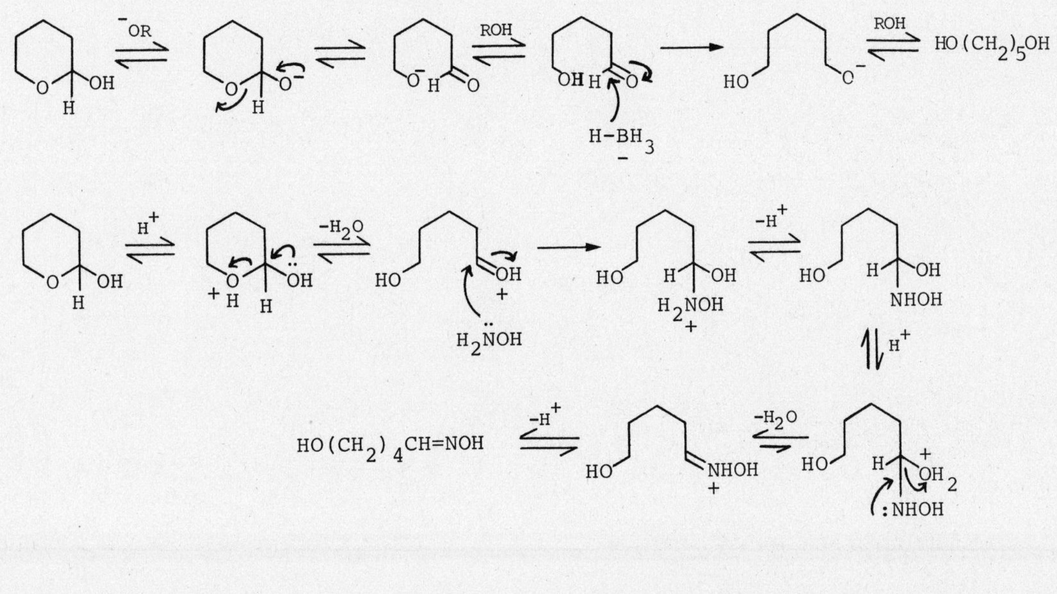

$-CH_4$

CH_3-MgBr

CH_3-MgBr

H_2O

$HOCH_2CH_2CH_2CH_2\overset{OH}{C}HCH_3$

$-H^+$

$-Cl$

$H_2Cr_2O_7$

$+ \left(Cr^{IV} \longrightarrow disproportionates\right)$

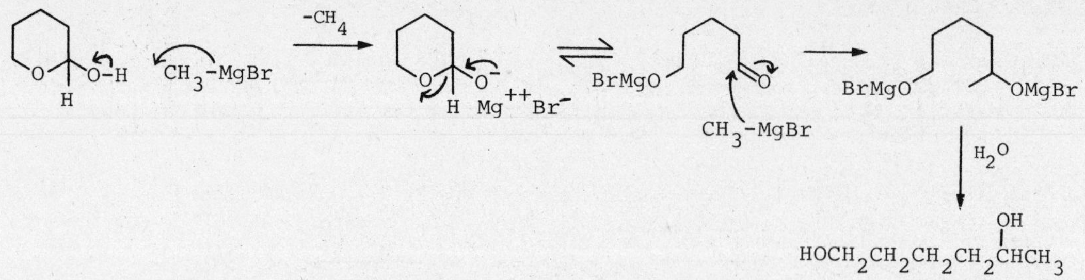

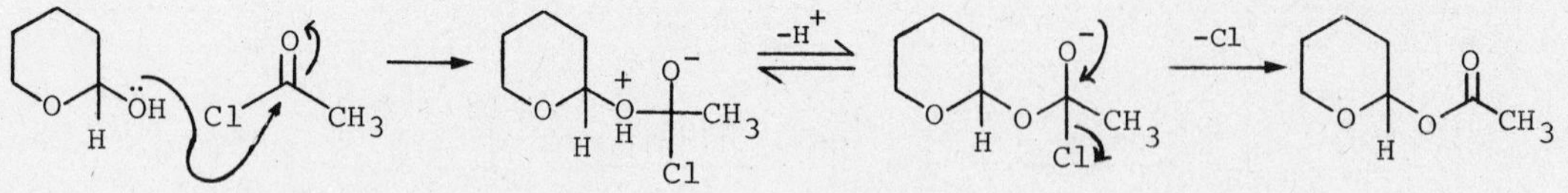

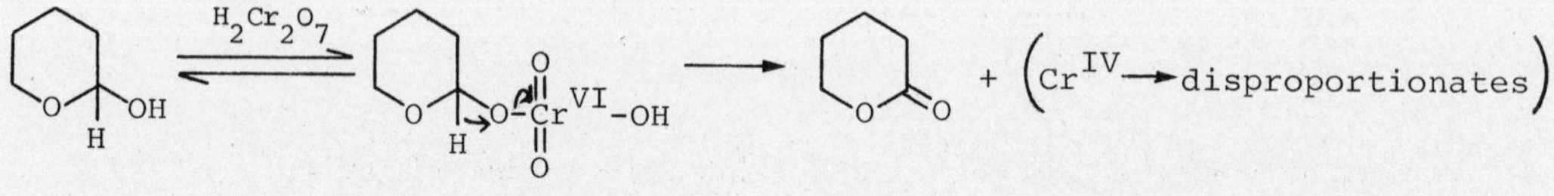

27.9 (a) $CH_3CH_2CH_2CH_2CO_2H \xrightarrow{P,\,Br_2} \xrightarrow{H_2O} CH_3CH_2CH_2\overset{Br}{C}HCO_2H \xrightarrow{NaOH} CH_3CH_2CH_2\overset{OH}{C}HCO_2H$

(b) $CH_3CH_2CH_2\overset{O}{\overset{||}{C}}H \xrightarrow{HCN} CH_3CH_2CH_2\overset{OH}{C}HC\equiv N \xrightarrow{H_2SO_4}$

$CH_3\overset{O}{\overset{||}{C}}OC_2H_5 \xrightarrow[THF,\,-70°]{LDA} CH_3CH_2\overset{O}{\overset{||}{C}}H \xrightarrow{OH^-} CH_3CH_2\overset{OH}{C}HCH_2CO_2H$

27.10

NaCN → CN → H_3O^+ → CO_2H

$\xrightarrow[(or\ Hg(OAc)_2;\ NaBH_4)]{aq.\ H_2SO_4}$

$\xrightarrow[-H_2O]{H^+}$ HO—...—CO_2H

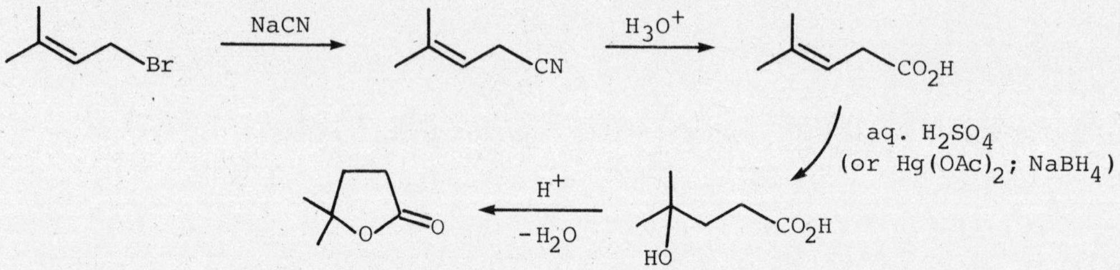

27.11

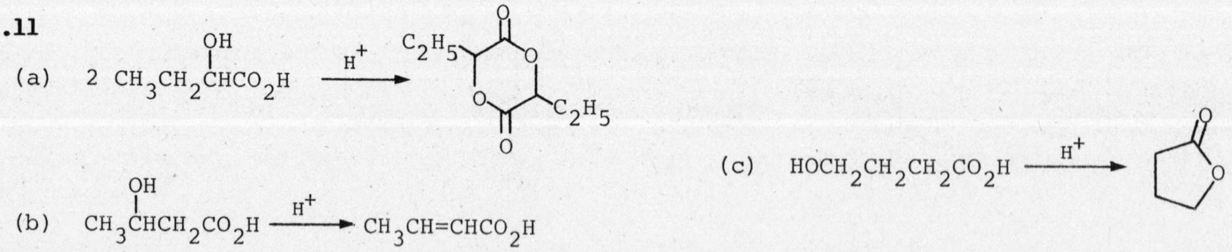

(a) $2\ CH_3CH_2\overset{OH}{C}HCO_2H \xrightarrow{H^+}$

(c) $HOCH_2CH_2CH_2CO_2H \xrightarrow{H^+}$

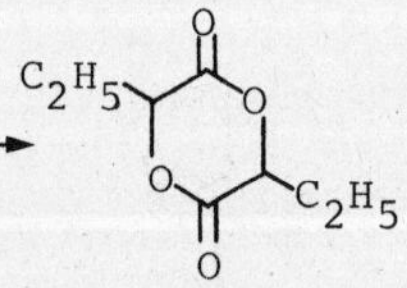

(b) $CH_3\overset{OH}{C}HCH_2CO_2H \xrightarrow{H^+} CH_3CH=CHCO_2H$

27.12

$+ CH_3CO_2Me \xrightarrow{MeO^-}$ —CO_2Me $\xrightarrow{NaCN}$ CN/CO_2Me $\xrightarrow[\Delta]{H_3O^+}$ CO_2H/CO_2H

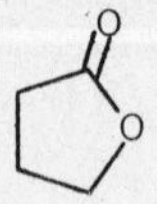

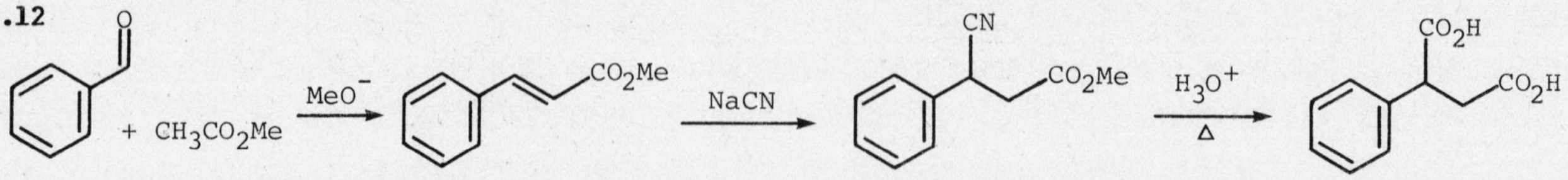

27.13

$HO_2CCH_2CH_2CH_2CO_2H \xrightarrow{\Delta}$ $+ H_2O$

$CH_3CH_2CH(CO_2H)_2 \xrightarrow{\Delta} CH_3CH_2CH_2CO_2H + CO_2$

$HO_2C\overset{}{C}HCH_2CO_2H$ (CH_3) $\xrightarrow{\Delta}$ $+ H_2O$

$(CH_3)_2C(CO_2H)_2 \xrightarrow{\Delta} (CH_3)_2CHCO_2H + CO_2$

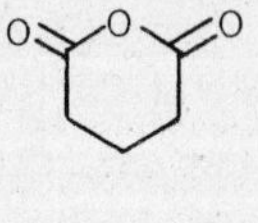

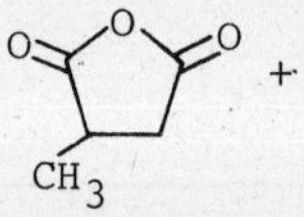

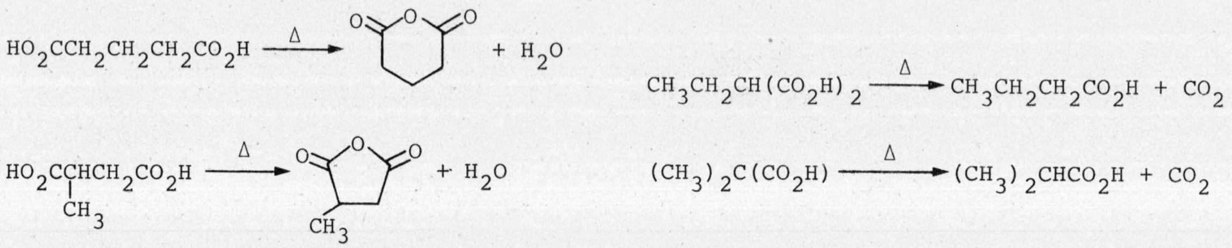

27.14

$$EtO_2CCH_2CH_2CH_2CH_2CO_2Et \xrightarrow{NaOEt} \rightleftharpoons EtO_2C\overset{-}{C}HCH_2CH_2CH_2\overset{O}{\underset{\parallel}{C}}OEt \rightleftharpoons$$

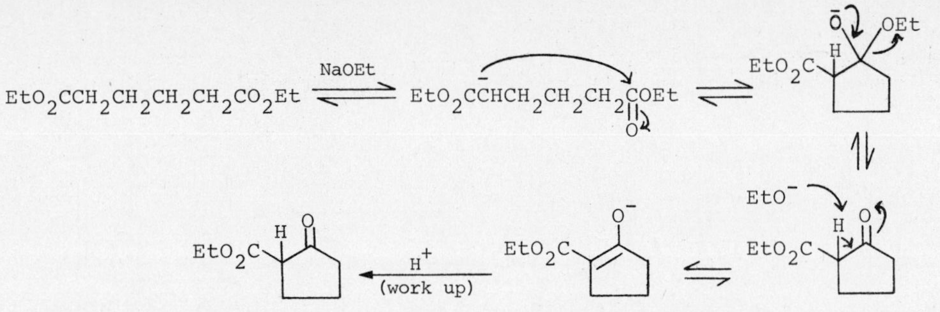

(among other resonance structures)

$$EtO_2C \overset{H}{\underset{O}{\rightleftharpoons}} \xleftarrow[\text{(work up)}]{H^+} EtO_2C \overset{O^-}{\rightleftharpoons} EtO_2C \overset{H}{\rightleftharpoons}$$

27.15

(a) $2\ CH_3CH_2CO_2Et \xrightarrow[\text{ether}]{Na} \xrightarrow{H_2O} CH_3CH_2\overset{O}{\underset{\parallel}{C}}\underset{OH}{CH}CH_2CH_3 \xrightarrow{Cu(Ac)_2} CH_3CH_2\overset{O}{\underset{\parallel}{C}}\overset{O}{\underset{\parallel}{C}}CH_2CH_3$

(b) $CH_3\overset{O}{\underset{\parallel}{C}}CH_3 + CH_3CO_2Et \xrightarrow{EtO^-} CH_3\overset{O}{\underset{\parallel}{C}}\overset{O}{\underset{\parallel}{C}}HCCH_3 \xrightarrow[\text{(work up)}]{H^+} CH_3\overset{O}{\underset{\parallel}{C}}CH_2\overset{O}{\underset{\parallel}{C}}CH_3$

(c) $2\ CH_3\overset{O}{\underset{\parallel}{C}}H \xrightarrow[\text{mild}]{OH^-} CH_3\underset{OH}{CH}CH_2\overset{O}{\underset{\parallel}{C}}H \xrightarrow[\text{pyridine}]{CrO_3} CH_3\overset{O}{\underset{\parallel}{C}}CH_2\overset{O}{\underset{\parallel}{C}}H$

27.16

from small amount of diketo form:

−CH₃ (area 6)

(area 1)

−OH (area 1)

27.18

+ MeO⁻ ⇌ + MeOH $K = 10^{6.5} = 3.2 \times 10^6$

pK$_a$:   9   15.5
(Table 10.3)

27.19

(a) $CH_3\overset{O}{\underset{\parallel}{C}}CH_2CO_2Et \xrightarrow[CH_2=CH-CH_2Br]{NaOEt} CH_3\overset{O}{\underset{\parallel}{C}}\underset{CH_2CH=CH_2}{CH}CO_2Et \xrightarrow{H_3O^+} \left[CH_3\overset{O}{\underset{\parallel}{C}}\underset{CH_2CH=CH_2}{CH}CO_2H \right] \xrightarrow{-CO_2}$

$$CH_3\overset{O}{\underset{\parallel}{C}}CH_2CH_2CH=CH_2$$

(b) $EtO_2CCH_2CO_2Et \xrightarrow[(CH_3)_2CHCH_2CH_2Br]{NaOEt} (CH_3)_2CHCH_2CH_2CH(CO_2Et)_2 \xrightarrow[\Delta]{H_3O^+}$

$$(CH_3)_2CHCH_2CH_2CH_2CO_2H \xleftarrow{-CO_2} \left[(CH_3)_2CHCH_2CH_2CH(CO_2H)_2 \right]$$

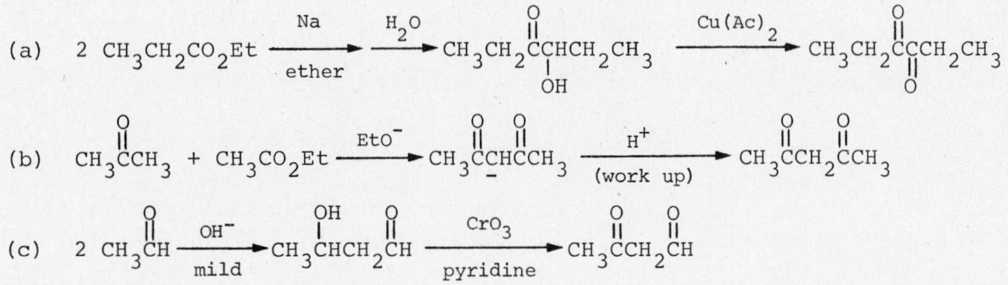

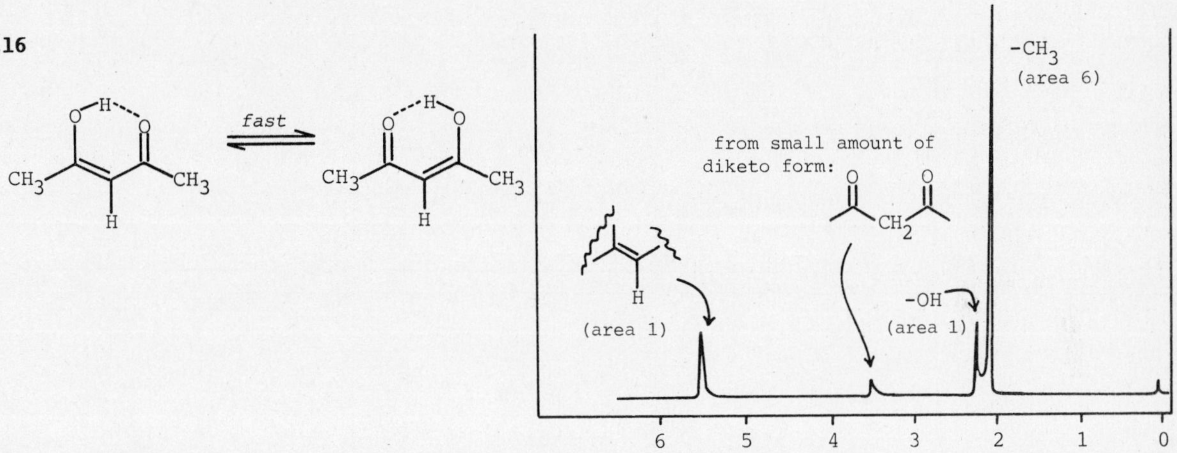

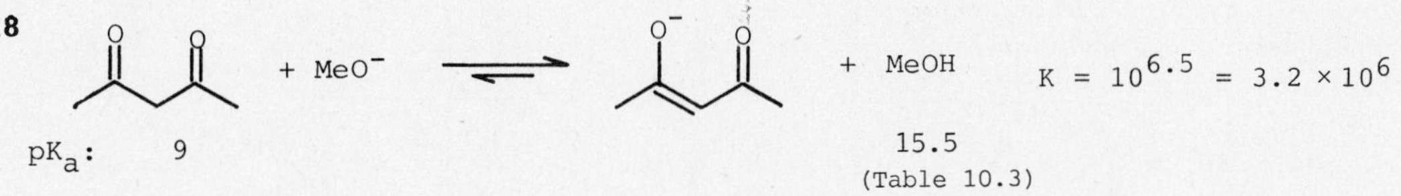

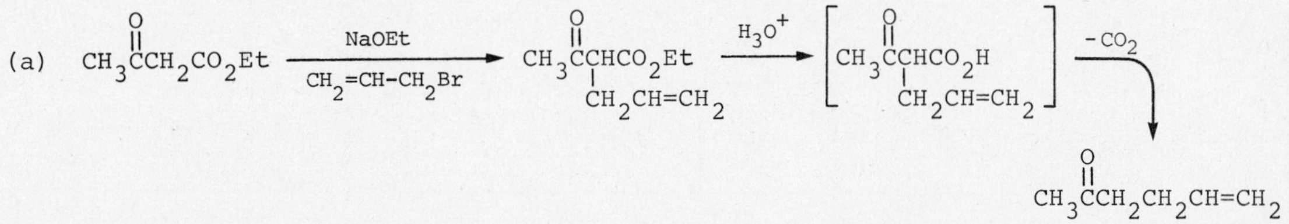

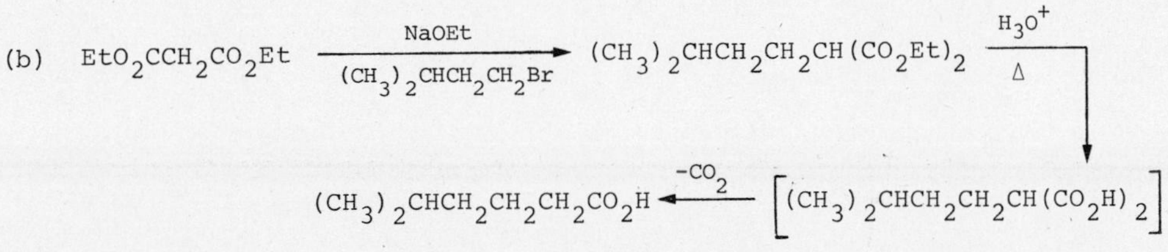

(c) $EtO_2CCH_2CO_2Et$ $\xrightarrow[C_2H_5I]{NaH}$ $EtO_2C\!-\!CO_2Et$ $\xrightarrow[CH_2=CH_2CH_2Br]{NaH}$ $\overset{CO_2Et}{\underset{CO_2Et}{\diagup}}$ $\xrightarrow[\Delta]{H_3O^+}$ CO_2H

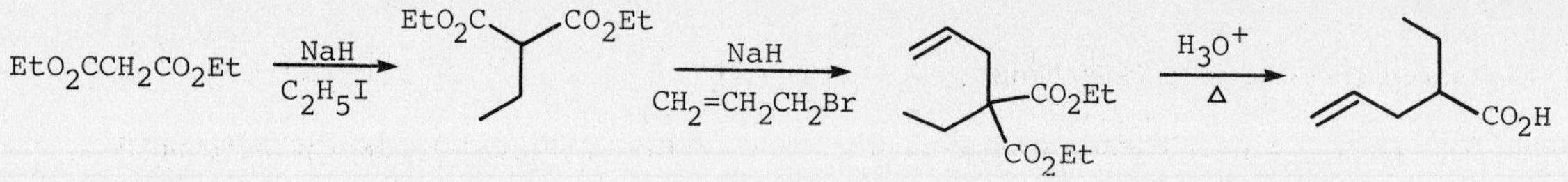

(d) $\underset{O}{\overset{\parallel}{C}}\!-\!OEt$ (acetoacetic ester) $\xrightarrow[BrCH_2CO_2Et]{NaH}$ $\overset{CO_2Et}{\diagup}\,CO_2Et$ $\xrightarrow[\Delta]{H_3O^+}$ CO_2Et

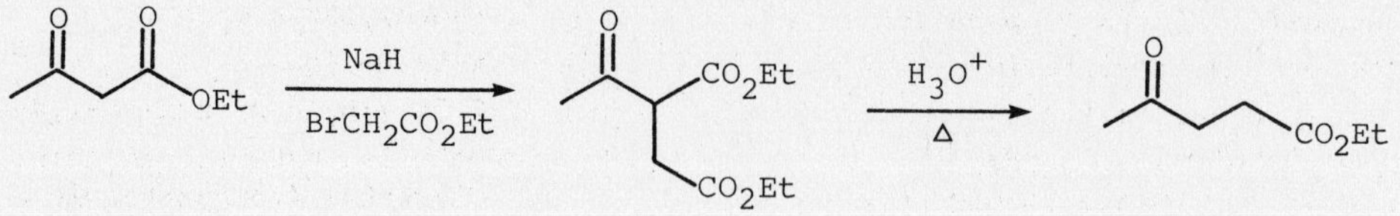

27.20

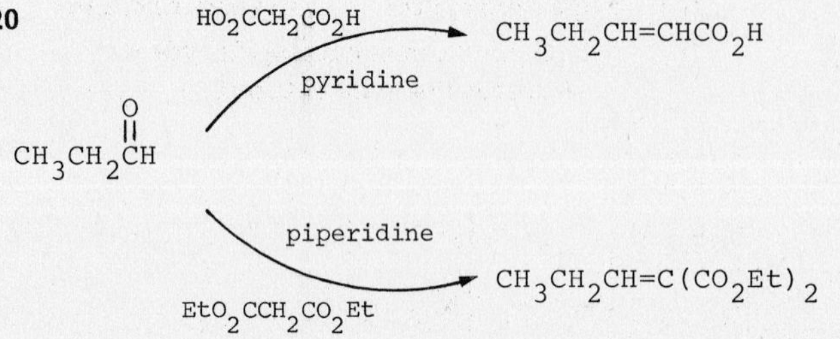

$HO_2CCH_2CO_2H$ $\xrightarrow{pyridine}$ $CH_3CH_2CH=CHCO_2H$

$CH_3CH_2\overset{O}{\overset{\parallel}{C}}H$

$\xrightarrow[EtO_2CCH_2CO_2Et]{piperidine}$ $CH_3CH_2CH=C(CO_2Et)_2$

27.21

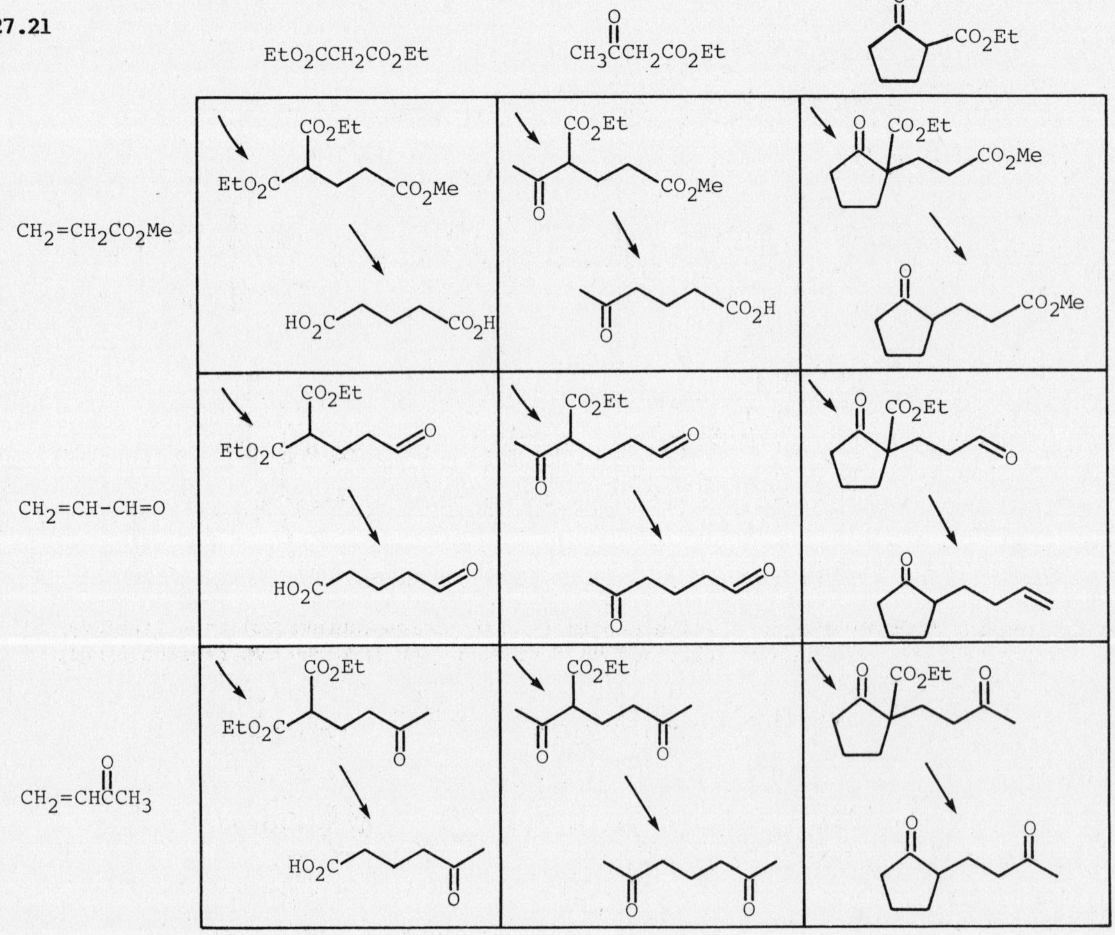

	$EtO_2CCH_2CO_2Et$	$CH_3\overset{O}{\overset{\parallel}{C}}CH_2CO_2Et$	$\overset{O}{\diagup}CO_2Et$ (2-carbethoxycyclopentanone)
$CH_2=CH_2CO_2Me$	(structures)	(structures)	(structures)
$CH_2=CH-CH=O$	(structures)	(structures)	(structures)
$CH_2=CH\overset{O}{\overset{\parallel}{C}}CH_3$	(structures)	(structures)	(structures)

27.22

$\overset{O}{\diagup}$ spiro ketone $\xleftarrow{KOH}$ (spiro diketoaldehyde) $\xleftarrow[KOH]{\overset{O}{\diagup}}$ (methyl vinyl ketone) $HC\overset{O}{\overset{\parallel}{}}\!-\!cyclopentyl$

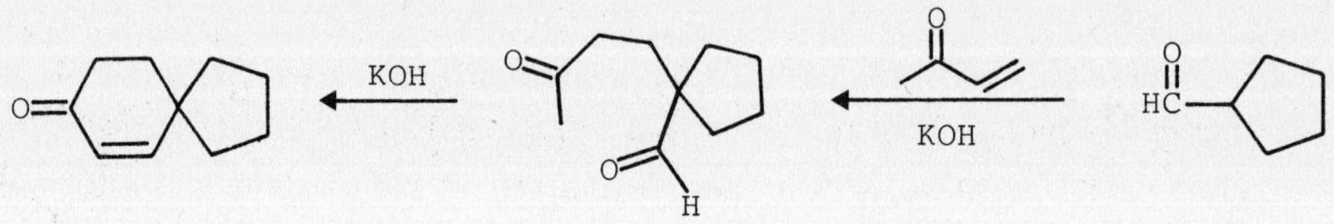

27.E   Answers and Explanations for Problems

1. (a) methyl 4-methyl-3-oxopentanoate
    (b) 2,2-dimethyl-1,3-propanediol
    (c) 4-hydroxybutanoic acid
    (d) 4-oxopentanenitrile
    (e) β-methylglutaric acid;
             3-methylpentanedioic acid

    (f) α-methyladipic acid;
             2-methylhexanedioic acid
    (g) dimethyl methylpropylmalonate;
           dimethyl 2-methyl-2-propylpropanedioate

    (h) 3-methyl-5-oxopentanoic acid
    (i) 4-hydroxybutanamide
    (j) hex-5-en-2-one
    (k) 2,2-dimethylcyclohexane-1,4-dione
    (l) α-methyl-γ-ketovaleric acid;
             2-methyl-4-oxopentanoic acid
    (m) glutaronitrile;   pentanedinitrile
    (n) ε-methyl-γ-ketoenanthaldehyde;
             6-methyl-4-oxoheptanal

2.

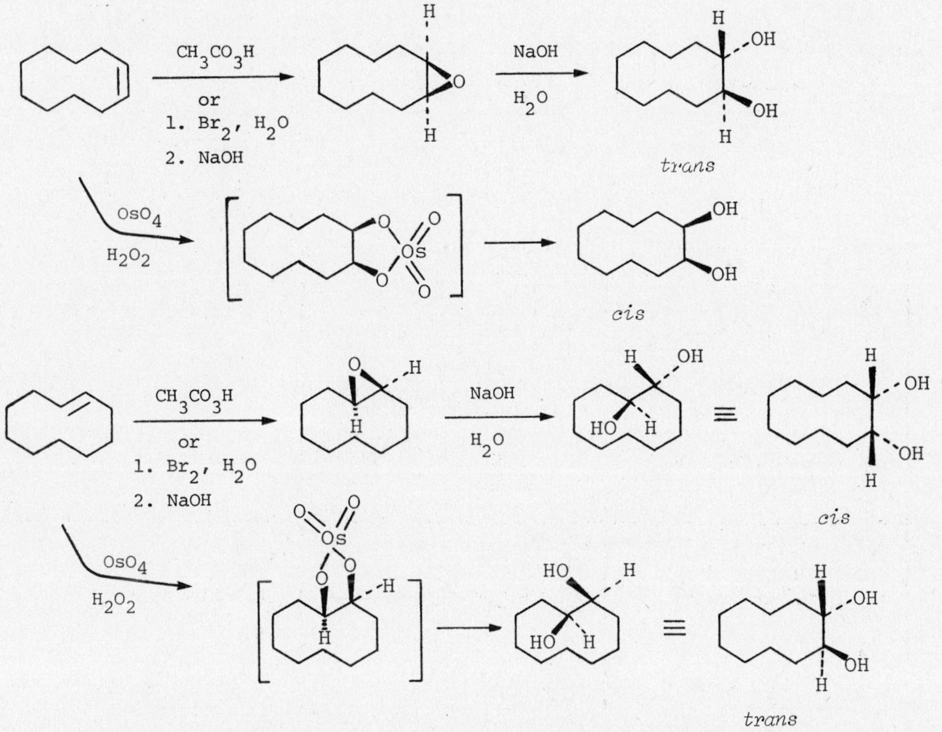

trans

cis

cis

trans

3. Loss of the two hydroxy groups can give a primary carbocation (unfavored) or a tertiary
    carbocation that can be further stabilized by delocalization into the two benzene rings.

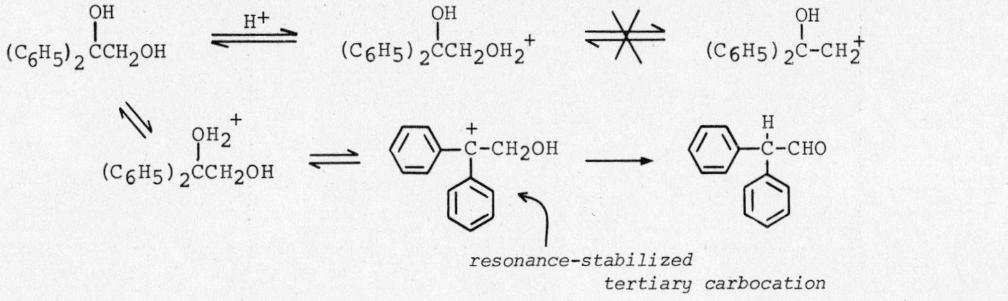

$(C_6H_5)_2CCH_2OH$ ⇌ $(C_6H_5)_2CCH_2OH_2^+$ ⇏ $(C_6H_5)_2C-CH_2^+$

$(C_6H_5)_2CCH_2OH$ ⇌ ⟶

resonance-stabilized
tertiary carbocation

4. (a) 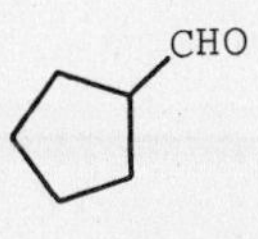   CHO

    (b) 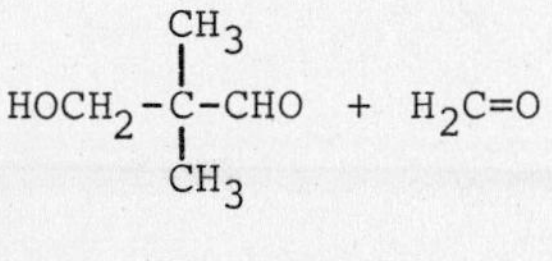 $HOCH_2-C(CH_3)_2-CHO$ + $H_2C=O$

    (c) $+O-(CH_2)_6-C(=O)+_n$
         polymer

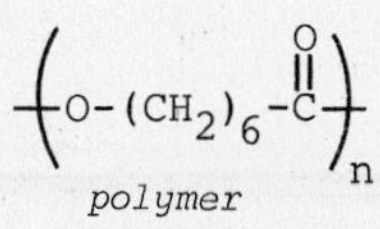

    (d)

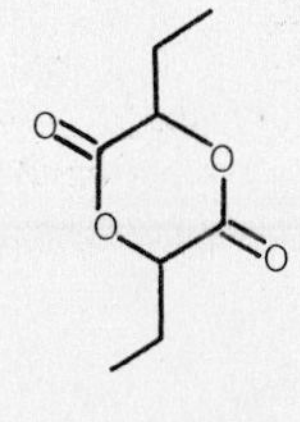

(e)

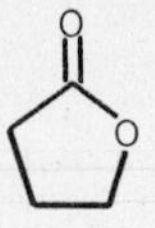

(f)

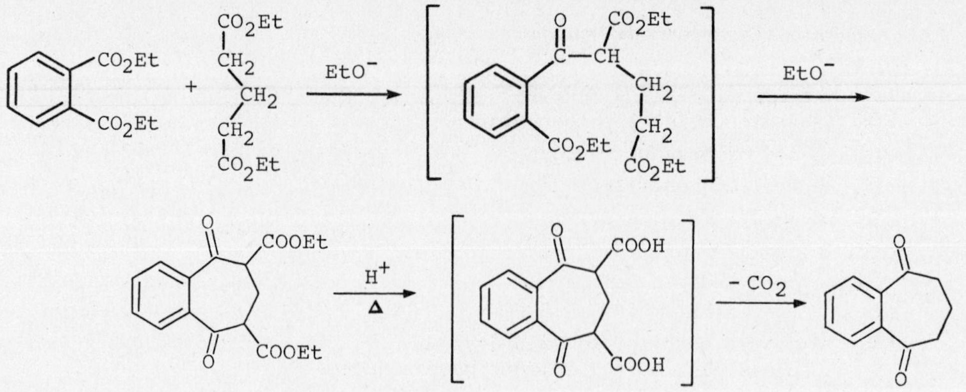

(EtO^-) ...

Note that both CO_2H groups are β-keto acids.

(g)

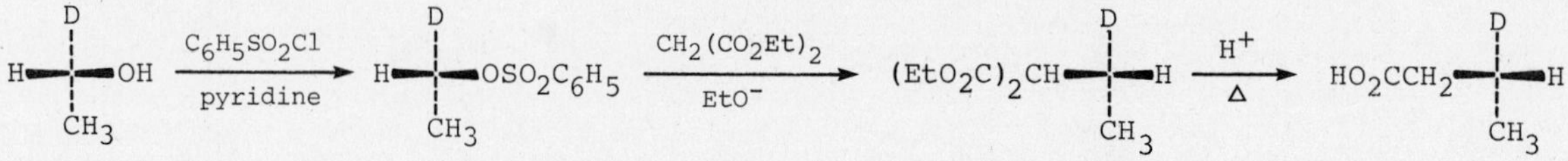

note inversion
of configuration

(h)

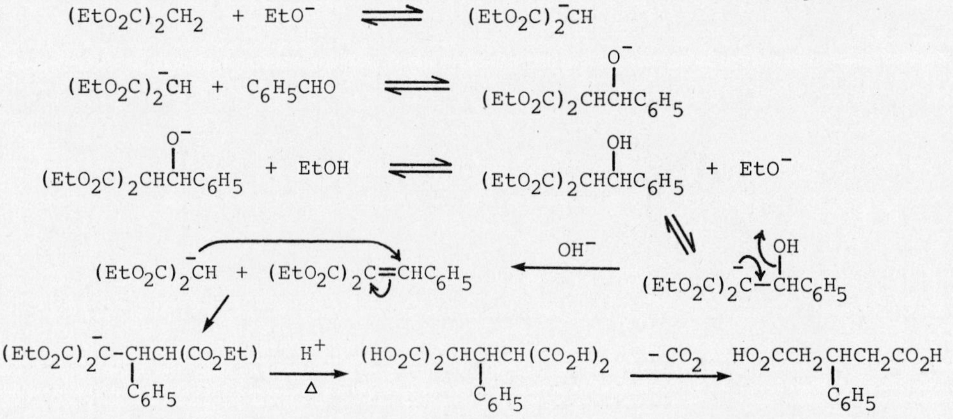

$(EtO_2C)_2CH_2 + EtO^- \rightleftharpoons (EtO_2C)_2^-CH$

$(EtO_2C)_2^-CH + C_6H_5CHO \rightleftharpoons (EtO_2C)_2CHCHC_6H_5$

$(EtO_2C)_2CHCHC_6H_5 + EtOH \rightleftharpoons (EtO_2C)_2CHCHC_6H_5 + EtO^-$

$(EtO_2C)_2^-CH + (EtO_2C)_2C=CHC_6H_5 \xleftarrow{OH^-} (EtO_2C)_2C-CHC_6H_5$

$(EtO_2C)_2^-C-CHCH(CO_2Et) \xrightarrow[\Delta]{H^+} (HO_2C)_2CHCHCH(CO_2H)_2 \xrightarrow{-CO_2} HO_2CCH_2CHCH_2CO_2H$
$\quad C_6H_5 \qquad\qquad\qquad\qquad C_6H_5 \qquad\qquad\qquad\qquad C_6H_5$

(i) 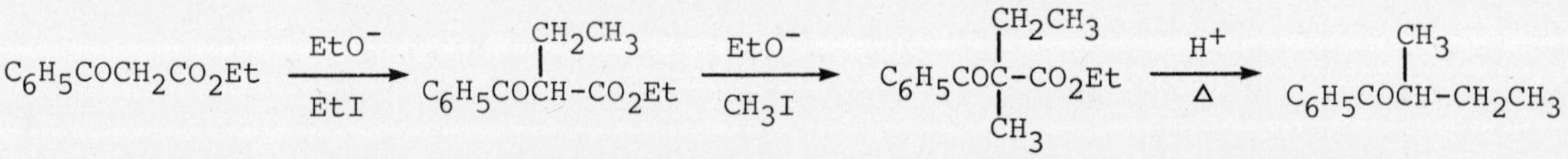 $C_6H_5COCH_2CO_2Et \xrightarrow[EtI]{EtO^-} C_6H_5COCH-CO_2Et \xrightarrow[CH_3I]{EtO^-} C_6H_5COC-CO_2Et \xrightarrow[\Delta]{H^+} C_6H_5COCH-CH_2CH_3$

(j) $CH_3CO_2Et + EtO_2CCO_2Et \xrightarrow{EtO^-} EtO_2CCH_2COCO_2Et$

5. (a)

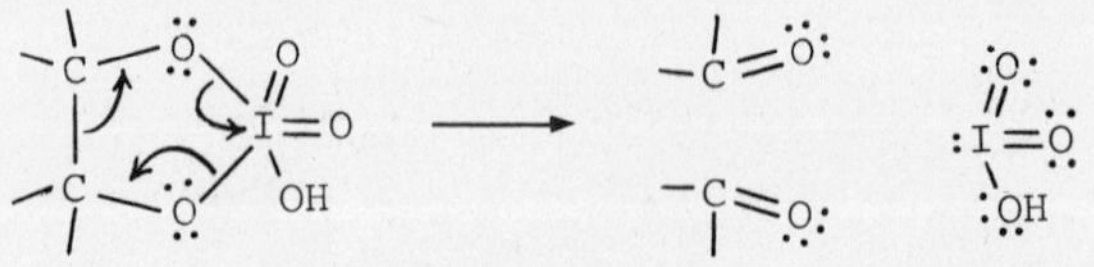

(b) Ease of formation of the cyclic iodate intermediate with the cis isomer. This is easier to see using molecular models.   vs.   farther apart

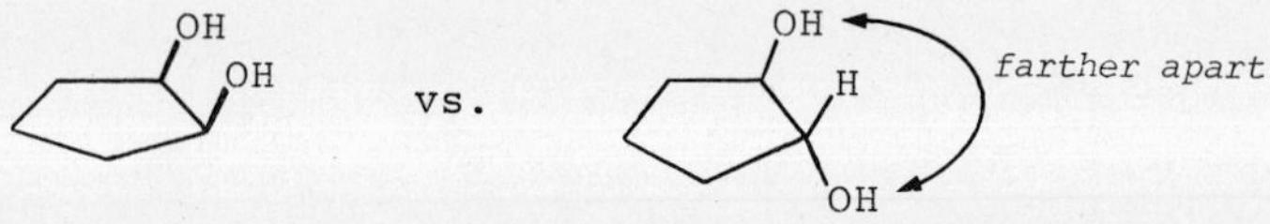

(c)

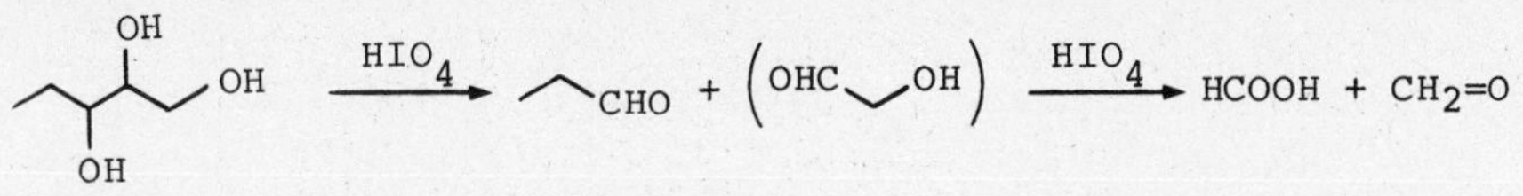

The 1,2,3-isomer will consume <u>two</u> equivalents of HIO_4.
The 1,2,4-isomer only reacts once.

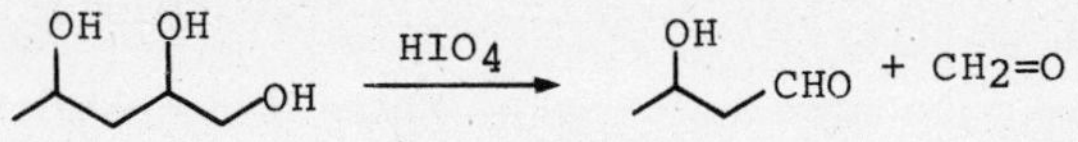

6. (a)

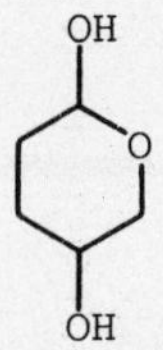

*major isomer; six-membered
saturated ring is preferred*

(b)

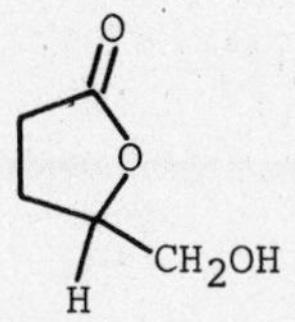

*five-membered lactone
ring is preferred*

7. (a)

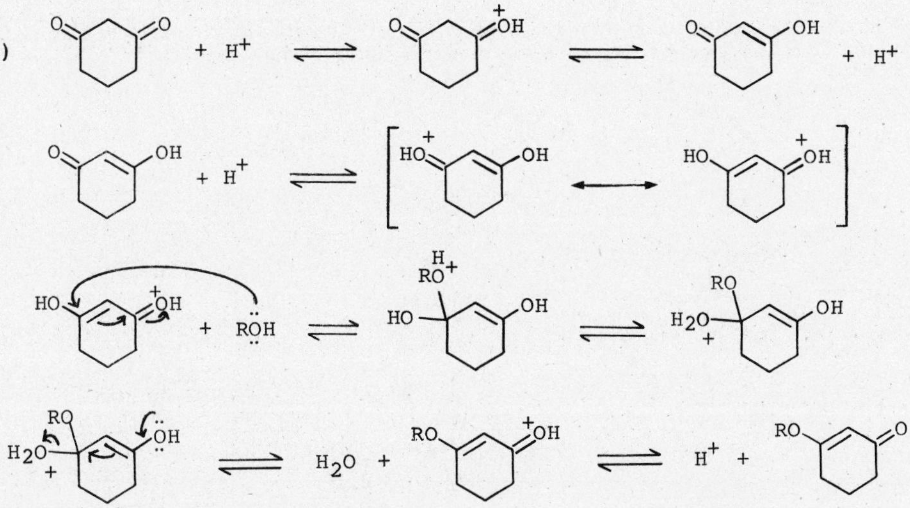

(b)

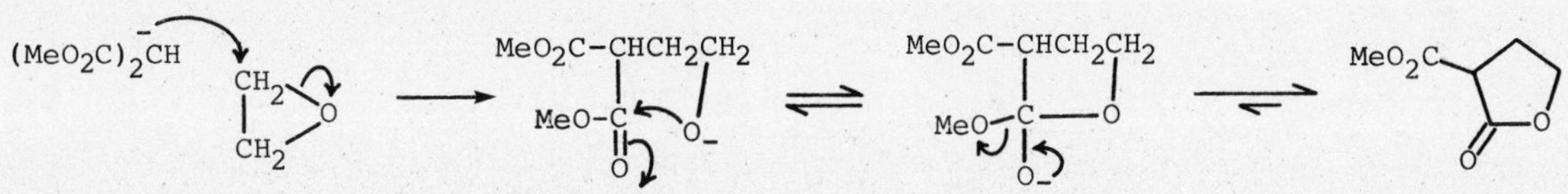

(c)

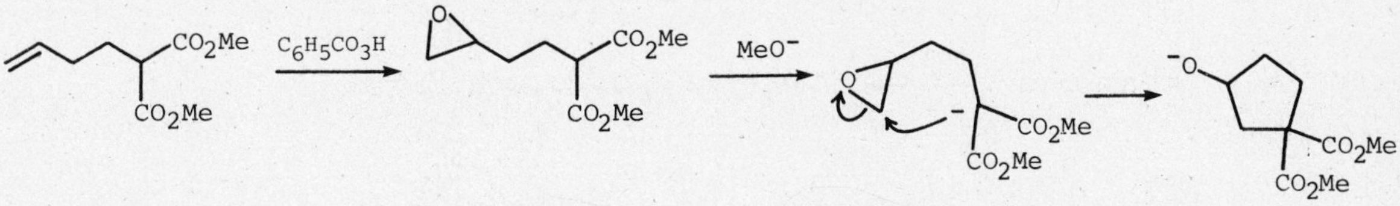

(d)

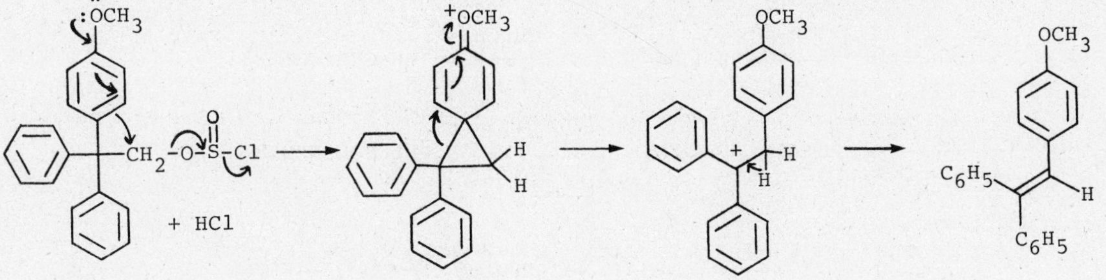

8. $CH_3CO\overset{-}{C}HCO_2Et$ + $BrCH_2CH_2CH_2Br$ $\longrightarrow$ $CH_3CO\underset{\underset{CH_2CH_2CH_2Br}{|}}{C}HCO_2Et$

While the first alkylation is normal,
the second would give a strained four-membered ring:

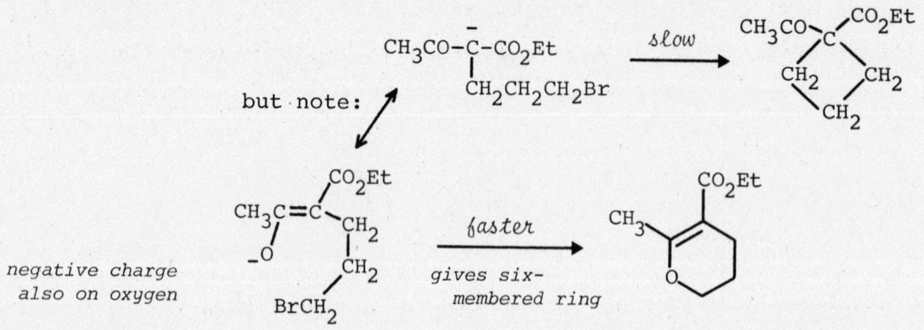

but note:

$CH_3CO-\overset{-}{C}-CO_2Et$ ... $\overset{slow}{\longrightarrow}$ ...

negative charge
also on oxygen

$\overset{faster}{\longrightarrow}$ gives six-
membered ring

O-alkylation is a side reaction that is normally not important in alkylations
of β-keto esters, but it can become dominant with some reagents.

9. (a)

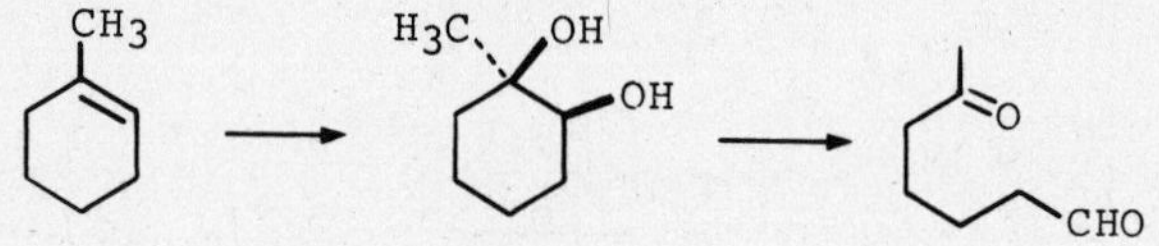

   (b)
   $(Et)_3C\overset{O}{\overset{||}{C}}Et$

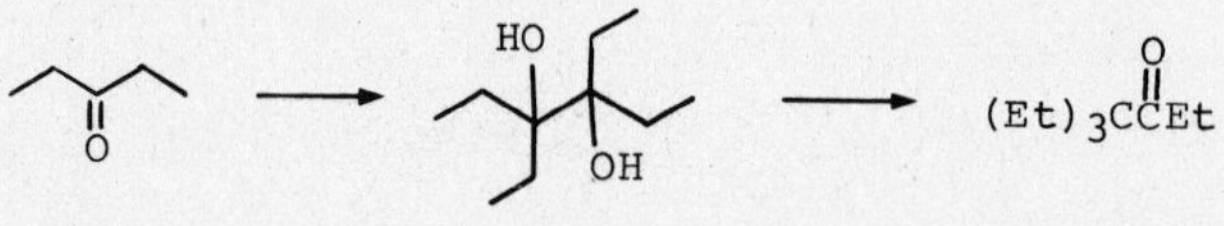

   (c)

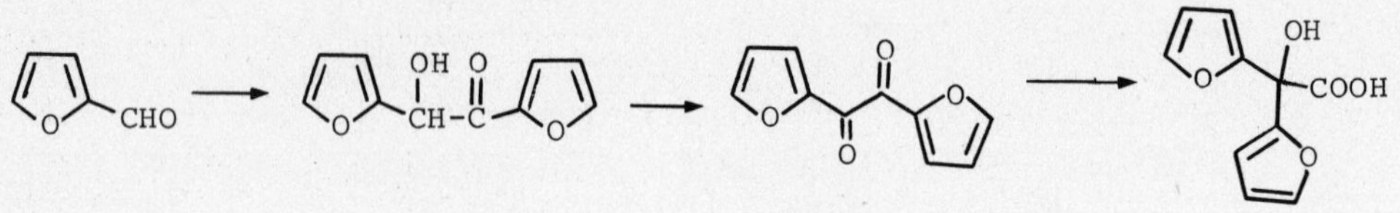

   (d)

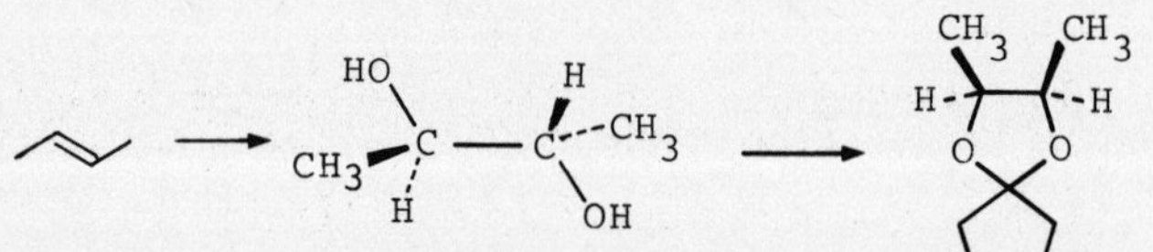

10. (a) CH_3CH_2COOH $\overset{SOCl_2}{\longrightarrow}$ CH_3CH_2COCl $\overset{H_2}{\underset{Pd/BaSO_4}{\longrightarrow}}$ CH_3CH_2CHO

   $\overset{dil.\ OH^-}{\longrightarrow}$ $CH_3CH_2CHOH\overset{\overset{CH_3}{|}}{C}HCHO$ $\overset{Ag_2O}{\longrightarrow}$ $CH_3CH_2CHOH\overset{\overset{CH_3}{|}}{C}HCOOH$

   or: CH_3CH_2COOH $\overset{PBr_3}{\underset{Br_2}{\longrightarrow}}$ $CH_3CHBrCOBr$ $\overset{CH_3OH}{\longrightarrow}$ $CH_3CHBrCOOCH_3$

   $\overset{Zn}{\underset{CH_3CH_2CHO}{\longrightarrow}}$ $CH_3CH_2CHOH\overset{\overset{CH_3}{|}}{C}HCOOCH_3$ $\overset{OH^-}{\underset{H_2O}{\longrightarrow}}$ $CH_3CH_2CHOH\overset{\overset{CH_3}{|}}{C}HCOOH$

   (b)

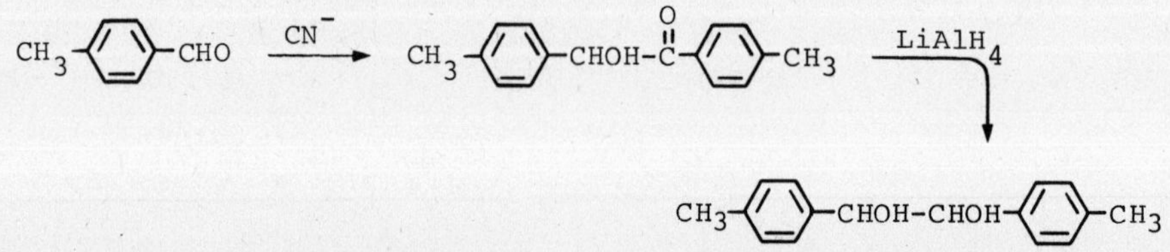

(c)

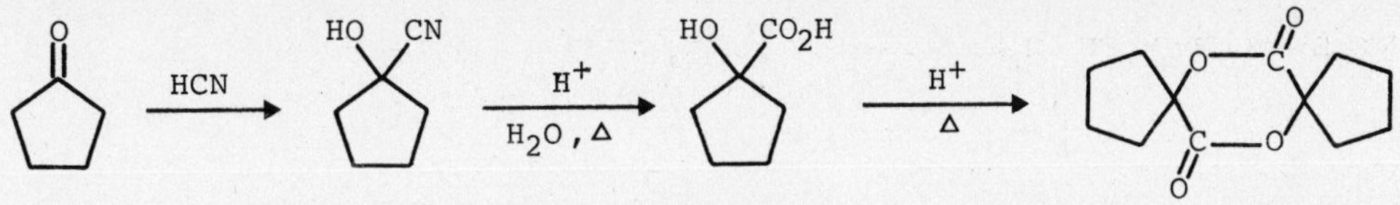

(d) 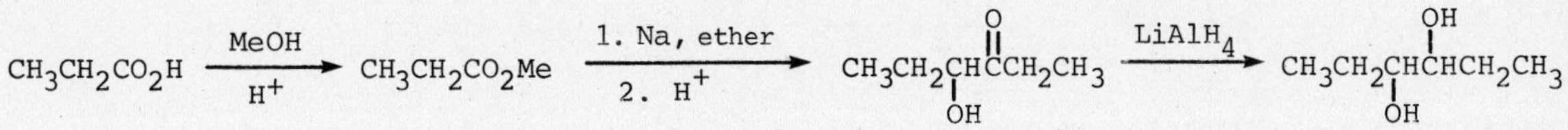 $CH_3CH_2CO_2H \xrightarrow[H^+]{MeOH} CH_3CH_2CO_2Me \xrightarrow[2.\ H^+]{1.\ Na,\ ether} CH_3CH_2\underset{OH}{\overset{O}{C}H}CCH_2CH_3 \xrightarrow{LiAlH_4} CH_3CH_2\underset{OH}{C}H\underset{OH}{C}HCH_2CH_3$

(e)

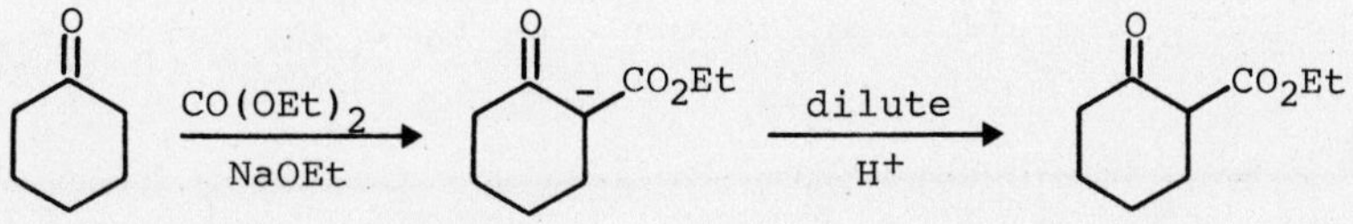

(f) 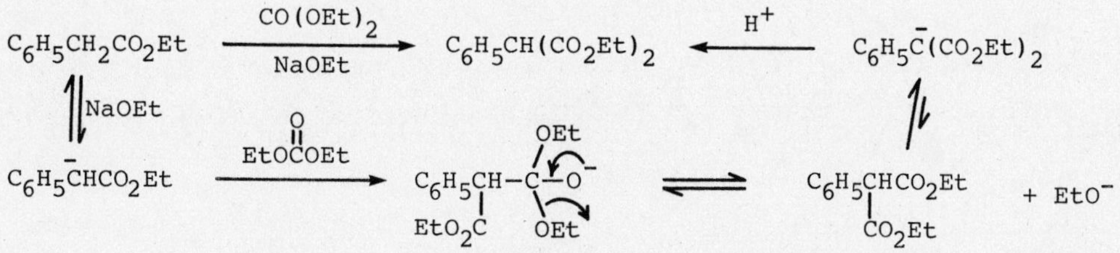 $C_6H_5CH_2CO_2Et \xrightarrow[NaOEt]{CO(OEt)_2} C_6H_5CH(CO_2Et)_2 \xleftarrow{H^+} C_6H_5\overset{-}{C}(CO_2Et)_2$

$\updownarrow NaOEt$ $\qquad\qquad\qquad\qquad\qquad\qquad\qquad\qquad\qquad \updownarrow$

$C_6H_5\overset{-}{C}HCO_2Et \xrightarrow{EtO\overset{O}{C}OEt} C_6H_5CH\underset{EtO_2C}{-}\overset{OEt}{\underset{OEt}{C}}-O^- \rightleftharpoons C_6H_5\underset{CO_2Et}{C}HCO_2Et \ +\ EtO^-$

(g) 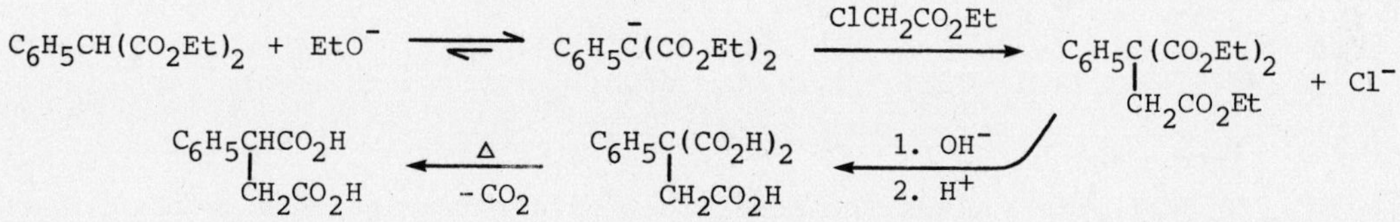 $C_6H_5CH(CO_2Et)_2 + EtO^- \rightleftharpoons C_6H_5\overset{-}{C}(CO_2Et)_2 \xrightarrow{ClCH_2CO_2Et} C_6H_5\underset{CH_2CO_2Et}{C}(CO_2Et)_2 \ +\ Cl^-$

$C_6H_5\underset{CH_2CO_2H}{C}HCO_2H \xleftarrow[-CO_2]{\Delta} C_6H_5\underset{CH_2CO_2H}{C}(CO_2H)_2 \xleftarrow[2.\ H^+]{1.\ OH^-}$

11. (a) $(CH_3)_2CHCH_2Br + CH_2(CO_2Et)_2 \xrightarrow{NaOEt} \xrightarrow{OH^-} \xrightarrow[\Delta]{H^+} (CH_3)_2CHCH_2CH_2CO_2H$

(b) a methylallylacetic acid:

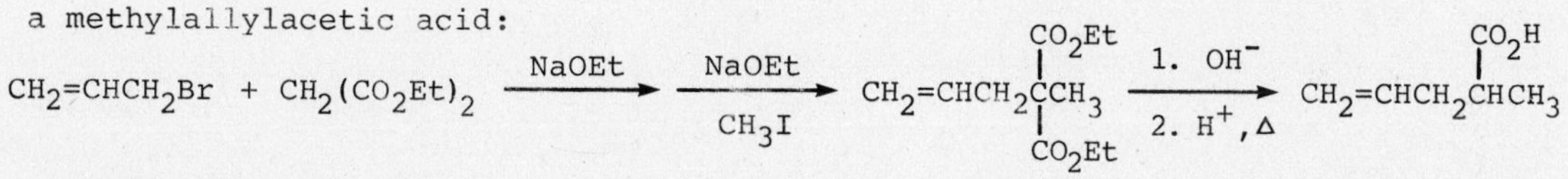

$CH_2=CHCH_2Br + CH_2(CO_2Et)_2 \xrightarrow{NaOEt} \xrightarrow[CH_3I]{NaOEt} CH_2=CHCH_2\underset{CO_2Et}{\overset{CO_2Et}{C}}CH_3 \xrightarrow[2.\ H^+,\Delta]{1.\ OH^-} CH_2=CHCH_2\overset{CO_2H}{C}HCH_3$

Note that the allyl group is added first. Some dialkylation occurs as a side reaction. Separation of mono- from dialkylated ester is easier when the first group is larger.

(c) 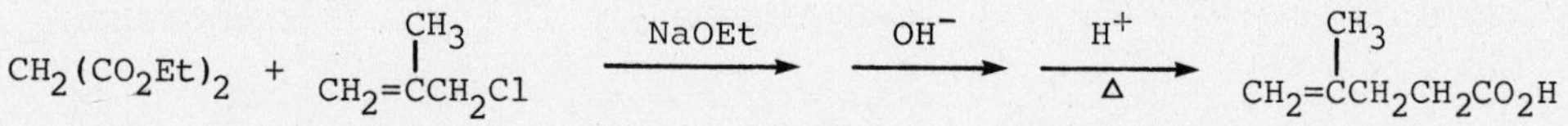 $CH_2(CO_2Et)_2 + CH_2=\underset{}{\overset{CH_3}{C}}CH_2Cl \xrightarrow{NaOEt} \xrightarrow{OH^-} \xrightarrow{H^+} CH_2=\overset{CH_3}{C}CH_2CH_2CO_2H$

(d) 1,5-keto acid; Michael addition:

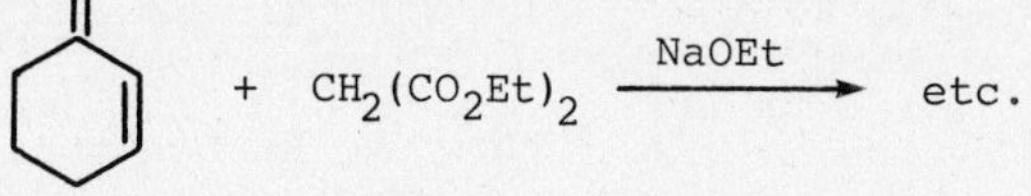

$+\ CH_2(CO_2Et)_2 \xrightarrow{NaOEt}$ etc.

(e) $CH_2(CO_2Et)_2 + BrCH_2CO_2Et \xrightarrow{NaOEt} (EtO_2C)_2CHCH_2CO_2Et \xrightarrow{H_3O^+} HO_2CCH_2CH_2CO_2H$

(f) $CH_2(COOEt)_2$ $\xrightarrow[\text{Br}(CH_2)_5Br]{\text{NaOEt (2 moles)}}$ $\left[(EtOOC)_2CHCH_2CH_2CH_2CH_2CH_2Br \right]$

$HOOC-\bigcirc$ $\xleftarrow[\Delta]{H^+}$ $\xleftarrow{OH^-}$ $(EtOOC)_2C\bigcirc$

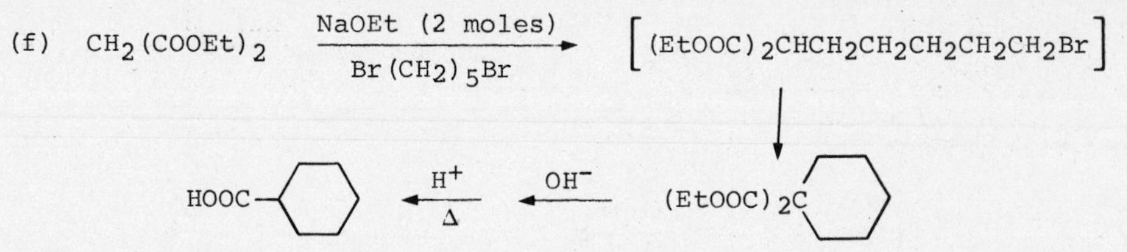

12. (a) "isopentylacetone":

$CH_3COCH_2CO_2Et + BrCH_2CH_2CH(CH_3)_2$ $\xrightarrow{\text{NaOEt}}$ $\underset{\underset{CH_3COCHCH_2CH_2CH(CH_3)_2}{|}}{\overset{CO_2Et}{}}$ $\xrightarrow[2.\ H^+, \Delta]{1.\ OH^-}$ $CH_3\overset{O}{\overset{\|}{C}}(CH_2)_3CH(CH_3)_2$

(b) a 1,5-keto acid; Michael addition:

$CH_3COCH_2CO_2Et + CH_2=CHCO_2Et$ $\xrightarrow{\text{NaOEt}}$ $\underset{\underset{CO_2Et}{|}}{CH_3COCHCH_2CH_2CO_2Et}$ $\longrightarrow$ etc.

(c) "propylethylacetone":

$CH_3COCH_2CO_2Et$ $\xrightarrow[CH_3CH_2CH_2Br]{\text{NaOEt}}$ $\xrightarrow[CH_3CH_2Br]{\text{NaOEt}}$ $\underset{\underset{CH_2CH_2CH_3}{|}}{\overset{\overset{CH_2CH_3}{|}}{CH_3CO-C-CO_2Et}}$ $\xrightarrow{OH^-}$ $\xrightarrow{H^+}_{\Delta}$

(d) Note symmetrical nature; both ends can be attached by an acetoacetic ester alkylation:

$CH_3COCH_2CO_2Et$ $\xrightarrow[CH_3I]{\text{NaOEt}}$ $\underset{\underset{CH_3}{|}}{CH_3COCHCO_2Et}$ $\xrightarrow[\underset{(0.5\ \text{mole})}{BrCH_2CH_2Br}]{\text{NaOEt}}$ $\left(\underset{\underset{CH_3}{|}}{\overset{\overset{CO_2Et}{|}}{CH_3CO-C-CH_2-}} \right)_2$ $\xrightarrow{OH^-}$ $\xrightarrow{H^+}_{\Delta}$

13. (a) This product is a substituted succinic acid. Two possible routes:

$CH_3CH_2CH=CHCOOEt$ $\xrightarrow{CN^-}$ $\underset{\overset{|}{CN}}{CH_3CH_2CHCH_2COOEt}$ $\xrightarrow{H^+}_{\Delta}$ $\underset{\overset{|}{COOH}}{CH_3CH_2CHCH_2COOH}$

or

$CH_2(COOEt)_2$ $\xrightarrow{\text{NaOEt}}$ $\xrightarrow{C_2H_5Br}$ $CH_3CH_2CH(COOEt)_2$ $\xrightarrow{\text{NaOEt}}$ $\xrightarrow{ClCH_2COOEt}$

$\underset{\overset{|}{CH_3CH_2CHCOOH}}{CH_2COOH}$ $\xleftarrow{-CO_2}$ $\left[\underset{\overset{|}{CH_3CH_2C(COOH)_2}}{CH_2COOH} \right]$ $\xleftarrow{H^+}_{\Delta}$ $\underset{\overset{|}{CH_3CH_2C(COOEt)_2}}{CH_2COOEt}$

(b) $\underset{\text{[from (a)]}}{CH_3CH_2CH(CO_2Et)_2}$ $\xrightarrow{\text{NaOEt}}$ $\xrightarrow[CH_3CHBrCO_2Et]{CH_3CHClCO_2Et\ \text{or}}$ $\underset{\underset{\overset{|}{CH_3}}{\overset{|}{CHCO_2Et}}}{CH_3CH_2C(CO_2Et)_2}$ $\xrightarrow[2.\ H^+, \Delta]{1.\ OH^-}$ $\underset{\overset{|}{CH_3CHCO_2H}}{CH_3CH_2CHCO_2H}$

Note that a mixture of two diastereomers results.

(c)

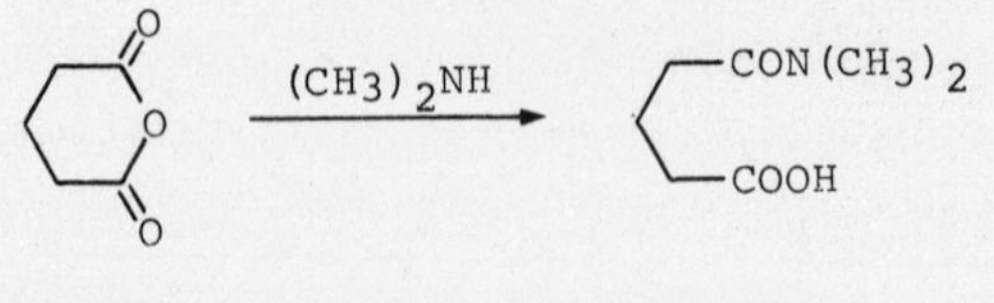

$\xrightarrow{(CH_3)_2NH}$ $\overset{-CON(CH_3)_2}{\underset{-COOH}{}}$

(d)

$\xrightarrow[CH_3I]{\text{NaOMe}}$

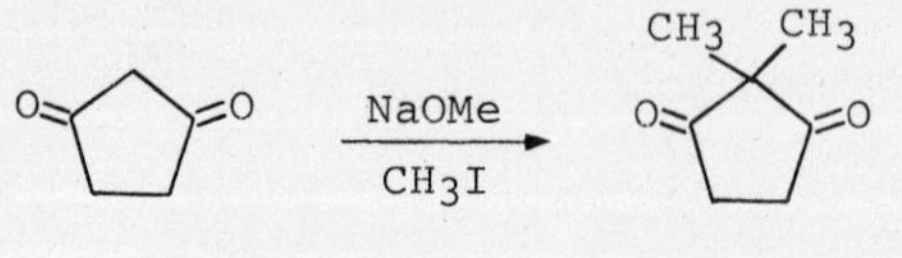

(e) This compound obviously can be prepared from $(CH_3)_2CHCOCH_2CO_2Et + ClCH_2CO_2Et$ $\xrightarrow{EtO^-}$ etc.

The problem is to make the β-keto ester. It cannot be made by the Claisen condensation, but it is available by a sequence starting with:

$$CH_3COCH(CH_3)_2 \xrightarrow[\substack{EtOH \\ HCO_2Et}]{NaOEt} (CH_3)_2CHCOCH_2CHO \xrightarrow{Ag_2O} R\text{-}CO_2H \xrightarrow[\text{or } CH_2N_2]{EtOH/H^+} \text{ester}$$

why must the condensation go in the methyl group?

(f)

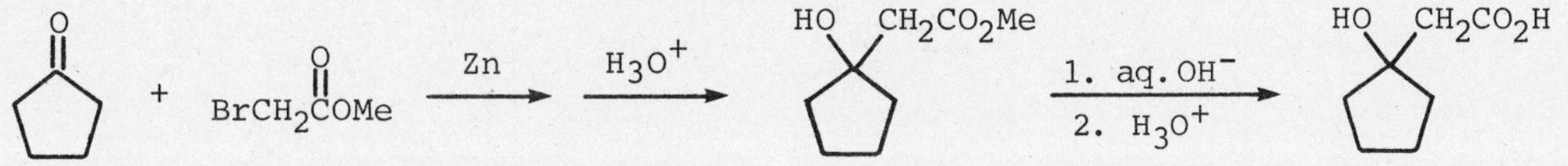

(g)

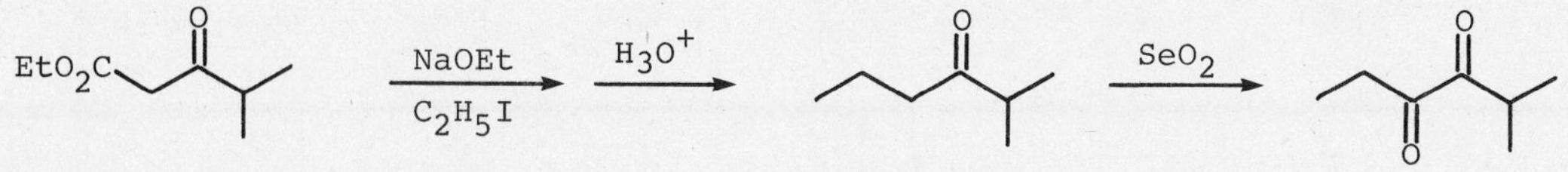

[from (e) above]

(h) This is a 1,6-dicarbonyl compound for which none of the special methods applies. Try treating it as a methyl ketone:

$$CH_3CO\bar{C}HCO_2Et + Br(CH_2)_3CO_2Me \longrightarrow \underset{CO_2Et}{CH_3COCH(CH_2)_3CO_2Me} \xrightarrow[\Delta]{H^+} CH_3CCH_2(CH_2)_3CO_2H$$

The bromoester can be made from commercially available γ-butyrolactone or by:

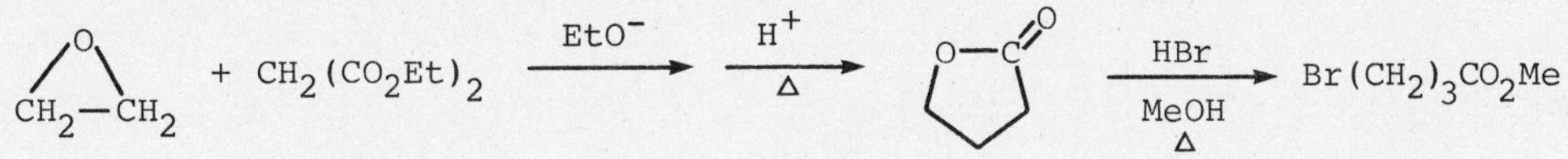

(i)

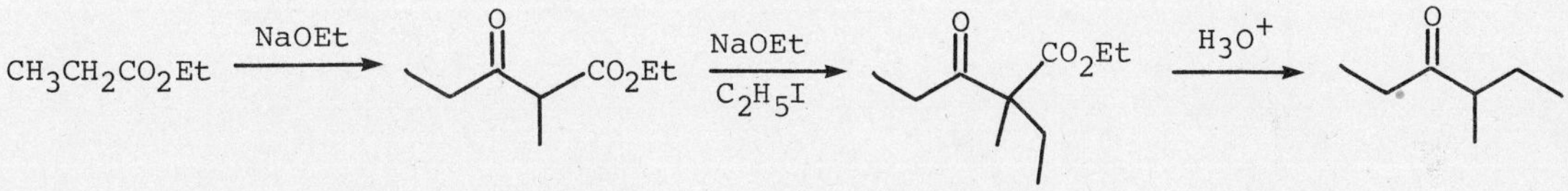

(j)

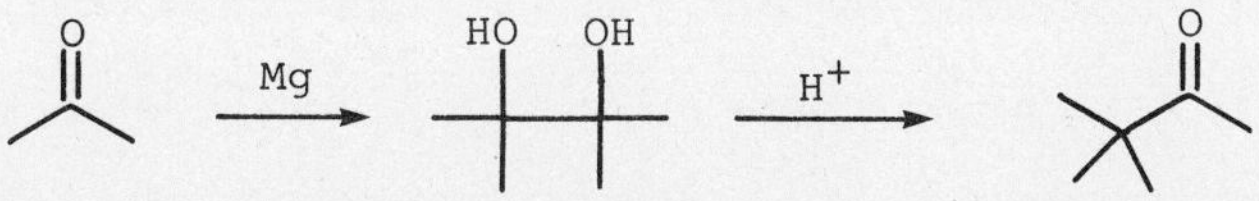

(k) α-Keto esters are available by Claisen condensations with diethyl oxalate:

$$CH_3CH_2CH_2CH_2COOEt + EtOOCCOOEt \xrightarrow{NaOEt} \underset{COOEt}{CH_3CH_2CH_2CHCOCOOEt}$$

$$CH_3CH_2CH_2CH_2\overset{O}{C}\text{-}COOH \xleftarrow[-CO_2]{\Delta} \left[\underset{COOH}{CH_3CH_2CH_2CHCOCOOH} \right] \xleftarrow[\Delta]{\substack{H^+ \\ OH^-}}$$

(an α-keto acid and a β-keto acid; β-COOH decarboxylates)

(l) Substituted glutaric acid available by Michael addition:

$$\underset{\text{[from (a)]}}{CH_3CH_2CH(CO_2Et)_2} \xrightarrow[\text{2. } CH_2=CHCO_2Et]{\text{1. NaOEt}} \underset{CO_2Et}{EtO_2CCH_2CH_2\overset{CO_2Et}{C}CH_2CH_3} \xrightarrow[\text{2. } H^+, \Delta]{\text{1. } OH^-} \underset{}{HO_2CCH_2CH_2\overset{CO_2H}{C}HCH_2CH_3}$$

(m) $(EtOOC)_2CH_2$ + CH_2-$CHCH_2CH_3$ $\xrightarrow{NaOEt}$ $[(EtOOC)_2CHCH_2\overset{O^-}{C}HCH_2CH_3]$

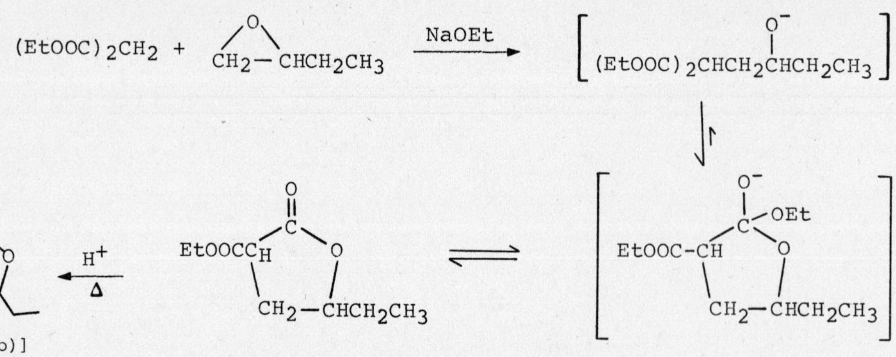

[See problem #7(b)]

(n) $\bigcirc$=O + HCN $\longrightarrow$ $\bigcirc\overset{OH}{\underset{CN}{}}$ $\xrightarrow[\Delta]{H_3O^+}$ $\bigcirc\overset{OH}{\underset{COOH}{}}$

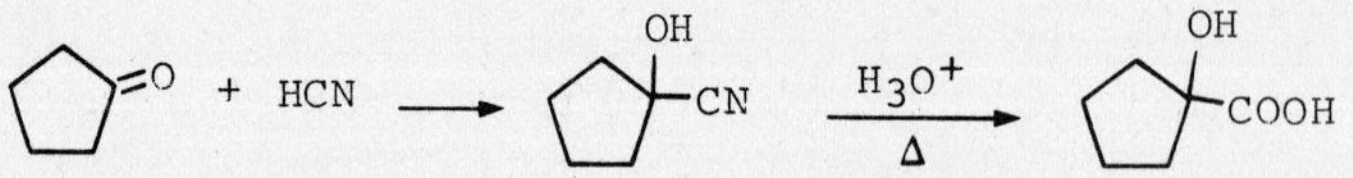

14. $EtO_2CCH_2CO_2Et$ + 2 $C_6H_5CH_2Cl$ $\xrightarrow[50\% \ KOH]{C_6H_5CH_2\overset{+}{N}Et_3Cl^-}$ $(C_6H_5CH_2)_2C(CO_2Et)$

(*In the organic phase, the following equilibrium occurs faster than ester hydrolysis:*

$EtO_2CCH_2CO_2Et$ + OH^- $\rightleftharpoons$ $EtO_2C\overset{-}{C}HCO_2Et$ + H_2O)

$\xrightarrow{NaOH \mid EtOH}$

$\xrightarrow{H^+ \mid \Delta}$

$(C_6H_5CH_2)_2CHCO_2H$

15. (a)

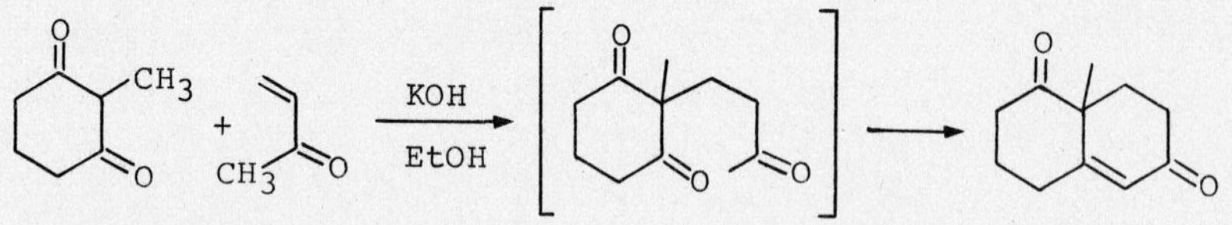

(b) 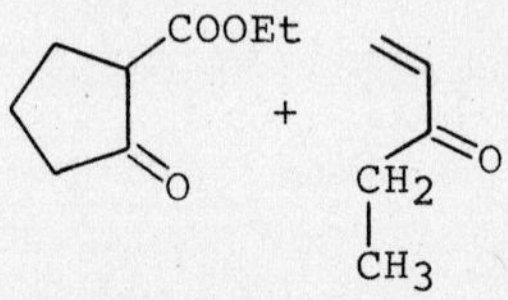   (c)

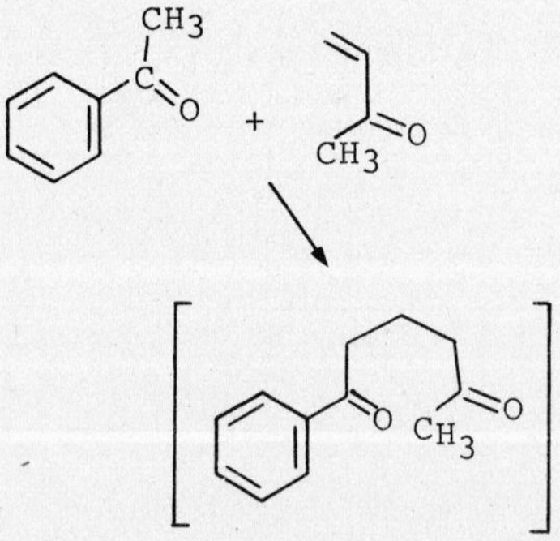

(d)

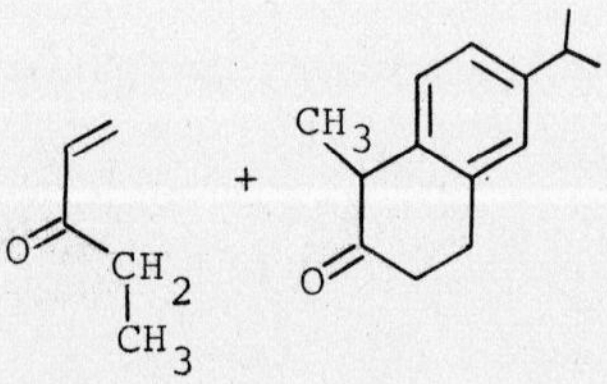

16.

(R)   (-) B   (-) C   (-) D
             (R)   (R)   (S)

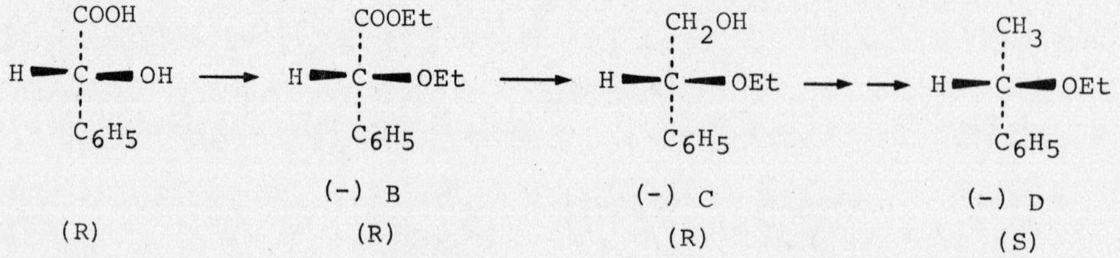

Note inversion of configuration in the conversion of (-) E to (-) F

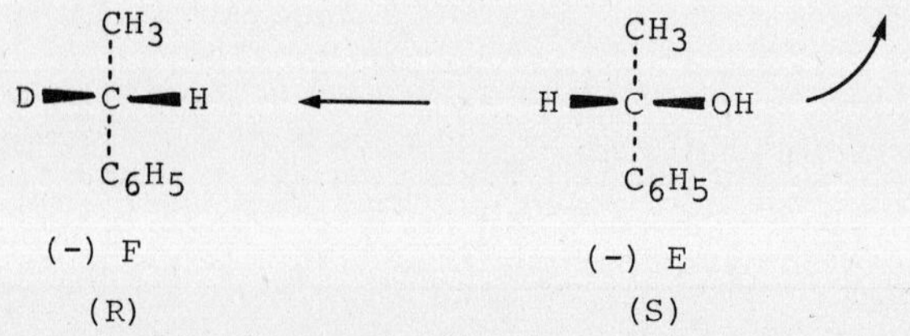

(-) F   (-) E
(R)   (S)

17. (a)

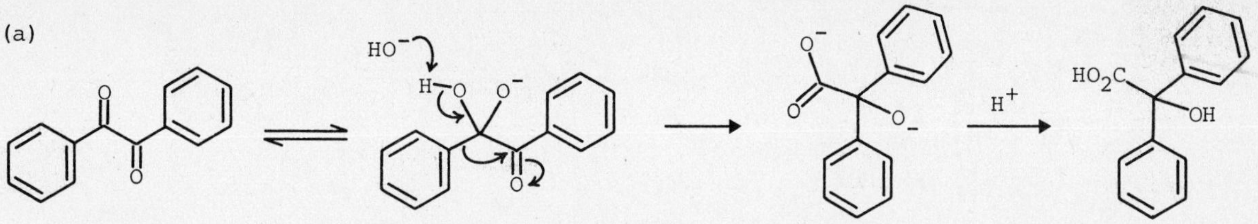

(b)

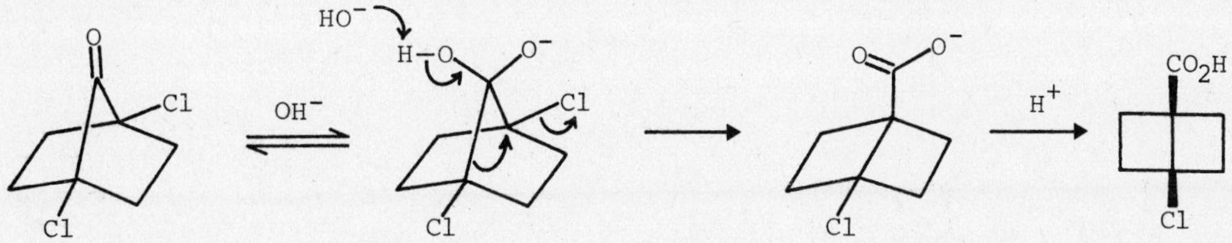

(c)

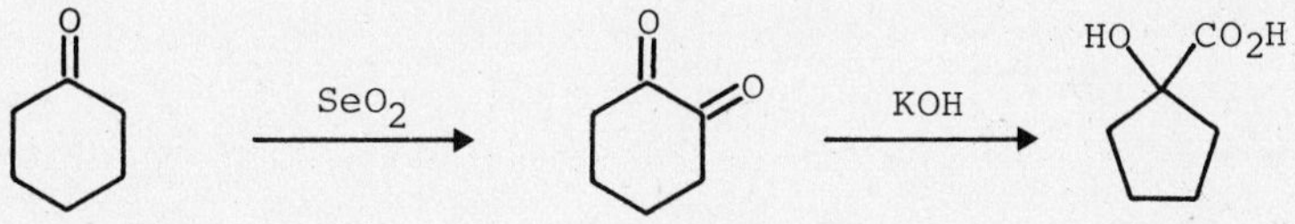

18.

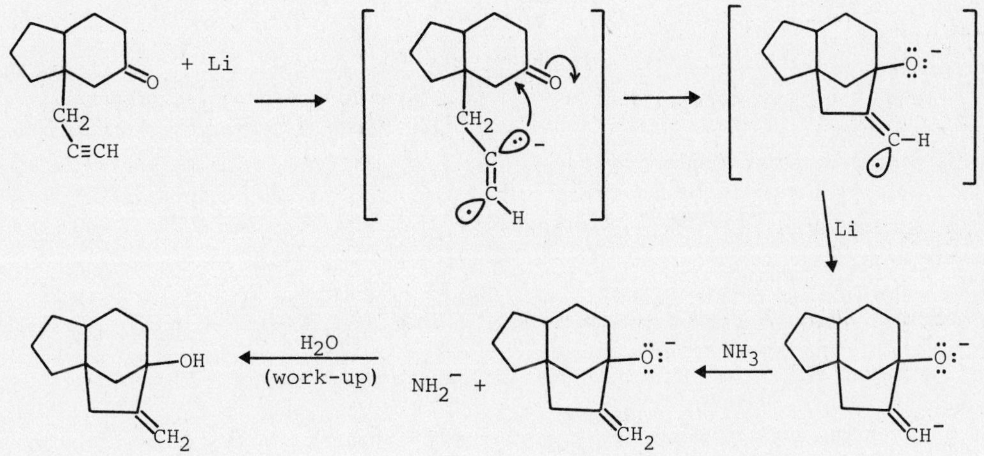

The first step is like the metal-ammonia reduction of an alkyne (see Section 12.6.A). The initial radical anion undergoes cyclization, with the nucleophilic carbon attacking the carbonyl group.

19. (a)

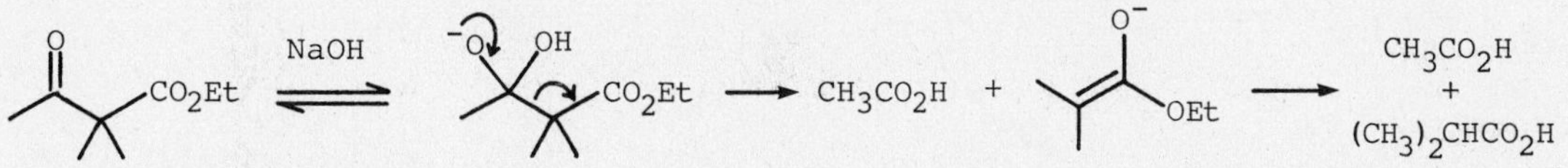

This process is known as the "retro-Claisen" reaction. It occurs readily with <u>non-enolizable</u> β-dicarbonyl compounds. An enolizable β-dicarbonyl compound is protected by formation of the enolate in basic solution.

(b)

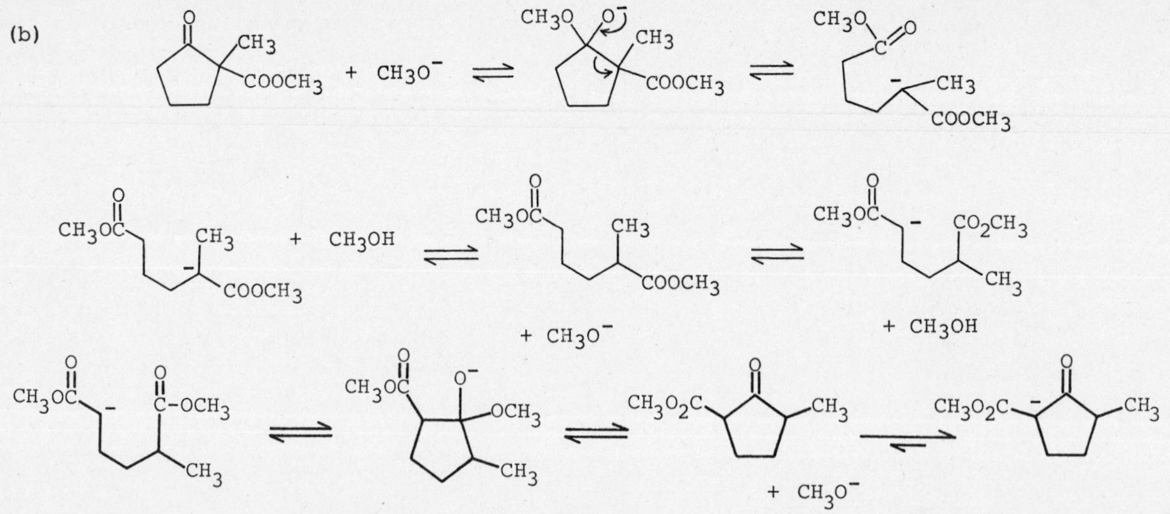

The product ion is a stabilized carbanion (anion of the β-keto ester), and pulls the entire set of equilibria.

27.F Supplementary Problems

S1. Write the structure of each of the following compounds.

(a) <u>trans</u>- 4-cyclopenten-1,3-diol   (e) (R)-2,3-dihydroxypropanal

(b) 4-hydroxy-3-hexanone   (f) methyl 2-oxocyclopentanecarboxylate

(c) 4-oxocyclohexanecarboxaldehyde   (g) diethyl methylmalonate

(d) (2R,4S)-2,4-dimethylpentanedioic acid   (h) 1,1,2,2-tetraphenyl-1,2-ethanediol

S2. Give the major product of each of the following reaction sequences:

(a) 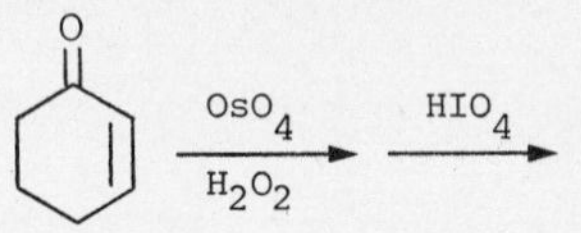 $\xrightarrow[\text{H}_2\text{O}_2]{\text{OsO}_4} \xrightarrow{\text{HIO}_4}$

(b) $(\text{CH}_3)_2\text{CHCOEt} \xrightarrow[\text{toluene}]{\text{Na}} \xrightarrow{\text{Cu(OAc)}_2}$

(c) $\text{EtO}_2\text{CCH}_2\text{CO}_2\text{Et} \xrightarrow[\text{NaOEt}]{\text{CH}_2=\text{CHCO}_2\text{Et}} \xrightarrow{\text{H}_3\text{O}^+} \xrightarrow{\Delta}$

(d) $\text{CH}_3\text{O}_2\text{CCH}_2\text{CH}_2\text{CO}_2\text{CH}_3 \xrightarrow{\text{Na}} \xrightarrow{\text{H}_2\text{O}}$

(e) 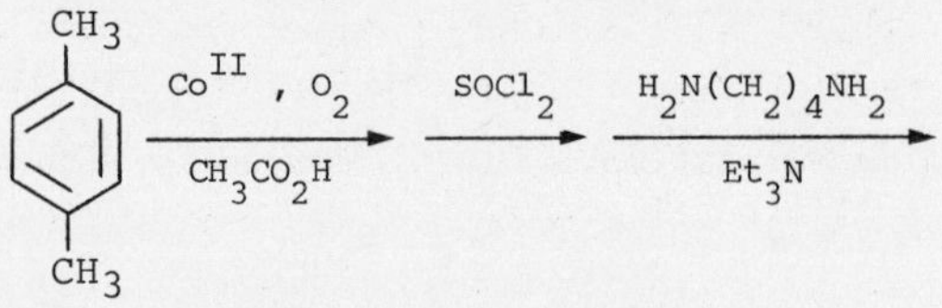 $\xrightarrow[\text{CH}_3\text{CO}_2\text{H}]{\text{Co}^{II}, \text{O}_2} \xrightarrow{\text{SOCl}_2} \xrightarrow[\text{Et}_3\text{N}]{\text{H}_2\text{N(CH}_2)_4\text{NH}_2}$

(f) 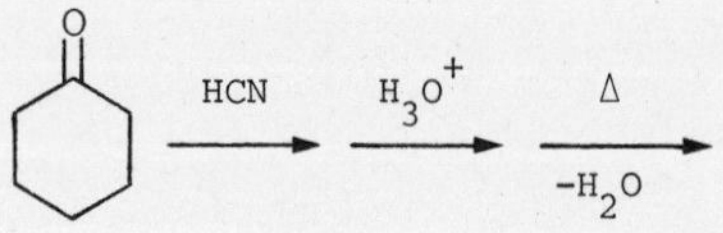 $\xrightarrow{\text{HCN}} \xrightarrow{\text{H}_3\text{O}^+} \xrightarrow[-\text{H}_2\text{O}]{\Delta}$

(g) 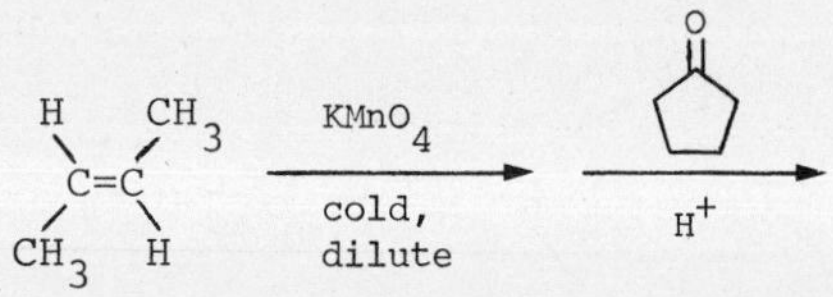 $\xrightarrow[\substack{\text{cold,}\\\text{dilute}}]{\text{KMnO}_4} \xrightarrow{\text{H}^+}$

(h) $\xrightarrow{\text{H}^+}$

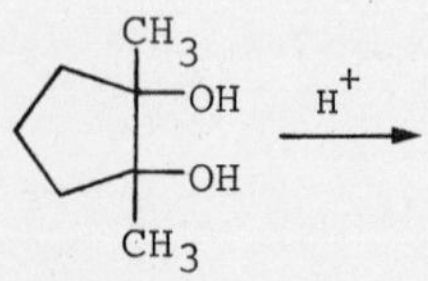

(i) 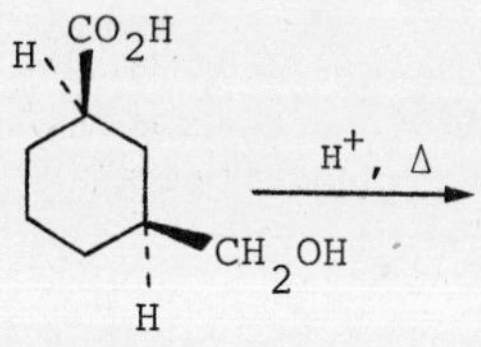 $\xrightarrow{\text{H}^+, \Delta}$

S3. Propose efficient syntheses of the following compounds, using any starting material containing five carbons or less.

(a) $CH_3CH_2\underset{\underset{CH_3}{|}}{CH}CH\underset{\underset{}{|}}{C}HCH_2CH_3$ with OH, OH groups

(b) cyclohexanone structure

(c) $CH_3\overset{O}{\overset{||}{C}}$ attached to a lactone ring with CH_3

(d) $(CH_3CH_2)_3C\overset{O}{\overset{||}{C}}CH_2CH_3$

(e) dioxane ring with CH_3 CH_3 and CH_3CH_2 and CH_3 substituents

(f) cyclohexane-dione ring with CO_2CH_3

(g) $(CH_3)_2CHCH_2\overset{O}{\overset{||}{C}}\underset{\underset{O}{||}}{C}CH_2CH(CH_3)_2$

(h) naphthalenyl/tetralin bicyclic structure *(You can use benzene as a starting material for this one.)*

(i) $CH_3\overset{O}{\overset{||}{C}}$ attached to cyclopentane

(j) geraniol structure with OH *geraniol (odor of geraniums)*

S4. Carbamates can be synthesized from an alcohol, NaN=C=O, and acid (see below). Given this reaction, outline a synthesis of the tranquilizer meprobamate.

$$ROH + NaN=C=O \xrightarrow{H^+} RO\overset{O}{\overset{||}{C}}-NH_2$$

$$NH_2\overset{O}{\overset{||}{C}}OCH_2\underset{\underset{CH_2CH_3}{|}}{\overset{\overset{CH_3}{|}}{C}}CH_2O\overset{O}{\overset{||}{C}}NH_2 \qquad meprobamate$$

S5. Provide structures which are consistent with the information given below.

$$B \xleftarrow[I_2]{NaOH} A \xrightarrow[CH_3OH]{H^+} C \xrightarrow{LiAlH_4} D \xrightarrow{H^+ \text{ (catalytic)}} E$$

B	A	C	D	E
$C_4H_6O_4$	$C_5H_8O_3$	$C_8H_{16}O_4$	$C_7H_{16}O_3$	$C_6H_{12}O_2$

NMR: δ 2.3 (s, area 2)
δ 12 (s, area 1)

IR (dilute solution): 1710, 1760, 2400-3400 cm^{-1}

IR: 1050, 1100, 3400 cm^{-1}

IR: 1070, 1120 cm^{-1}

S6. The benzilic acid rearrangement (see Problem #17) is a useful way to contract the ring of a cyclic α-diketone. Show how this rearrangement could be applied in a synthesis of bicyclo[2.1.1]-5-hexanone from bicyclo[2.2.1]-2-heptanone.

bicyclic ketone structure $\xrightarrow{?}$ bicyclic ketone structure

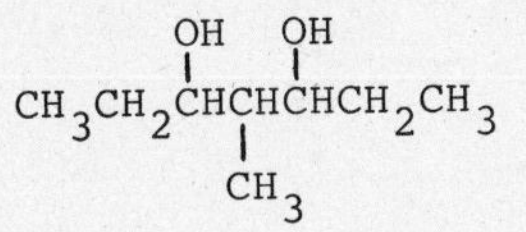

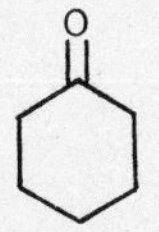

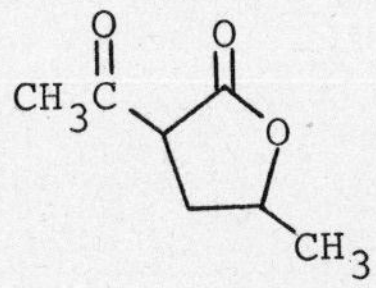

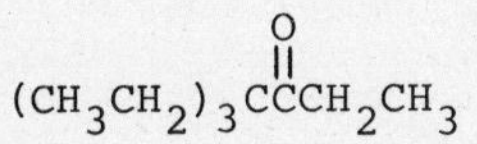

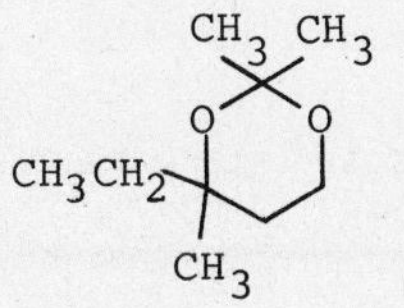

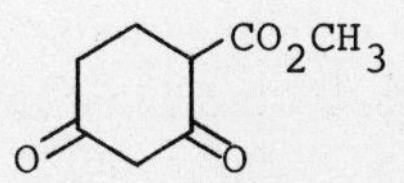

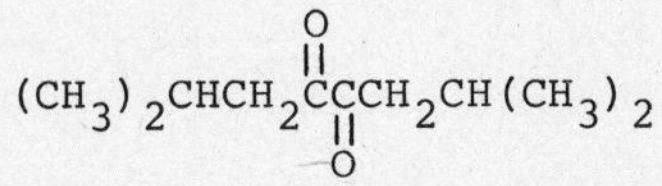

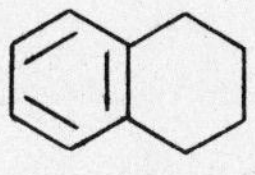

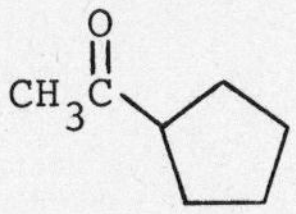

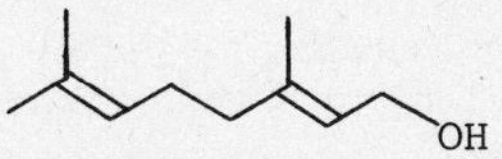

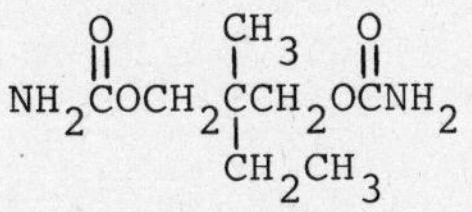

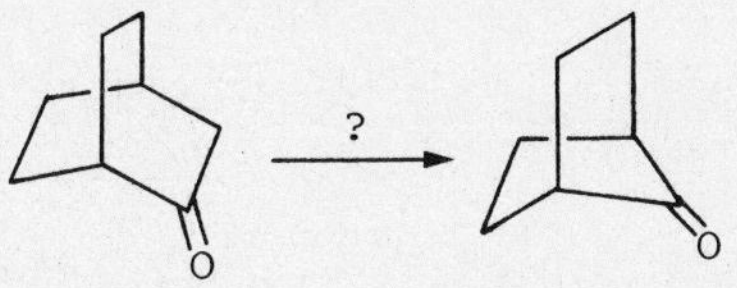

S7. α-Cyanocarboxylic acids also lose carbon dioxide on heating, although less readily than malonic or β-keto acids do. Write a mechanism for this decarboxylation, showing all of the intermediates involved.

$$N\equiv CCH_2CO_2H \xrightarrow{\Delta} N\equiv CCH_3 + CO_2$$

S8. Write mechanisms for each of the following transformations, showing all of the steps involved.

(a) 2 $(EtO_2C)_2CH_2$ + $CH_2=O$ $\xrightarrow[\text{EtOH}]{\text{NaOEt}}$ $(EtO_2C)_2CHCH_2CH(CO_2Et)_2$

(b) 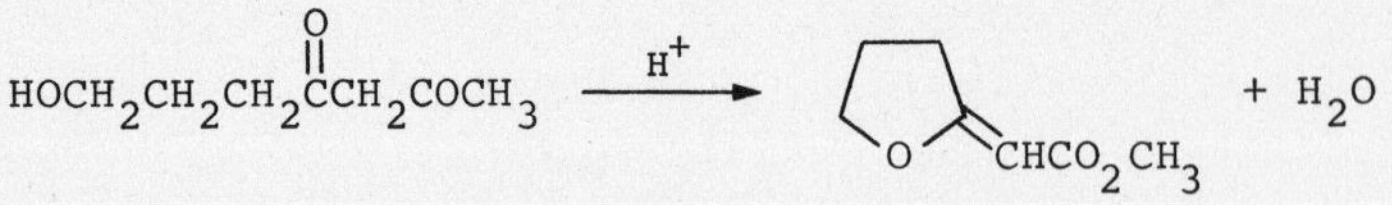 $HOCH_2CH_2CH_2\overset{\displaystyle O}{\overset{\displaystyle \|}{C}}CH_2COCH_3$ $\xrightarrow{H^+}$ $+ H_2O$

S9. The molecule illustrated at the right is very unstable, rapidly decomposing with loss of CO_2. What is the product and how is it formed?

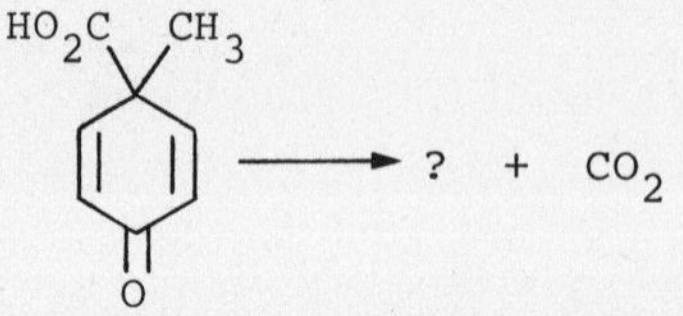

$\longrightarrow$? + CO_2

S10. A byproduct which can sometimes be isolated during the course of a Robinson annelation is the β-hydroxy ketone drawn below.

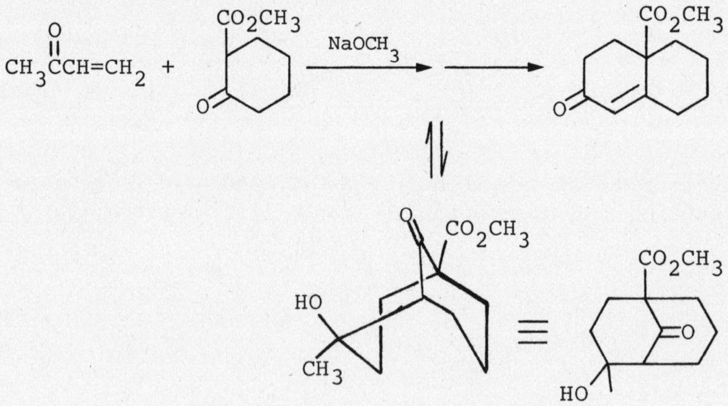

(a) Write a mechanism for the formation of this compound.

(b) The formation of this β-hydroxy ketone is reversible, and on continued treatment with base it is converted to the normal annelated product. Why doesn't it undergo the normal dehydration reaction of β-hydroxy ketones and lead to an unsaturated ketone with the same carbon skeleton?

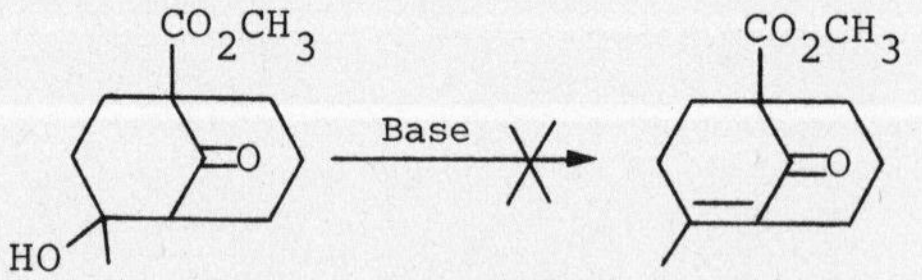

S11. Write a reasonable mechanism for the following transformation.

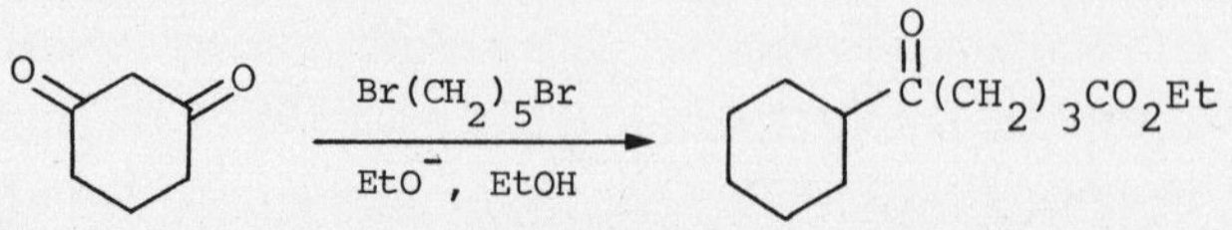

27.G　Answers to Supplementary Problems

S1.

(a)

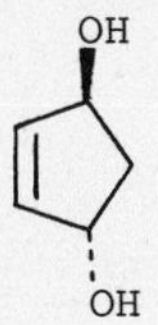

(b) $CH_3CH_2\overset{O}{\overset{\|}{C}}CHCH_2CH_3$
　　　　　　　$\underset{OH}{}$

(c)

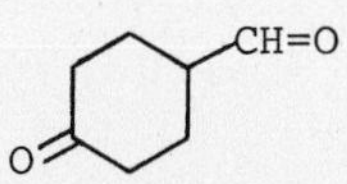

(d) 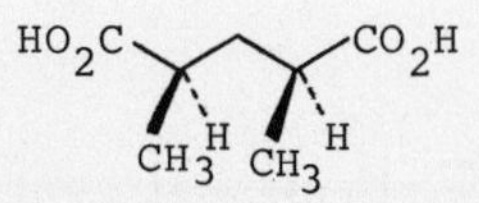
　　HO_2C　　　CO_2H
　　　　$CH_3\ H\ CH_3\ H$

(e) 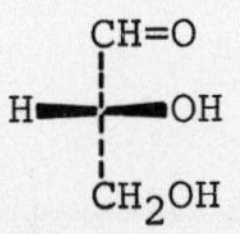
　　$CH=O$
　　$H—OH$
　　CH_2OH

(f) 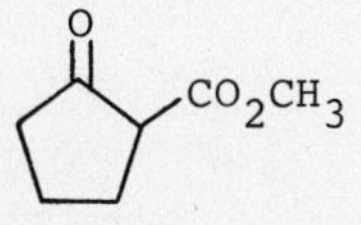
　　CO_2CH_3

(g) $CH_3CH_2O_2CCHCO_2CH_2CH_3$
　　　　　　　$\underset{CH_3}{}$

(h) $(C_6H_5)_2\overset{OH\ \ OH}{C—C}(C_6H_5)_2$

S2.　(a)　$HO_2CCH_2CH_2CH_2CH=O + HCO_2H$

(b)

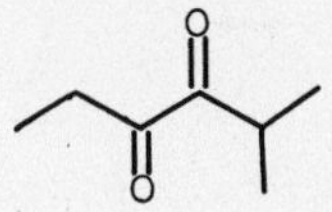

(c)

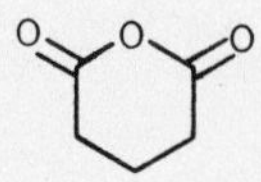

(d)

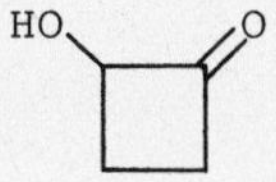

(e) 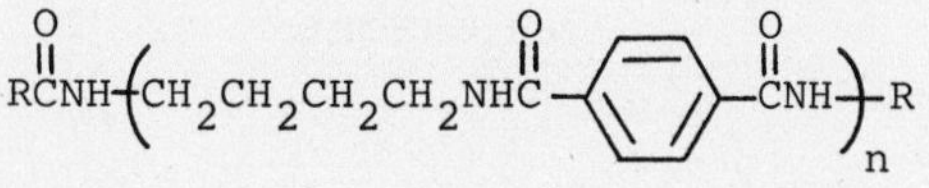 $R\overset{O}{\overset{\|}{C}}NH\left(CH_2CH_2CH_2CH_2NH\overset{O}{\overset{\|}{C}}\text{—}\bigcirc\text{—}\overset{O}{\overset{\|}{C}}NH\right)_n R$

(f)

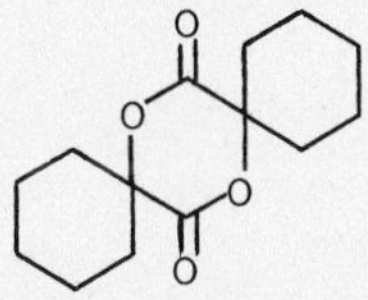

(g)

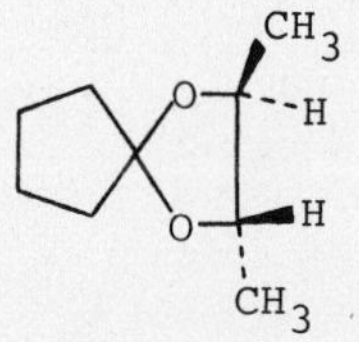

(h)

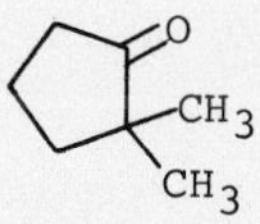

(i)

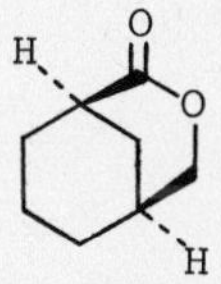

S3.　(a)　$CH_3CH_2CO_2CH_3 + CH_3CH_2\overset{O}{\overset{\|}{C}}CH_2CH_3 \xrightarrow{NaOCH_3} CH_3CH_2\overset{O}{\overset{\|}{C}}\underset{CH_3}{\overset{O}{\overset{\|}{C}}}CHCH_2CH_3 \xrightarrow{NaBH_4}$

(b)　$BrCH_2CH_2CH_2CH_2CH_2Br \xrightarrow{2\ NaCN} \xrightarrow[\Delta]{H_3O^+} HO_2C(CH_2)_5CO_2H \xrightarrow{\Delta}$

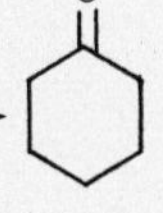

(c) 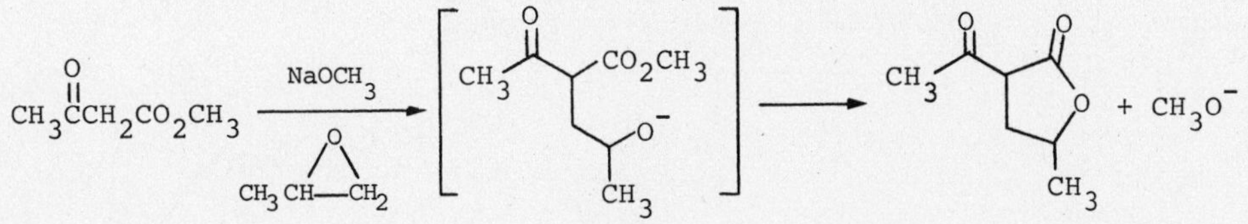　$CH_3\overset{O}{\overset{\|}{C}}CH_2CO_2CH_3 \xrightarrow[\underset{CH_3CH—CH_2}{\triangle O}]{NaOCH_3} \left[CH_3\overset{O}{\overset{\|}{C}}\text{—}\underset{\underset{CH_3}{O^-}}{CH\text{—}CO_2CH_3} \right] \longrightarrow$ $+ CH_3O^-$

(d)　$2\ (CH_3CH_2)_2C=O \xrightarrow{Mg} (CH_3CH_2)_2\underset{HO}{\overset{OH}{C}}\text{-}C(CH_2CH_3)_2 \xrightarrow{H^+} (CH_3CH_2)_3C\overset{O}{\overset{\|}{C}}CH_2CH_3$

(e) 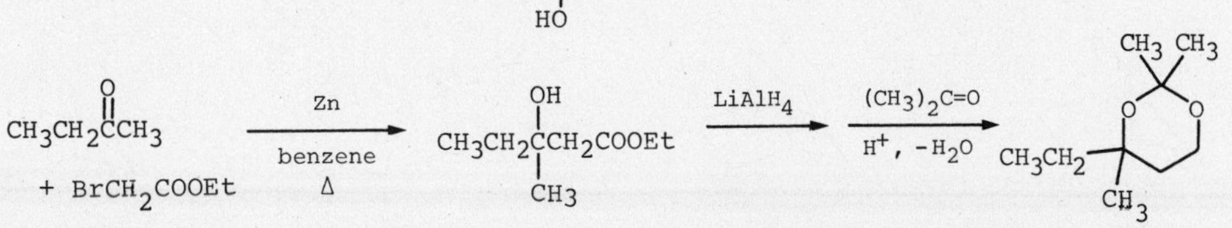　$CH_3CH_2\overset{O}{\overset{\|}{C}}CCH_3$ $+ BrCH_2COOEt \xrightarrow[\Delta]{\underset{benzene}{Zn}} CH_3CH_2\underset{CH_3}{\overset{OH}{C}}CH_2COOEt \xrightarrow{LiAlH_4} \xrightarrow[H^+,\ -H_2O]{(CH_3)_2C=O}$

(f) [structure: methyl vinyl ketone] + $CH_2(CO_2CH_3)_2$ $\xrightarrow{NaOCH_3}$ [intermediate with CO_2CH_3, CH_3, CO_2CH_3] $\longrightarrow$ [cyclohexane with CO_2CH_3 and two ketones]

(g) $(CH_3)_2CHCH_2COOH$ $\xrightarrow[H^+]{CH_3OH}$ $\xrightarrow[2.\ H_2O]{1.\ Na}$ $(CH_3)_2CHCH_2\overset{O}{\overset{\|}{C}}\underset{OH}{CH}CH_2CH(CH_3)_2$ $\xrightarrow{Cu(OAc)_2}$ $R\overset{O}{\overset{\|}{C}}-\overset{O}{\overset{\|}{C}}R$

(h) [benzene] + [succinic anhydride] $\xrightarrow{AlCl_3}$ $\xrightarrow[HCl]{Zn}$ [benzene-CH2CH2CH2-HO_2C] $\xrightarrow{HF}$ $\xrightarrow[HCl]{Zn}$ [tetralin]

(i) $CH_3\overset{O}{\overset{\|}{C}}CH_2CO_2CH_3$ $\xrightarrow[Br(CH_2)_4Br]{2\ NaOCH_3}$ [cyclopentane with $CH_3\overset{O}{\overset{\|}{C}}$ and CO_2CH_3] $\xrightarrow[\Delta]{H_3O^+}$ $CH_3\overset{O}{\overset{\|}{C}}$[cyclopentane]

(j) $CH_3\overset{O}{\overset{\|}{C}}CH_2CO_2CH_3$ $\xrightarrow[(CH_3)_2C=CHCH_2Br]{NaOCH_3}$ [structure with CO_2CH_3] $\xrightarrow[\Delta]{H_3O}$ [structure]

[structure] $\xrightarrow[\ (CH_3O)_2\overset{O}{\overset{\|}{P}}CHCO_2CH_3\ ]{\Delta}$

[structure $CHCO_2CH_3$] $\xleftarrow{LiAlH_4}$ [structure $CHCH_2OH$]

(mixture of isomers)

S4. $(CH_3OOC)_2CH_2$ $\xrightarrow[(CH_3O)_2SO_2]{NaOCH_3}$ $\xrightarrow[CH_3CH_2Br]{NaOCH_3}$ $CH_3OOC\underset{CH_2CH_3}{\overset{CH_3}{\underset{\|}{\overset{\|}{C}}}}COOCH_3$ $\xrightarrow{LiAlH_4}$ $\xrightarrow[H^+]{2\ NaNCO}$

$H_2N\overset{O}{\overset{\|}{C}}OCH_2\underset{CH_2CH_3}{\overset{CH_3}{\underset{\|}{\overset{\|}{C}}}}CH_2O\overset{O}{\overset{\|}{C}}NH_2$

S5. $CH_3\overset{O}{\overset{\|}{C}}CH_2CH_2COOH$ $HOOCCH_2CH_2COOH$ $CH_3\underset{OCH_3}{\overset{OCH_3}{\underset{\|}{\overset{\|}{C}}}}CH_2CH_2COOCH_3$

A   B   C

$CH_3\underset{OCH_3}{\overset{OCH_3}{\underset{\|}{\overset{\|}{C}}}}CH_2CH_2CH_2OH$ $\underset{CH_3}{\overset{CH_3O}{C}}$[tetrahydrofuran ring] E

D

S6. [bicyclic ketone] $\xrightarrow[\Delta]{SeO_2}$ [bicyclic diketone] $\xrightarrow{NaOH}$ [bicyclic with COOH and OH] $\xrightarrow{HIO_4}$ [bicyclic ketone]

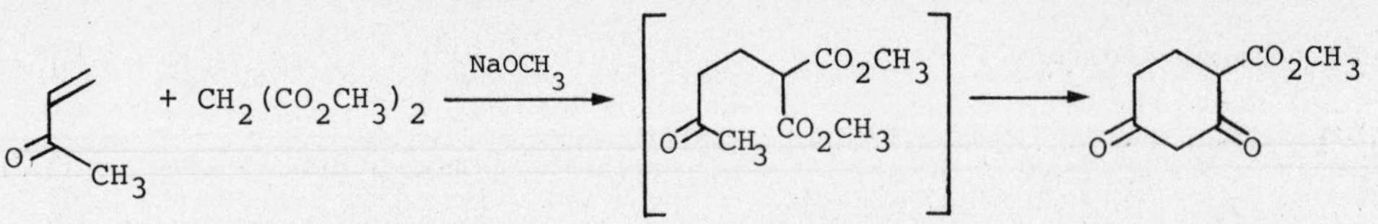

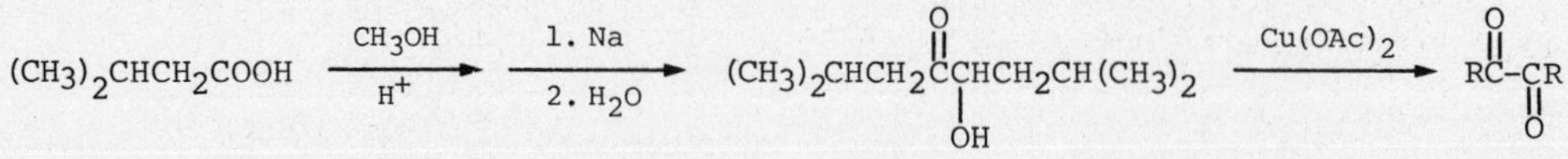

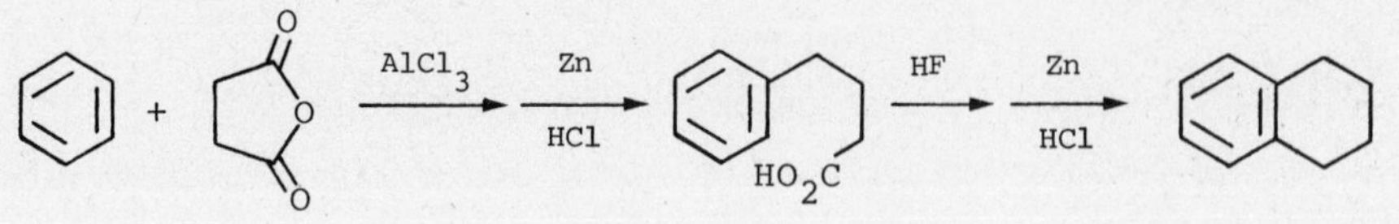

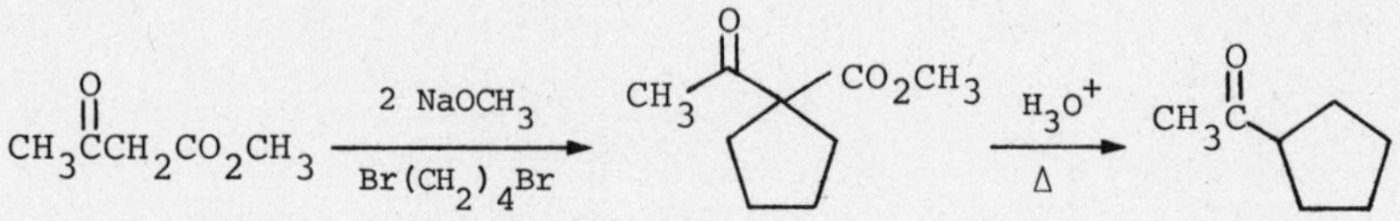

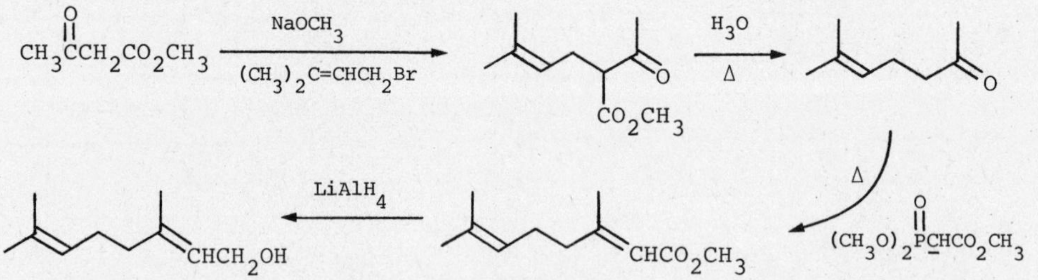

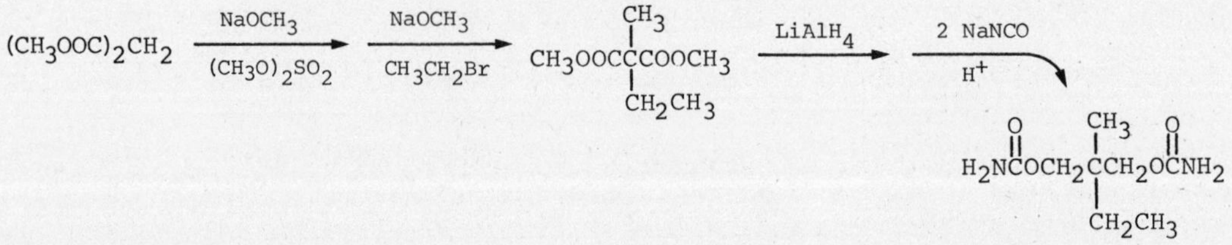

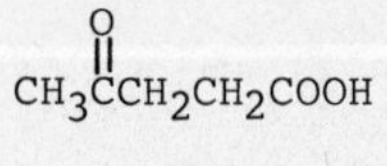

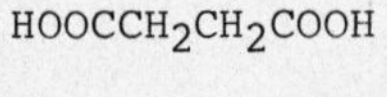

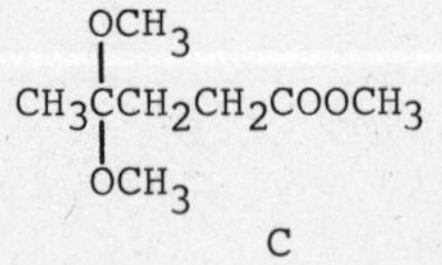

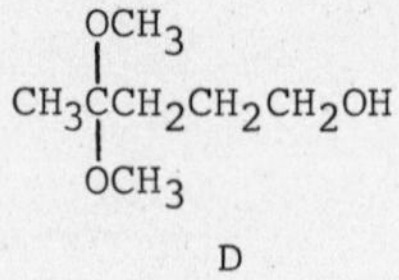

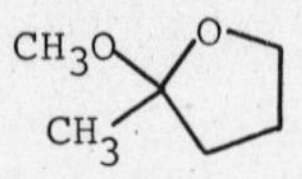

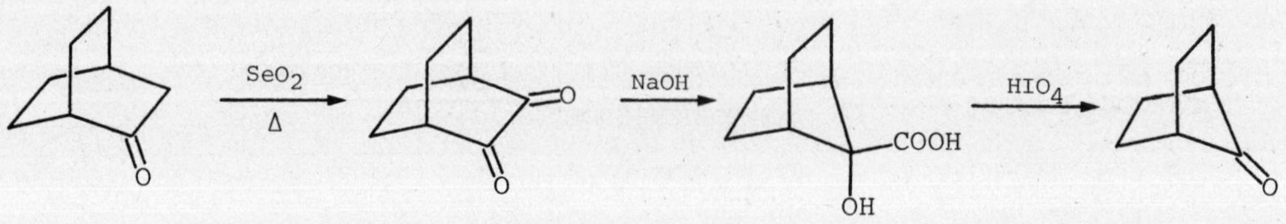

S7.

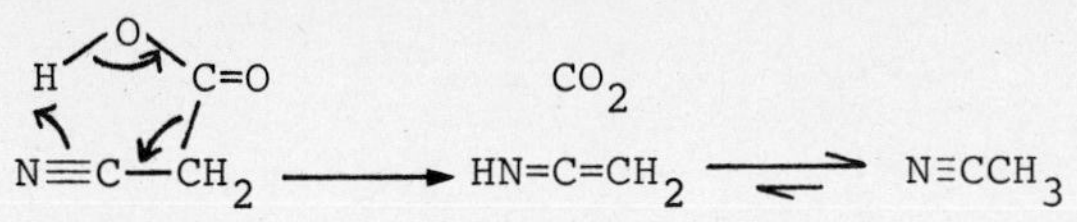

S8. (a)

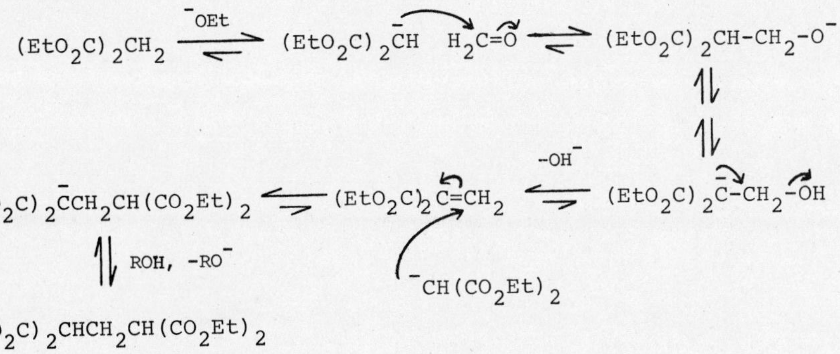

(b)

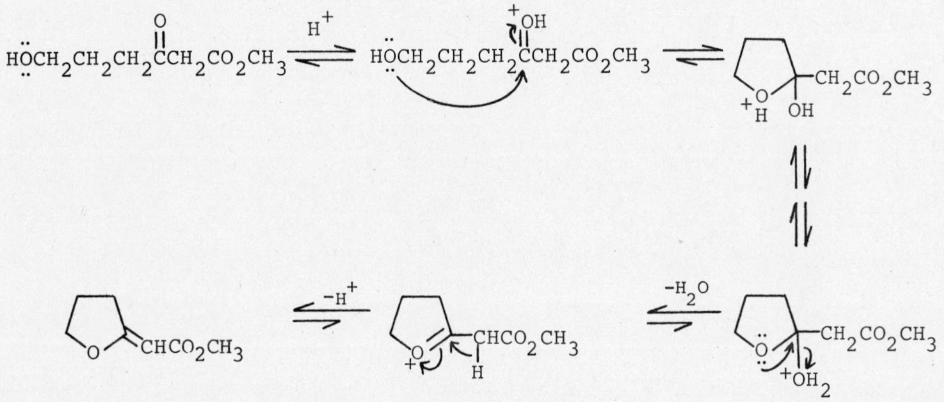

S9.

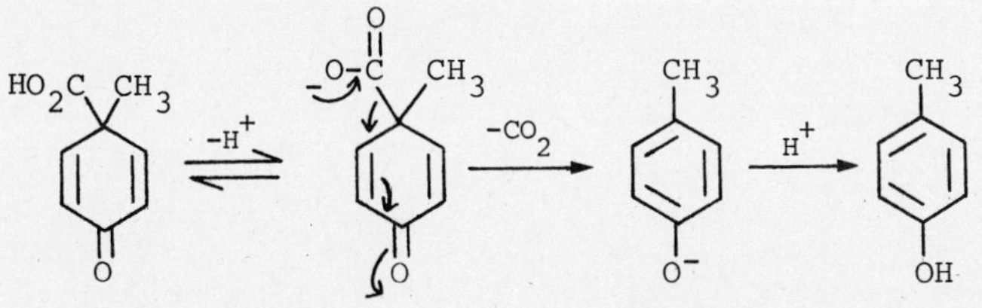

S10. (a)

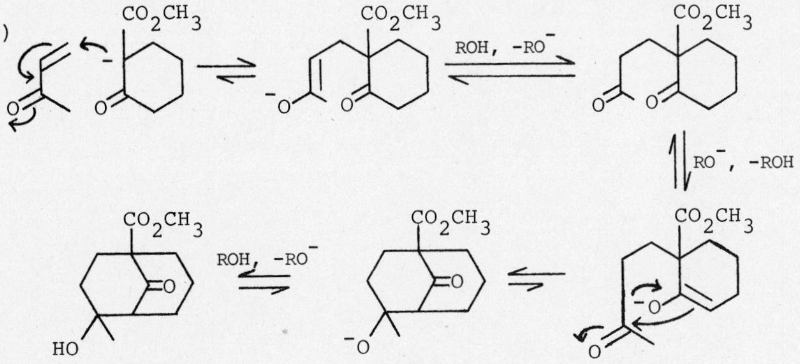

(b) Elimination of water from this bicyclic ketol would involve
     1) formation of the enolate of the ketone, as well as
     2) loss of hydroxide to generate the double bond.
     Neither of these occurrences is possible in this system, because either one would
     require the formation of a π-bond between two orbitals which are perpendicular to
     each other:

           no overlap possible;   *no overlap possible;*
         the enolate is not formed   *no double bond is formed*

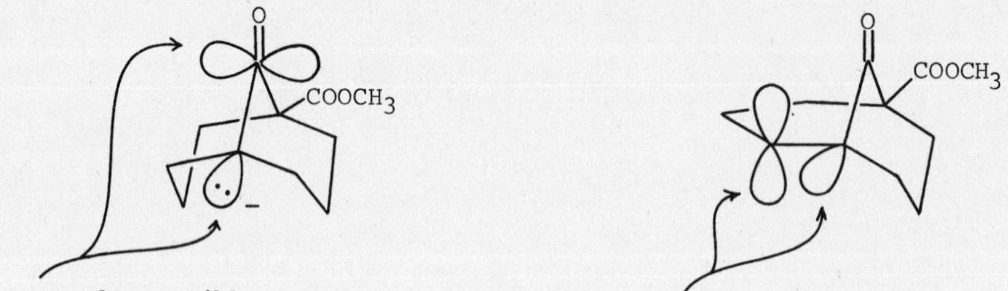

S11.

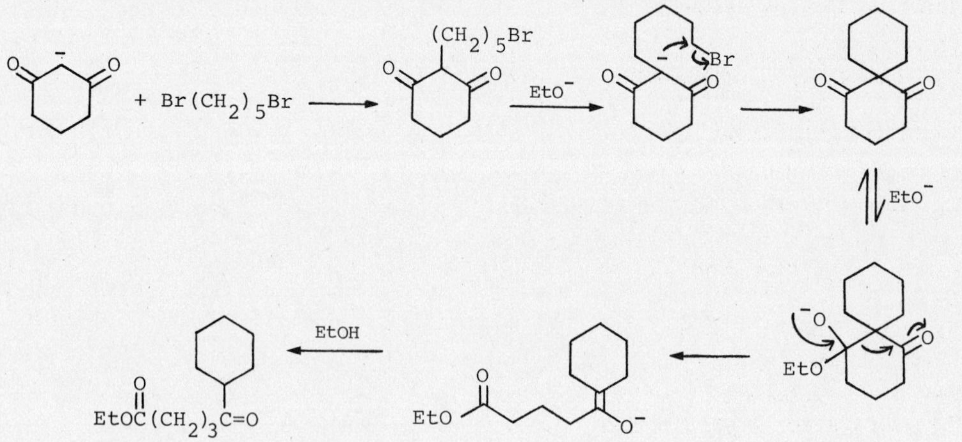

28. CARBOHYDRATES

28.A   Chapter Outline and Important Terms Introduced

28.1   Introduction

    carbohydrate: $(CH_2O)_n$ aldose, aldopentose, etc.

    sugar   ketose, ketohexose, etc.

    mono-, di-, tri-, tetra-, oligo-, and polysaccharides

28.2   Stereochemistry and Configurational Notation of Sugars

    R,S vs. D,L   meso compounds

    Fischer projections

28.3   Cyclic Hemiacetals: Anomerism; Glycosides

    α- and β-anomers   mutarotation

    Haworth projections   glycoside

    pyranose vs. furanose   glucoside, mannoside

28.4   Conformations of the Pyranoses

    chair conformations

    axial vs. equatorial substituents

28.5   Reactions of Monosaccharides

    A. Ether Formation

         glycoside formation (see Section 28.3)

         protection of anomeric carbon   methylation

    B. Formation of Cyclic Acetals and Ketals

    C. Esterification

         equatorial anomeric hydroxyl faster than axial

         anomeric effect

    D. Reduction: Alditols

    E. Oxidation: Aldonic and Saccharic Acids

         Tollens and Fehling's tests   saccharic acid

         reducing vs. non-reducing sugars

    F. Oxidation by Periodic Acid

    G. Phenylhydrazones and Osazones

         for derivatization and identification

    H. Chain Extension: The Kiliani-Fischer Synthesis

    I. Chain Shortening: The Ruff and Wohl Degradations

28.6   Relative Stereochemistry of the Monosaccharides: The Fischer Proof

    use of symmetry

    relative vs. absolute configuration

28.7   Oligosaccharides

    structure proof via methylation/cleavage

    invertase enzymes

28.8   Polysaccharides

    starch   amylose, amylopectin

    cellulose, cellulase

28.9   Sugar Phosphates

    ribonucleic acid (RNA)   deoxyribonucleic acid (DNA)

28.10   Natural Glycosides

    glycosyl residue vs. aglycon

    laetrile vs. erythromycin

28.B   Important Reactions Introduced

> *NOTE:* There are essentially no **new** reactions introduced in this Chapter; it is simply the context -- the fact that the substrates are sugars -- that makes the reactions different from what you have already learned.

Mutarotation (28.3)

Equation:

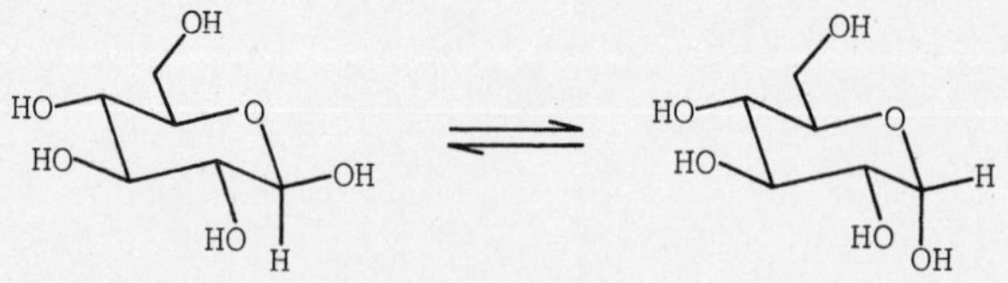

Generality: acid- or base-catalyzed
 saccharide must be a free hemiacetal
 observed for a wide variety of saccharides

Key features: mechanism involves equilibration between hemiacetal and hydroxy aldehyde

Glycoside formation and hydrolysis (28.3)

Equation:

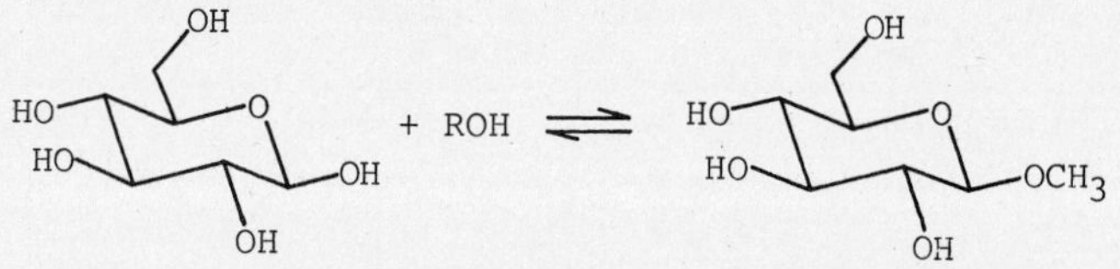

+ ROH

(α- and β-anomers)

Generality: catalyzed by acid or glycosidase enzyme
 mixture of anomers often formed

Key features: mechanism is simply formation of a cyclic acetal
 useful for protection of anomeric (= carbonyl) carbon toward basic reagents

Methylation (28.5.A)

Equation:

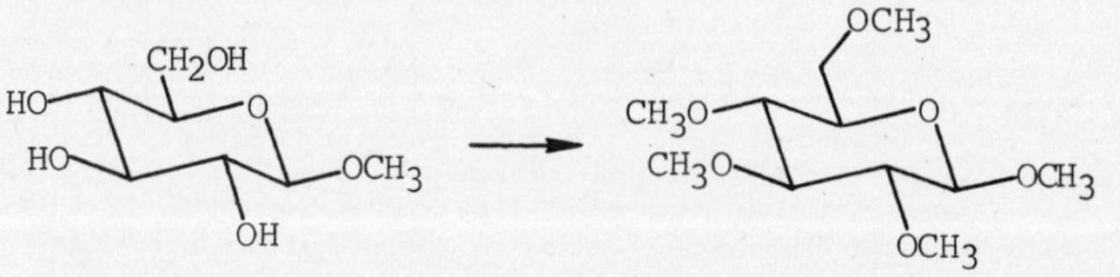

Generality: strongly basic conditions (= Williamson ether synthesis) require anomeric carbon to
 be protected as glycoside (acetal)

Key features: used in structure elucidation to determine acetal ring size

Formation of cyclic acetals and ketals (28.5.B)

Equation:

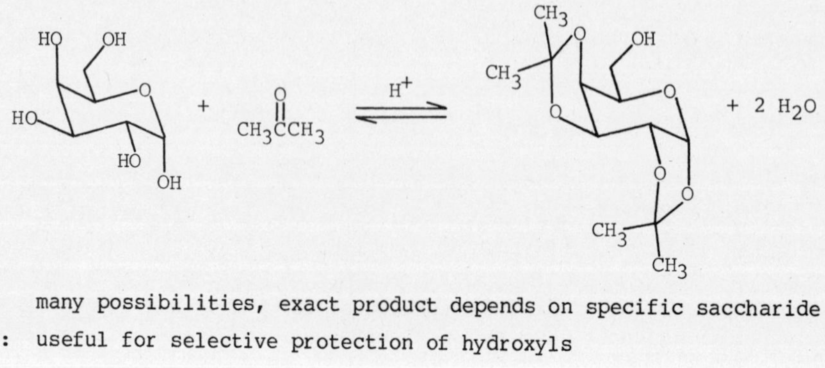

+ $CH_3\overset{O}{\overset{\|}{C}}CH_3$ $\overset{H^+}{\rightleftharpoons}$ + 2 H_2O

Generality: many possibilities, exact product depends on specific saccharide

Key features: useful for selective protection of hydroxyls

Reduction to alditols   (28.5.D)

Equation:

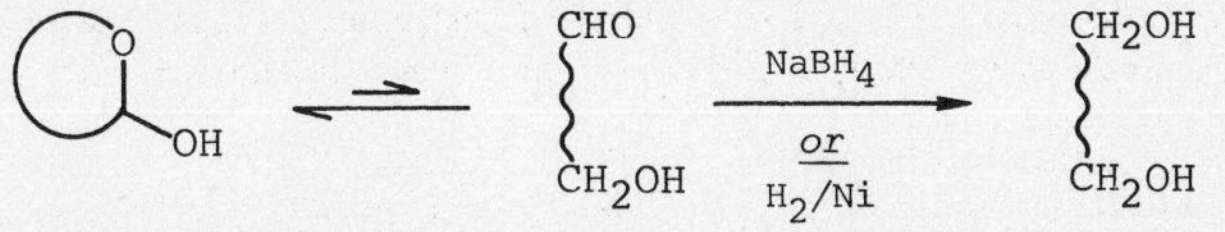

CHO — NaBH₄ or H₂/Ni → CH₂OH (structure diagram with pyranose hemiacetal, open-chain CHO/CH₂OH, and CH₂OH/CH₂OH alditol)

Key features: requires hemiacetal form of saccharide
                reaction proceeds via open chain (hydroxy aldehyde) form
                useful in symmetrization for structure elucidation

Oxidation to aldonic acids   (28.5.E)

Equation:

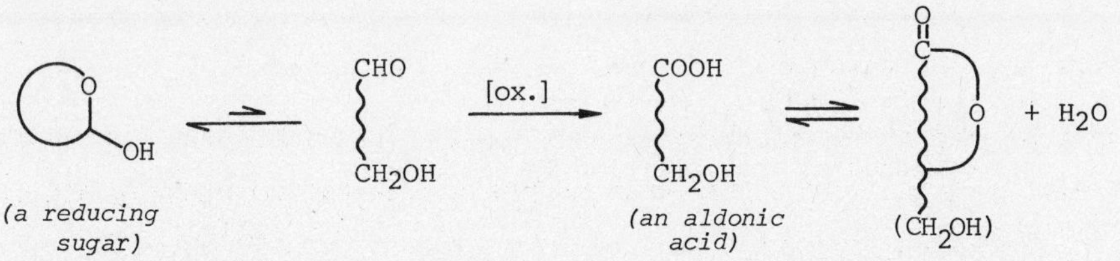

(structure diagram: pyranose hemiacetal ⇌ CHO/CH₂OH open chain → [ox.] → COOH/CH₂OH ⇌ lactone + H_2O)

(a reducing
sugar)   (an aldonic
                                                       acid) (CH_2OH)

Generality: [Ox] = $Ag^+(NH_3)_2$ (Tollens reagent), $Cu(OH)_2$ (Fehling's reagent),
                or Br_2 in H_2O (bromine water)

Key features: requires hemiacetal form of saccharide
                product often lactonizes

Oxidation to saccharic acids   (28.5.E)

Equation:

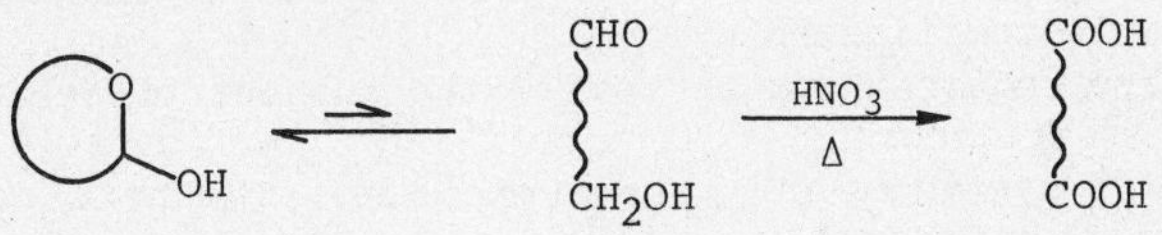

(structure diagram: pyranose hemiacetal ⇌ CHO/CH₂OH open chain → HNO₃, Δ → COOH/COOH)

                                                    (a saccharic acid)

Key features: useful in symmetrization for structure elucidation

Oxidation by periodic acid   (28.5.F; see Section 27.4.B)

Formation of osazones   (28.5.G)

Equation:

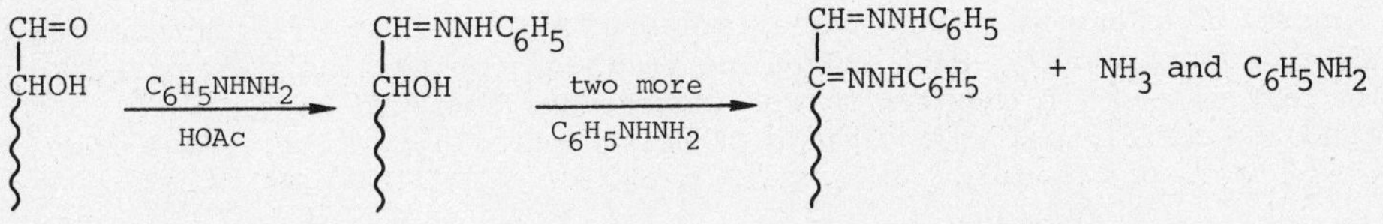

CH=O — C₆H₅NHNH₂/HOAc → CH=NNHC₆H₅ — two more C₆H₅NHNH₂ → CH=NNHC₆H₅, C=NNHC₆H₅   + NH_3 and $C_6H_5NH_2$
CHOH   CHOH

Key features: important as crystalline derivatives of saccharides, with characteristic mp as well
                as rate of formation for each saccharide
                stereocenter at C-2 destroyed, hence C-2 epimeric saccharides give the same osazone
                (albeit at different rates)

Kiliani-Fischer synthesis   (28.5.H)

Equation:

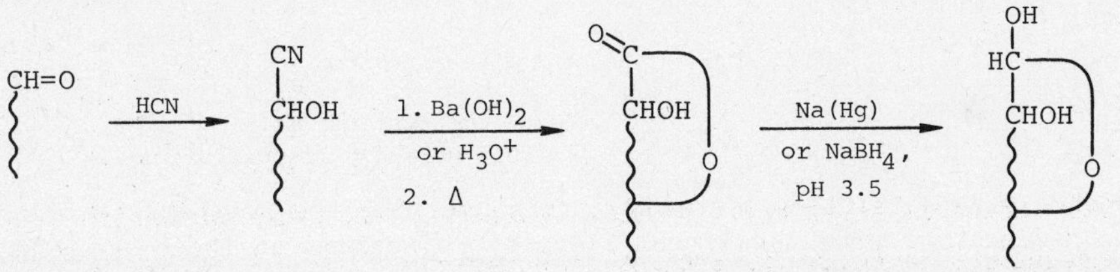

CH=O — HCN → CN/CHOH — 1. Ba(OH)₂ or H₃O⁺, 2. Δ → (lactone C=O/CHOH) — Na(Hg) or NaBH₄, pH 3.5 → (HC-OH/CHOH lactone)

Key features: leads to formation of both C-2 epimers of the chain-extended saccharide

Chain degradations (28.5.I)

Equations:

Ruff degradation

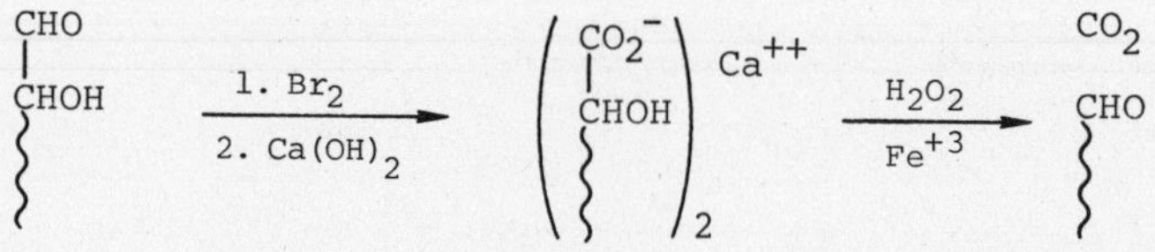

$$\begin{array}{c}CHO \\ | \\ CHOH \\ \sim\sim\sim\end{array} \xrightarrow[\text{2. Ca(OH)}_2]{\text{1. Br}_2} \left(\begin{array}{c}CO_2^- \\ | \\ CHOH \\ \sim\sim\sim\end{array}\right)_2 Ca^{++} \xrightarrow[\text{Fe}^{+3}]{\text{H}_2\text{O}_2} \begin{array}{c}CO_2 \\ CHO \\ \sim\sim\sim\end{array}$$

Wohl degradation

$$\begin{array}{c}CHO \\ | \\ CHOH \\ \sim\sim\sim\end{array} \xrightarrow{\text{H}_2\text{NOH}} \begin{array}{c}CH=NOH \\ | \\ CHOH \\ \sim\sim\sim\end{array} \xrightarrow[\text{NaOAc}]{\text{Ac}_2\text{O}} \begin{array}{c}N \\ |||| \\ C \\ | \\ CHOH \\ \sim\sim\sim\end{array} \xrightarrow{\text{NaOCH}_3} \begin{array}{c}CHO \\ \sim\sim\sim\end{array} + \text{NaCN}$$

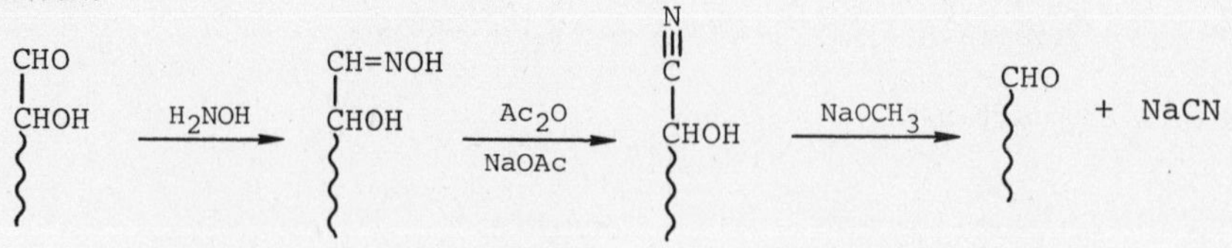

Key features: saccharides which are epimeric at C-2 give the same degradation product, since the stereocenter at that position is destroyed

28.C Important Concepts and Hints

Appropriately, the chemistry of carbohydrates follows the discussion of difunctional compounds. With only a couple of exceptions, all of the reactions presented in this chapter are ones you have seen before. What makes them different is the fact that the molecules involved have a functional group on every carbon! Nonetheless, these molecules behave according to the principles outlined in the preceding chapter, and only a few transformations which are specific to carbohydrate chemistry have to be learned. In essence, this topic requires you to apply the knowledge you've already gained to more complicated systems.

The topic of sugar chemistry also requires you to review the subject of stereochemistry. You have to be able to manipulate Fischer projections, determine R and S configurations, and recognize the presence or absence of planes of symmetry and meso compounds. The presence or absence of optical activity has been the single most important observation in schemes for the determination of the relative stereochemistry of sugars. Many of the techniques devised for probing the stereochemistry of a sugar have involved bringing the two ends of the carbon chain to the same oxidation state ($-CH_2OH$ or $-CO_2H$) and then looking for optical activity. An optically active compound cannot be meso, and an optically inactive compound is assumed to be meso.

Fischer projections are by convention drawn with the carbon chain extending vertically and the most oxidized end of the molecule at the top, if there is a difference. To determine whether a Fischer projection represents a meso compound, draw (or imagine) a line across the picture exactly half-way down. If there is an even number of carbons, this line will cross one of the carbon-carbon bonds; if there is an odd number of carbons, the line will cut across the middle carbon atom and its substituents. With this line in place (or in mind), compare the pattern above the line with that below: if they are mirror images, the compound is meso; if they differ in any way the compound is chiral, and thus capable of being optically active. Some examples are illustrated below:

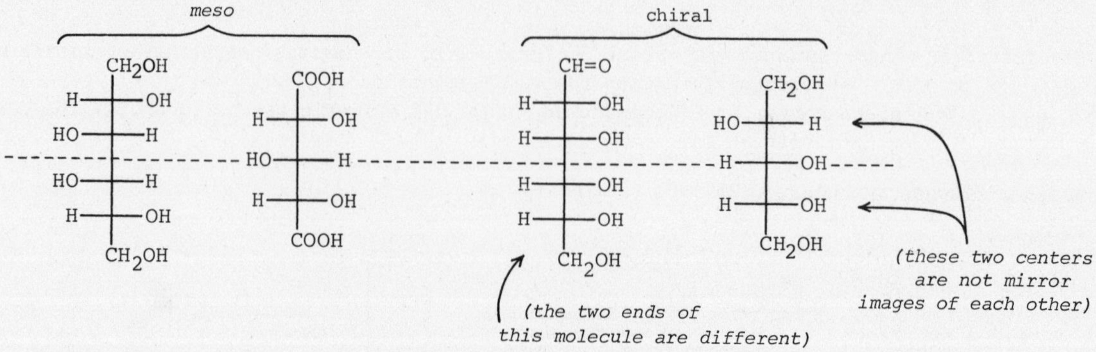

Many students have difficulty mentally interconverting the perspective diagrams of the chair forms of sugar hemiacetals with the linear Fischer projections of their open-chain isomers. Can you tell whether the two structures illustrated on the next page represent the same sugar or not? (They do.)

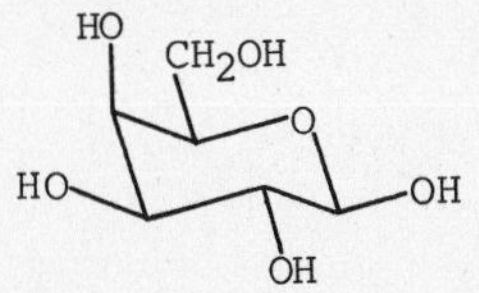

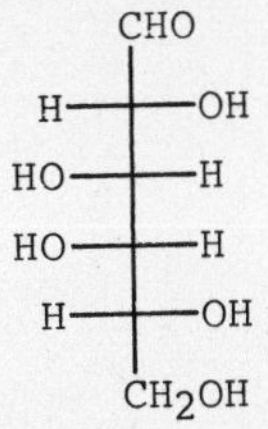

One hint that we can give you (in addition to **using models**!!) is to become familiar with Haworth projections. These are intermediate between the perspective formulas and Fischer projections, and serve to relate the two in a logical way. A Haworth projection is essentially a flattened form of the cyclic structure; the distinction between axial and equatorial is ignored and all that matters is whether substituents stick up or down. To go from the perspective formula to the Haworth projection, you simply look for up or down orientations. The Haworth projection of the sugar above is:

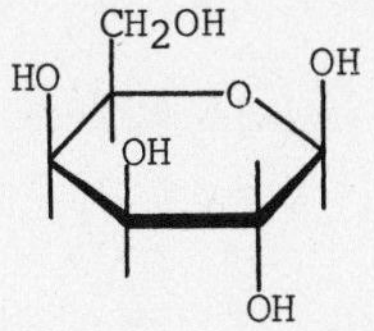

The substituents that stick **up** in a Haworth formula are on the **left** in a Fischer projection, with two exceptions:

1. the next-to-last carbon gets mixed up because the substituent in the Haworth formula is part of the carbon chain itself (if -CH$_2$OH sticks up (D-sugar), the hydroxy group is on the right);

2. the configuration of the anomeric carbon (α or β) is not represented in the open-chain Fischer projection.

As usual, these correlations can be most easily visualized and understood with the help of models.

28.D   Answers to Exercises

28.1   One of the epimeric hexaols has an axis of symmetry, such that carbons 1-3 are equivalent to carbons 6-4, respectively. The other hexaol is not symmetrical, and every carbon is different in the CMR spectrum.

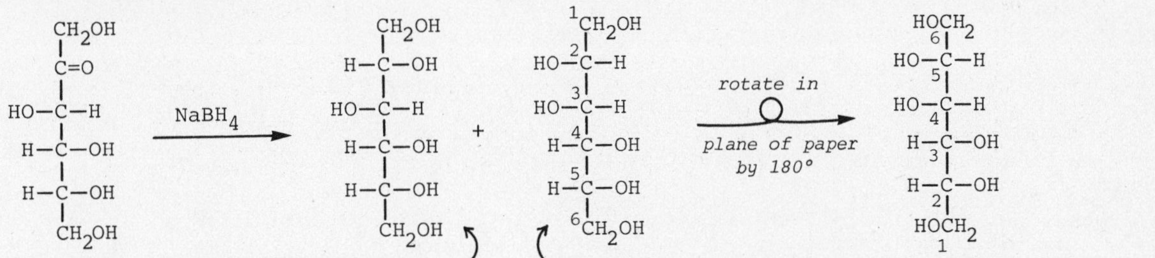

These projections represent the same structure, therefore C-1 = C-6, C-2 = C-5, and C-3 = C-4.

(NOTE: the CH$_2$OH groups are not stereocenters, so it does not matter whether they are written CH$_2$OH or HOCH$_2$.)

28.3

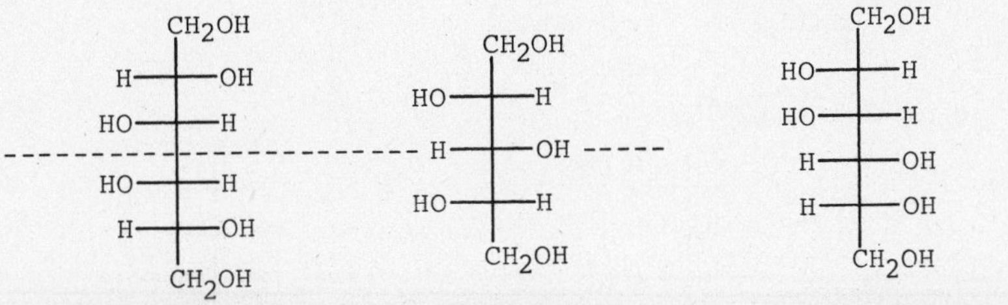

from D-galactose *(achiral)*   from L-xylose *(achiral)*   from D-mannose *(chiral)*

28.4

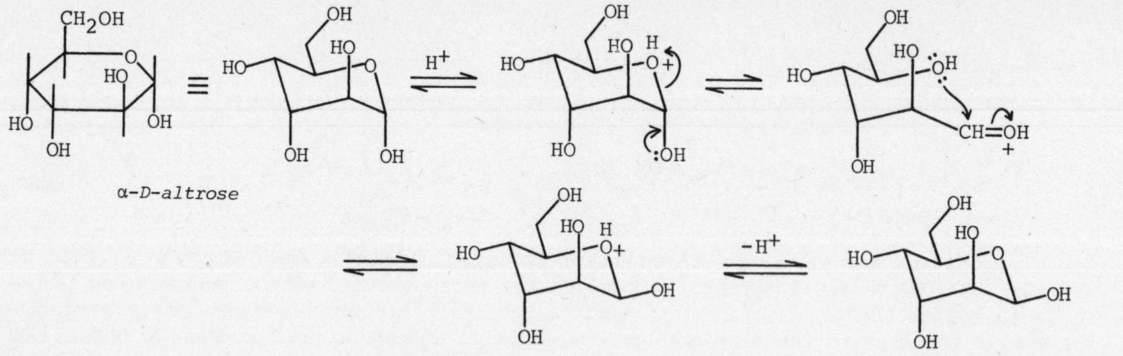

α-D-altrose

β-D-altrose

28.5

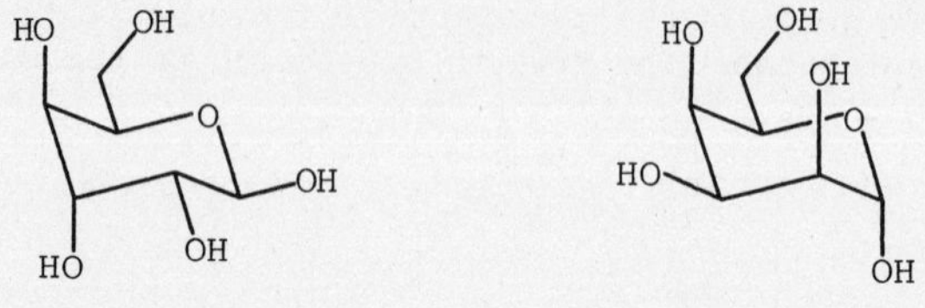

β-D-gulose

α-D-talose

28.6

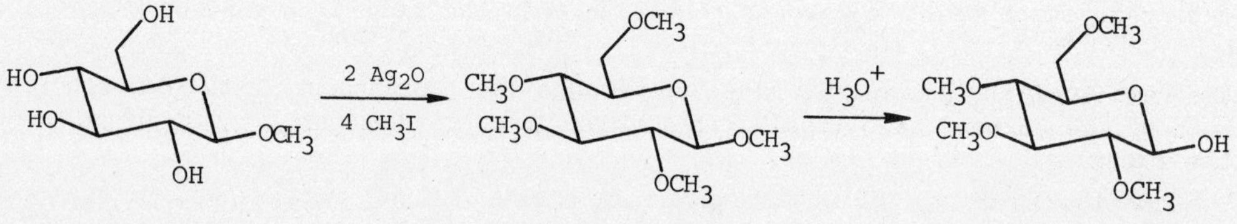

$\xrightarrow[\text{4 CH}_3\text{I}]{\text{2 Ag}_2\text{O}}$

$\xrightarrow{\text{H}_3\text{O}^+}$

$+\ 4\ \text{AgI}\ +\ 2\ \text{H}_2\text{O}$

(plus α-anomer)

28.7

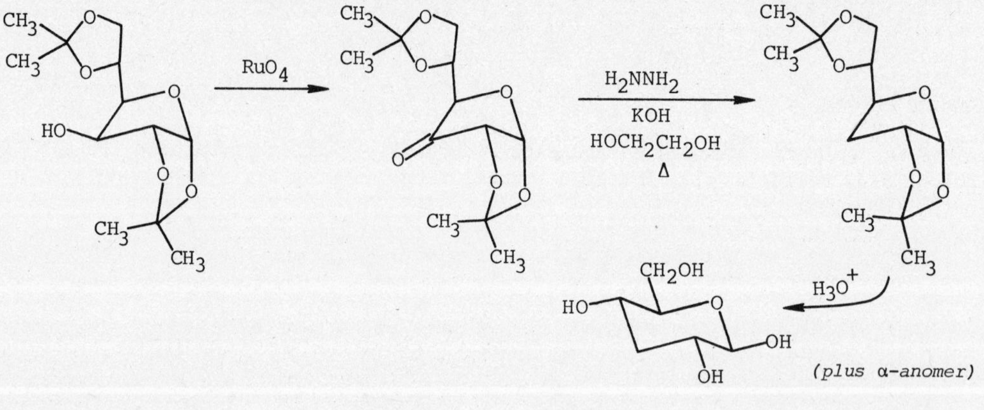

$\xrightarrow{\text{RuO}_4}$

$\xrightarrow[\substack{\text{KOH} \\ \text{HOCH}_2\text{CH}_2\text{OH} \\ \Delta}]{\text{H}_2\text{NNH}_2}$

$\xleftarrow{\text{H}_3\text{O}^+}$

(plus α-anomer)

28.8

COOH
H——OH
HO——H
HO——H
H——OH
CH$_2$OH
(chiral)

COOH
H——OH
HO——H
HO——H
H——OH
COOH
(achiral)

from D-galactose

COOH
HO——H
HO——H
H——OH
H——OH
CH$_2$OH
(chiral)

COOH
HO——H
HO——H
H——OH
H——OH
COOH
(chiral)

from D-mannose

COOH
H——OH
HO——H
H——OH
CH$_2$OH
(chiral)

COOH
H——OH
HO——H
H——OH
COOH
(achiral)

from D-xylose

C=O
H——OH
HO——H
H
H——OH
CH$_2$OH

O=C
HO——H
HO——H
H
H——OH
CH$_2$OH

O=C
H——OH
HO——H
H
CH$_2$OH

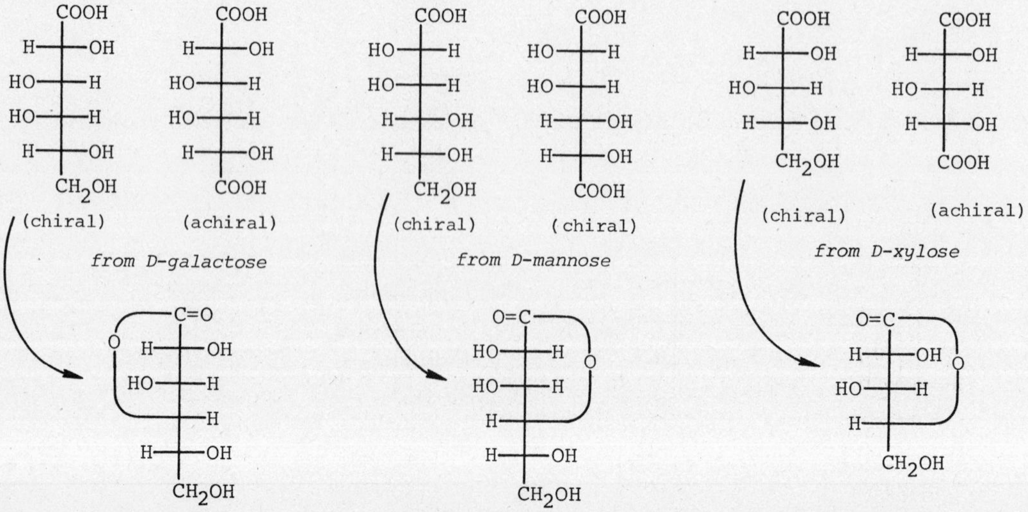

28.9

(a)

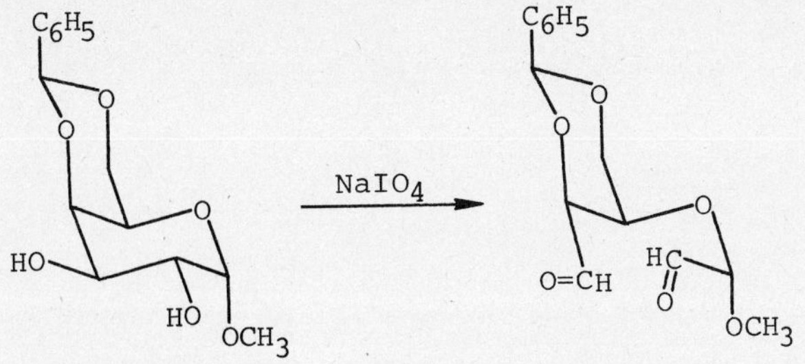

$\xrightarrow{\text{NaIO}_4}$

(one equivalent of NaIO$_4$ consumed)

(b)

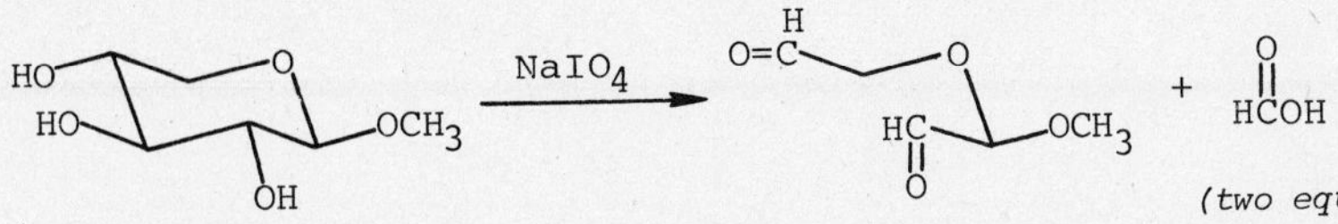

$\xrightarrow{\text{NaIO}_4}$

+

(two equivalents of NaIO$_4$ consumed)

(c)

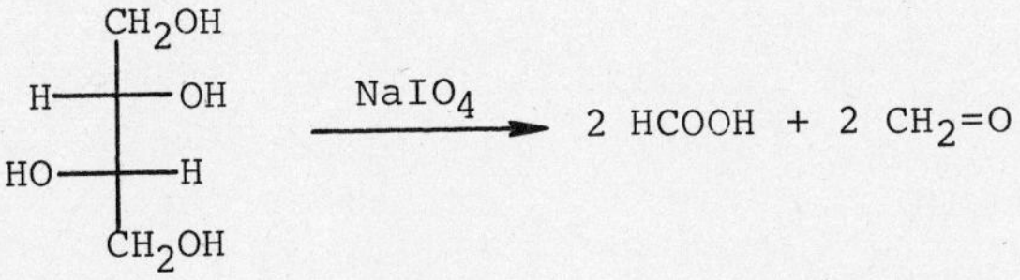

$\xrightarrow{\text{NaIO}_4}$ 2 HCOOH + 2 CH$_2$=O   *(three equivalents of NaIO$_4$ consumed)*

28.10

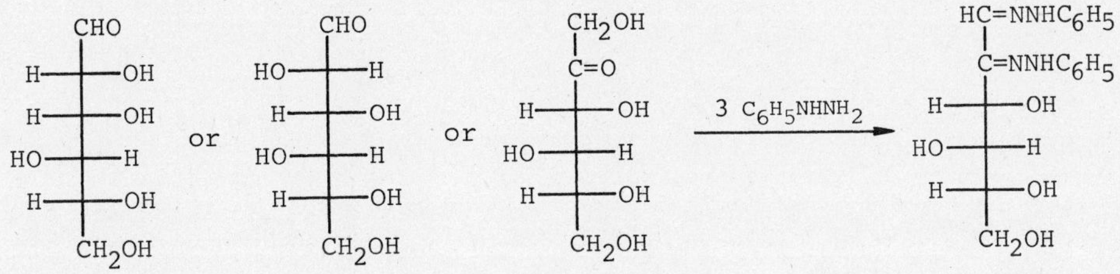

or

or

$\xrightarrow{\text{3 C}_6\text{H}_5\text{NHNH}_2}$

D-(−)-gulose   *D-(−)-idose*   *D-(+)-sorbose*

28.11

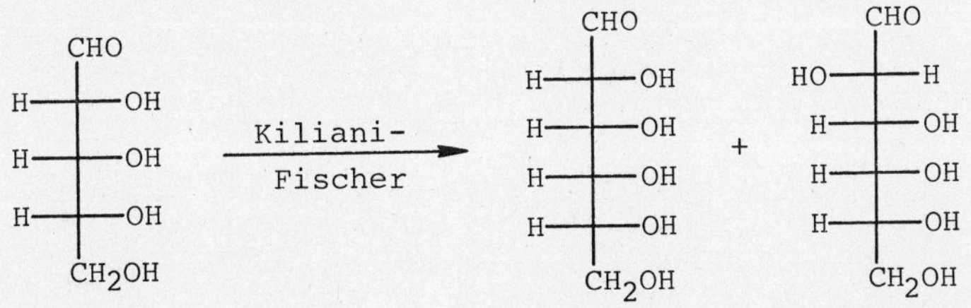

$\xrightarrow[\text{Fischer}]{\text{Kiliani-}}$

+

D-ribose   *D-allose*   *D-altrose*

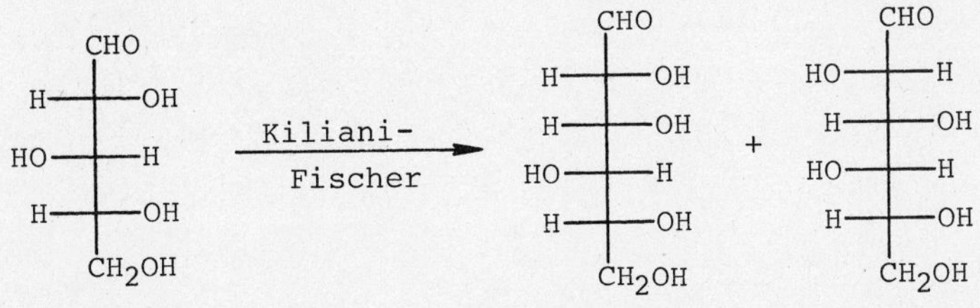

$\xrightarrow[\text{Fischer}]{\text{Kiliani-}}$

+

D-xylose   *D-gulose*   *D-idose*

28.12

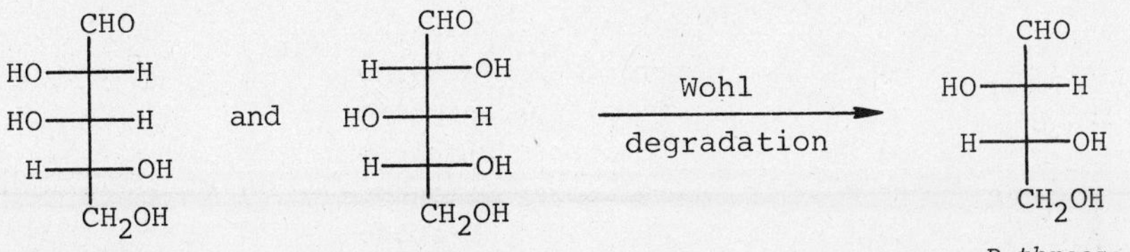

and

$\xrightarrow[\text{degradation}]{\text{Wohl}}$

D-lyxose   *D-xylose*   *D-threose*

488

28.14

28.E   Answers and Explanations for Problems

1.
D-glyceraldehyde	2R
D-erythrose	2R, 3R
D-threose	2S, 3R
D-ribose	2R, 3R, 4R
D-arabinose	2S, 3R, 4R
D-xylose	2R, 3S, 4R
D-lyxose	2S, 3S, 4R

D-allose	2R, 3R, 4R, 5R
D-altrose	2S, 3R, 4R, 5R
D-glucose	2R, 3S, 4R, 5R
D-mannose	2S, 3S, 4R, 5R
D-gulose	2R, 3R, 4S, 5R
D-idose	2S, 3R, 4S, 5R
D-galactose	2R, 3S, 4S, 5R
D-talose	2S, 3S, 4S, 5R

2.

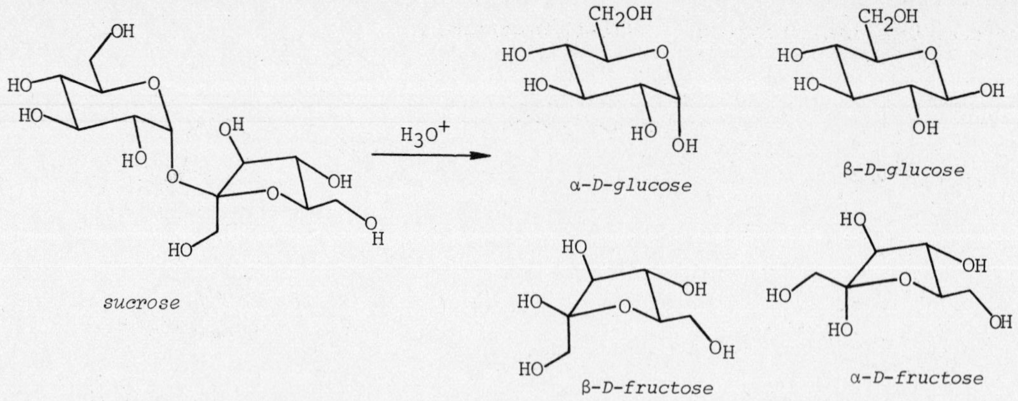

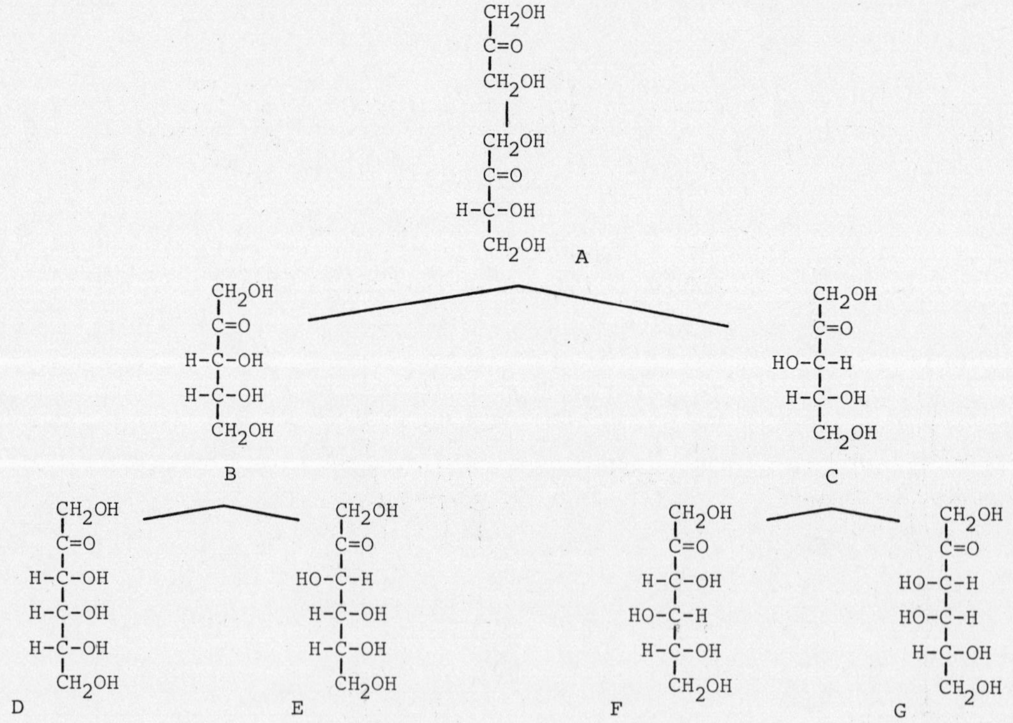

IDENTICAL OSAZONES	Ketose	Hexoses
	A	D-erythrose, D-threose
	B	D-ribose, D-arabinose
	C	D-xylose, D-lyxose
	D	D-allose, D-altrose
	E	D-glucose, D-mannose
	F	D-gulose, D-idose
	G	D-galactose, D-talose

3.   D-erythrose, D-ribose, D-xylose, D-allose, D-galactose

4.

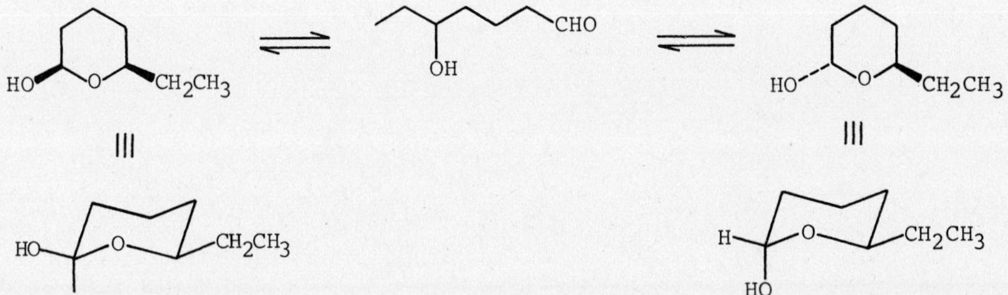

diequatorial
(more stable)

axial-equatorial
(less stable)

Mechanism:

Acid:

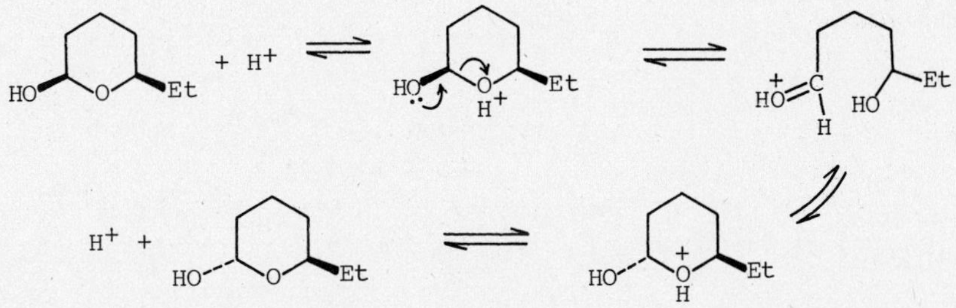

Base:

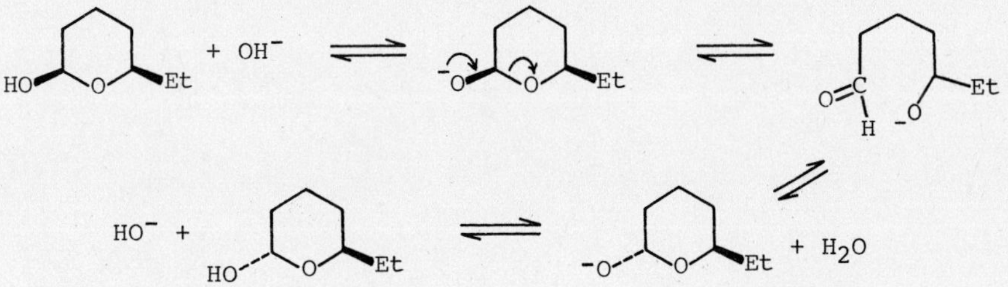

5.   (a)

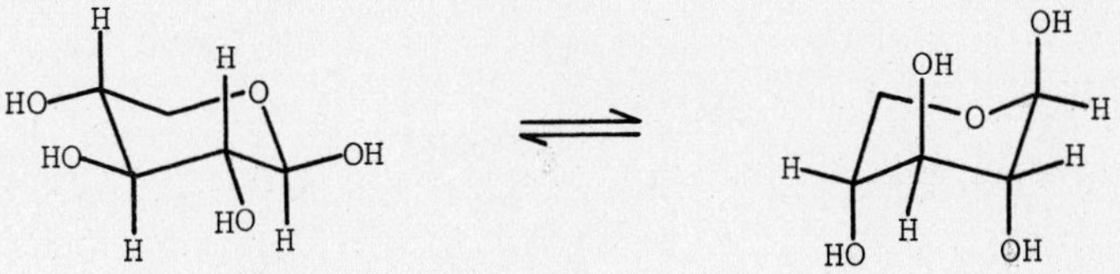

more stable

less stable
(four axial groups)

(b)

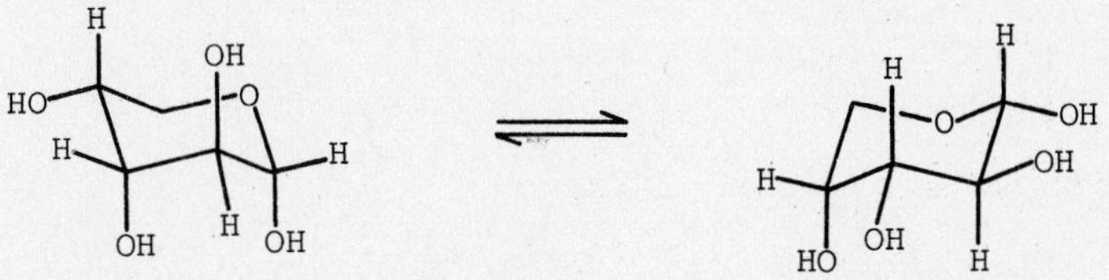

less stable
(three axial groups)

more stable
(one axial group)

6.

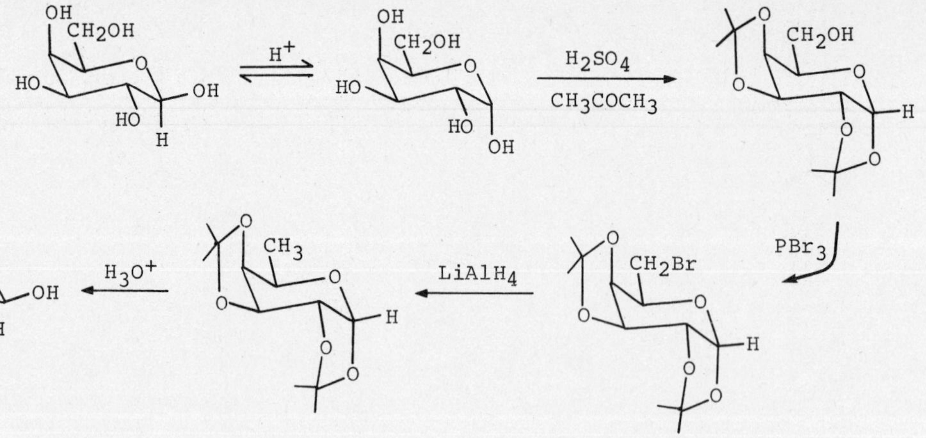

7. Kiliani-Fischer chain extension follows the aldose tree in Table 28.1.

8. Reverse of the aldose tree in Table 28.1.

9.

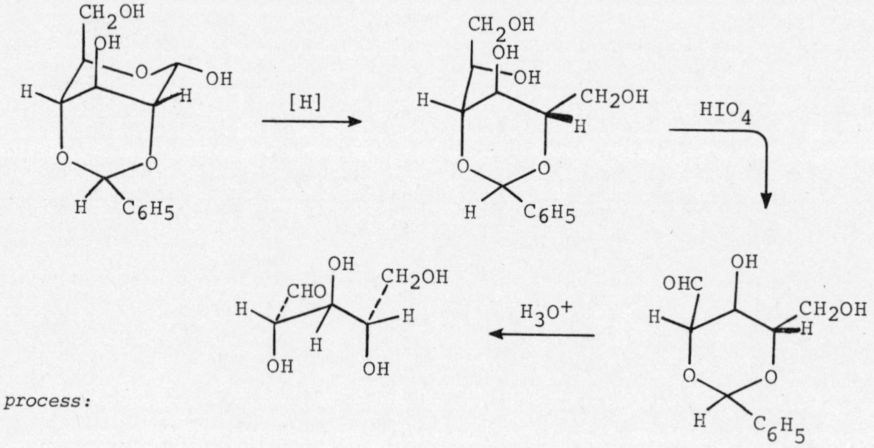

Overall process:

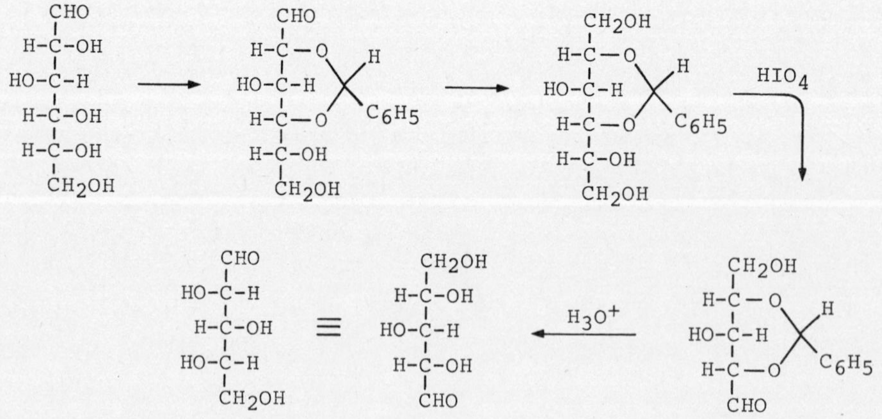

L-xylose

10.

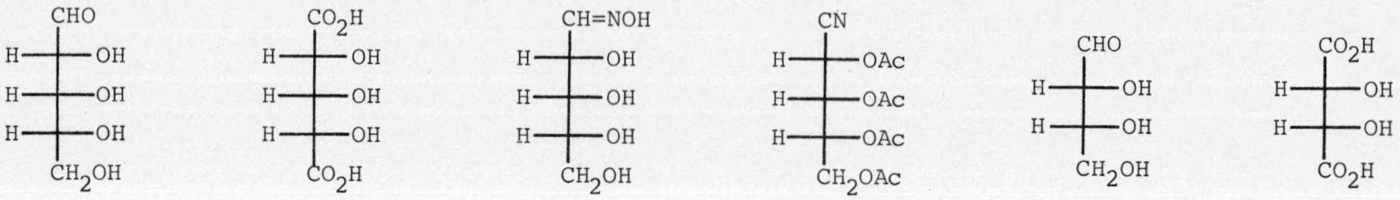

A   B   C   D   E   F

11.

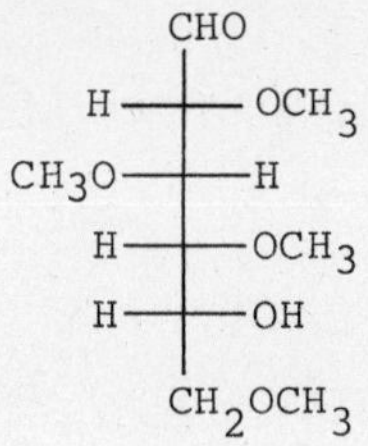

CHO
H——OCH₃
CH₃O——H
H——OCH₃
H——OH
CH₂OCH₃

2,3,4,6-tetra-O-methyl-D-glucose

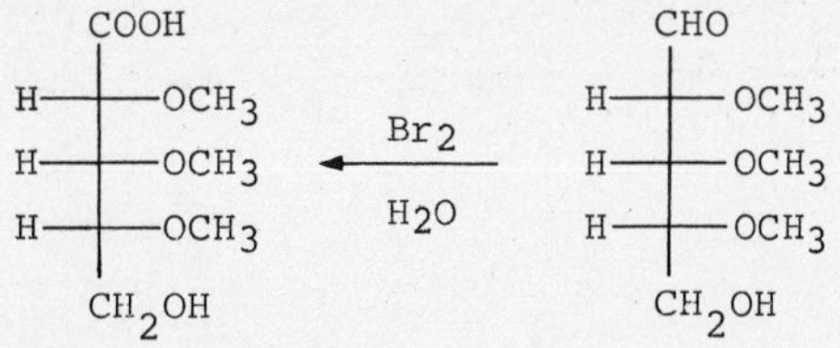

COOH
H——OCH₃
H——OCH₃
H——OCH₃
CH₂OH

2,3,4-tri-O-methyl-D-ribonic acid

$\xleftarrow{\text{Br}_2 / \text{H}_2\text{O}}$

CHO
H——OCH₃
H——OCH₃
H——OCH₃
CH₂OH

Therefore, H must be:

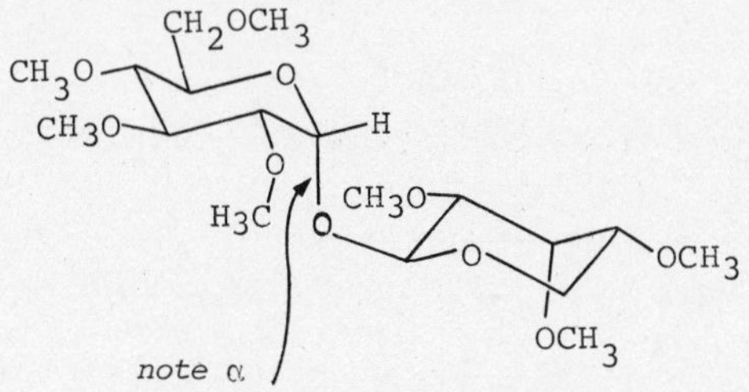

and G is:

note α linkage

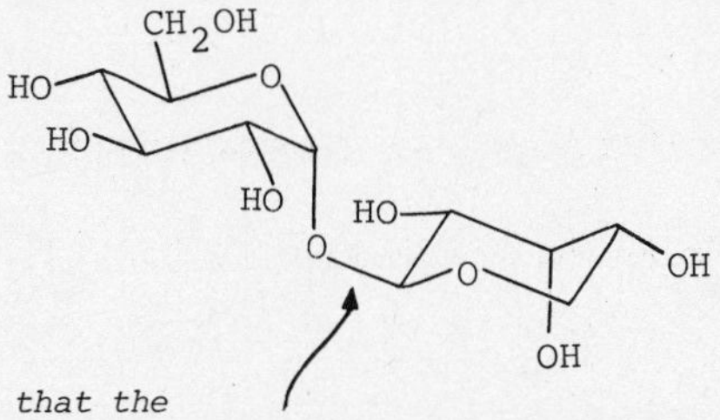

Note that the stereochemistry at the pentose anomeric carbon is not established. Either α or β is compatible with the data provided.

12.

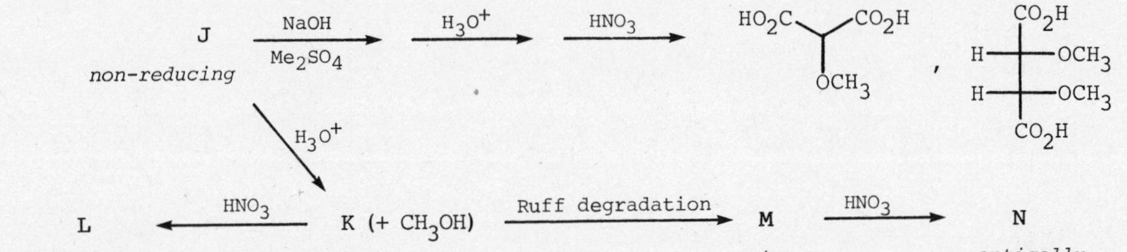

J
non-reducing

$\xrightarrow[\text{Me}_2\text{SO}_4]{\text{NaOH}}$ $\xrightarrow{\text{H}_3\text{O}^+}$ $\xrightarrow{\text{HNO}_3}$

HO₂C——CO₂H
OCH₃

,

CO₂H
H——OCH₃
H——OCH₃
CO₂H

$\searrow \text{H}_3\text{O}^+$

L
optically inactive diacid

$\xleftarrow{\text{HNO}_3}$ K (+ CH₃OH)
hexose

$\xrightarrow{\text{Ruff degradation}}$ M
pentose

$\xrightarrow{\text{HNO}_3}$ N
optically active diacid

1) **N** is optically <u>active</u>:

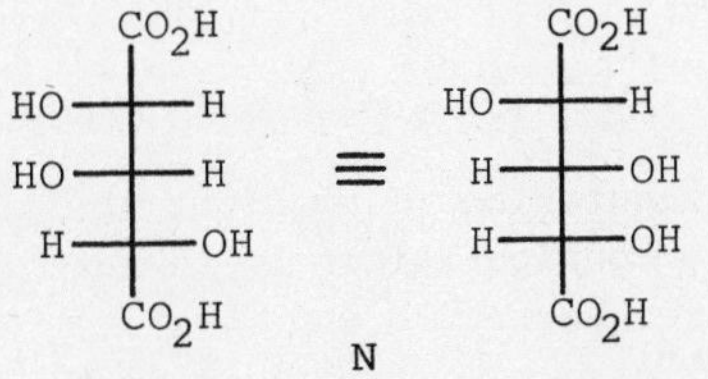

CO₂H
HO——H
HO——H
H——OH
CO₂H

≡

CO₂H
HO——H
H——OH
H——OH
CO₂H

N

2) M $\xrightarrow{\text{HNO}_3}$ N :

Therefore, **M** can be

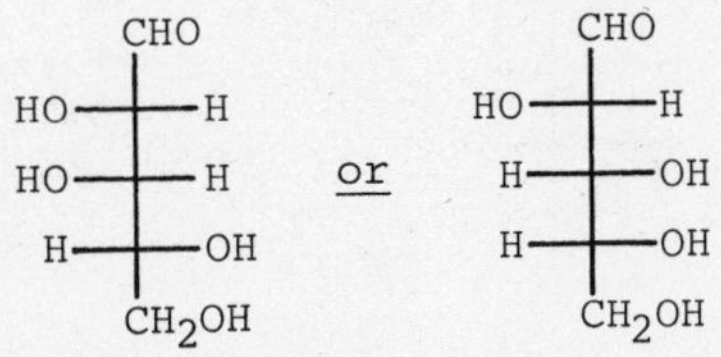

CHO
HO——H
HO——H
H——OH
CH₂OH

or

CHO
HO——H
H——OH
H——OH
CH₂OH

3) K $\xrightarrow{\text{Ruff}}$ M :

Therefore **K** can be

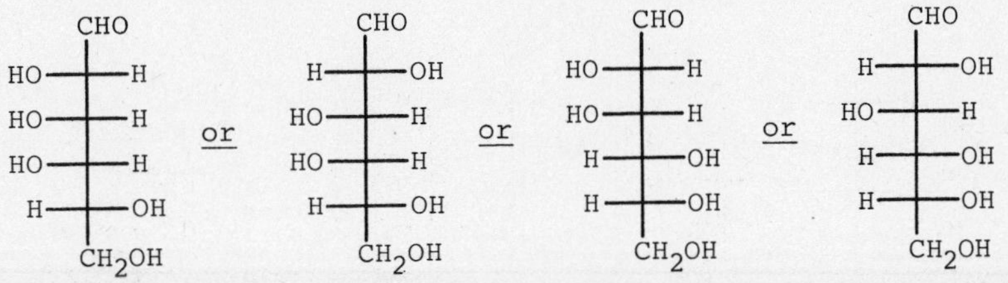

CHO
HO——H
HO——H
HO——H
H——OH
CH₂OH

or

CHO
H——OH
HO——H
HO——H
H——OH
CH₂OH

or

CHO
HO——H
HO——H
H——OH
H——OH
CH₂OH

or

CHO
H——OH
HO——H
H——OH
H——OH
CH₂OH

4)   K $\xrightarrow{\text{HNO}_3}$ L *(optically <u>inactive</u>)* :

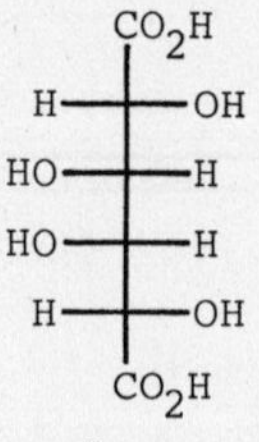

```
        CO2H                 CHO
   H ——— OH            H ——— OH
  HO ——— H            HO ——— H
  HO ——— H            HO ——— H
   H ——— OH            H ——— OH
        CO2H                CH2OH
         L                   K
```

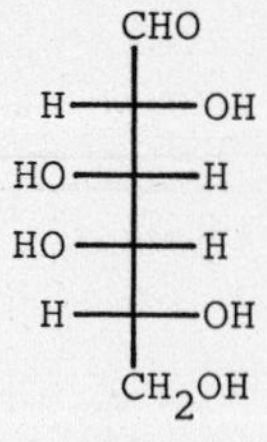

J is evidently a methyl glycoside of K. The reaction with $NaOH/(CH_3)_2SO_4$ converts all hydroxyl groups to methyl ether groups. The aqueous HCl hydrolyzes the glycoside acetal and nitric acid oxidizes at the resulting CHO and C-OH groups. From the products, we deduce the hydrolysis product to be:

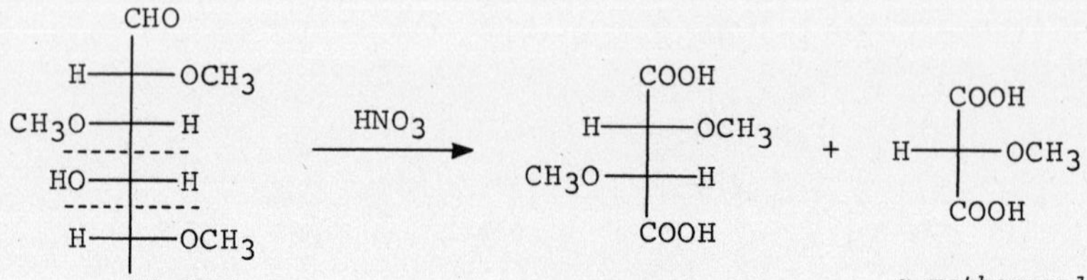

```
        CHO
    H ——— OCH3
 CH3O ——— H
 ---------
   HO ——— H
 ---------
    H ——— OCH3
       CH2OCH3
```
$\xrightarrow{\text{HNO}_3}$

```
       COOH
   H ——— OCH3
CH3O ——— H
       COOH
```
α,β-*dimethoxy-succinic acid*

+

```
       COOH
   H ——— OCH3
       COOH
```
α-*methoxymalonic acid*

Thus, J must be:

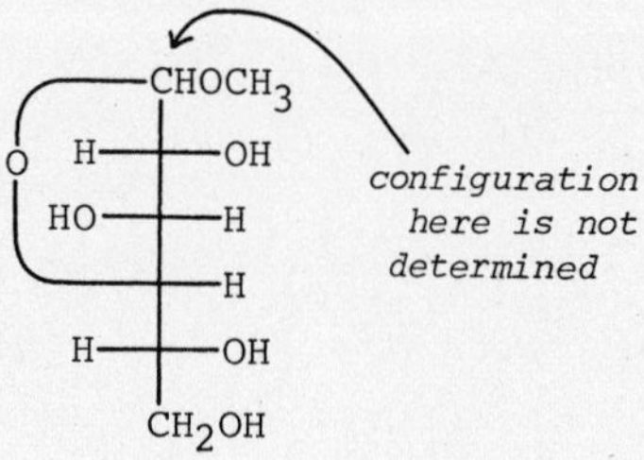

```
       CHOCH3
  O  H ——— OH
    HO ——— H
       H
    H ——— OH
       CH2OH
```
configuration here is not determined

Note that
```
       CHO
   H ——— OCH3
  HO ——— H
 CH3O ——— H
   H ——— OCH3
      CH2OCH3
```

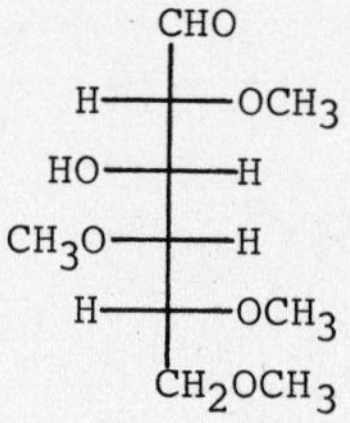

could give α,β-dimethoxysuccinic acid and α-methoxymalonic acid on oxidation, but the corresponding cyclic acetal has a four-membered ring and is not a reasonable structure.

NOTE also that the α-methoxymalonic acid could derive from further oxidation of the dimethoxysuccinic acid, rather than from oxidation of the 6-methoxy ether.

(b) Not only has the configuration (α or β) of the anomeric carbon not been established, but we have assumed D-configurations in the above structures. The available data do not allow a distinction between D and L.

13.

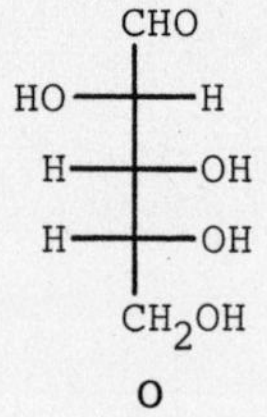

```
       CHO                 CO2H                 CHO                 CO2H
  HO ——— H            HO ——— H            H ——— OH            H ——— OH
   H ——— OH            H ——— OH            H ——— OH            H ——— OH
   H ——— OH            H ——— OH               CH2OH                CO2H
      CH2OH                CO2H
        O                   P                   Q                   R
```

14.

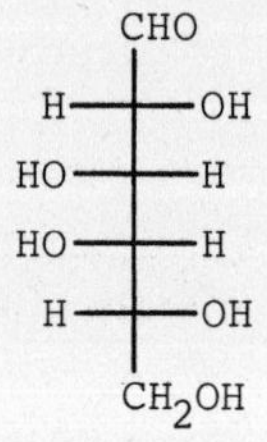

```
       CHO                CH2OH                 CHO                 CO2H
   H ——— OH            H ——— OH            HO ——— H            HO ——— H
  HO ——— H            HO ——— H            HO ——— H            HO ——— H
  HO ——— H            HO ——— H            HO ——— H            HO ——— H
   H ——— OH            H ——— OH            H ——— OH            H ——— OH
      CH2OH               CH2OH               CH2OH                CO2H
        S                   T                   U                   V
```

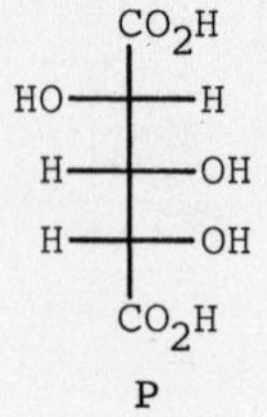

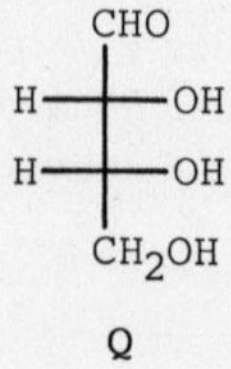

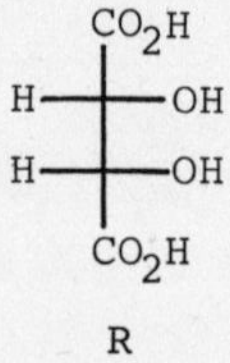

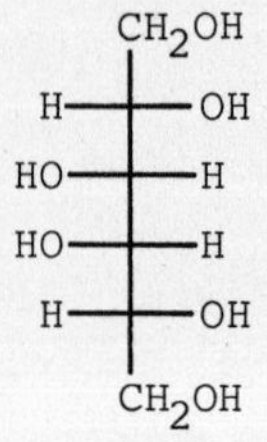

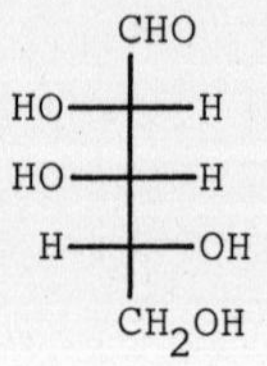

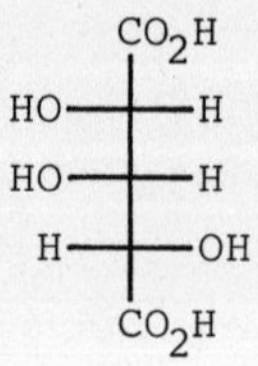

15.

W: CHO / HO—H / H—OH / HO—H / H—OH / CH₂OH

X: COOH / HO—H / H—OH / HO—H / H—OH / COOH

Y: CHO / H—OH / HO—H / H—OH / CH₂OH

Z: COOH / H—OH / HO—H / H—OH / COOH

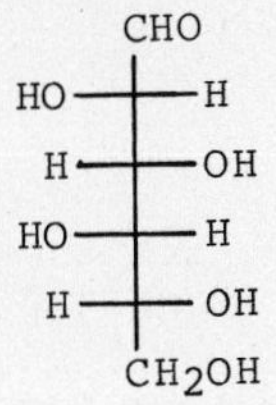

W   X   Y   Z

16. Let n_α = fraction α, and $1 - n_\alpha$ = fraction β

$$n_\alpha(29.3) + (1-n_\alpha)(-17.0) = 14.2$$

$$n_\alpha = 0.674, \text{ or } 67.4\% \qquad n_\beta = 0.326, \text{ or } 32.6\%$$

17.

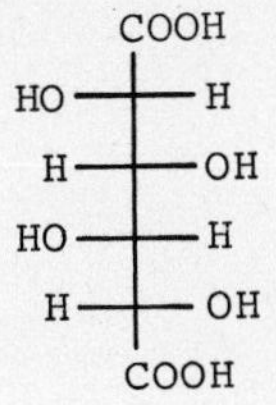

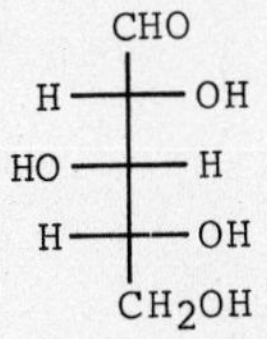

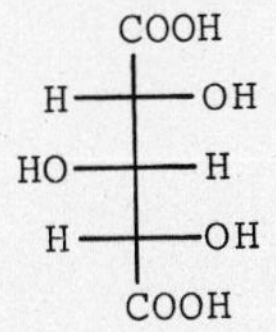

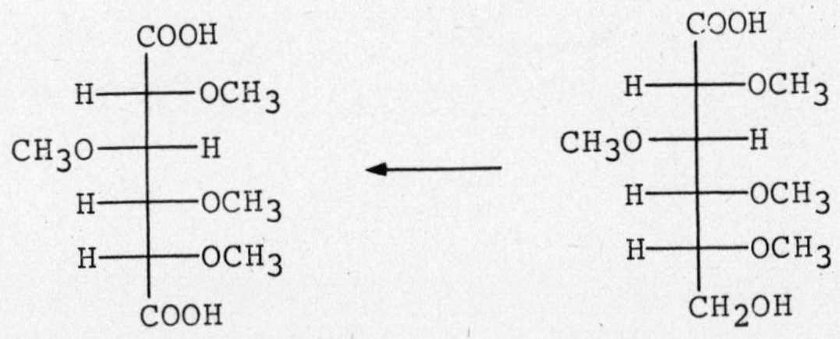

tetra-*O*-methylglucaric
acid

←

AA, tetra-*O*-methylgluconic acid

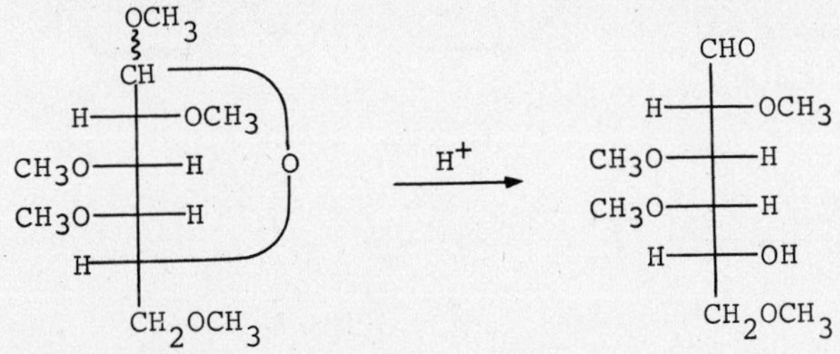

methyl-2,3,4,6-tetra-*O*-methyl-
galactopyranoside

$\xrightarrow{H^+}$

BB, tetra-*O*-methylgalactose

Melibionic acid must join C-6 of gluconic acid to C-1 of galactose:

note α-linkage

melibionic acid

or:

α-glycoside

hemiacetal;
reducing sugar

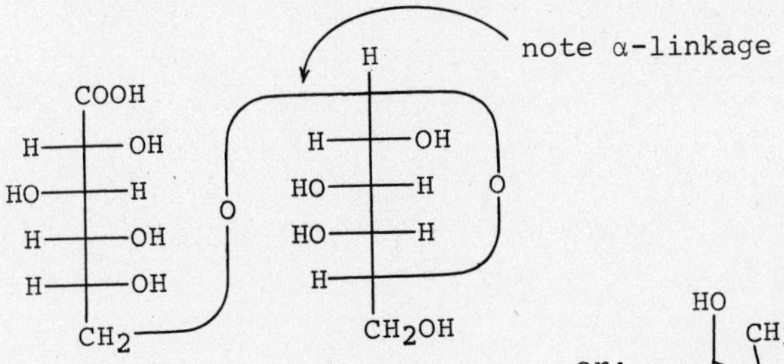

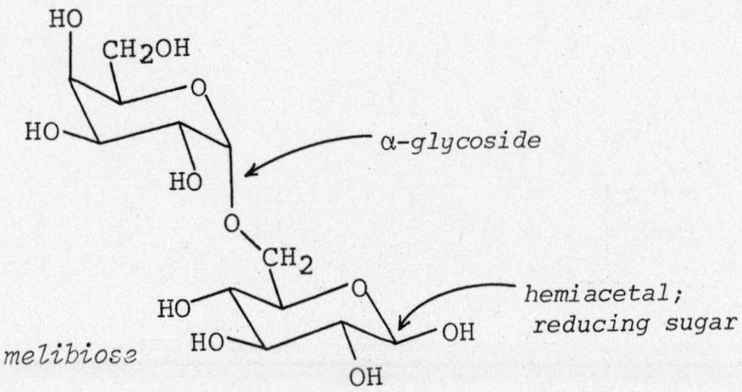

melibiose

18.

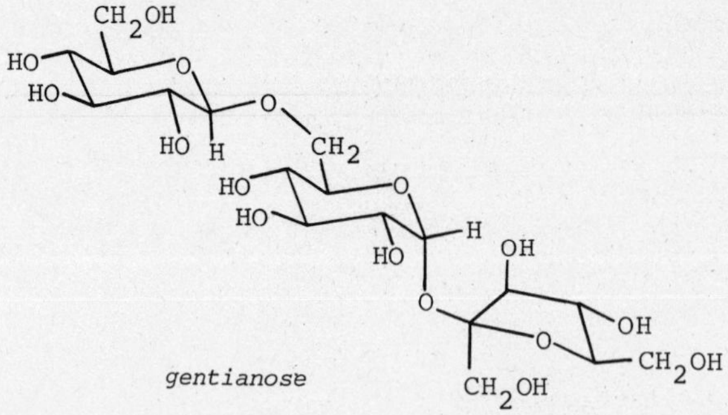

gentianose

19.

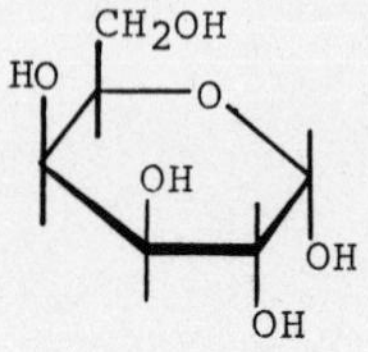

α-D-galactopyranose

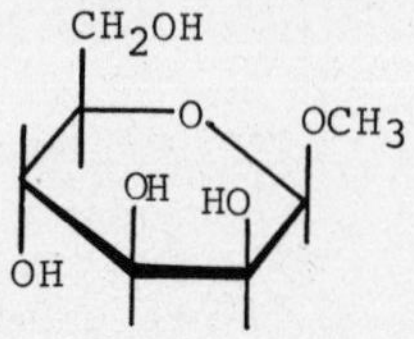

methyl β-D-mannoside

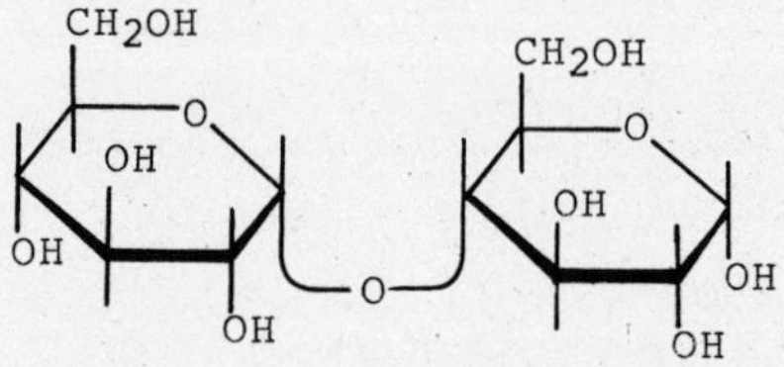

α-maltose

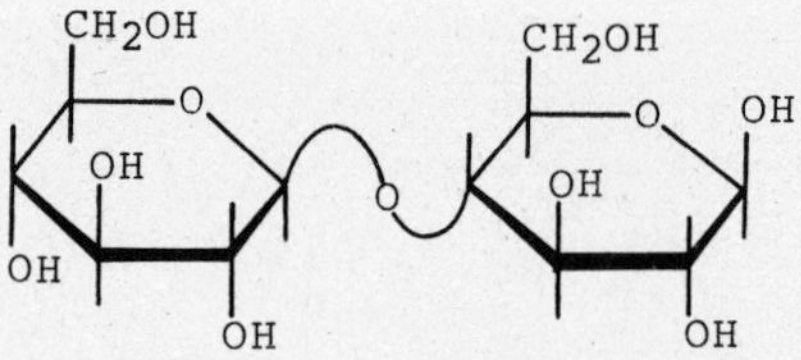

β-cellobiose

20.

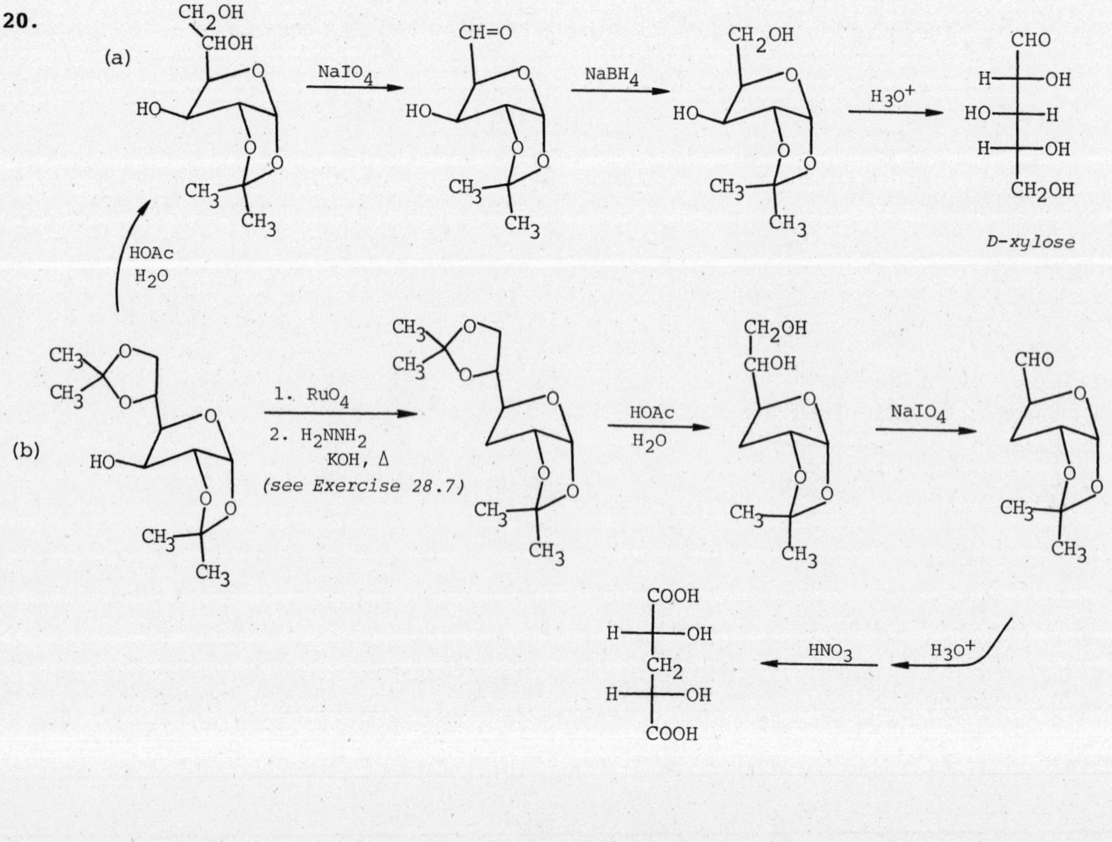

(a)

(b)

(c)

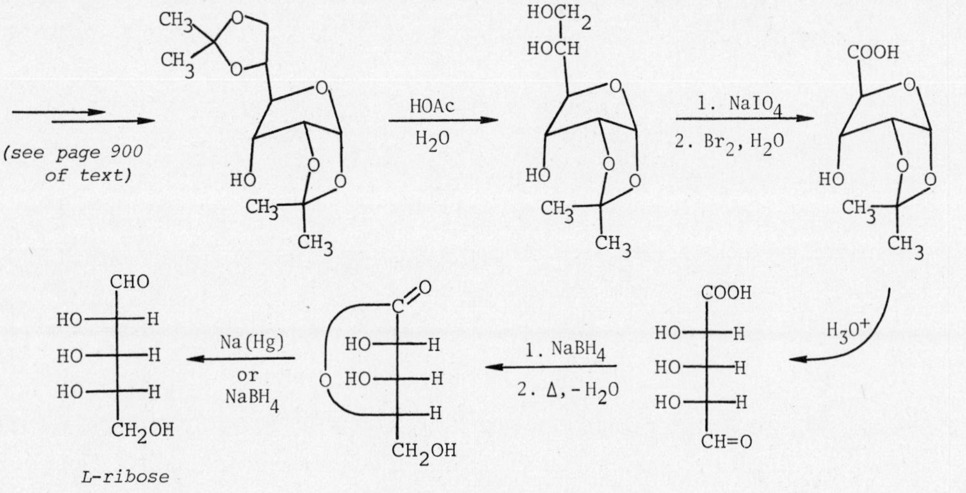

(see page 900 of text)

CH₃ / CH₃

HOAc
H₂O

HOCH₂
HOCH

1. NaIO₄
2. Br₂, H₂O

COOH

CH₃ / CH₃

CHO
HO——H
HO——H
HO——H
CH₂OH

L-ribose

Na(Hg)
or
NaBH₄

C=O
HO——H
HO——H
——H
CH₂OH

1. NaBH₄
2. Δ, -H₂O

COOH
HO——H
HO——H
HO——H
CH₂OH

H₃O⁺

COOH
HO——H
HO——H
HO——H
CH=O

21.

CH₂OH
HO——H
HO——H
H——OH
H——OH
CH₂OH

D-mannitol

CH_3CCH_3
H⁺

CH₃ / CH₃
CH₃ / CH₃

O—CH₂
O——H
HO——H
H——OH
H——O
CH₂—O

NaIO₄

2

CH=O
H——O CH₃
CH₂—O CH₃

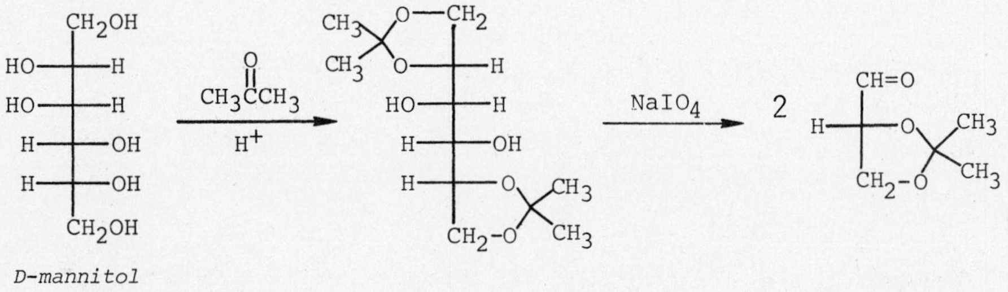

28.F Supplementary Problems

S1. Write a Fischer projection of the open-chain form of each of the sugars illustrated below.

(a)   (b) 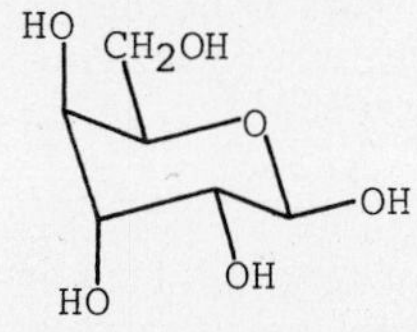   (c)

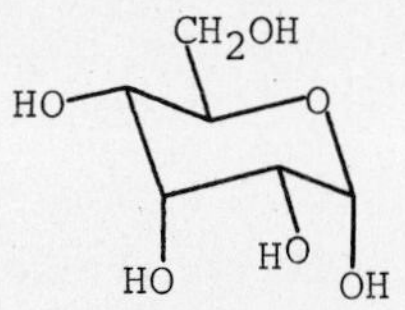

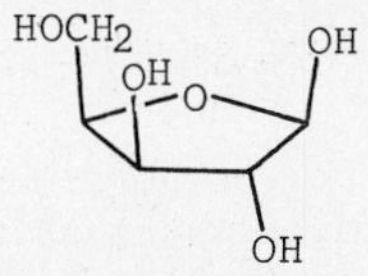

(d) 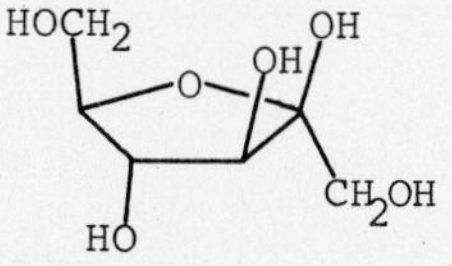   (e) 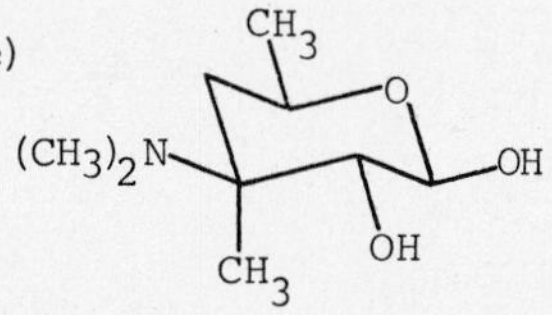   (f)

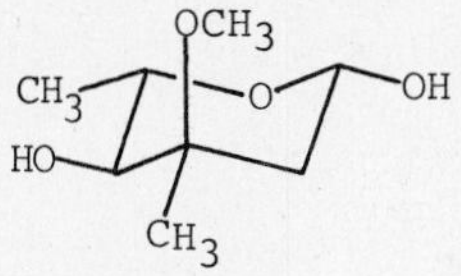

S2. Write perspective formulas of the pyranose β-anomers of each of the sugars illustrated below, choosing the most stable conformation where appropriate.

(a)
CHO
HO——H
HO——H
H——OH
H——OH
CH₂OH

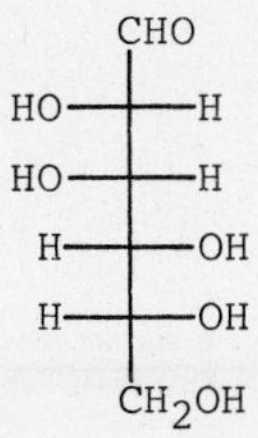

(b)
CHO
HO——H
H——OH
HO——H
H——OH
CH₂OH

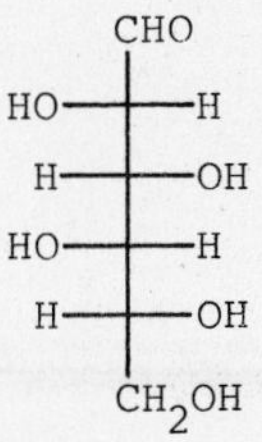

(c)
CHO
H——OH
CH₂
HO——H
CH₂OH

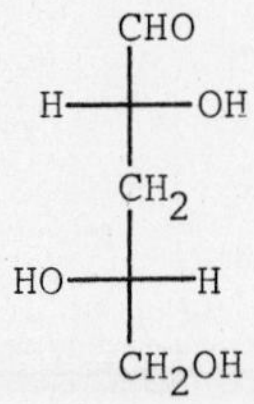

(d)
CHO
H——NHCCH₃
HO——H
H——OH
H——OH
CH₂OH

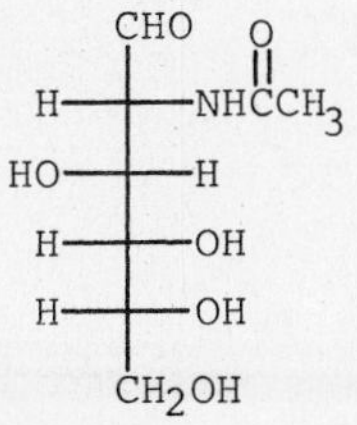

S3. Write a step-by-step mechanism for the base-catalyzed interconversion of the furanose and pyranose forms of fructose:

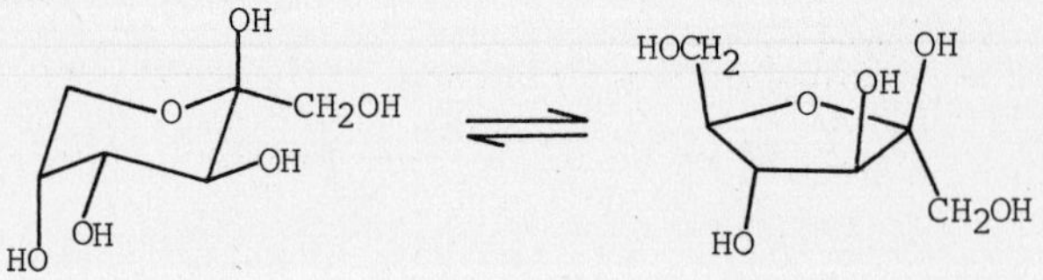

S4. Predict the major product(s) from each of the following reaction sequences:

(a)

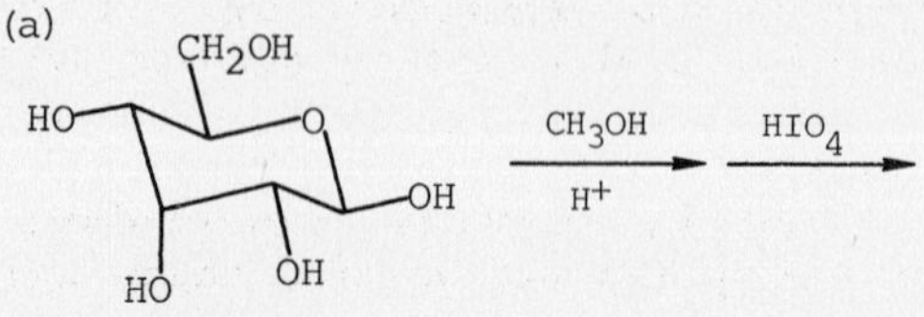

$$\xrightarrow[H^+]{CH_3OH} \xrightarrow{HIO_4}$$

(b)

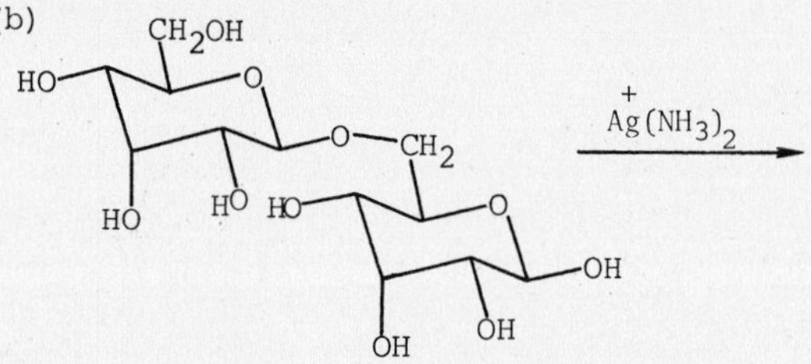

$$\xrightarrow{Ag(NH_3)_2^+}$$

(c)

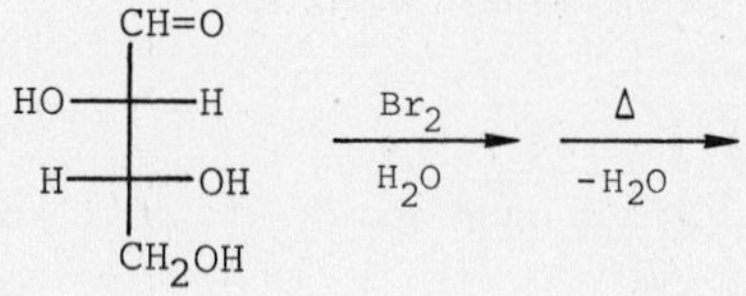

$$\xrightarrow[H_2O]{Br_2} \xrightarrow[-H_2O]{\Delta}$$

(d)

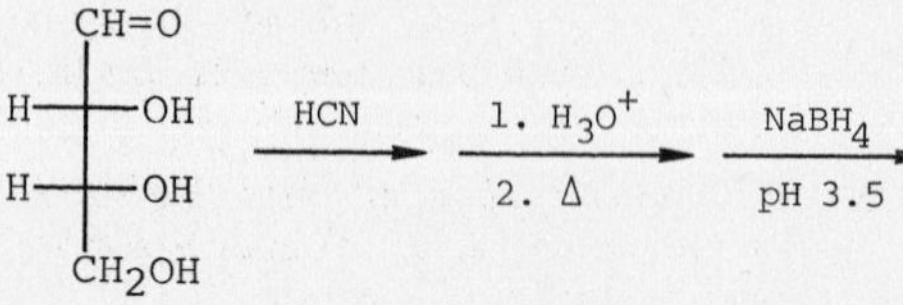

$$\xrightarrow{HCN} \xrightarrow[2.\ \Delta]{1.\ H_3O^+} \xrightarrow[pH\ 3.5]{NaBH_4}$$

(e)

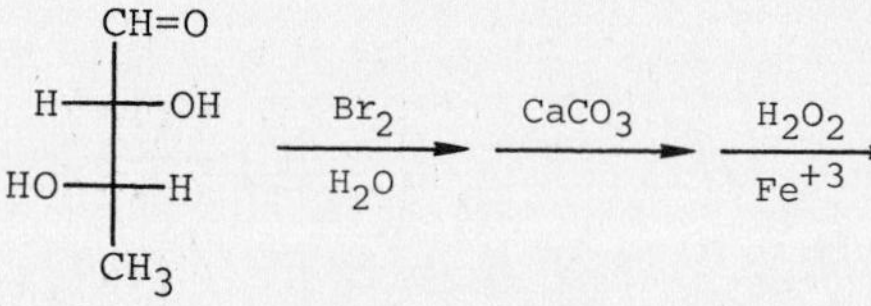

$$\xrightarrow[H_2O]{Br_2} \xrightarrow{CaCO_3} \xrightarrow[Fe^{+3}]{H_2O_2}$$

(f)

$$\xrightarrow[(CH_3)_2SO_4]{NaOH} \xrightarrow{H_3O^+}$$

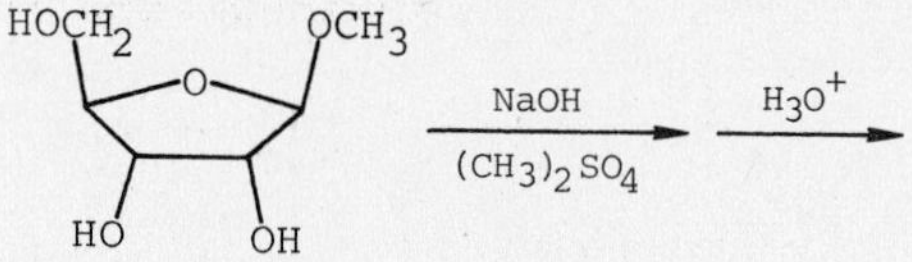

S5. Treatment of D-aldopentose A with sodium borohydride gives an optically inactive alditol, B. Reaction of A with HCN, followed by acid-catalyzed hydrolysis, produces two aldonic acids, C and D, **both** of which afford optically active saccharic acids after treatment with nitric acid. What are A, B, C, and D?

S6. Oxidation of L-aldohexose E with nitric acid leads to an optically active product. Ruff degradation of E provides an aldopentose F, which loses all optical activity on reaction with sodium borohydride. Kiliani-Fischer chain extension of F gives E back again, along with an isomeric aldohexose G. G reacts with nitric acid to afford an optically inactive diacid. What are E, F, and G?

S7.

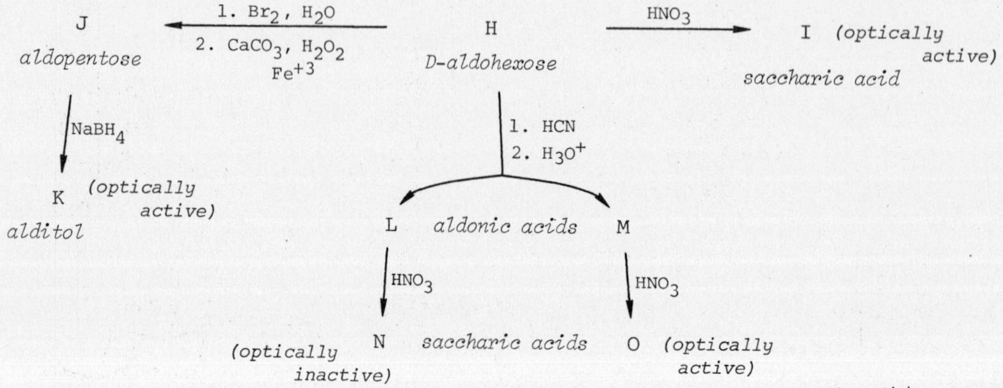

[cont'd on next page]

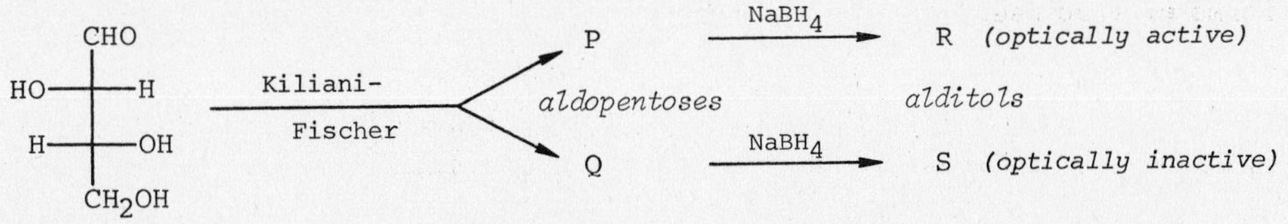

S8. Hydrolysis of the disaccharide sophorose furnishes two moles of D-glucose; it is not hydrolyzed by α-glucosidase. Oxidation of sophorose with bromine water, followed by permethylation with sodium hydroxide and dimethyl sulfate, leads to an octamethylsophoronic acid derivative. Mild acid treatment of this compound produces a solution which reduces periodic acid. What is the structure of sophorose?

S9. Formation of a triphenylmethyl ("trityl") ether from an alcohol and triphenylmethyl chloride with pyridine is selective for the reaction of primary alcohols in carbohydrate derivatives, as illustrated below:

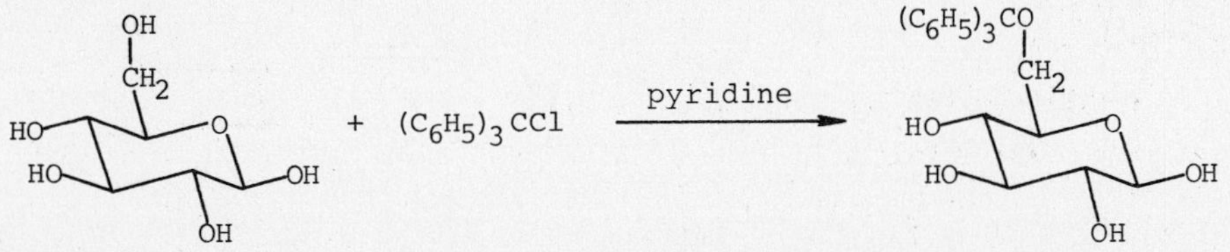

A trityl ether is stable to alkaline reaction conditions, but is hydrolyzed in dilute acid. Using this information, show how to synthesize L-fucose from D-galactose.

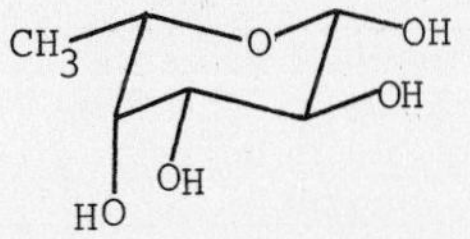

L-fucose

28.G   Answers to Supplementary Problems

S1.

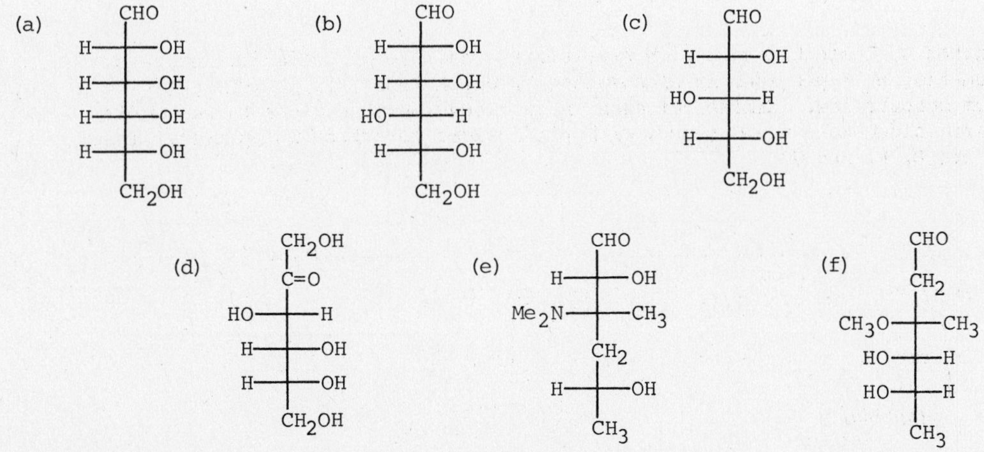

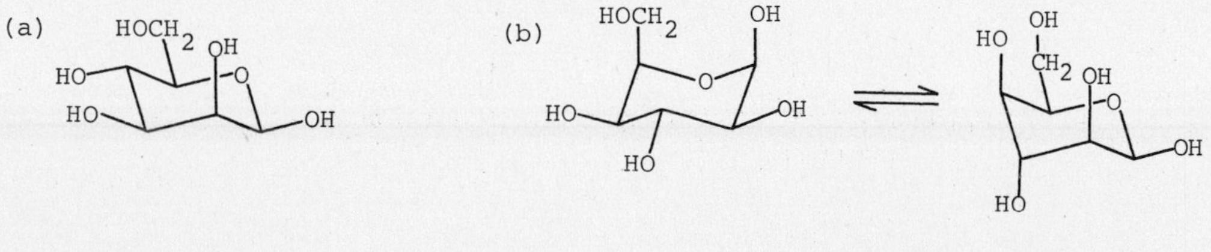

(c)

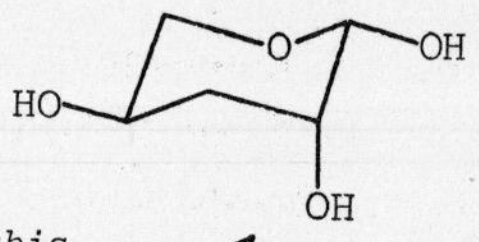

NOTE: *for
an L-sugar, this
is the β-anomer*

(d)

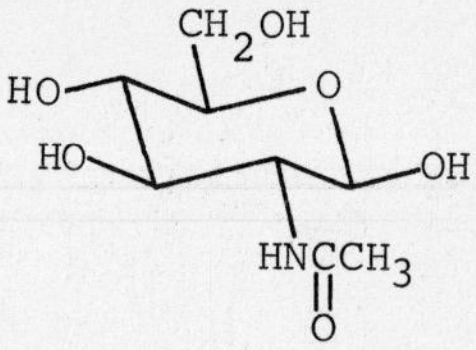

S3.

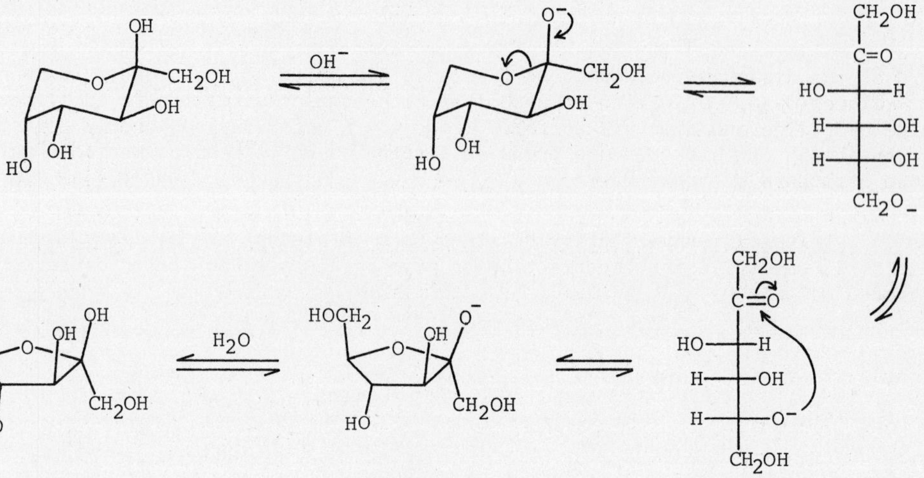

OH^- H_2O

S4. (a)

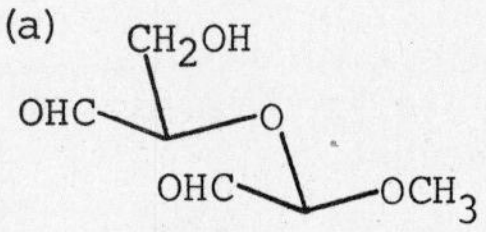

+ HCOOH

(b)

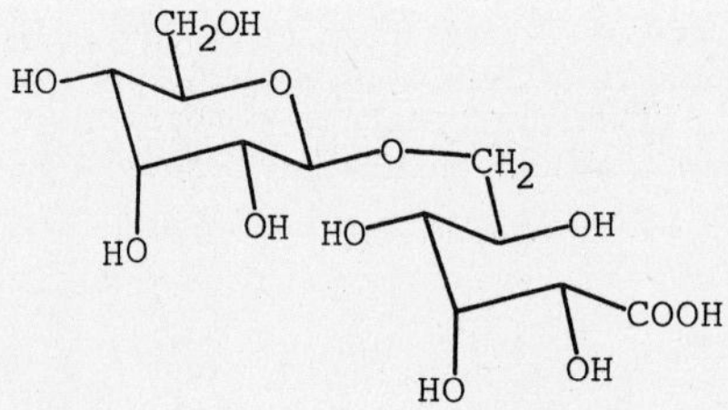

(c)

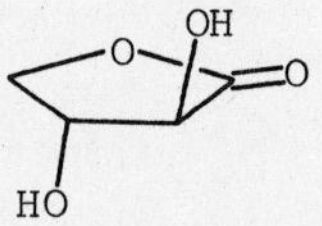

(d) 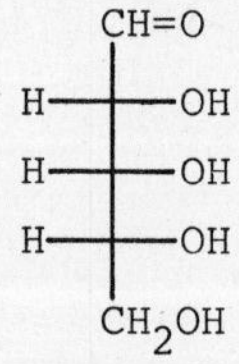   and 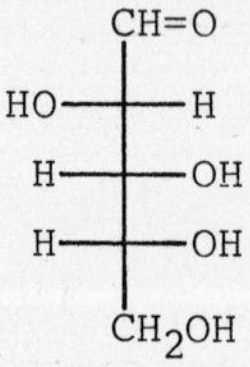   (e) 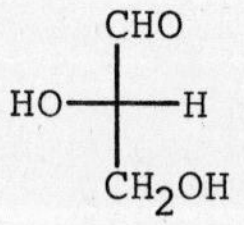   (f)

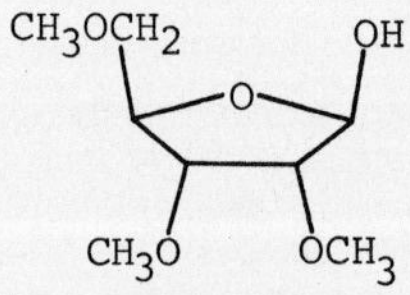

S5.

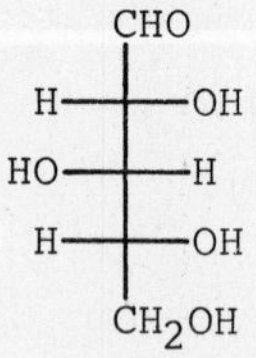

A 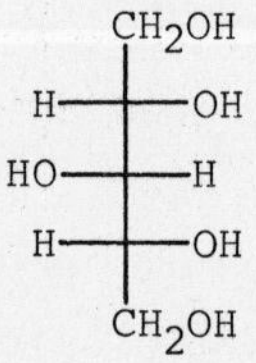   B 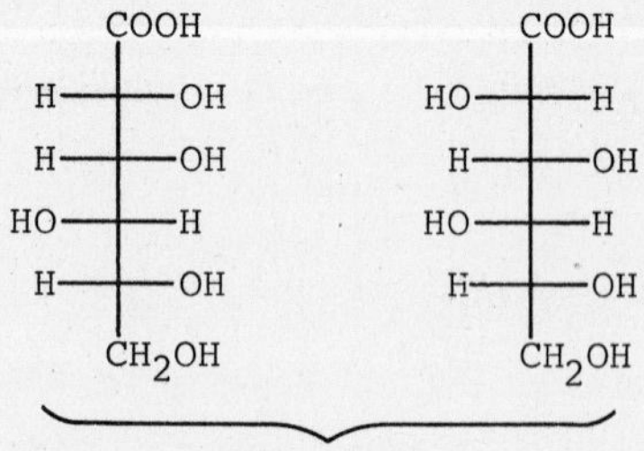   C and D

S6.

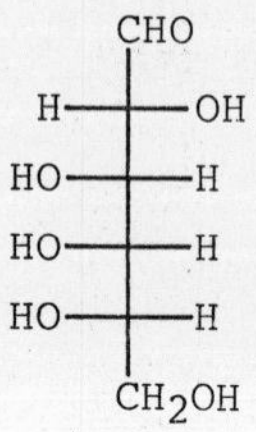

E 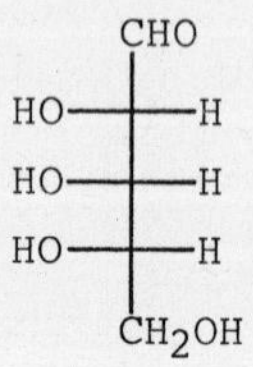   F 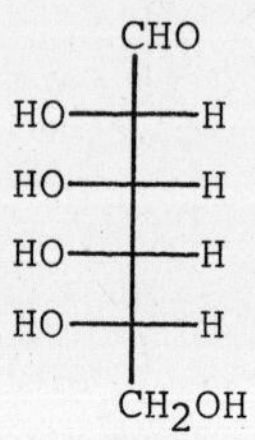   G

S7.

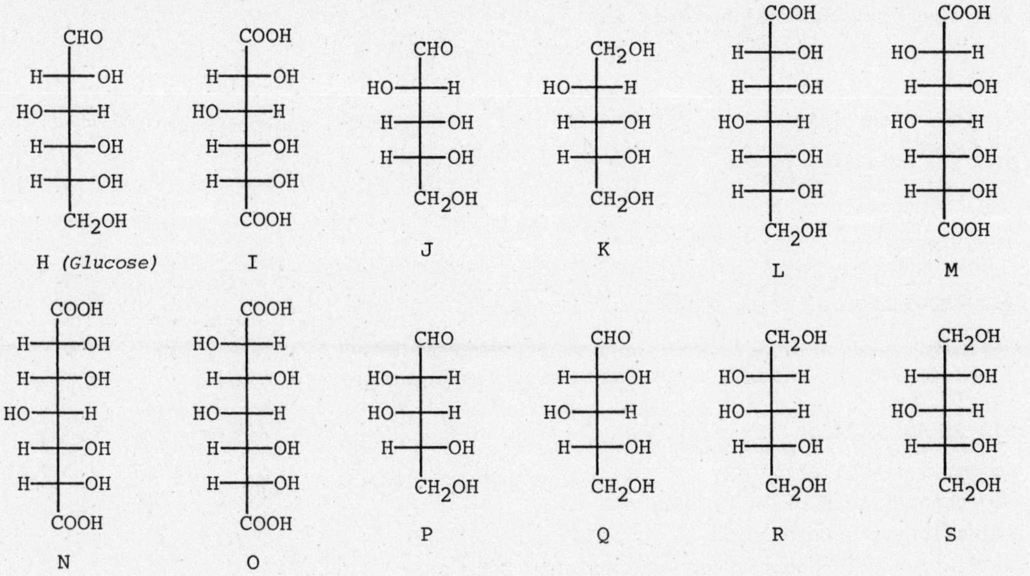

H *(Glucose)*   I   J   K   L   M

N   O   P   Q   R   S

S8.

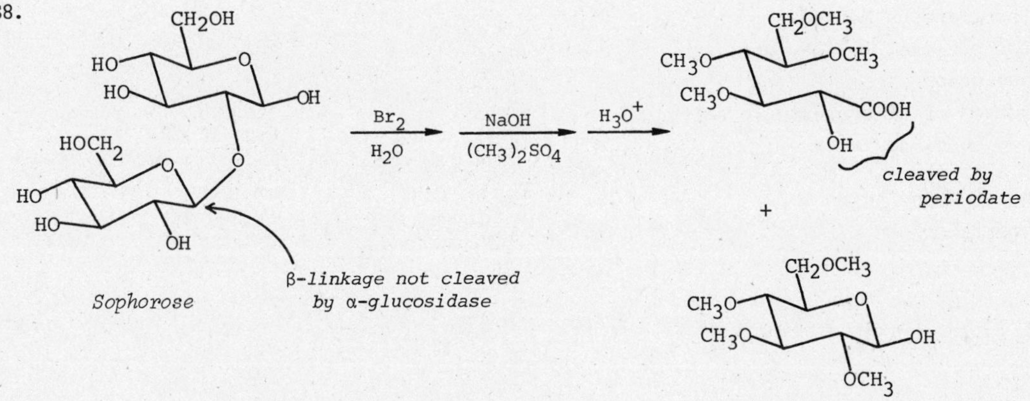

$$\xrightarrow[\text{H}_2\text{O}]{\text{Br}_2} \quad \xrightarrow[\text{(CH}_3\text{)}_2\text{SO}_4]{\text{NaOH}} \quad \xrightarrow{\text{H}_3\text{O}^+}$$

cleaved by periodate

+

Sophorose

β-linkage not cleaved by α-glucosidase

S9.

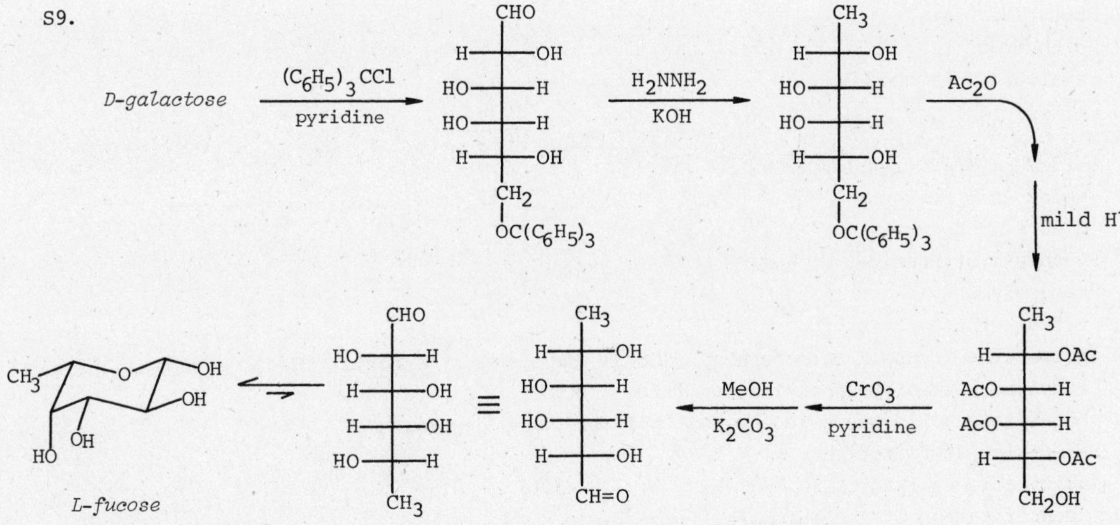

D-galactose $\xrightarrow[\text{pyridine}]{\text{(C}_6\text{H}_5\text{)}_3\text{CCl}}$

$\xrightarrow[\text{KOH}]{\text{H}_2\text{NNH}_2}$

$\xrightarrow{\text{Ac}_2\text{O}}$

$\downarrow \text{mild H}^+$

$\xleftarrow[\text{K}_2\text{CO}_3]{\text{MeOH} \quad \text{CrO}_3 \quad \text{pyridine}}$

L-fucose

29. AMINO ACIDS, PEPTIDES, AND PROTEINS

29.A   Chapter Outline and Important Terms Introduced

29.1   Introduction

zwitterion, inner salt   di-, tri-, tetra-, and polypeptides
peptide bond   protein

29.2   Structure, Nomenclature, and Physical Properties of Amino Acids

D,L vs. R,S   (D = R, L = S)

29.3   Acid-Base Properties of Amino Acids

amphoterism   isoelectric point
pK_a's = 2.4, 9.8 for α-amino acids (plus side chain groups)

29.4   Synthesis of Amino Acids

A.   Commercial Availability
       L- cheaper than D-
B.   Amination of α-Halo Acids
C.   Alkylation of N-Substituted Aminomalonic Esters
D.   Strecker Synthesis
E.   Miscellaneous Methods
       for proline, lysine, etc.
F.   Resolution
       method of diastereomeric salts
       hog renal acylase

29.5   Reactions of Amino Acids

A.   Esterification

$$^+H_3N-\underset{\underset{R}{|}}{CH}-CO_2H \ + \ HOR' \ \xrightarrow{H^+} \ ^+H_3N-\underset{\underset{R}{|}}{CH}-CO_2R'$$

B.   Amide Formation

$$^+H_3N-\underset{\underset{R}{|}}{CH}-CO_2^- \ + \ R'-\overset{\overset{O}{||}}{C}-X \ \xrightarrow{base} \ R'-\overset{\overset{O}{||}}{C}-NH-\underset{\underset{R}{|}}{CH}-CO_2^- \quad (X = Cl, \ O_2CR')$$

C.   Oxidative Deamination
       ninhydrin
       analytical method

29.6   Peptides

A.   Structure and Nomenclature
       amino acid sequence   N-terminal vs. C-terminal amino acids
       disulfide bond
B.   Synthesis of Peptides
       homopolymer
       2,5-diketopiperazine formation
       protecting groups: carbobenzoxy ("Cbz") and t-butoxycarbonyl ("Boc") groups
       coupling with dicyclohexylcarbodiimide ("DCC")
       Merrifield solid-phase technique; polymer-bound peptides
C.   Structure Determination
       amino acid analyzer
       identification of the N-terminal amino acid
          Sanger method   Edman degradation
       identification of the C-terminal amino acid
          sequential removal of C-terminal amino acids with carboxypeptidase

        fragmentation of the peptide chain
            proteases: trypsin, chymotrypsin, pepsin
            cyanogen bromide (cleaves at methionine carbonyl)
            partial degradation and peptide mapping

29.7 Proteins

    A. Molecular Shape

        fibrous vs. globular   enzymes

        prosthetic group

    B. Factors that Influence Molecular Shape

        primary structure
            amino acid sequence

        secondary structure
            hydrogen bonds   disulfide bridges

        tertiary structure
            electronic and steric properties of the side chain groups
            hydrophobic vs. hydrophilic

    C. Structure of the Fibrous Proteins

        α-helix   super helix

        random coil   β-pleated sheet

    D. Structure of the Globular Proteins

        denaturation/renaturation

    E. Biological Function of Proteins and Polypeptides

        enzymes   defensive substances

        transport   hormones

        storage   (amphiphilic character)

29.B Important Reactions Introduced

    NOTE: Just as in the last Chapter, there are very few **new** reactions introduced; it is the combination of
    an acidic and a basic functional group in the same molecule that makes the chemistry look different.

Synthesis of α-amino acids by amination of α-haloacids (29.4.B)

Equation:

$$R\text{--CH--}CO_2H \xrightarrow{\ NH_3\ } R\text{--CH--}CO_2H$$
$$\hspace{1.2cm}\underset{X}{|} \hspace{3.3cm} \underset{NH_2}{|}$$

Generality: X is usually Br

Key features: reaction proceeds better than most direct aminations with NH_3 because NH_2 group in
               product is less reactive than normal alkyl amine (see Section 23.6.A)

Synthesis of α-amino acids by alkylation of N-substituted malonic esters (29.4.C)

Equation:

$$EtO_2C\text{--CH--}CO_2Et + R'X \xrightarrow{\ EtO^-\ } EtO_2C\overset{R'}{\underset{RCONH}{\text{--C--}}}CO_2Et \xrightarrow{\ H_3O^+\ } {}^+H_3N\text{--CH--}CO_2H$$
$$\hspace{1.0cm}\underset{RCONH}{|} \hspace{8.8cm}\underset{R'}{|}$$

Generality: RCONH = AcNH, CbzNH, Phthaloyl-N, tBocNH, etc.

Key features: version of the classic malonic ester synthesis adapted to preparation of amino acids
               (see Section 27.7.D)

Strecker amino acid synthesis (29.4.D)

Equation:

$$NH_3 + R\text{--CH=O} + HCN \longrightarrow H_2N\text{--CH--C}\equiv N \xrightarrow{\ H_3O^+\ } {}^+H_3N\text{--CH--}CO_2H$$
$$\hspace{5.2cm}\underset{R}{|} \hspace{3.5cm}\underset{R}{|}$$

Key features: amino version of cyanohydrin formation (Section 14.8.B)

reaction proceeds via ⁻CN addition to immonium intermediate

Resolution of racemic amino acids with hog renal acylase (29.4.F)

Equation:

$$^+H_3N-CH-CO_2^- \xrightarrow{Ac_2O} CH_3-\overset{\overset{O}{\|}}{C}-NH-CH-CO_2H \xrightarrow[acylase]{hog\ renal} H_3\overset{+}{N}\underset{\underset{H\ \ R}{}}{\diagup}CO_2^- + CH_3CONH\underset{\underset{R\ \ H}{}}{\diagup}CO_2H$$

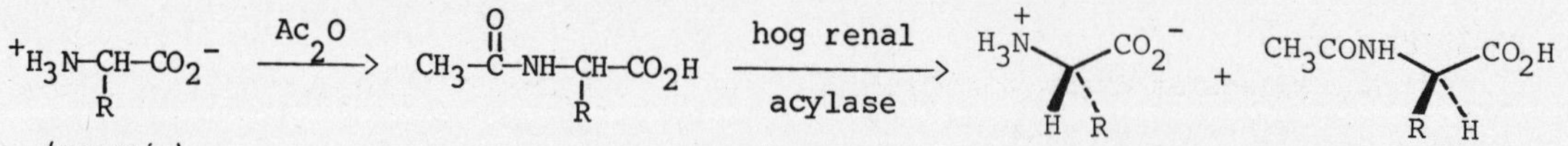

(racemic)   L-enantiomer   D-enantiomer

Ninhydrin reaction (29.5.C)

Equation:

$$\underset{R}{\overset{^+NH_3}{R-CH-CO_2^-}} \xrightarrow{ninhydrin} R-\overset{HN}{\overset{\|}{C}}-CO_2^- \xrightarrow{H_2O} R-\overset{\overset{O}{\|}}{C}-CO_2^- + NH_3 \xrightarrow{ninhydrin} purple\ color$$

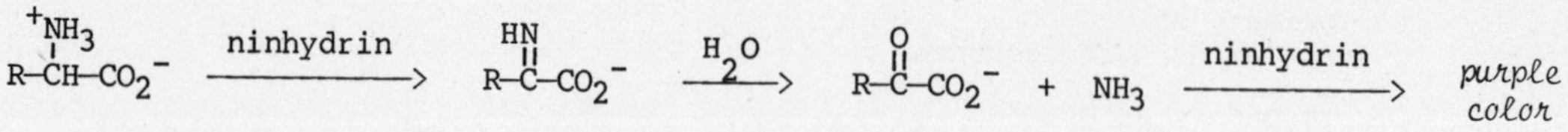

Key features: used as analytical reaction to detect presence of α-amino acids; not used preparatively

gives a different reaction with proline

Diketopiperazine formation (29.6.B)

Equation:

$$2\ ^+H_3N-\underset{R}{CH}-CO_2^- \xrightarrow{-H_2O}$$

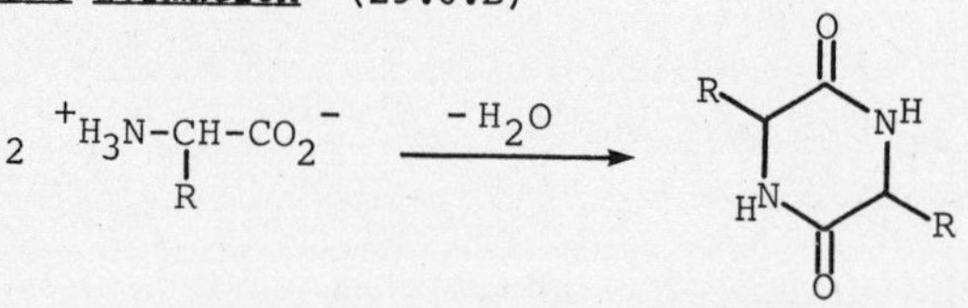

Key feature: generally a reaction to be avoided in the synthesis of peptides

Introduction and removal of N-protecting groups for peptide synthesis (29.6.B)

Equation:

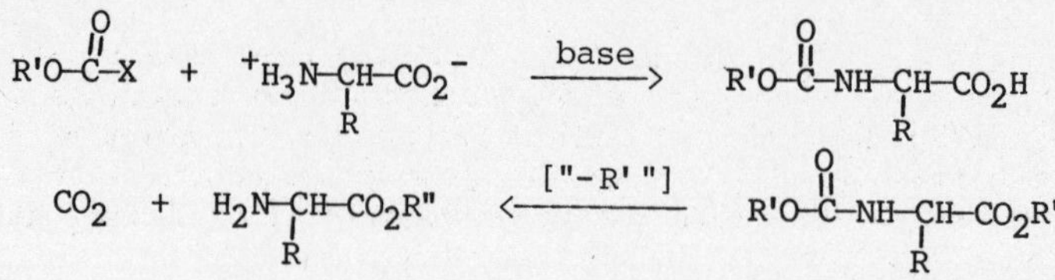

$$R'O-\overset{\overset{O}{\|}}{C}-X + {}^+H_3N-\underset{R}{CH}-CO_2^- \xrightarrow{base} R'O-\overset{\overset{O}{\|}}{C}-NH-\underset{R}{CH}-CO_2H$$

$$CO_2 + H_2N-\underset{R}{CH}-CO_2R'' \xleftarrow{["-R'\,"]} R'O-\overset{\overset{O}{\|}}{C}-NH-\underset{R}{CH}-CO_2R''$$

Generality: "R'O₂CX" is usually $C_6H_5CH_2O_2CCl$ ("CbzCl") or $tBuO_2CON=C(CN)C_6H_5$ ("Boc-ON")

["-R'"] = H_2/Pt or HBr for Cbz protecting group

= HCl or CF_3CO_2H for Boc protecting group

Peptide synthesis with dicyclohexylcarbodiimide (DCC) (29.6.B)

Equation:

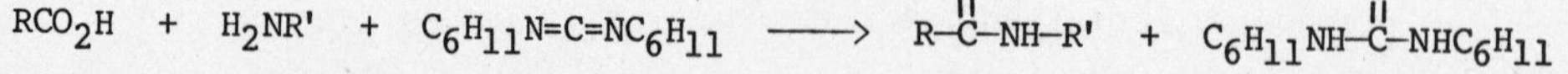

$$RCO_2H + H_2NR' + \underset{DCC}{C_6H_{11}N=C=NC_6H_{11}} \longrightarrow R-\overset{\overset{O}{\|}}{C}-NH-R' + \underset{dicyclohexylurea\ (DCU)}{C_6H_{11}NH-\overset{\overset{O}{\|}}{C}-NHC_6H_{11}}$$

Generality: general method for formation of amide and ester bonds

Key features: reaction proceeds via O-acylisourea, an activated carboxylic acid derivative

in combination with polymer-bound amino acid derivative (R' part above), used with Merrifield automated technique for peptide synthesis

Sanger method for N-terminal amino acid identification (29.6.C)

Equation:

+ amino acids

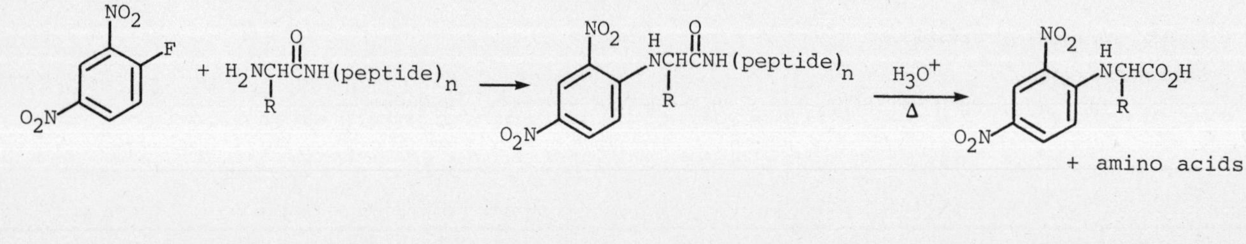

Key features: hydrolysis of polypeptide gives free amino acids, with the N-terminal one
                        derivatized with the dinitrophenyl group (lysine ε-amino group derivatized too)
                reaction is example of nucleophilic aromatic substitution (Section 26.3.A)

Edman method for sequential degradation of polypeptide chains   (29.6.C)

Equation:

$$C_6H_5N=C=S \; + \; H_2N\overset{O}{\overset{\|}{C}}HCNH(peptide) \; \longrightarrow \; C_6H_5NH-\overset{S}{\overset{\|}{C}}-NH\overset{O}{\overset{\|}{C}}HCNH(peptide) \; \xrightarrow{\;HCl\;}$$

(+ peptide)

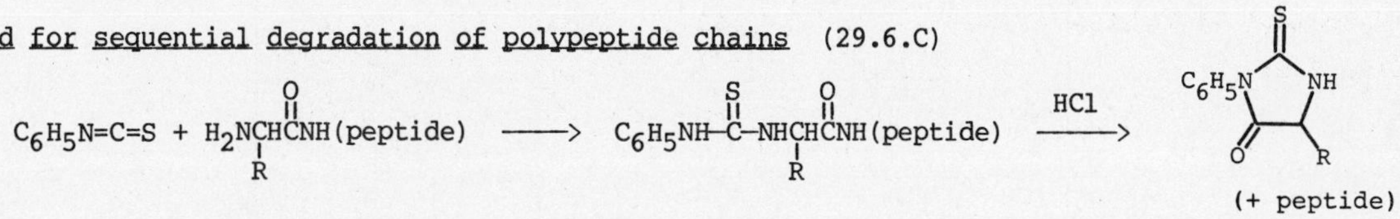

Key features: can be repeated sequentially to remove one amino acid at a time from N-terminus of
                        peptide chain
                cyclic product (thiohydantoin) is isolated and identified

Cyanogen bromide cleavage of methionine peptide bonds   (29.6.C)

Equation:

$$\xrightarrow{\;CNBr\;}$$ + H_2N—B + MeSCN

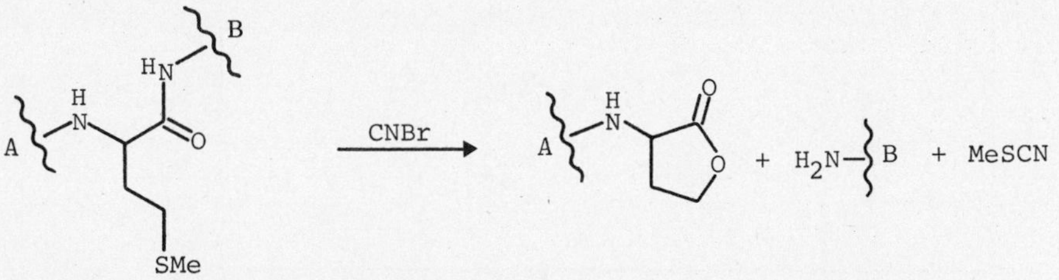

Key features: cleaves peptide chain **only** at methionine carbonyl position
                useful in selective peptide degradation and sequence analysis

29.C   Important Concepts and Hints

Like the last chapter, this one discusses the special chemistry that arises when two familiar functional groups are present in the same molecule. Although most of the reactions of amino acids are ones you've seen before, complications can arise because of the juxtaposition of the acidic and basic groups. For example, a sequence of protection and deprotection steps is necessary for controlled formation of the amide linkage in a polypeptide, whereas it is a very straightforward process in monofunctional molecules.

The topic of this chapter is important not only for the chemistry it presents, but also because of the biological significance of amino acids, oligopeptides, and proteins. The frontiers of biology have reached the molecular level, and it is necessary to understand the chemistry of one of its most important groups of building blocks. It really is useful to know the structures, names, and abbreviations of the amino acids, and we urge you to learn them if you have any interest in the life sciences.

29.D   Answers to Exercises

29.1   This is especially important for biology and biochemistry students.

29.2   (D) = (R) and (L) = (S) for the α-position of amino acids (except for the amino acid
                                                            cysteine).

29.3 $\overset{+}{H_3}N-CH_2-CO_2H$ $\overset{+}{H_3}N-CH_2-CO_2^-$ $H_2N-CH_2-CO_2^-$

               pH 2   pH 4   pH 8   pH 11

29.4

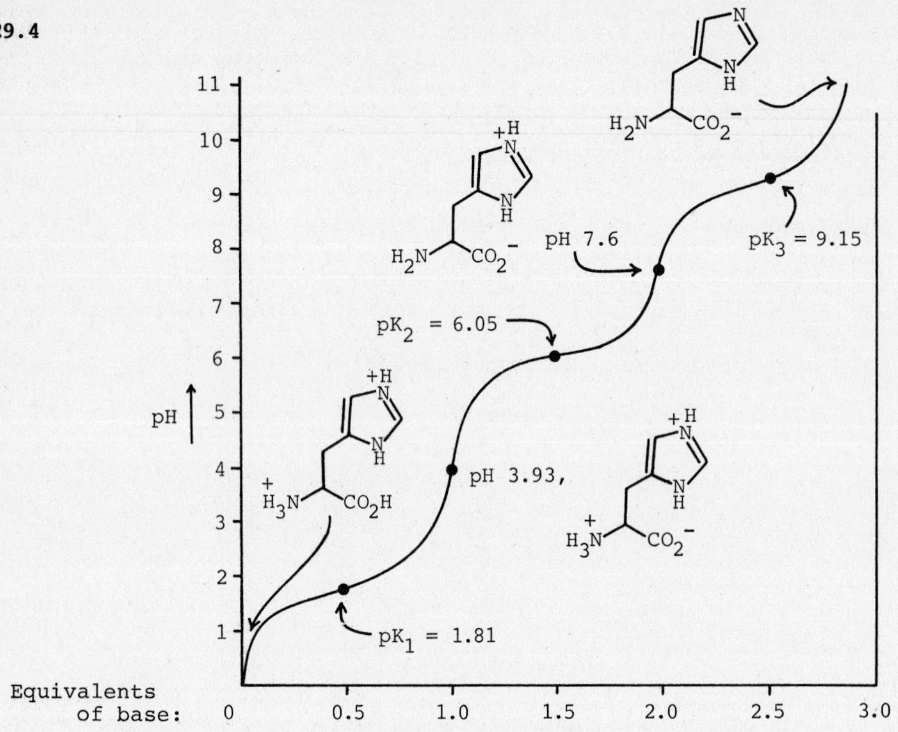

29.5

$$C_6H_5CH_2CH_2CO_2H \xrightarrow[\Delta]{P, Br_2} \xrightarrow{H_2O} C_6H_5CH_2\underset{Br}{C}HCO_2H \xrightarrow{NH_3} C_6H_5CH_2\underset{\overset{+}{N}H_3}{C}HCO_2^- + NH_4Br$$

$$(CH_3)_2CHCH_2CO_2H \xrightarrow[\Delta]{P, Br_2} \xrightarrow{H_2O} (CH_3)_2CH\underset{Br}{C}HCO_2H \xrightarrow{NH_3} (CH_3)_2CH\underset{\overset{+}{N}H_3}{C}HCO_2^- + NH_4Br$$

$$(CH_3)_2CHCH_2CH_2CO_2H \xrightarrow[\Delta]{P, Br_2} \xrightarrow{H_2O} (CH_3)_2CHCH_2\underset{Br}{C}HCO_2H \xrightarrow{NH_3} (CH_3)_2CHCH_2\underset{\overset{+}{N}H_3}{C}HCO_2^- + NH_4Br$$

for serine:

$$HOCH_2CH_2CO_2H \xrightarrow[\Delta]{P, Br_2} \xrightarrow{H_2O} BrCH_2\underset{Br}{C}HCO_2H$$

for tyrosine:

activated aromatic ring

29.6

aspartic acid
(if R = CH₂CO₂Et)

or

phenylalanine
(if R = CH₂C₆H₅)

or

valine
(if R = CH(CH₃)₂)

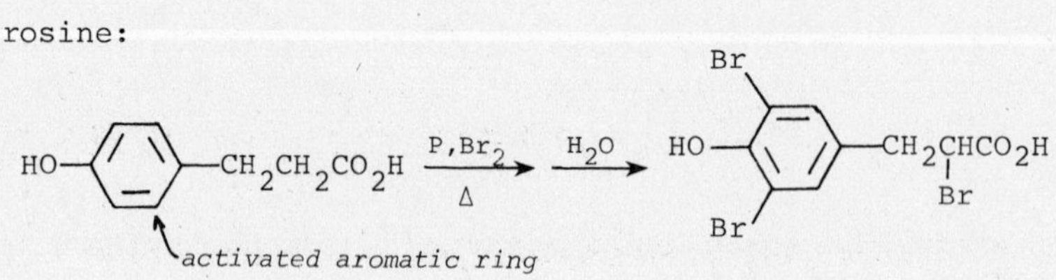

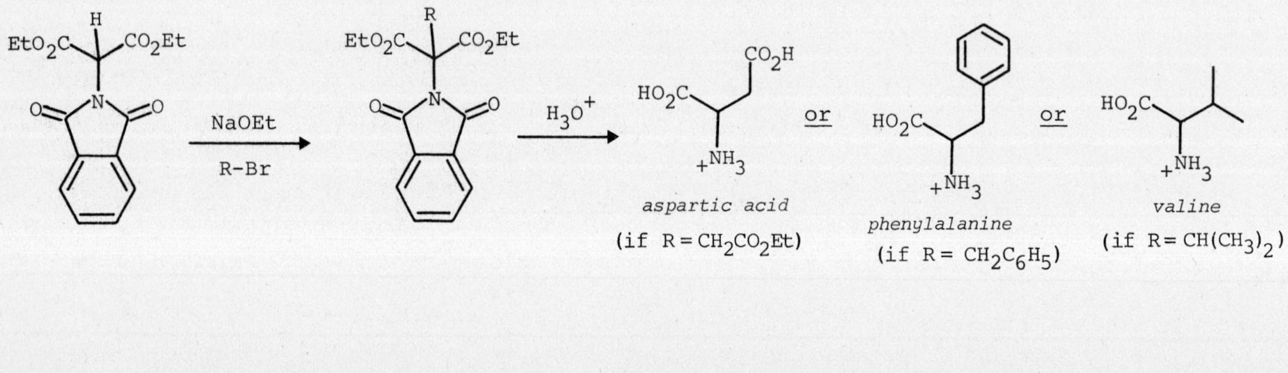

29.7

or

or

serine

(from $CH_2=O$)

tyrosine

(from

valine

(from $(CH_3)_2CHBr$)

followed by hydrogenation
to remove protecting group)

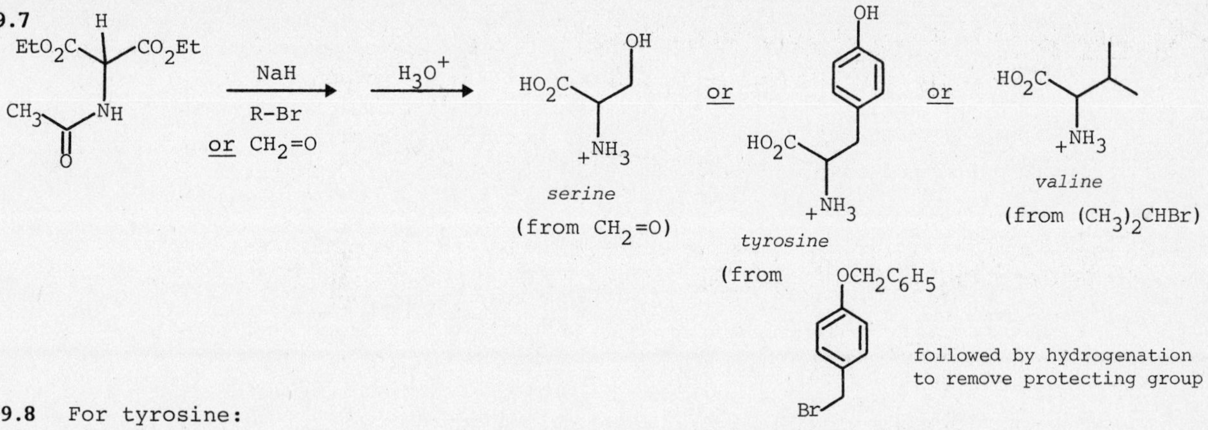

29.8 For tyrosine:

for lysine:

This intramolecular Strecker synthesis is the dominant reaction.

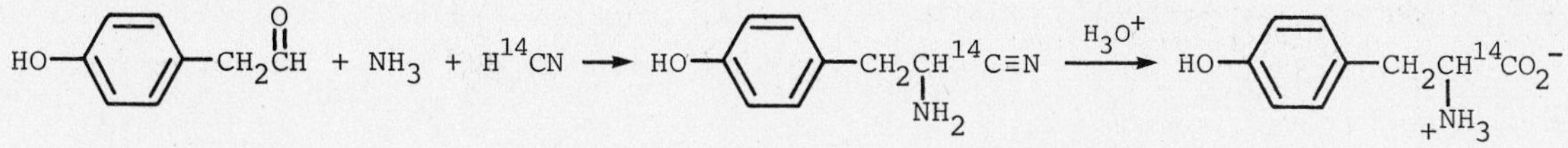

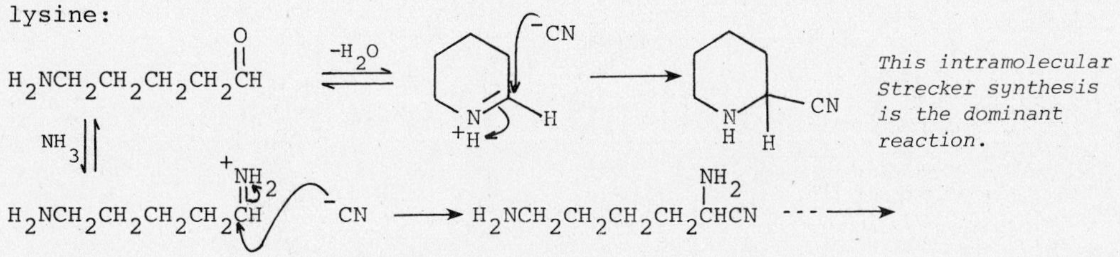

29.9

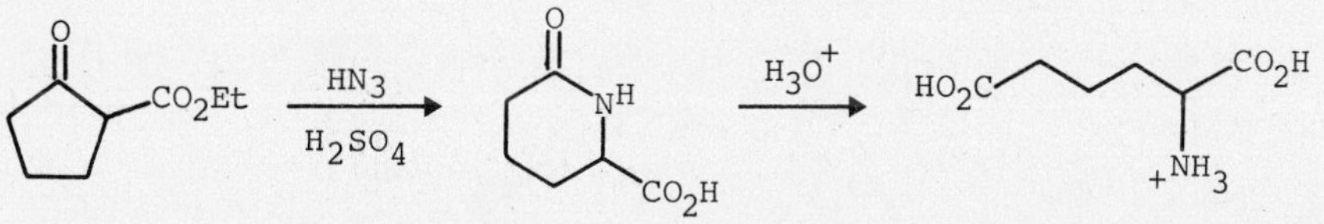

29.10

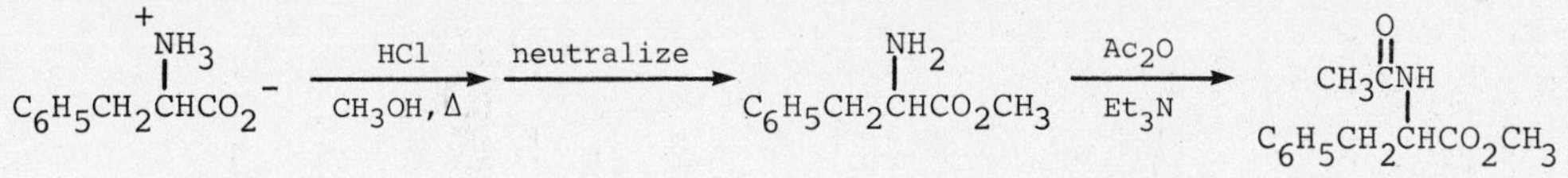

29.11

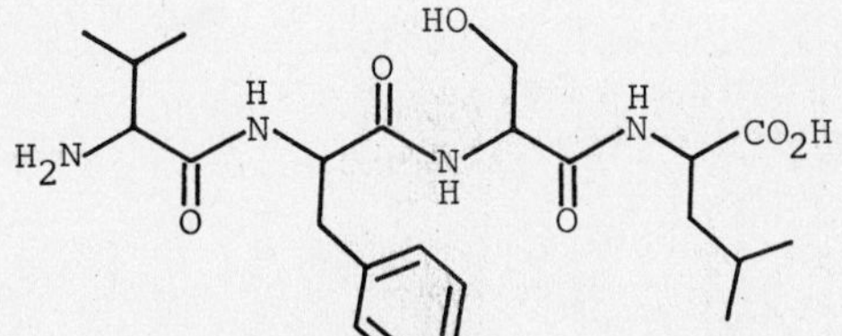

29.12 When the dimer, Gly-Gly, is formed, the next step of the cyclization to form 2,5-diketo-piperazine is much faster (six-membered ring formation) than intermolecular reaction with another glycine. Hence, the glycine is converted most rapidly to the diketopiperazine, and thereafter it is the diketopiperazine which polymerizes. Since this is then a polymerization of dimers, even-numbered peptides predominate.

29.13

$$Cbz\text{-}Ala + \underset{\underset{CH_3}{|}}{H_2NCHCO_2Et}\ (\equiv Ala\text{-}Et) \xrightarrow{DCC} Cbz\text{-}Ala\text{-}Ala\text{-}Et \xrightarrow{H_2\text{-}Pd/C} Ala\text{-}Ala\text{-}Et \xrightarrow[DCC]{Cbz\text{-}Phe}$$

$$\xleftarrow{H_2\text{-}Pd/C} Cbz\text{-}Val\text{-}Phe\text{-}Ala\text{-}Ala\text{-}Et \xleftarrow[DCC]{Cbz\text{-}Val} Phe\text{-}Ala\text{-}Ala\text{-}Et \xleftarrow{H_2\text{-}Pd/C} Cbz\text{-}Phe\text{-}Ala\text{-}Ala\text{-}Et$$

$$Val\text{-}Phe\text{-}Ala\text{-}Ala\text{-}Et \xrightarrow[DCC]{Cbz\text{-}Ala} Cbz\text{-}Ala\text{-}Val\text{-}Phe\text{-}Ala\text{-}Ala\text{-}Et \xrightarrow{H_2\text{-}Pd/C} Ala\text{-}Val\text{-}Phe\text{-}Ala\text{-}Ala\text{-}Et$$

$$Ala\text{-}Val\text{-}Phe\text{-}Ala\text{-}Ala \xleftarrow[hydrolysis]{mild}$$

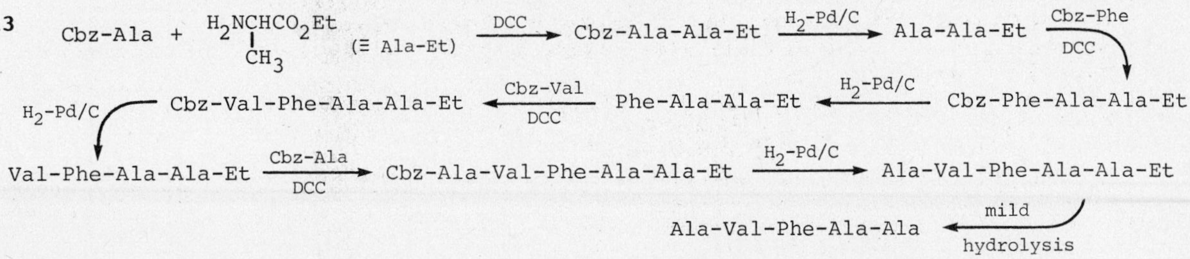

Since there are nine steps in this synthesis (starting with the commercially available protected amino acids), the overall yield from the sequence would be $(0.95)^9 = 63\%$.

29.14   1. Edman degradation of tetrapeptide -- N-terminal is Val: Val-( )-( )-( )

2. Edman degradation of tripeptide -- next is Ser: Val-Ser-( )-( )

3. Sanger method on dipeptide -- then Ala: Val-Ser-Ala-( )

4. Amino acid decomposition -- all that is left is Gly: Val-Ser-Ala-Gly

First Edman:

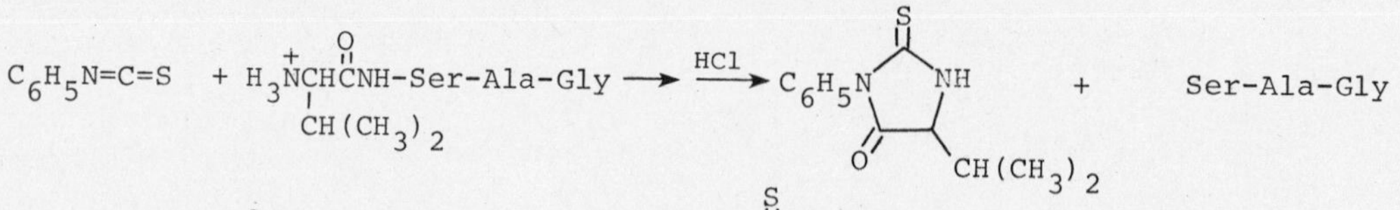

$$C_6H_5N=C=S \ + \ H_3\overset{+}{N}CH\overset{O}{\overset{\|}{C}}NH\text{-Ser-Ala-Gly} \ \xrightarrow{\text{HCl}} \ C_6H_5N \ \text{(ring)} \ + \ \text{Ser-Ala-Gly}$$
with CH(CH₃)₂ and CH(CH₃)₂ on ring

Second Edman:

$$C_6H_5N=C=S \ + \ H_3\overset{+}{N}CH\overset{O}{\overset{\|}{C}}NH\text{-Ala-Gly} \ \xrightarrow{\text{HCl}} \ C_6H_5N \ \text{(ring)} \ + \ \text{Ala-Gly}$$
with CH₂OH and CH₂OH on ring

Sanger:

$$O_2N\text{-}\bigcirc\text{-}F \ + \ H_3\overset{+}{N}CH\overset{O}{\overset{\|}{C}}NHCH_2CO_2^- \ \xrightarrow[\Delta]{H_3O^+} \ O_2N\text{-}\bigcirc\text{-}NHCHCO_2H \ + \ H_3\overset{+}{N}CH_2CO_2^-$$
with CH₃, NO₂, CH₃, NO₂ substituents

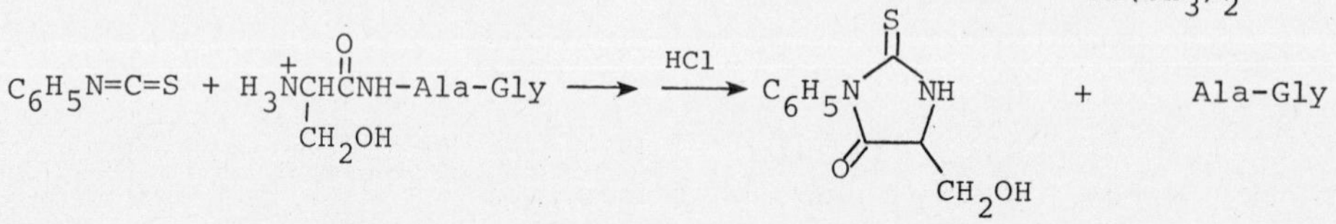

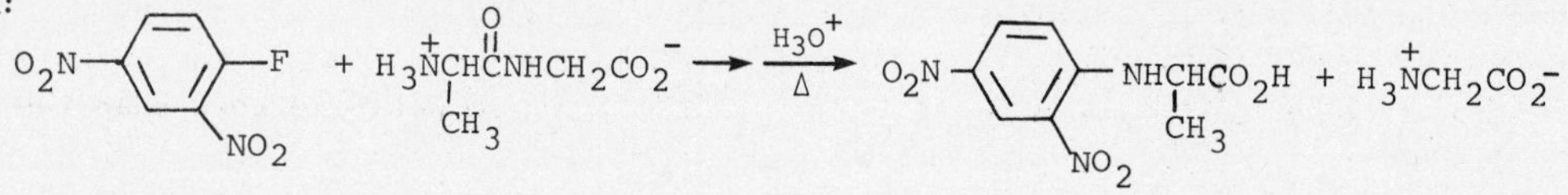

29.15   Gly-Ser-Phe

29.16   Gly-Ala-Leu—Leu—Phe

↑   ↑   *pepsin cleavage*

29.17

natural melittin:

Kaiser's peptide:

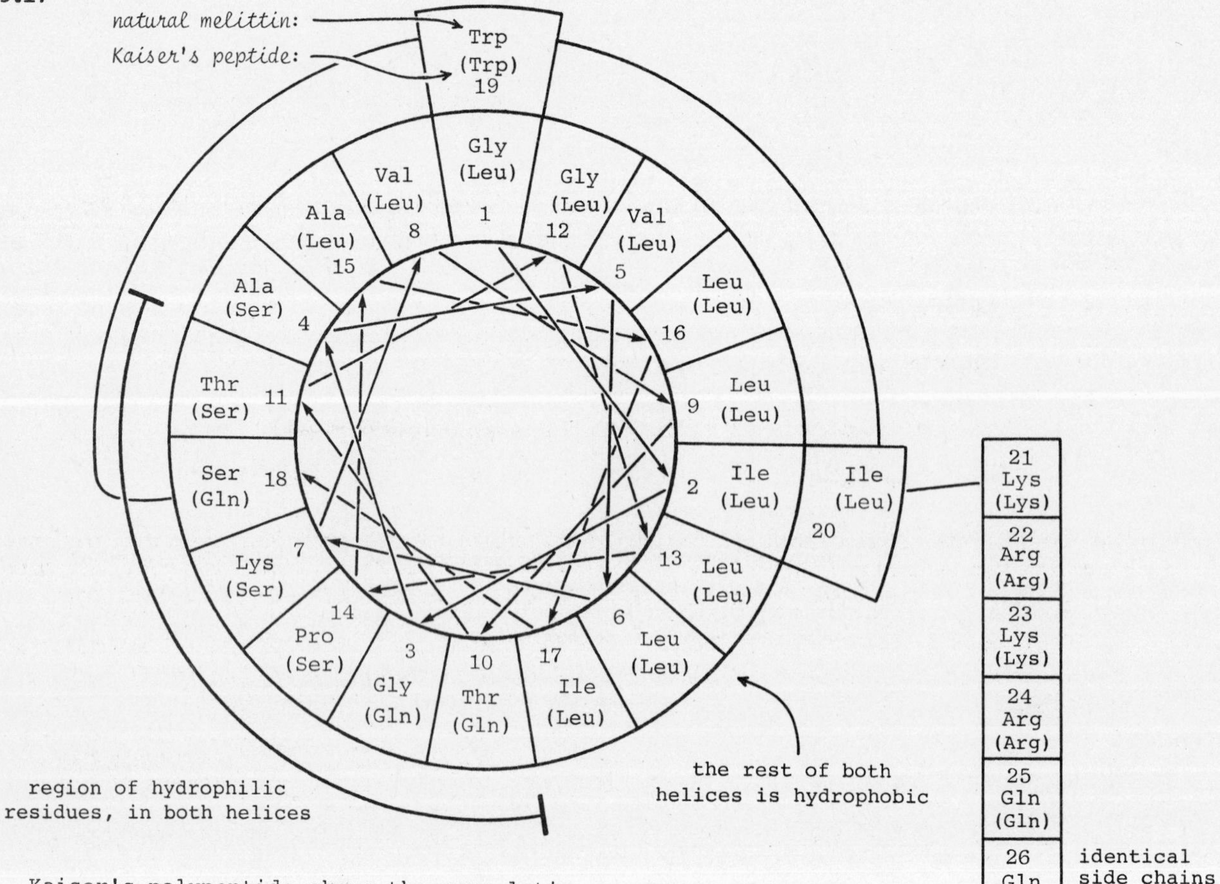

Kaiser's polypeptide shows the same lytic
activity that melittin does

region of hydrophilic
residues, in both helices

the rest of both
helices is hydrophobic

identical
side chains

29.E   Answers and Explanations for Problems

1.   This question requires Tables 29.2 and 29.4.

<u>pH = 2</u>   <u>pH = 7</u>   <u>pH = 12</u>

(a) $\overset{\overset{\displaystyle H_3C \quad NH_3^+}{|\qquad\quad|}}{CH_3CH_2CH-CHCO_2H}$ $\overset{\overset{\displaystyle H_3C \quad NH_3^+}{|\qquad\quad|}}{CH_3CH_2CH-CHCO_2^-}$ $\overset{\overset{\displaystyle H_3C \quad NH_2}{|\qquad\quad|}}{CH_3CH_2CH-CHCO_2^-}$

(b) $\overset{\overset{\displaystyle NH_3^+}{|}}{HO_2CCHCHCO_2^-}$ $\overset{\overset{\displaystyle NH_3^+}{|}}{{}^-O_2CCH_2CHCO_2^-}$ $\overset{\overset{\displaystyle NH_2}{|}}{{}^-O_2CCH_2CHCO_2^-}$

(c) $\overset{\overset{\displaystyle NH_3^+}{|}}{H_3\overset{+}{N}(CH_2)_4CHCO_2^-}$ $\overset{\overset{\displaystyle NH_3^+}{|}}{H_3\overset{+}{N}(CH_2)_4CHCO_2^-}$ $\overset{\overset{\displaystyle NH_2}{|}}{H_2N(CH_2)_4CHCO_2^-}$

(d) $H_3\overset{+}{N}CH_2CONHCH_2CO_2H$ $H_3\overset{+}{N}CH_2CONHCH_2CO_2^-$ $H_2NCH_2CONHCH_2CO_2^-$

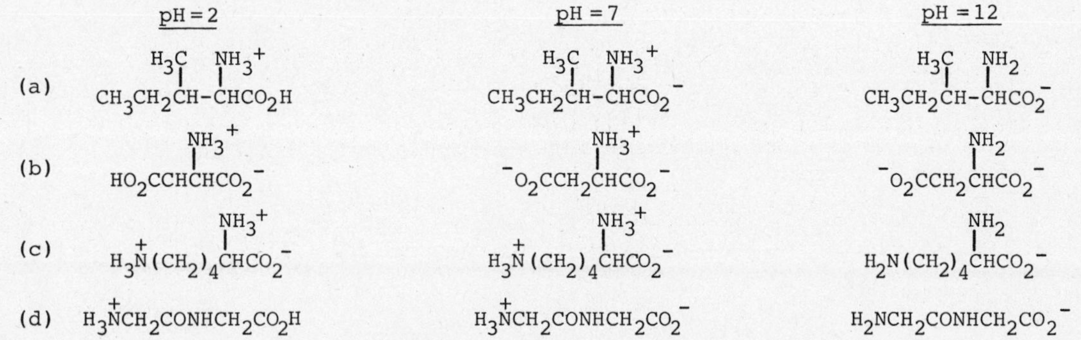

The remainder of the question requires two generalizations:

1. The $-CO_2H$ of the peptide is less acidic (higher pK_a) than that in the amino acid, because the $-NH_3^+$ group, with its positive charge, is farther away;
2. The $-NH_3^+$ group of the peptide is more acidic (lower pK_a) than that in the amino acid, because the $-CONH-$ group has greater electron-attracting inductive effect than the $-CO_2^-$ group.

(e) Because the terminal NH_2 of Lys in the peptide is approximately the same as in the amino acid:

$\overset{\overset{\displaystyle NH_3^+}{|}}{\overset{+}{H_3N}(CH_2)_4CHCONHCH_2CO_2H}$ $\overset{\overset{\displaystyle NH_3^+}{|}}{H_3N(CH_2)_4CHCONHCH_2CO_2^-}$ $\overset{\overset{\displaystyle NH_2}{|}}{H_2N(CH_2)_4CHCONHCH_2CO_2^-}$

and

$\overset{\overset{\displaystyle NH_2}{|}}{\overset{+}{H_3N}(CH_2)_4CHCONHCH_2CO_2^-}$

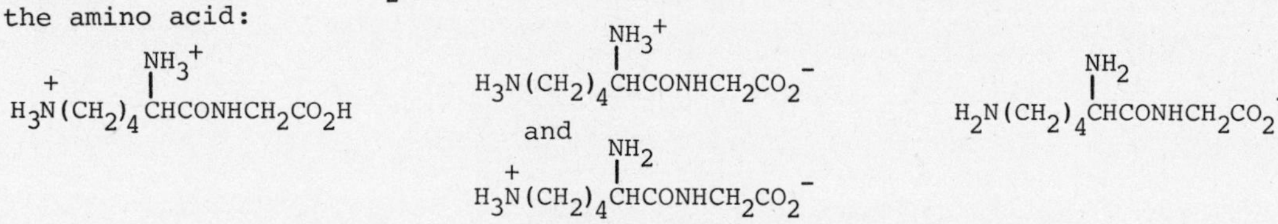

(similar amounts)

this case is ambiguous because the
α-NH_3^+ in Lys-Gly is close to 7

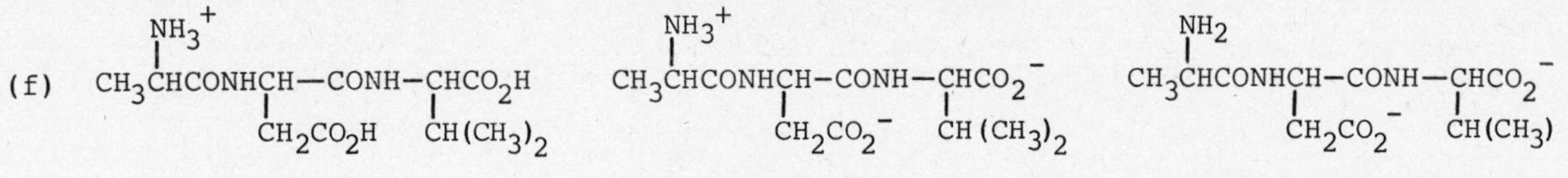

(f) $\overset{\overset{\displaystyle NH_3^+}{|}}{CH_3CHCONH\underset{\underset{\displaystyle CH_2CO_2H}{|}}{CH}-CONH-\underset{\underset{\displaystyle CH(CH_3)_2}{|}}{CHCO_2H}}$ $\overset{\overset{\displaystyle NH_3^+}{|}}{CH_3CHCONH\underset{\underset{\displaystyle CH_2CO_2^-}{|}}{CH}-CONH-\underset{\underset{\displaystyle CH(CH_3)_2}{|}}{CHCO_2^-}}$ $\overset{\overset{\displaystyle NH_2}{|}}{CH_3CHCONH\underset{\underset{\displaystyle CH_2CO_2^-}{|}}{CH}-CONH-\underset{\underset{\displaystyle CH(CH_3)}{|}}{CHCO_2^-}}$

2. $K_1 = \dfrac{[H_3\overset{+}{N}\text{\scriptsize$\sim\!\sim\!\sim$}CO_2^-][H^+]}{[H_3\overset{+}{N}\text{\scriptsize$\sim\!\sim\!\sim$}CO_2H]}$ $K_2 = \dfrac{[H_2N\text{\scriptsize$\sim\!\sim\!\sim$}CO_2^-][H^+]}{[H_3\overset{+}{N}\text{\scriptsize$\sim\!\sim\!\sim$}CO_2^-]}$ $K_1K_2 = \dfrac{[H_2N\text{\scriptsize$\sim\!\sim\!\sim$}CO_2^-]}{[H_3\overset{+}{N}\text{\scriptsize$\sim\!\sim\!\sim$}CO_2^-]} \cdot [H^+]^2$

At the isoelectric point, $[H_2N\text{\scriptsize$\sim\!\sim\!\sim$}CO_2^-] = [H_3\overset{+}{N}\text{\scriptsize$\sim\!\sim\!\sim$}CO_2H]$

At this point, $[H^+] = (K_1K_2)^{1/2}$;   or, $pH = \dfrac{1}{2}[pK_1 + pK_2]$

3.   The $-CO_2H$ of Ala is more acidic than that of β-alanine; i.e., the distance to the $-NH_3^+$ group is greater in β-alanine. Thus there is lower electrostatic attraction in the conjugate base, $^+H_3N\text{\scriptsize$\sim\!\sim\!\sim$}CO_2^-$.   The NH_3^+ group in $H_3\overset{+}{\underset{\underset{\displaystyle CH_3}{|}}{N}}CHCO_2^-$ is more acidic than that in $H_3NCH_2CH_2CO_2^-$.

The difference is probably associated with solvation. When (+) and (−) are far apart they can be separately solvated, but when they are close together the solvation is less efficient.

solvent molecules in this region don't know which way to point!

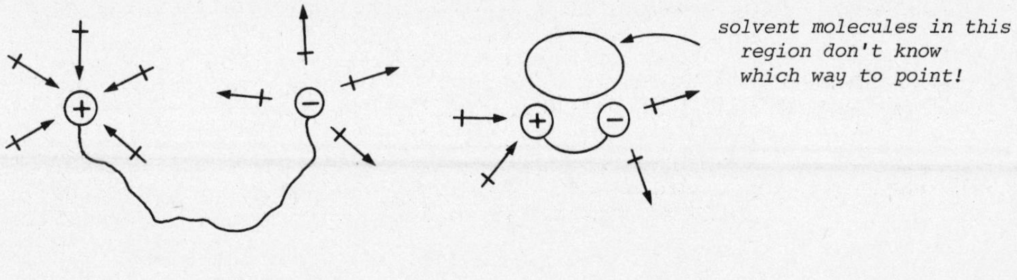

The same arguments apply to 4-aminobutanoic acid.

  <u>Isoelectric points</u>:   β-alanine   6.90

                          4-aminobutanoic acid   7.30

4.   8.60 ⟶ $H_3\overset{+}{N}CH_2CONHCHCO_2H$ ← 2.81
                              |
                         CH_2CO_2H ← 4.45

The value of 4.45 is close to that for simple aliphatic carboxylic acids; 2.81 is typical of peptide $-CO_2H$.

5.

(a) $CH_3(CH_2)_4COOH$ $\xrightarrow{P, Br_2}$ $CH_3(CH_2)_3CHBrCOOH$ $\xrightarrow{NH_3}$ $CH_3(CH_2)_3\overset{\overset{+NH_3}{|}}{C}HCO_2^-$

       caproic acid

or $CH_3(CH_2)_3Br$ + $^-\overset{\overset{NHCOCH_3}{|}}{C}(COOEt)_2$ ⟶ $CH_3(CH_2)_3\overset{\overset{NHCOCH_3}{|}}{C}(COOEt)_2$ $\xrightarrow{OH^-}$ $\xrightarrow[\Delta]{H^+}$

(b) —CHO + NH_3 + HCN ⟶ —$\overset{\overset{NH_2}{|}}{C}HCN$ $\xrightarrow[\Delta]{aq.\ NaOH}$ $\xrightarrow{H^+}$ —$\overset{\overset{NH_3^+}{|}}{C}HCO_2^-$

(c) $(CH_3)_3CCHO$ + NH_3 + HCN ⟶ $(CH_3)_3C\overset{\overset{NH_2}{|}}{C}HCN$ $\xrightarrow[\Delta]{aq.\ NaOH}$ $\xrightarrow{H^+}$ $(CH_3)_3C\overset{\overset{NH_3^+}{|}}{C}HCO_2^-$

(d) $CH_2(COOEt)_2$ $\xrightarrow[EtBr]{NaOEt}$ $EtCH(COOEt)_2$ $\xrightarrow[MeI]{NaOEt}$ $CH_3CH_2\overset{\overset{CH_3}{|}}{C}(COOEt)_2$ $\xrightarrow{OH^-}$

$CH_3CH_2\overset{\overset{CH_3}{|}}{\underset{\underset{NH_3^+}{|}}{C}}CO_2^-$ $\xleftarrow[H_2SO_4]{HN_3}$ $CH_3CH_2\overset{\overset{CH_3}{|}}{\underset{\underset{COOH}{|}}{C}}COOH$ $\xleftarrow{H^+}$

                              (Schmidt reaction)

(e) + NH_3 + HCN ⟶ $\xrightarrow[\Delta]{OH^-}$ $\xrightarrow{H^+}$

or $CH_2(COOEt)_2$ $\xrightarrow[Br(CH_2)_5Br]{\overset{NaOEt}{(2\ moles)}}$ $\xrightarrow{OH^-}$ $\xrightarrow{H^+}$ $\xrightarrow[H_2SO_4]{HN_3}$

(f) $\xrightarrow[Br(CH_2)_4Br]{NaOEt}$ $\xrightarrow[EtOH]{NaOH}$

$\xleftarrow[\Delta]{H^+}$

6.   (a) CH_3CHO + NH_3 + H^*CN ⟶ etc.

(b) CH_3MgX + $^*CO_2$ ⟶ $CH_3^*CO_2H$ $\xrightarrow{LiAlH_4}$ $CH_3^*CH_2OH$ $\xrightarrow[H_2SO_4]{Na_2Cr_2O_7}$ CH_3^*CHO $\xrightarrow[HCN]{NH_3}$ etc.

(c) $RO-\overset{\overset{O}{||}}{C}-OR$ $\xrightarrow{LiAlD_4}$ CD_3OH $\xrightarrow{HI}$ CD_3I $\xrightarrow[EtOH,\ NaOEt]{CH_3CONHCH(CO_2Et)_2}$ etc.

       a carbonate ester

       <u>or</u> $CO + D_2$ $\xrightarrow[catalyst]{\Delta}$ <u>NOTE</u>: would you use dimethyl carbonate for the first step?

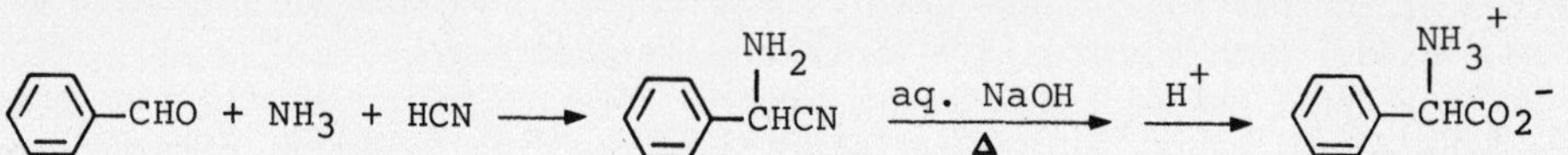

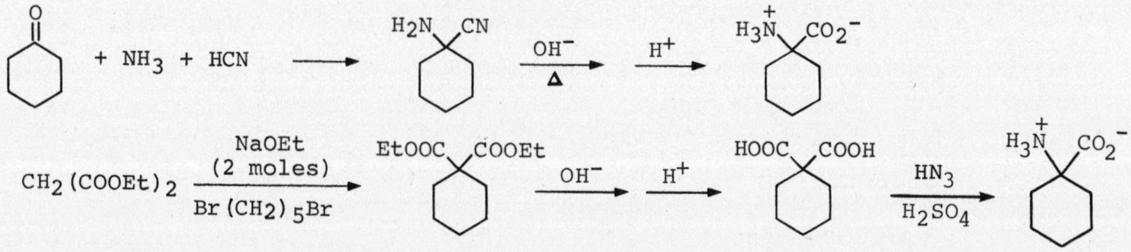

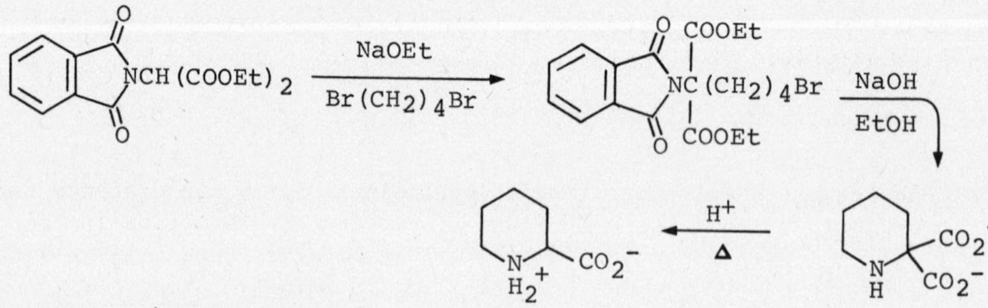

(d)

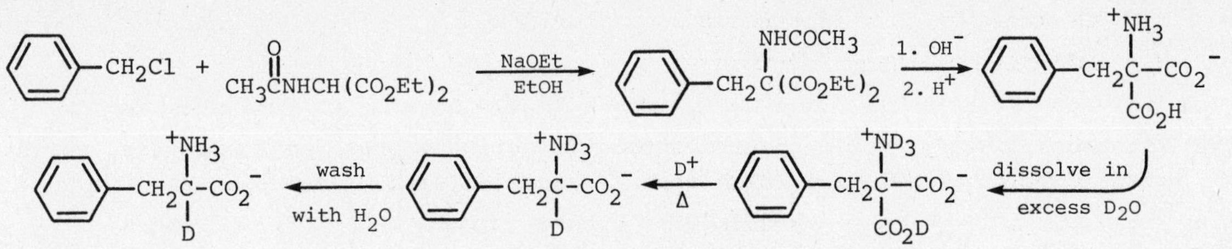

$$\text{C}_6\text{H}_5\text{-CH}_2\text{Cl} + \text{CH}_3\overset{\text{O}}{\text{C}}\text{NHCH(CO}_2\text{Et)}_2 \xrightarrow[\text{EtOH}]{\text{NaOEt}}$$

$$\text{C}_6\text{H}_5\text{-CH}_2\overset{\text{NHCOCH}_3}{\underset{}{\text{C}}}\text{(CO}_2\text{Et)}_2 \xrightarrow[\text{2. H}^+]{\text{1. OH}^-}$$

$$\text{C}_6\text{H}_5\text{-CH}_2\overset{+\text{NH}_3}{\underset{\text{CO}_2\text{H}}{\text{C}}}\text{-CO}_2^-$$

$$\xrightarrow{\text{dissolve in excess D}_2\text{O}}$$

$$\text{C}_6\text{H}_5\text{-CH}_2\overset{+\text{ND}_3}{\underset{\text{CO}_2\text{D}}{\text{C}}}\text{-CO}_2^- \xrightarrow[\Delta]{\text{D}^+} \text{C}_6\text{H}_5\text{-CH}_2\overset{+\text{ND}_3}{\underset{\text{D}}{\text{C}}}\text{-CO}_2^- \xrightarrow[\text{with H}_2\text{O}]{\text{wash}} \text{C}_6\text{H}_5\text{-CH}_2\overset{+\text{NH}_3}{\underset{\text{D}}{\text{C}}}\text{-CO}_2^-$$

(e)

$$*\text{CO}_2 \xrightarrow{\text{LiAlH}_4} *\text{CH}_3\text{OH} \xrightarrow{\text{HI}} *\text{CH}_3\text{I} \xrightarrow{\text{SH}^-} *\text{CH}_3\text{SH} \xrightarrow[\overset{\text{O}}{\text{CH}_2\text{-CH}_2}]{\text{OH}^-} *\text{CH}_3\text{SCH}_2\text{CH}_2\text{OH}$$

$$\downarrow \text{HBr}$$

$$\text{etc.} \xleftarrow{\text{NaOEt}} *\text{CH}_3\text{SCH}_2\text{CH}_2\text{Br}$$

$$\overset{\text{O}}{\underset{\text{O}}{\text{phthalimide}}}\text{NCH(COOEt)}_2$$

(f)

$$\text{CH}_3\text{COCH}_3 \xrightarrow[\text{Na}_2\text{CO}_3]{\text{D}_2\text{O}} \text{CD}_3\text{COCD}_3 \xrightarrow{\text{LiAlH}_4} \text{CD}_3\underset{\text{OH}}{\text{CHCD}_3} \xrightarrow{\text{HBr}} (\text{CD}_3)_2\text{CHBr} \xrightarrow[\text{of (e) above}]{\text{see last step}} \text{etc.}$$

(g)

$$\text{CH}_3\text{MgX} + *\text{CO}_2 \longrightarrow \text{CH}_3*\text{CO}_2\text{H} \xrightarrow[\text{P}]{\text{Br}_2} \text{BrCH}_2*\text{CO}_2\text{H} \xrightarrow[\text{H}^+]{\text{EtOH}} \text{BrCH}_2*\text{CO}_2\text{Et} \xrightarrow[\text{of (e)}]{\text{last step}} \text{etc.}$$

(h)

$$\overset{\text{O}}{\underset{\text{O}}{\text{phthalimide}}}\text{N-}\overset{\text{COOEt}}{\underset{\text{COOEt}}{\text{C}}}\text{CH}_2\text{CH}_2\text{CH}_2\text{Br} + \text{CN}^- \longrightarrow \overset{\text{O}}{\underset{\text{O}}{\text{phthalimide}}}\text{N-}\overset{\text{COOEt}}{\underset{\text{COOEt}}{\text{C}}}\text{CH}_2\text{CH}_2\text{CH}_2\text{CN}$$

(*Section 29.4.E*)

$$\downarrow \text{D}_2/\text{catalyst}$$

$$\text{H}_2\text{N-CH(CH}_2)_3\text{CD}_2\text{NH}_3^+ \xleftarrow{\text{H}^+} \xleftarrow[\text{EtOH}]{\text{NaOH}} \overset{\text{O}}{\underset{\text{O}}{\text{phthalimide}}}\text{N-}\overset{\text{COOEt}}{\underset{\text{COOEt}}{\text{C}}}\text{CH}_2\text{CH}_2\text{CH}_2\text{CD}_2\text{ND}_2$$
$$\underset{\text{CO}_2^-}{}$$

LiAlD_4 clearly cannot be used in the reduction step because of the other reducible groups present; however, the catalytic reduction is not straightforward either. If excess NH_3 is present to cut down secondary amine formation (Section 23.6.F), some catalysts will promote exchange:

$$\text{NH}_3 + \text{D}_2 \xrightarrow{\text{catalyst}} \text{ND}_3 + \text{H}_2, \text{ etc.}$$

and the deuterium will become diluted. In practice, experiments would be required to find the best conditions for the hydrogenation with D_2.

7. Acid-catalyzed esterification starts with a protonated carbonyl:

$$\text{R-}\overset{+\text{OH}}{\underset{\text{OH}}{\text{C}}}$$

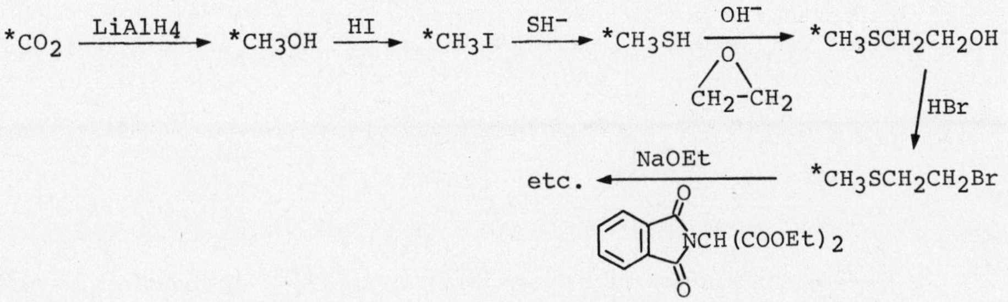

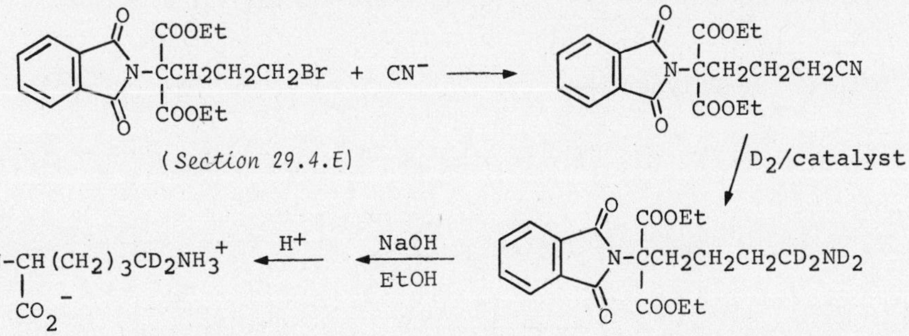

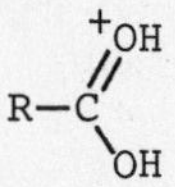

Protonation of an amino acid is more difficult because of electrostatic repulsion with the $-\text{NH}_3^+$ group:

$$\text{-CH-}\overset{+\text{OH}}{\underset{\text{OH}}{\text{C}}}$$
$$\underset{+\text{NH}_3}{}$$

repulsion

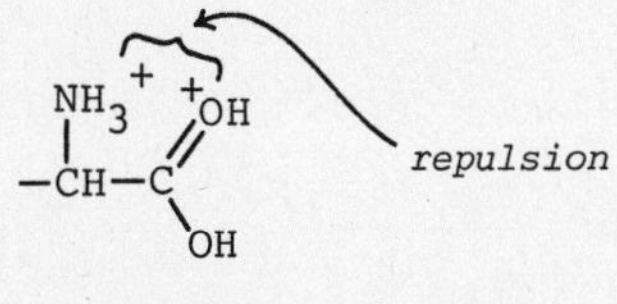

8. Hydrolysis of the benzoyl amide group requires conditions that also cause hydrolysis of the peptide bond; both are normal amide functions.

9. (a)

$$\text{BrCH}_2\overset{\text{O}}{\text{C}}\text{-Br} + \text{CH}_3\overset{\text{NH}_2}{\underset{}{\text{CH}}}\text{CO}_2^- \longrightarrow \text{BrCH}_2\text{CONH}\overset{\text{CH}_3}{\underset{}{\text{CH}}}\text{CO}_2^- \xrightarrow{\text{NH}_3} \text{H}_3\overset{+}{\text{N}}\text{CH}_2\text{CONH}\overset{\text{CH}_3}{\underset{}{\text{CH}}}\text{CO}_2^-$$

$$\text{BrCH}_2\overset{\text{O}}{\text{C}}\text{-Br} + \text{H}_2\text{NCH}_2\text{CONH}\overset{\text{CH}_3}{\underset{}{\text{CH}}}\text{CO}_2^- \longrightarrow \text{BrCH}_2\text{CONHCH}_2\text{CONH}\overset{\text{CH}_3}{\underset{}{\text{CH}}}\text{CO}_2^- \xrightarrow{\text{NH}_3} \text{Gly-Gly-Ala}$$

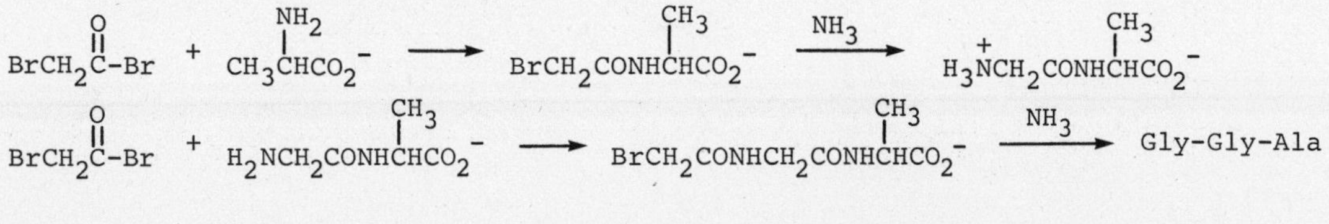

(b) $CH_3\overset{Br}{CHCOBr}$; $(CH_3)_2\overset{Br}{CHCHCOBr}$

(c) Val-Ala or Ala-Ala   Note the the amino acid used forms the CO_2H end of the peptide.

(d) Stereochemistry: would require optically active α-bromo acyl bromides, which are difficult to prepare and which readily racemize with mild base:

$$R\text{-CHBrCOBr} + \text{base} \rightleftharpoons R\text{-CBrCOBr} + \text{base-}H^+$$

                                    ↑— *configuration lost*

Thus a mixture of diastereomers would result. As an example, in (c) above, the use of racemic acid bromides will produce L-Ala-L-Ala, D-Ala-L-Ala, L-Ala-D-Ala, D-Ala-D-Ala, etc.

10.   (structure) + $H_3\overset{+}{N}CHCO_2^-$ (R) → (structure) $O_2CNHCHCO_2H$ (R) ≡ Cbz-amino acid

$H_3NCHCO_2CH_2CH_3$ / $CH(CH_3)_2$ (Val-Et) $\xrightarrow[\text{DCC}]{\text{Cbz-Ala}}$ Cbz-Ala-Val-Et $\xrightarrow{H_2/\text{Pt}}$ Ala-Val-Et $\xrightarrow[\text{DCC}]{\text{Cbz-Ala}}$ Cbz-Ala-Ala-Val-Et $\downarrow H_2/\text{Pt}$

Pro-Ala-Ala-Val-Et $\xleftarrow{H_2/\text{Pt}}$ Cbz-Pro-Ala-Ala-Val-Et $\xleftarrow[\text{DCC}]{\text{Cbz-Pro}}$ Ala-Ala-Val-Et

$\downarrow \xrightarrow[\text{DCC}]{\text{Cbz-Ala}}$ Cbz-Ala-Pro-Ala-Ala-Val-Et $\xrightarrow{H_2/\text{Pt}}$ Ala-Pro-Ala-Ala-Val-Et

Gly-Ala-Pro-Ala-Ala-Val $\xleftarrow[\text{2. OH}^-]{\text{1. } H_2/\text{Pt}}$ Cbz-Gly-Ala-Pro-Ala-Ala-Val-Et $\xleftarrow[\text{DCC}]{\text{Cbz-Gly}}$

11. Boc-Gly + $ClCH_2$—(ring)—Polymer → Boc-Gly-CH_2—Ⓟ $\xrightarrow{H^+}$ Gly-CH_2—Ⓟ $\xrightarrow[\text{DCC}]{\text{Boc-Gly}}$

$\xrightarrow{}$ Boc-Gly-Gly-CH_2—Ⓟ $\xleftarrow{H^+}$ $BocNH$-CH-CO_2H / CH_2 / $CH_2CO_2CH_2C_6H_5$

Boc-Glu(δ-Bz)-Gly-Gly-CH_2—Ⓟ $\xleftarrow[\text{DCC}]{H^+}$ Boc-Lys(ε-Cbz)

Boc-Lys(ε-Cbz)-Glu(δ-Bz)-Gly-Gly-CH_2—Ⓟ $\xrightarrow{H^+}$ $\xrightarrow[\text{DCC}]{\text{Boc-Ala}}$ Boc-Ala-Lys(ε-Cbz)-Glu(δ-Bz)-Gly-Gly-CH_2—Ⓟ

Ala-Lys-Glu-Gly-Gly $\xleftarrow{H_2/\text{Pt}}$ $\xleftarrow{\text{HF}}$ $\xleftarrow{H^+}$

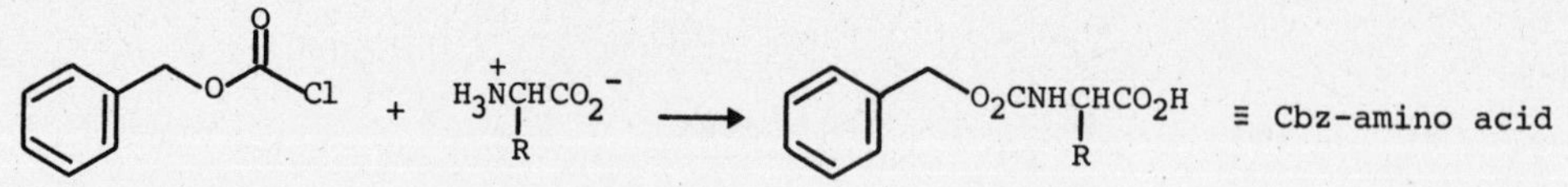

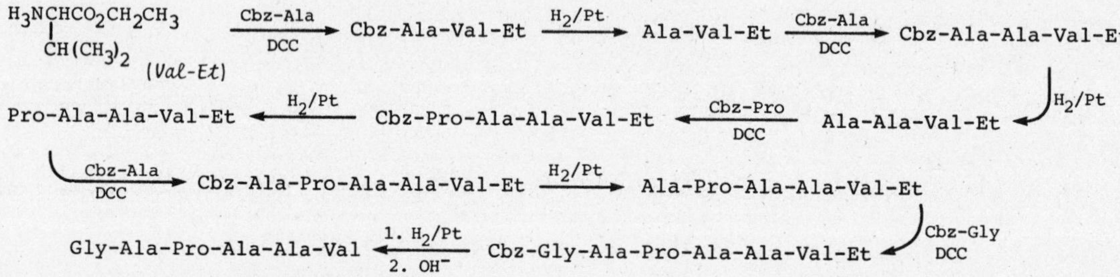

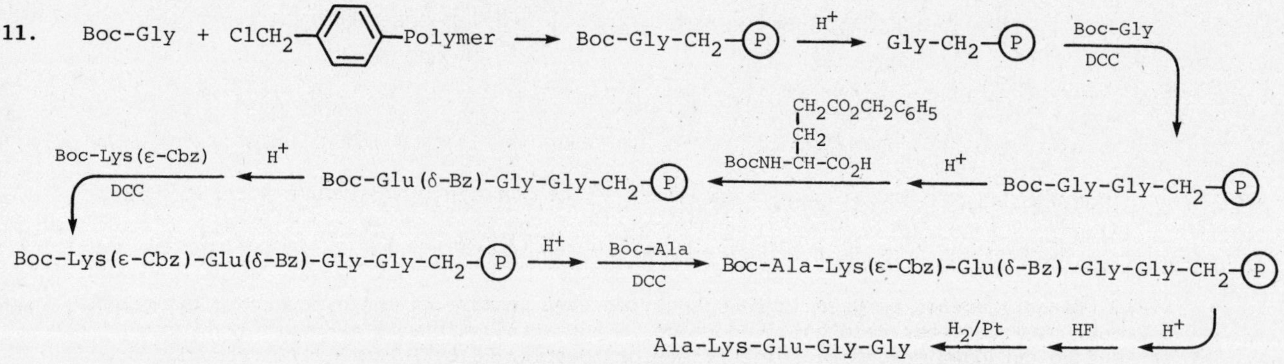

12. Either of the methods depicted in answers #10 or #11 can be used by continuing to add groups in the sequence Ala, Ala, Phe, Val, Ala. However, the first and second halves of this decapeptide are the same. Hence, one could simply couple two of the pentapeptides:

Cbz-Ala-Val-Phe-Ala-Ala-Et $\xrightarrow{H_2\text{-Pd/C}}$ Ala-Val-Phe-Ala-Ala-Et

                        +

             $\xrightarrow[\text{hydrolysis}]{\text{mild}}$ Cbz-Ala-Val-Phe-Ala-Ala }DCC

Cbz-Ala-Val-Phe-Ala-Ala-Ala-Val-Phe-Ala-Ala-Et $\longleftarrow$

$\downarrow H_2\text{-Pd/C}$

$\xrightarrow[\text{hydrolysis}]{\text{mild}}$ Ala-Val-Phe-Ala-Ala-Ala-Val-Phe-Ala-Ala

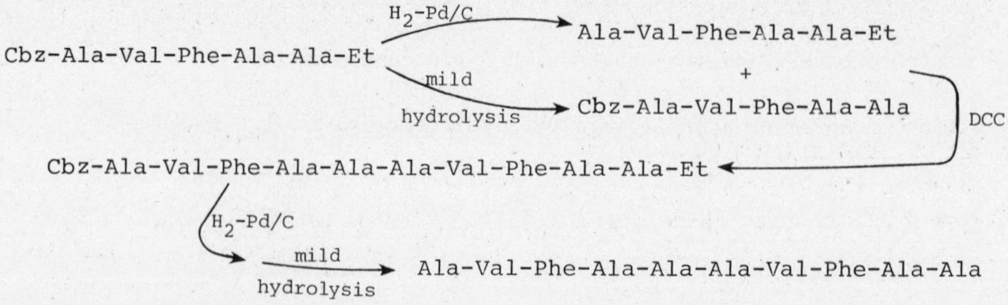

13. TRH ≡ pyroGlu-His-Pro-NH_2 or

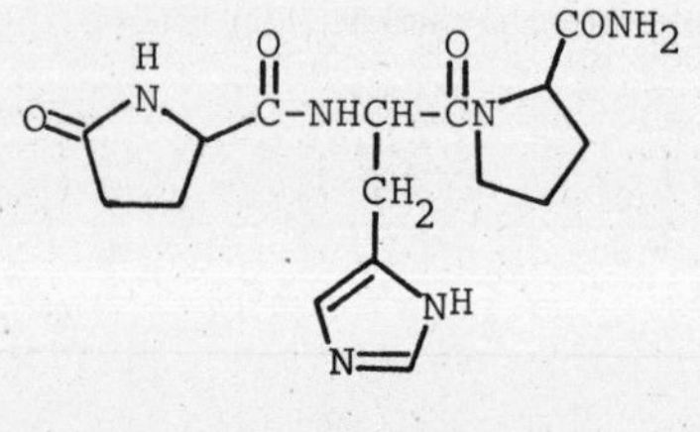

Synthesis:

Cbz-His + (≡ Pro-Et) $\xrightarrow{DCC}$ Cbz-His-Pro-Et $\xrightarrow{H_2-Pd/C}$ His-Pro-Et

pyroGlu-His-Pro-NH$_2$ $\xleftarrow[\substack{1.\ \text{mild hydrolysis} \\ 2.\ NH_3,\ DCC}]{NH_3\ or}$ pyroGlu-His-Pro-Et $\xleftarrow[DCC]{pyroGlu}$ His-Pro-Et

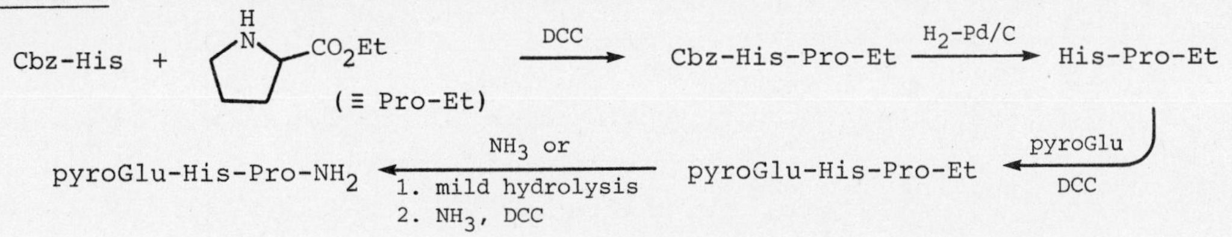

NOTE: conversion to the acid chloride with SOCl$_2$, followed by treatment with NH$_3$ to form the final amide is an alternative, but will probably cause some racemization at the proline α-carbon to give a mixture of diastereomers.

14.

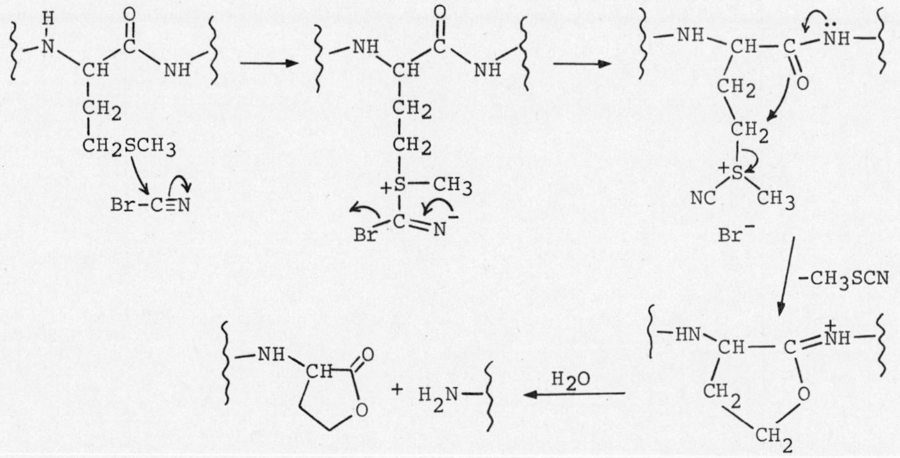

15. (a) Lys; Glu-Thr-Ala-Ala-Ala-Lys; Phe-Glu-Arg; Glu-His〜〜〜〜〜〜Met-Lys; Ser-Arg;

(positions 15 20 25 30)

Asn-Leu-Thr-Lys; Asp-Arg; Cys-Lys; Pro-Val〜〜〜〜〜Glu-Lys; Asn-Val-Ala-Cys-Lys;

(positions 45 50 55 60)

Asn-Gly〜〜〜〜〜Cys-Arg; Glu-Thr-Gly-Ser-Ser-Lys; Tyr-Pro-Asn-Cys-Ala-Tyr-Lys;

(positions 70 75 80 85)

Thr-Thr-Glu-Ala-Asn-Lys; His〜〜〜〜〜Val

(positions 105 110 115 120 124)

(b) Ten polypeptides: three ending with Phe, six with Tyr, and one with Val (terminal piece). No Trp is present.

(c) BrCN cleaves only at Met, of which four are present (two of which are joined). Five pieces will be formed, one of which is cyclized Met itself:

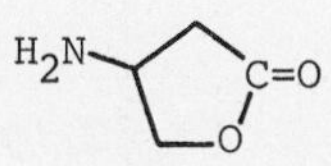

16. I-II-IV-III or I-IV-II-III. I must be the amino end because it is the only fragment that starts with Glu; similarly, III must be the carboxy end. Positions of II and IV are not established.

17. Consider the following logic:

a) T-1 through T-8 contain all 56 amino acids. T-9 is clearly (T-7) - (T-6). T-7 must be a product of abnormal cleavage, since trypsin does not normally hydrolyze at Tyr. Thus, T-9 presumably is the primary hydrolysis product that partially hydrolyzed to T-6 and T-7.

b) Since the protein N-end starts with Thr and the C-end is Cys, the sequence can initially be represented as   (T-4)〜〜〜〜〜(T-3).

c) Furthermore, this also tells us that the chains from chymotrypsin digestion are in the sequence: (Ch-1) — (Ch-2) — (Ch-3).

d) Comparing the amino acid compositions, we find that Ch-2 is the same as T-7 + Tyr + Ile. Similarly, T-8 is part of Ch-1 (note that there is only one Ala in the protein). Since T-6 follows T-7, we can write the protein as:

$$\text{(T-4)} - \text{(T-8)} - \overbrace{\text{(T-7)} - \text{(T-6)}}^{\text{(T-9)}} - \text{(T-5,1,2)} - \text{(T-3)}$$

e) The only question left is where the single units, T-1 and T-2, fit with relation to T-5. For this answer we turn to the T* series. T*-2 contains the Cys and comes at the end; in fact, the composition of T*-2 is that of T-5 and T-3. Thus, T-1 and T-2 come between (T-6) and (T-5), but with CH₃NCS, Lys has been modified so that it will not cleave; hence, T*-3 must terminate with Asp.

f) We conclude that the complete sequence is:

$$(T-4) - (T-8) - (T-7) - (T-6) - (T-1) - (T-2) - (T-5) - (T-3)$$

29.F Supplementary Problems

S1. What is the principal ionic form of the dipeptide histidyltyrosine (His-Tyr) at pH 2, 5, 8, and 11?

S2. What is the approximate isoelectric point of the following amino acids?

    (a) Valine   (b) Glutamic acid   (c) Lysine

S3. Show how to synthesize the following amino acids.

(a) $H_3\overset{+}{N}$ CO_2^- (on a cyclopentane ring)

(c) $HO-\langle\text{ring}\rangle-\overset{14}{C}H_2CHCO_2^-$ with $\overset{+}{N}H_3$ (^{14}C available as $Ba^{14}CO_3$ or $Na^{14}CN$)

(b) $HO_2CCH_2CH_2CHCO_2^-$ with $\overset{+}{N}H_3$

(d) pyrrolidine ring with $\overset{+}{N}(H)-CH_2CO_2^-$

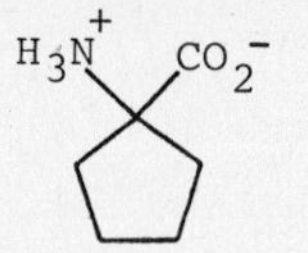

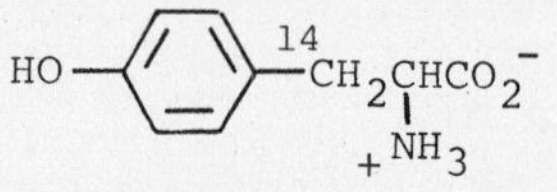

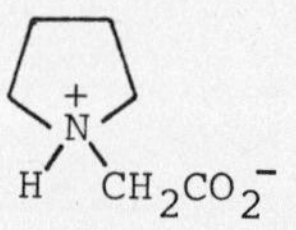

S4. Outline syntheses of the following tripeptides, using the N-protecting group indicated and appropriate coupling reagents and other protecting groups as necessary.

    (a) Ser-Leu-Tyr (t-Boc)
    (b) Phe-Ile-Asp (Cbz)
    (c) Gly-Val-Met (t-Boc)

S5. How many isomers are produced in the Strecker synthesis of isoleucine? What methods may be used to separate them from each other?

S6. Conversion of an N-acyl amino acid to the acid chloride often leads to formation of an azlactone and racemization. Write reasonable mechanisms for these reactions.

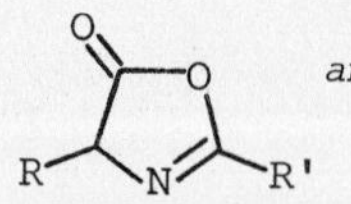

an azlactone

S7. Another method for peptide bond formation is the "mixed-anhydride" coupling method, which is illustrated in the example below:

$$CbzNHCH_2CO_2H \xrightarrow[\text{2. } H_3\overset{+}{N}CHCO_2^-, Et_3N]{\text{1. } ClCOCH_2CH_3, Et_3N} CbzNHCH_2-\overset{O}{\overset{\|}{C}}NH-CHCO_2^-$$

(with CH_3 groups on the amino acid carbon)

(a) Write a balanced equation for this reaction sequence and indicate what intermediates are involved.

(b) What would happen if an unprotected amino acid were used as the starting material?

(c) What do you expect is the major side product to result from this sequence?

S8. The enkephalins are believed to be the natural compounds in the central nervous system whose activity is imitated by morphine. The amino acid composition of one of the enkephalins is Gly-Gly-Met-Phe-Tyr. Reaction of this pentapeptide with 8-dimethylaminonaphthalenesulfonyl chloride (dansyl chloride) and subsequent acid-catalyzed hydrolysis affords the dansyl derivative of tyrosine as the only modified amino acid. When the enkephalin is treated with cyanogen bromide, no cleavage of the chain takes place. Partial hydrolysis of the penta-peptide with chymotrypsin gives only tyrosine, methionine, and a tripeptide.

(a)   What is the most likely structure of the dansyl derivative of tyrosine?

(b)   What is the sequence of the enkephalin?

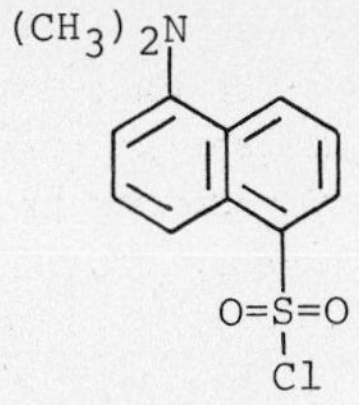

Dansyl Chloride

29.G   Answers to Supplementary Problems

S1.   pH 2:

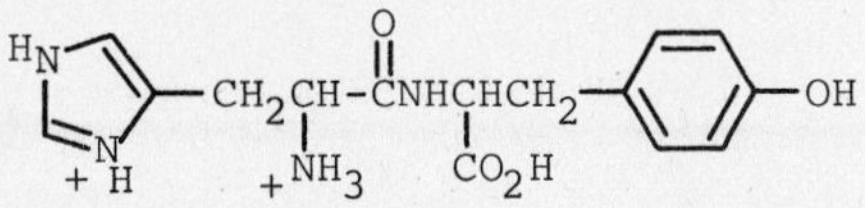

pH 5:

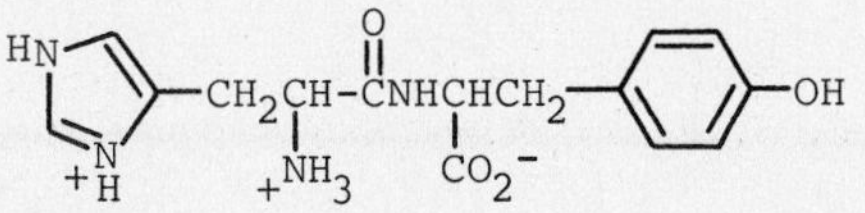

pH 8:

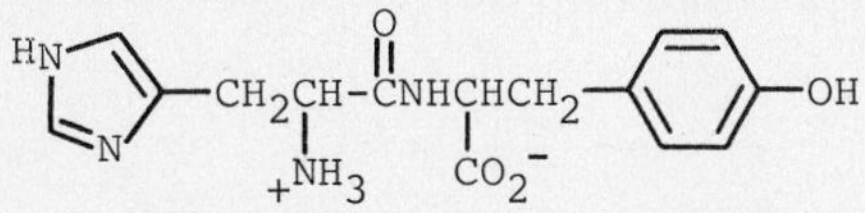

pH 11:

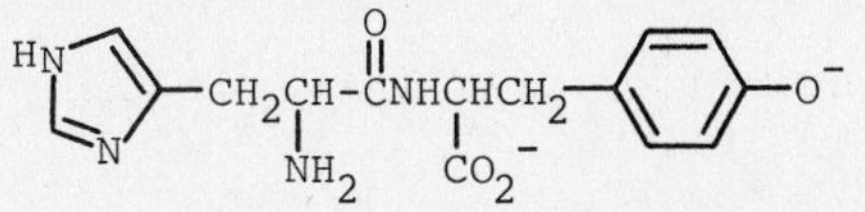

S2.   (a) $\dfrac{2.29\ (CO_2H)\ +\ 9.72\ (\overset{+}{N}H_3)}{2} = 6.0$

(b) $\dfrac{2.13\ (\alpha\text{-}CO_2H)\ +\ 4.32\ (\gamma\text{-}CO_2H)}{2} = 3.23$

(c) $\dfrac{9.20\ (\alpha\text{-}NH_2)\ +\ 10.8\ (\epsilon\text{-}NH_2)}{2} = 10.0$

Write out the major ionic forms and their net charge at various pH's to see how the answers to (b) and (c) were obtained.

S3. (a)

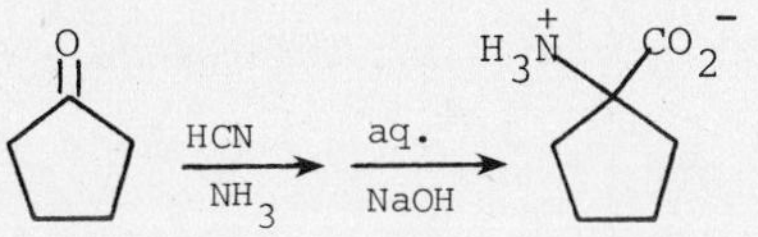

(b) $(EtO_2C)_2CH\underset{NHAc}{} + CH_2=CHCO_2Et \xrightarrow[EtOH]{NaOEt} (EtO_2C)_2CCH_2CH_2CO_2Et\underset{NHAc}{} \xrightarrow[\Delta]{H_3O^+} {}^-O_2CCHCH_2CH_2CO_2^-\underset{+NH_3}{}$

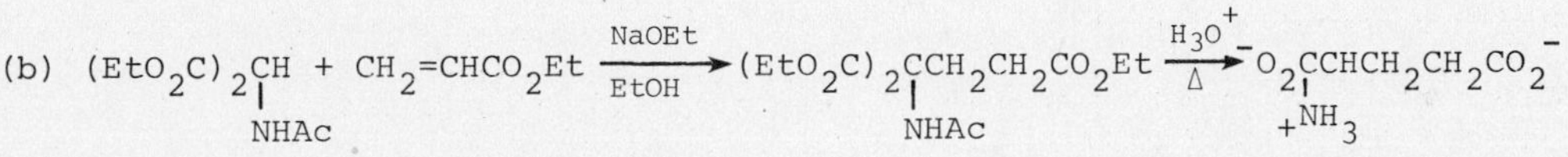

(c)

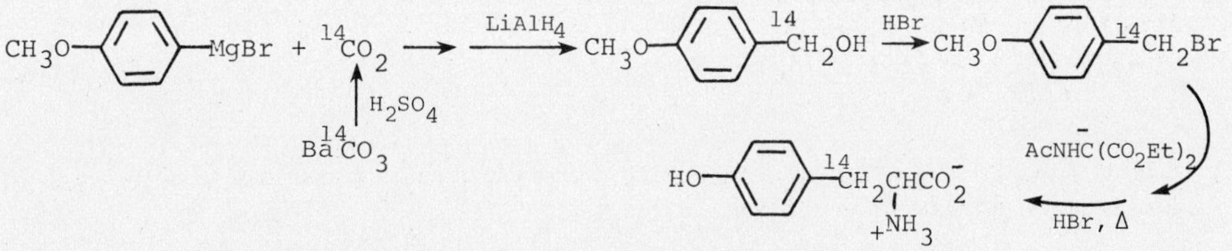

(d)

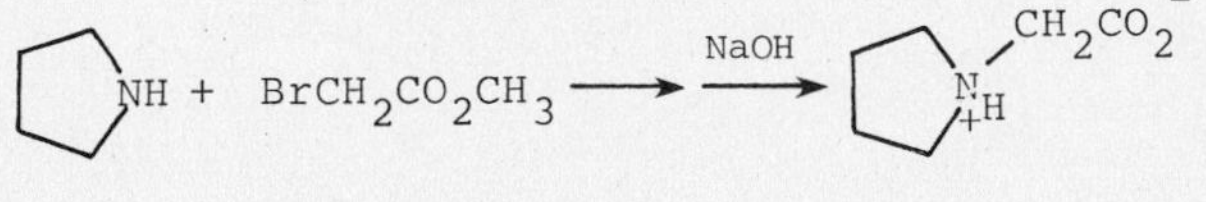

S4. (a)

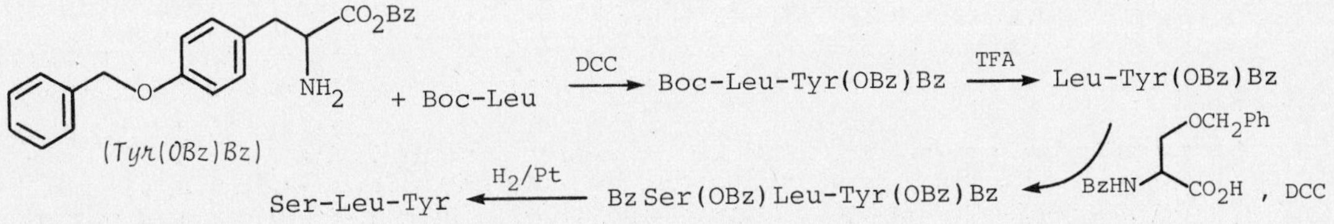

(b)

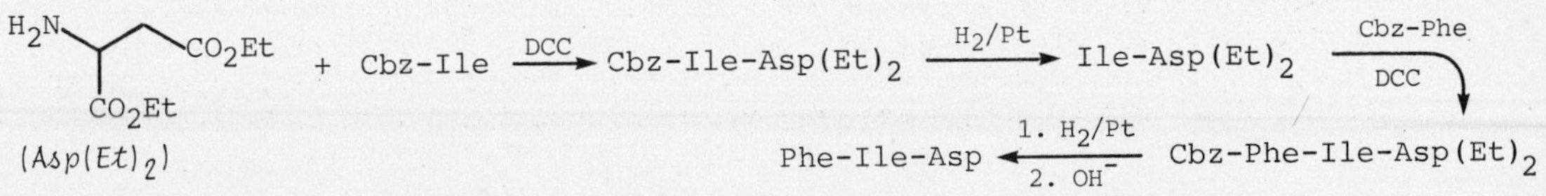

(c)   Met-Et + Boc-Val $\xrightarrow{\text{DCC}}$ Boc-Val-Met-Et $\xrightarrow[\text{(= TFA)}]{\text{CF}_3\text{CO}_2\text{H}}$ Val-Met-Et $\xrightarrow[\text{DCC}]{\text{Boc-Gly}}$

Gly-Val-Met $\xleftarrow[\text{2. OH}^-]{\text{1. TFA}}$ Boc-Gly-Val-Met-Et

S5.

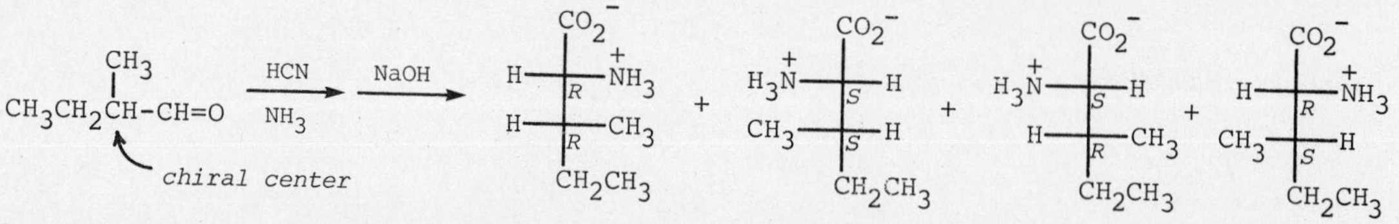

The racemic mixture of RS and SR isomers can be separated from the RR,SS racemate by crystallization or chromatography because they are diastereomeric. Separation of the RS enantiomer from the SR enantiomer, and separation of the RR from the SS enantiomer, require resolution procedures such as those discussed in Section 29.4.F.

S6.

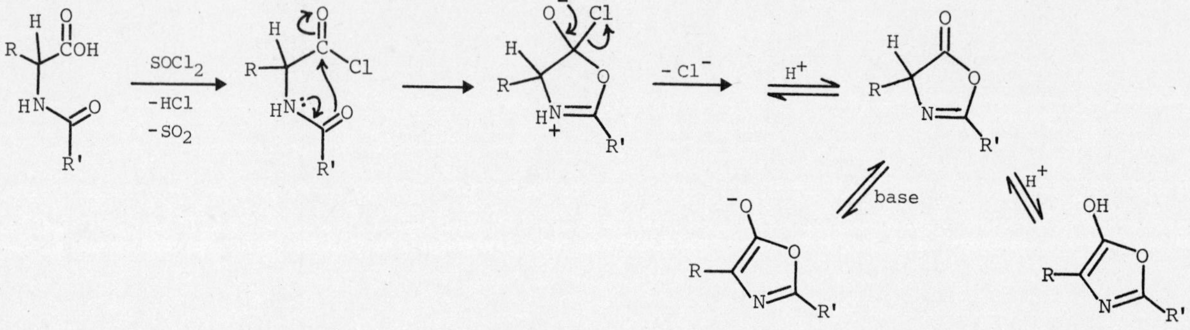

both planar and achiral

S7. (a) CbzNHCH$_2$CO$_2^-$ Et$_3\overset{+}{\text{N}}$H $\xrightarrow{\text{ClCOOEt}}$ CbzNHCH$_2$COCOOEt + Et$_3\overset{+}{\text{N}}$H Cl$^-$

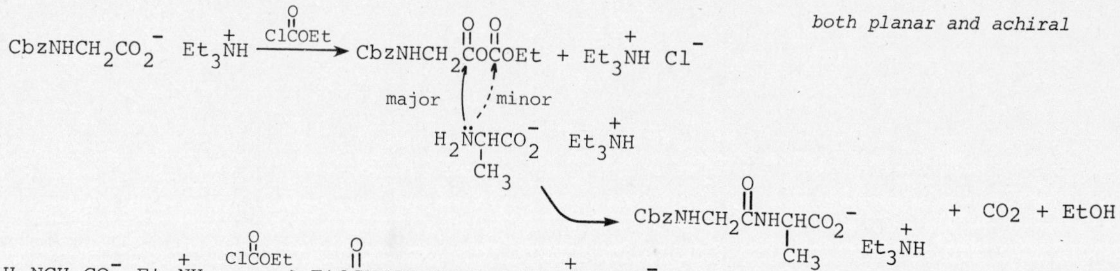

major | minor

H$_2\overset{..}{\text{N}}$CHCO$_2^-$ Et$_3\overset{+}{\text{N}}$H
          |
          CH$_3$

CbzNHCH$_2$CNHCHCO$_2^-$ + CO$_2$ + EtOH
                      | Et$_3\overset{+}{\text{N}}$H
                      CH$_3$

(b) H$_2$NCH$_2$CO$_2^-$ Et$_3\overset{+}{\text{N}}$H $\xrightarrow{\text{ClCOOEt}}$ EtOCNHCH$_2$CO$_2$H + Et$_3\overset{+}{\text{N}}$H Cl$^-$

(c) EtOCNHCHCO$_2^-$, from attack at the wrong carbonyl of the mixed anhydride.
        |
        CH$_3$

S8.   (a)   (CH$_3$)$_2\overset{+}{\text{N}}$H

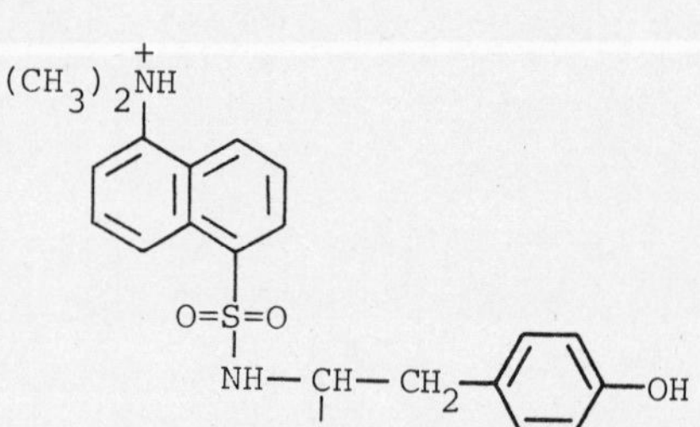

(b) 1. Enkephalin $\xrightarrow[\text{chloride}]{\text{dansyl}}$ $\xrightarrow{\text{H}_3\text{O}^+}$ modified Tyr: Tyr is N-terminal residue.

2. Enkephalin $\xrightarrow{\text{BrCN}}$ no cleavage: Met must be C-terminal residue (otherwise cleavage would have occurred).

3. Enkephalin $\xrightarrow{\text{chymotrypsin}}$ Tyr, tripeptide, Met: C-terminal amino acid of tripeptide must be Phe.

4. Therefore the sequence is: Tyr-Gly-Gly-Phe-Met

30. POLYCYCLIC AROMATIC HYDROCARBONS

30.A   Chapter Outline and Important Terms Introduced

30.1   Nomenclature

   biaryls

   fused-ring systems: naphthalene, anthracene, phenanthrene

30.2   Biphenyl

   A. Synthesis

      pyrolysis of benzene

$$2\ C_6H_6 \longrightarrow C_6H_5-C_6H_5 + H_2$$

      benzidine rearrangement   (see Section 24.1.C)
      Ullmann reaction   (see Section 26.3.B)
      Gomberg-Bachmann reaction   (see Section 24.5.F)

   B. Structure

      chirality of 2,2',6,6'-tetrasubstituted derivatives

   C. Reactions

      electrophilic aromatic substitution   (usually favors para)

   D. Related Compounds

      terphenyls
      fluorene (pK$_a$ = 23)

30.3   Naphthalene

   A. Structure and Occurrence

      resonance energy
      cis and trans decalins

   B. Synthesis

      annelation routes
      aromatization of hydroaromatics
      Diels-Alder reactions of p-benzoquinone

   C. Electrophilic Substitution

      favors 1-position kinetically
      sulfonation can provide 2-naphthalenesulfonic acid thermodynamically

   D. Oxidation and Reduction of Naphthalene

      naphthalene to 1,4-naphthoquinone or phthalic anhydride
      Birch reduction

   E. Substituted Naphthalenes

      transformations of substituent groups
      directive effects in electrophilic aromatic substitution reactions
      Bucherer reaction

30.4   Anthracene and Phenanthrene

   A. Structure and Stability

   B. Preparation of Anthracenes and Phenanthrenes

      annelation methods

   C. Reactions

      oxidation to quinones
      reduction to dihydro compounds
      Diels-Alder reactions of anthracene
      electrophilic aromatic substitution (occurs on central ring)

30.5   Higher Polybenzenoid Hydrocarbons

   acene   benz-, benzo- derivatives
   graphite   carcinogens

30.B Important Reactions Introduced

Synthesis of polycyclic aromatic hydrocarbons by annelation:

Friedel-Crafts acylation (30.3.B)

Equation:

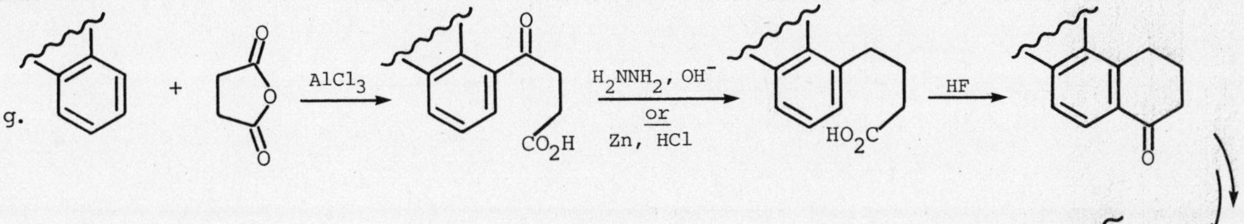

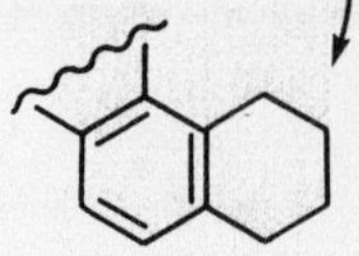

Diels-Alder reaction (30.3.B)

Equation:

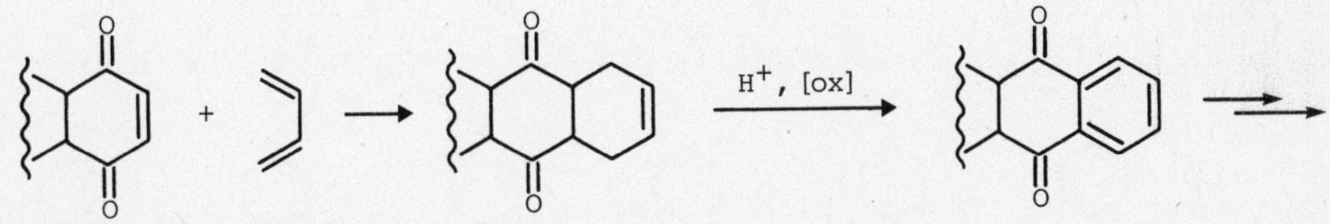

Bucherer reaction (30.3.E)

Equation:

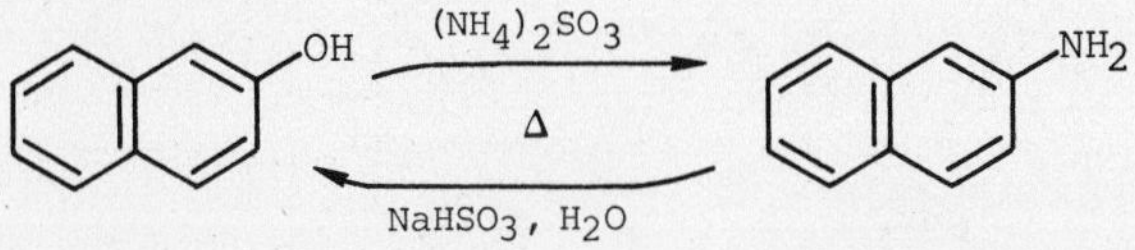

Generality: Reversible, requires catalysis by sulf**ite**
Specific for naphthalenes and higher fused polycyclics

Diels-Alder reaction of anthracene (30.4)

Equation:

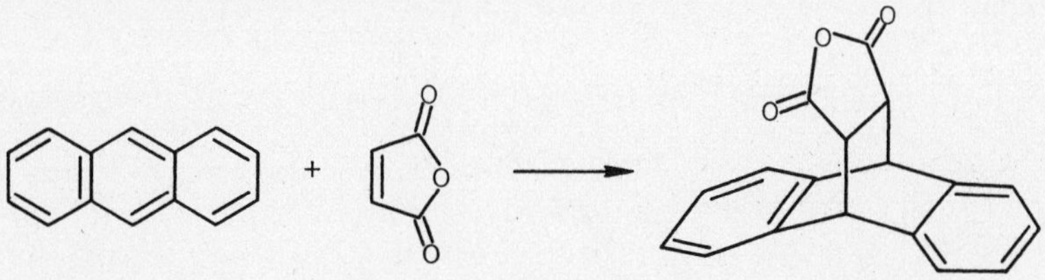

30.D Answers to Exercises

30.1 (a) 6-bromonaphthalene-2-carboxylic acid
(b) 1-bromo-2,5-dimethylanthracene
(c) 3-chloro-9,10-dihydrophenanthrene

30.2 (a)

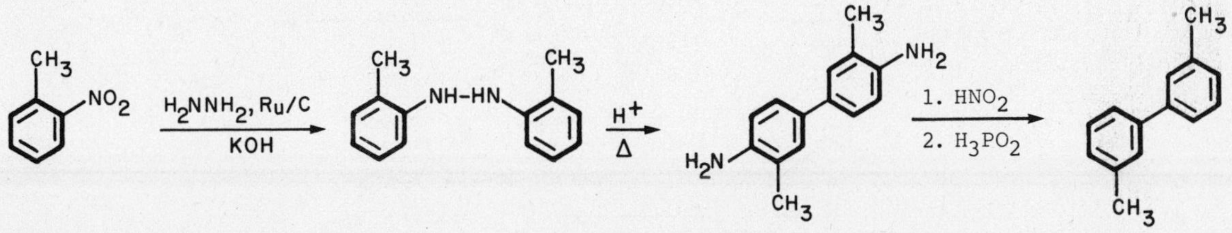

(b)

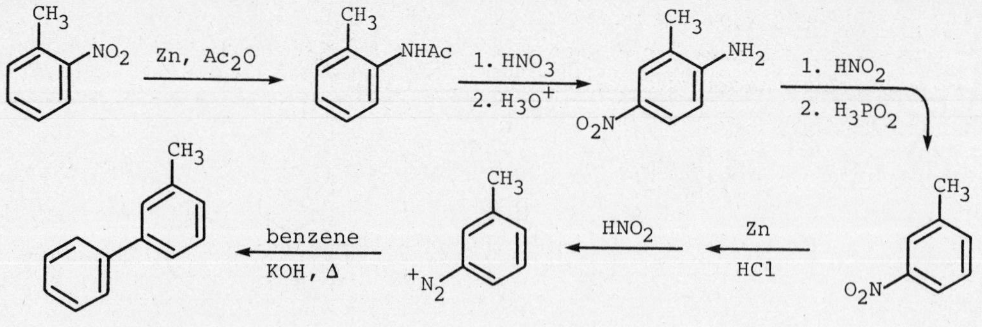

Zn, Ac₂O → 1. HNO₃ / 2. H₃O⁺ → 1. HNO₂ / 2. H₃PO₂ →

benzene / KOH, Δ ← HNO₂ ← Zn / HCl ←

30.3   [there is no answer for (a)]

(b)

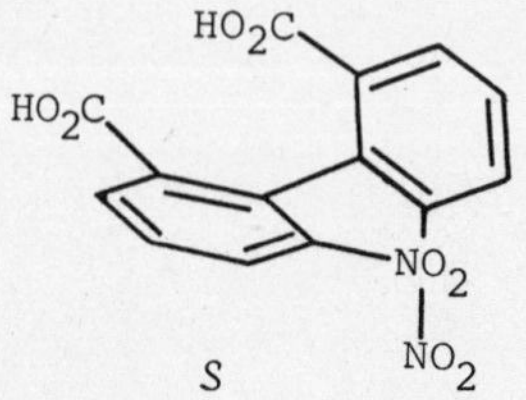

S

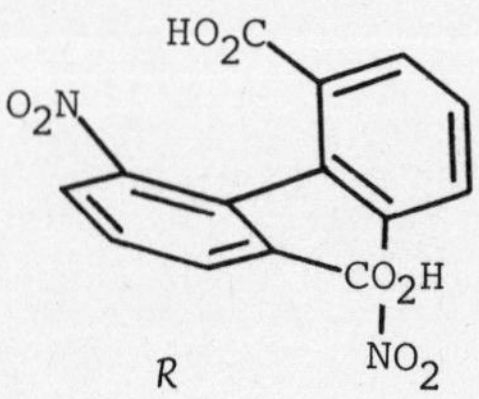

R

30.4   <u>para</u> attack:

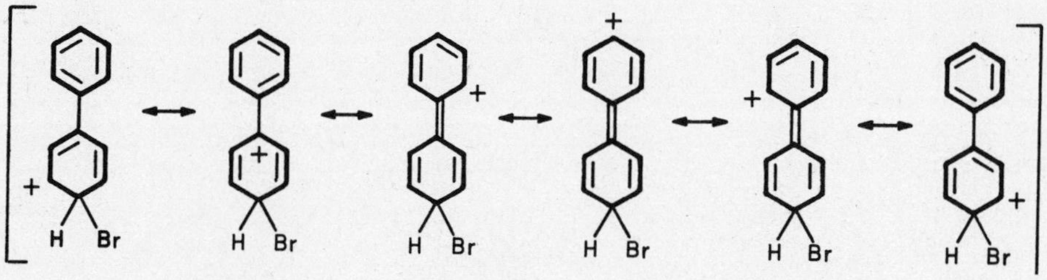

<u>meta</u> attack:

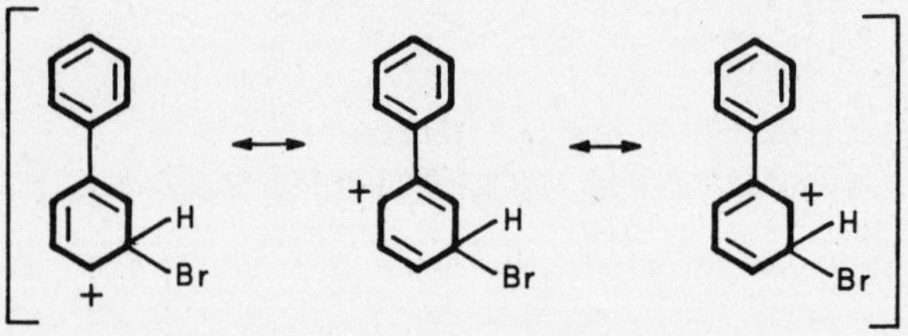

The phenyl substituent itself can stabilize the
positive charge via resonance when it is in the <u>para</u> position.

30.5 (a)

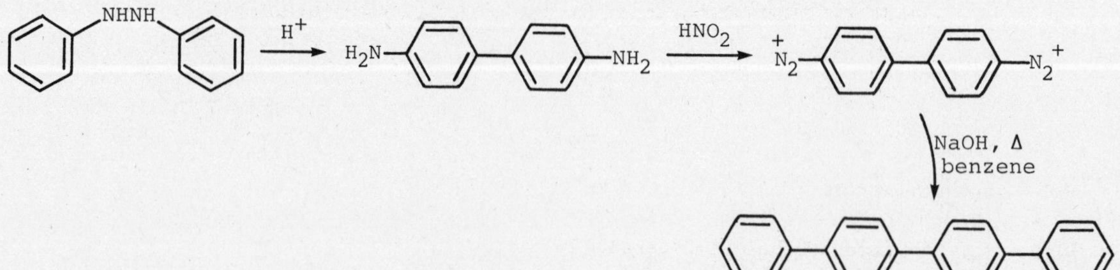

H⁺ → HNO₂ →

NaOH, Δ
benzene ↓

(b)

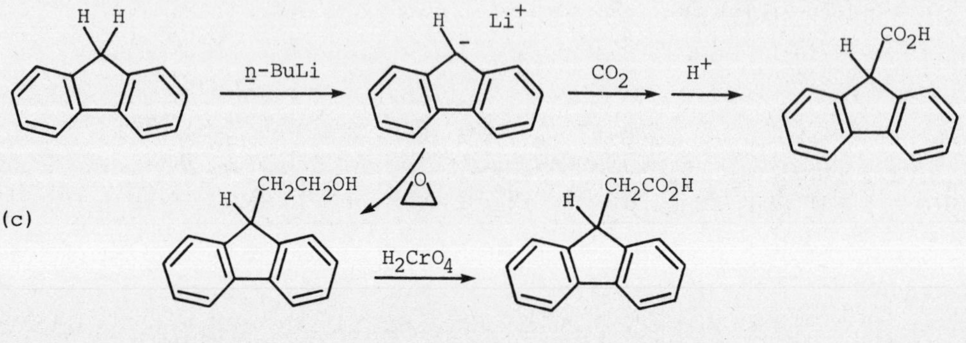

<u>n</u>-BuLi → CO₂   H⁺ →

↓ O (epoxide)

(c)   H₂CrO₄ →

30.6   Fractional double bond character = the number of resonance structures with a double bond divided by the total number of resonance structures:

1/3   2/3
1/3
1/3

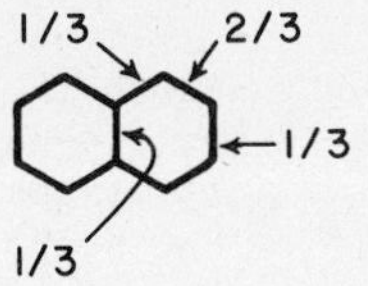

The prediction is roughly correct.

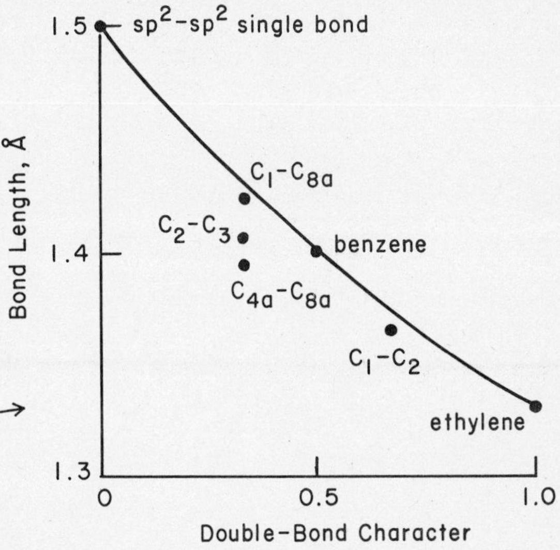

Bond Length, Å

1.5 — sp²-sp² single bond

C_1-C_{8a}

C_2-C_3

1.4   benzene

C_{4a}-C_{8a}

C_1-C_2

1.3

ethylene

0   0.5   1.0
Double-Bond Character

30.7   (a)

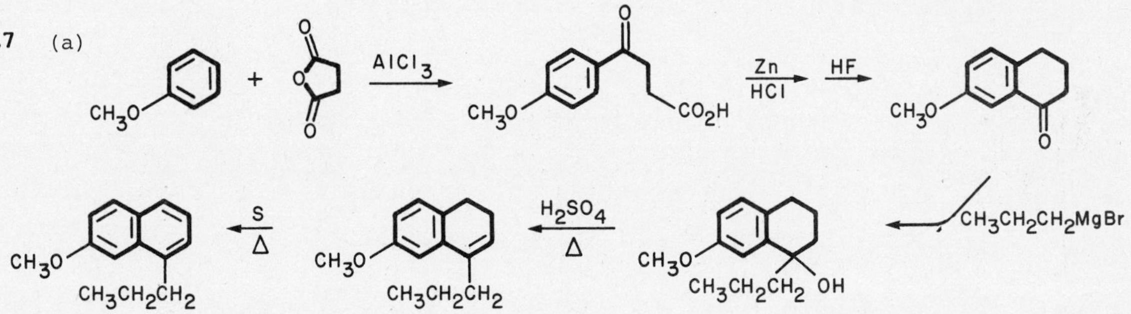

CH_3O + (anhydride) $\xrightarrow{AlCl_3}$ CH_3O—(C=O)—$CH_2CH_2CO_2H$ $\xrightarrow[HCl]{Zn}$ $\xrightarrow{HF}$ CH_3O—(tetralone)

CH_3O—(naphthalene)—$CH_3CH_2CH_2$ $\xleftarrow[\Delta]{S}$ CH_3O—(dihydronaphthalene)—$CH_3CH_2CH_2$ $\xleftarrow[\Delta]{H_2SO_4}$ CH_3O—(tetrahydronaphthalene)—$CH_3CH_2CH_2$, OH $\xleftarrow{CH_3CH_2CH_2MgBr}$

(b)

CH_3, CH_3 (quinone) + (diene) $\rightarrow$ CH_3, CH_3 (adduct) $\xrightarrow[H_2SO_4]{Na_2Cr_2O_7}$ CH_3, CH_3 (naphthoquinone)

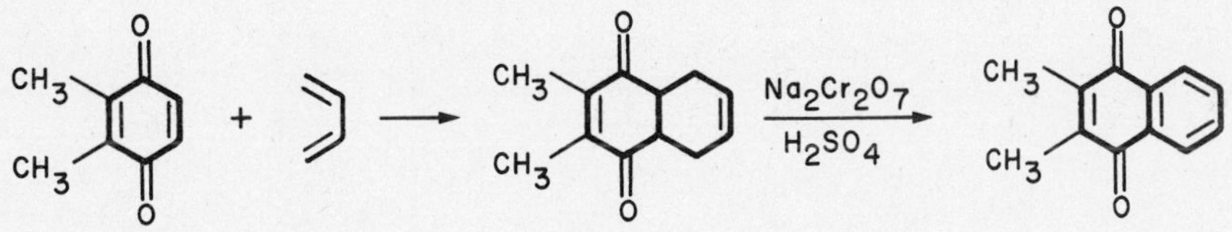

NOTE: The reaction sequence outlined below, which is depicted in the text, often confuses students. It is intended to illustrate that, with proper choice of reagents, it is possible to carry out the sequence in a stepwise fashion.

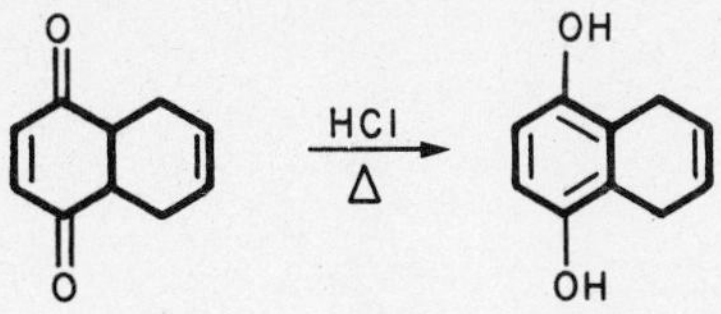

(diketone) $\xrightarrow[\Delta]{HCl}$ (diol)   (This reaction is simply a double enolization.)

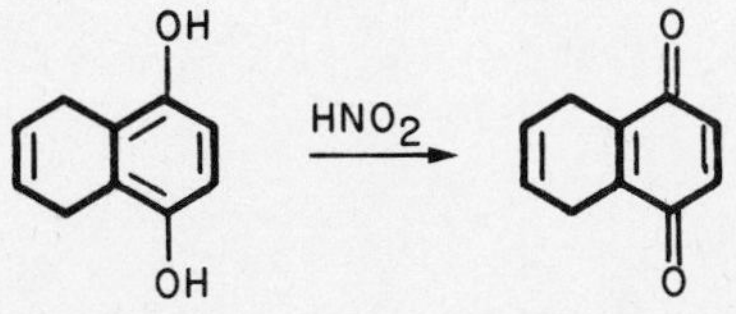

(diol) $\xrightarrow{HNO_2}$ (quinone)   (This is an oxidation, which stops at this stage when HNO_2 is the oxidant. Note that HNO_2 is a mild oxidizing agent and a weak acid)

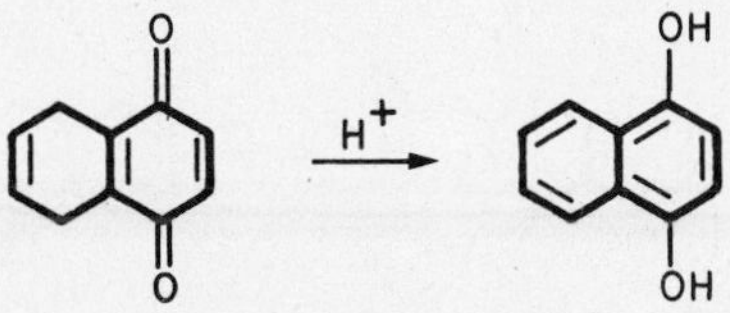

(diketone) $\xrightarrow{H^+}$ (diol)   (This reaction is another double enolization. It occurs under the acidic conditions of $K_2Cr_2O_7/H_2SO_4$ oxidation.)

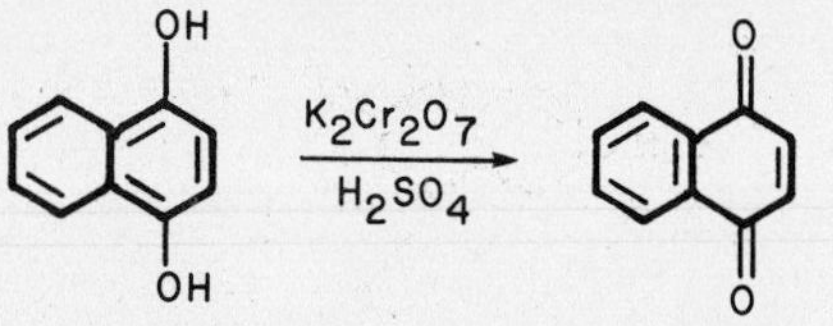

(This is the final oxidation step.)

It is _not_ necessary to use each one of these reagents sequentially in order to achieve the overall transformation from the Diels-Alder adduct to the 1,4-naphthoquinone. The transformation can be accomplished all at once under the acidic conditions of the chromic acid oxidation (below). However, you should bear in mind that all of the steps depicted above are involved.

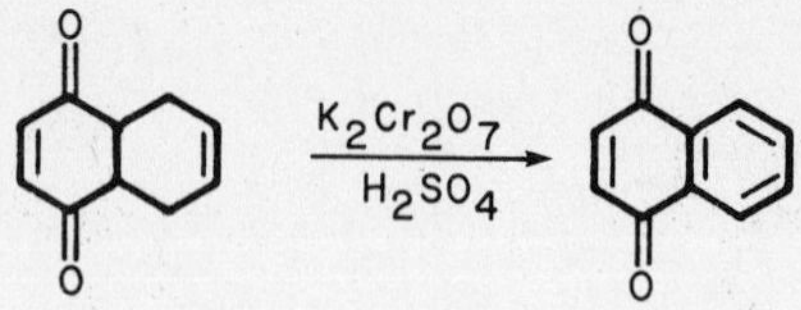

30.8 (a)

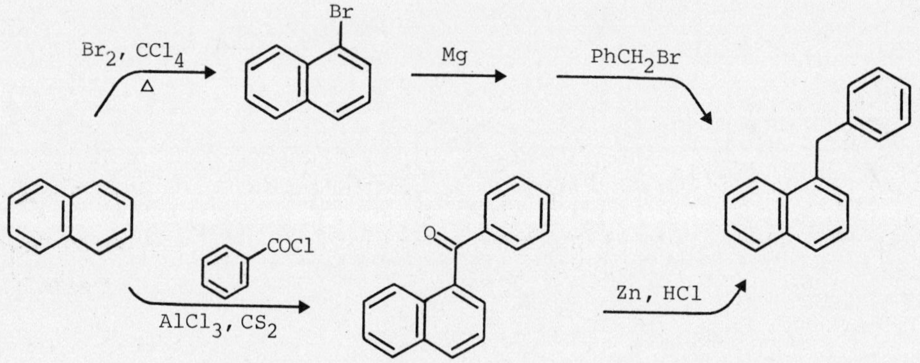

(b)

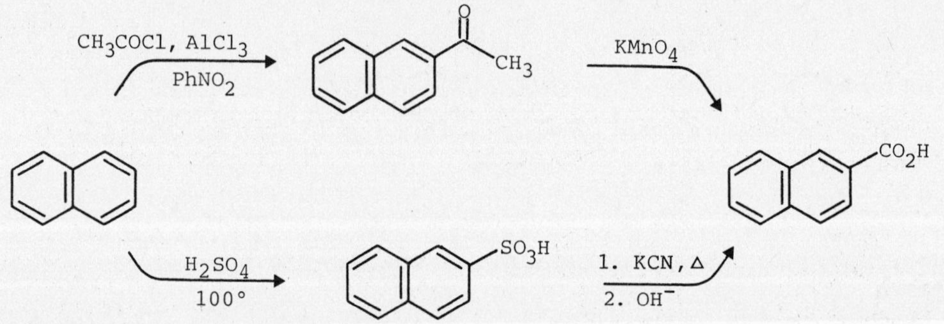

30.9 (a)

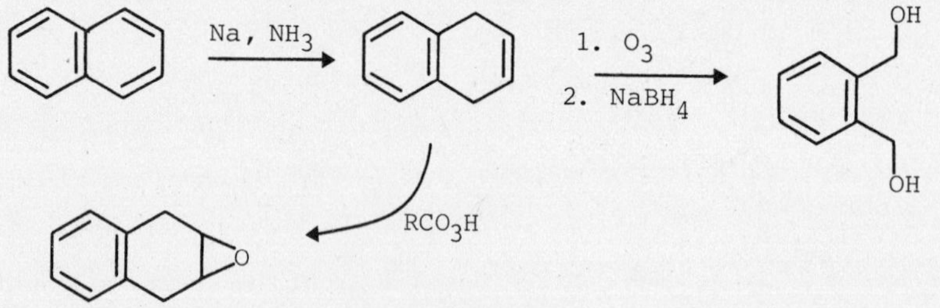

(b)

30.10

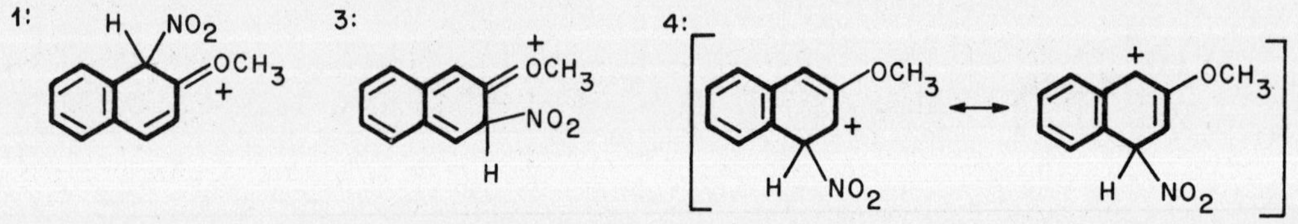

1:    3:   4:

5:

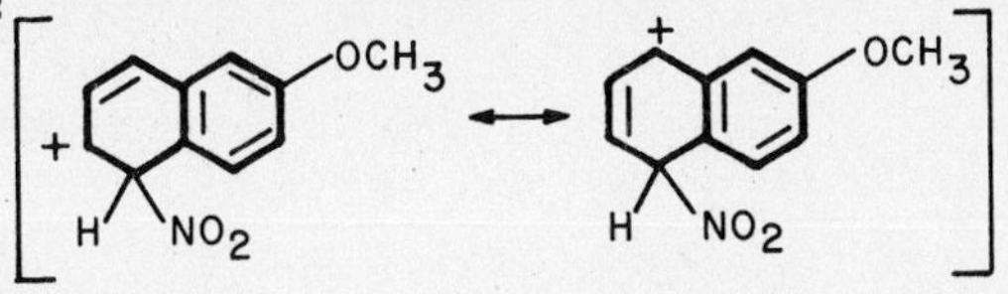

6:

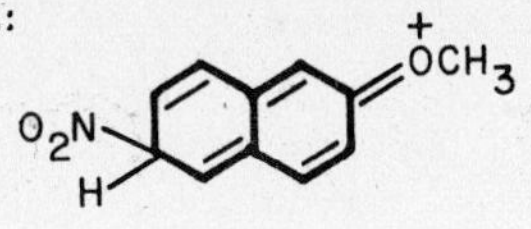

7:

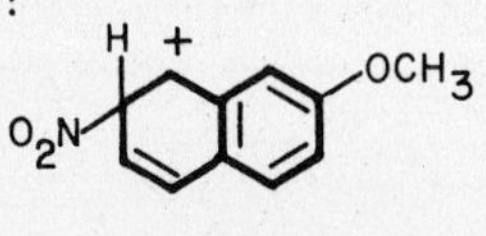

8:

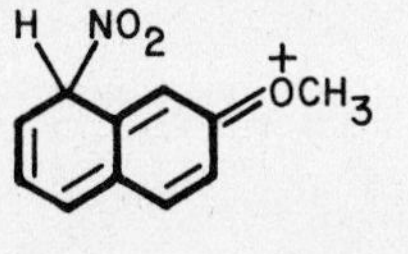

Only the 1-substitution intermediate can utilize the oxygen lone pair electrons to stabilize the positive charge and maintain an aromatic ring.

30.11

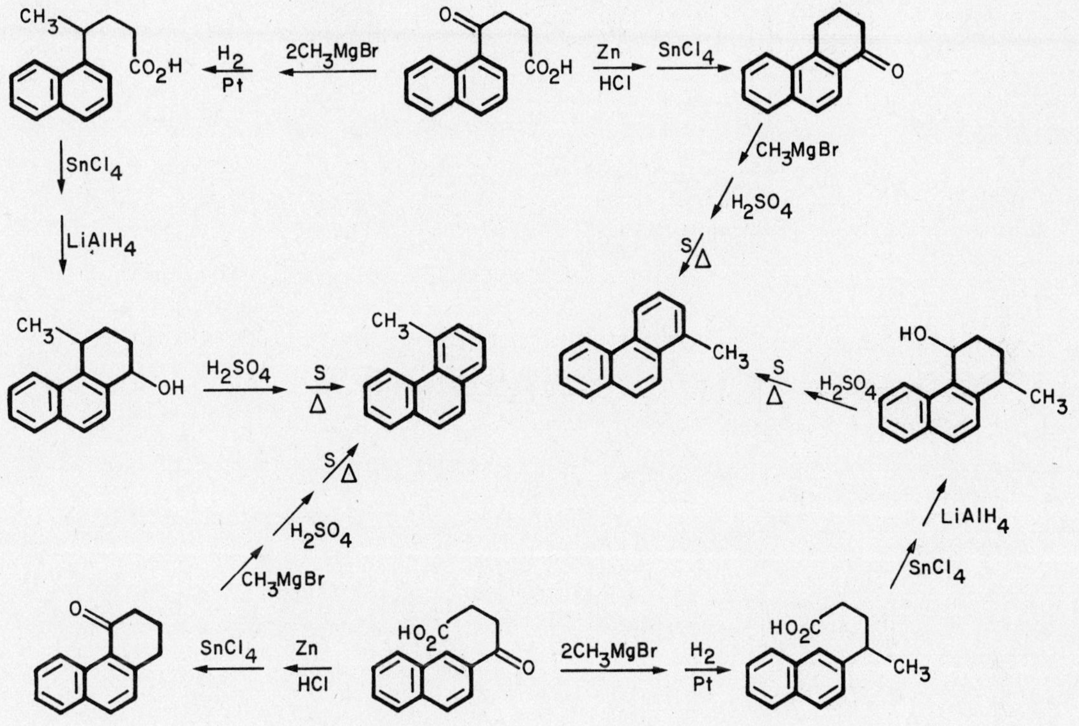

30.12

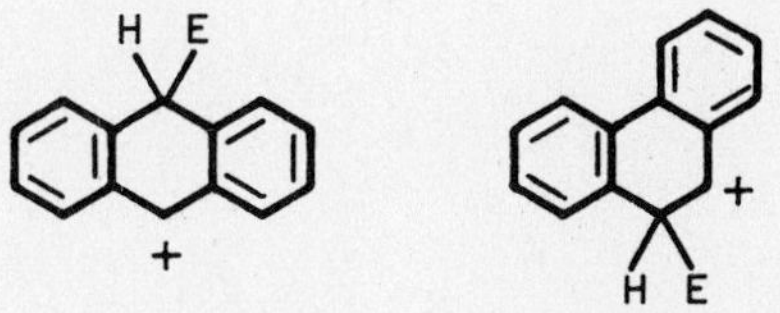

These are the two most favored resonance structures, because each allows two of the rings to remain fully aromatic as benzene rings.

30.13

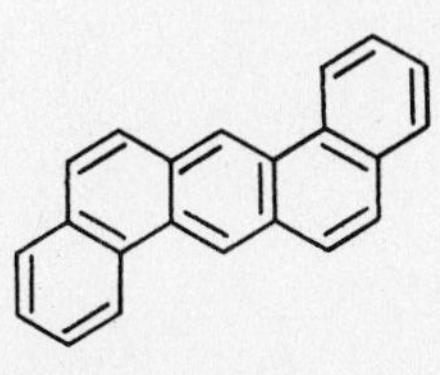

dibenz[a,h]-
anthracene

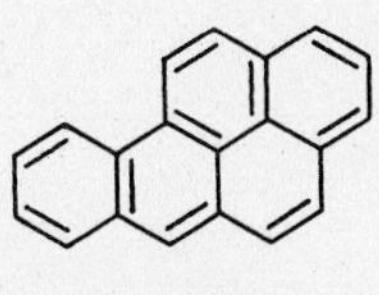

benzo[a]pyrene

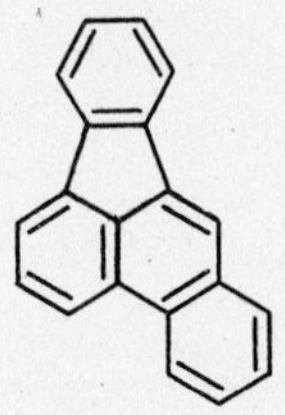

benzo[b]fluoranthene

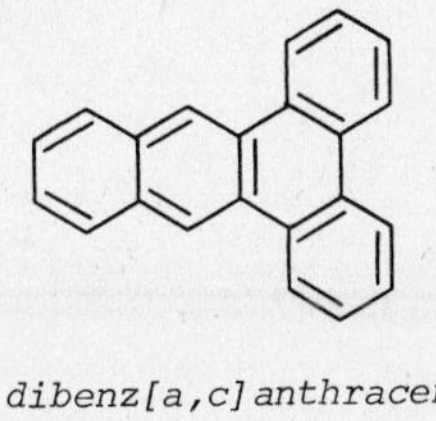

dibenz[a,c]anthracene

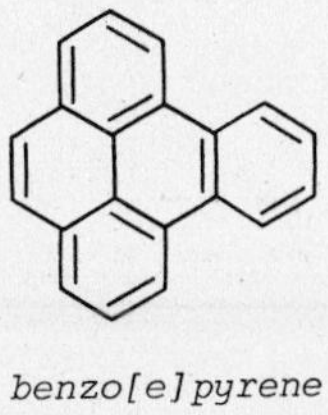

benzo[e]pyrene

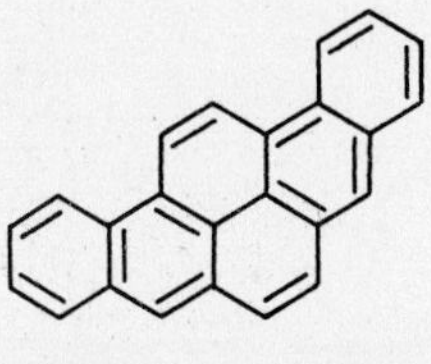

dibenzo[a,i]pyrene

30.E   Answers and Explanations for Problems

1.

(a) The reaction sequence shows benzene + succinic anhydride with $AlCl_3$ giving a phenyl ketone with $COOH$, then Zn/Hg, HCl (*Clemmensen reduction*) giving the reduced acid, then PPA, Δ (*polyphosphoric acid*) or HF giving the tetralone.

The tetralone reacts with phenyl $MgBr$, then H^+ giving the tertiary alcohol (OH), then H^+, Δ giving the dihydronaphthalene, then Se or S, Δ giving *1-phenyl-naphthalene*.

(b) The ketoacid (*from (a)*) reacts with CH_3MgBr (2 moles), then H^+ [first mole reacts with $-COOH$ to form $-COOMgX$, which is now inert to further CH_3MgX] giving HO, CH_3 product with $COOH$, then H^+, Δ giving the alkene CH_3 with $COOH$, then H_2/Pt.

or Pd/H_2, $HClO_4$ giving the CH_3 phenyl acid with $COOH$, then PPA or HF; Δ giving the CH_3 tetralone.

then 1. CH_3MgBr 2. H^+ giving the CH_3 ... HO CH_3 product, then 1. H^+, Δ 2. Se or S, Δ giving *1,4-dimethylnaphthalene*.

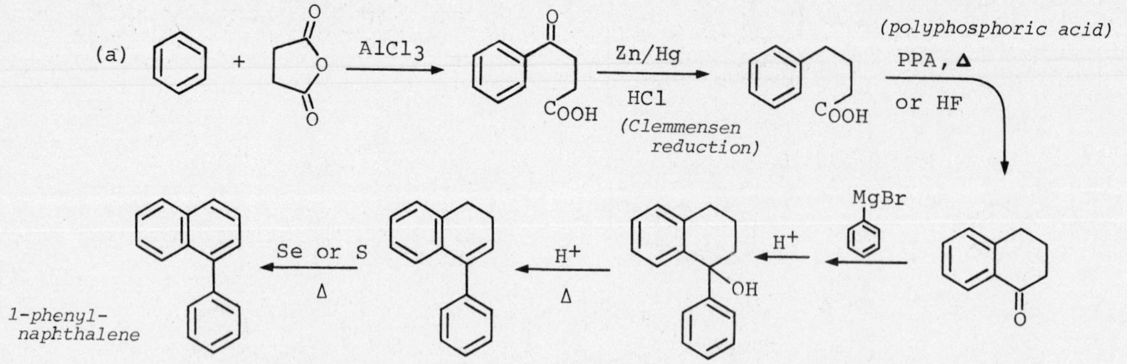

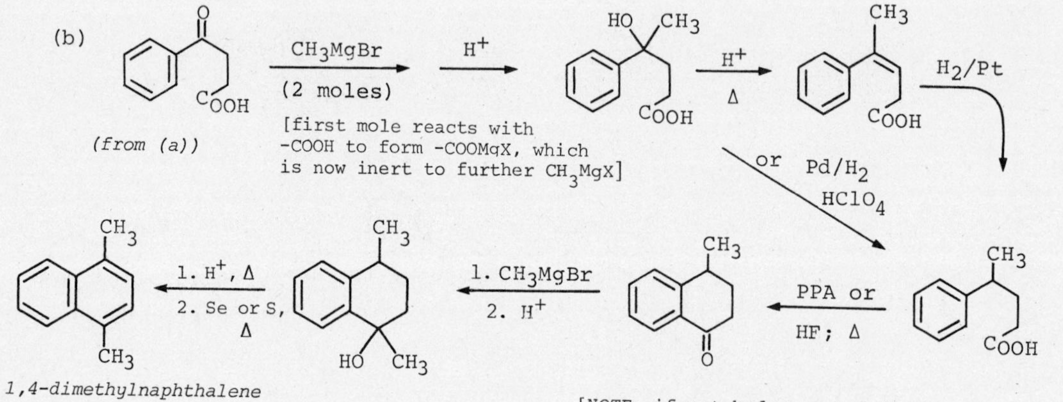

[*NOTE*: if not hydrogenated first, we would obtain a naphthol at this point]

<u>Alternative:</u> p-xylene + succinic anhydride $\rightarrow$ the CH_3 ketoacid with $COOH$ $\rightarrow$ etc.

(c) benzoquinone + 2,3-dimethylbutadiene $\rightarrow$ the Diels-Alder adduct, H^+ giving the dihydroxy dimethyl compound (OH ... OH), HNO_2

then $Na_2Cr_2O_7$, H_2SO_4 giving *6,7-dimethyl-1,4-naphthoquinone*

(d) toluene + succinic anhydride, $AlCl_3$ giving the CH_3 ketoacid with $COOH$, then Zn/Hg HCl or H_2NNH_2 glycol, KOH giving the CH_3 acid with $COOH$, then HF

giving the CH_3 tetralone, then $(CH_3)_2CHMgBr$ giving the CH_3 ... HO $CH(CH_3)_2$ product, then H^+, Δ then Se or S, Δ giving *1-isopropyl-7-methylnaphthalene*.

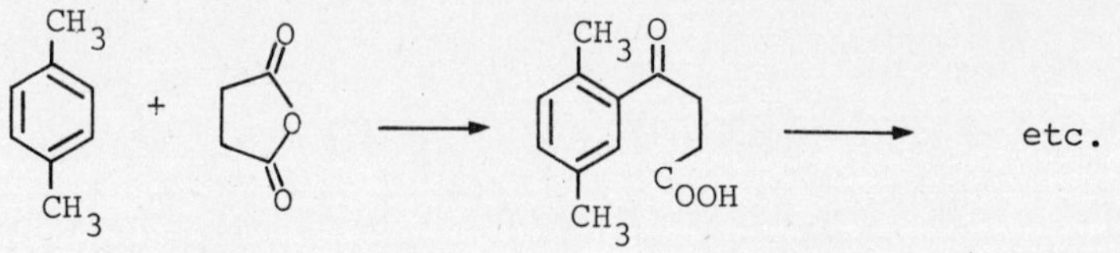

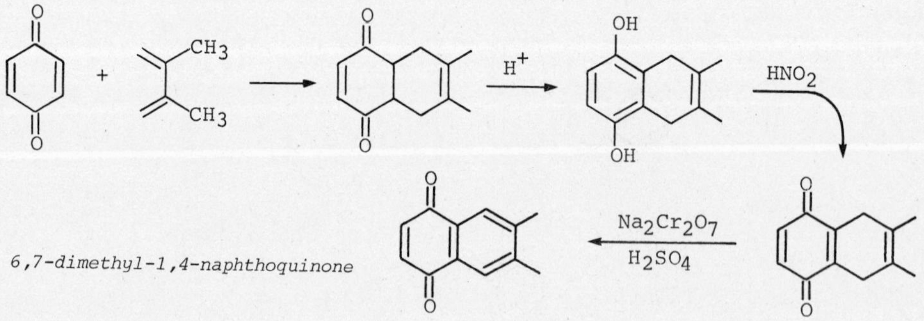

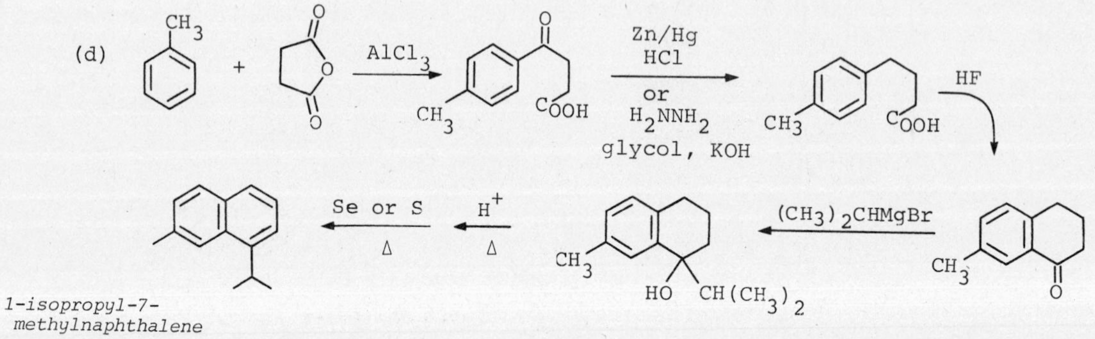

(e)

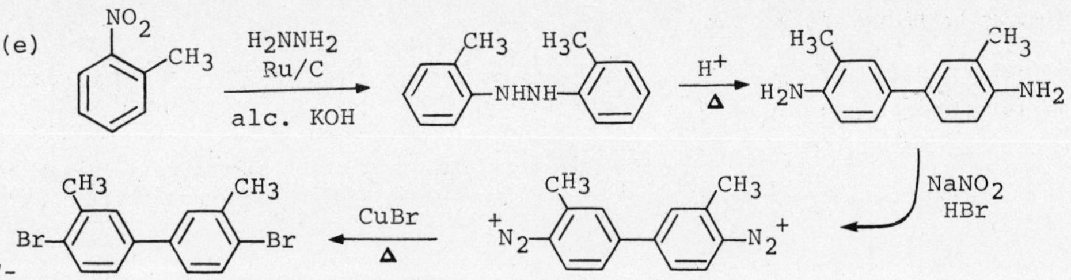

4,4'-dibromo-3,3'-
dimethylbiphenyl

(f)

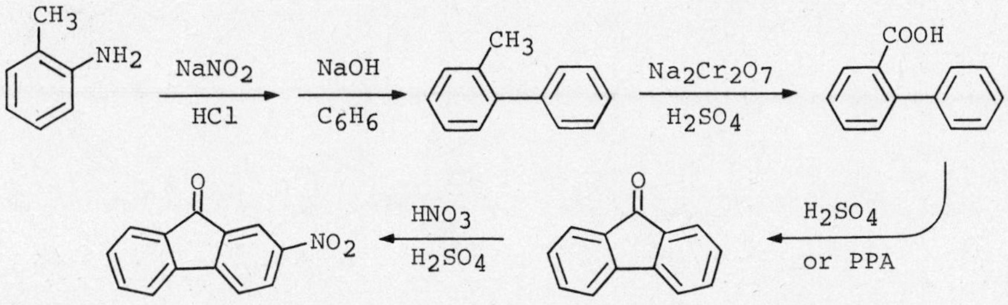

2-nitrofluorenone

(g)

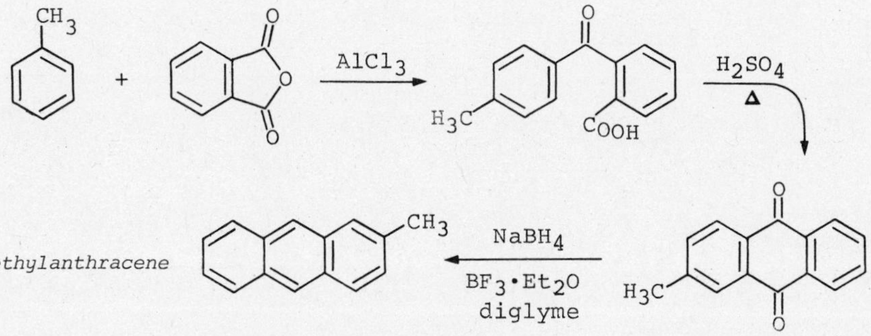

2-methylanthracene

(h)

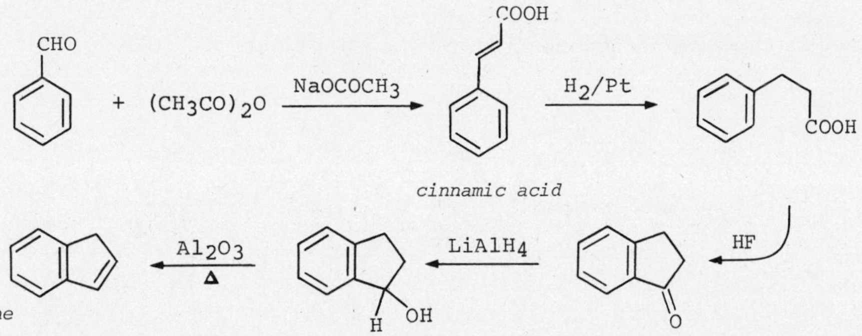

cinnamic acid

indene

2.

anthranilic acid

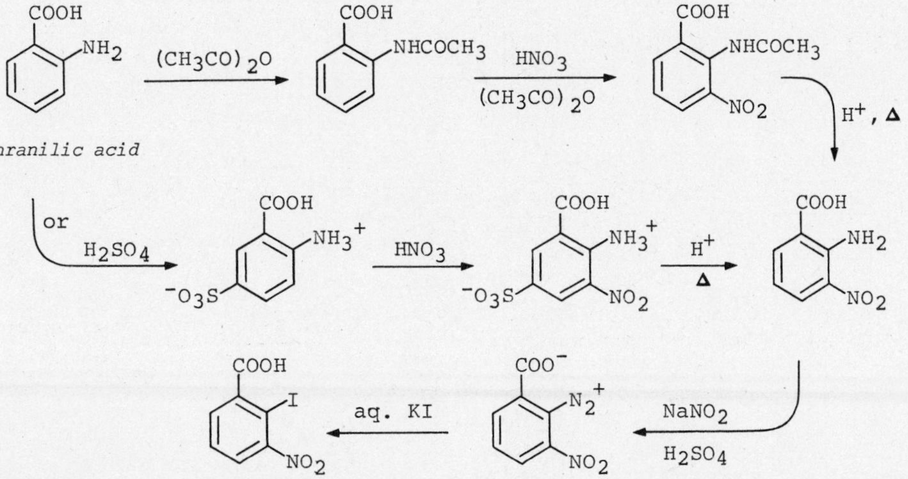

3. The 6-position conjugates
with the 2-methyl.
The 7-position does not.

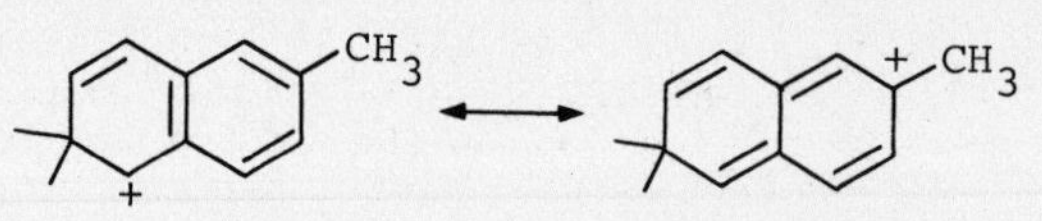

No such tertiary carbocation structure is possible
for attack at the 7-position.

4.

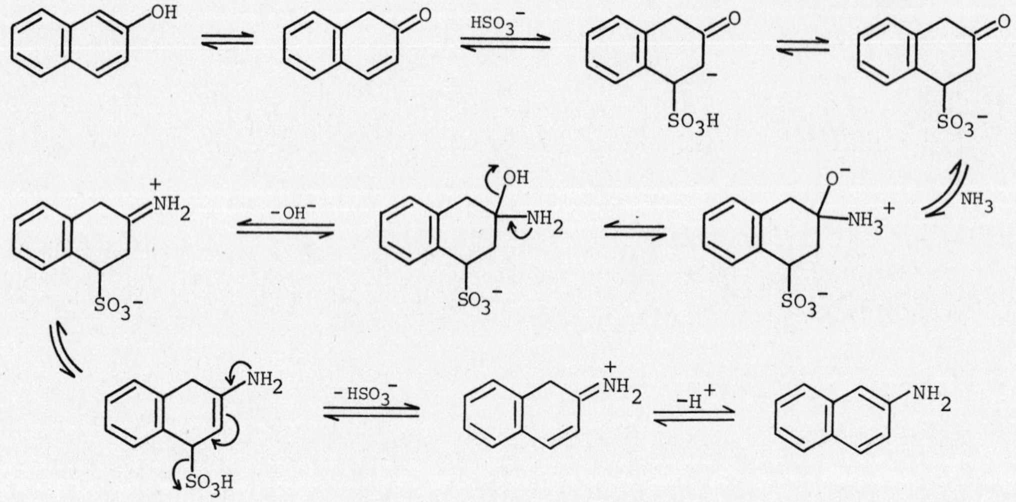

5. (a) $\Delta H^{\circ}_{hydrog.} = -43.5 - 36.1 = -79.6$ kcal mole^{-1}

(b) For cyclohexene, $\Delta H^{\circ}_{hydrog.} = -28.4$ kcal mole^{-1}
For five double bonds, the value for $\Delta H^{\circ}_{hydrog.}$ would be $5 \times (-28.4) = -142.0$ kcal mole^{-1}

(c) Empirical resonance energy = $142.0 - 79.6 = 62.4$ kcal mole^{-1}

6. (a) 1,6-dimethyl-4-isopropylnaphthalene

(b)

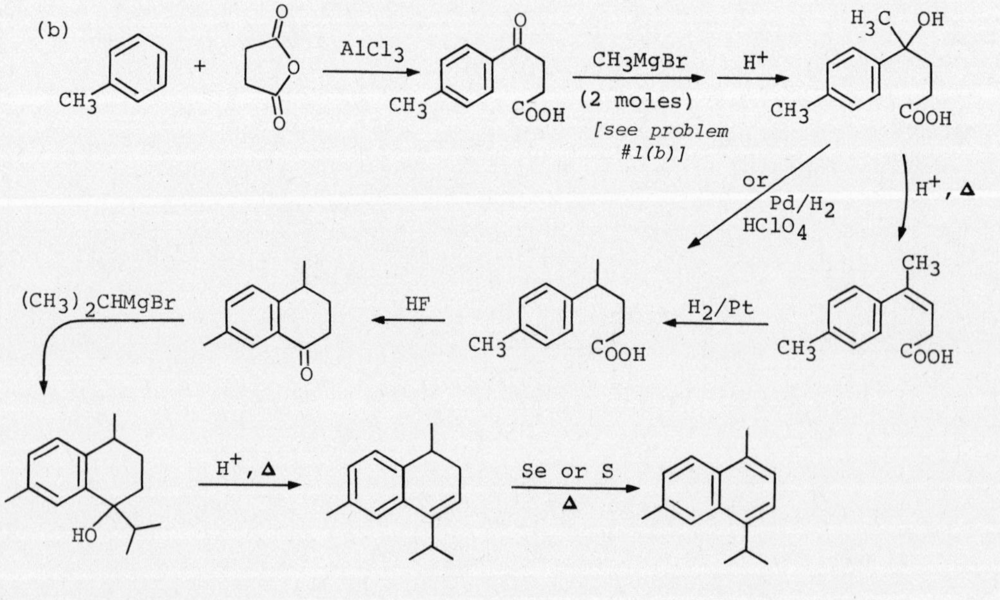

7.

(a)

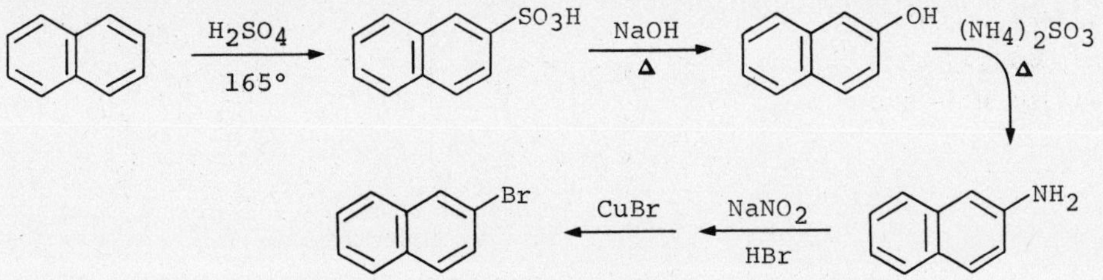

(b)

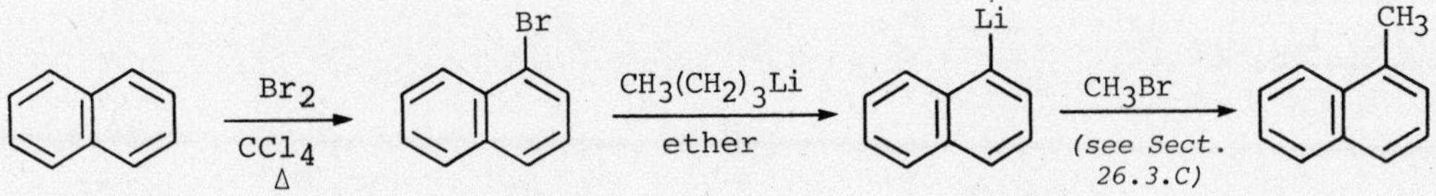

(c)

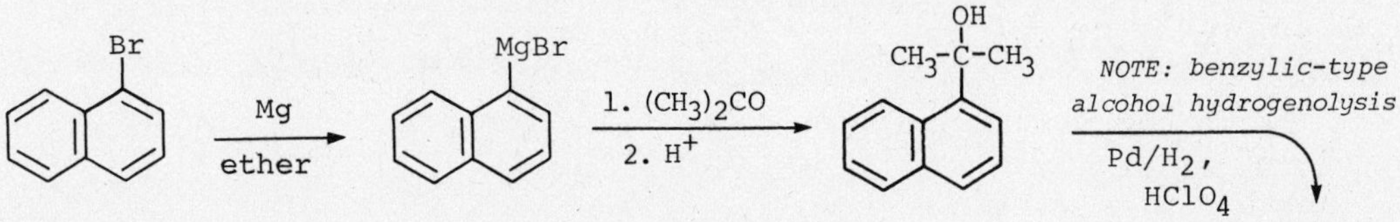

[from (b)]

NOTE: benzylic-type alcohol hydrogenolysis

(d)

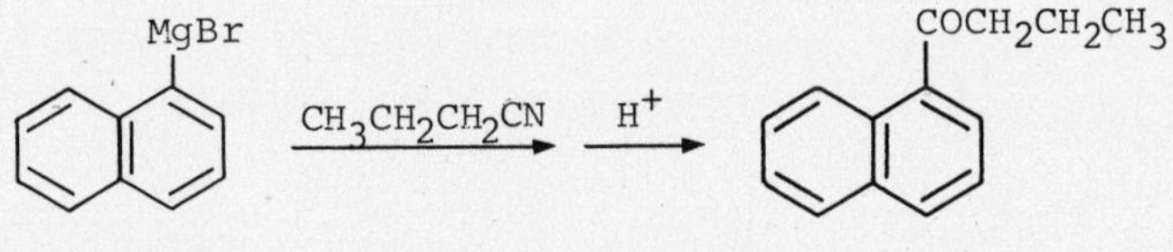

[from (c)]

(e)

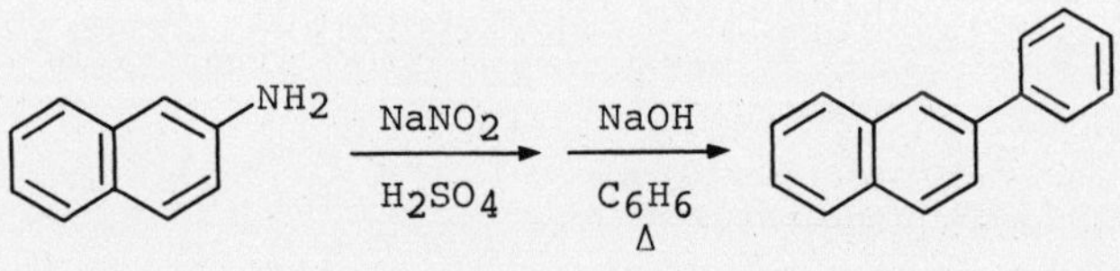

[from (a)]

(f)

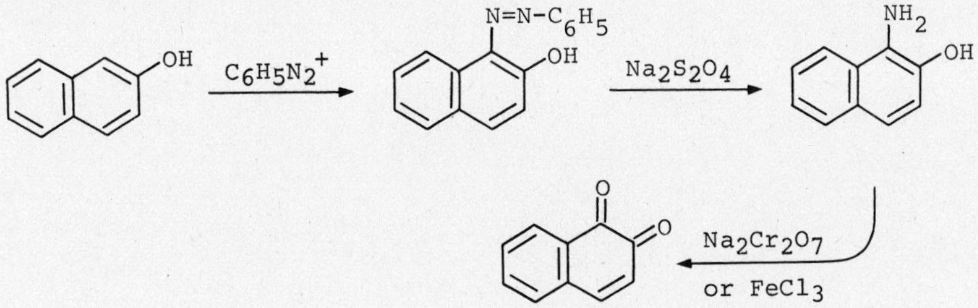

(g)

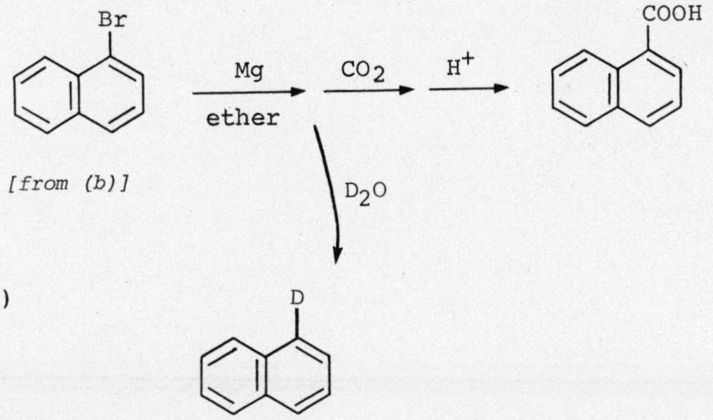

[from (b)]

(h)

8.

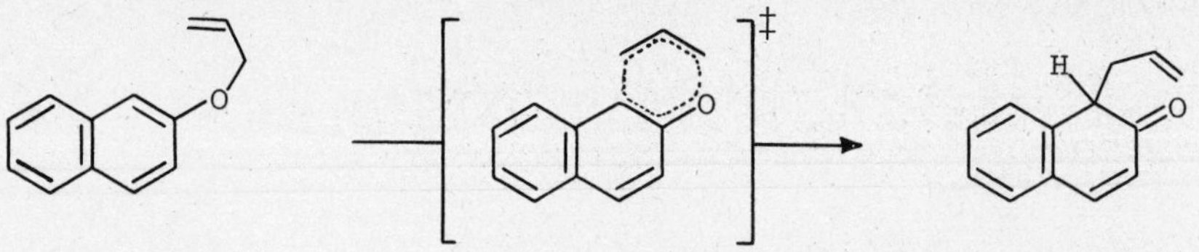

This transition state and intermediate both still have an intact benzene ring.

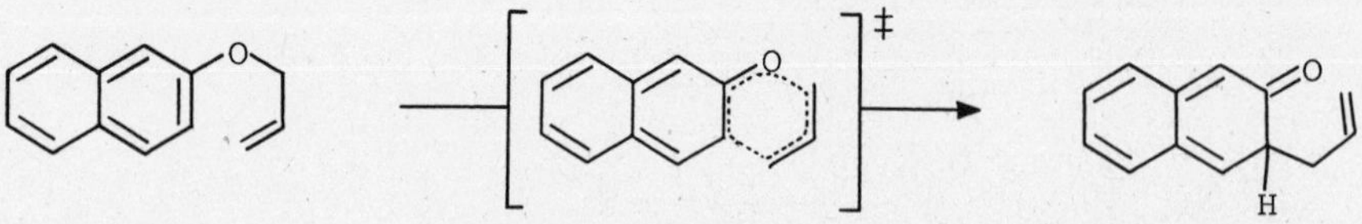

In this transition state and intermediate, the resonance stabilization of both benzene rings has been lost.

9.   (a)

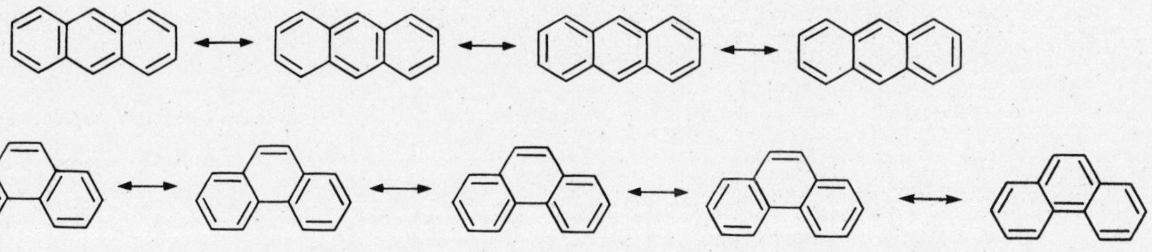

(b)

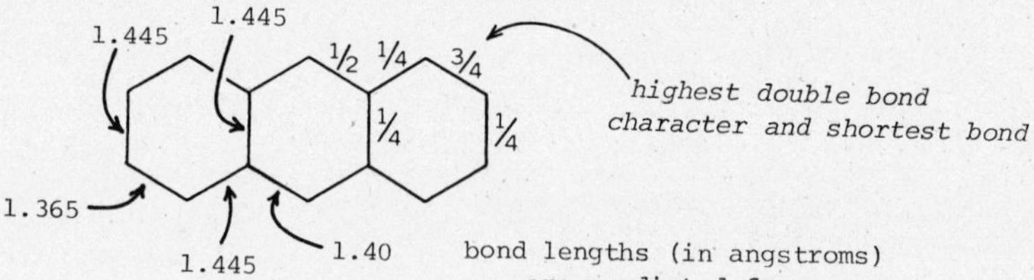

highest double bond character and shortest bond

bond lengths (in angstroms) are predicted from curve

10.

(a)

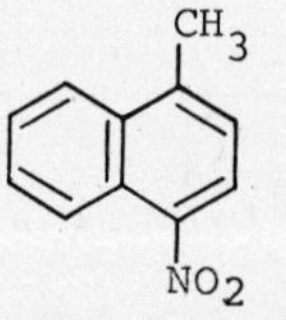

(b) +

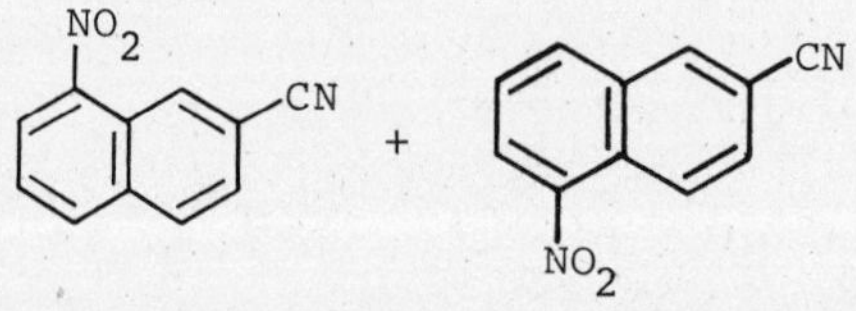

(c)

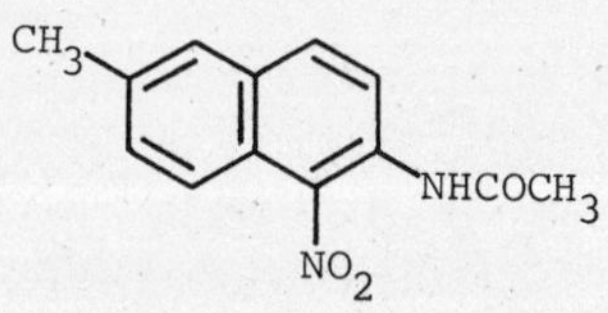

(d)

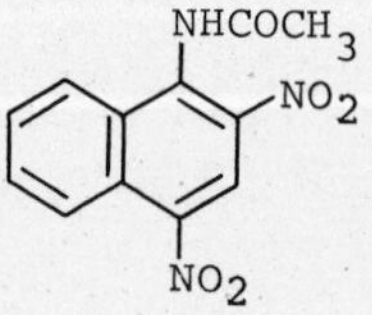

(e)

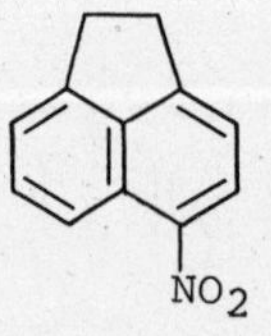

(α-alkylnaphthyl type)

(f)

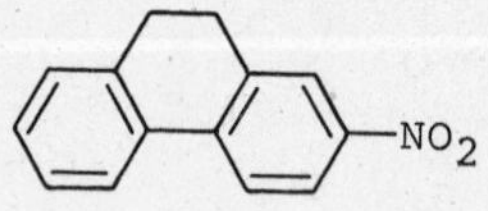

(biphenyl type)

(g)

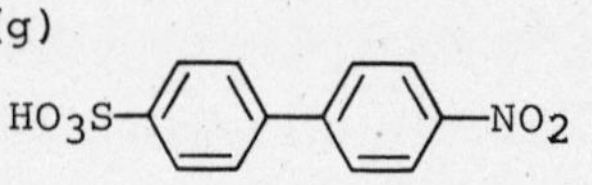

(h)

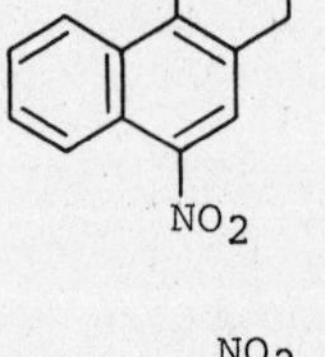

(i)

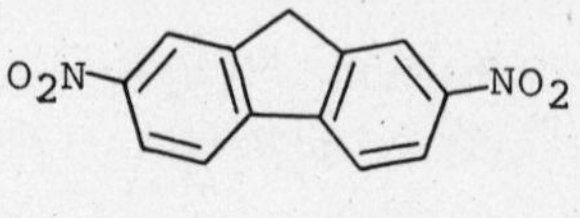

(j)

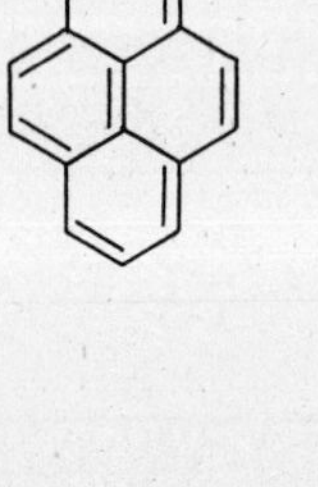

(k)

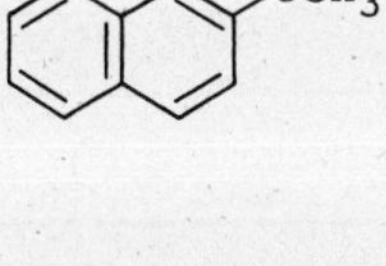

(l)

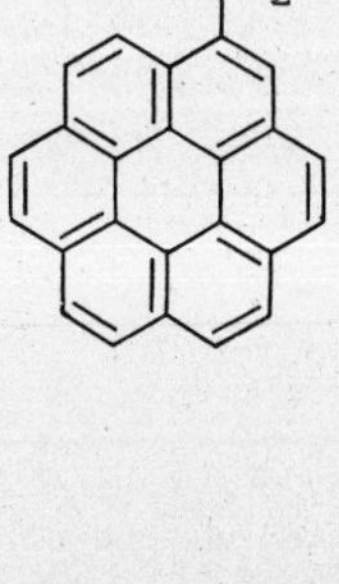

NOTE: all positions are equivalent!

11. (a)

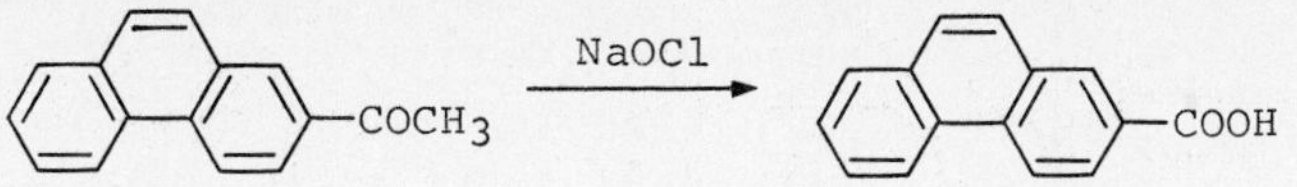

(b)

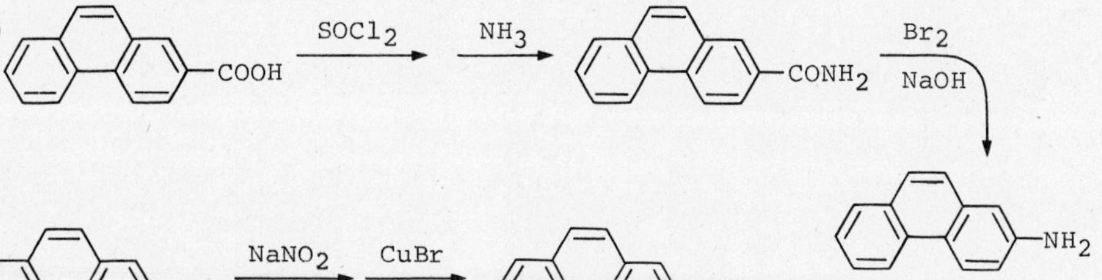

(c)

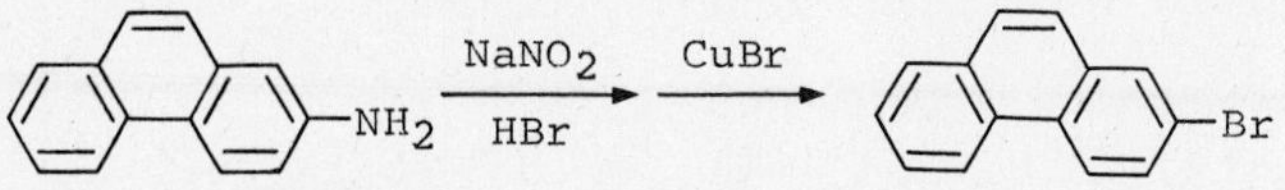

(d)

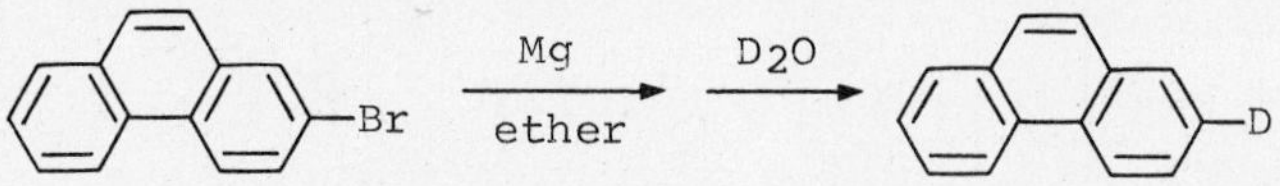

The same sequences apply, starting with the 3-acetyl compound.

12. (a)

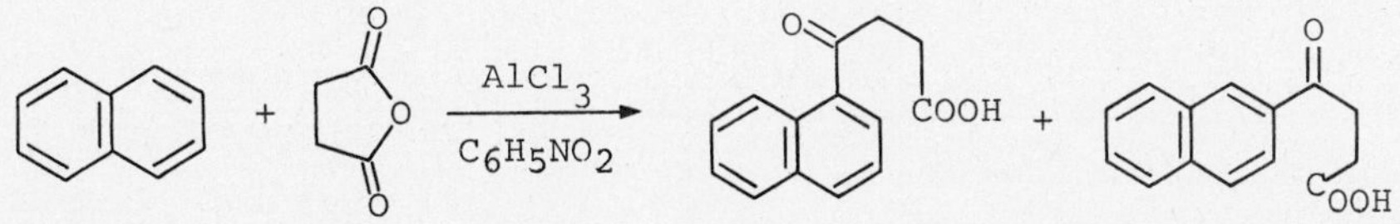

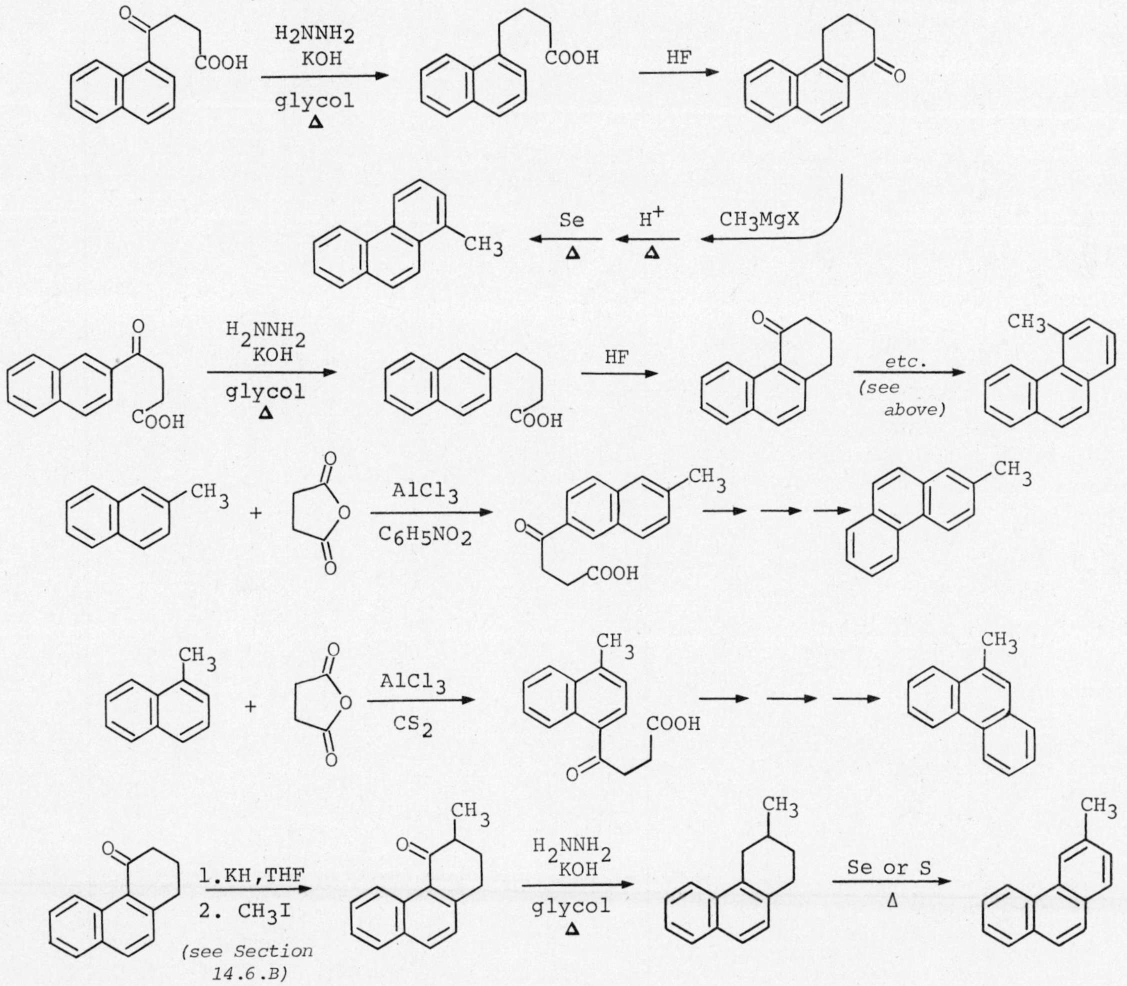

(b)

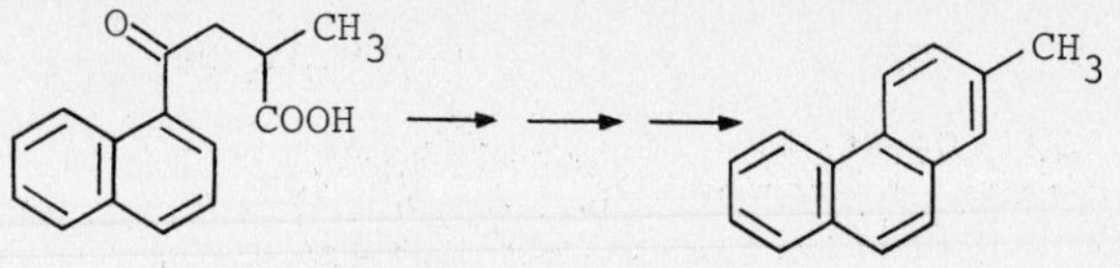

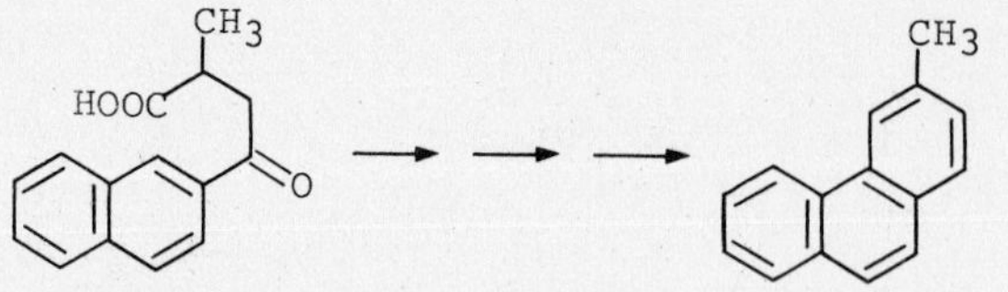

13.

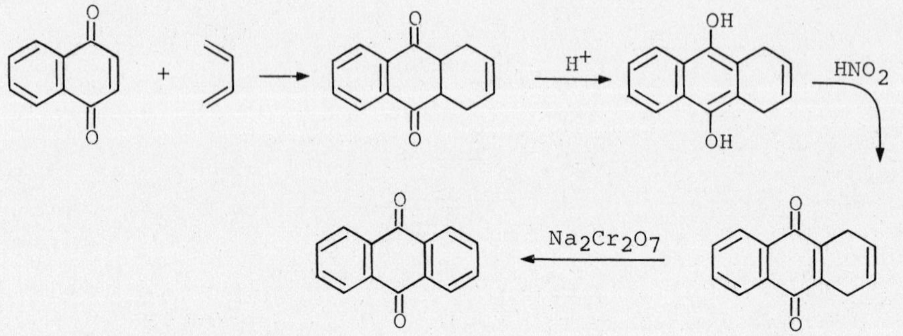

14.   1-methylpyrene;   1,2,3,4-tetramethylphenanthrene;   5,6-dimethylchrysene

Note that in benzo derivatives the numbering changes. For example, the numbering in benz[a]anthracene is:

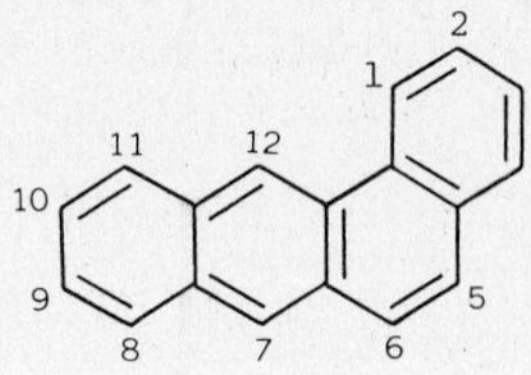

The name of a carcinogenic derivative is given:

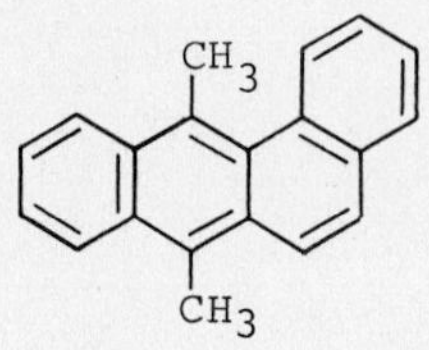

(see Section 30.5)

7,12-dimethylbenz[a]anthracene

15.   (a)

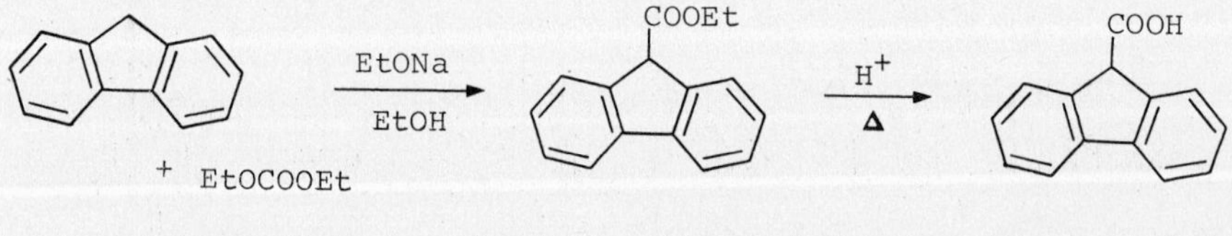

+ EtOCOOEt

(b)

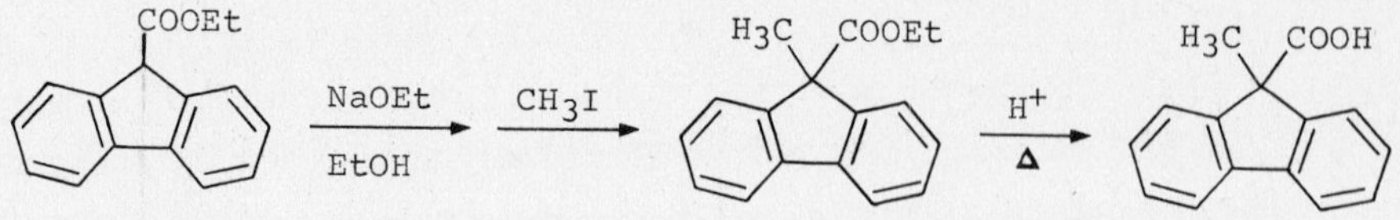

[from (a)]

(c)

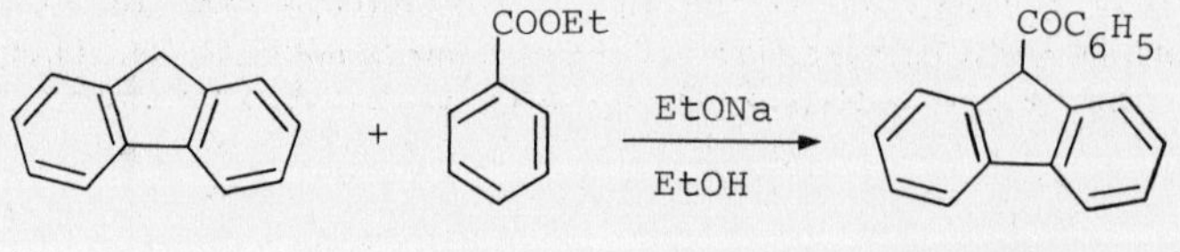

(d)

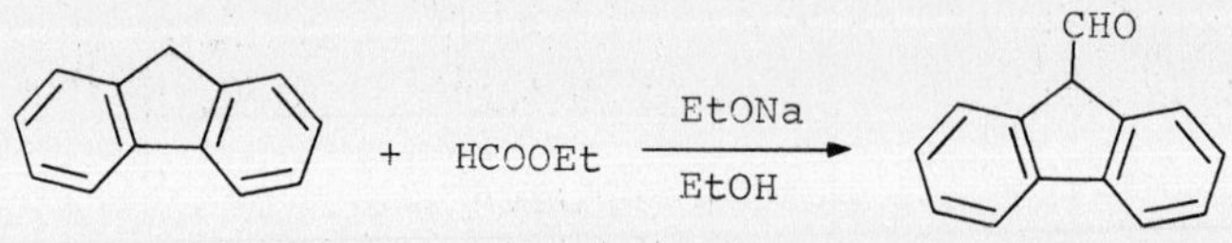

16.

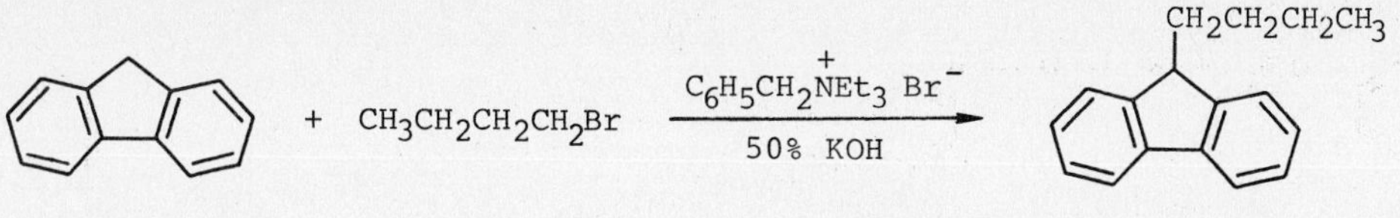

17. (a)

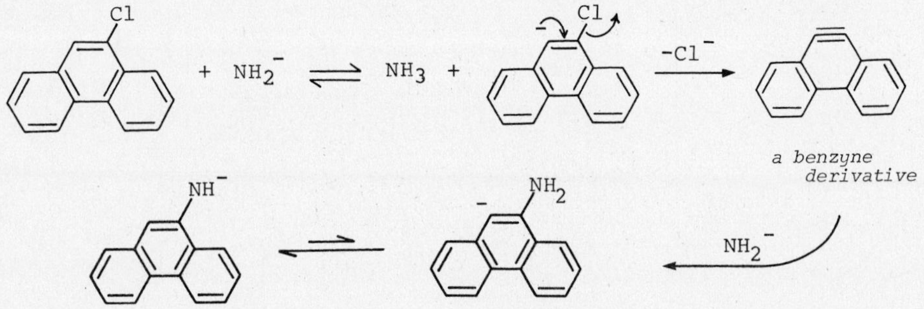

a benzyne derivative

(b)

A mixture of two isomers is obtained.

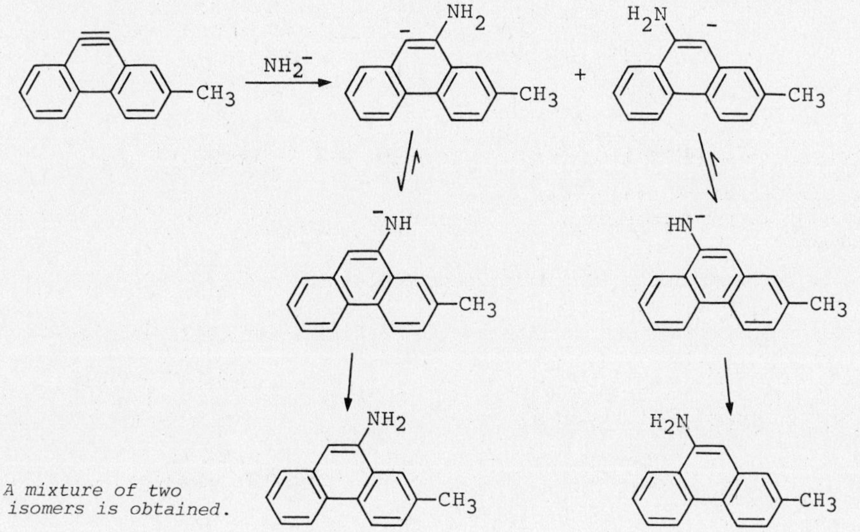

18.

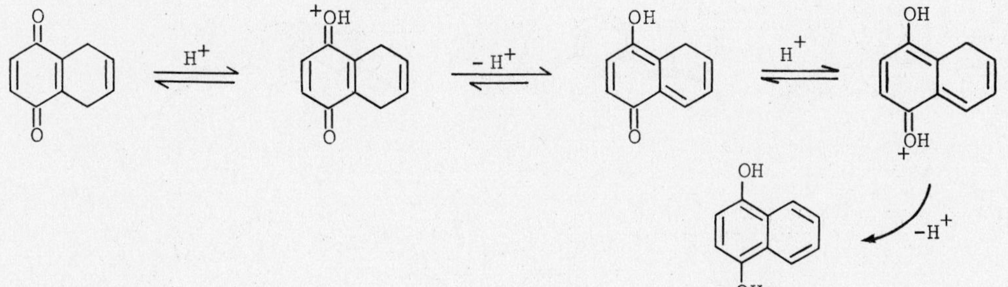

19. 1,2-Naphthoquinone has one benzene ring. On reduction, a naphthalene ring is generated, with a consequent increase in resonance stabilization. 2,6-Naphthoquinone has no benzene ring. On reduction to naphthalene, the entire stabilization energy of the two aromatic rings is gained.

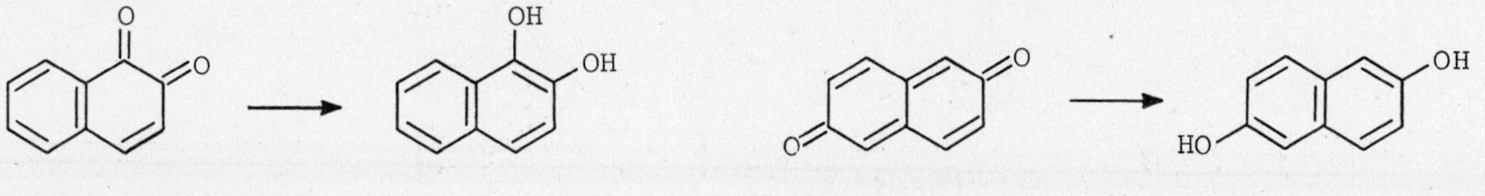

1,2-naphthoquinone

2,6-naphthoquinone (no benzene conjugation)

These relationships may be summarized by the following energy diagram:

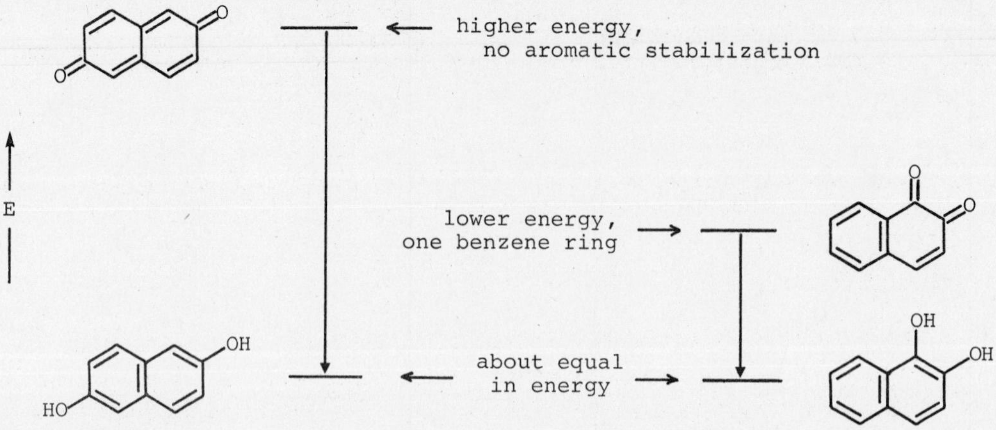

20. Steganone and isosteganone differ in their conformation about the biphenyl bond:

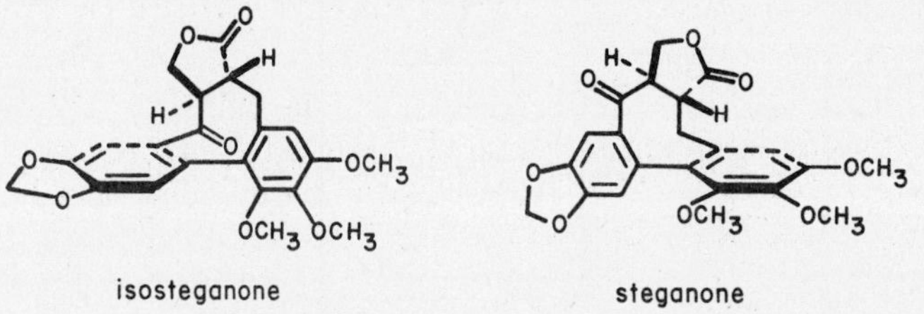

isosteganone   steganone

21. Removal of the bridgehead proton from triptycene places the negative charge in an orbital that cannot overlap with any of the p-orbitals of the aromatic rings. It lies in the nodal plane of all of the π-systems, and so receives no stabilization by resonance:

22.

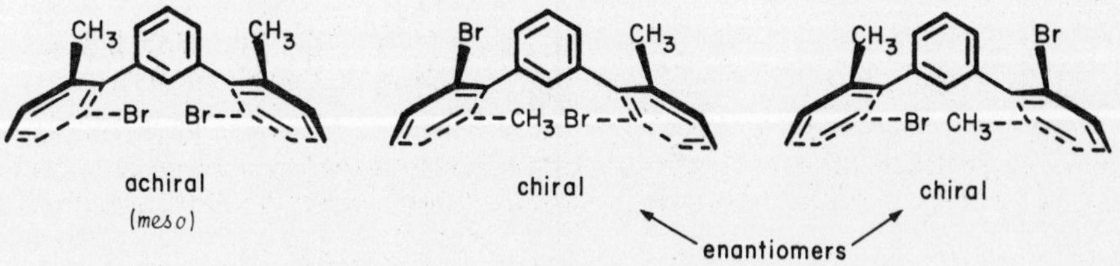

achiral   chiral   chiral
(*meso*)

enantiomers

23.

all except
this structure
are equivalent

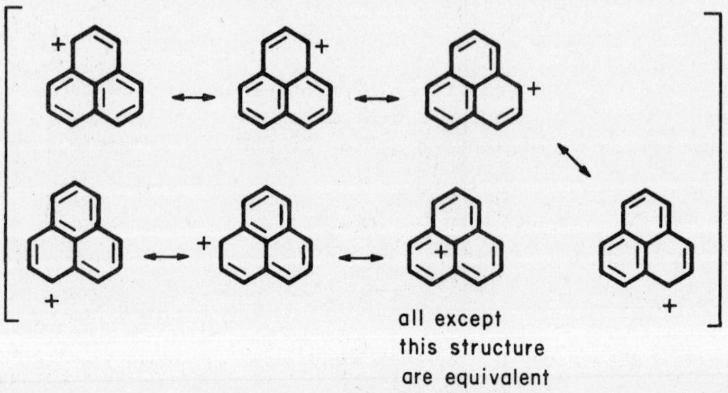

Substitution at the 1-position of
pyrene results in the formation
of a perinaphthenyl-like cation:

perinaphthenyl-like system

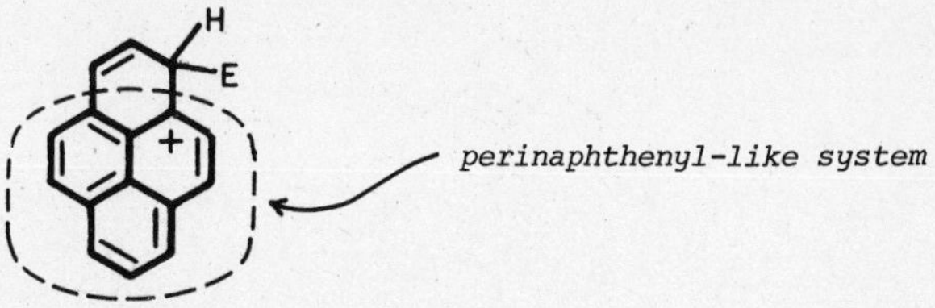

24. Oxidation by vanadium pentoxide involves electrophilic attack on the aromatic ring, hence it
occurs at the ring with the highest electron density.

30.F   Supplementary Problems

S1.   Write the structure of each of the following compounds.

(a) 5-dimethylamino-1-naphthalenesulfonic acid   (d) 1,4-phenanthraquinone

(b) 3-bromo-4,4'-dimethylbiphenyl   (e) benzo[a]chrysene

(c) 2,7-dinitrofluorene   (f) dibenzo[b,e]fluoranthene

S2.   Write the major product from each of the following reaction sequences:

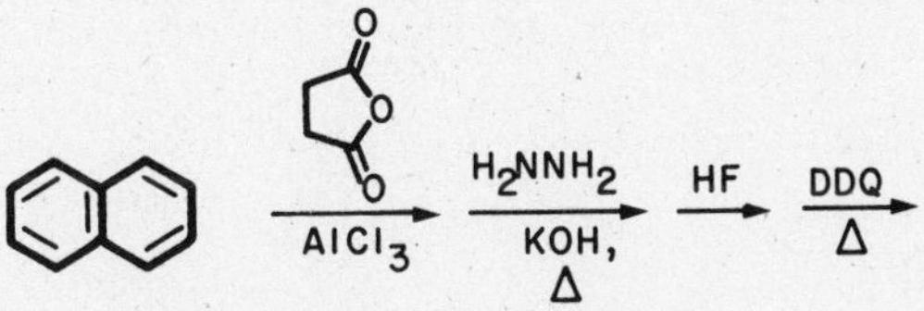

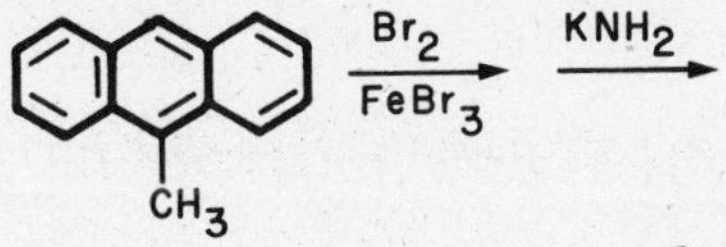

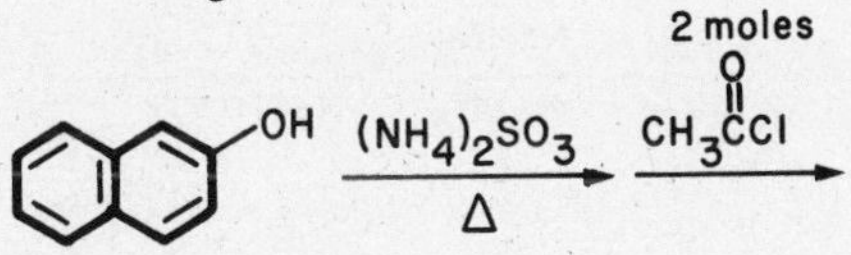

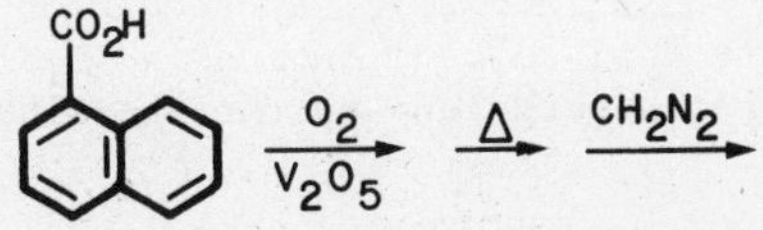

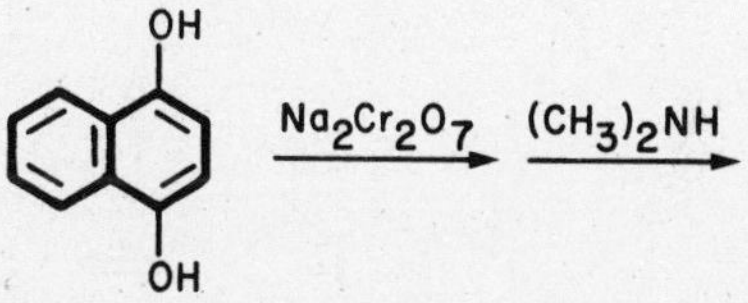

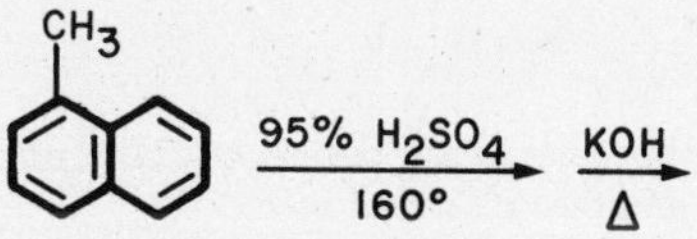

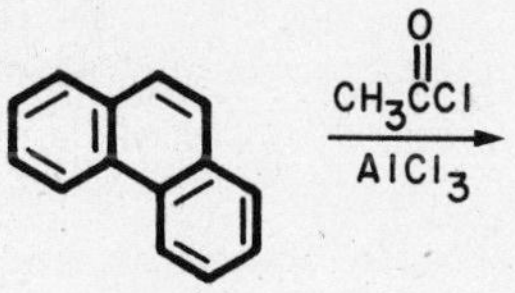

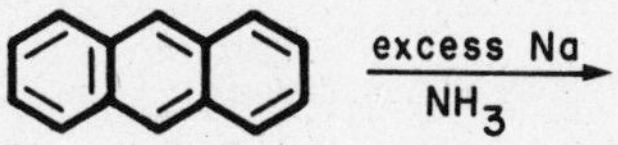

S3.   Outline a synthesis for each of the compounds illustrated below, starting from benzene,
naphthalene, or any monosubstituted benzene, and any other non-aromatic compounds.

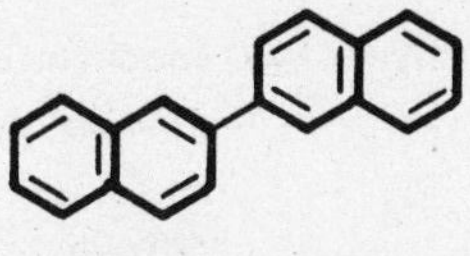

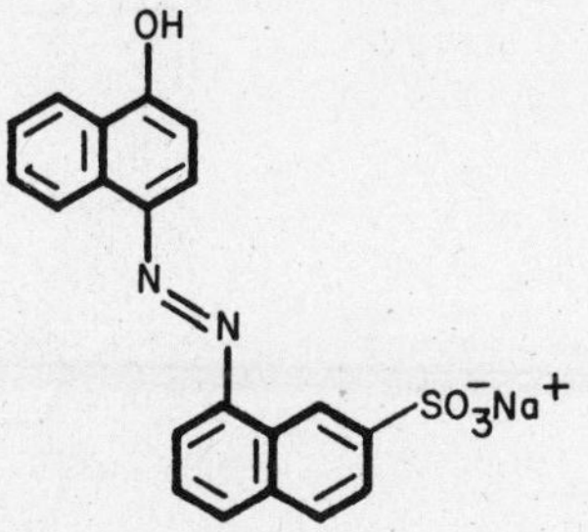

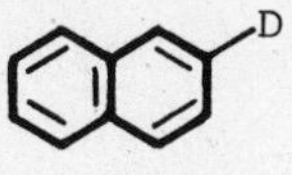

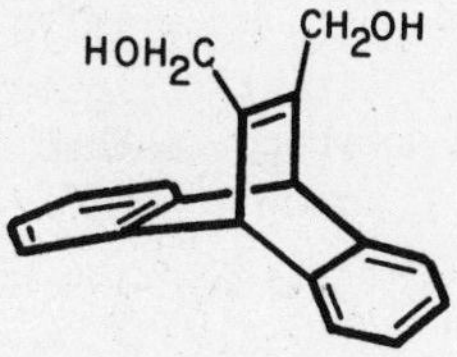

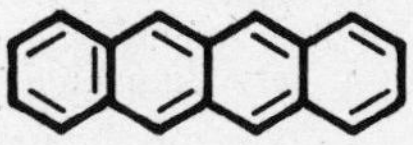

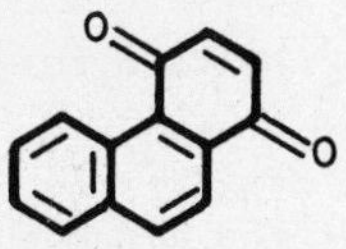

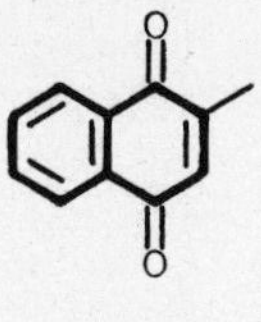

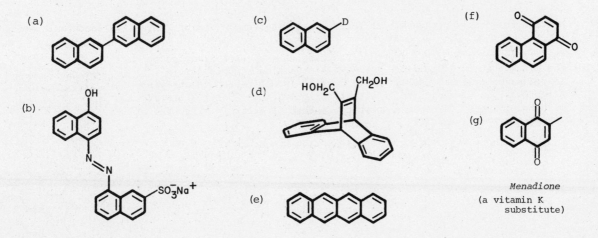

(h)

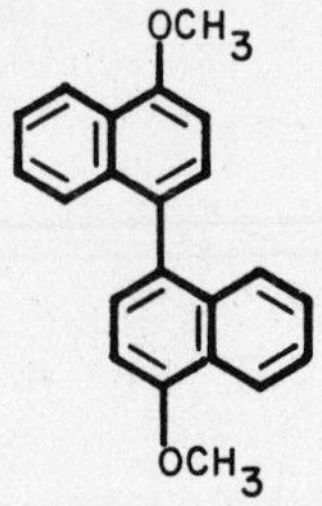

S4. Predict the positions of the following equilibria and justify your answers.

(a)

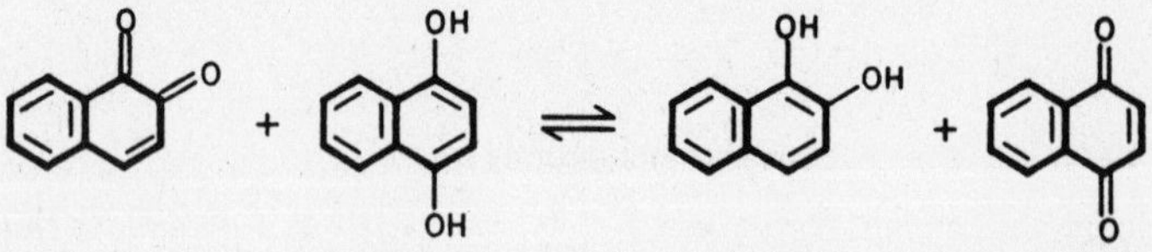

(b)

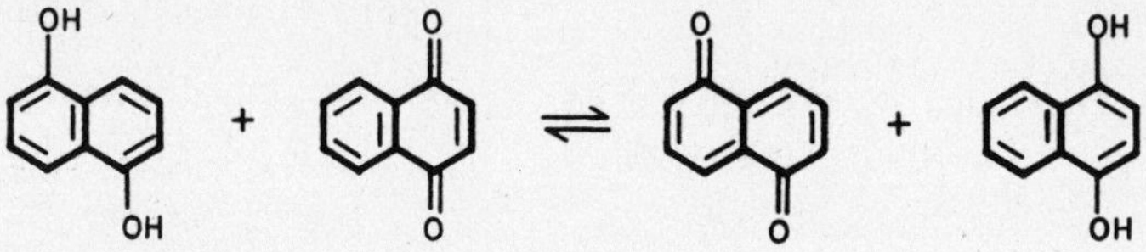

(c)

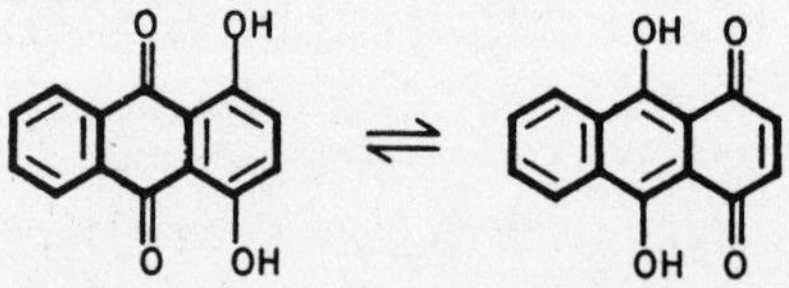

S5. Write the structures of the six intermediates which are produced during the following sequence of reactions.

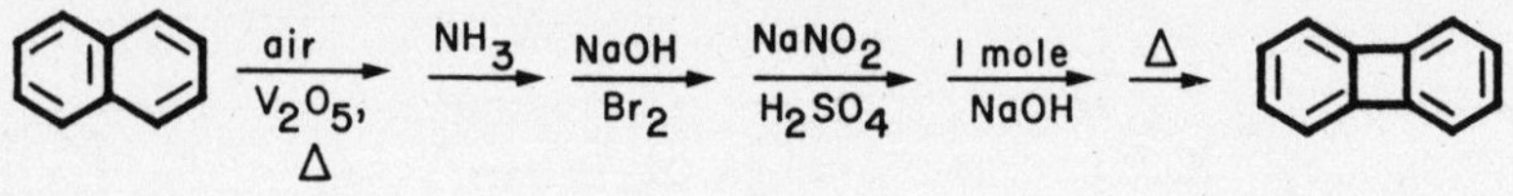

$$\text{air} \atop V_2O_5, \Delta \quad NH_3 \quad \frac{NaOH}{Br_2} \quad \frac{NaNO_2}{H_2SO_4} \quad \frac{1\ mole}{NaOH} \quad \Delta$$

S6. 6-Methoxy-1-tetralone is an important intermediate in an industrial synthesis of estrone, as well as a number of contraceptive drugs which are derived from estrone. Devise an efficient preparation of 6-methoxy-1-tetralone, using naphthalene as the starting material.

6-methoxy-1-tetralone: estrone:

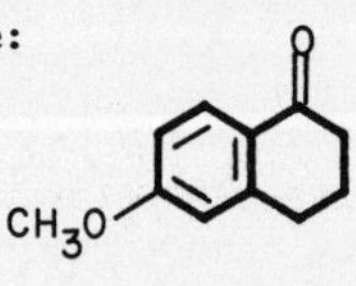

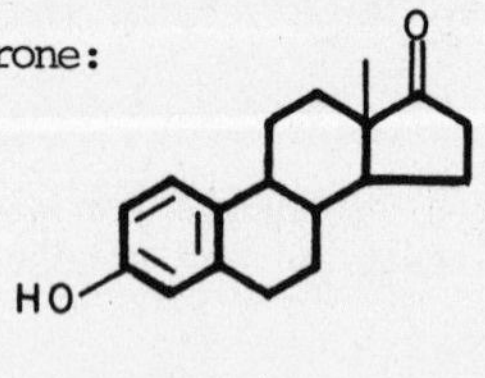

CH_3O— HO—

S7. Write a reasonable mechanism for the thermal decarboxylation of 2-hydroxy-1-naphthoic acid.

S8. The streptovaricins are a group of antibiotics which are produced by the microorganism *Streptomyces spectabilis*. Heating streptovaricin C in refluxing toluene results in its partial isomerization to atropiso-streptovaricin C. Reaction of either streptovaricin C or its isomer with $NaIO_4$ leads to the same compound. What is a likely structure of atropisostreptovaricin C?

(The structure of streptovaricin C is depicted at the right.)

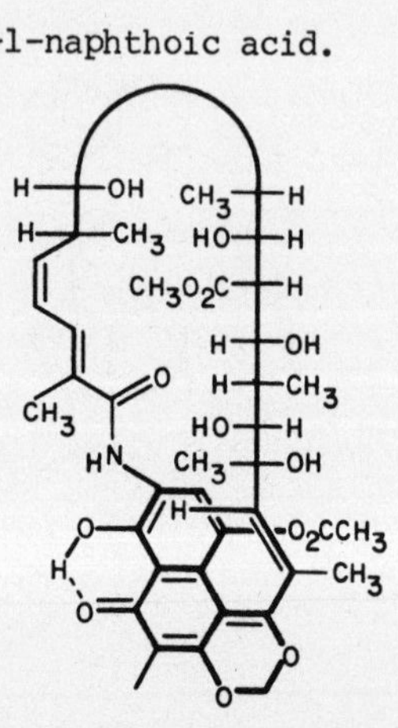

30.G   Answers to Supplementary Problems

S1.

(a)

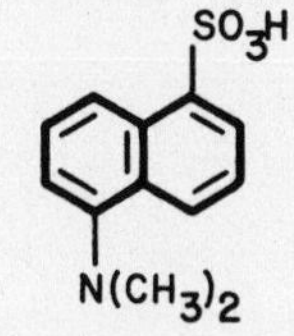

(b)

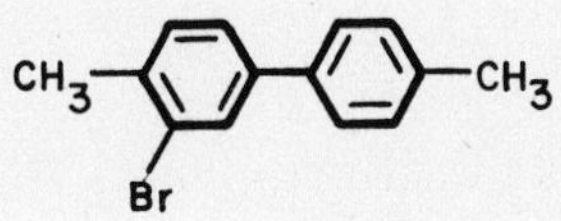

(c)

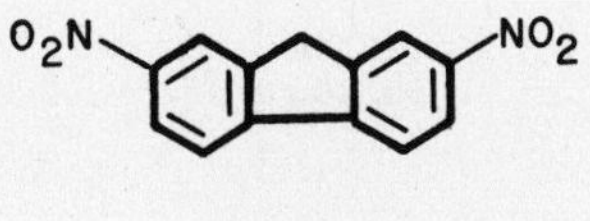

(d)

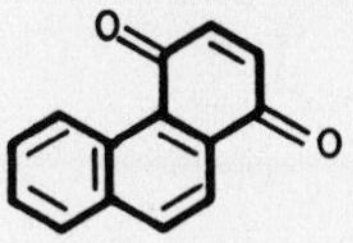

(e)

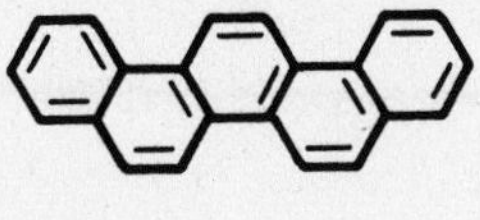

(f)

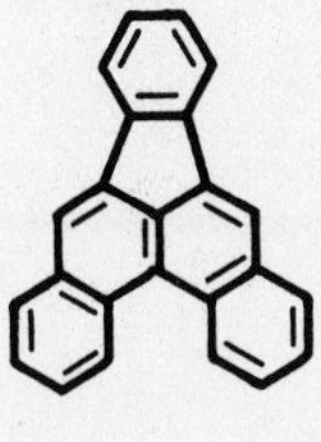

S2.

(a)

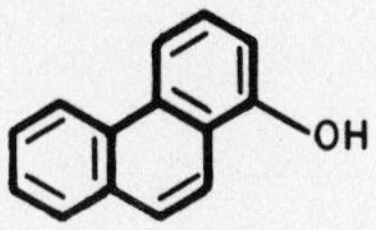

(b)

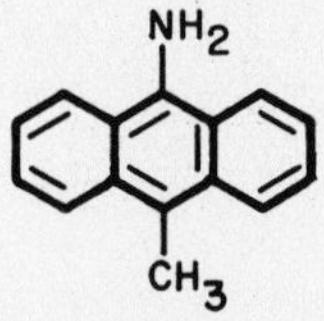

(c)

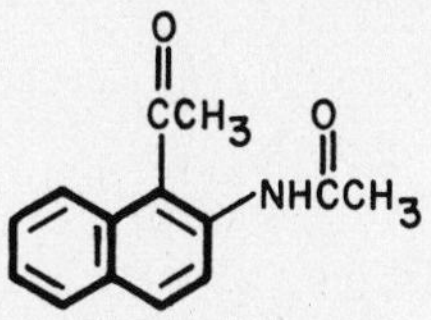

(d)

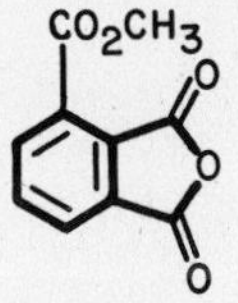

(e)   and

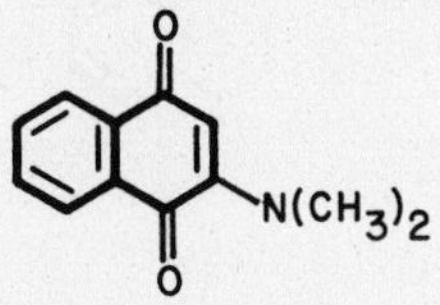

1/2 mole   1/2 mole

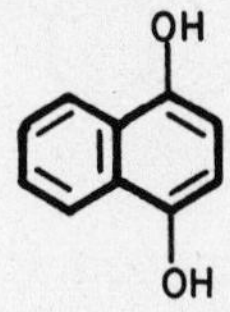

(see Problem #S10 in Chapter 26 of this Study Guide)

(f)

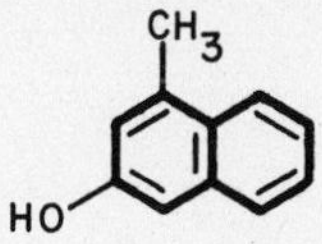

(g)

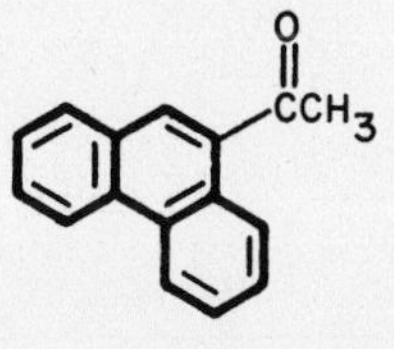

(h)

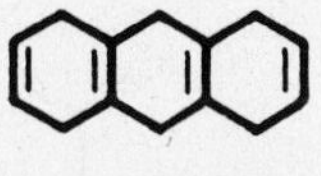

S3.

(a)

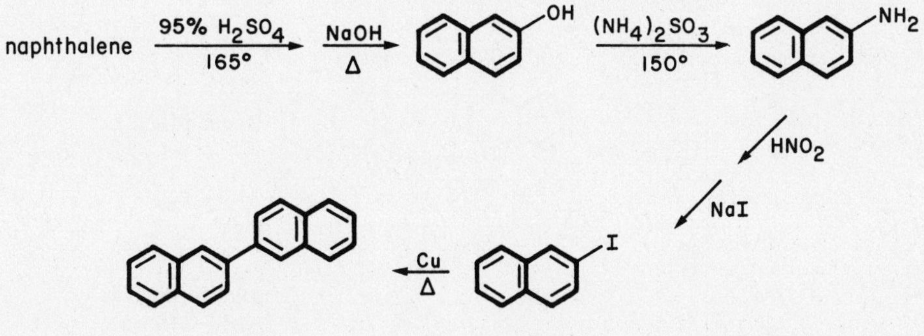

(b) naphthalene $\xrightarrow[165°]{95\%\ H_2SO_4}$ $\xrightarrow[H_2SO_4]{HNO_3}$ [1-nitronaphthalene-2-sulfonic acid] (separate from 2,5-isomer)

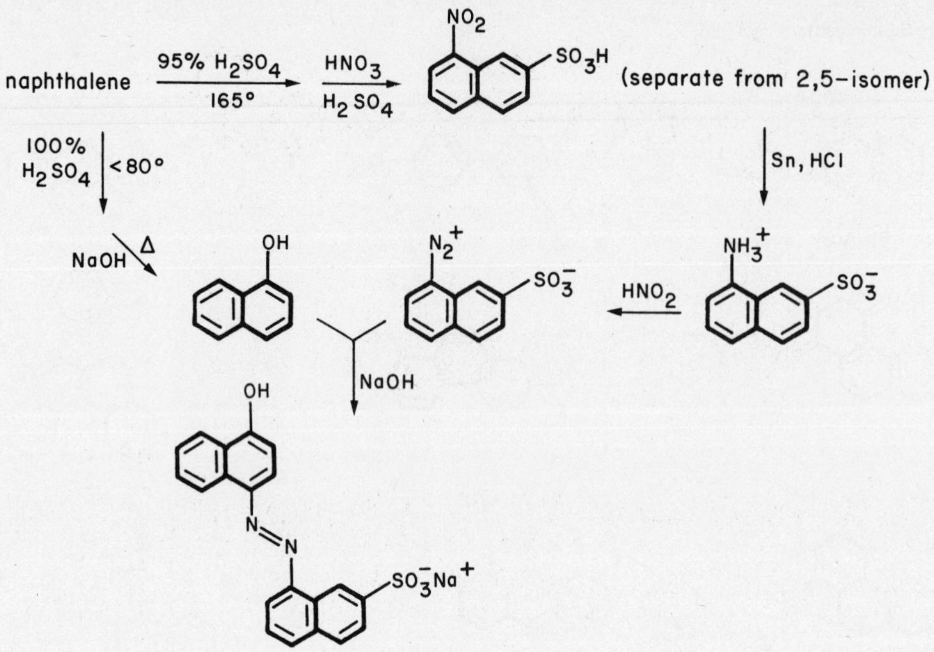

$\downarrow$ $\xrightarrow[<80°]{100\%\ H_2SO_4}$

$\xrightarrow[]{NaOH\ \Delta}$

[naphthol structure] [diazonium naphthalene sulfonate] $\xleftarrow{HNO_2}$ [amino naphthalene sulfonate] $\xleftarrow{Sn,\ HCl}$

$\downarrow NaOH$

[azo dye structure with OH and SO₃⁻Na⁺]

(c) [2-iodonaphthalene] (from (a)) $\xrightarrow{Mg}$ $\xrightarrow{D_2O}$ [2-deuteronaphthalene]

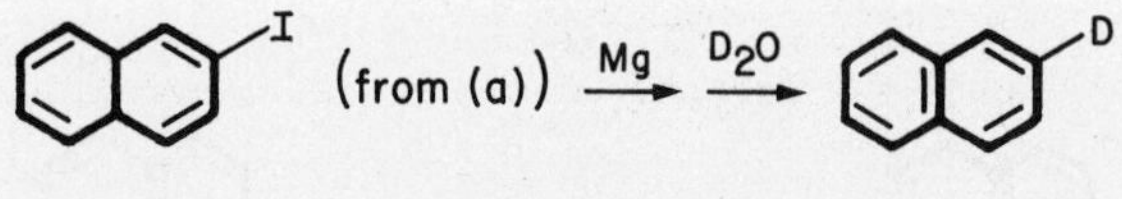

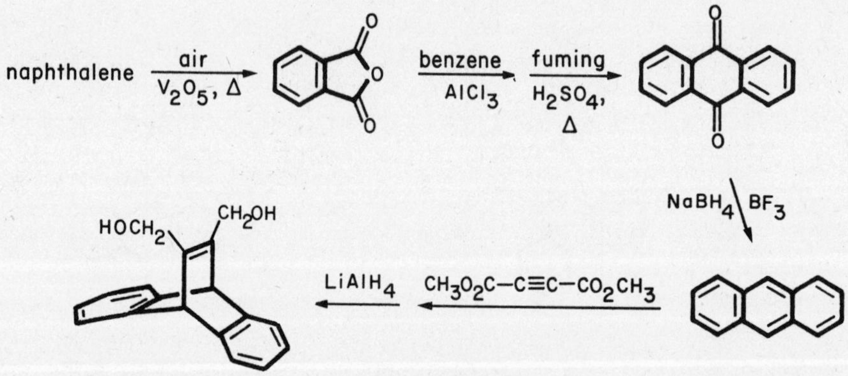

(d) naphthalene $\xrightarrow[V_2O_5,\ \Delta]{air}$ [phthalic anhydride] $\xrightarrow[AlCl_3]{benzene}$ $\xrightarrow[\Delta]{fuming\ H_2SO_4,}$ [anthraquinone]

$\downarrow NaBH_4\ BF_3$

[bridged diol structure with HOCH₂ and CH₂OH] $\xleftarrow{LiAlH_4}$ $\xleftarrow{CH_3O_2C-C\equiv C-CO_2CH_3}$ [anthracene]

(e) [1,4-dihydroxynaphthalene] (from (c)) $\xrightarrow[(CH_3)_2SO_4]{NaOH}$ [1,4-dimethoxynaphthalene] + [phthalic anhydride] (from (d))

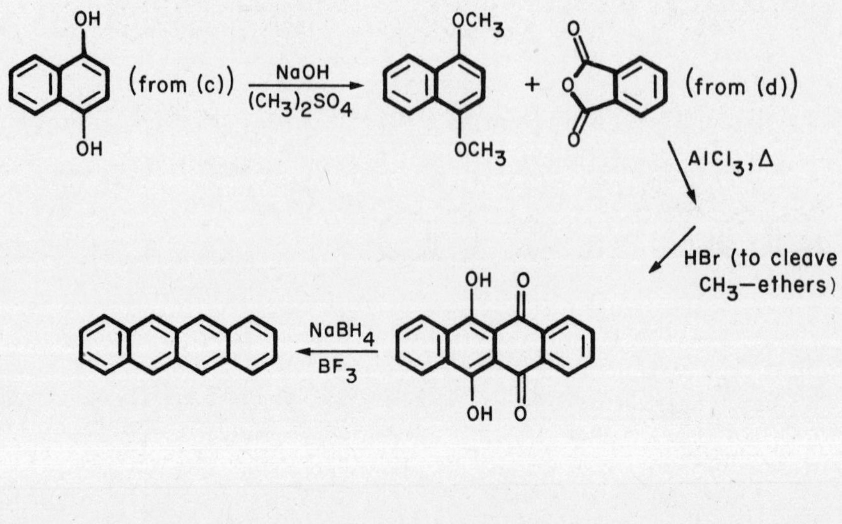

$\downarrow AlCl_3,\ \Delta$

$\downarrow$ HBr (to cleave CH₃–ethers)

[naphthacene/tetracene structure] $\xleftarrow[BF_3]{NaBH_4}$ [dihydroxy anthraquinone structure]

(f)

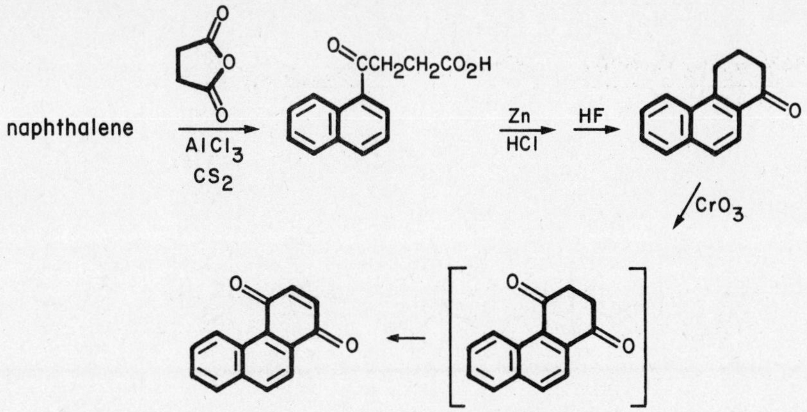

naphthalene $\xrightarrow[\text{CS}_2]{\text{AlCl}_3}$ O=CCH$_2$CH$_2$CO$_2$H $\xrightarrow[\text{HCl}]{\text{Zn}}$ HF $\xrightarrow{}$

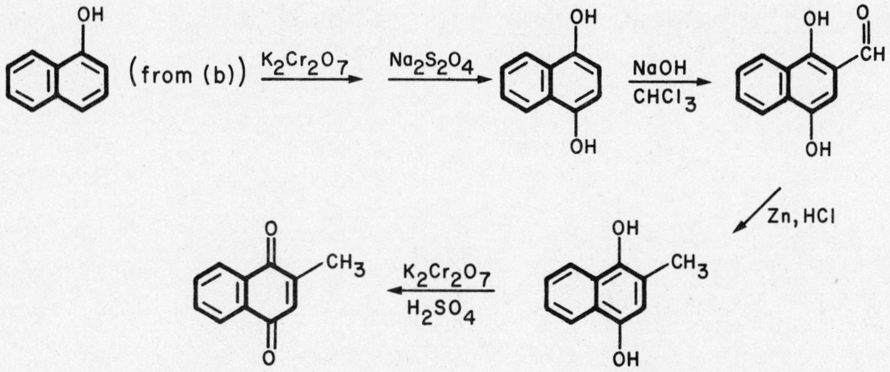

$\searrow$ CrO$_3$

(g)

OH (from (b)) $\xrightarrow{\text{K}_2\text{Cr}_2\text{O}_7}$ $\xrightarrow{\text{Na}_2\text{S}_2\text{O}_4}$ $\xrightarrow[\text{CHCl}_3]{\text{NaOH}}$

$\searrow$ Zn, HCl

$\xleftarrow[\text{H}_2\text{SO}_4]{\text{K}_2\text{Cr}_2\text{O}_7}$

(h)

naphthalene $\xrightarrow[\text{H}_2\text{SO}_4]{\text{HNO}_3}$ $\xrightarrow[\text{KOH}]{\begin{array}{c}\text{H}_2\text{NNH}_2\\ \text{Ru/C}\end{array}}$ $\xrightarrow[\Delta]{\text{H}^+}$ $\xrightarrow[\Delta]{\begin{array}{c}\text{1. HNO}_2\\ \text{2. CH}_3\text{OH}\end{array}}$

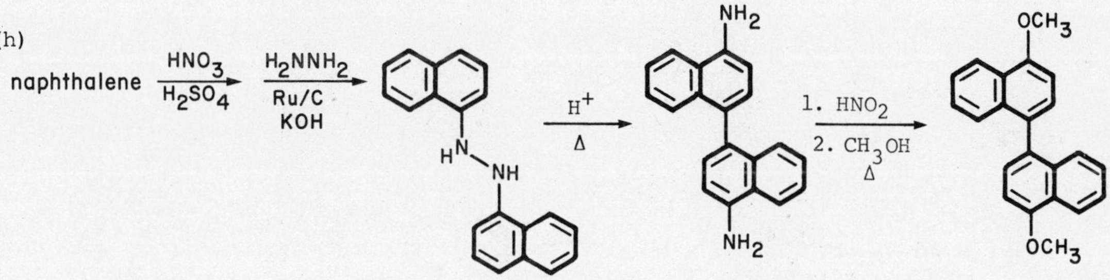

S4.   (a) favors

+

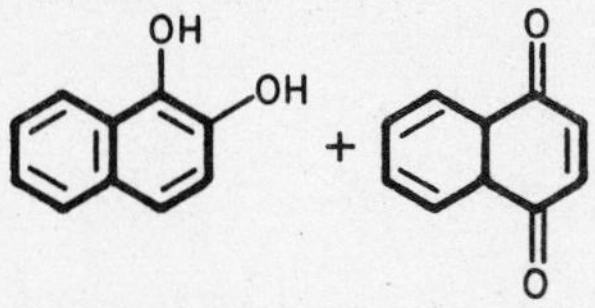

1,2-Naphthoquinone and 1,2-benzoquinone both have higher reduction potentials than their 1,4-isomers (see Table 30.2) because of unfavorable interaction between their aligned dipoles:

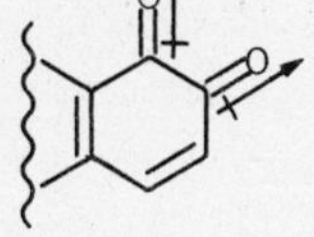

(b) favors

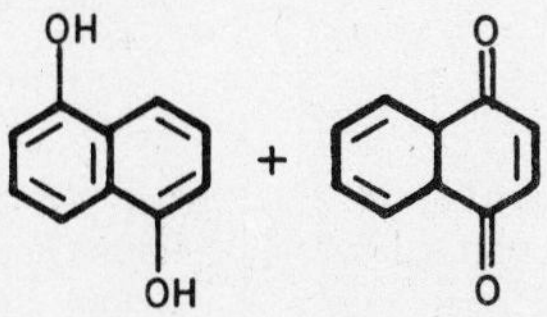

+

See answer to problem #19 of this chapter.

(c) favors

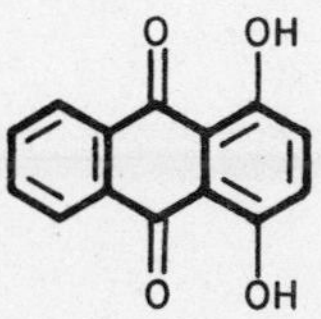

This structure has the aromatic stabilization of the two benzene rings, which is greater than the stabilization of the naphthalene system present in the 1,4-quinone tautomer.

S5.

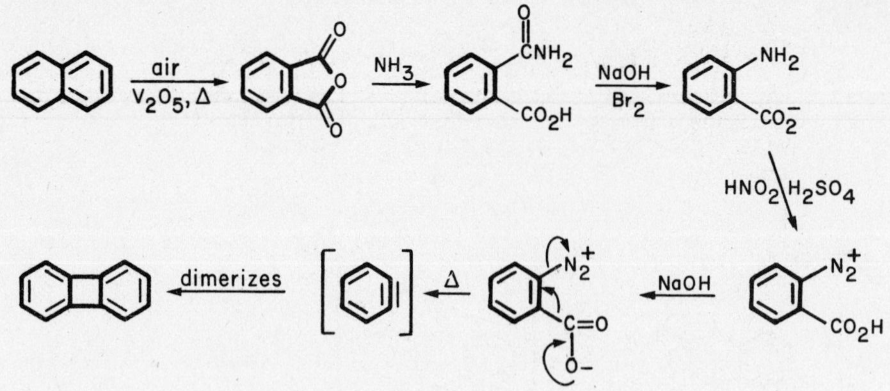

S6.

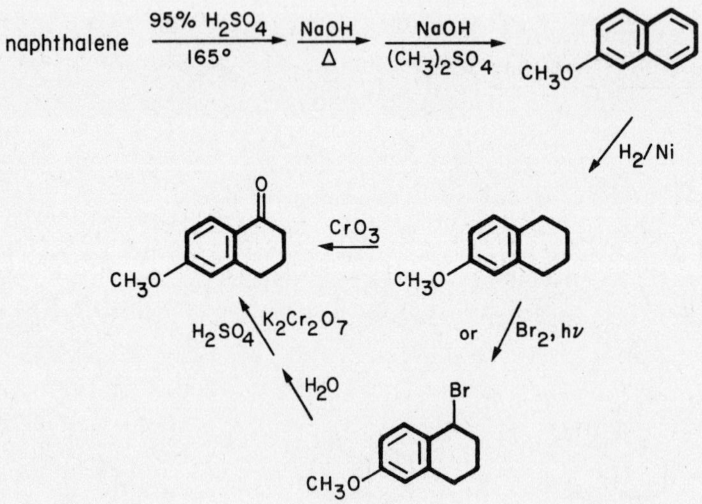

S7.

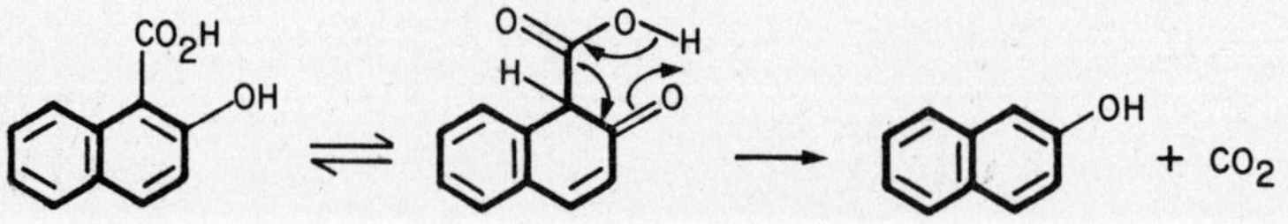

S8. The aromatic ring system and the highly-substituted bridging chain of streptovaricin C can be represented schematically, as illustrated below:

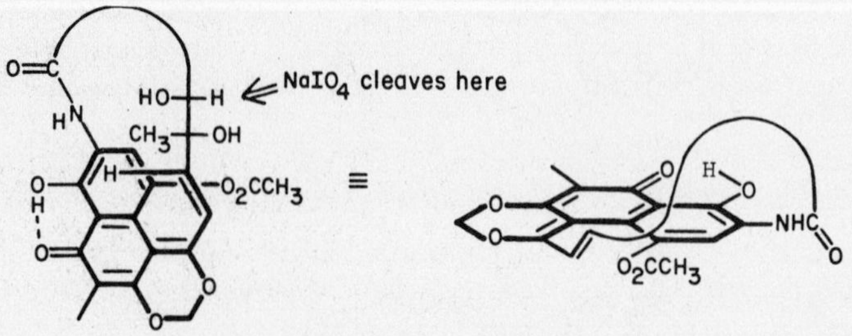

This compound reacts with NaIO$_4$ only at the vicinal diol position indicated at the left above, to cleave the bridging chain. Because atropisostreptovaricin gives the same product upon cleavage by NaIO$_4$, it can differ only in conformation, and most likely is the "ring-flipped" conformer drawn below:

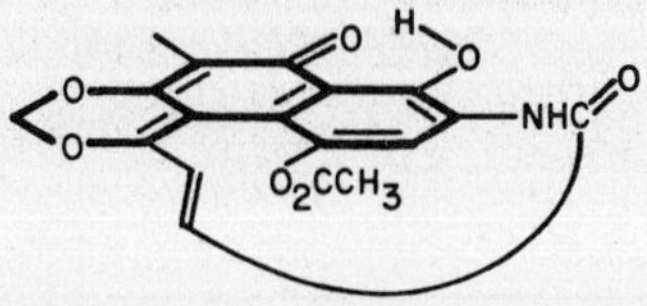

31. HETEROCYCLIC COMPOUNDS

31.A and 31.B   Chapter Outline and Reactions Discussed

NOTE: *since this Chapter is primarily an outline of reactions, there does not seem to be any point in separating Parts A. and B. in this Chapter of the Study Guide.*

31.1   Introduction

definition of heterocycles   (-iran (3), -etan (4), -olan (5), -ane (6))
aza- (N), oxa- (O), thia- (S)

31.2   Non-aromatic Heterocycles

A. Nomenclature

B. Three-Membered Rings

epoxides = oxiranes (see Sections 10.11.A and 11.6.E)

aziridines via intramolecular alkylation:

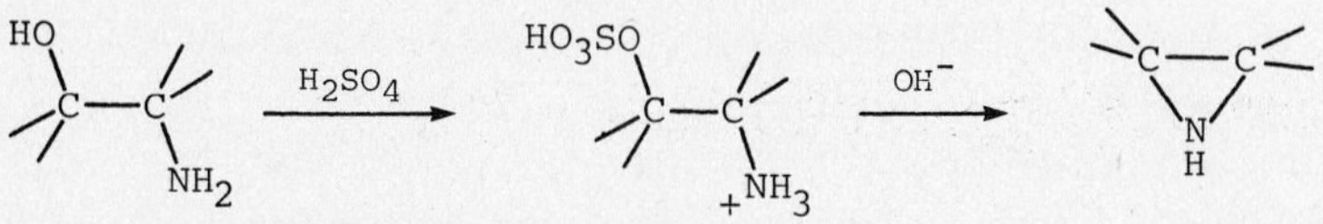

aziridines via iodoisocyanates:

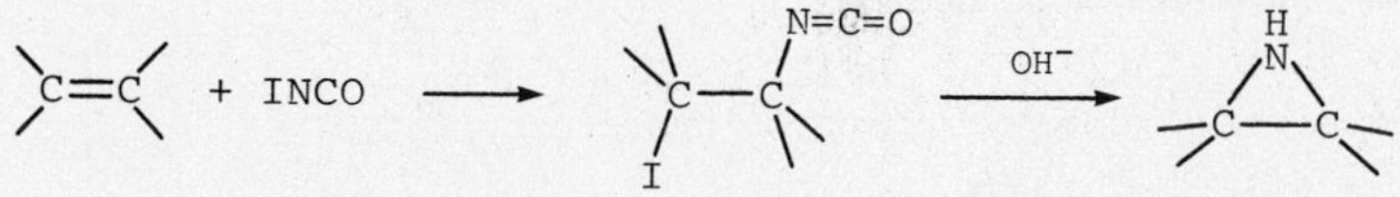

thiiranes from epoxides:

reactions: ring opening

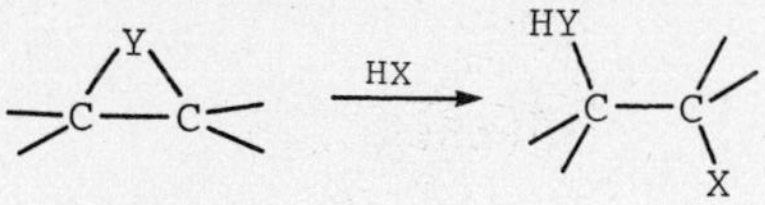

X = halogen, OR;   Y = O, S, NR'

C. Four-Membered Rings

oxetane, azetidine, thietane
via ring closure:

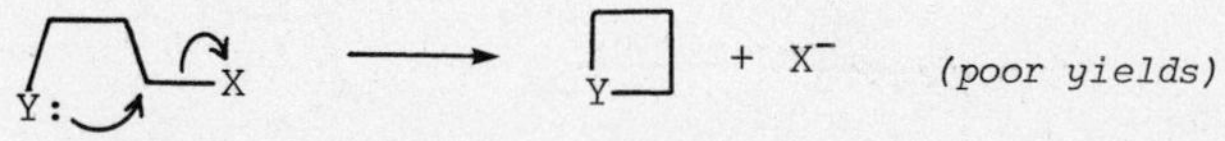

X = good leaving group; Y: = O⁻, S⁻, or NHR

β-lactones and β-lactams via cycloaddition:

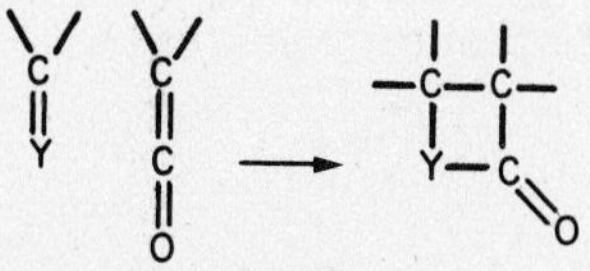

Y = O or NR

ring-opening reactions; similar to three-membered rings

537

D. Five- and Six-Membered Rings
    by hydrogenation of the aromatic heterocycles (furan, pyrrole):
    e.g.,

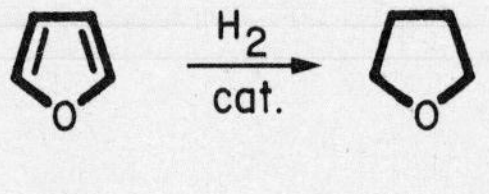

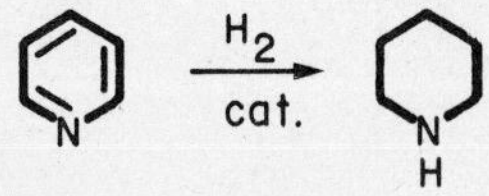

    nucleophilic ring closure:

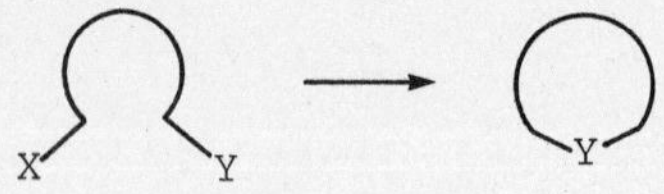

31.3 <u>Furan, Pyrrole, and Thiophene</u>

A. Structure and Properties
    use of lone pair electrons of heteroatom to attain aromatic six-π-electron system
    effect of aromaticity on pK_a
    position of protonation of pyrrole

B. Synthesis
    furan derivatives from dehydration of pentoses   (industrial synthesis)
    pyrrole from distillation of coal-tar
    thiophene from pyrolysis of butenes and sulfur   (industrial synthesis)
    Paal-Knorr synthesis:

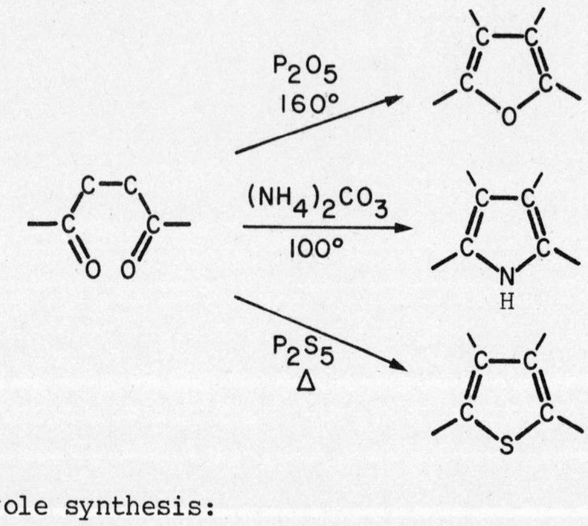

    Knorr pyrrole synthesis:

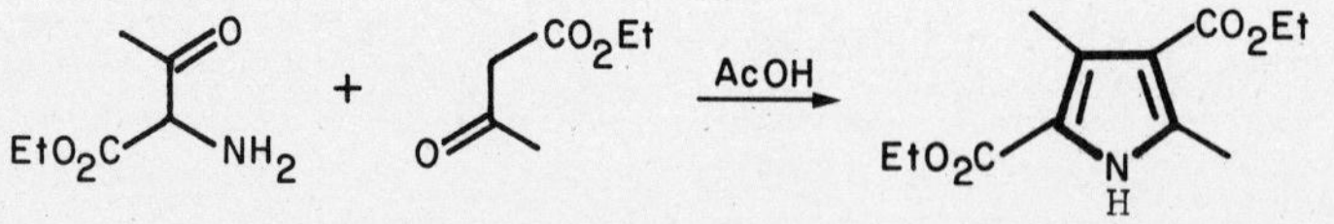

C. Reactions
    reactivity toward electrophiles: pyrrole > furan > thiophene >> benzene
    electrophilic aromatic substitution oriented toward 2-positions
    hydrolysis (primarily of furans):

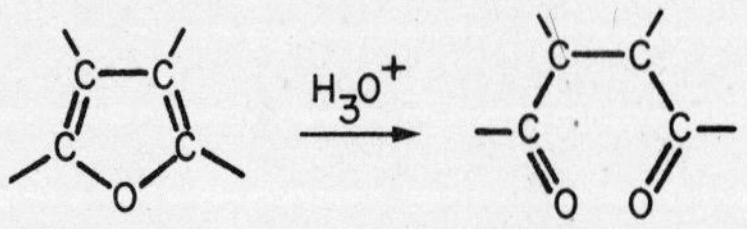

31.4 <u>Condensed Furans, Pyrroles, and Thiophenes</u>

A. Structure and Nomenclature
    indole

B. Synthesis
    Fischer indole synthesis:

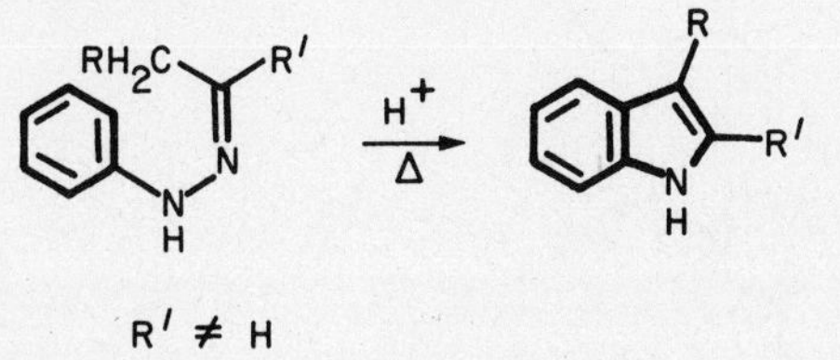

(use R = H, R' = COOH, then decarboxylate
to obtain indole itself)

R' ≠ H

C. Reactions
    electrophilic aromatic substitution:

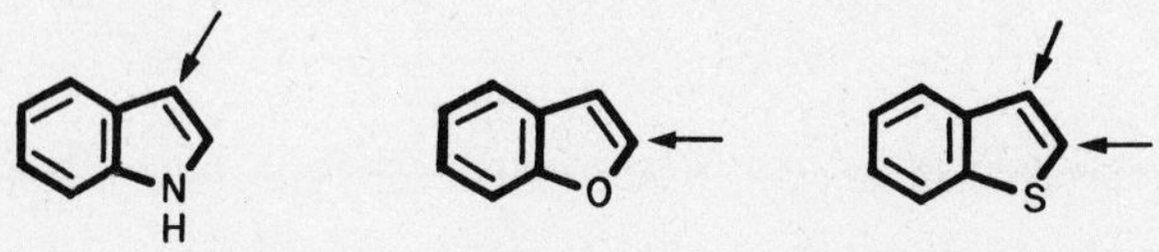

31.5 <u>Azoles</u>

A. Structure and Nomenclature
    oxazole, imidazole, thiazole
    isoxazole, pyrazole, isothiazole
    basicity
    occurrence in nature

B. Synthesis
    isoxazoles and pyrazoles from 1,3-dicarbonyl compounds:

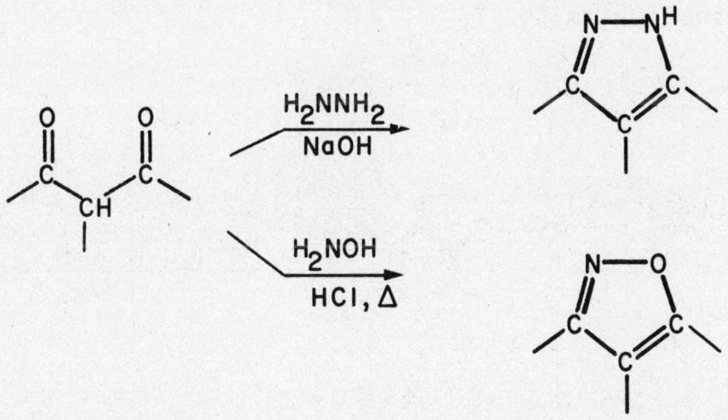

isoxazoles via nitrile oxide-1,3-dipolar cycloaddition:

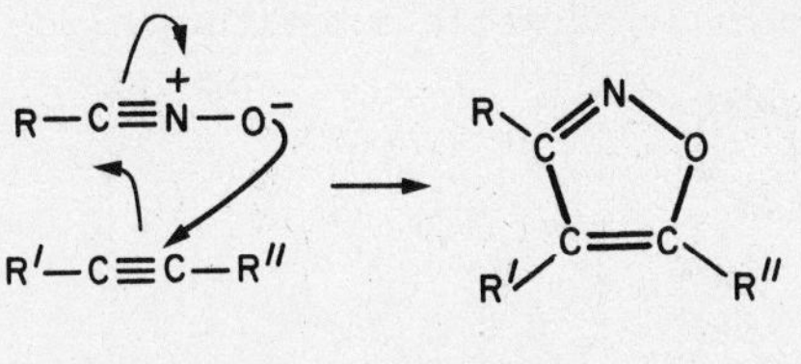

pyrazoles via diazomethane-1,3-dipolar cycloaddition:

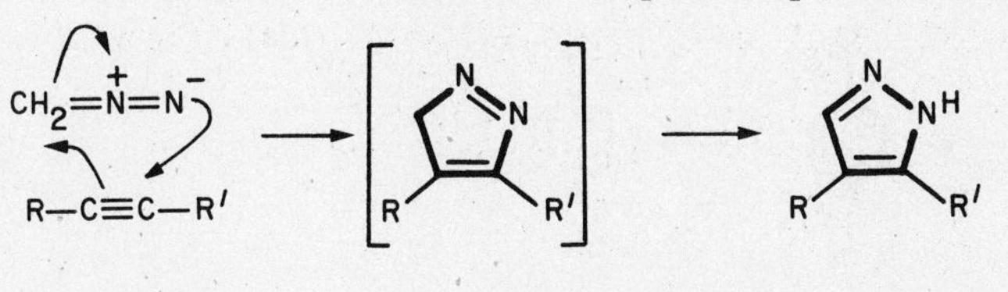

Paal-Knorr-like cyclization:

$$\begin{array}{c} \text{H}_2\text{SO}_4 \\ \Delta \end{array}$$

$$\begin{array}{c} \text{NH}_4\text{OAc} \\ \Delta \end{array}$$

$$\begin{array}{c} \text{P}_2\text{S}_5 \\ \Delta \end{array}$$

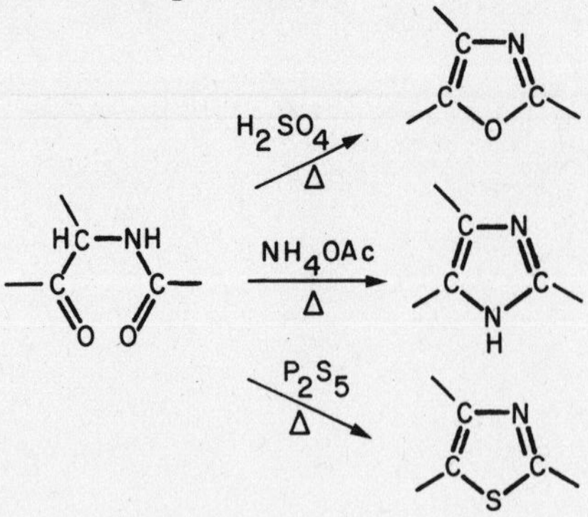

C. Reactions

less reactive toward electrophilic aromatic substitution than the monohetero analogs:

pyrazole > isothiazole > isoxazole

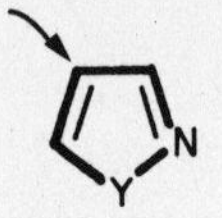

Y = O, S, NH

substitution occurs at C-4

imidazole > thiazole > oxazole

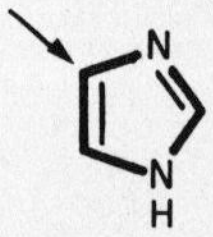

31.6 Pyridine

A. Structure and Physical Properties

basicity (pK_a of pyridinium ion is 5.2)

B. Synthesis

Hantzsch pyridine synthesis:

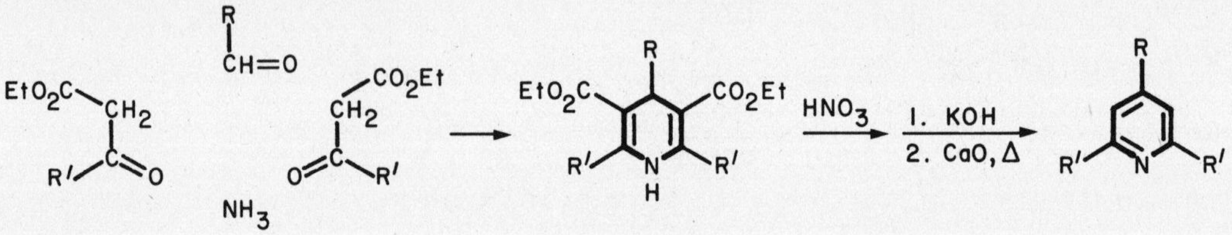

C. Reactions

as a base and nucleophile, and as solvent

resistant to oxidation and electrophilic aromatic substitution:

e.g.,

$$\begin{array}{c} \text{KNO}_3, \text{HNO}_3 \\ \hline \text{H}_2\text{SO}_4, \text{Fe} \\ \underline{\underline{300°\text{C}}} \end{array}$$ 22%

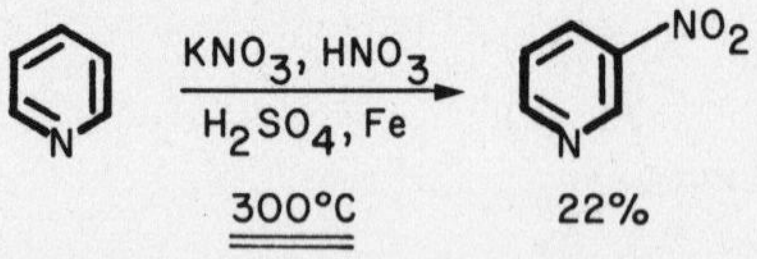

substitution facilitated by activating groups or by N-oxide:

$$\begin{array}{c} \text{HNO}_3 \\ \hline \text{H}_2\text{SO}_4 \end{array}$$ $$\xrightarrow{\text{PCl}_3}$$

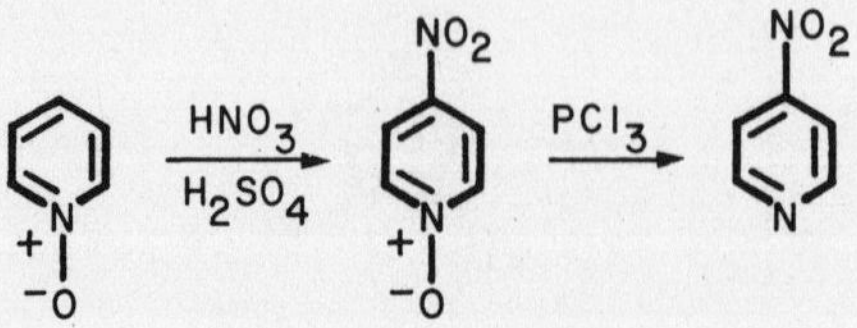

nucleophilic substitution; Chichibabin reaction:

$$\xrightarrow{\text{NaNH}_2}$$ + H$_2$

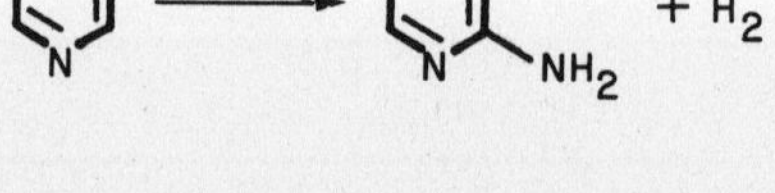

diazotization of aminopyridines to make pyridones:

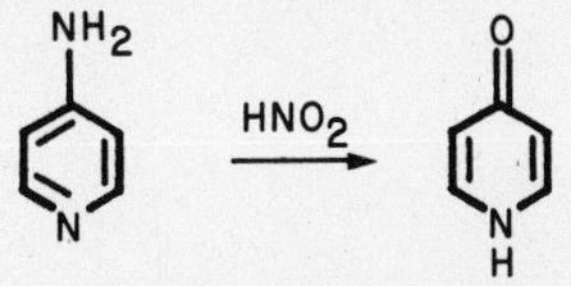

(major tautomer)

acidity of α- and γ-alkyl groups:

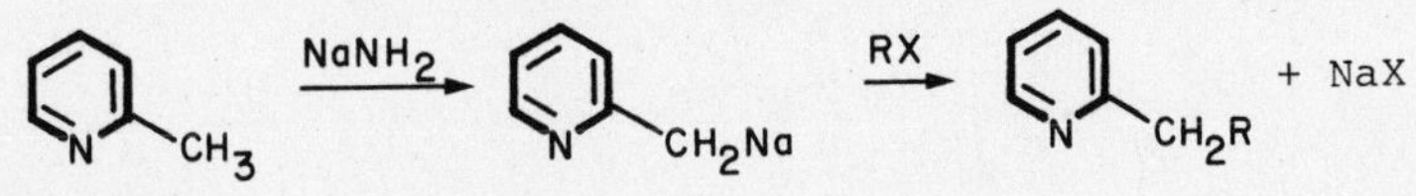

+ NaX

31.7 Quinoline and Isoquinoline

A. Structure and Nomenclature

B. Synthesis

Skraup reaction:

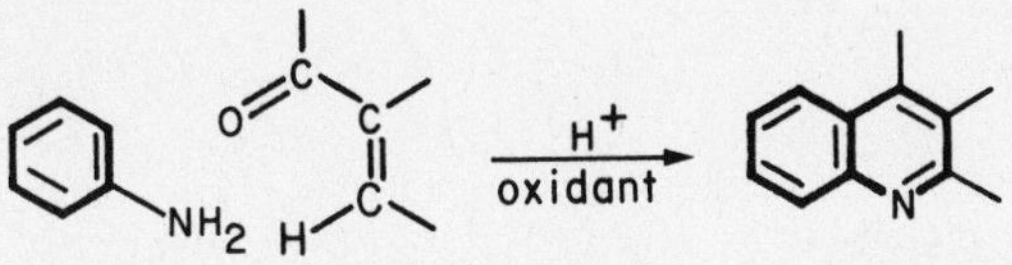

(in Döbner-Miller reaction, the unsaturated carbonyl component is synthesized in situ)

Friedländer synthesis:

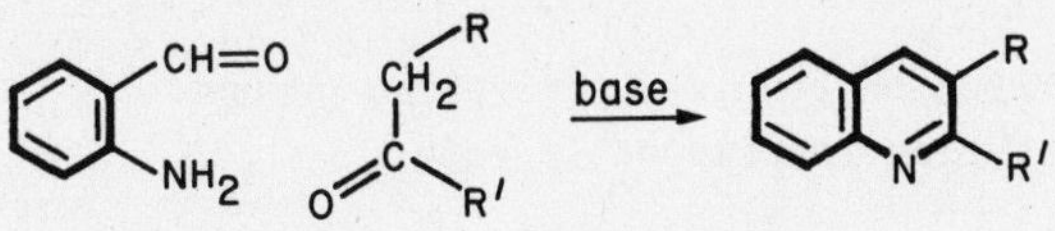

Bischler-Napieralski synthesis:

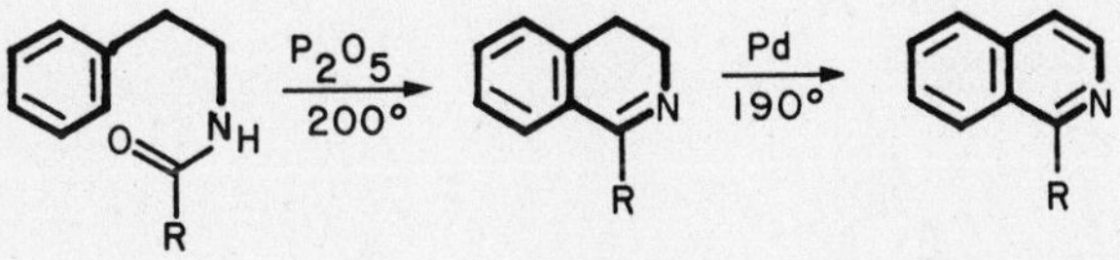

C. Reactions

electrophilic aromatic substitution (avoids pyridine ring):

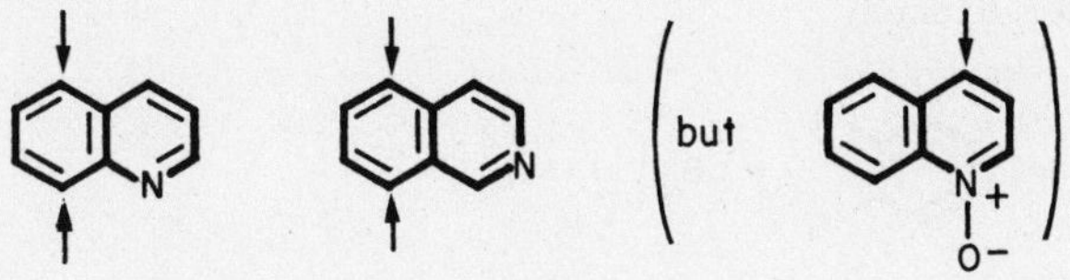

(but)

nucleophilic aromatic substitution:

acidity of alkyl derivatives:

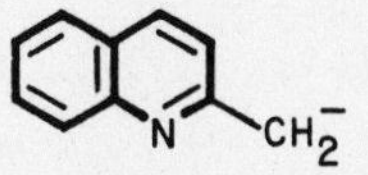

31.8 Diazines

A. Structure and Occurrence

pyridazine, pyrimidine, pyrazine

purine

nucleic acid components

B. Synthesis

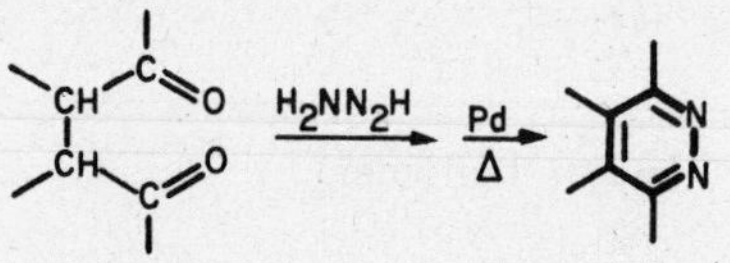

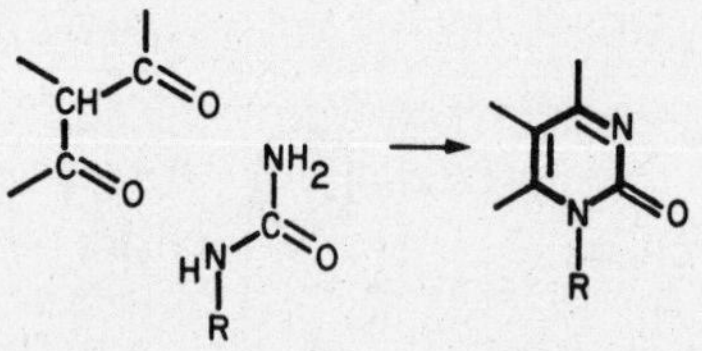

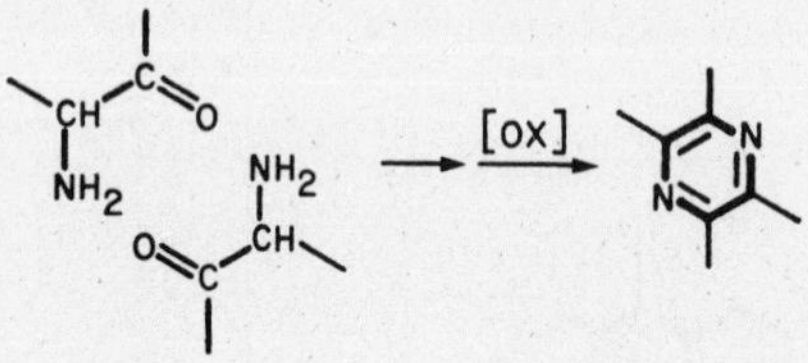

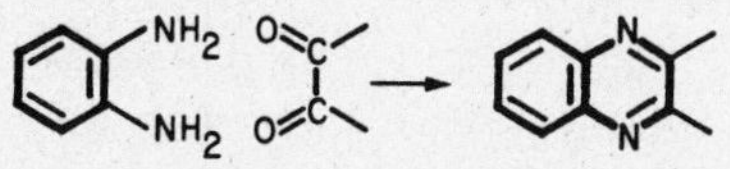

C. Reactions

electrophilic aromatic substitution requires activating groups
nucleophilic aromatic substitution is reasonably easy

31.9 Pyrones and Pyrylium Salts

A. Pyrones

α-pyrone from pyrolysis of malic acid

γ-pyrones from 1,3,5-triketones:

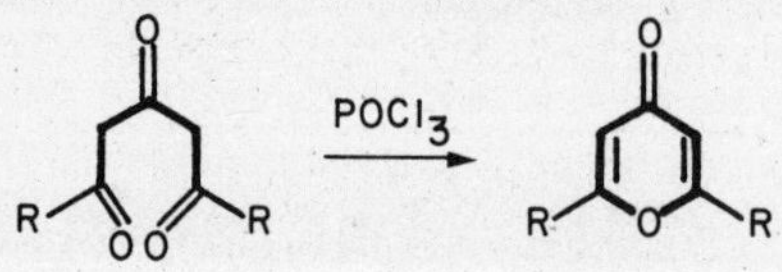

α-pyrones as Diels-Alder dienes:

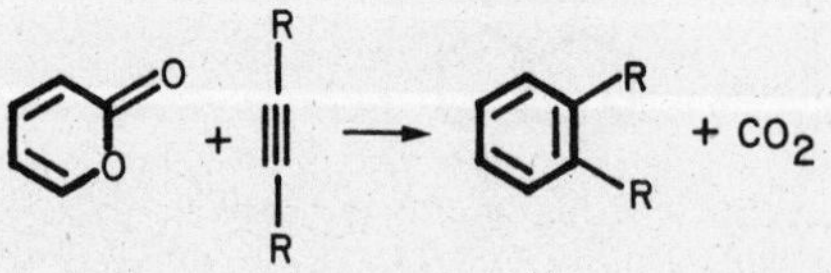

pyridones from γ-pyrones:

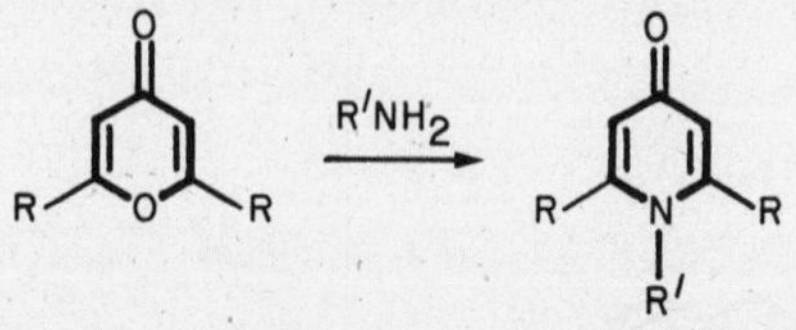

basicity of pyrones:

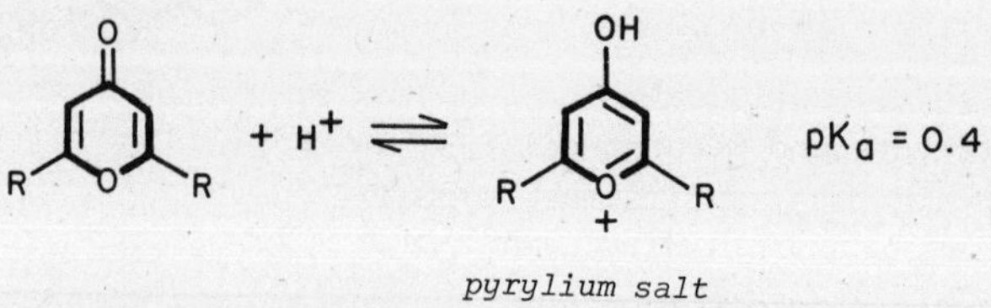

$pK_a = 0.4$

pyrylium salt

B. Pyrylium Salts

from pyrones and a Grignard reagent:

$$\text{(pyrone)} \xrightarrow{R'MgBr} \xrightarrow{H^+} \text{(pyrylium salt)}$$

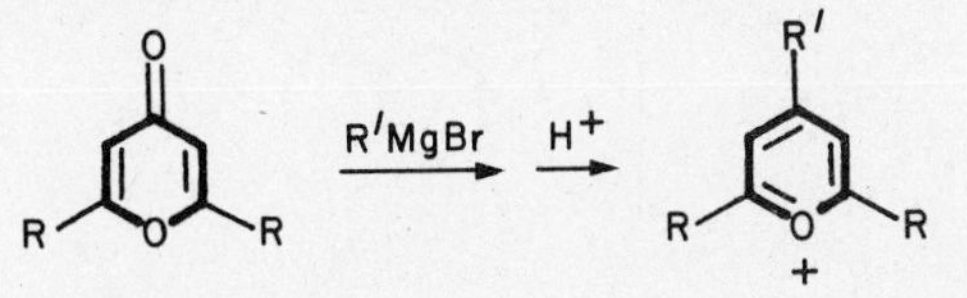

from enone condensation:

e.g.,

$$(CH_3)_2C=CHCCH_3 + 2\,Ac_2O \xrightarrow{H^+} \text{(trimethylpyrylium salt)}$$

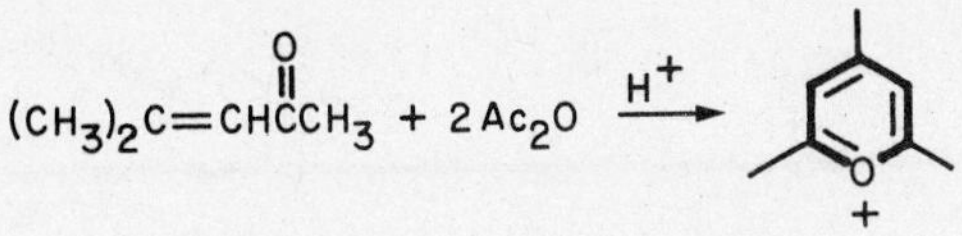

reactions with nucleophiles:

$$\text{(pyrylium salt)} + \ ^-CH_2NO_2 \longrightarrow \text{(nitromethyl aromatic, NO_2)}$$

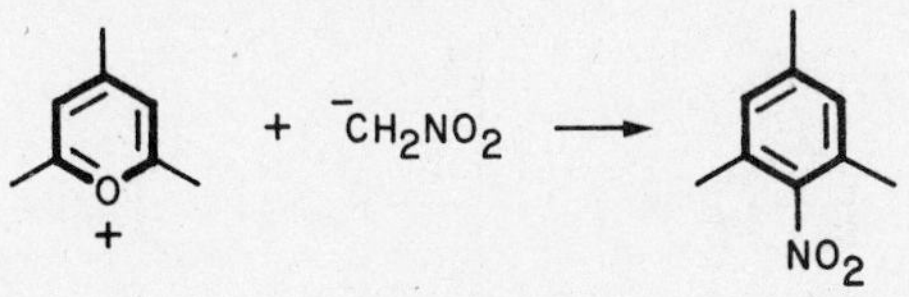

31.C   Important Concepts and Hints

There is an astounding amount of material presented in this chapter on heterocyclic compounds. That the chapter is organized as it is reflects both your chemical sophistication as the end of your organic course approaches ("you know more so you can learn more") and the importance and breadth of the field of heterocyclic chemistry itself. Many biologically significant compounds, both naturally-occurring and man-made, are heterocycles, and most organic chemists encounter heterocyclic compounds either directly or indirectly during the course of their research.

The subject is divided between saturated and unsaturated (usually aromatic) heterocycles. The syntheses and reactions of the saturated heterocycles are almost the same as those of acyclic compounds which have the same functional groups. However, special syntheses and greater reactivity are seen for the three- and four-membered ring compounds. The saturated rings themselves are prepared either by hydrogenation of the aromatic analogs or by intramolecular alkylation reactions. (Peracid epoxidation is an exception.)

The classification of aromatic heterocycles encompasses a vast range of compounds, including five- and six-membered and polycyclic systems, and many combinations and orientations of one or more nitrogens, oxygens, and sulfurs (and others!). There is a correspondingly large number of methods for the synthesis of these compounds. A few can be made by cycloaddition reactions, but by far the greatest number arise from condensation reactions. The single most important characteristic of the condensation reactions that produce unsaturated heterocycles is the following: the ring carbons which are directly attached to the heteroatom were originally either carbonyl carbons or were adjacent to carbonyl carbons. To convince yourself of this fact, go through the chapter outline preceding this section of the Study Guide and look for **exceptions** to this generalization. In a sense, the synthesis of aromatic heterocycles is simply another aspect of the chemistry of carbonyl compounds.

31.D   Answers to Exercises

31.1   (a)

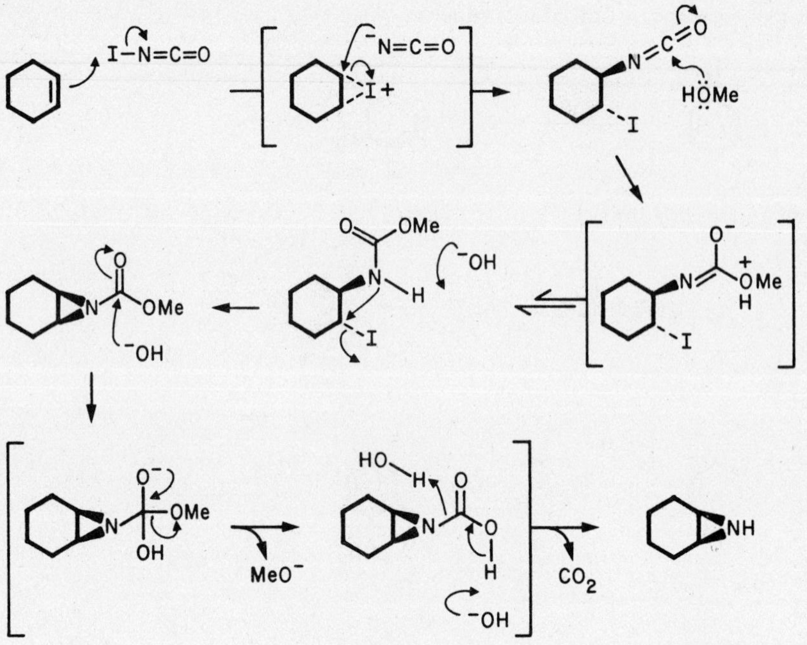

(b)

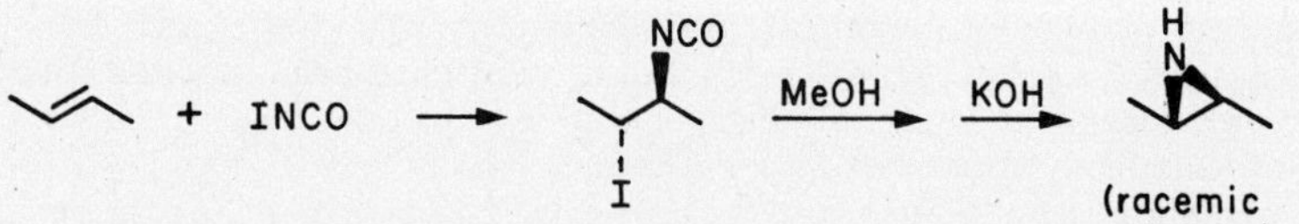

(racemic mixture)

31.2

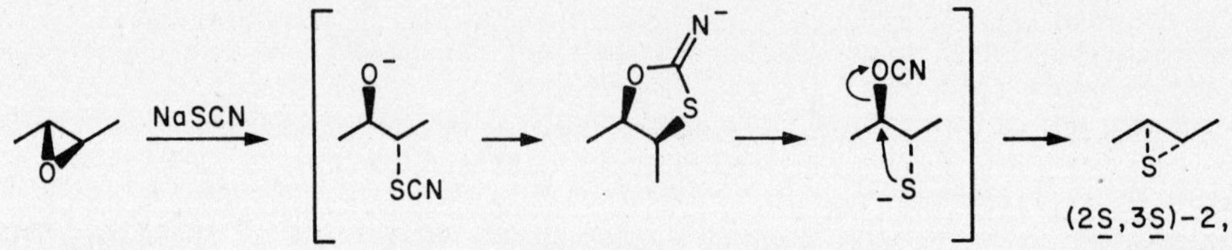

(2$\underline{S}$,3$\underline{S}$)-2,3-dimethylthiirane

31.3

$CH_3OCH_3 \longrightarrow$ CH$_2$—CH$_2$ (epoxide) + H$_2$

$\Delta H^\circ_f = \quad -44.0 \qquad\qquad -12.6 \qquad 0 \qquad\qquad \Delta H^\circ = +31.4$ kcal mole^{-1}

$CH_3SCH_3 \longrightarrow$ CH$_2$—CH$_2$ (thiirane) + H$_2$

$\Delta H^\circ_f = \quad -8.9 \qquad\qquad 19.7 \qquad 0 \qquad\qquad \Delta H^\circ = +28.6$ kcal mole^{-1}

The thiirane ring is less strained because less distortion of the C–S–C bond angle is required to close the ring. In dimethyl sulfide the C–S–C bond angle is 98.9° (see Section 25.1) vs. the C–O–C bond angle of 111.7° of dimethyl ether (see Section 10.1).

31.4

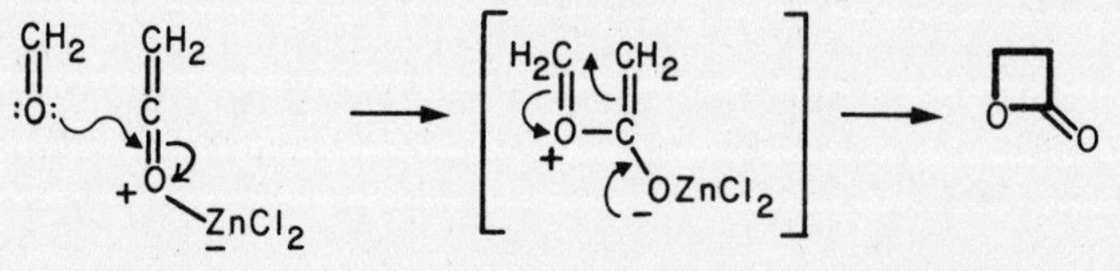

31.5   C-protonation gives a highly delocalized cation:

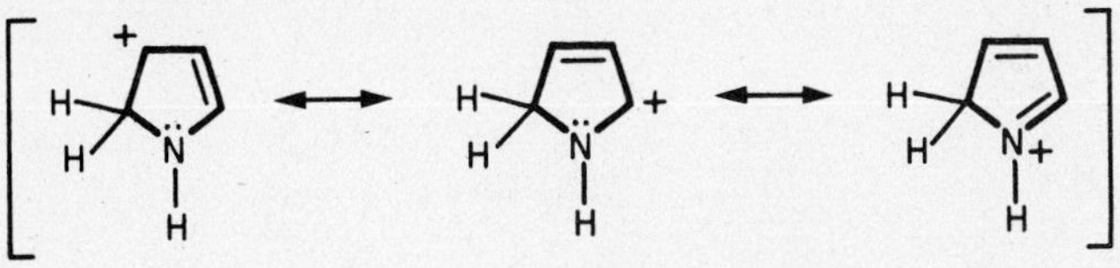

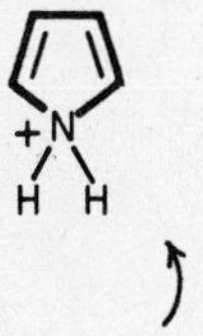

N-protonation gives a localized cation:

31.6

			H° (kcal mole^{-1})	Aromatic Stabilization (kcal mole^{-1})
	+ 2 H$_2$ →		−50.3	(0)
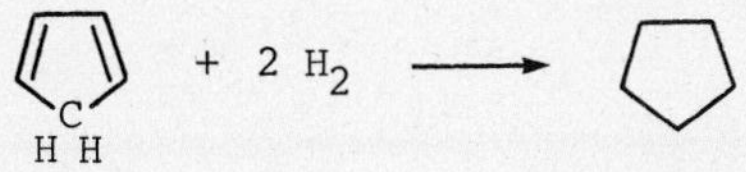 ΔH°$_f$ = 31.9	0	−18.4		
	+ 2 H$_2$ →		−35.7	14.6
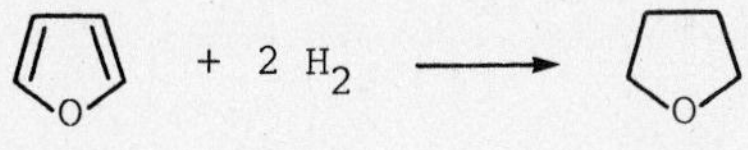 ΔH°$_f$ = −8.3	0	−44.0		
	+ 2 H$_2$ →		−26.7	23.6
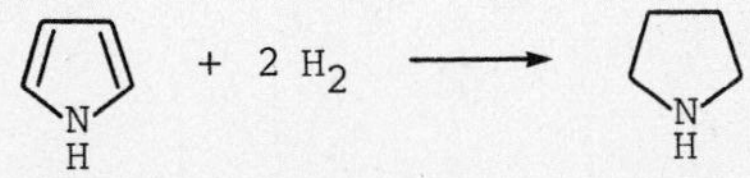 ΔH°$_f$ = 25.9	0	−0.8		
	+ 2 H$_2$ →		−35.7	14.6
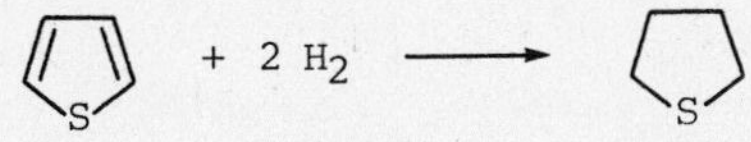 ΔH°$_f$ = 27.6	0	−8.1		

The resonance structures which contribute to aromatic stabilization are those which involve a positive charge on the heteroatom:

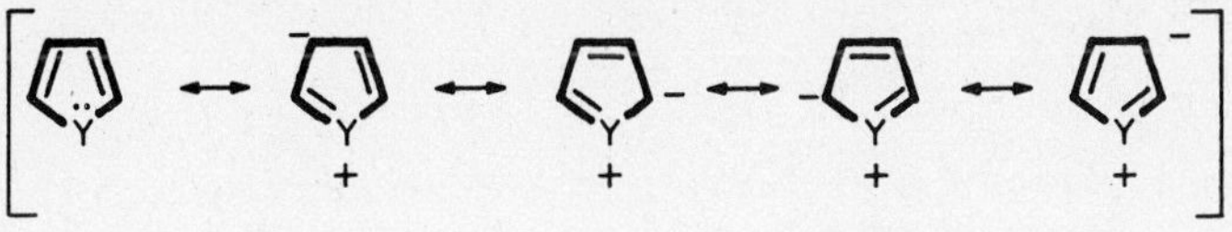

This is easier for the more basic nitrogen atom than for oxygen or sulfur.

31.7

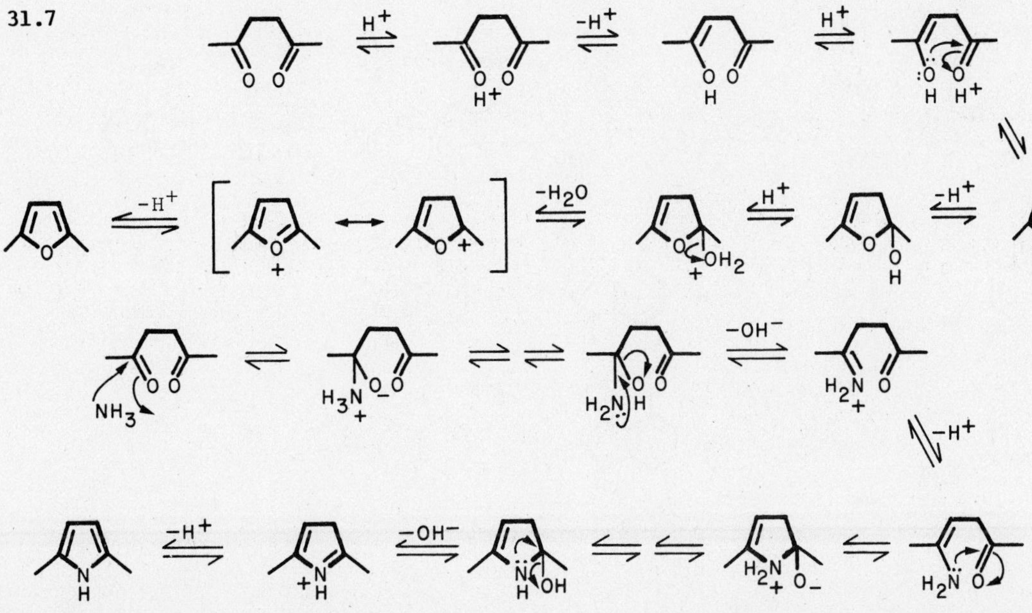

31.8

(a)

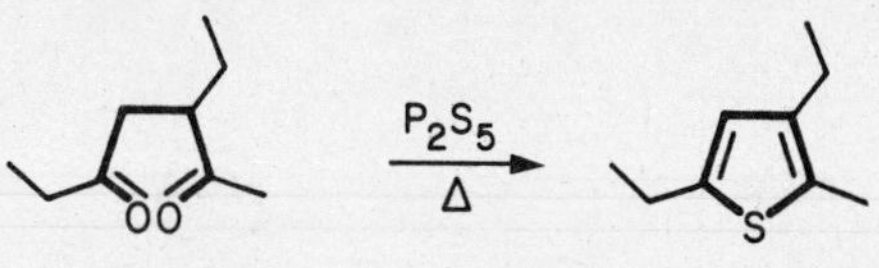

(b)

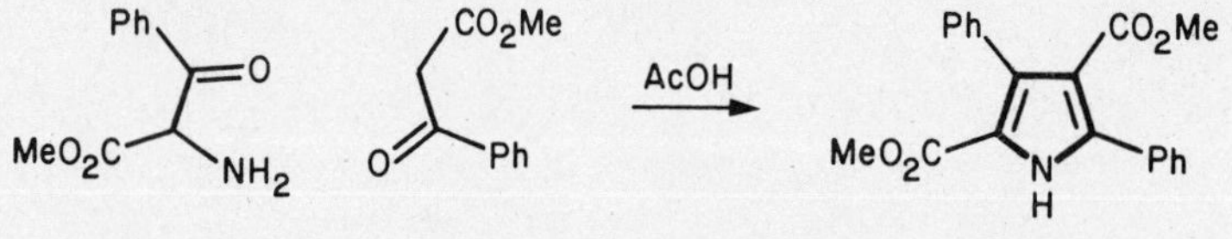

31.9

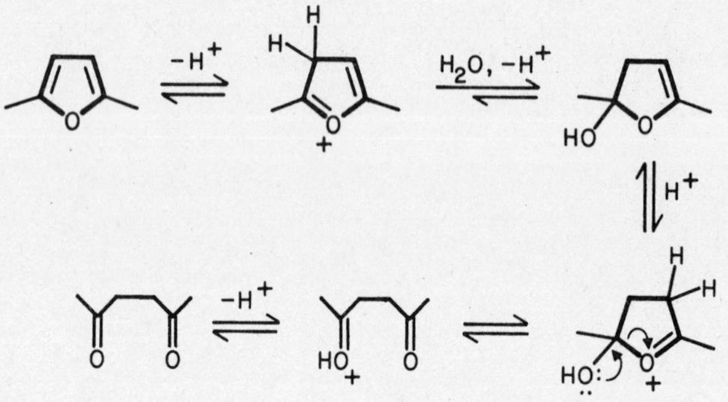

31.10

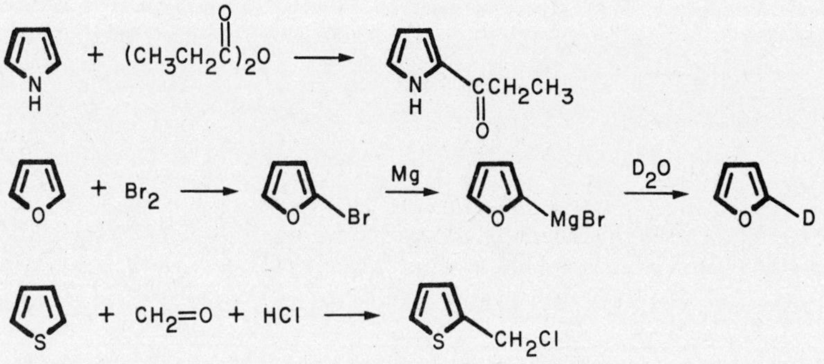

31.11

(a)

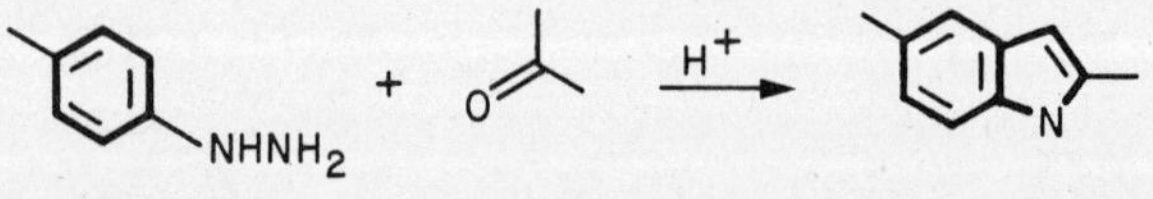

(b)

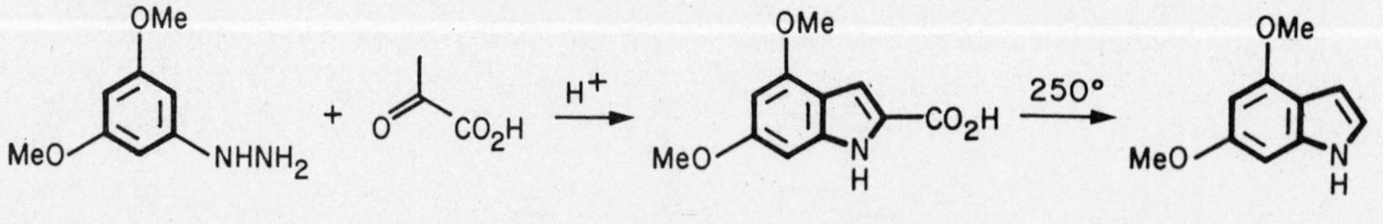

(c)

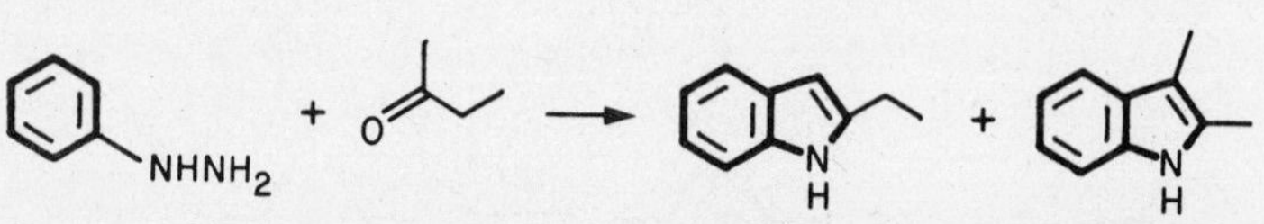

2,3-dimethylindole is formed as well

(d)

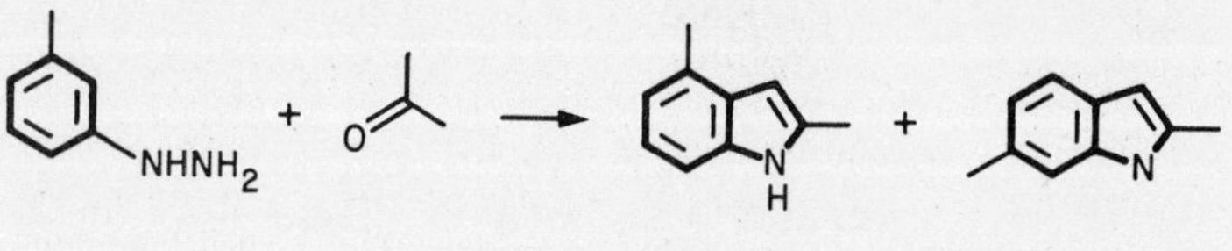

2,6-dimethylindole is formed as well

31.12

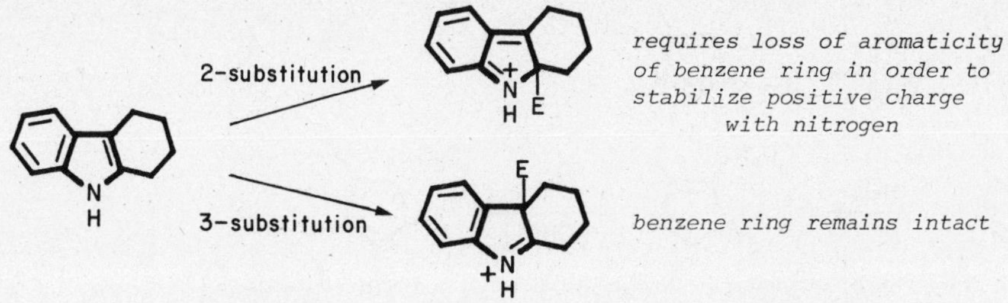

2-substitution → *requires loss of aromaticity of benzene ring in order to stabilize positive charge with nitrogen*

3-substitution → *benzene ring remains intact*

31.13

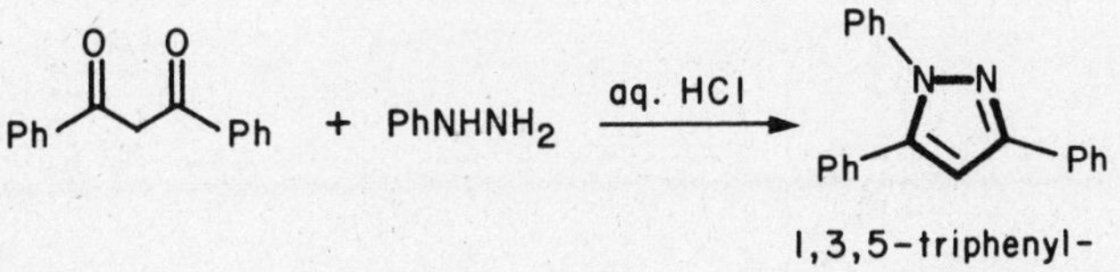

$$Ph\text{-}CO\text{-}CH_2\text{-}CO\text{-}Ph + PhNHNH_2 \xrightarrow{\text{aq. HCl}}$$

1,3,5-triphenyl-pyrazole

31.14

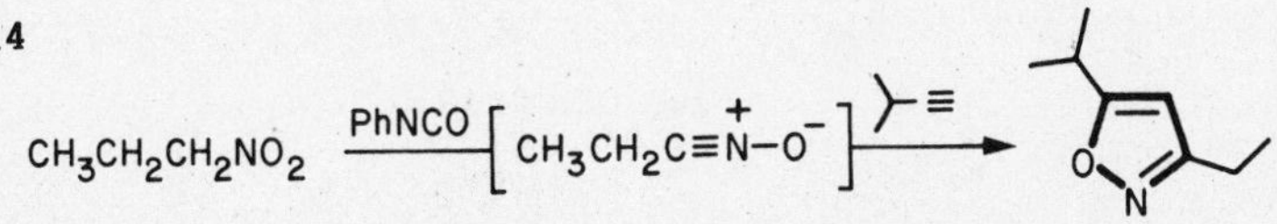

$$CH_3CH_2CH_2NO_2 \xrightarrow{PhNCO} [CH_3CH_2C\equiv \overset{+}{N}-O^-] \longrightarrow$$

31.15

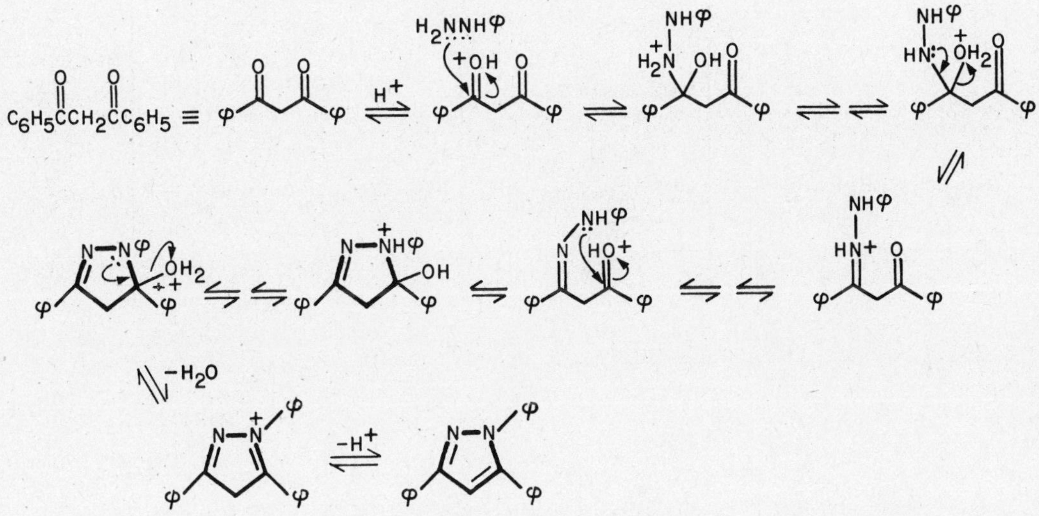

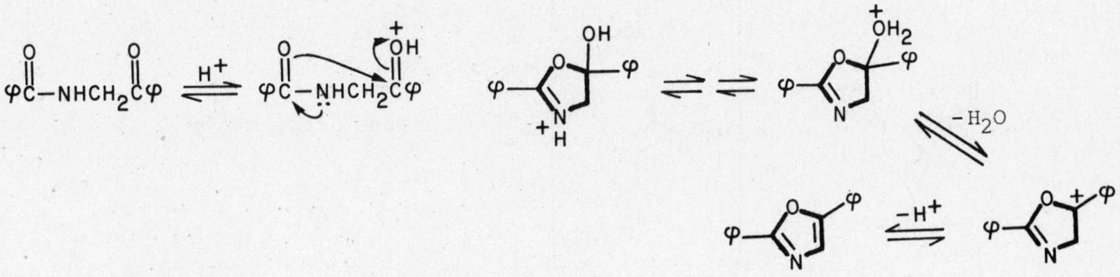

$$C_6H_5\overset{O}{C}CH_2\overset{O}{C}C_6H_5 \equiv$$

31.16

4-substitution:

5-substitution:

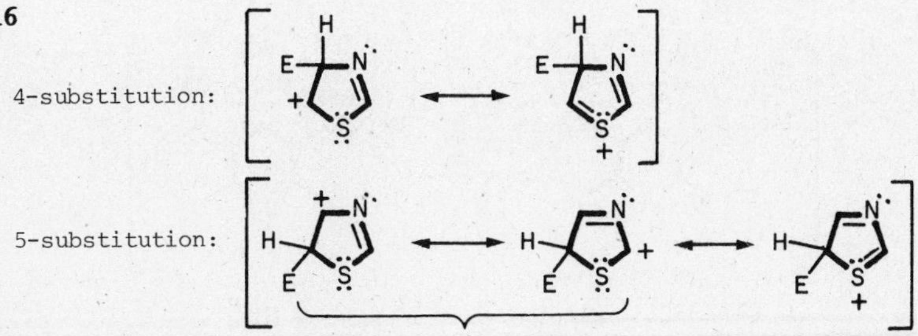

both of these are poor because the positive charge is next to an electron-withdrawing nitrogen

31.17

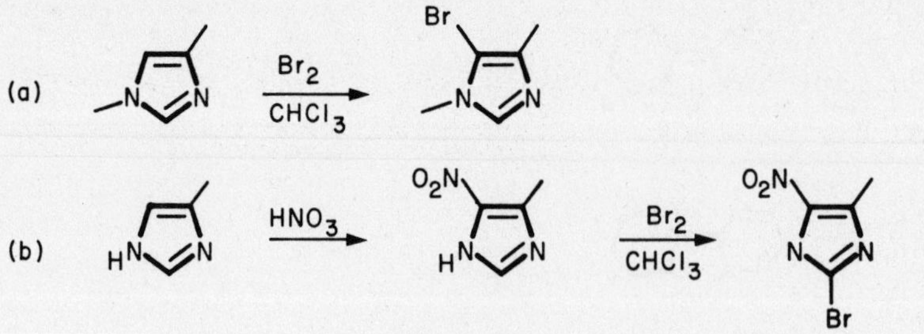

(a)

(b)

31.18

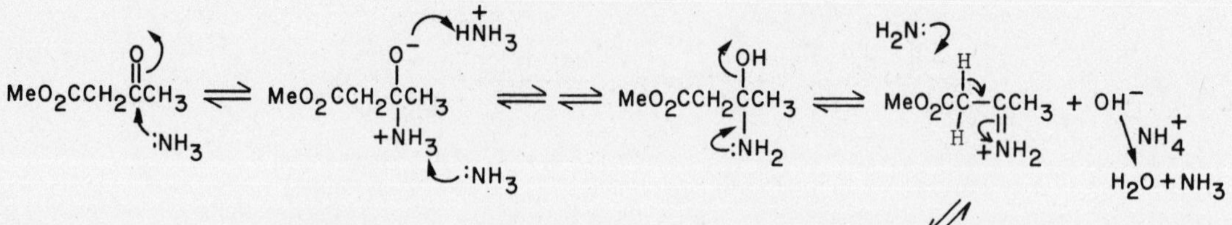

The proton source is NH_4^+;
the base is $:NH_3$

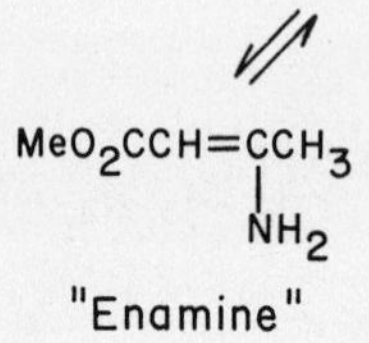

"Enamine"

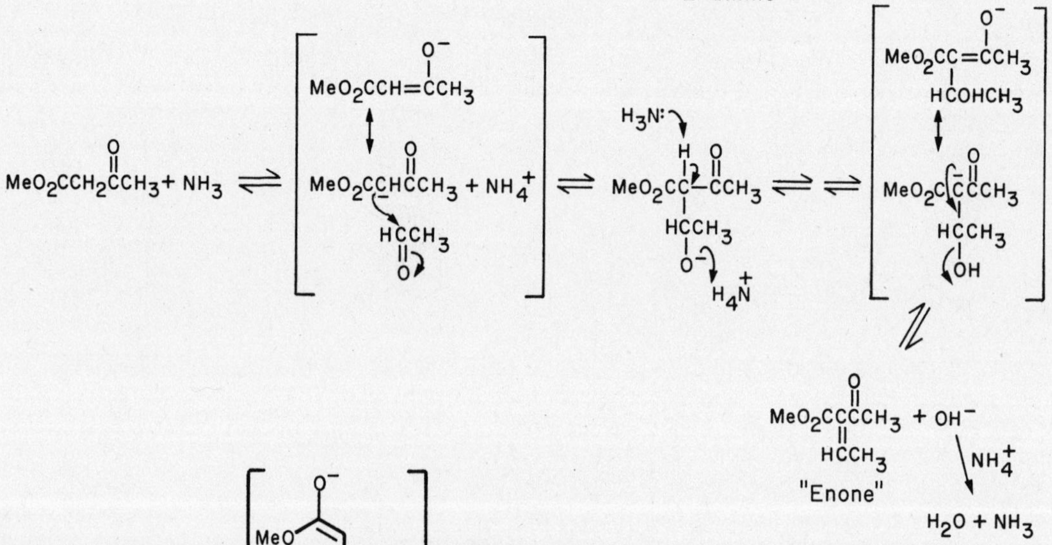

"Enone"

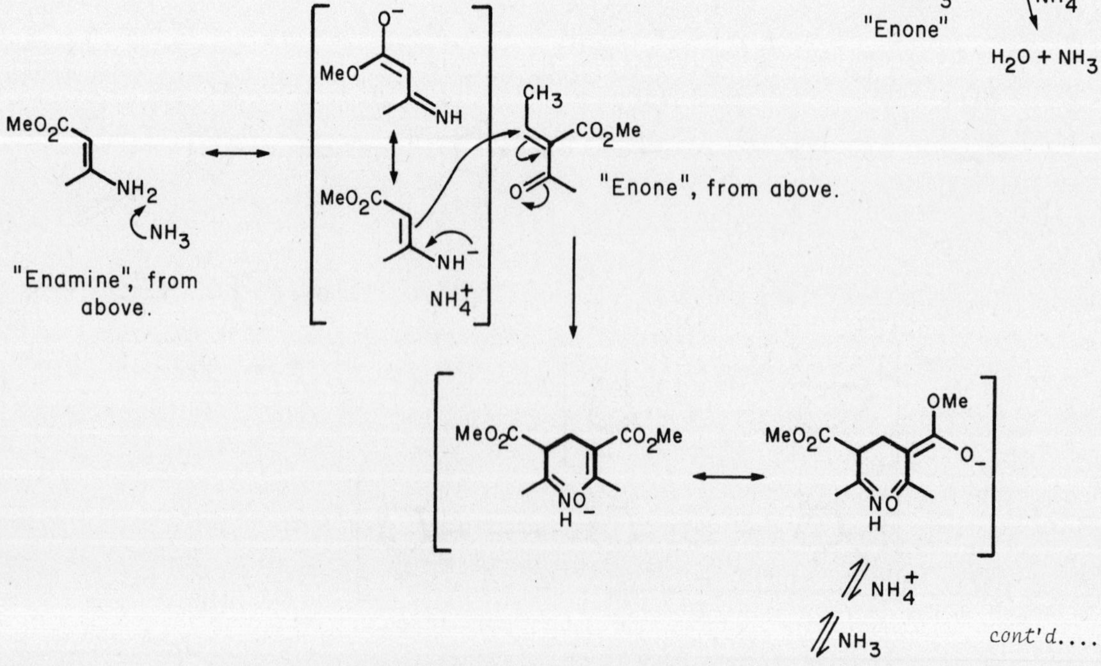

"Enamine", from
above.

"Enone", from above.

cont'd....

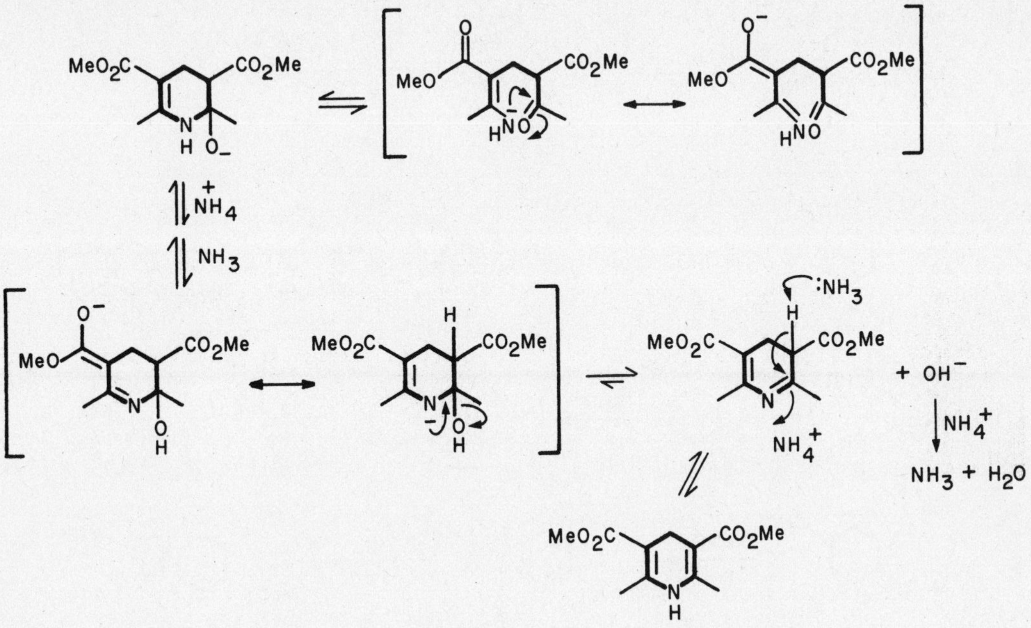

31.19

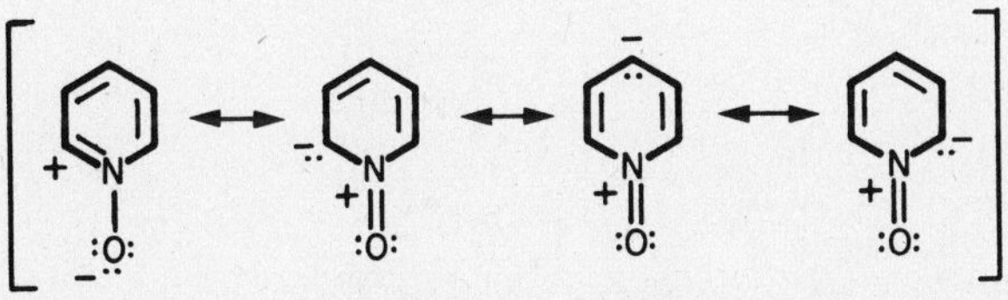

These resonance structures suggest that electrophilic attack will occur at the 2-, 4-, and 6-positions.

31.20

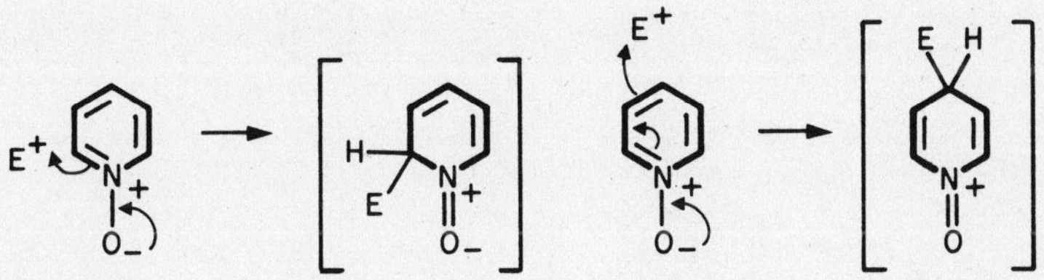

Intermediates with resonance structures having full octets are possible from attack at C-2 and C-4.

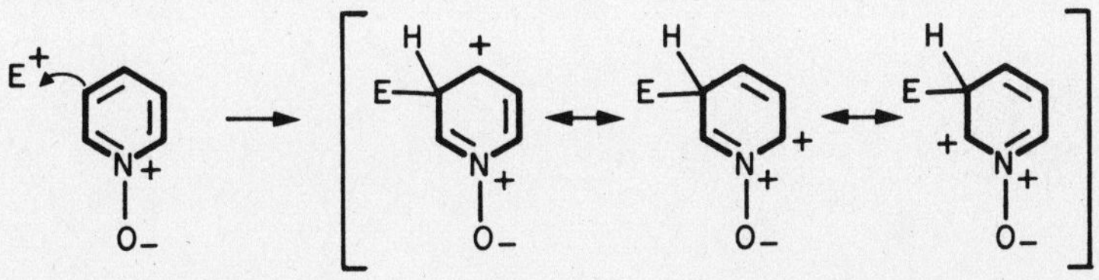

No resonance structure of the intermediate from attack at C-3 has a filled shell.

31.21

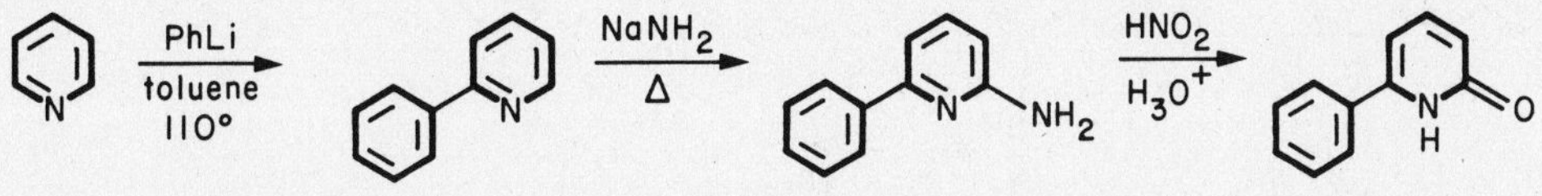

31.22

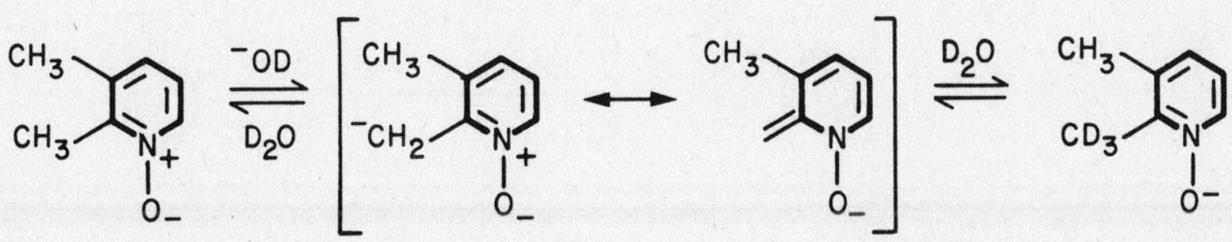

31.23

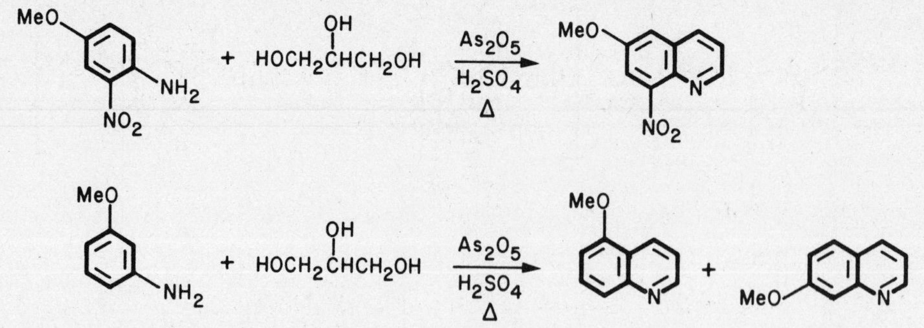

31.24

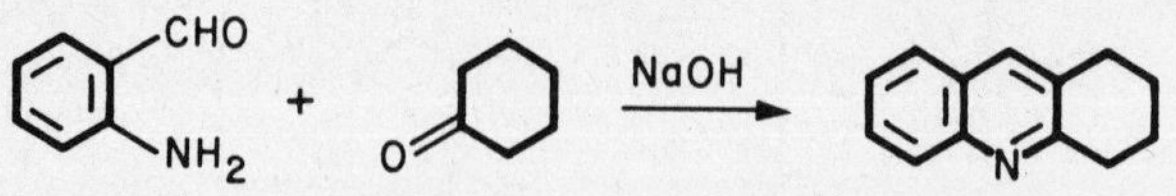

31.25

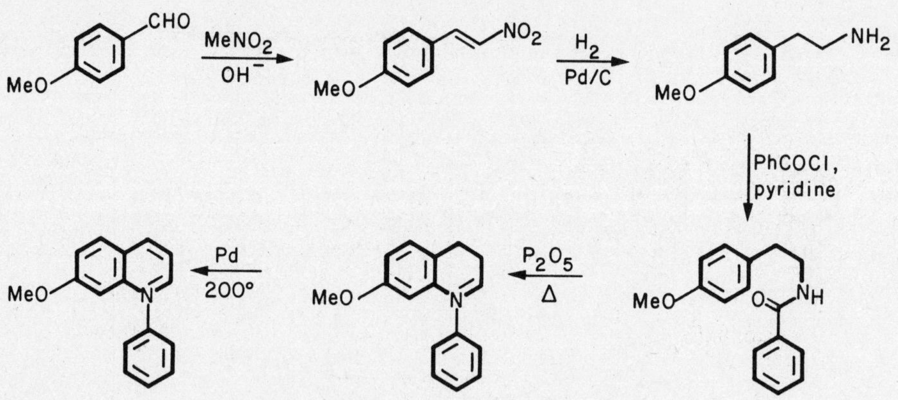

31.26

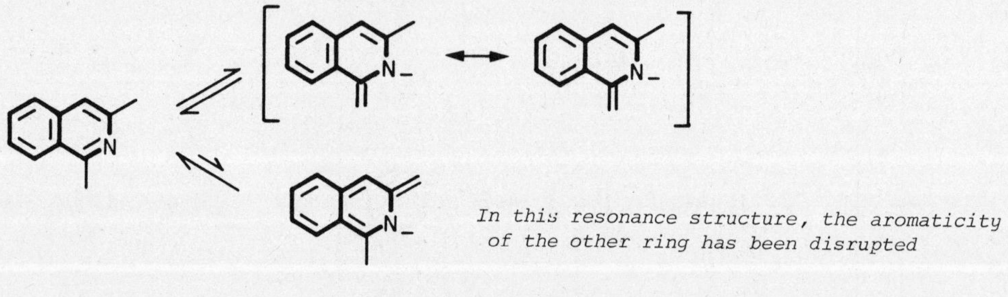

In this resonance structure, the aromaticity of the other ring has been disrupted

31.27

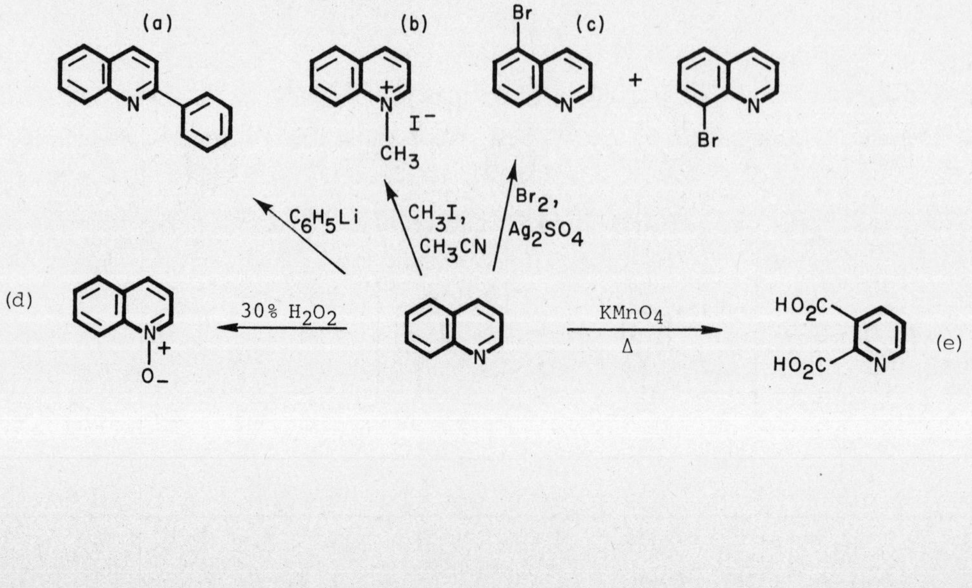

(a) (b) (c)

(d)

(e)

30% H₂O₂

C₆H₅Li

CH₃I, CH₃CN

Br₂, Ag₂SO₄

KMnO₄ Δ

31.28

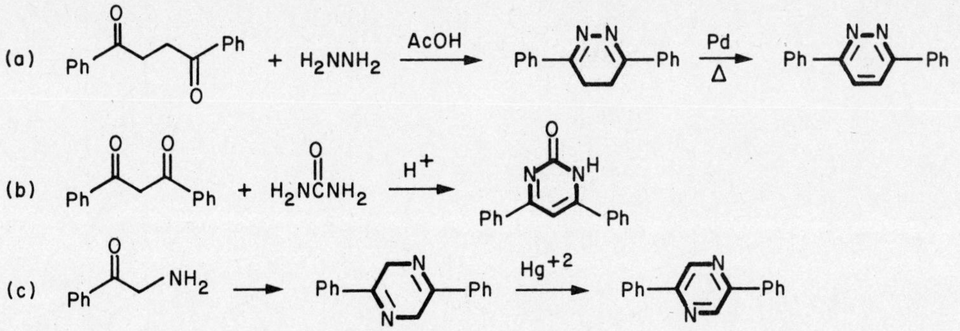

(a) $Ph\text{-}CO\text{-}CH_2CH_2\text{-}CO\text{-}Ph$ + H_2NNH_2 $\xrightarrow{\text{AcOH}}$ Ph—(pyridazine)—Ph $\xrightarrow[\Delta]{Pd}$ Ph—(pyridazine)—Ph

(b) $Ph\text{-}CO\text{-}CH_2\text{-}CO\text{-}Ph$ + $H_2N\overset{O}{\overset{||}{C}}NH_2$ $\xrightarrow{H^+}$ (pyrimidinone with Ph, Ph)

(c) $Ph\text{-}CO\text{-}CH_2\text{-}NH_2$ $\longrightarrow$ Ph—(dihydropyrazine)—Ph $\xrightarrow{Hg^{+2}}$ Ph—(pyrazine)—Ph

31.29

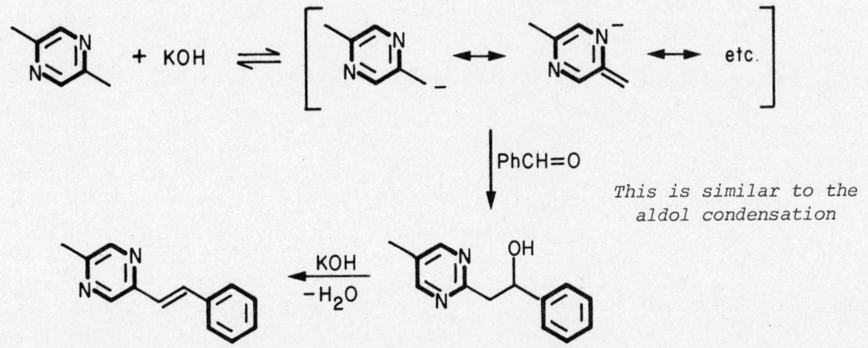

(dimethylpyrazine) + KOH $\rightleftharpoons$ [(anion) $\leftrightarrow$ (anion) $\leftrightarrow$ etc.]

$\downarrow$ PhCH=O

This is similar to the aldol condensation

(styryl methylpyrazine) $\xleftarrow[-H_2O]{KOH}$ (methylpyrazine with CH(OH)Ph)

31.30

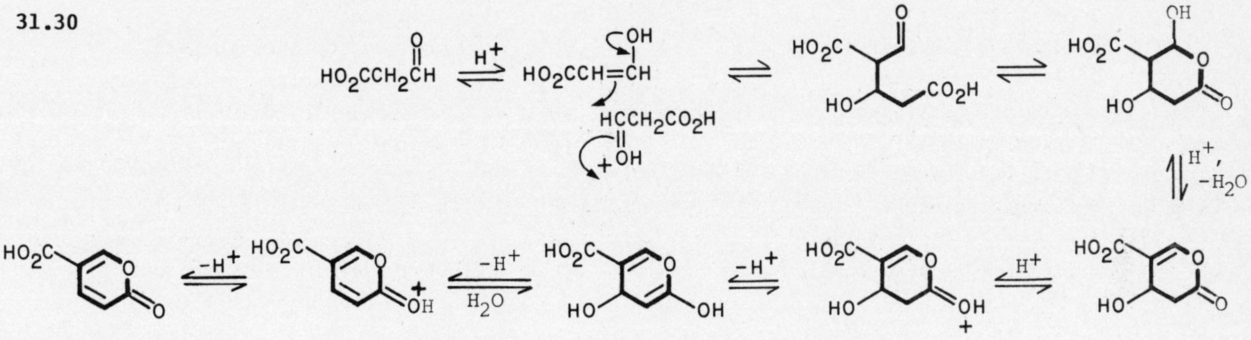

HO_2CCH_2CHO $\underset{H^+}{\rightleftharpoons}$ $HO_2CCH=CH\text{-}OH$ $\rightleftharpoons$ (branched aldehyde acid) $\rightleftharpoons$ (lactone)

$HCCH_2CO_2H$
$+OH$

$\Updownarrow H^+, -H_2O$

(pyranone) $\underset{}{\overset{-H^+}{\rightleftharpoons}}$ (pyranol cation) $\underset{H_2O}{\overset{-H^+}{\rightleftharpoons}}$ (dihydropyran) $\overset{-H^+}{\rightleftharpoons}$ (dihydropyranone cation) $\overset{H^+}{\rightleftharpoons}$ (dihydropyranone)

31.31

(mesityl oxide) $\underset{}{\overset{H^+}{\rightleftharpoons}}$ (enol) $\rightarrow$ (cation) $\overset{-H^+}{\rightleftharpoons}$ (pyrylium type)

$(CH_3C)_2O$
$||$
O

$\Updownarrow H^+$

(2,4,6-trimethylpyrylium) $\underset{}{\overset{-H_2O}{\rightleftharpoons}}$ (intermediate) $+OH_2$ $\rightleftharpoons$ (cation) $HO\,H$ $\rightleftharpoons$ (cation) $+HH$

$PhCOCH_3 + CH_3COCH_3 \longrightarrow$ (phenyl enone) $\xrightarrow[H^+]{2\,Ac_2O}$ (2-methyl-4-methyl-6-phenylpyrylium cation)

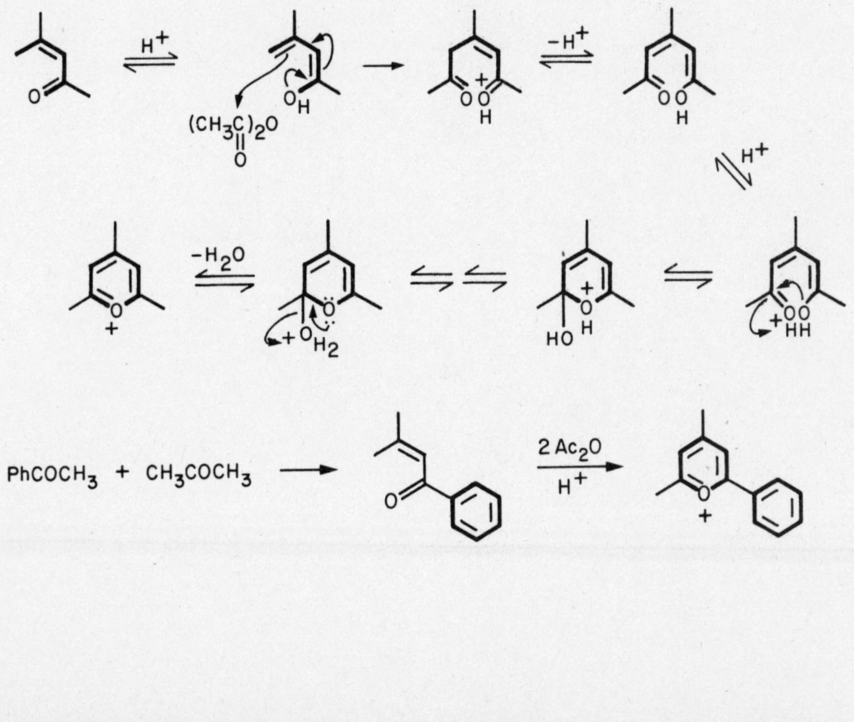

31.32

(mechanism schemes)

31.E Answers and Explanations for Problems

1.

(a) 3-methyltetrahydropyran
(b) 3-azetidinone
(c) 2-methyl-2-ethyloxirane
(d) 2-nitro-3-bromofuran
(e) 5-chloro-2-furoic acid
(f) 2-amino-thiazole
(g) 4-methyl-3-isoxazolecarboxylic acid
(h) 5-nitroisothiazole
(i) 4-nitro-1-phenylimidazole
(j) 6-bromoindole-3-carboxylic acid

(k) 3-pyridinecarboxylic acid
(l) 4-methylpyridine oxide
(m) 7-chloro-1-methylisoquinoline
(n) 2,3-dimethylquinoline
(o) 2-amino-4-methylpyrimidine
(p) 3,6-dimethylpyrazine
(q) 3-chlorobenzofuran
(r) 2-(2-hydroxyethyl)thiophene
(s) 2-(4-methoxyphenyl)-6-phenyl-1,4-pyrone
(t) 4-t-butyl-2,6-dimethylpyrylium tetrafluoroborate

2.

(a) (structure)   (b) (structure)   (c) (structure)   (d) (structure)

(e)

(f)

(g)

(h) 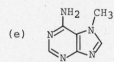   (i) (structure)   (j) (structure)

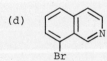

(k) (structure)   (l) (structure)   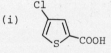   (m) (structure)   (n) (structure)

3. **(a)** $C_6H_5CH=CH_2$ $\xrightarrow[\substack{1.\ HOCl \\ 2.\ NaOH}]{C_6H_5CO_3H\ or}$ (epoxide: $C_6H_5CH\overset{O}{-\!\!\frown\!\!-}CH_2$) $\xrightarrow{^-SCN}$ (thiirane: $C_6H_5CH\overset{S}{-\!\!\frown\!\!-}CH_2$) *(see Section 31.2.B)*

(b) $C_6H_5C\equiv CH$ $\xrightarrow[\text{liq. }NH_3]{NaNH_2}$ $\xrightarrow{CH_3I}$ $C_6H_5C\equiv CCH_3$ $\xrightarrow[NH_3]{Na}$ (alkene with C_6H_5, H, H, CH_3) $\xrightarrow{C_6H_5CO_3H}$ (epoxide)

(c) (methylenecyclohexane) $+ INCO \longrightarrow$ (cyclohexane with NCO and CH_2I) $\xrightarrow{MeOH}$ (cyclohexane with $NHCO_2Me$ and CH_2I) $\xrightarrow[EtOH]{KOH}$ (spiro aziridine)

(d) (acetone, H_3C, CH_3, C=O) $+$ (CHC_6H_5 / N / C_6H_5 imine) $\longrightarrow$ (β-lactam: CH_3, CH_3, C_6H_5, C_6H_5)

   NOTE: $(CH_3)_2\overset{Br}{C}COBr$ $\xrightarrow{Zn}$ $(CH_3)_2C=C=O$ $\underline{and}$ $C_6H_5NH_2 + O=CHC_6H_5 \longrightarrow C_6H_5N=CHC_6H_5$
   (Section 19.3.C)

(e) (pyridine) $+ CH_3(CH_2)_3Li \longrightarrow$ (2-substituted pyridine $(CH_2)_3CH_3$) $\xrightarrow{H_2/cat.}$ (2-substituted piperidine $(CH_2)_3CH_3$)

(f) (cyclopentanone with COOEt) $+$ (CH₂=CH–C≡N) $\xrightarrow{base}$ (cyclopentanone with COOEt and CH_2CH_2CN) $\xrightarrow{OH^-}$ $\xrightarrow[\Delta]{H^+}$ (cyclopentanone with CH_2CH_2CN) $\xrightarrow{H_2/cat.}$

$\longrightarrow$ $\left[\text{(cyclopentanone with } CH_2CH_2CH_2NH_2)\right]$ $\xrightarrow{}$ $\left[\text{(bicyclic imine)}\right]$ $\longrightarrow$ (octahydroindole, N–H)

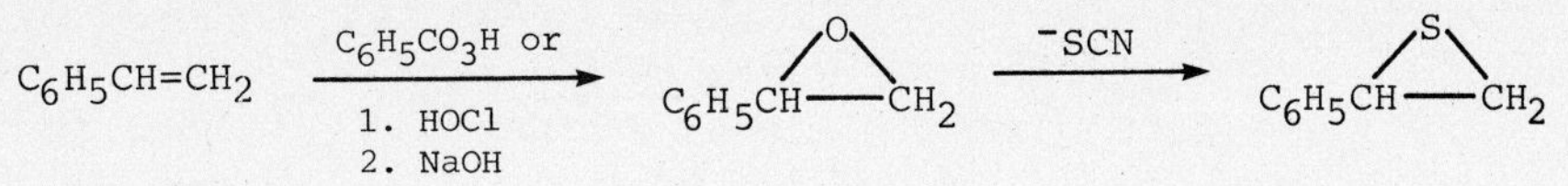

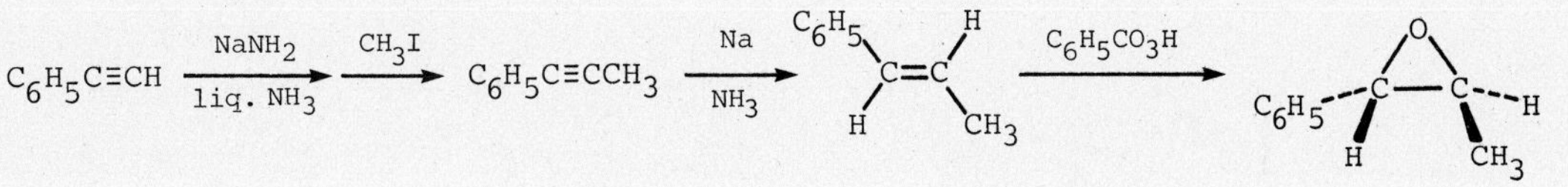

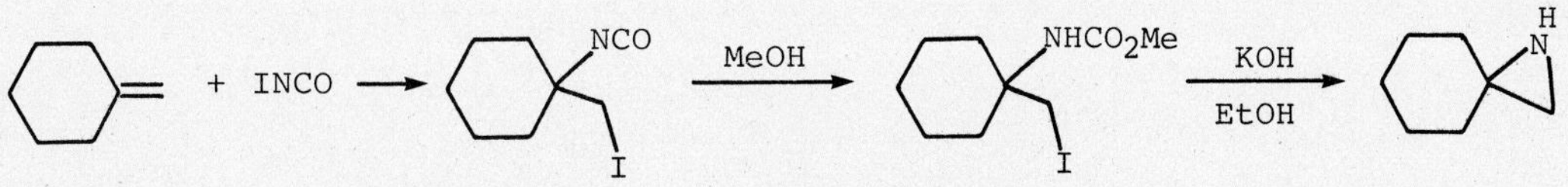

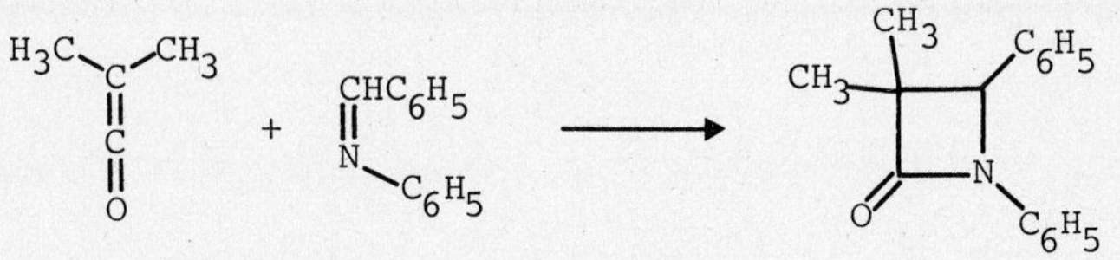

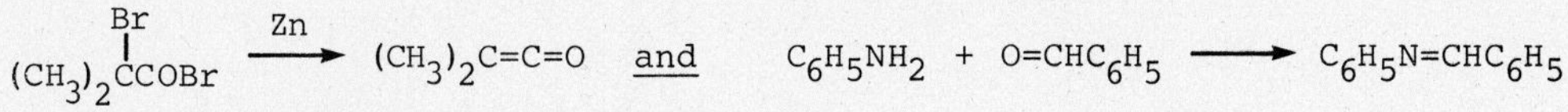

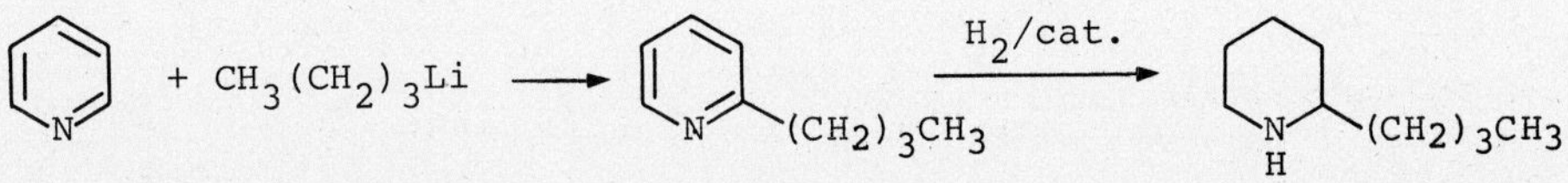

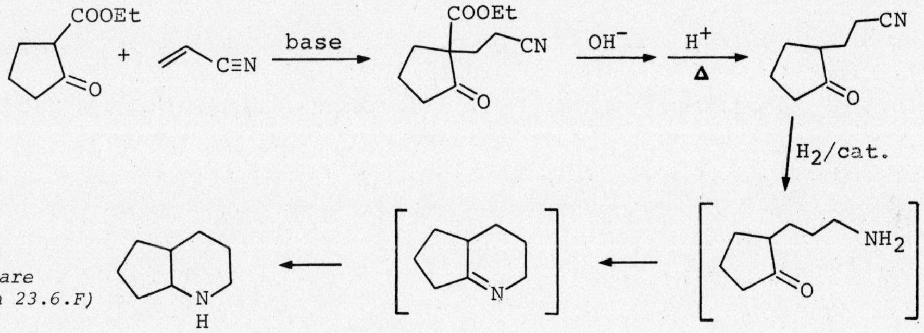

(compare Section 23.6.F)

4. In these syntheses, note the type of heterocyclic ring system that is present and use the appropriate synthetic route.

   (a) This problem requires a 1,4-diketone:

   (cyclohexanone with CH_2COCH_3) $\xrightarrow[100°]{P_2O_5}$ (tetrahydrobenzofuran with CH_3)

   The 1,4-diketone may be prepared in several ways. One possibility is:

   (cyclohexanone with CO_2Et) $\xrightarrow[\substack{2.\ \text{(methallyl chloride)}}]{1.\ NaOEt}$ (cyclohexanone with CO_2Et and methallyl) $\xrightarrow[\Delta]{H_3O^+}$ (cyclohexanone with methallyl) $\xrightarrow[MeOH]{O_3}$ $\xrightarrow{Me_2S}$ (cyclohexanone with CH_2COCH_3)

   (b) Knorr pyrrole synthesis *(Section 31.3.B)*:

   (MeO_2C, C_6H_5, C=O) $+$ (O=C–C_6H_5 / H_2N / CO_2Me) $\xrightarrow{CH_2CO_2H}$ (pyrrole: MeO_2C, C_6H_5, C_6H_5, CO_2Me, N–H)

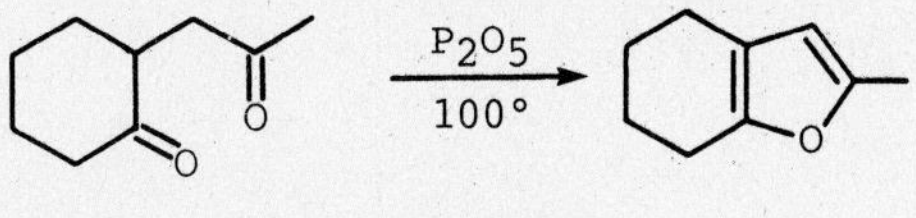

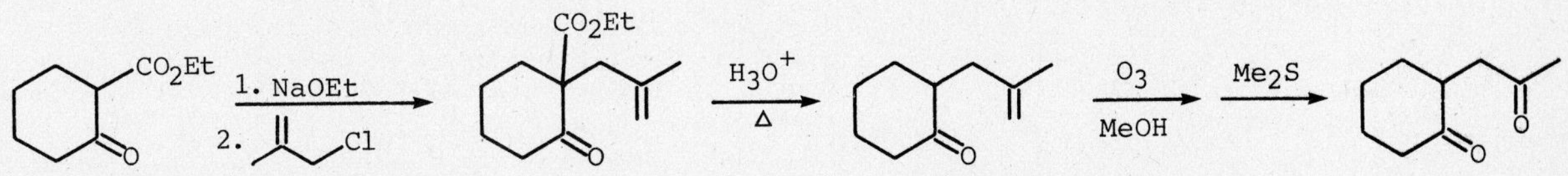

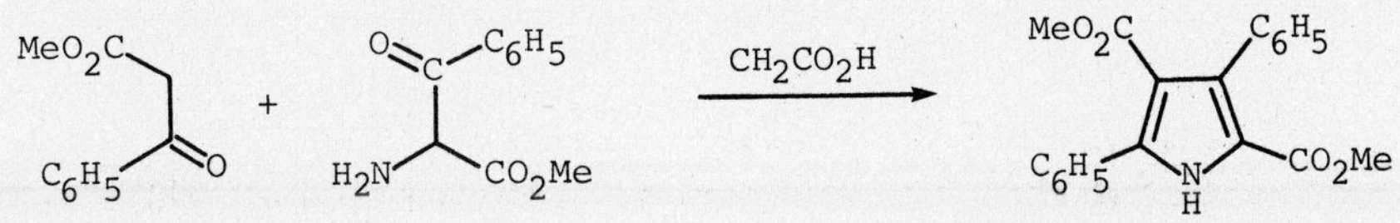

$$C_6H_5CO_2Me + CH_3CO_2Me \xrightarrow[NaOMe]{MeOH} C_6H_5\overset{O}{\underset{||}{C}}CH_2CO_2Me \xrightarrow{HONO} C_6H_5\overset{NOH}{\underset{O}{C}}CCO_2Me \xrightarrow[(CH_3CO)_2O]{H_2/Pt}$$

$$C_6H_5\overset{NH_2}{\underset{O}{C}}CH-CO_2Me \xleftarrow[H^+,\Delta]{MeOH} C_6H_5\overset{NHCOCH_3}{\underset{O}{C}}CHCO_2Me$$

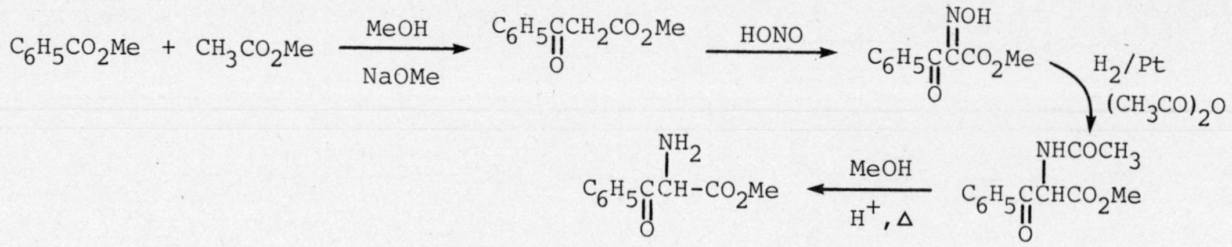

(c) Fischer indole synthesis *(Section 31.4.B)*:

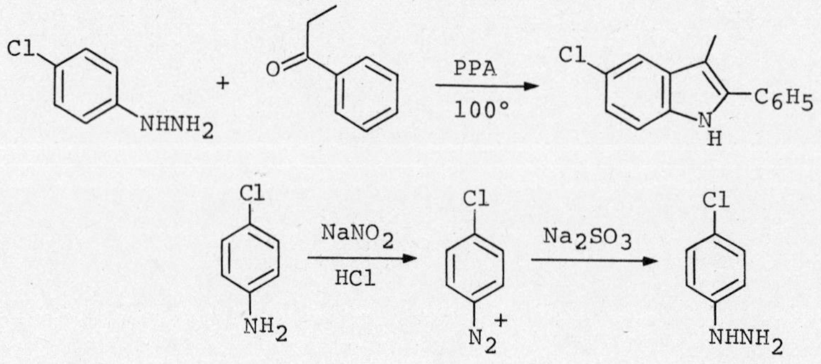

4-chlorophenylhydrazine + propiophenone $\xrightarrow[100°]{PPA}$ 5-chloro-3-methyl-2-phenylindole

4-chloroaniline $\xrightarrow[HCl]{NaNO_2}$ 4-chlorobenzenediazonium $\xrightarrow{Na_2SO_3}$ 4-chlorophenylhydrazine

(d) 2-nitrophenol $\xrightarrow{(CH_3)_2SO_4}$ 2-nitroanisole $\xrightarrow{H_2/cat.}$ 2-methoxyaniline $\xrightarrow[HCl]{NaNO_2}$ 2-methoxybenzenediazonium

2-methoxybenzenediazonium $\xrightarrow{Na_2SO_3}$ 2-methoxyphenylhydrazine $\xrightarrow{(CH_3)_2CO}$ acetone 2-methoxyphenylhydrazone $\xrightarrow[100°]{PPA}$ 2-methyl-7-methoxyindole

(e) phenylhydrazine + 3-pentanone $\xrightarrow[100°]{PPA}$ 3-methyl-2-ethylindole

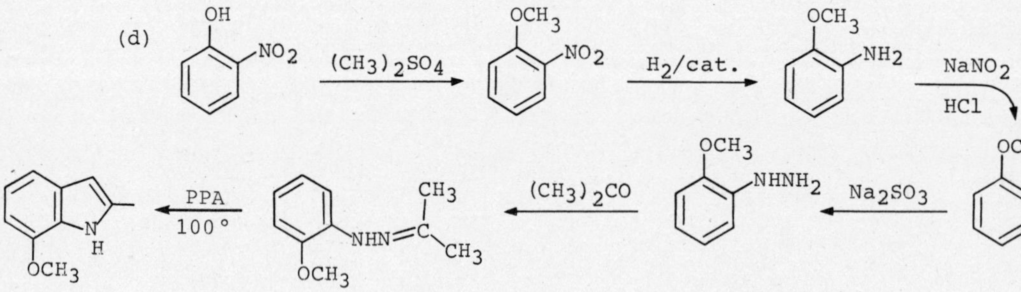

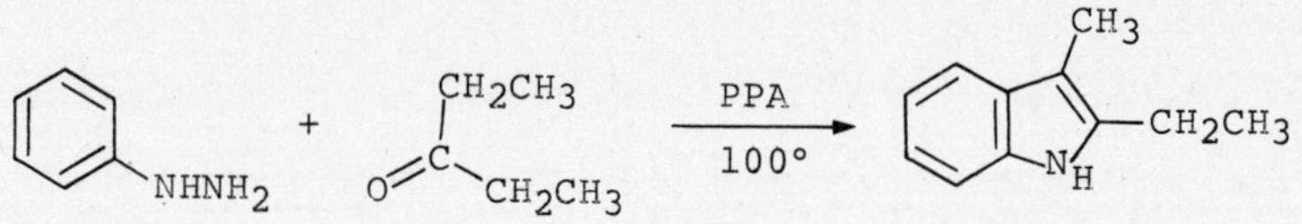

(f) hydroxylamine + 1,3-dicarbonyl compound *(Section 31.5.B)*:

$$\left. \begin{array}{l} C_6H_5\overset{CH_2}{\underset{O}{C}}\overset{}{\underset{O}{C}}C_6H_5 \\ HO-NH_2 \end{array} \right\} \xrightarrow[\Delta]{HCl}$$

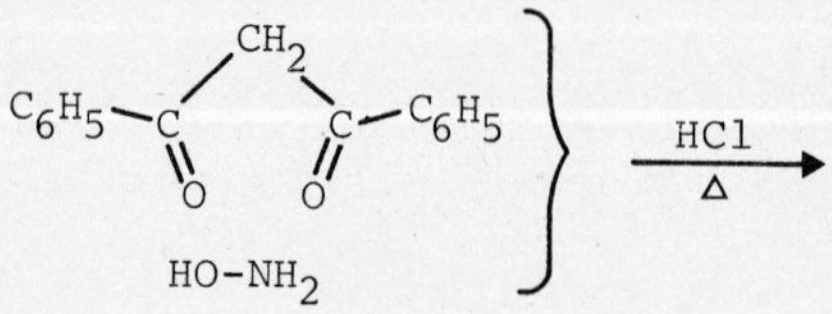

β-Diketones are prepared from esters + ketones:

$$C_6H_5\overset{O}{\underset{||}{C}}CH_3 + EtO_2C-C_6H_5 \xrightarrow[EtOH]{EtO^-} C_6H_5\overset{O}{\underset{||}{C}}-CH_2-\overset{O}{\underset{||}{C}}C_6H_5$$

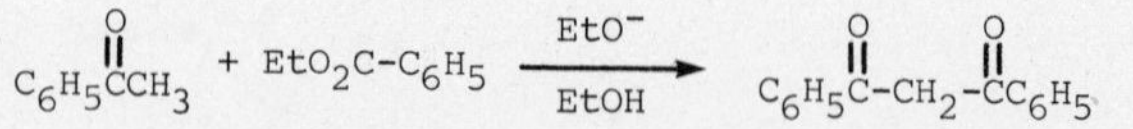

(g) β-diketone + hydrazine:

$$\left. \begin{array}{l} C_6H_5\overset{CH_2}{\underset{O}{C}}\overset{}{\underset{O}{C}}CH_3 \\ H_2N-NH_2 \end{array} \right\}$$

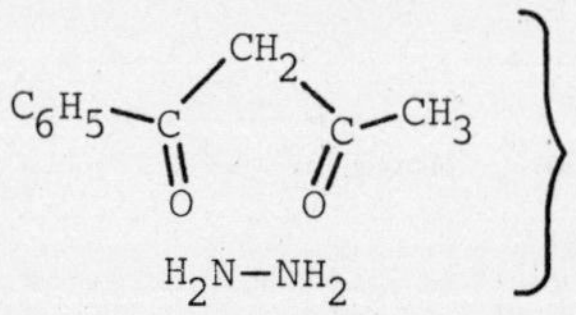

Note that unsymmetrical pyrazoles can be prepared because hydrazine is symmetrical. With hydroxylamine, this β-diketone would give a mixture of isoxazoles.

The β-diketone can be made by: $C_6H_5COCH_3 + CH_3CO_2Et \xrightarrow{EtO^-}$

or: $C_6H_5CO_2Et + CH_3COCH_3 \xrightarrow{EtO^-}$

(h) This isoxazole is unsymmetrical, and the required β-diketone is hard to make. An alternative preparation is a cycloaddition with nitrile oxides *(see Section 31.5.B)*:

$$C_6H_5CH=NOH \xrightarrow{Cl_2} C_6H_5CCl=NOH \xrightarrow{NaOH} C_6H_5C\equiv N-O^- \xrightarrow{MeO_2C-C\equiv C-CO_2Me}$$

(MeO_2C, C_6H_5 substituted isoxazole with MeO_2C)

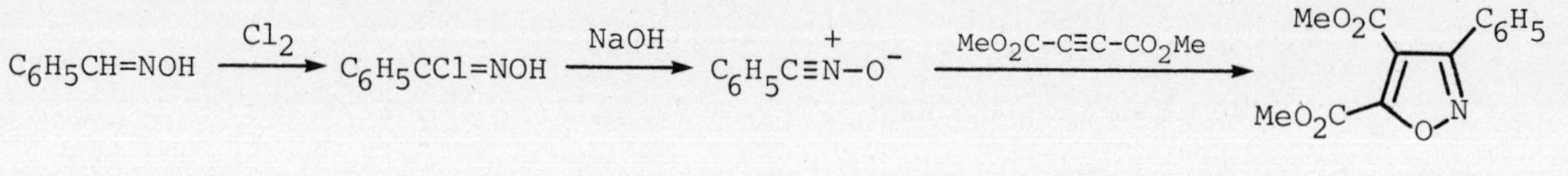

(i) Here also, the β-dicarbonyl approach does not look promising. An alternative preparation uses diazomethane *(Section 31.5.B)*:

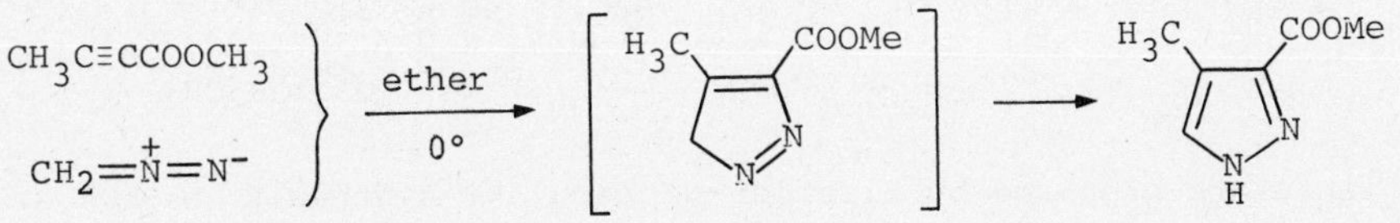

$$CH_3C\equiv CCOOCH_3$$

$$CH_2=\overset{+}{N}=N^-$$

$$\xrightarrow[0°]{ether}$$

The acetylene compound may be prepared by:

$$CH_3C\equiv CH \xrightarrow{RMgX} CH_3C\equiv CMgX \xrightarrow[H^+]{CO_2} CH_3C\equiv CCO_2H \xrightarrow[H^+]{MeOH}$$

(j) Don't be fooled by the way this compound is written. Imidazoles are in rapid tautomeric equilibrium (remember their basicity):

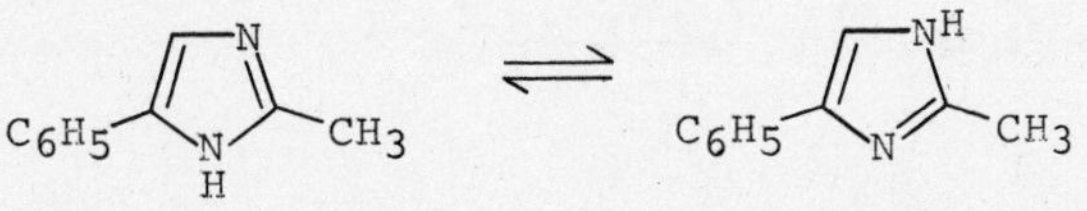

The Paal-Knorr cyclization can be designed in two ways *(Section 31.5.B)*:

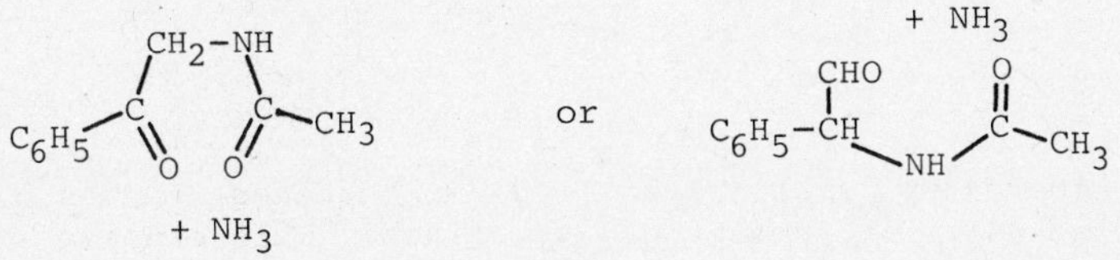

or

The first is a better approach since it does not involve a sensitive aldehyde. Ketones are better than aldehydes in all of these cyclizations.

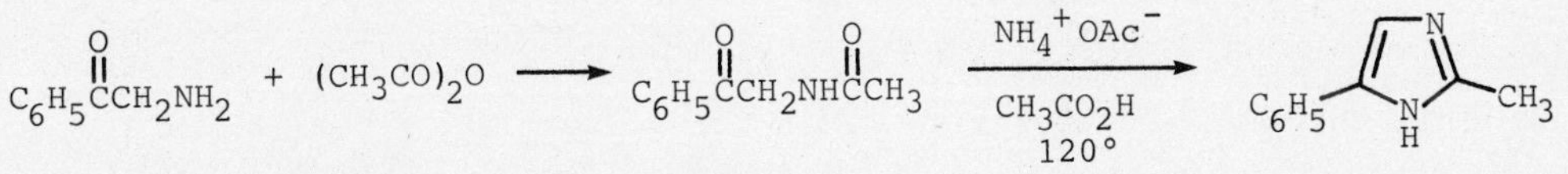

$$C_6H_5\overset{O}{C}CH_2NH_2 + (CH_3CO)_2O \longrightarrow C_6H_5\overset{O}{C}CH_2NH\overset{O}{C}CH_3 \xrightarrow[\substack{CH_3CO_2H \\ 120°}]{NH_4^+OAc^-}$$

(k) Hantzsch pyridine synthesis *(Section 31.6.B)*:

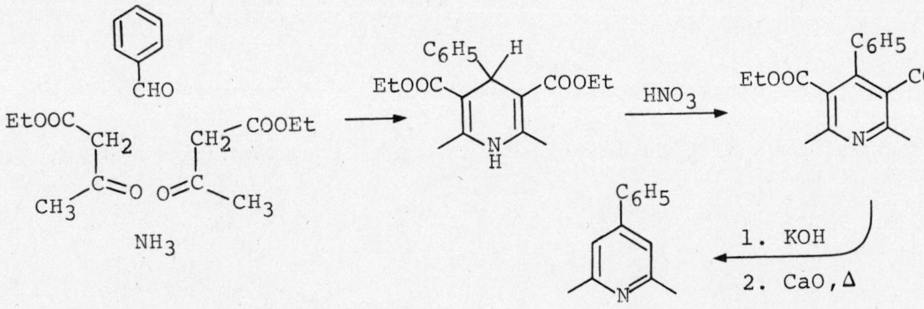

$$\xrightarrow{HNO_3}$$

1. KOH
2. CaO, Δ

(l) Skraup reaction *(Section 31.7.B)*:

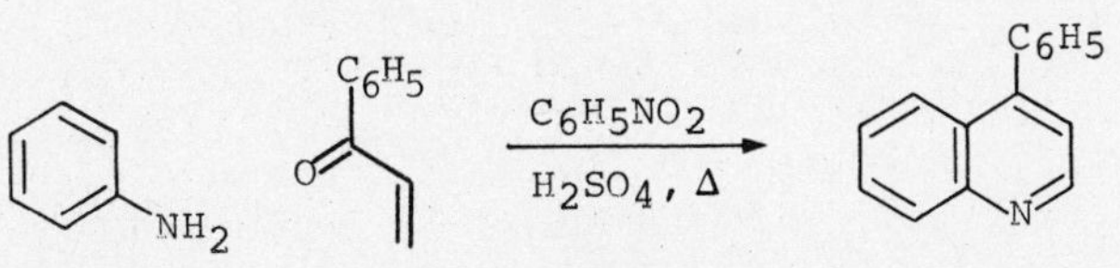

$$\xrightarrow[H_2SO_4, \Delta]{C_6H_5NO_2}$$

(m) Skraup reaction with:

$$\xrightarrow[As_2O_5]{H_2SO_4}$$

or p-CH₃C₆H₄NO₂

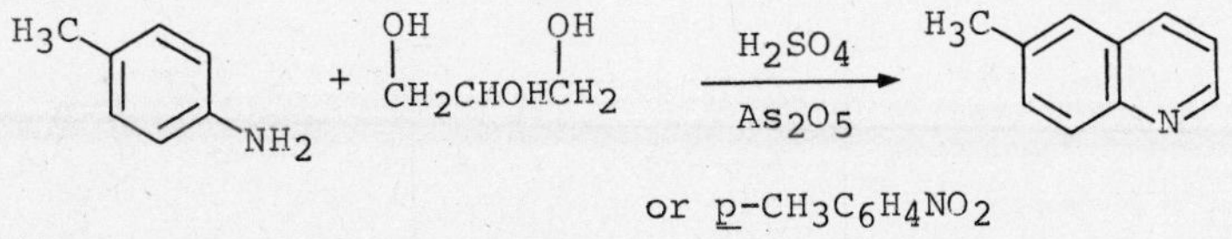

(n) This kind of quinoline is best prepared by the Friedländer method *(Section 31.7.B)*:

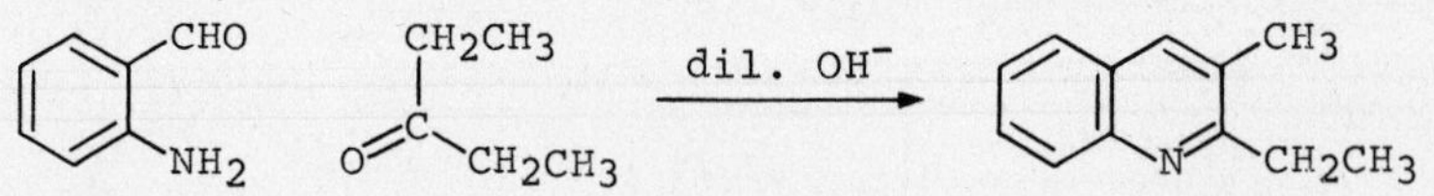

(o) Isoquinolines are prepared by Bischler-Napieralski synthesis *(Section 31.7.B)*:

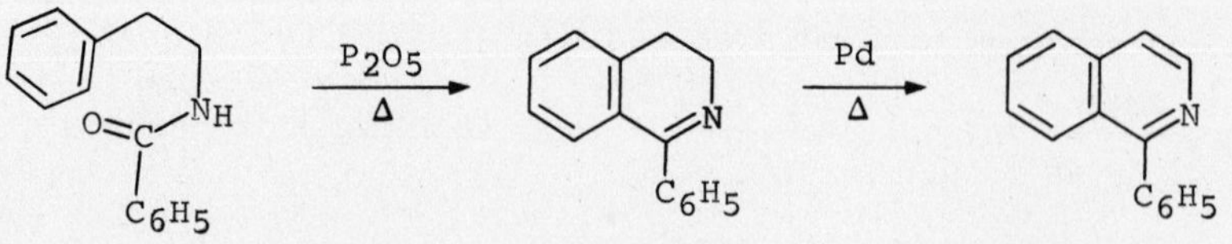

$$C_6H_5CH_2CH_2NH_2 \quad + \quad Cl-\overset{O}{\underset{||}{C}}-C_6H_5$$

benzoyl chloride

The amide is prepared from

$$C_6H_5CH_2Cl + CN^- \longrightarrow C_6H_5CH_2CN \xrightarrow[\text{or } H_2/\text{cat., } NH_3]{LiAlH_4}$$

(p) Section 31.8.B:

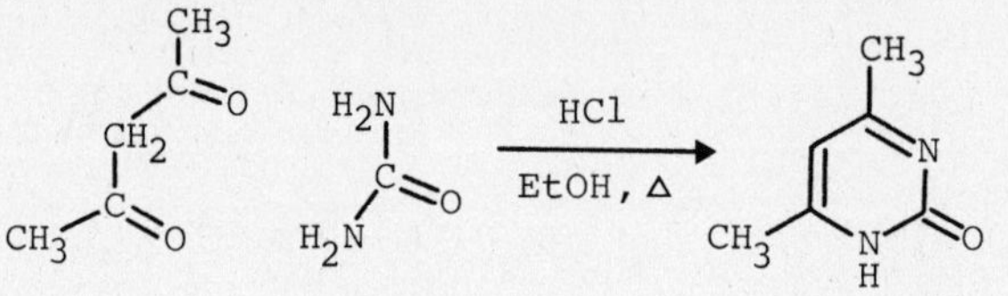

$$\xrightarrow[\text{EtOH, } \Delta]{HCl}$$

(q) Pyrazines can be prepared by dimerization of α-aminoketones *(Section 31.8.B)*, but this method is useful only for symmetrical pyrazines. This example is symmetrical:

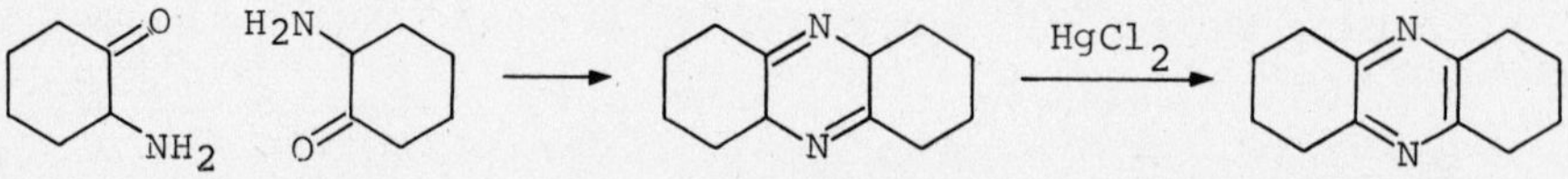

$$\xrightarrow{HgCl_2}$$

(r) This unsymmetrical pyrazine is of the quinoxaline type *(Section 31.8.B)*:

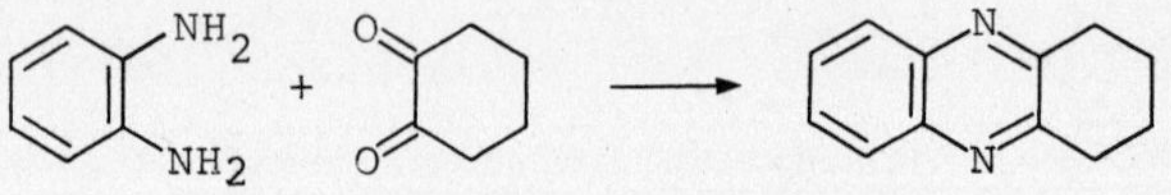

The diketone can be prepared in several ways; one method is given in Section 27.7.A.

(s) This compound is a barbituric acid derivative, prepared from a β-keto ester and urea.

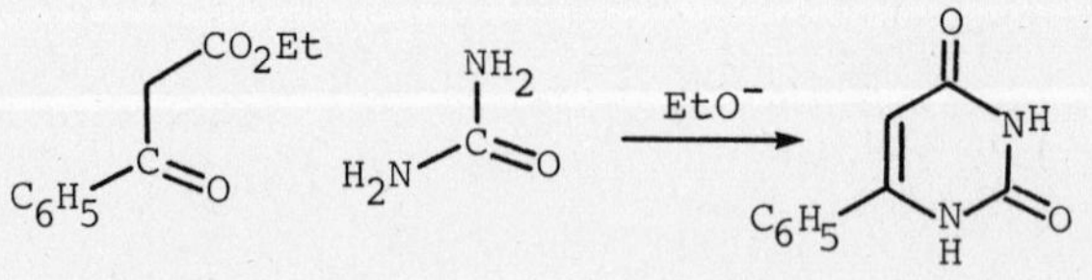

$$\xrightarrow{EtO^-}$$

(t) $CH_3\overset{O}{\overset{||}{C}}CH_3$ + 2 CH_3COOEt $\xrightarrow{NaOEt}$ $CH_3\overset{O}{\overset{||}{C}}CH_2\overset{O}{\overset{||}{C}}CH_2\overset{O}{\overset{||}{C}}CH_3$ $\xrightarrow{POCl_3}$ $\xrightarrow[\text{2. } H^+]{\text{1. } CH_3CH_2MgBr}$

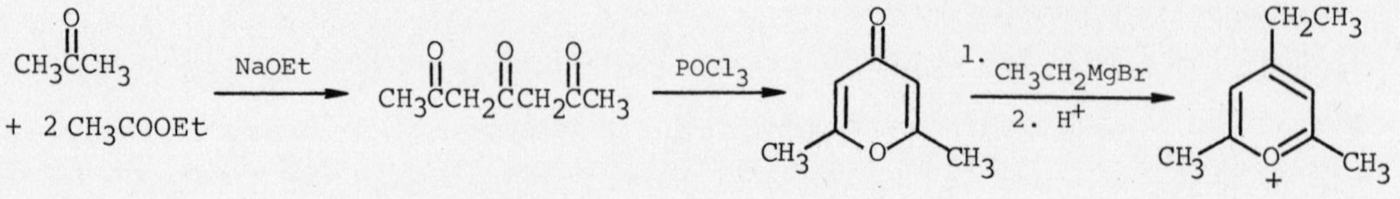

(u) $CH_3\overset{O}{\overset{||}{C}}CH_3$ + 2 C_6H_5COOEt $\xrightarrow{NaOEt}$ $C_6H_5\overset{O}{\overset{||}{C}}CH_2\overset{O}{\overset{||}{C}}CH_2\overset{O}{\overset{||}{C}}C_6H_5$ $\xrightarrow{POCl_3}$

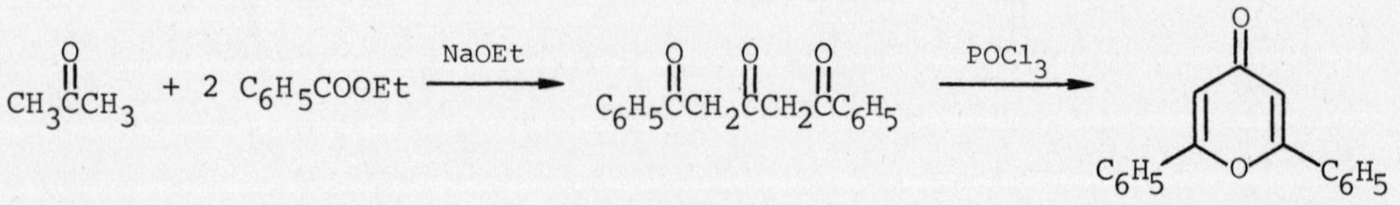

5. (a)

$$+ \quad \overset{O}{\overset{||}{HC}}N(CH_3)_2 \quad \xrightarrow{POCl_3} \quad \left[\quad \right] \quad \xrightarrow{H_2O}$$

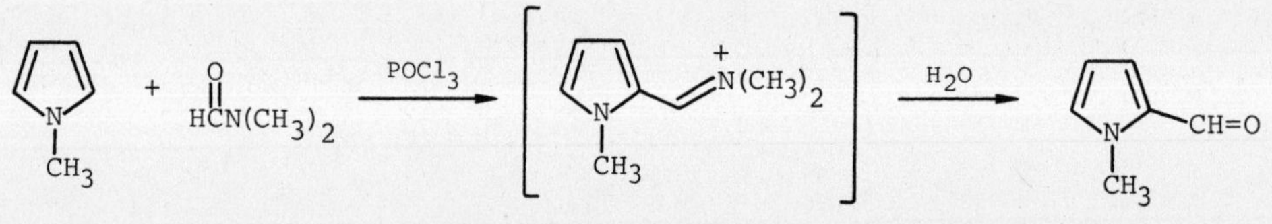

(b) [thiophene] + I_2 $\xrightarrow[\text{benzene}]{\text{HgO}}$ [2-iodothiophene] $\xrightarrow[\text{ether}]{\text{Mg}}$ $\xrightarrow{CH_3COCH_3}$ [2-(2-thienyl)propan-2-ol]

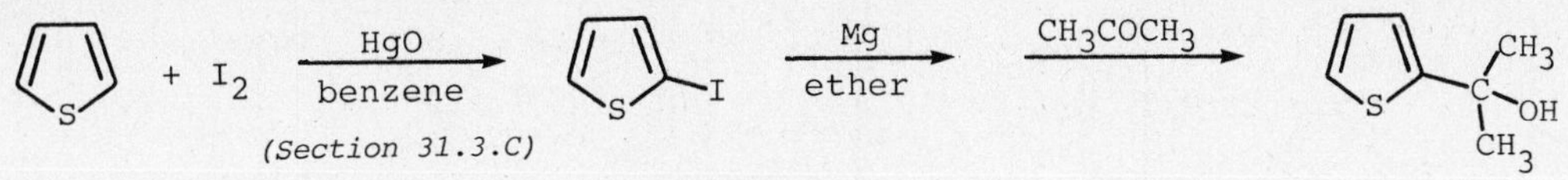

(Section 31.3.C)

(c) [isoquinoline] $\xrightarrow{C_6H_5Li}$ [1-phenylisoquinoline]

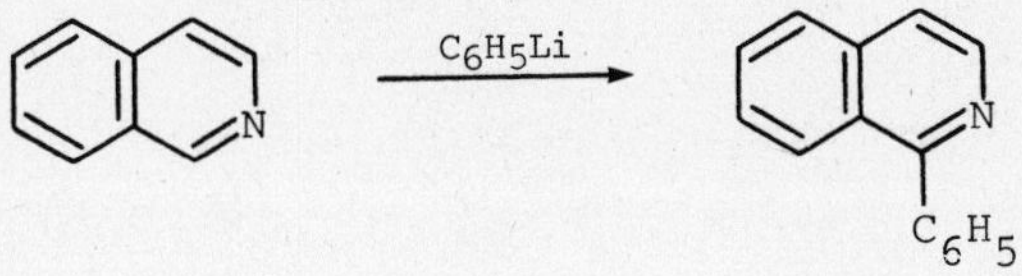

(d) [furan] $\xrightarrow[\text{dioxane}]{Br_2}$ [2-bromofuran] $\xrightarrow[\text{ether}]{\text{Mg}}$ [2-furyl MgBr] $\xrightarrow{\text{(cyclohexanone)}}$ [1-(2-furyl)cyclohexanol]

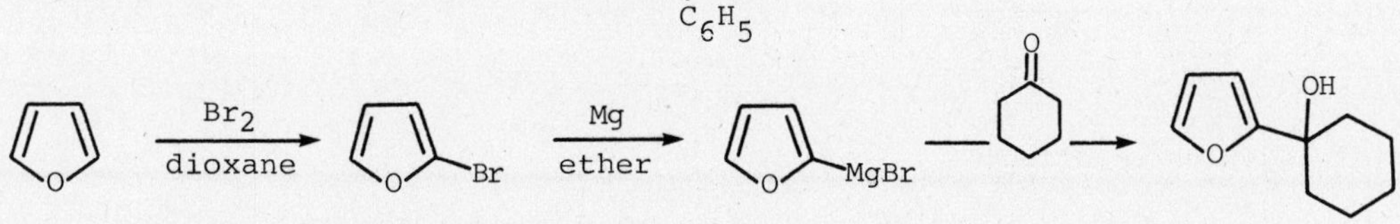

(e) Friedel–Crafts acylations occur readily on furan; only mild Lewis acids are required, if any:

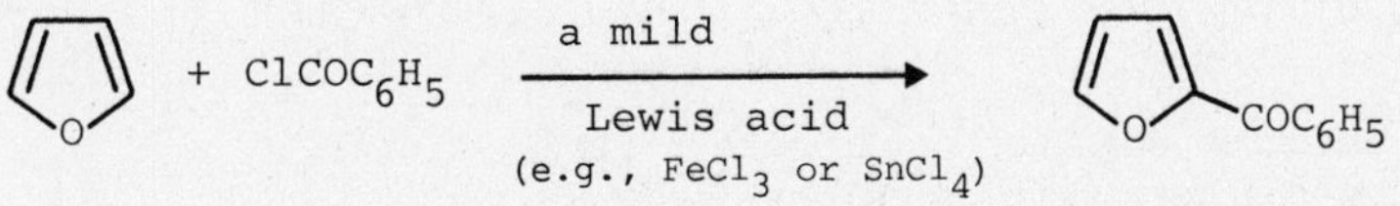

[furan] + $ClCOC_6H_5$ $\xrightarrow[\substack{\text{Lewis acid} \\ \text{(e.g., FeCl}_3 \text{ or SnCl}_4)}]{\text{a mild}}$ [2-benzoylfuran COC_6H_5]

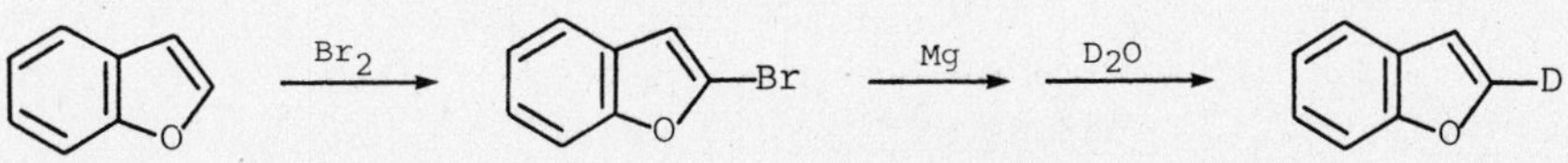

(f) [benzofuran] $\xrightarrow{Br_2}$ [2-bromobenzofuran] $\xrightarrow{\text{Mg}}$ $\xrightarrow{D_2O}$ [2-deuteriobenzofuran $-D$]

(g) [indole] + Br_2 $\xrightarrow{\text{AcOH}}$ [3-bromoindole]

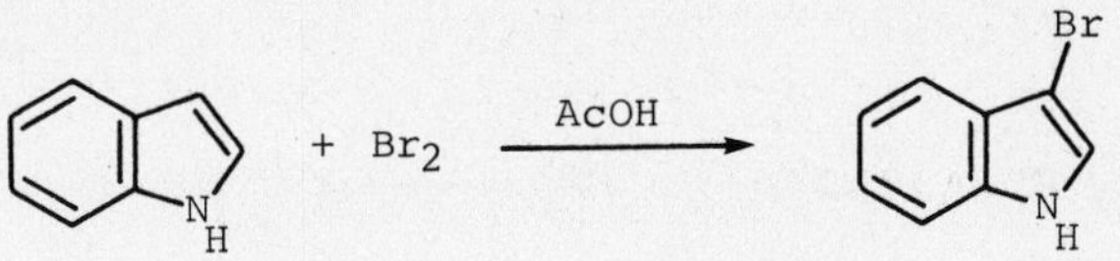

(h) [pyridine] $\xrightarrow[\substack{\text{vigorous} \\ \text{nitrating} \\ \text{conditions:}}]{}$ $\xrightarrow[\substack{H_2SO_4, \text{ Fe} \\ 300°}]{KNO_3, HNO_3}$ [3-nitropyridine NO_2]

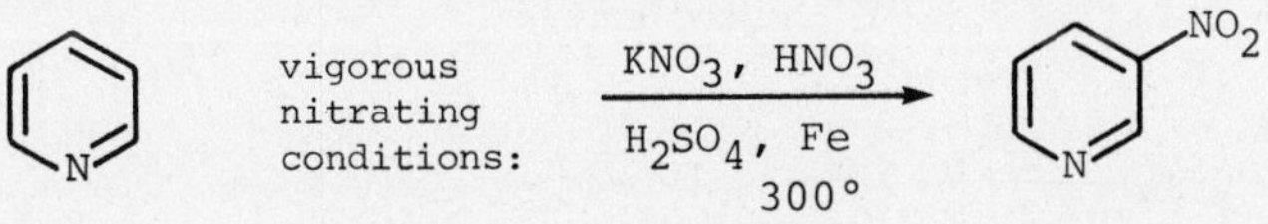

(i) α-Picoline must first be converted into the N-oxide so that nitration will occur at the γ-position:

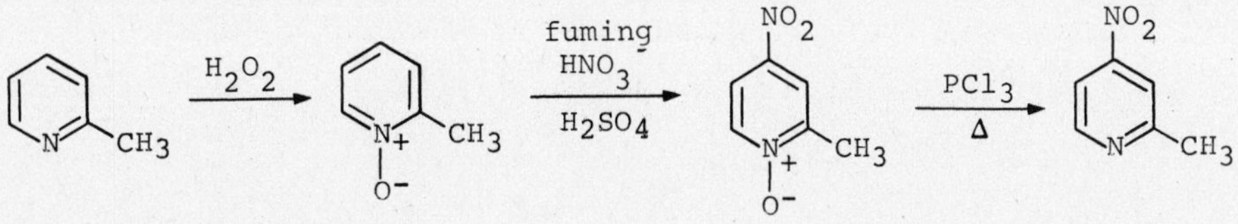

[2-methylpyridine CH_3] $\xrightarrow{H_2O_2}$ [2-methylpyridine N-oxide CH_3, O^-] $\xrightarrow[H_2SO_4]{\substack{\text{fuming} \\ HNO_3}}$ [4-nitro-2-methylpyridine N-oxide NO_2, CH_3, O^-] $\xrightarrow[\Delta]{PCl_3}$ [4-nitro-2-methylpyridine NO_2, CH_3]

(j) Chichibabin reaction:

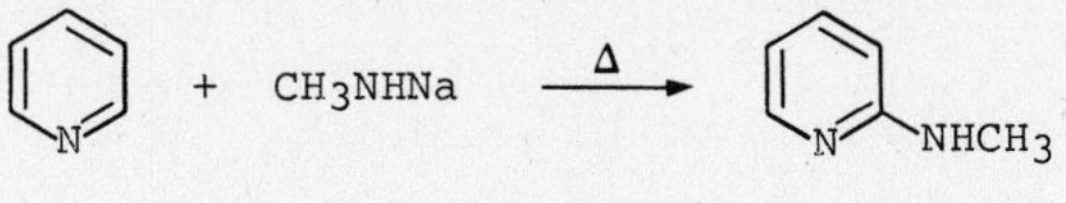

[pyridine] + CH_3NHNa $\xrightarrow{\Delta}$ [2-(methylamino)pyridine $NHCH_3$]   (Section 31.6.C)

(k) [pyridine] + CH_3CH_2Br $\longrightarrow$ [1-ethylpyridinium CH_2CH_3] $\xrightarrow{OH^-}$ [2-hydroxy-1-ethyl-1,2-dihydropyridine OH, H, CH_2CH_3] $\xrightarrow[Fe(CN)_6^{\equiv}]{[O]}$ [1-ethyl-2-pyridone CH_2CH_3]

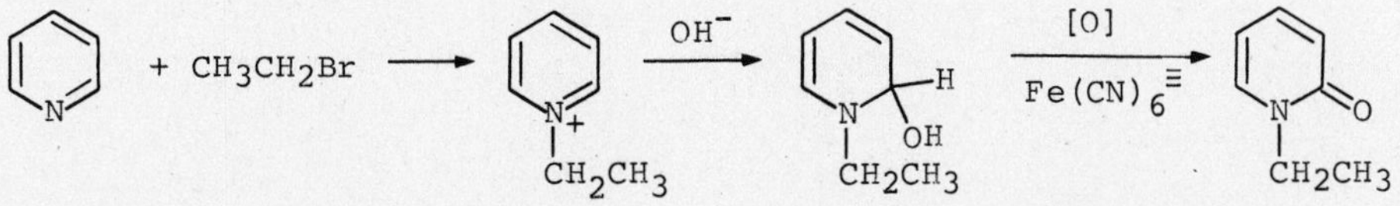

(ℓ) [2-methylquinoline CH_3] $\xrightarrow{H_2O_2}$ [2-methylquinoline N-oxide CH_3, O^-] $\xrightarrow[\substack{H_2SO_4 \\ \Delta}]{HNO_3}$ [4-nitro-2-methylquinoline N-oxide NO_2, O^-] $\xrightarrow{PCl_3}$ [4-nitro-2-methylquinoline NO_2]

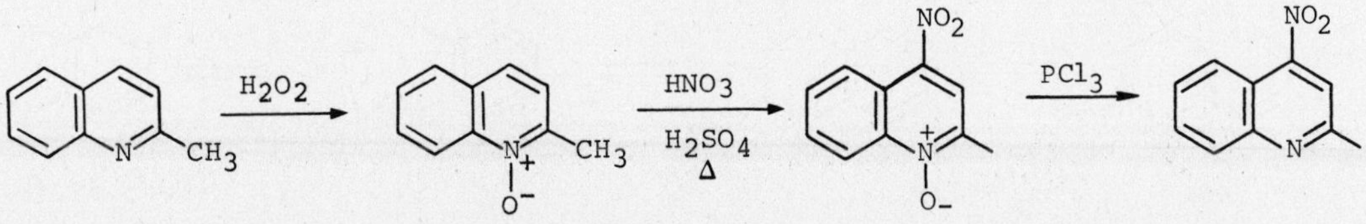

(m)

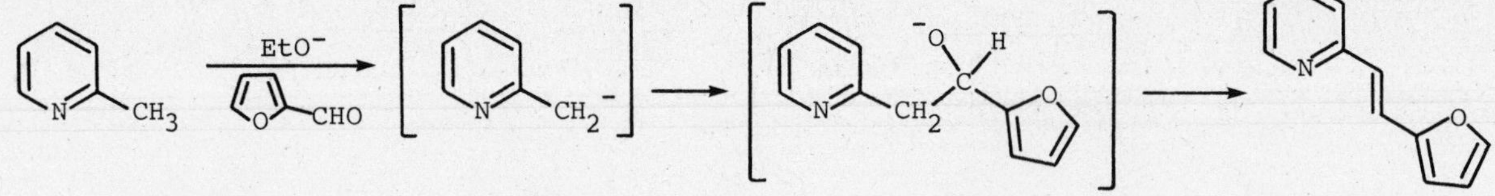

(n)

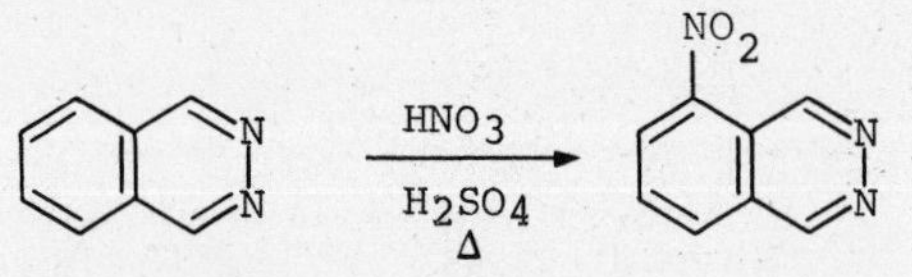

6. Michael addition reaction:

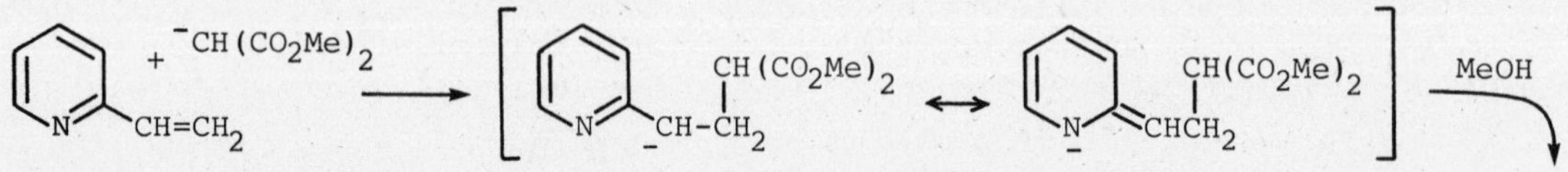

The corresponding reaction does not occur with 3-vinylpyridine because the negative charge cannot be delocalized onto the nitrogen via resonance.

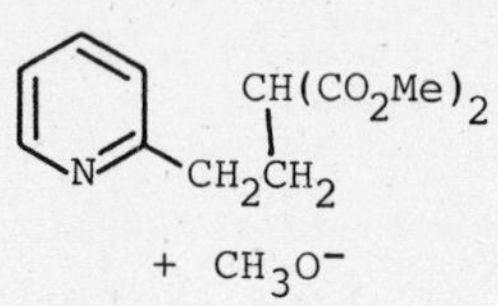

7. (a)

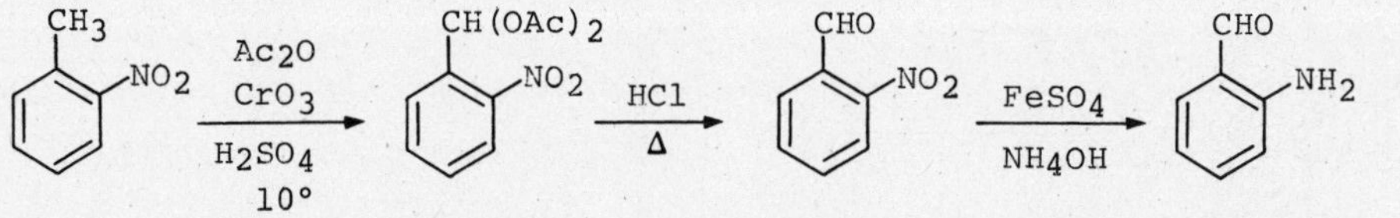

(23-24%)   (74%)   (69-75%)

(b)

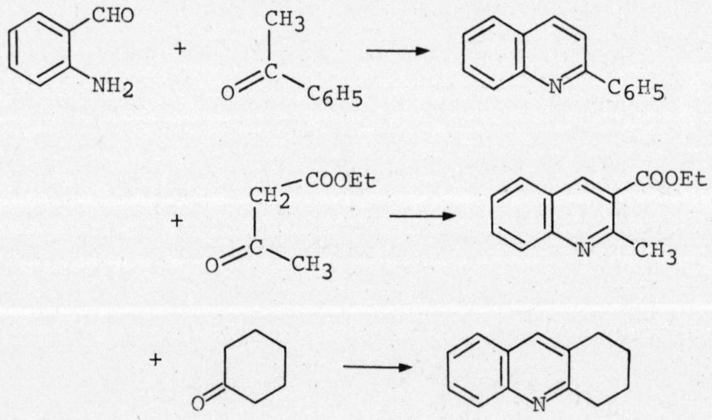

(c)

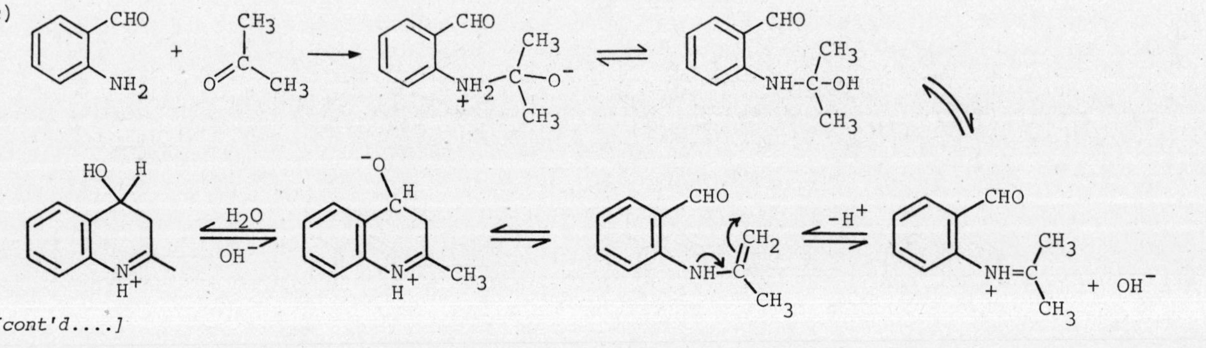

[cont'd....]

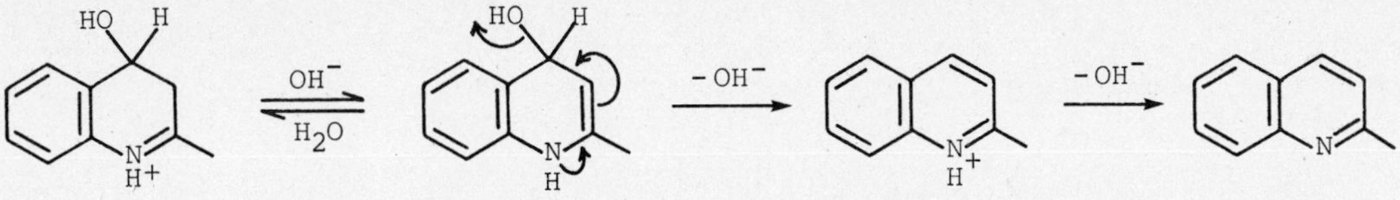

8.

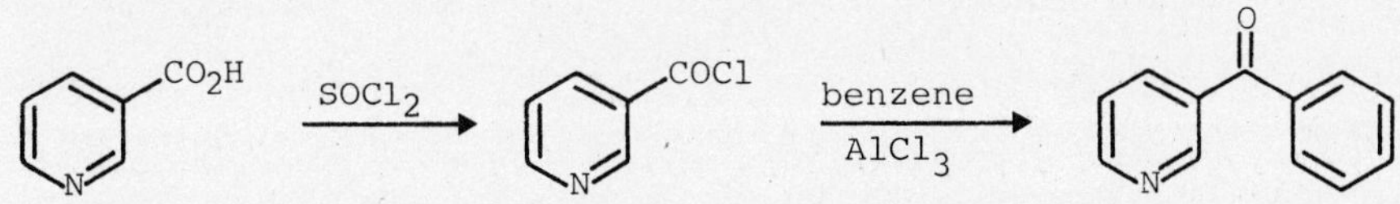

Although Friedel-Crafts acylations cannot be performed <u>on</u> pyridine, a β-pyridinecarboxylic halide can be utilized to acylate benzene. This procedure, however, does not work with the α- or γ-acids.

9.   (a) 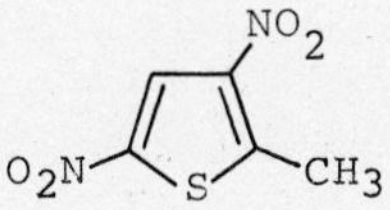   (b) 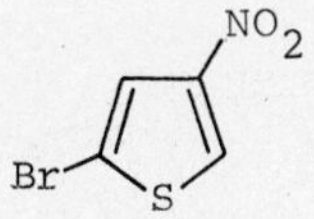   (c)

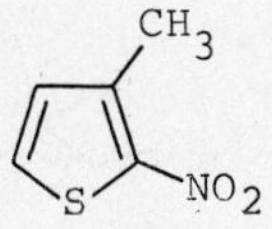

For (a)-(c), see Section 31.3.C.

(d) 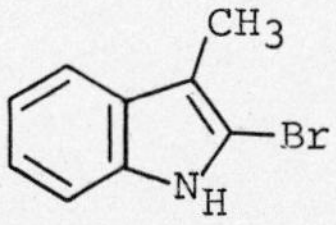   (e) 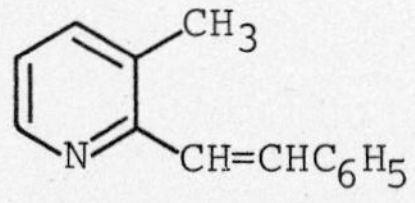   only the methyl which is conjugated to the nitrogen will react (α- or γ-methyl)

See Section 31.4.C   (see Exercise at the end of Section 31.6.C)

(f)   a Fischer indole synthesis: (g)

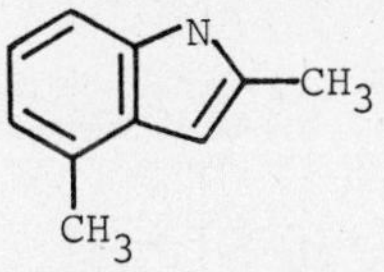

and

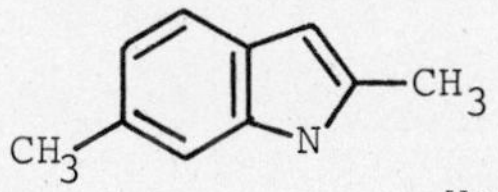

We expect a greater amount of this product, since there is less steric hindrance for the cyclization reaction.

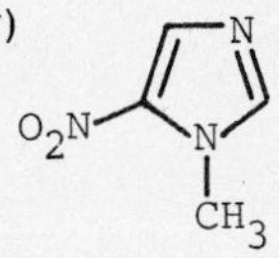

10.

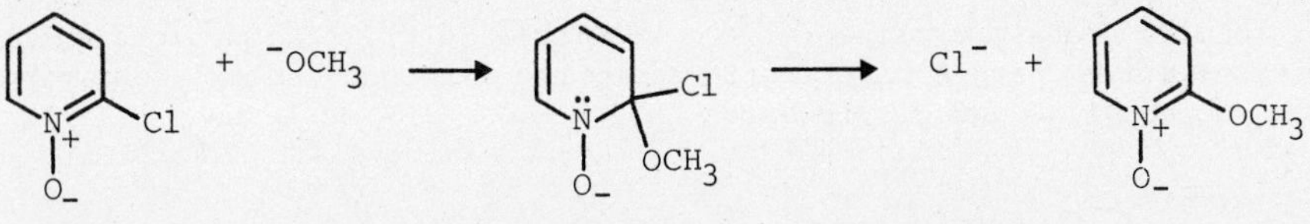

11.

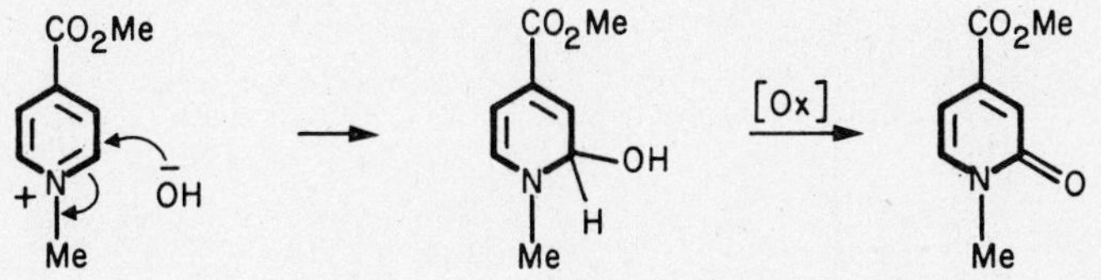

12.

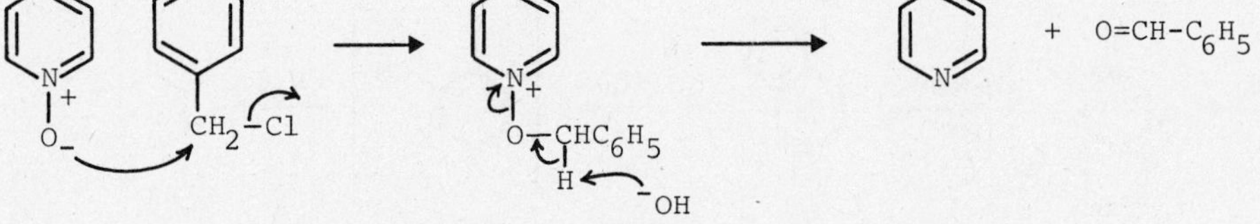

Pyridine serves as a leaving group in a reaction that is essentially an E2 reaction, and which constitutes a new aldehyde synthesis.

13.

I

II

II

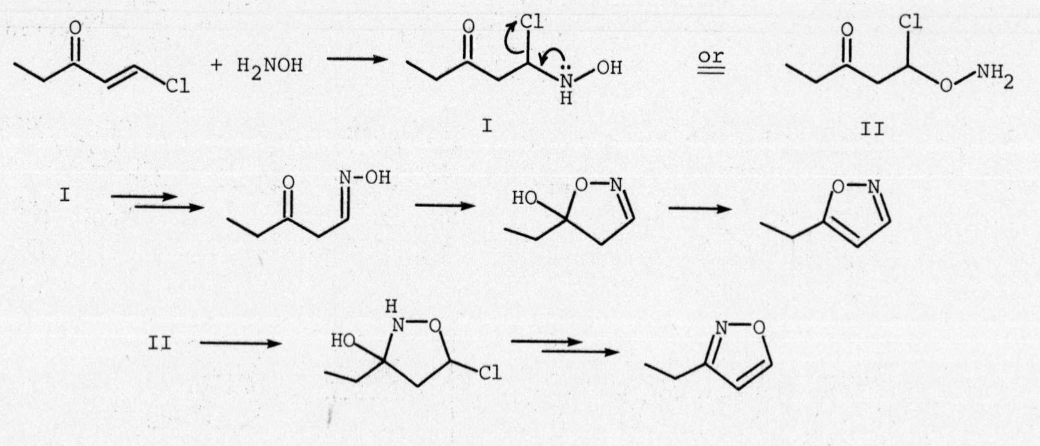

14.

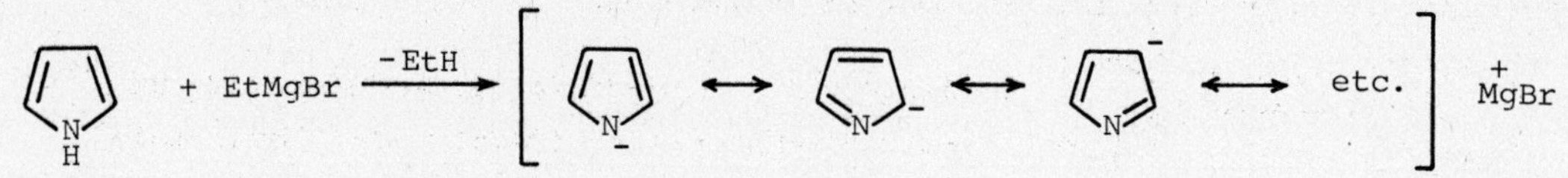

Pyrrole is rather acidic; recall cyclopentadiene (in Table 30.1). The pyrrole anion is an ambident anion with negative charges distributed among the nitrogen and all four ring carbons. The carbon is more nucleophilic and displaces on CH_3I.

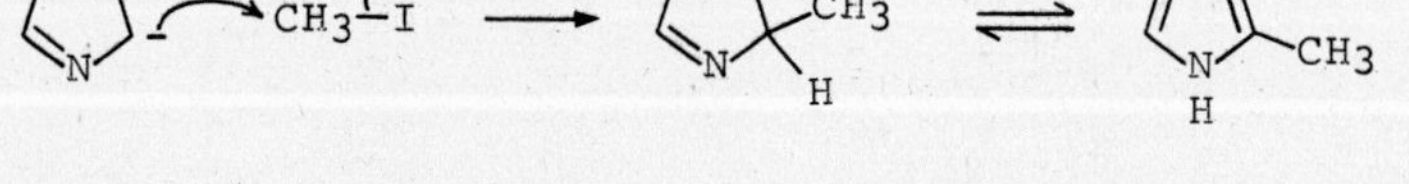

15.

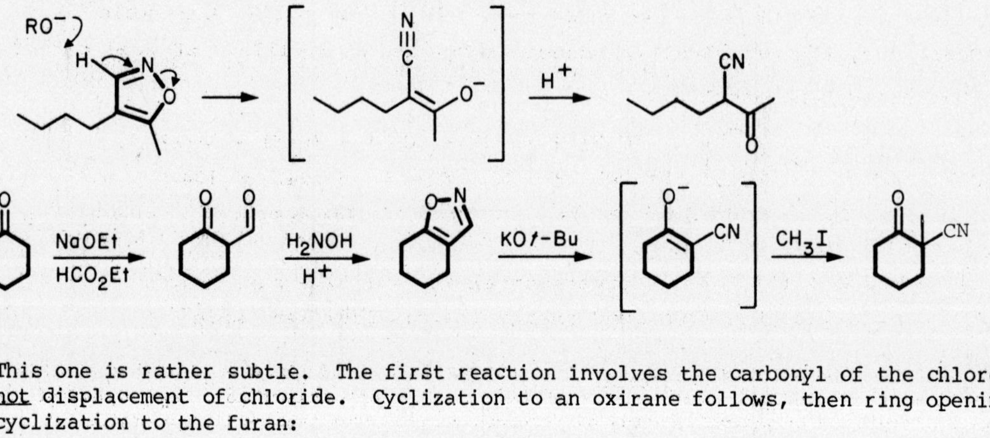

16. This one is rather subtle. The first reaction involves the carbonyl of the chloroketone, _not_ displacement of chloride. Cyclization to an oxirane follows, then ring opening and cyclization to the furan:

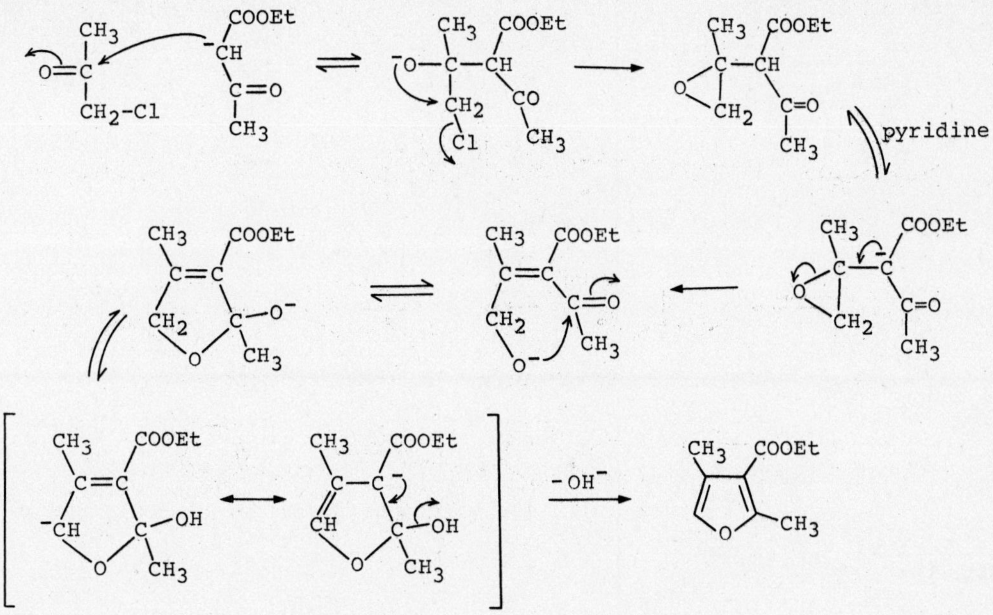

(chemical reaction schemes with structures showing CH₃, COOEt, CH₂-Cl, pyridine, etc.)

17.

(a)

$$H_2 + \text{(cyclohexene)} \longrightarrow \text{(cyclohexane)} \qquad \Delta H° = -28.4 \text{ kcal mole}^{-1}$$

   −1.1   −29.5

$$H_2 + \text{(dihydropyridine)} \longrightarrow \text{(piperidine)} \qquad \Delta H° = -21 \text{ kcal mole}^{-1}$$

Therefore, for pyridine (two C=C bonds and one C=N bond), we would expect:

$$\text{(pyridine)} \xrightarrow{3\,H_2} \text{(piperidine)}$$

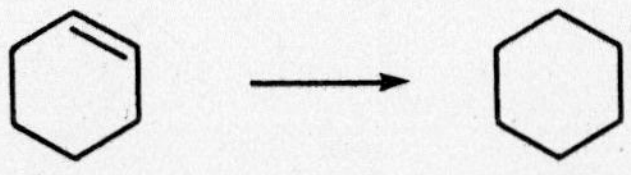

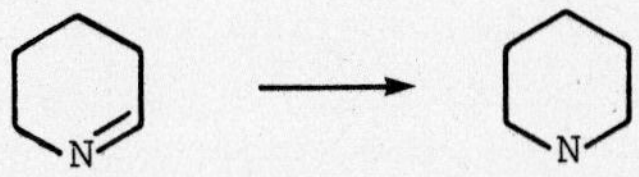

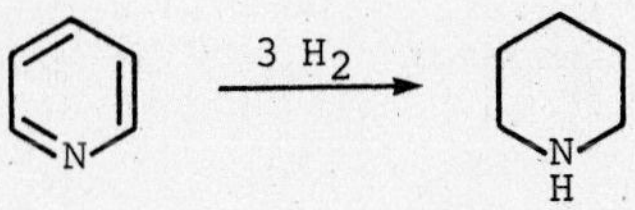

predicted $\Delta H° = 2 \times (-28.4) - 21 = -77.8$ kcal mole^{-1}

actual $\Delta H° = -11.8 - (34.6) = -46.4$ kcal mole^{-1}

The resonance energy is $-46.4 - (-77.8) = 31.4$ kcal mole^{-1}
This empirical resonance energy is similar to that of benzene.

(b)

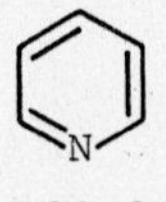

$$\text{(pyridine)} \longrightarrow 5\,C + 5\,H + N \qquad \Delta H°_{atomiz.} = 1193.4 \text{ kcal mole}^{-1}$$

                    $5 \times 170.9 \quad 5 \times 52.1 \quad 113.0$
+34.6

Bond energies: $5\,C\text{-}H + 2\,C\text{=}C + 2\,C\text{-}C + N\text{-}C + N\text{=}C$

$5 \times 99 + 2 \times 146 + 2 \times 83 + 73 + 147 = 1173$ kcal mole^{-1}

Therefore, the empirical resonance energy is $1193 - 1173 = 20$ kcal mole^{-1}

Note that using bond energies,

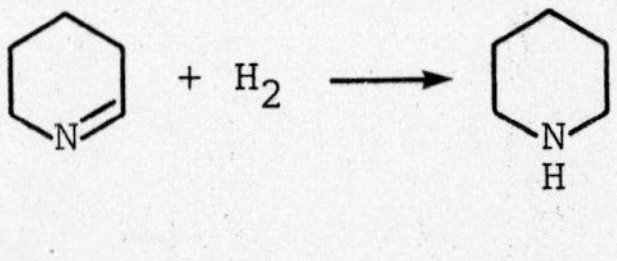

$$\text{(dihydropyridine)} + H_2 \longrightarrow \text{(piperidine)}$$

$(C\text{-}H) + (N\text{-}H) + (C\text{-}N) - (C\text{=}N) - (H\text{-}H)$

$= 99 + 93 + 73 - 147 - 104$

$\Delta H° = -14$ kcal mole^{-1} The experimental value used in
                                   part (a) is -21 kcal mole^{-1}.

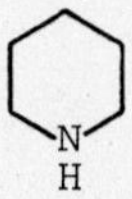

$$\text{(piperidine)} \longrightarrow 5\,C + 11\,H + N \qquad \text{experimental } \Delta H° = 1552.4 \text{ kcal mole}^{-1}$$

calculated from bond energy Table: 1561 kcal mole^{-1}

The Table of bond energies gives $\Delta H°_{atomiz.}$ that are accurate to ±1% or less, but this still amounts to several kcal mole^{-1}; i.e., in practice, the $\Delta H°$ we calculate only amount to a few percent of the total atomization energies. In general, energy differences derived from average bond energies can have substantial errors.

18. Compare the bond dipole of $C-Br$ in [structure] with that for [furan-Br structure]

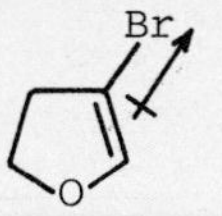

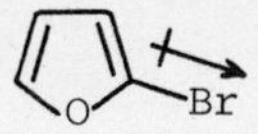

0.91 D < 1.46 D; therefore [furan structure]

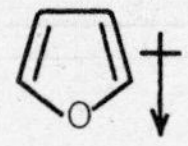

The similarity between   [Br–thiophene–Br, 1.1 D] – [thiophene, 0.51 D] = 0.6 D

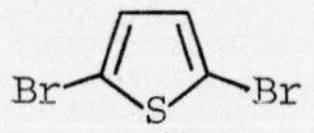

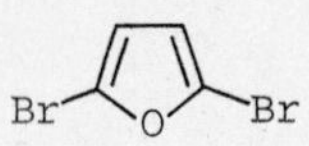

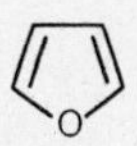

and   [Br–furan–Br, 1.63 D] – [furan, 0.70 D] = 0.9 D

suggests [thiophene structure] for thiophene. If the thiophene dipole were in the opposite direction, the effect of the bromines could not be rationalized.

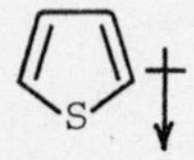

In the case of pyrrole, [oxazole structure] net 2.8 D , but [imidazole structure, 6.2 D] strongly suggests [pyrrole structure, 1.81 D]

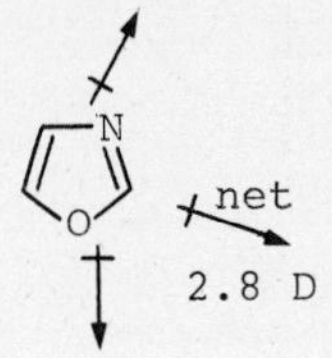

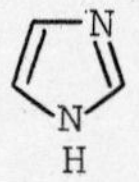

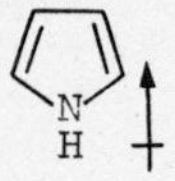

19. 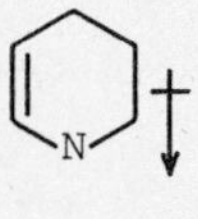 [dihydropyridine structure] ; [piperidine structure] is also ↓ , and pyridine is expected to be enhanced in this direction by polarization, as suggested by resonance structures such as: [pyridine resonance structure]

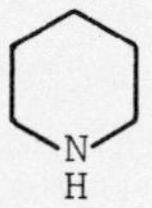

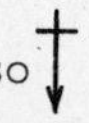

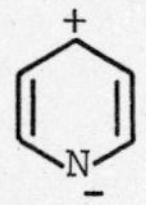

20.

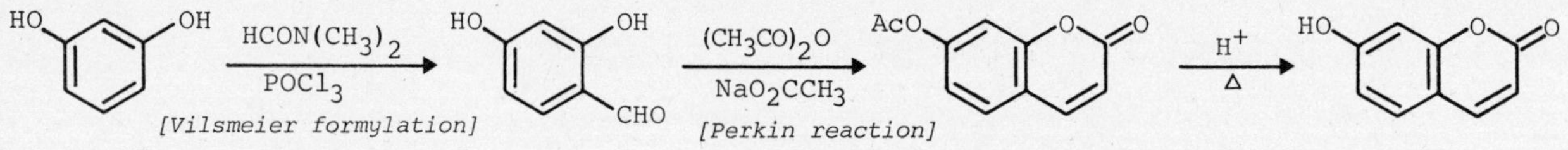

[resorcinol] $\xrightarrow[\text{POCl}_3]{\text{HCON(CH}_3)_2}$ [2,4-dihydroxybenzaldehyde] $\xrightarrow[\text{NaO}_2\text{CCH}_3]{\text{(CH}_3\text{CO)}_2\text{O}}$ [AcO-coumarin] $\xrightarrow[\Delta]{\text{H}^+}$ [7-hydroxycoumarin]

[Vilsmeier formylation]   [Perkin reaction]

$$\begin{bmatrix} \text{or Reimer-Tiemann:} \\ \text{CHCl}_3, \text{ OH}^- \end{bmatrix}$$

NOTE: the lactone ring hydrolyzes less readily than a normal phenol ester, especially in acid.

21. For $C_{20}H_{21}O_4N$, Zeisel determination gives the partial formula $C_{19}H_9N(OCH_3)_4$. The oxidation to a ketone indicates: $C_{15}H_7N(CH_2)(OCH_3)_4 \longrightarrow C_{15}H_7N(CO)(OCH_3)_4$

The oxidation products from the ketone can be explained on the basis that the initial products undergo further reaction:

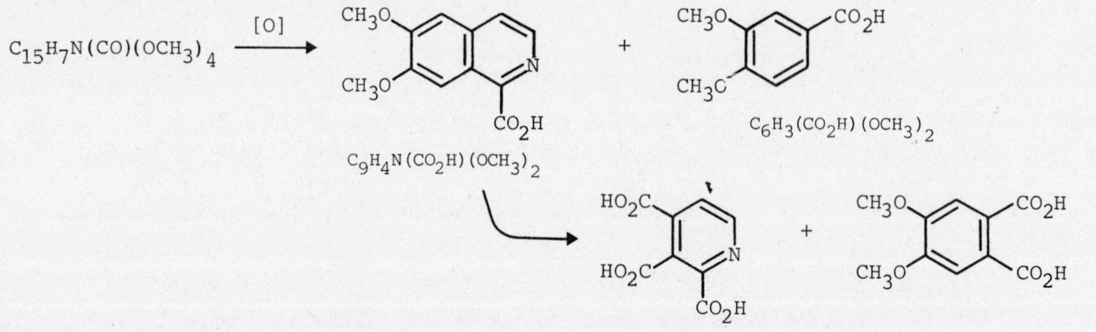

$C_{15}H_7N(CO)(OCH_3)_4 \xrightarrow{[O]}$ [isoquinoline-CO₂H structure, $C_9H_4N(CO_2H)(OCH_3)_2$] + [benzene structure, $C_6H_3(CO_2H)(OCH_3)_2$]

[pyridine tricarboxylic acid structure] + [dimethoxy benzene dicarboxylic acid structure]

Note that the two primary products are $C_{15} \rightarrow C_9 + C_6$; this is the only combination that can give the molecular formula of the ketone by working backwards. Furthermore, the CO_2H of both primary product carboxylic acids must come from the same ketone carbonyl. Thus, the structures of the ketone and of papaverine must be:

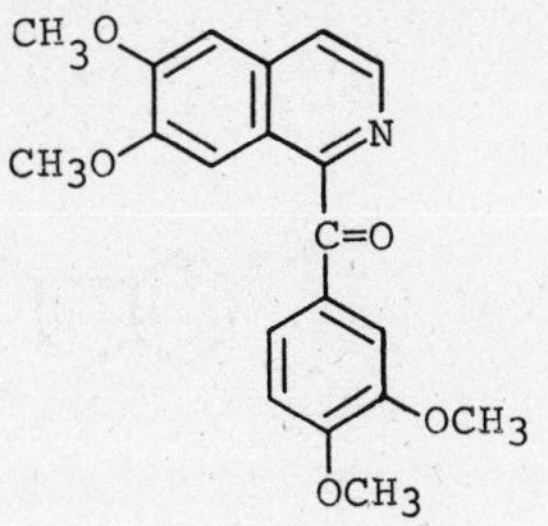

ketone 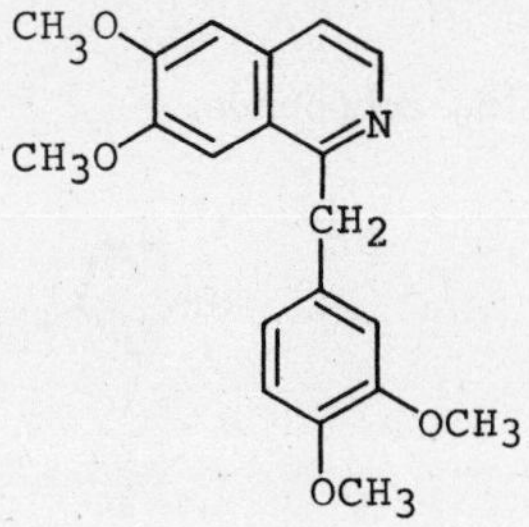   *papaverine*

22.

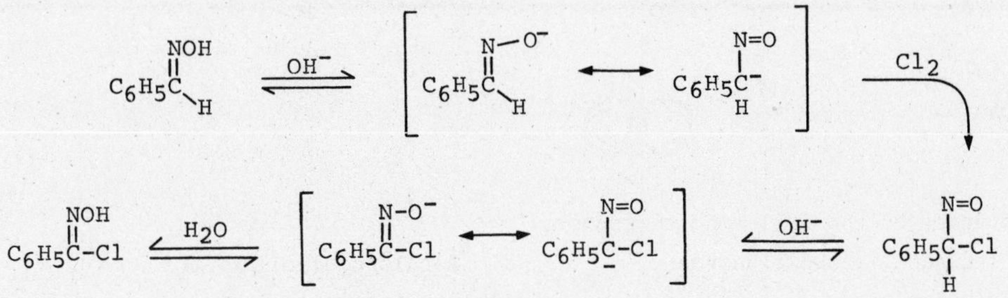

This mechanism is actually similar to the chlorination of phenol in basic solution *(Section 26.6.A)*.

23.

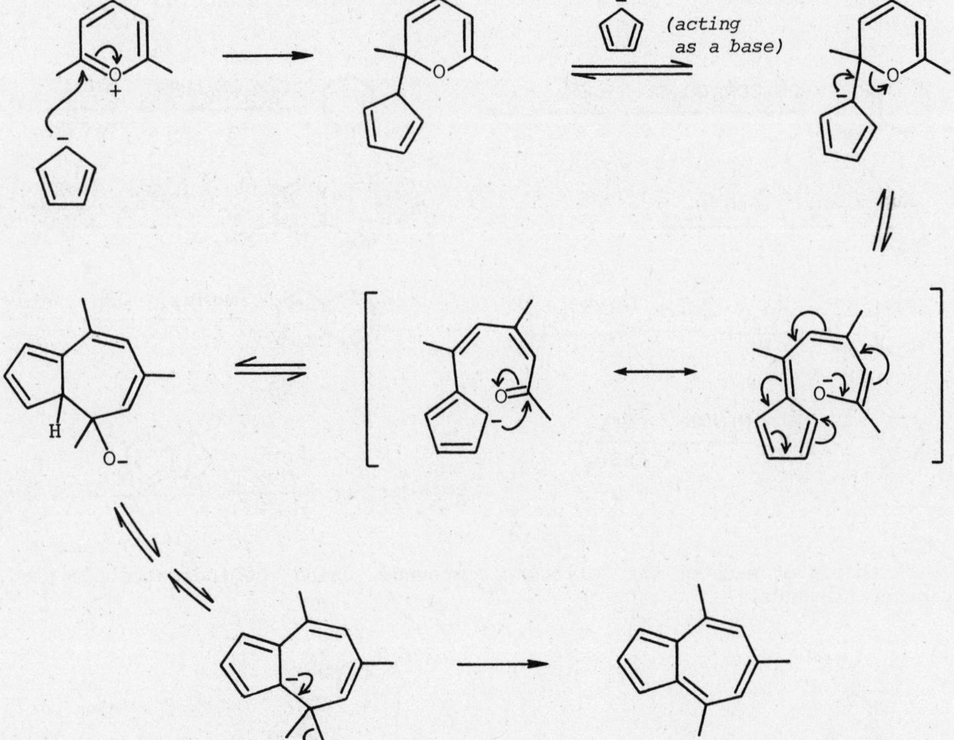

(acting as a base)

31.F   **Supplementary Problems**

S1.   Name each of the following compounds.

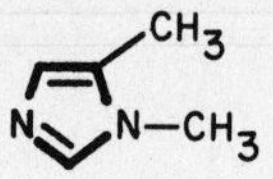

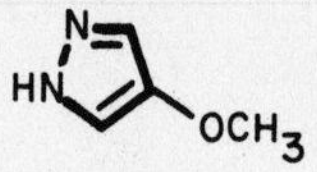

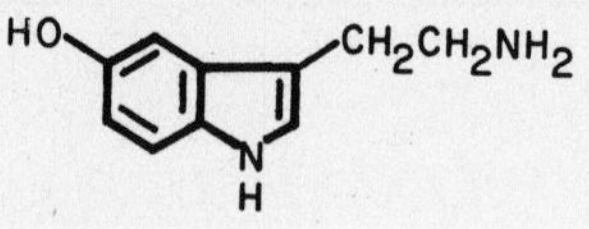

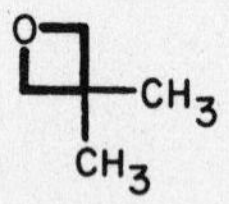

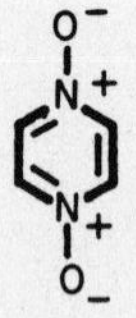

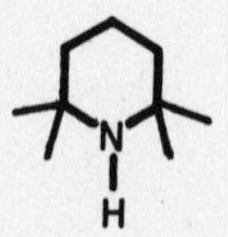

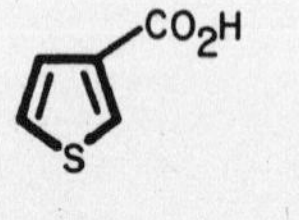

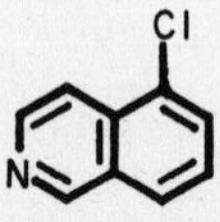

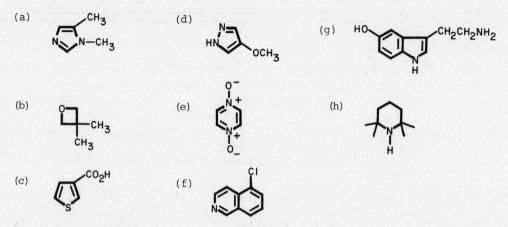

S2.   Write the structures of the following compounds.

    (a)   4-bromofuran-3-carboxaldehyde   (e)   2-chloroquinoline

    (b)   3-nitrobenzofuran   (f)   5-nitroisoxazole

    (c)   trans-2,3-diphenyloxirane   (g)   6-methylthiopurine

    (d)   N-acetylpyrrole   (h)   2-methylthietane

S3.   What is the major product to result from each of the following reaction sequences?

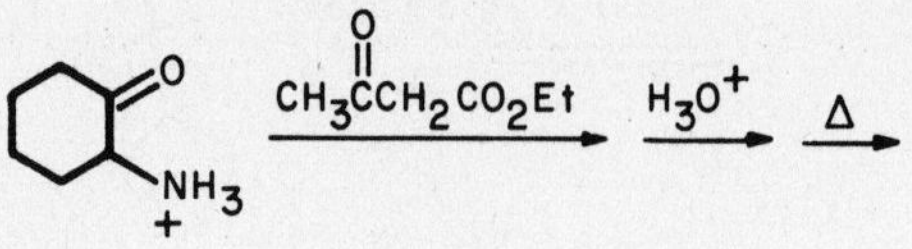

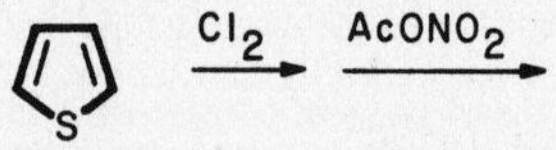

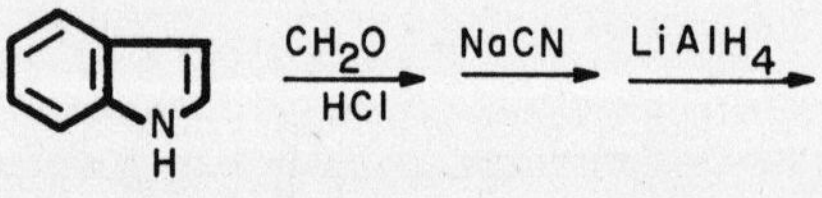

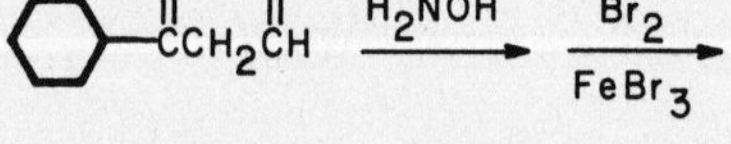

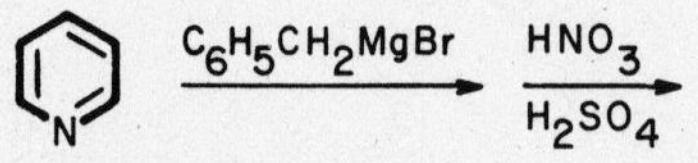

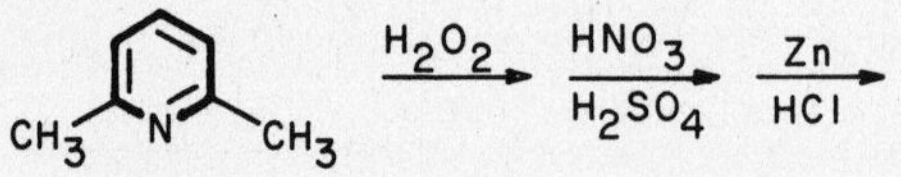

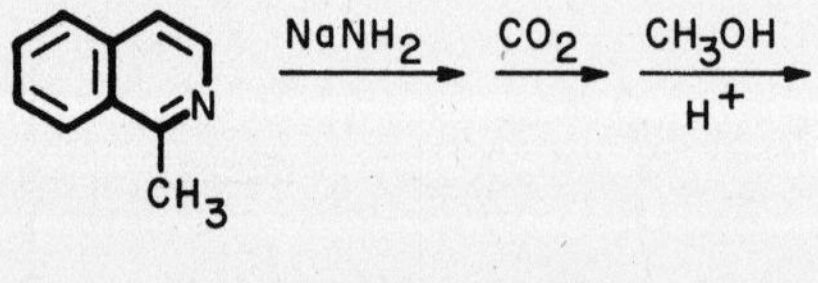

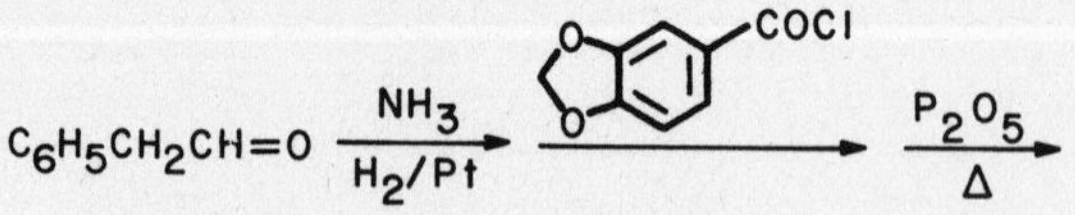

S4.   Devise a synthesis of each of the following compounds, using the indicated starting material and any other reagents.

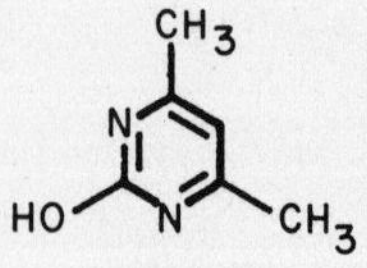

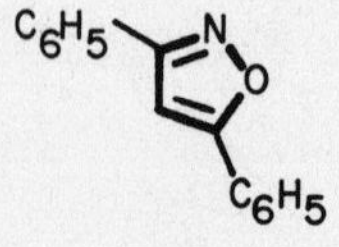

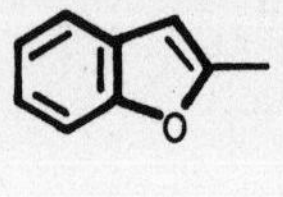

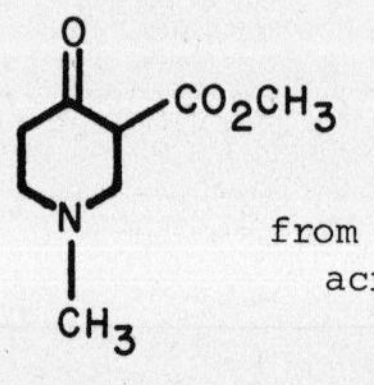

(e) 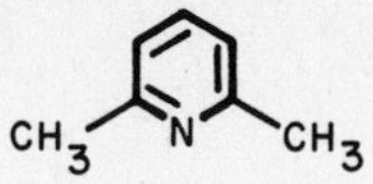 from acetic acid

(g) 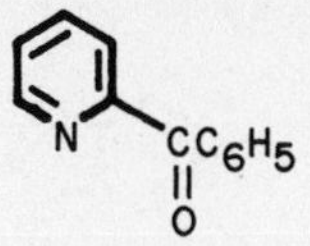 from pyridine

(f) 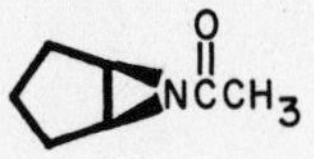 from cyclopentane

(h) 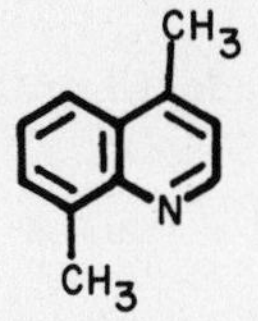 from toluene

S5. Show how to synthesize each of the following compounds from non-heterocyclic precursors.

(a)

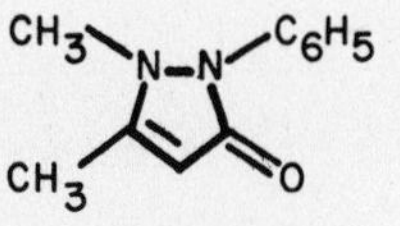

antipyrine, an ingredient in many
commercial headache remedies

(b)

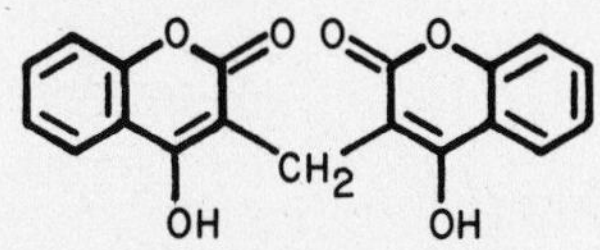

dicumarol, a compound isolated from sweet clover
which causes a severe bleeding tendency in cattle

(c)

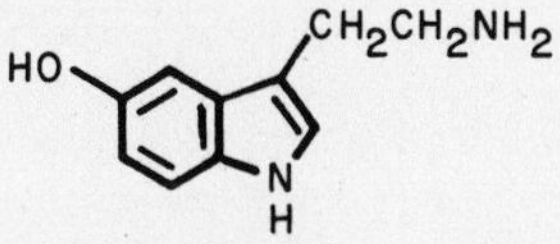

serotonin, one of the molecules involved in
the transmission of nerve impulses in the brain

(d)

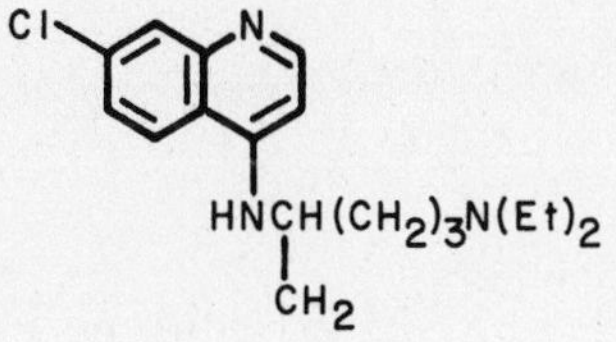

chloroquine, an important
antimalarial drug

(e)

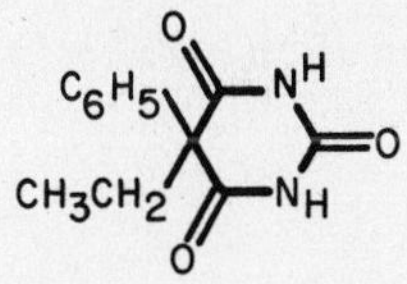

phenobarbital, one of the
barbiturates (sedatives, depressants)

S6. Write a reasonable mechanism for each of the following transformations.

(a)

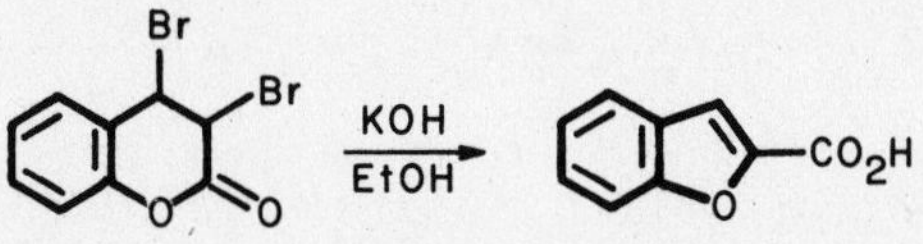

(b)

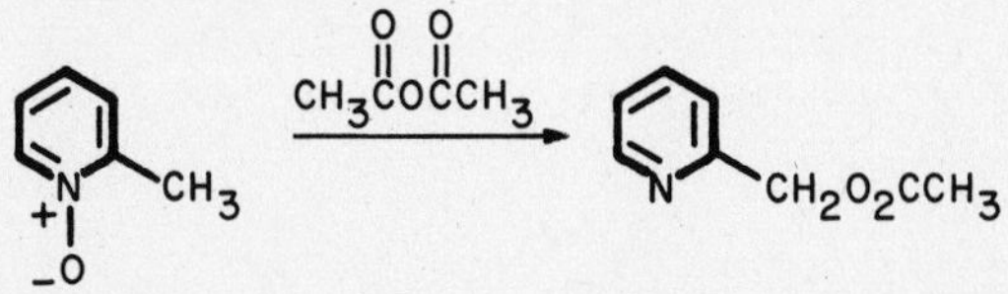

(c)

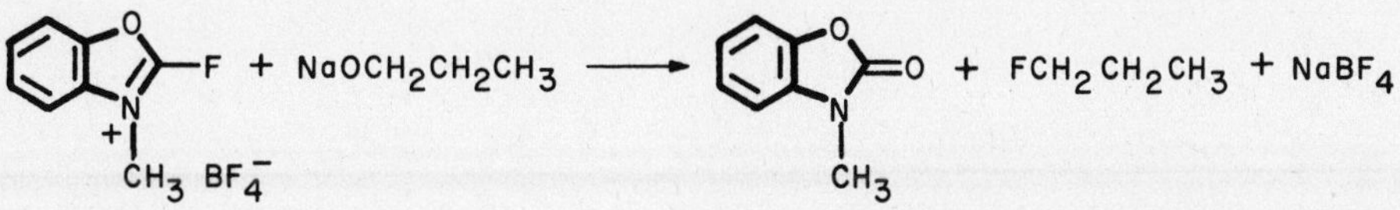

(d)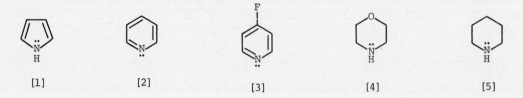

S7. Rank the following compounds in order of **basicity**.

[1]   [2]   [3]   [4]   [5]

S8. Explain the differences in reactivity of the three furan derivatives illustrated below:

*very fast reaction,
even at −50 °C*

reacts at room temperature

no reaction, even at 100 °C

31.G   Answers to Supplementary Problems

S1.   (a)   1,5-dimethylimidazole   (e)   pyrazine di-N-oxide
         (b)   3,3-dimethyloxetane   (f)   5-chloroisoquinoline
         (c)   3-thiophenecarboxylic acid   (g)   3-(2-aminoethyl)-5-hydroxyindole   (serotonin)
         (d)   4-methoxypyrazole   (h)   2,2,6,6-tetramethylpiperidine

S2.

(a) 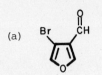   (b) 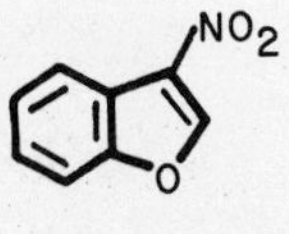 [structure: benzofuran with NO₂]   (c) [C₆H₅ epoxide C₆H₅]   (d) 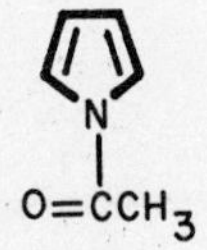 [N-acetyl pyrrole]

(e) 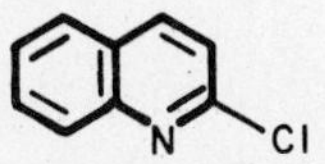 [2-chloroquinoline]   (f) 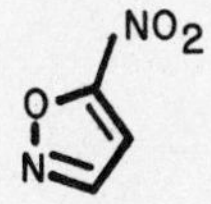 [5-nitroisoxazole]   (g) 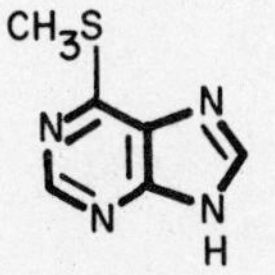 [6-(methylthio)purine]   (h) 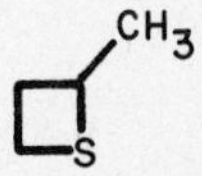 [2-methylthietane]

S3.

(a) 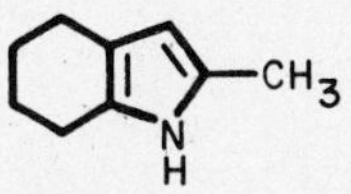 [4,5,6,7-tetrahydro-2-methylindole]   (b) 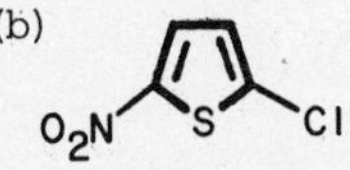 [2-chloro-5-nitrothiophene]   (c) 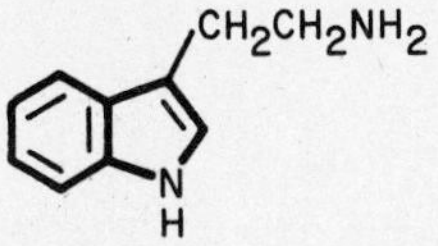 [3-(2-aminoethyl)indole]   (d) [5-cyclohexyl-4-bromoisoxazole]

(e) 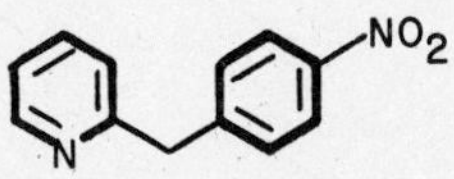 [2-(4-nitrobenzyl)pyridine]   (f) 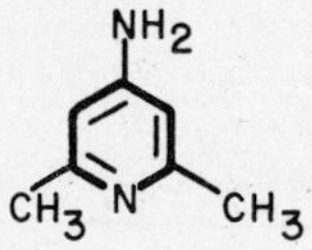 [4-amino-2,6-dimethylpyridine]   (g) 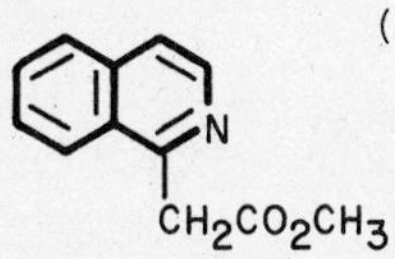 [1-isoquinolyl CH₂CO₂CH₃]   (h) 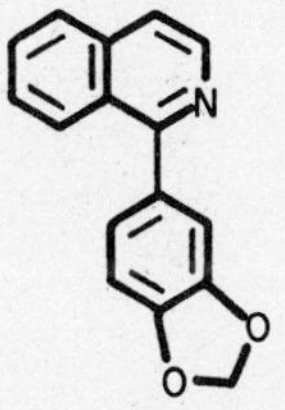 [1-(benzodioxolyl)isoquinoline]

S4.

(a)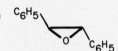

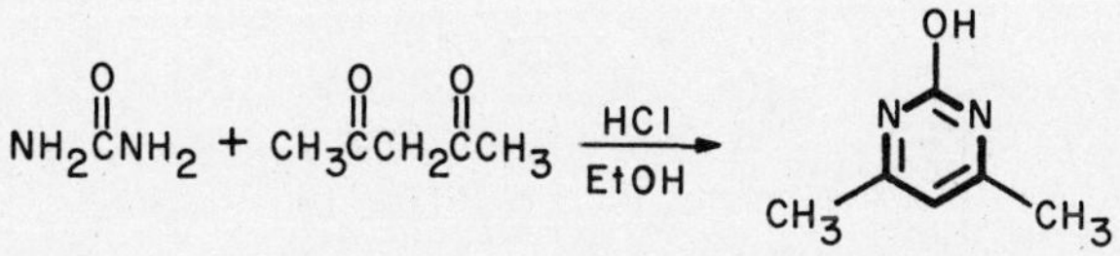

$$NH_2\overset{\overset{\displaystyle O}{\|}}{C}NH_2 + CH_3\overset{\overset{\displaystyle O}{\|}}{C}CH_2\overset{\overset{\displaystyle O}{\|}}{C}CH_3 \xrightarrow[\text{EtOH}]{\text{HCl}}$$ [2-hydroxy-4,6-dimethylpyrimidine]

(b) $C_6H_5OH \xrightarrow[\underset{\underset{CH_3}{|}}{CH_2=C-CH_2Br}]{NaOH} \xrightarrow{\Delta}$ [o-methallylphenol] $\xrightarrow[P_2O_5]{O_3}$ [2-methylbenzofuran]

(c) $C_6H_5CH_3 \xrightarrow[h\nu]{Br_2} \xrightarrow{NaNO_2} C_6H_5CH_2NO_2 \xrightarrow{C_6H_5NCO} C_6H_5\overset{+}{C}\equiv\overset{-}{N}-O^-$

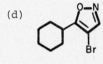 [3,5-diphenylisoxazole: C₆H₅ ... C₆H₅]

$C_6H_5CH_3 \downarrow \overset{2Br_2,}{\underset{h\nu}{}}$

$\downarrow NaOH$

$C_6H_5CH=O \xrightarrow{CH_3MgBr} \xrightarrow{H_2SO_4} C_6H_5CH=CH_2 \xrightarrow{Br_2} \xrightarrow{NaNH_2} C_6H_5C\equiv CH$

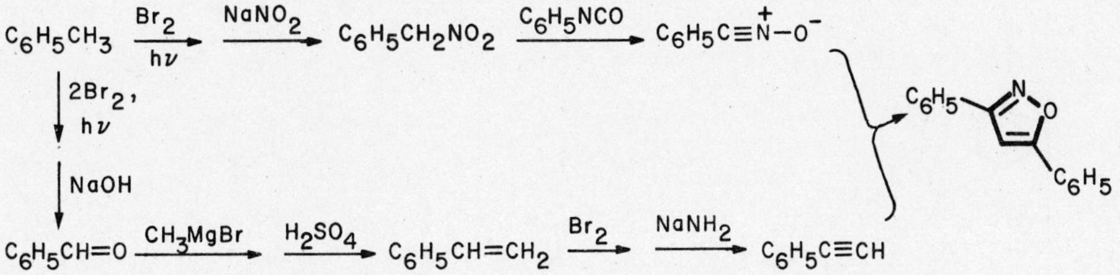

or

$C_6H_5CH_3 \xrightarrow{KMnO_4} C_6H_5CO_2H \xrightarrow[H^+]{CH_3OH} C_6H_5CO_2CH_3$

$\downarrow CH_3Li$

$C_6H_5\overset{\overset{\displaystyle O}{\|}}{C}CH_3 \xrightarrow{NaOCH_3}$ $C_6H_5\overset{\overset{\displaystyle O}{\|}}{C}CH_2\overset{\overset{\displaystyle O}{\|}}{C}C_6H_5 \xrightarrow[H^+,\Delta]{H_2NOH}$ [3,5-diphenylisoxazole: C₆H₅ ... C₆H₅]

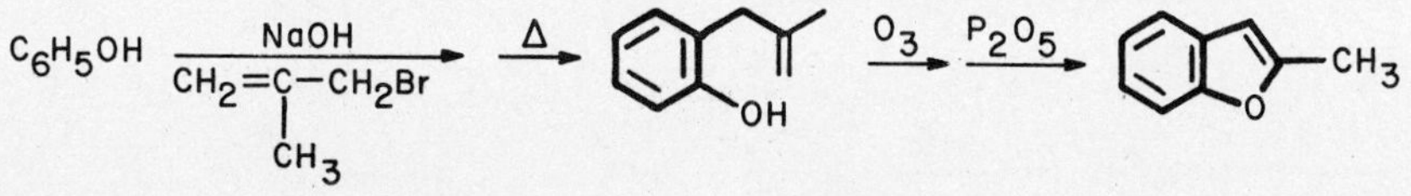

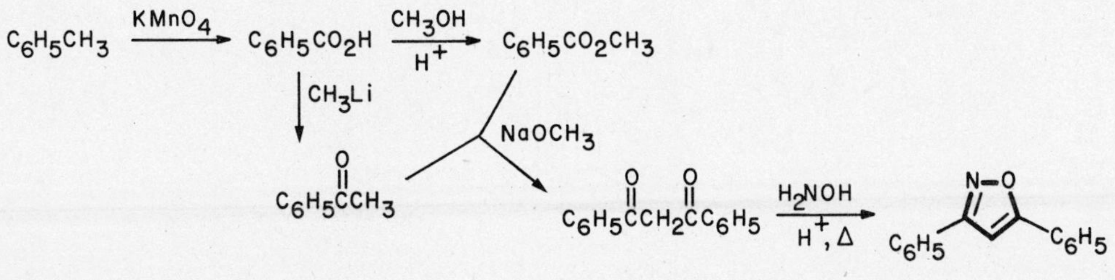

(d) CH_3NH_2 + $2CH_2=CH_2CO_2CH_3$ ⟶ [structure] $\xrightarrow[\Delta]{NaOCH_3}$ [structure]

(e) CH_3CO_2H $\xrightarrow[H^+,\Delta]{CH_3OH}$ $\xrightarrow[\Delta]{NaOCH_3}$ $CH_3CCH_2CO_2CH_3$ $\xrightarrow[CH_2O]{NH_3}$ [structure]

$\xleftarrow[\Delta]{H_3O^+}$ [structure] $\xleftarrow{HNO_3}$

(f) [structure] $\xrightarrow{INCO}$ $\xrightarrow{NaOH}$ [structure] $\xrightarrow{Ac_2O}$ [structure]

(g) [structure] + $C_6H_5CH_2Li$ ⟶ [structure] $\xrightarrow{CrO_3}$ [structure] $\xrightarrow{PCl_3}$ [structure]

(h) toluene $\xrightarrow[H_2SO_4]{HNO_3}$ $\xrightarrow[HCl]{Zn}$ [structure] $\xrightarrow[FeCl_3, ZnCl_2]{CH_2=CHCCH_3}$ [structure]

S5. (a) $CH_3CCH_2CCH_3$ + $CH_3NHNHC_6H_5$ $\xrightarrow{-H_2O}$ [structure] $\xrightarrow{-CH_3OH}$ [structure]

(b) [structure] + $CH_3CO_2CH_3$ $\xrightarrow{NaOCH_3}$ [structure] ⟶ [structure]

[structure] $\xleftarrow{-H_2O}$ [structure] $\xleftarrow{CH_2O}$ [structure] ⟲ $NaOCH_3$

⟶ [structure]

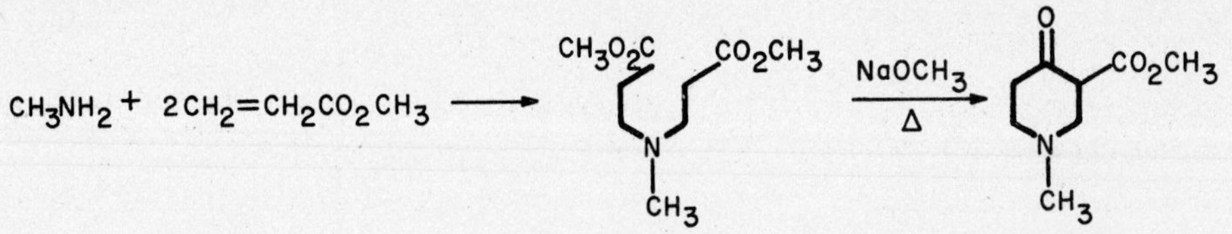

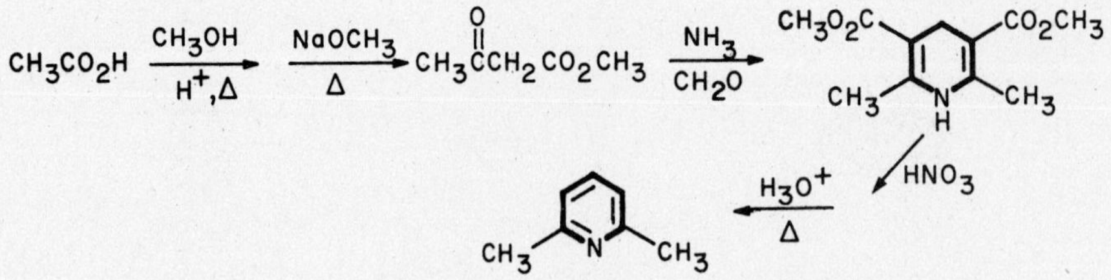

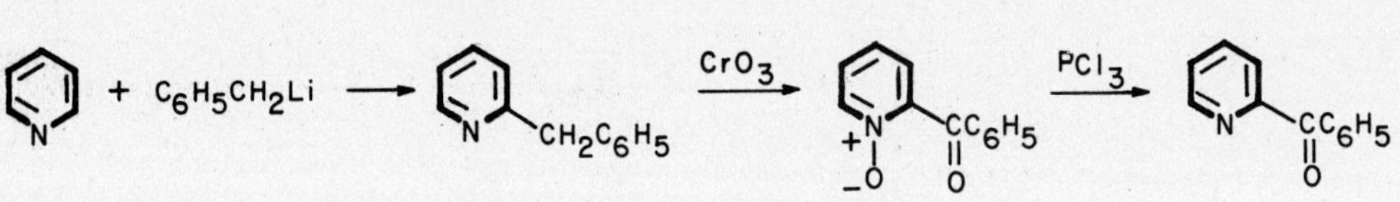

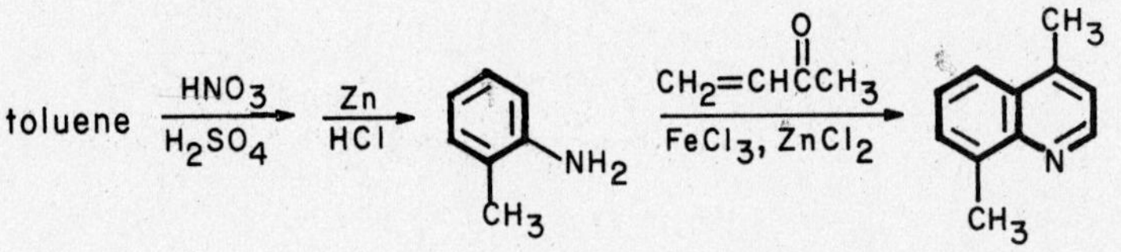

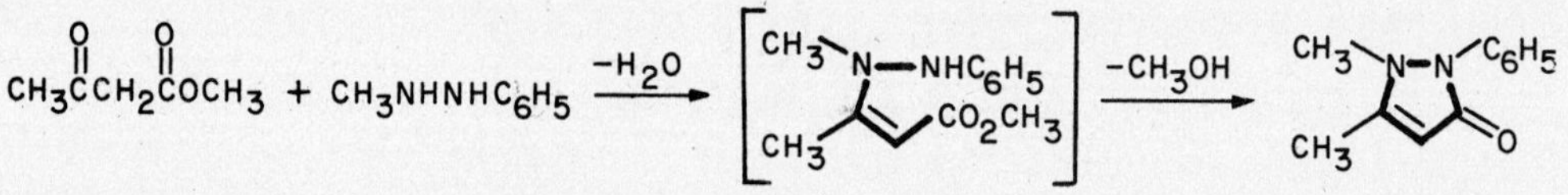

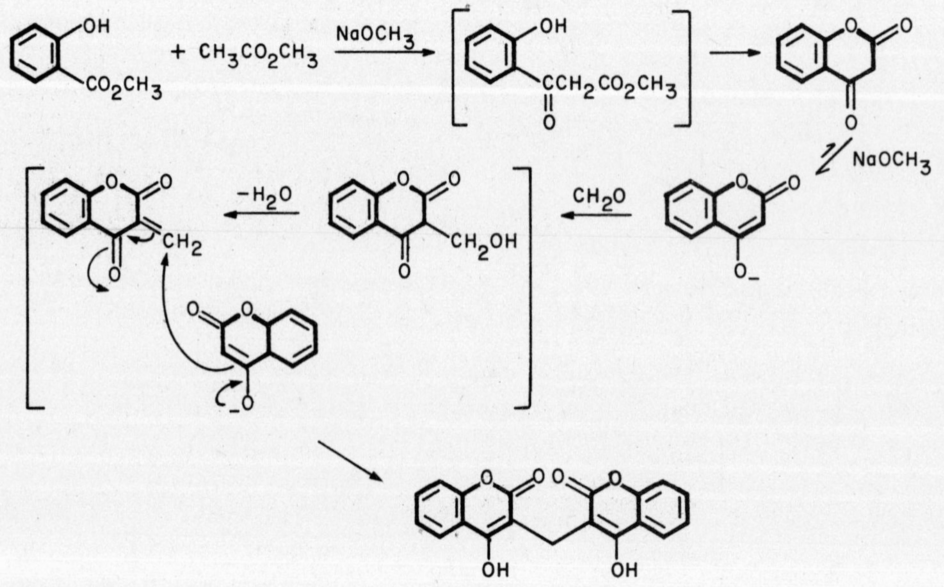

(c)

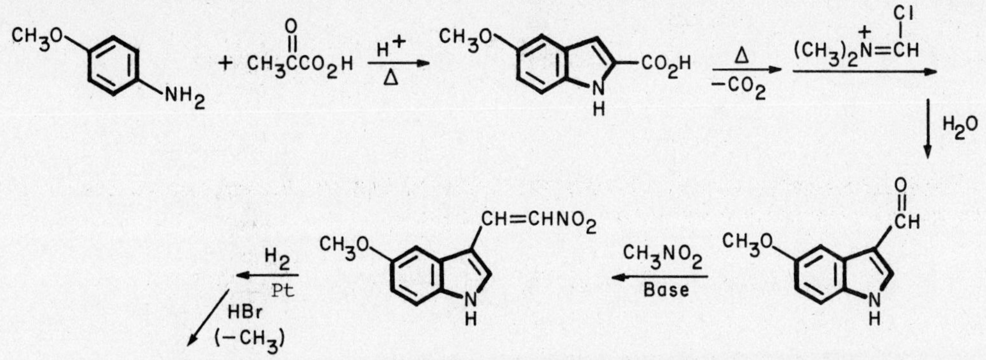

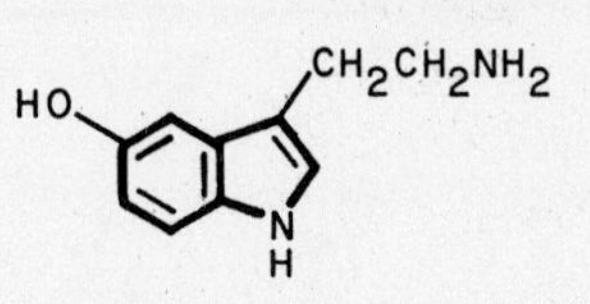

(alternatively, refer to the sequence given
in problem #S3 (c) above)

(d)

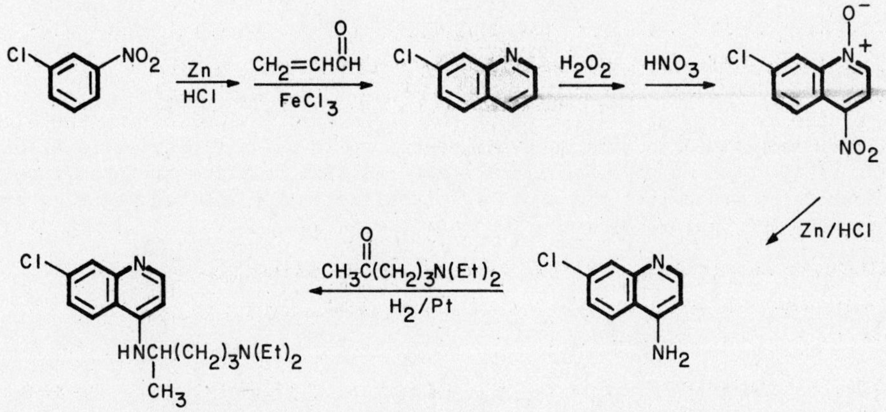

(e)

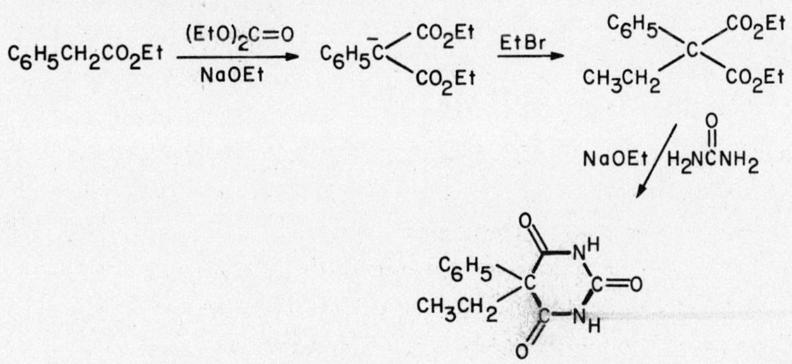

S6. (a)

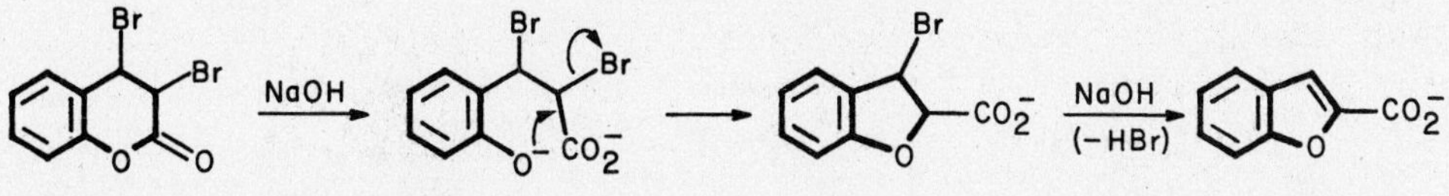

(b)

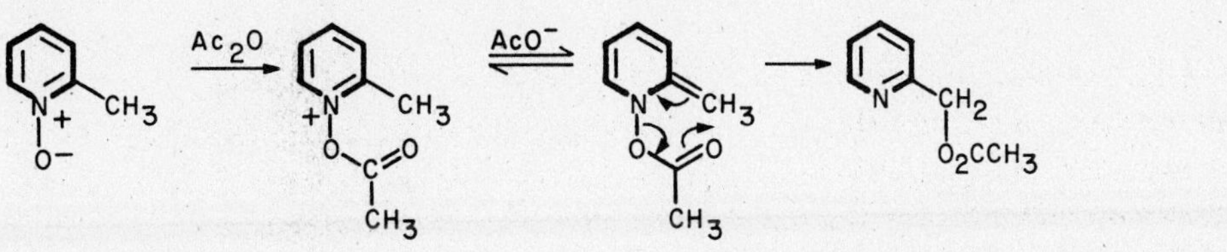

(c)

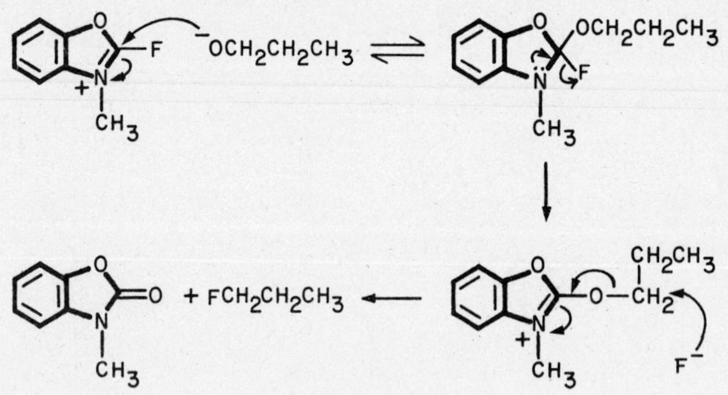

$^-OCH_2CH_2CH_3$ $\rightleftharpoons$

$OCH_2CH_2CH_3$

CH_3

CH_3

O + $FCH_2CH_2CH_3$ $\leftarrow$

CH_2CH_3

CH_3

F^-

CH_3

(d)

CO_2H

$\rightleftharpoons$

$-CO_2$

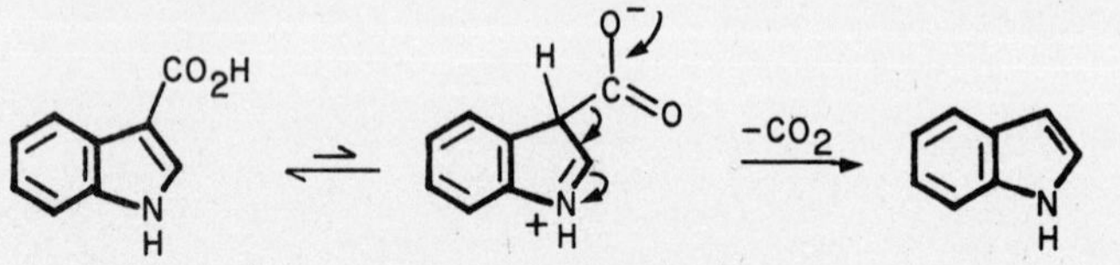

S7.   [5] > [4] > [2] > [3] > [1]

S8.   In each case, the aromatic stabilization of the furan ring is lost during the Diels-Alder
         reaction. When isobenzofuran undergoes the reaction, it gains the aromatic stabilization
         of a benzene ring, which helps to accelerate the reaction relative to furan itself. In
         contrast, benzofuran would lose the aromatic stabilization of its benzene ring as well,
         and that prevents the Diels-Alder reaction from occurring.

32. MASS SPECTROMETRY

32.A Chapter Outline and Important Terms Introduced

32.1 Introduction

radical cation

mass spectrometer

mass spectrum

32.2 Instrumentation (the physics behind the technique)

magnetic sector mass spectrometer

magnetic scanning

$m/z = H^2r^2/2V$

32.3 The Molecular Ion: Molecular Formula

nominal mass

high resolution

M+1 peaks

32.4 Fragmentation

A. Simple Bond Cleavage

(to give most stable cationic fragment)

B. Two-bond Cleavage, Elimination of a Neutral Molecule

alcohols: loss of water

carbonyl compounds: McLafferty rearrangement

32.B Important Reactions Introduced (none in this Chapter)

32.C New Concepts and Hints

HOW TO INTERPRET A MASS SPECTRUM ≡ HOW TO SOLVE MASS SPECTRAL PROBLEMS

**All the rules listed below apply to molecules containing only C, H, and O. For halogen-
or nitrogen-containing compounds, see item #6, entitled "Complications".**

1. Decide whether the particle of highest mass/charge ratio (m/z) is the molecular ion (M^+).
    (**NOTE:** The **height** of the peak (**intensity**) is something completely different; the tallest peak
    is usually not M^+.)
    (a) If the formula of the molecule is given, you can determine M^+ right away by calculating
         the molecular weight.
    (b) If m/z for the largest particle is **odd**, then it's **not** M^+.
    (c) If the next smaller fragment corresponds to loss of an impossible piece (loss of 7, say,
         or 22 mass units), then the larger fragment is not M^+. The spectrum of 2-methyl-2-
         propanol (Figure 32.15) provides an example of both of these generalizations.
    (d) If the particle of highest m/z is **not** M^+ and no hints or formula were provided, try
         adding water (to the even-numbered fragments) or alkyl groups (to the odd-numbered frag-
         ments) to come up with something reasonable. For instance, in the spectrum of 2-methyl-
         2-propanol, addition of 18 (water) to the next largest fragment and 15 (methyl) to the
         largest fragment suggest the same molecular ion (m/z 88).

2. Look at the major fragment ions, and decide what pieces have been lost (subtract each m/z from
    M^+ and/or from a higher m/z).
    (a) Odd-mass pieces are radicals: methyl = 15, ethyl = 29, propyl = 43, butyl = 57, etc.
    (b) Even-mass pieces are neutral molecules: water = 18, ROH = 17 + alkyl; ethylene (from
         McLafferty rearrangement) = 28; higher alkenes = 28 + 14 for each additional CH_2 group.

3. Before you attempt to interpret cleavage patterns, see what you can deduce about the molecule
    from other sources. Is there oxygen in the molecule? Is it a ketone or an alcohol? Because
    you can predict how different classes of compounds will fragment, interpreting an actual
    cleavage pattern becomes much easier if you know what to expect.

4. Look at even-mass fragments first, the ones that correspond to loss of a neutral molecule.
   (a) Loss of 18 (water) is strong evidence for an alcohol; loss of 17 + alkyl (ROH) is evidence for an ether.
   (b) Loss of 28 ($CH_2=CH_2$) or a higher alkene from a carbonyl-containing molecule is the result of McLafferty rearrangement. This means that a carbon γ to the carbonyl group has a hydrogen attached. It also gives you an indication of the type of alkyl group (see problem #9, for example).

5. Finally, look at the odd-mass fragments, which correspond to loss of a radical from the molecule. Such cleavages occur to give the most stable cations and (less importantly) most stable radicals.
   (a) Hydrocarbons cleave at branch points so that secondary or tertiary cations can be formed.
   (b) Alcohols, ethers, amines, and carbonyl compounds undergo cleavage adjacent to the functional group (so-called α-cleavage) so that oxonium or immonium ions can be formed:

$$\left[\begin{array}{c} R' \\ | \\ O \\ | \\ -C-R \\ | \end{array} \right]^{+} \cdot \longrightarrow \begin{array}{c} R'-O^+ \\ \| \\ C \end{array} + R\cdot \qquad\qquad \left[\begin{array}{c} N \\ | \\ -C-R \\ | \end{array} \right]^{+}\cdot \longrightarrow \begin{array}{c} N^+ \\ \| \\ C \end{array} + R\cdot$$

$$\left[\begin{array}{c} O \\ \| \\ C \\ R \end{array} \right]^{+}\cdot \longrightarrow -C\equiv O^+ + R\cdot$$

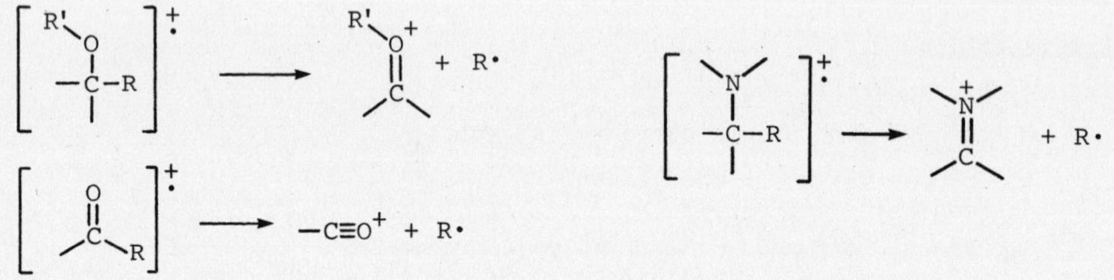

6. **COMPLICATIONS:**
   (a) Chlorine- and bromine-containing ions show doubled peaks because of the presence of two isotopes for each.
   (b) The presence of an odd number of nitrogen atoms changes statement 1(b) above: molecular ions containing an odd number of nitrogens have **odd** mass.
   (c) Molecules which contain several functional groups will obviously produce more complex mass spectra. Cyclic molecules, especially bicyclic molecules, often give fragmentation patterns which are difficult to interpret because more than one bond must be broken to remove a piece.

32.D   Answers to Exercises

32.1 The electron is removed from a π-orbital in forming the radical cation $[CH_2=CH_2]^{+}\cdot$. This orbital is higher in energy (= less energy required to **remove** an electron) than the σ-orbitals in methane.

32.2 $CH_3-\overset{+}{C}=O \longleftrightarrow CH_3-C\equiv O^+$

32.3
$$\frac{M+1}{M} = 0.01119\ c\ +\ 0.00015\ h\ +\ 0.00367\ n\ +\ 0.00037\ o\ +\ 0.0080\ s$$

   (a) $C_{10}H_{22}$: M+1/M = 0.1152 = 11.52%;   (b) $C_{10}H_{22}O$: 11.56%;   (c) $C_{10}H_{23}N$: 11.90%

32.4

Formula	(Mass)	% Abundance	
$C_2H_4{}^{79}Br_2$	186	$(50.54)^2$	= 25.5%
$C_2H_4{}^{79}Br{}^{81}Br$	188	$(50.54 \times 49.46) \times 2$	= 50.5%
$C_2H_4{}^{81}Br_2$	190	$(49.46)^2$	= 24.5%

186   190

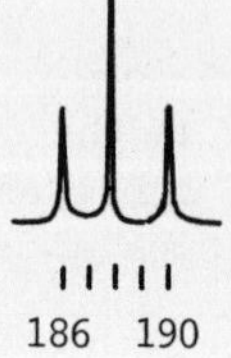

32.5

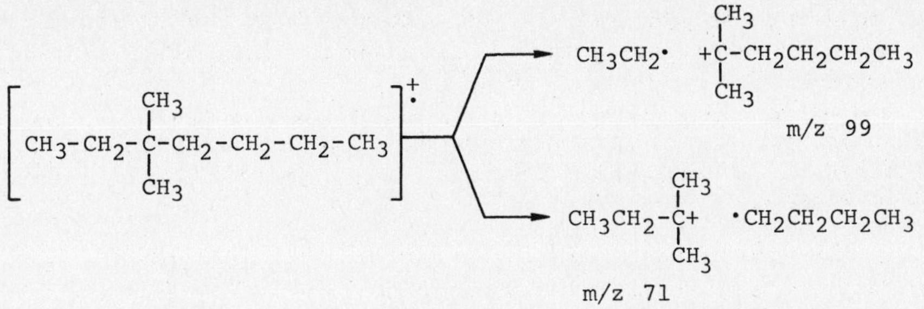

$$CH_3CH_2 \cdot \quad \overset{CH_3}{\underset{CH_3}{+C-CH_2CH_2CH_2CH_3}}$$

m/z 99

$$CH_3CH_2-\overset{CH_3}{\underset{CH_3}{C}}+ \quad \cdot CH_2CH_2CH_2CH_3$$

m/z 71

32.6 For molecules containing only C,H, and O, the molecular ions will have even mass and the fragments resulting from single bond cleavage will all have odd mass. The situation is reversed for monoamines: the molecular ions have odd mass and the single-bond-cleavage fragments have even mass.

32.7 (a)

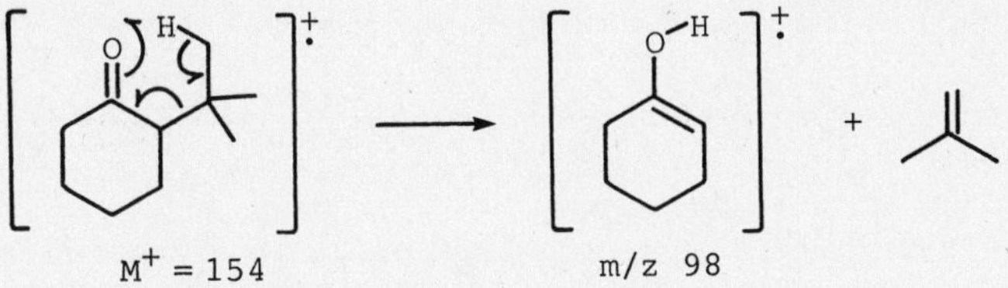

$M^+ = 154$ m/z 98

(b)

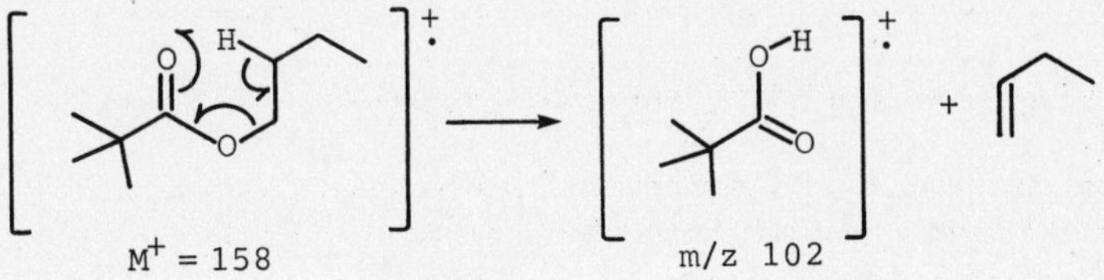

$M^+ = 158$ m/z 102

32.8

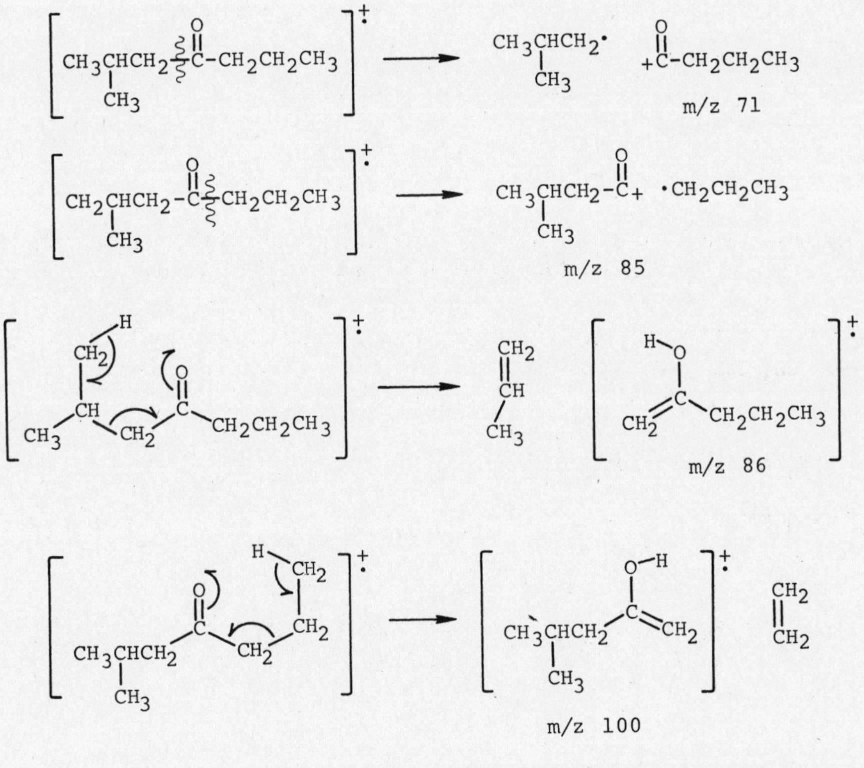

$$CH_3\underset{CH_3}{CHCH_2} \cdot \quad \overset{O}{\underset{}{+C-CH_2CH_2CH_3}}$$

m/z 71

$$CH_3\underset{CH_3}{CHCH_2}-\overset{O}{C}+ \quad \cdot CH_2CH_2CH_3$$

m/z 85

m/z 86

m/z 100

32.E   Answers and Explanations to Problems

1. (a)   Relative probabilities are: $C_3H_6{}^{35}Cl_2$, $(0.7553)^2$ = 57%

$C_3H_6{}^{37}Cl{}^{35}Cl$, $(0.7553)(0.2447) \times 2$ = 37%

$C_3H_6{}^{37}Cl_2$, $(0.2447)^2$ = 6%

(b)   Predicted M+1/M, according to equation 32-5:

$C_{10}H_{18}$: **0.1146**; $C_8H_{10}O_2$: 0.0918; $C_8H_{14}N_2$: 0.0990

2.
$$\frac{M+1}{M} = 0.01119\,c + 0.00015\,h + 0.00367\,n + 0.00037\,o + 0.0080\,s$$

(a) $C_8H_{14}O_4$: 9.31%   (b) $C_{10}H_{10}N_2$: 12.1%   (c) $C_{13}H_{20}$: 14.8% (d) $C_{60}H_{122}$: (69.0%)

The equation above is only accurate for formulas with relatively few carbons. Note that the M+1 peak approaches the intensity of the M peak for compounds containing many carbons.

(e) CH_3I: 1.1%   (f) C_2F_6: 2.2%

Since ^{127}I and ^{19}F are the only isotopes of these halogens, ^{13}C makes the only significant contribution to M+1.

3.   The positive charge in the M-29 fragment from N-propylaniline is localized on the nitrogen atom as an immonium ion. The presence of a p-nitro substituent destabilizes this charge and disfavors the formation of this fragment the same way it decreases the basicity of the aniline itself.

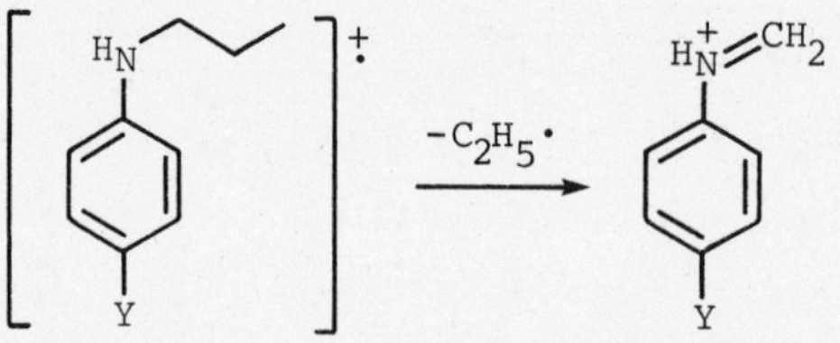

4.   (1) $M^+ = 128$: $C_{10}H_8$ or C_9H_{20}

(2)   weak M^+: likely to be a saturated hydrocarbon, therefore C_9H_{20}

(3)   fragment at m/z 113 = M-15: $[R-CH_3]^+ \longrightarrow R^+ + \cdot CH_3$

(4)   no significant fragment at m/z 99 (= $M-C_2H_5$): **not** $R'-CH_2CH_3$

(5)   m/z 43 = $C_3H_7{}^+$: $(CH_3)_2CH^+$

(6)   Structure is 2,6-dimethylheptane:

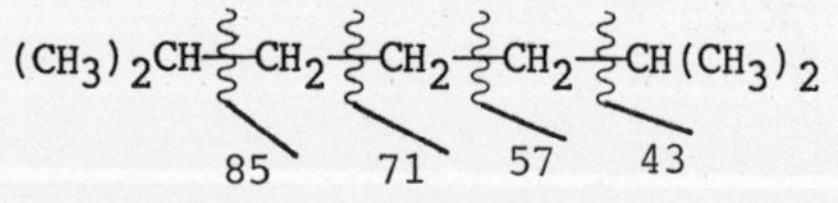

Notice how the fragmentations correspond with important peaks.

$(CH_3)_2CH\!-\!CH_2\!-\!CH_2\!-\!CH_2\!-\!CH(CH_3)_2$

85   71   57   43

5.   Saturated hydrocarbons frequently present problems in mass spectral analyses because of the prevalence of peaks derived from carbocation rearrangements. This example illustrates some of these difficulties. Assignments must be based not just on the presence or absence of given m/z peaks, but on their relative intensities.

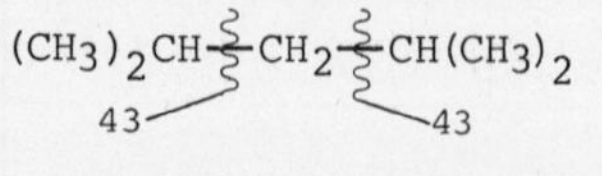

$(CH_3)_2CH\!-\!CH_2\!-\!CH(CH_3)_2$
43   43

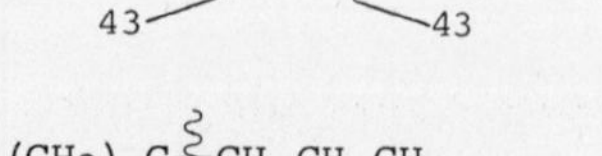

This isomer has two isopropyl ends and is expected to have the largest m/z 43 peak; therefore, c.

$(CH_3)_3C\!-\!CH_2CH_2CH_3$
57

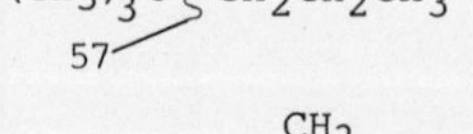

This isomer is the only one with a t-butyl group and is expected to have the largest m/z 57 peak; therefore, b.

$(CH_3)_2CHCH\!-\!CH_2CH_3$ with CH_3 branch
71

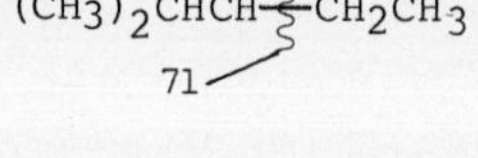

This isomer is expected to have the largest m/z 71 peak; hence, a.

6.   (1)   peaks at m/z 90 and 92: compound contains Cl (75% ^{35}Cl, 25% ^{37}Cl)

   (2) M^+ = 90 (92): formula is C_4H_7Cl

   (3)   m/z 55 = M-Cl: R = C_4H_7

   (4)   strength of m/z 55 peak suggests that R^+ is quite stable: $CH_3CH=CHCH_2^+$ or $CH_2=C-CH_2^+$ with CH_3 branch

   (5)   IR bands at 1650, 890 cm^{-1} confirm double bond, and suggest that it is $=CH_2$ (Table 15.4).

   (6)   Structure is 3-chloro-2-methylpropene ("methallyl chloride"): $CH_2=CCH_2Cl$ with CH_3 branch

7.   (1) M^+ = 254: $C_{20}H_{14}$, $C_{19}H_{26}$, or $C_{18}H_{38}$

   (2)   weak M^+ suggests saturated hydrocarbon: $C_{18}H_{38}$

   (3)   Compound A: major fragments at m/z 239 (M-15 = M-CH$_3$), 155 (M-99 = M-C$_7$H$_{15}$), and 127 (M-127 = M-C$_9$H$_{19}$) account for all but one carbon. Since fragmentation of saturated hydrocarbons favors cleavage at branch points, these prominent peaks suggest the structure of 8-methyl-heptadecane:

   (4)   Compound B: similarly, the fragments at m/z 239 (M-CH$_3$), 169 (M-C$_6$H$_{13}$), and 113 (M-C$_{10}$H$_{21}$) are consistent with 7-methylheptadecane:

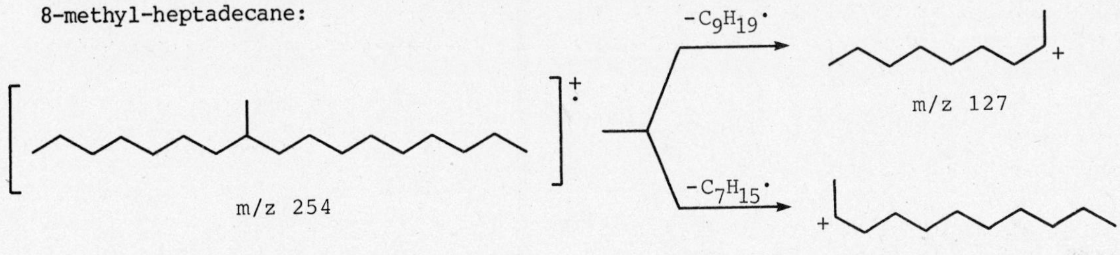

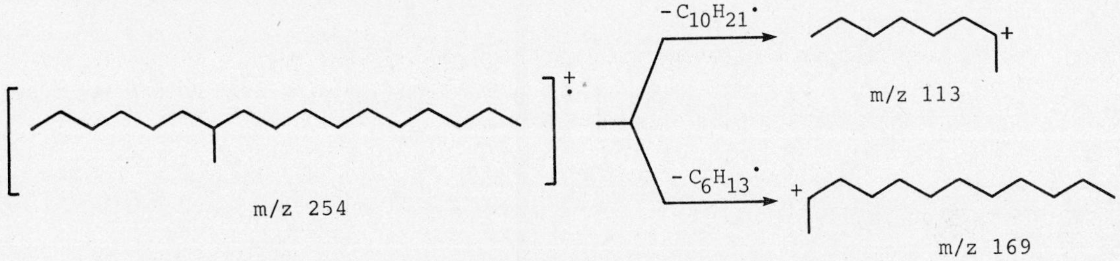

8.   (1)   The largest ion (101) has odd mass, and most of the large fragments (m/z = 86, 70, 58) are of even mass, suggesting that the compound contains an odd number of nitrogens.

   (2)   For M^+ = 101, a formula of $C_6H_{15}N$ can be proposed.

   (3)   Major fragment is M-15 peak, resulting from loss of a methyl group.

   (4)   If compound is a simple amine, M-15 would be expected to result from α-cleavage:

   (5)   Absence of other major fragments suggests that only **one** mode of α-cleavage is possible. Four structures are possible with this property:

   (6)   If there are only two resonances in the CMR spectrum, $\underline{t}$-butylethylamine and $\underline{t}$-butyldimethyl amine are excluded.

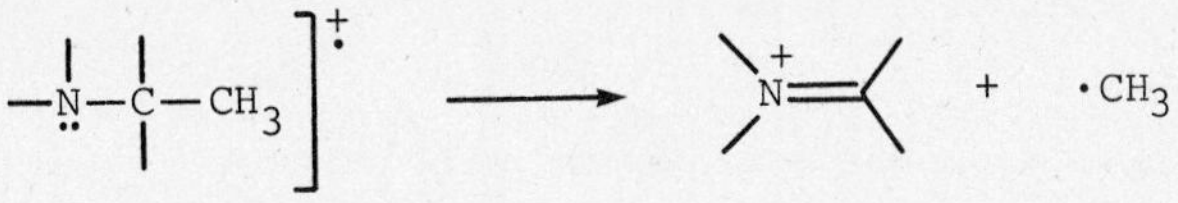

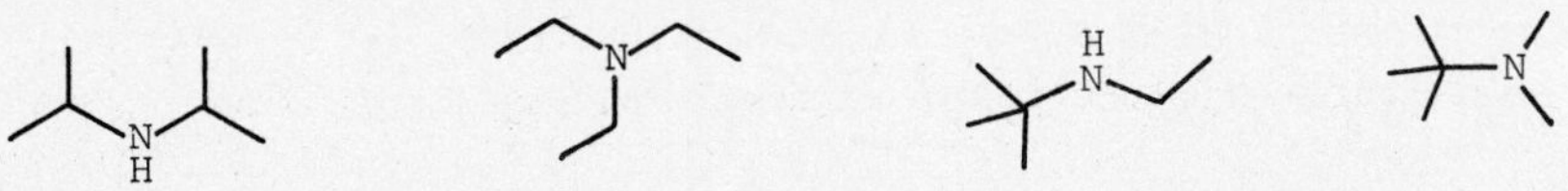

9.   (1)   IR band at 1710 cm^{-1}: ketone

   (2) M^+ = 100: $C_6H_{12}O$

   (3)   m/z 85: $[RCOCH_3]^+ \longrightarrow RC\equiv O^+ + \cdot CH_3$

   (4)   m/z 43: $[RCOCH_3]^+ \longrightarrow R\cdot + {}^+O\equiv CCH_3$

(5) m/z 58: even mass fragment must arise from two bond cleavage process; for a ketone this is most likely the McLafferty rearrangement; the fragment lost (100 - 58 = 42) corresponds to $CH_3CH=CH_2$, and could arise from either 2-hexanone or 4-methyl-2-pentanone:

$$[M^+ = 100] \longrightarrow [m/z\ 58] \quad + \quad CH_3CH=CH_2 \quad \longleftarrow \quad [M^+ = 100]$$

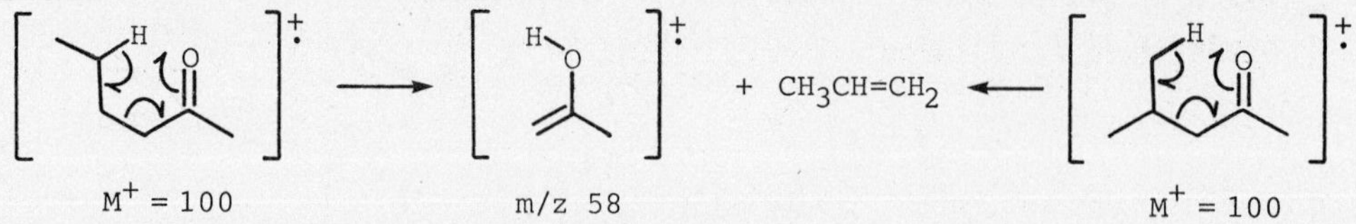

(6) To distinguish between these two possibilities is not easy. The fact that the m/z 43 fragment is so intense suggests that the structure is 4-methyl-2-pentanone, since this molecule can give rise to fragments of m/z 43 in two ways:

$$[m/z\ 100] \longrightarrow$$

$$m/z\ 43 \quad + \quad \cdot CH_2CCH_3$$

$$+ \quad ^+O\equiv CCH_3$$
$$m/z\ 43$$

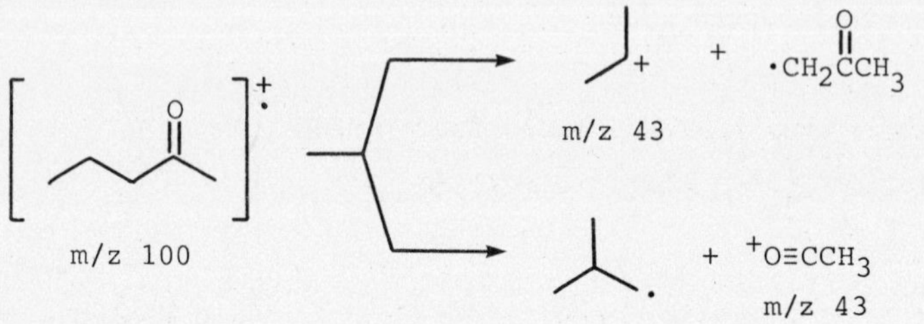

10. (1) IR band at 1710 cm^{-1}: ketone

(2) $M^+ = 114$: $C_7H_{14}O$

(3) odd mass fragments of m/z 71 and 43 cannot be the two α-cleavage fragments $R—C\equiv O^+$ and $^+O\equiv C—R'$, because they don't account for enough carbons (the mass of the two α-cleavage fragments must add up to M+28)

(4) m/z 71 must be **both** α-cleavage fragments: ketone is $C_3H_7\overset{O}{\overset{||}{C}}C_3H_7$

(5) There are **no** even mass peaks, therefore no fragments arising from McLafferty rearrangement

(6) Structure must therefore be diisopropyl ketone:

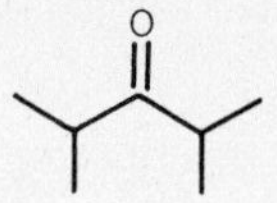

11. (1) IR band at 3400 cm^{-1}: alcohol

(2) $M^+ = 126$ suggests formula of $C_8H_{13}OH$, with two degrees of unsaturation

(3) m/z 111 (M-CH$_3$) and 69 (M-C$_4$H$_9$) suggest 3-methyl-1-heptyn-3-ol as structure:

$$C_4H_9-\overset{OH}{\underset{CH_3}{\overset{|}{C}}}-C\equiv CH$$

(4) But where does m/z 87 come from? And why isn't there a strong fragment at m/z 108 for loss of H_2O?

(5) Assume that m/z 126 is **not** M^+, but represents M-H_2O instead; M = 144 would then be a saturated alcohol: $C_9H_{19}OH$

(6) m/z 87 (M-C$_4$H$_9$) is α-cleavage fragment: part structure = $R_2\overset{OH}{\overset{|}{C}}+$

(7) m/z 69 cannot be an α-cleavage product, because no formula with $C_nH_{2n+1}O = 69$)

(8) with a single α-cleavage product observed, the structure must be $C_4H_9CHOHC_4H_9$

(9) m/z 111 = M-H_2O-CH$_3$ suggests that there are methyl branches

(10) absence of m/z 97 for M-H_2O-C$_2H_5$ suggests that there are not any ethyl branches

(11) most reasonable structure is 2,6-dimethyl-4-heptanol:

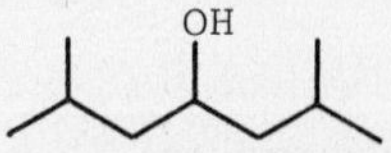

(12) The m/z 69 peak is left unexplained, but must result from a more deep-seated rearrangement. This is also a loose end, but the second hypothesis explains much more of the data than the first. Notice how the **absence** of expected peaks can be more significant than the presence of additional ones.

12. 2-Octanone is $C_8H_{16}O$ and has a molecular weight of 128; 113 = 128 - 15 (CH_3), 43 = 128 - 85 (C_6H_{13}):

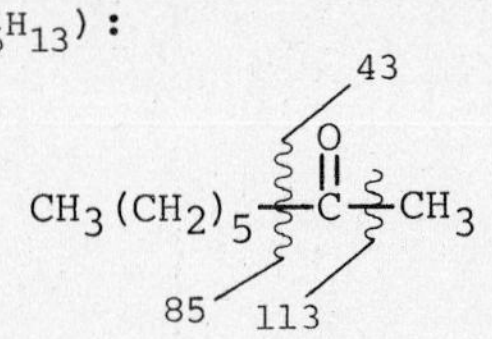

McLafferty rearrangement gives:

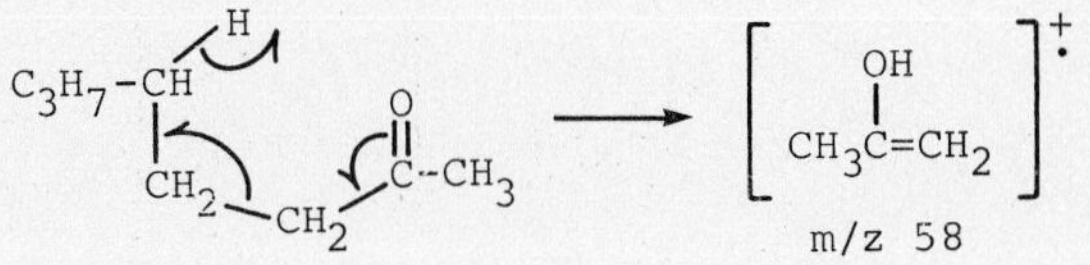

m/z 58

13. (1) odd M^+, even fragments: an amine

(2) M^+ = 73: $C_4H_{11}N$

(3) m/z 58 = M-15: loss of CH_3 by α-cleavage $\quad CH_3–\overset{+}{C}–NR_2 \longrightarrow CH_3\cdot + \rangle C{=}\overset{+}{N}R_2$

(4) m/z 44 = M-29: loss of CH_3CH_2 by α-cleavage $\quad CH_3CH_2–\overset{+}{C}–NR_2 \longrightarrow CH_3CH_2\cdot + \rangle C{=}\overset{+}{N}R_2$

(5) structure must be 1-methylpropanamine: $CH_3CH_2\underset{NH_2}{CH}CH_3$

14.

$$\left[(CH_3)_2CHCH_2CH_3\right]^+ \longrightarrow$$

	ΔH° (kcal mole^{-1})
$CH_3^+ + (CH_3)_2CHCH_2\cdot$	74
$CH_3\cdot + (CH_3)_2CHCH_2^+$	38
$(CH_3)_2CH^+ + CH_3CH_2\cdot$	11
$(CH_3)_2CH\cdot + CH_3CH_2^+$	35
$CH_3\cdot + CH_3\overset{+}{C}HCH_2CH_3$	25
$CH_3^+ + CH_3\dot{C}HCH_2CH_3$	72

$(CH_3)_2CH^+ > CH_3\overset{+}{C}HCH_2CH_3 > (CH_3)_2CHCH_2^+ > CH_3CH_2^+ \gg CH_3^+$

NOTE: These calculations were made using the ΔH°_f values from Appendix I.

32.F Supplementary Problems

S1. Predict the major peaks in the mass spectra of the following compounds:

(a) $CH_3CH_2\overset{\underset{\displaystyle CH_3}{|}}{C}HCH_2CH_2CH(CH_3)_2$

(b) $(CH_3)_2CH\overset{\underset{\displaystyle OH}{|}}{C}HCH_2CH_3$

(c) $(CH_3)_3CCH_2CH_2CH_2CH_2OH$

(d) $CH_3\overset{\underset{\displaystyle}{\overset{\displaystyle O}{||}}}{C}CH_2CH_2CH(CH_2CH_3)_2$

(e) $(CH_3)_2CHCH_2OC(CH_3)_3$

(f) cyclopentyl$-CH_2\overset{\underset{\displaystyle}{\overset{\displaystyle O}{||}}}{C}CH_3$

(g) $CH_3CH_2CH_2\overset{\underset{\displaystyle CH_3}{|}}{C}HN(CH_3)_2$

(h) phenyl$-CH_2CH_2CH_2CH_3$

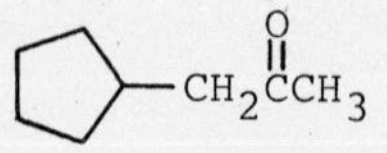

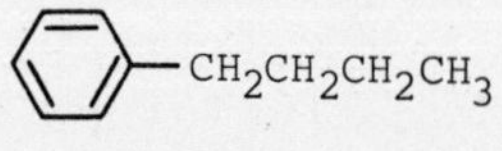

S2. From the following accurate mass measurements, determine the most likely formula for the molecule or fragment.

(a) m/z = 70.0419   (b) m/z = 56.0373   (c) m/z = 81.0861

S3. Deduce the structure of each of the compounds below, and write a mechanism showing the principal fragments in each mass spectrum.

(a) $A \xrightarrow[\text{2. } H_2O_2, \text{ OH}^-]{\text{1. } B_2H_6} B + C$ *Both B and C show a strong band at 1710 cm^{-1} in the ir.*

mass spectrum of B: m/z 114, 86, 85, 57

mass spectrum of C: m/z 114, 99, 58, 43

(b) $D \xrightarrow{(C_6H_5)_3P=CH_2} E \underset{\xrightarrow[\text{dilute } H_2SO_4]{}}{\xrightarrow[\text{2. } NaBH_4]{\text{1. } Hg(OAc)_2, H_2O}}} \begin{matrix} F \\ \\ G \end{matrix}$

mass spectrum of D: m/z 86, 58, 29

mass spectrum of F: m/z 102, 87, 84, 45

mass spectrum of G: m/z 87, 84, 73

(c) $H \xrightarrow{C_3H_7MgCl} \xrightarrow[\Delta]{H_2SO_4} I \xrightarrow[\text{2. } H_2O_2, \text{ OH}^-]{\text{1. } B_2H_6} J \xrightarrow[H_2SO_4]{K_2Cr_2O_7} K$

NMR spectrum of H: δ 0.9 (3H,t), 1.2-1.4 (4H,m), 2.1 (2H,dt), 9.5 (1H,t).

mass spectrum of K: m/z 128, 86, 85, 71

(d) $L \xrightarrow[H_2SO_4]{HgSO_4} M \xrightarrow[H_2/Ni]{NH_3} N \xrightarrow[HCO_2H, HCl]{CH_2=O} O$

mass spectrum of L: m/z 82

IR spectrum of M: 1710 cm^{-1}

mass spectrum of M: m/z 100, 72, 71, 57

mass spectrum of N: m/z 101, 72, 58

mass spectrum of O: m/z 129, 100, 86

32.G Answers to Supplementary Problems

S1. (a)

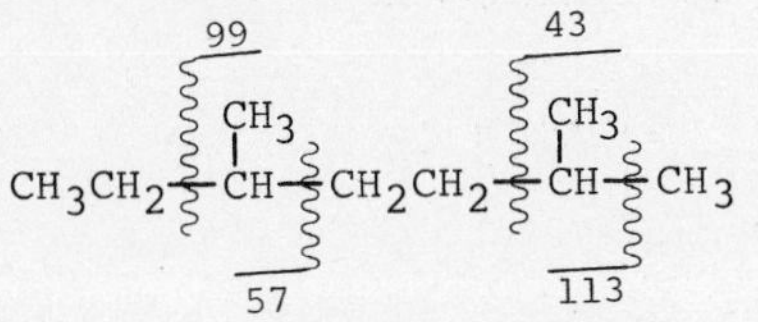

$CH_3CH_2 - CH(CH_3) - CH_2CH_2 - CH(CH_3) - CH_3$

99 — 43
57 — 113

$M^+ = 128$

(b)

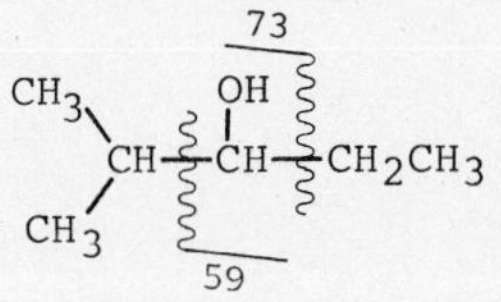

$(CH_3)_2CH - CH(OH) - CH_2CH_3$

73
59

$M^+ = 102; \quad M - H_2O = 84$

(c)

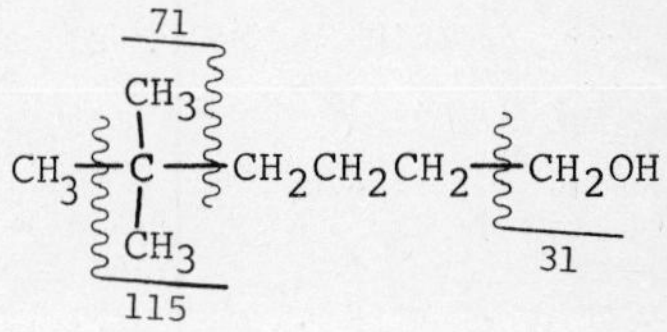

$CH_3 - C(CH_3)(CH_3) - CH_2CH_2CH_2 - CH_2OH$

71
115 — 31

$M^+ = 130; \quad M - H_2O = 112$

(d)

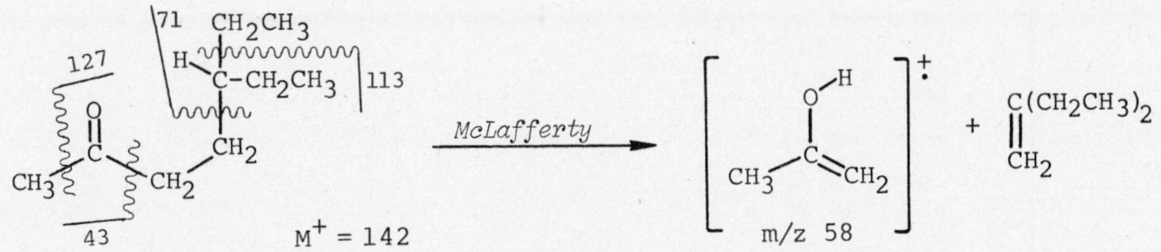

127
71 — 113
43

$M^+ = 142$

$\xrightarrow{McLafferty}$

$\left[CH_3 - C(OH) = CH_2 \right]^{+\bullet} \quad + \quad C(CH_2CH_3)_2 = CH_2$

m/z 58

(e)

$(CH_3)_2CH - CH_2OC(CH_3)_2 - CH_3$

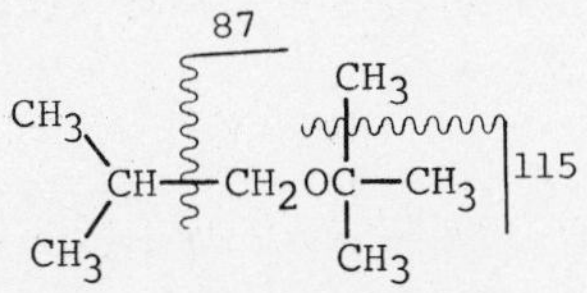

87
115

$(M^+ = 130); \quad M - (ROH) = 56$

(f)

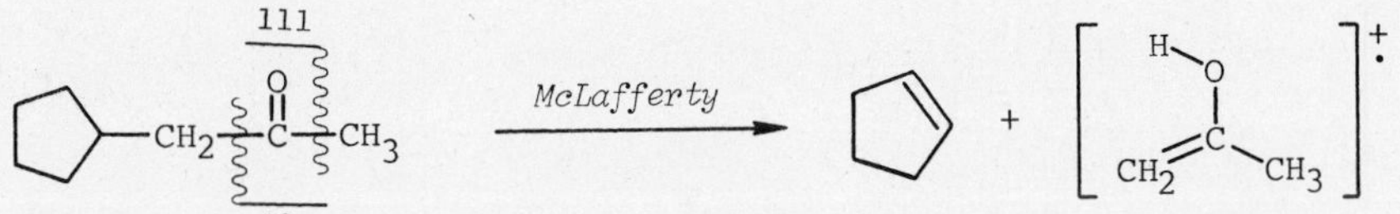

111
43

$\xrightarrow{McLafferty}$

+ $\left[CH_2 = C(OH) - CH_3 \right]^{+\bullet}$

m/z 58

$M^+ = 126$

(g)

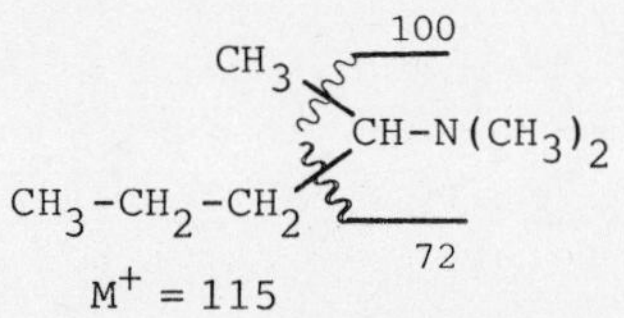

$CH_3 - CH_2 - CH_2 - CH(CH_3) - N(CH_3)_2$

100
72

$M^+ = 115$

(h)

$C_6H_5 - CH_2 - CH_2 - CH_2 - CH_3$

91

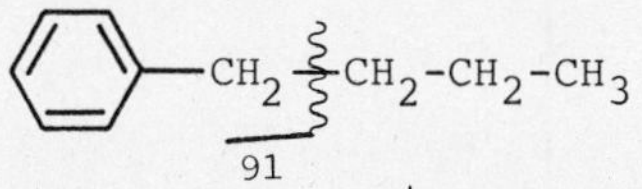

$M^+ = 134$

S2. (a)

Formula	Calculated Exact Mass
C_5H_{10}	70.07825
C_4H_6O	70.04186 ←
$C_3H_6N_2$	70.05305
$[C_4H_8N]^{\bullet}$	70.06565

(b)

Formula	Calculated Exact Mass
C_4H_8	56.0626
C_3H_4O	56.0262
$C_2H_4N_2$	56.0374 ←
$[C_3H_6N]^{\bullet}$	56.0500

(c)

Formula	Calculated Exact Mass
$[C_5H_{11}]^{\bullet}$	81.08608 ←
$[C_4H_7O]^{\bullet}$	81.04969
$[C_3H_7N_2]^{\bullet}$	81.06088
C_4H_9N	81.07348

S3.

(a) $CH_3C\equiv CCHCH_2CH_3$ $\xrightarrow[\text{2. } H_2O_2, OH^-]{\text{1. } B_2H_6}$ $CH_3CH_2\overset{\mid}{C}\overset{O}{\underset{\mid}{C}}CHCH_2CH_3$ + $CH_3\overset{O}{\underset{\mid}{C}}CH_2CHCH_2CH_3$

with CH_3 below; labeled 57, 85 on B; 43, 99 on C

A

B   C

$M^+ = 114$ $M^+ = 114$

McLafferty:

$\left[\begin{array}{c} OH \\ CH_3CH_2C=CH \\ CH_3 \end{array} \right]^{+\cdot}$ $\left[\begin{array}{c} OH \\ CH_3C=CH_2 \end{array} \right]^{+\cdot}$

m/z 86   m/z 58

(b) $CH_3CH_2\overset{CH_3}{\underset{}{CH}}CH=O$ $\xrightarrow{(C_6H_5)_3P=CH_2}$ $CH_3CH_2\overset{CH_3}{\underset{}{CHCH}}=CH_2$ $\xrightarrow[\text{2. } NaBH_4]{\text{1. } Hg^{++}, H_2O}$ $CH_3CH_2\overset{CH_3}{\underset{}{CH}}\overset{}{\underset{OH}{CH}}CH_3$

D (labeled 29)   E   F (labeled 87, 43)

$M^+ = 86$ $M^+ = 102$; $M - H_2O = 84$

McLafferty:

$\left[CH_3CH=CHOH \right]^{+\cdot}$

m/z 58

dilute H_2SO_4

$\left[\begin{array}{c} CH_3 \\ CH_3CH_2CH-CH-CH_3 \\ + \end{array} \right. \rightarrow \left. \begin{array}{c} CH_3 \\ CH_3CH_2CCH_2CH_3 \\ + \end{array} \right]$ $\xrightarrow{H_2O}$ $CH_3CH_2\overset{CH_3}{\underset{CH_2}{\overset{\mid}{C}}}\overset{}{\underset{OH}{C}}CH_3$

G (labeled 73, 87)

$M - H_2O = 84$
($M^+ = 102$ not seen)

(c) $CH_3CH_2CH_2CH_2\overset{O}{\overset{\parallel}{C}}H$ $\xrightarrow{C_3H_7MgCl}$ $\xrightarrow[\Delta]{H_2SO_4}$ $CH_3CH_2CH_2CH_2CH=C(CH_3)_3$ $\xrightarrow[\text{2. } H_2O_2 \; OH^-]{\text{1. } B_2H_6}$

H   I

McLafferty:

$CH_3CH_2CH_2CH_2\overset{O}{\underset{\parallel}{C}}CH(CH_3)_2$ $\xleftarrow[H_2SO_4]{K_2Cr_2O_7}$ $CH_3CH_2CH_2CH_2\overset{}{\underset{OH}{CH}}CH(CH_3)_2$

K (labeled 85, 71)   J

$\left[\begin{array}{c} OH \\ CH_2=CCH(CH_3)_2 \end{array} \right]^{+\cdot}$

m/z 86 $M^+ = 128$

(d) $CH_3CH_2C\equiv CCH_2CH_3$ $\xrightarrow[H_2SO_4]{HgSO_4}$ $CH_3-CH_2\overset{O}{\underset{\parallel}{C}}CH_2-CH_2-CH_3$

L   M (labeled 71, 57)

McLafferty = m/z 72 $M^+ = 100$

$\xrightarrow[H_2/Ni]{NH_3}$

$CH_3-CH_2\overset{N(CH_3)}{\underset{}{CH}}CH_2-CH_2-CH_3$ $\xleftarrow{CH_2=O, \; HCO_2H}$ $CH_3-CH_2\overset{NH_2}{\underset{}{CH}}CH_2-CH_2-CH_3$

O (labeled 100, 86)   N (labeled 72, 58)

$M^+ = 129$ $M^+ = 101$

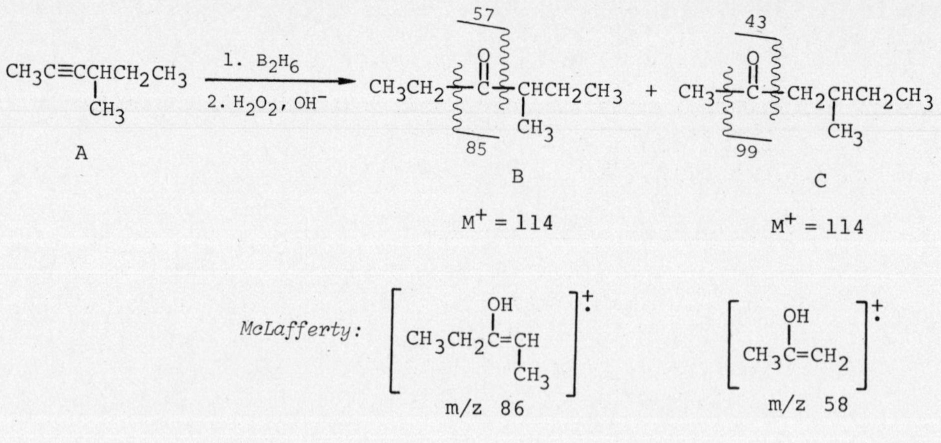

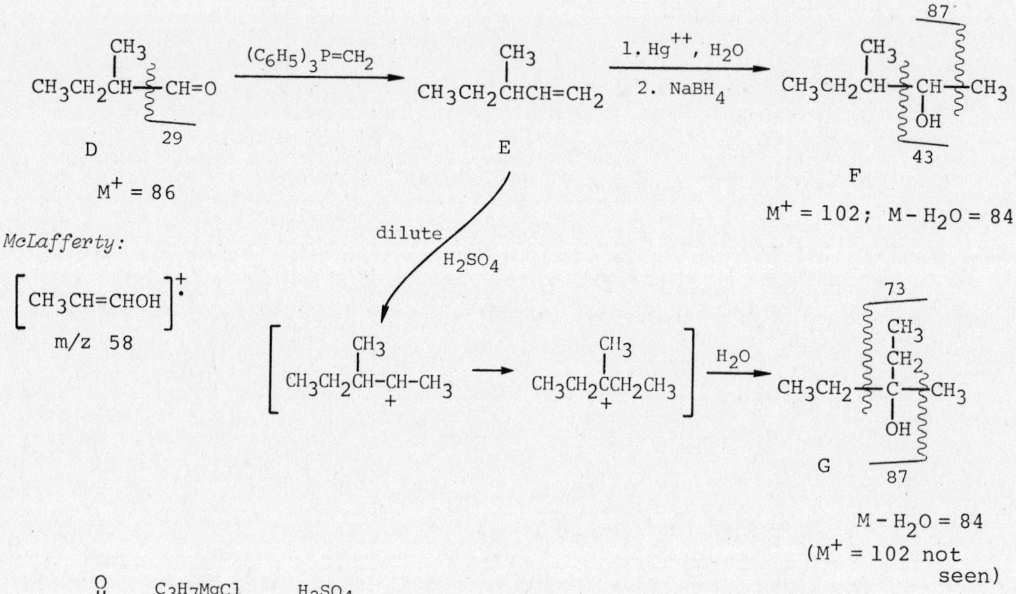

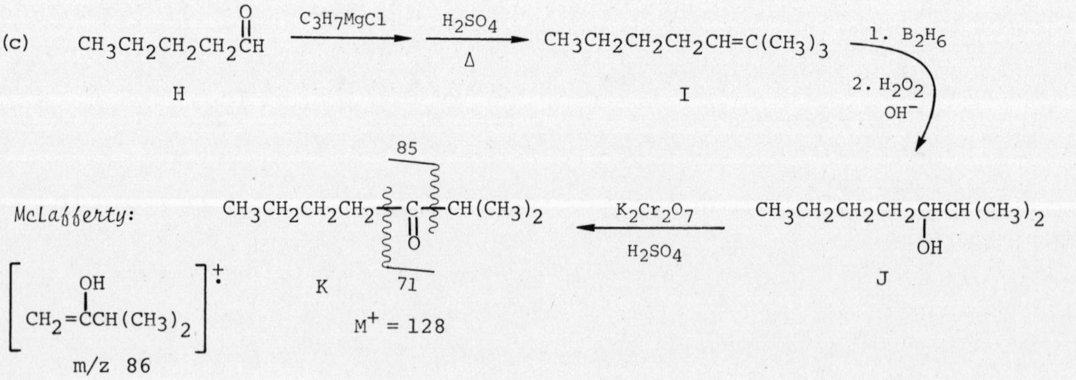

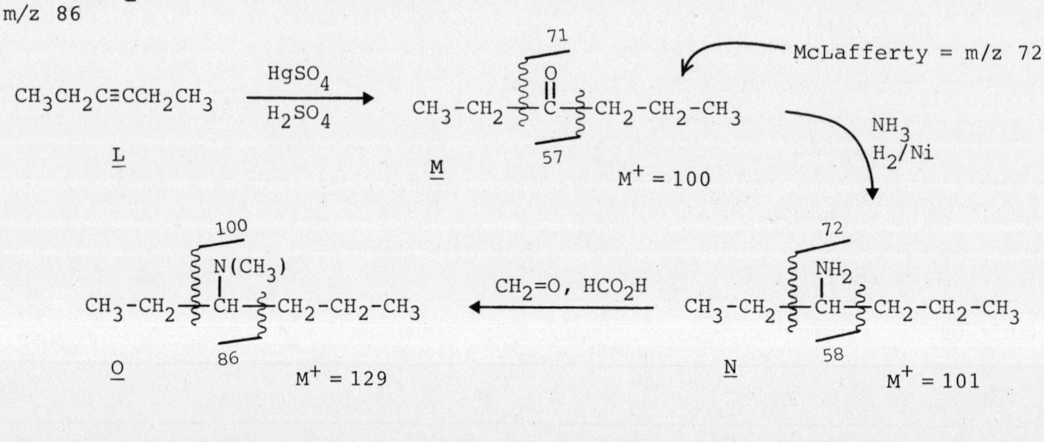

34. SPECIAL TOPICS

34.A Chapter Outline

34.1 The Hammett Equation: An Example of a Linear Free Energy Relationship

A. Acidity of Substituted Benzoic Acids

B. The Hammett $\sigma\rho$ Equation

34.2 Transition Metal Organometallic Compounds

ligand — coordinatively unsaturated — decarbonylation

1. Lewis Acid Association-Dissociation
2. Lewis Base Association-Dissociation
3. Oxidative Addition-Reductive Elimination
4. Insertion-Deinsertion

34.3 Organic Coloring Matters

A. Color

B. Natural Coloring Matters

- anthocyanins
- naphthoquinones, anthraquinones
- ommochromes
- porphyrins
- carotenoids
- melanins
- pterins
- indigoids

C. Dyes and Dyeing

- vat dyes
- direct dyes
- chromophore
- triphenylmethane dyes
- indigoid dyes
- phthalocyanines
- mordant dyes
- disperse dyes
- azo dyes
- anthraquinone dyes
- azine dyes

34.4 Photochemistry

A. Electronically Excited States

- singlet vs. triplet state
- internal conversion
- fluorescence
- phosphorescence
- vertical transition = Franck-Condon transition
- Jablonski diagram
- intersystem crossing
- triplet energy transfer

B. Photochemical Reactions

- Norrish type I and II processes
- triplet sensitizer
- quantum yield

34.5 Polymer Chemistry

- monomers
- addition vs. condensation polymers

A. Carbocation Polymerization of Alkenes

B. Free Radical Vinyl Polymerization

- branched chain vs. linear polyethylene
- plasticizer
- cross-linking

C. Anionic and Organometallic Polymerization

- Ziegler-Natta catalyst
- isotactic vs. atactic vs. syndiotactic

D. Diene Polymers

- copolymer vs. homopolymer
- drying oil

E. Condensation Polymers

- nylon
- polyurea
- polyurethane

34.6 <u>Nucleic</u> <u>Acids</u>

      nucleotide vs. nucleoside   DNA replication
      genes, genetic code   DNA sequencing
                                 Maxam–Gilbert method

34.7 <u>Natural</u> <u>Products</u>: <u>Terpenes</u>, <u>Steroids</u>, <u>and</u> <u>Alkaloids</u>

       metabolism   primary and secondary metabolites
   A. Terpenes
       essential oils   mono-, sesqui-, di-, and triterpenes
   B. Steroids
       estrogens and androgens   cardiac glycosides
   C. Alkaloids

34.8 <u>Biosynthesis</u>

      photosynthesis   acetyl coenzyme A
      mevalonic acid   NADPH
      ATP and ADP

34.D   Answers to (Selected) Exercises

34.2

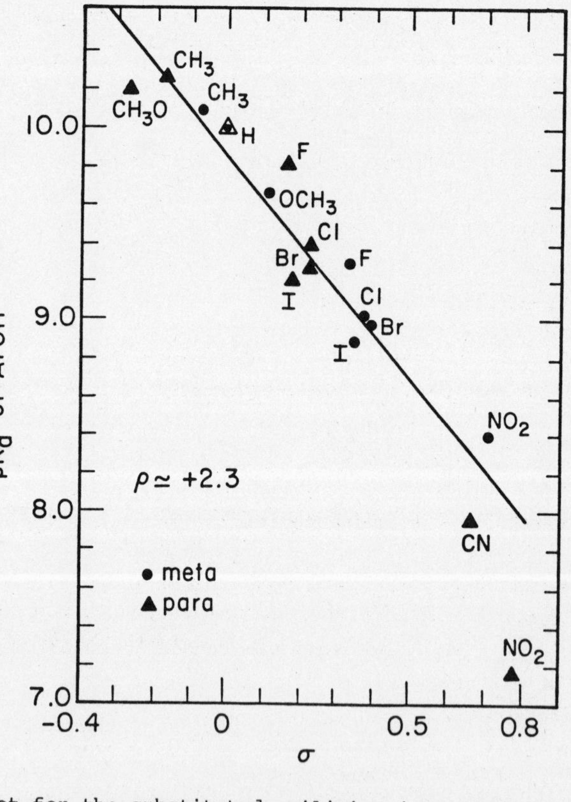

A similar plot for the substituted anilinium ions gives a value for ρ of about 3.1. Rho (ρ) is greater for ionization of phenols and anilinium ions than it is for benzoic acids, because in the first two cases, the negative or positive charge is on an atom which is attached directly to the ring. Not only is the inductive influence greater, but the π-system of the ring is directly involved through resonance.

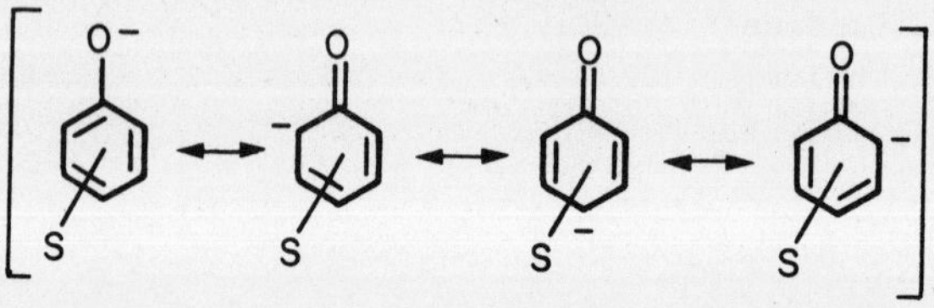

34.3 pK of $C_6H_5CO_2H$ = 4.20 - σ (m-IO_2) = 4.20 - 3.50 = 0.70.
                                σ (p-IO_2) = 4.20 - 3.44 = 0.76.

The -IO_2 group has the Lewis structure that is depicted in (i) below.
If iodine is allowed to expand its octet, we may also write:

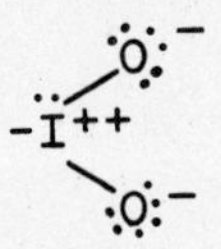

(i)

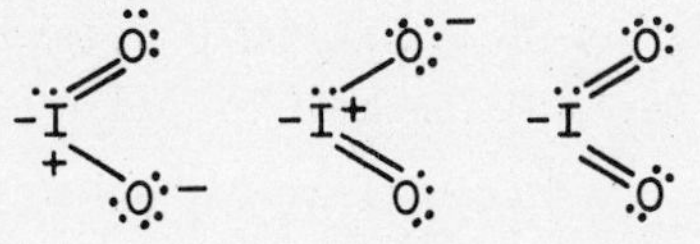

The net result gives the -IO_2 group a polar character similar to that of an NO_2 group.
Note that -NO_2 has similar σ values.

34.4 Electron-donating groups should stabilize the partial (+) charge of the transition state,
so ρ is negative.

34.5 ρ should be greater in magnitude when the positive charge of the transition state is
closer to the benzene ring; that is, the magnitude of ρ is greater for the reaction in
Exercise 34.4 than for this reaction.

34.6 The transition state has a negative charge, so ρ is positive.

34.7 A plot of log k vs. σ gives a good straight line with ρ = +1.6. m-Trifluoromethyl has σ =
0.43. From the plot, the calculated log k is -3.91, or k = 1.23×10^{-4} sec^{-1}.

34.8 (a) To satisfy the 18-electron rule, Cr (6 electrons) needs six CO ligands: $Cr(CO)_6$.
         Fe (8 electrons) needs five CO ligands: $Fe(CO)_5$.
      (b) $^-Mn(CO)_5$ and $^-Co(CO)_4$ each have 18 electrons in the valence shell of the metal.

34.9 The steps involved in this reaction are:

$$Ni(CO)_4 \rightleftharpoons Ni(CO)_3 + CO$$
$$Ni(CO)_3 + (C_6H_5)_3P \rightleftharpoons (C_6H_5)_3PNi(CO)_3$$

The rate expression for formation of product is: dP/dt = k[$Ni(CO)_3$][R_3P]. $Ni(CO)_3$ is in
equilibrium with $Ni(CO)_4$, and its concentration is related to that of $Ni(CO)_4$ and CO as shown
by the equilibrium constant
$$K = \frac{[Ni(CO)_3][CO]}{[Ni(CO)_4]}$$

Combining these two expressions gives the following equation: $\frac{dP}{dt} = kK \frac{[Ni(CO)_4][R_3P]}{[CO]}$

and the inverse dependence of rate on CO concentration can be seen.
(The concentration of CO in solution is proportional to the pressure of CO in contact with
the solution.)

34.10

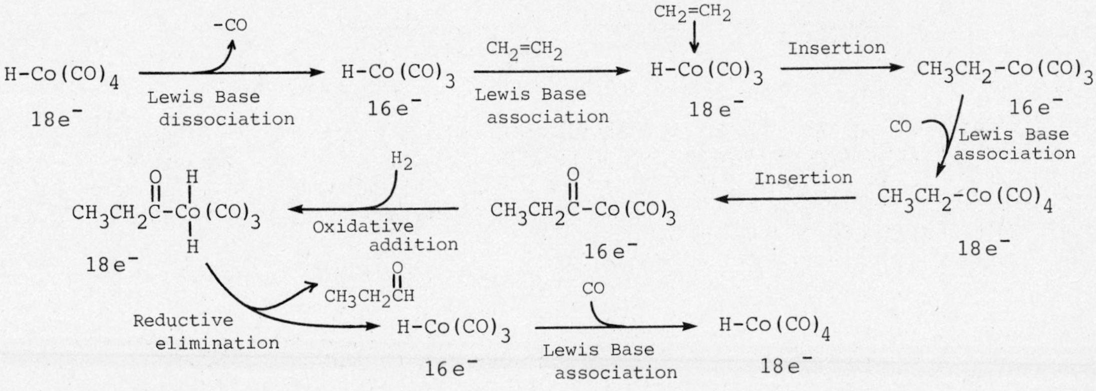

34.11

$[(C_6H_5)_3P]_3RhCl = L_3RhCl =$ Wilkinson's catalyst

$CH_3CH_2CH_2CH_2CCl = RCOCl$ (with O on the carbonyl carbon)

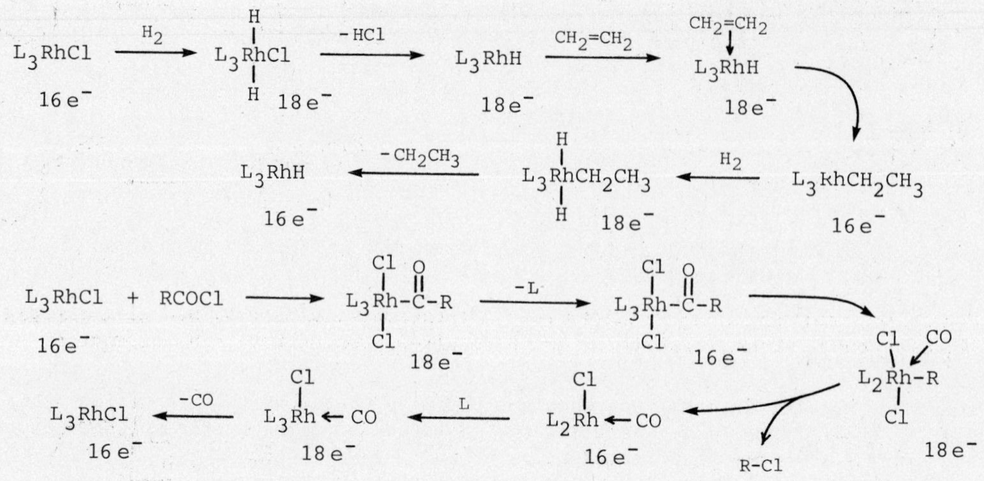

34.12

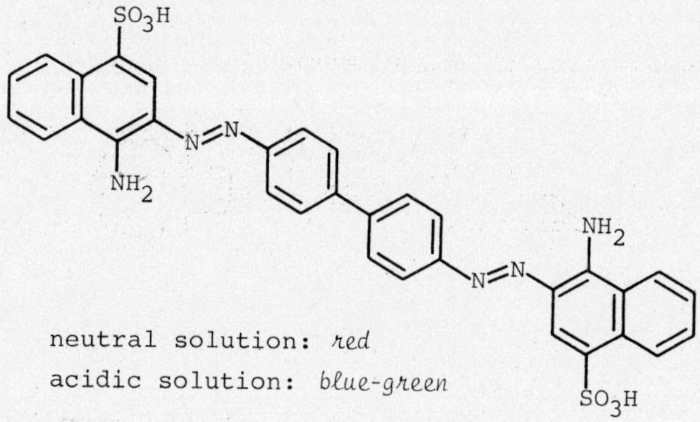

neutral solution: *red*
acidic solution: *blue-green*

34.13

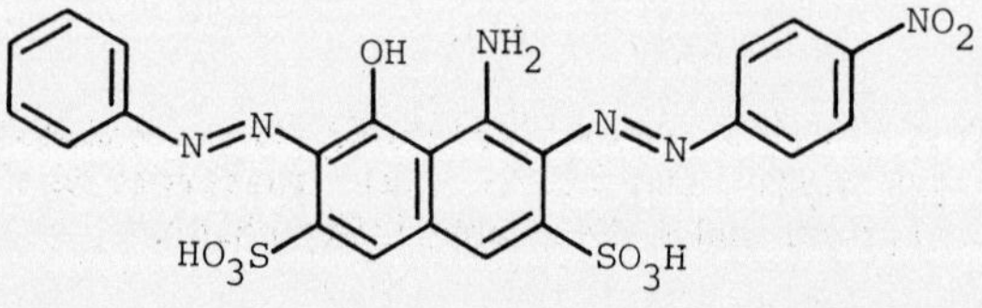

Naphthol Blue Black H

34.14

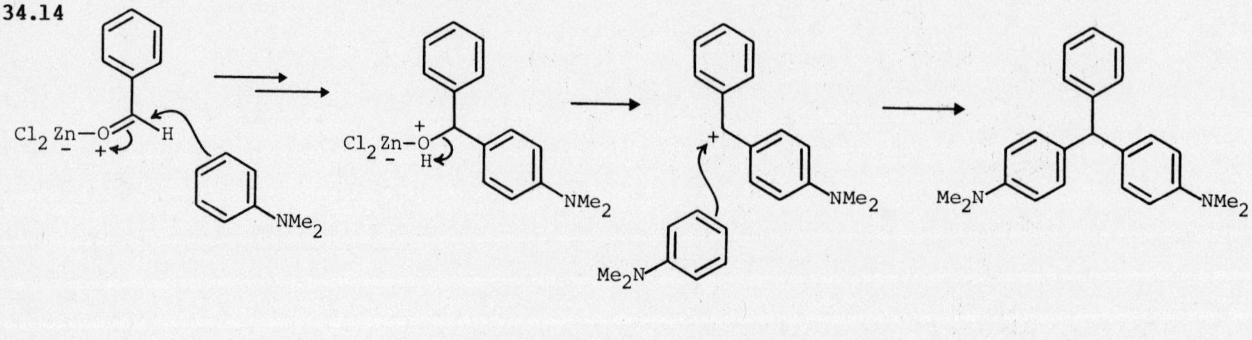

34.15

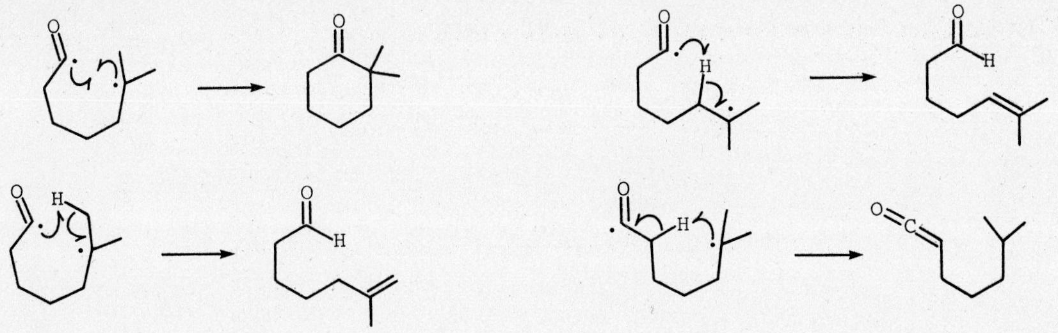

34.16   Molecular orbital theory predicts that the thermal reaction should give the _cis_ isomer (4n electrons, Möbius transition state required, conrotatory ring closure):

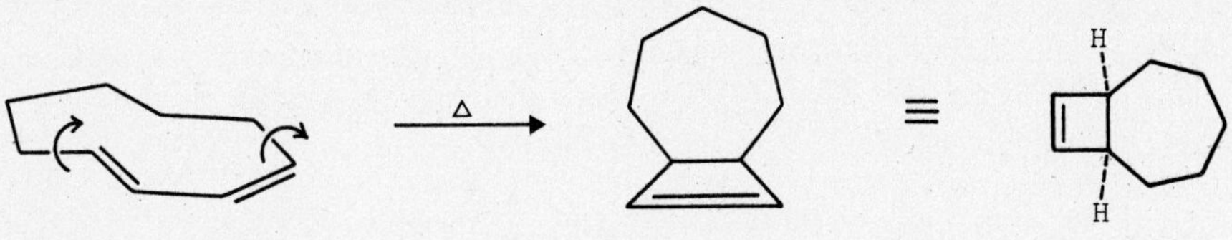

The excited state photochemical process gives the _trans_ isomer:

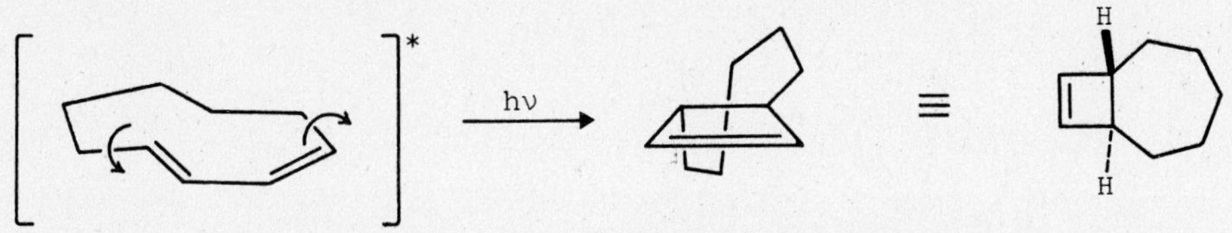

34.17

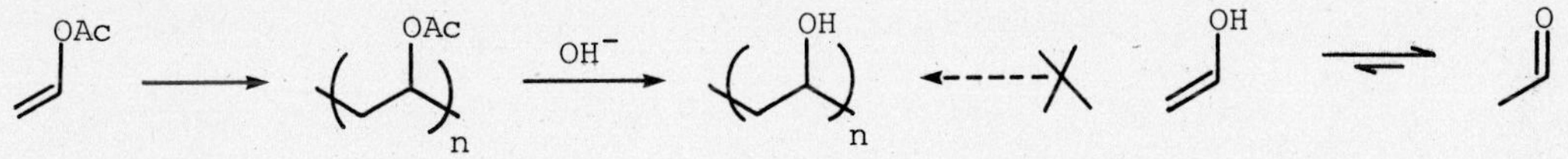

34.18   If both copolymerization ratios are small, there is more likelihood that a radical from styrene addition will react with maleic anhydride, and vice versa; therefore the polymer will tend to be composed of alternating styrene and maleic anhydride units.

34.19

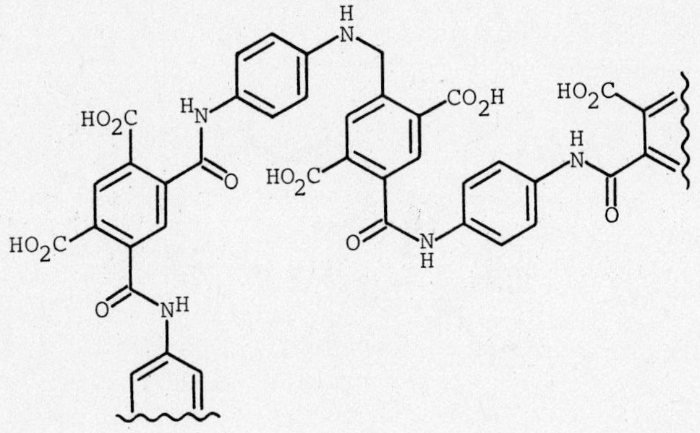

34.20 Poly(U) would be the messenger RNA arising from poly(dA). Since poly(dA) contains only AAA codons, poly(U) will give rise to poly(Phe). Poly(A) likewise arises from poly(dT), which codes for poly(Lys). A random copolymer of equal parts of uridylate and guanidylate will contain (on the average) equal amounts of the eight triads shown below:

RNA Triad	Precursor Sequence in Parent DNA (codon)	Amino Acid Encoded
UUU	AAA	Phe
GUU	CAA	Val
UGU	ACA	Cys
UUG	AAC	Leu
GGU	CCA	Gly
GUG	CAC	Val
UGG	ACC	Trp
GGG	CCC	Gly

The polypeptide produced is therefore expected to have the approximate composition:

$PheVal_2CysLeuGly_2Trp$

34.21

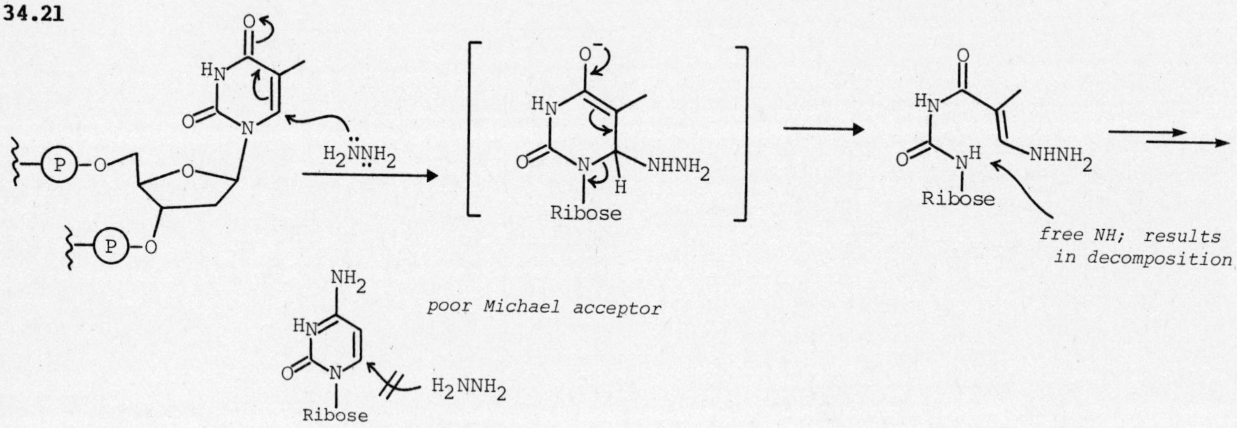

poor Michael acceptor

free NH; results in decomposition

34.22

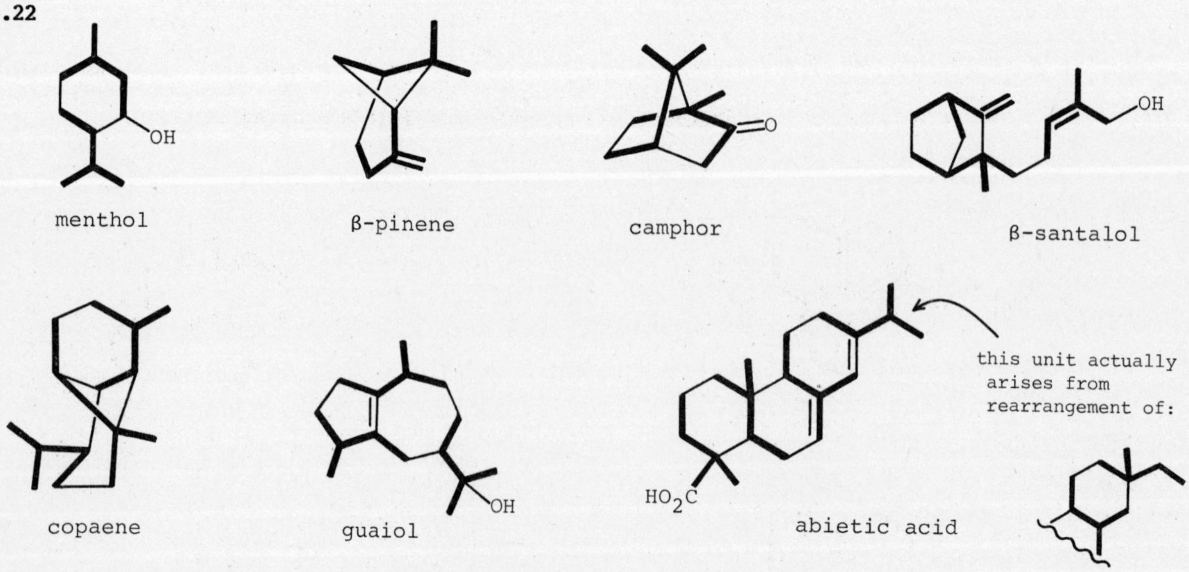

menthol   β-pinene   camphor   β-santalol

copaene   guaiol   abietic acid

this unit actually arises from rearrangement of:

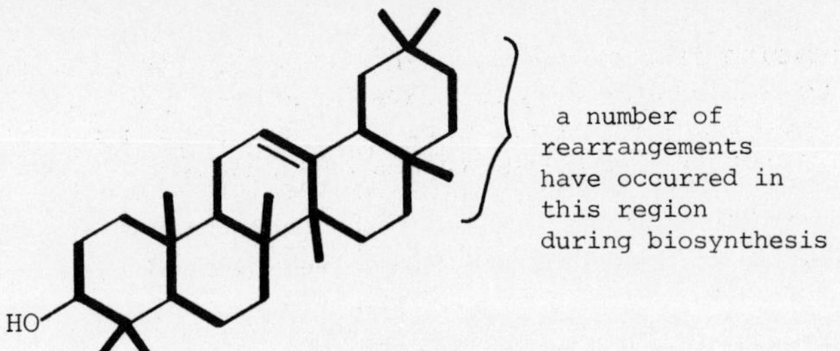

β-amyrin

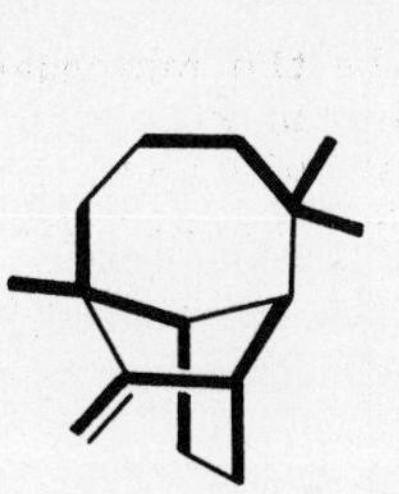

a number of
rearrangements
have occurred in
this region
during biosynthesis

longifolene

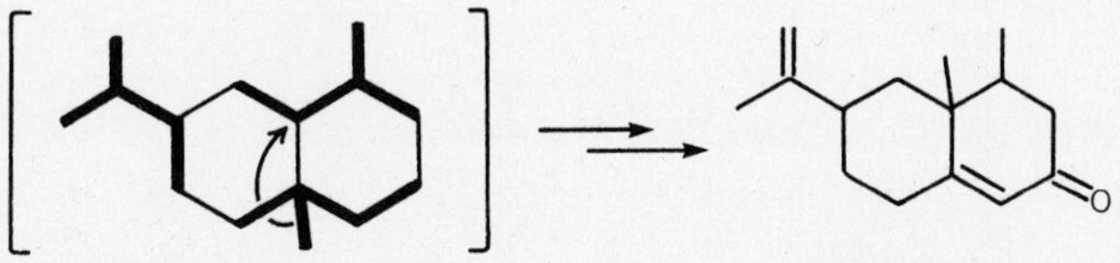

nootkatone

34.23

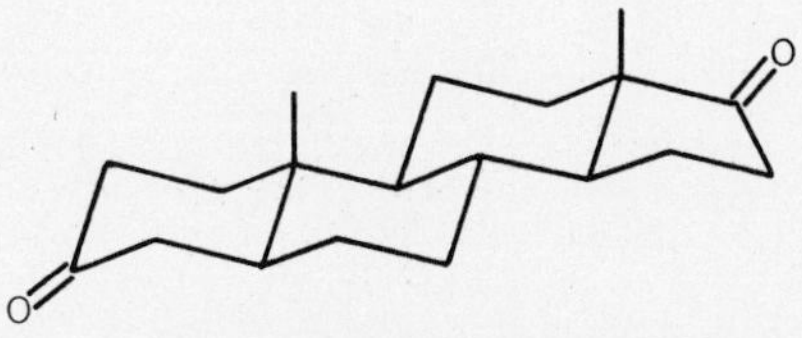

Androsterone

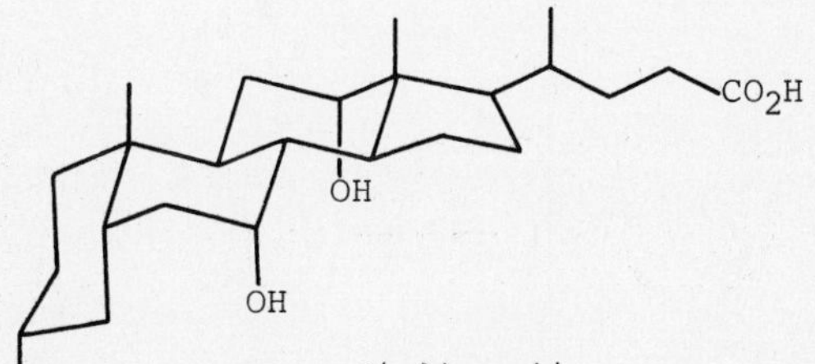

Cholic acid

34.24

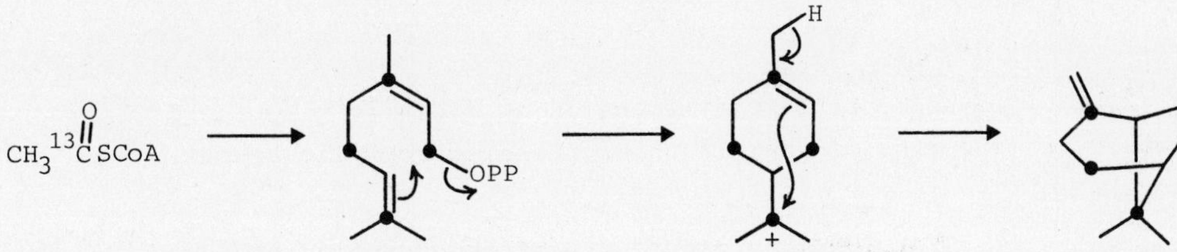

$CH_3\overset{O}{\underset{}{^{13}C}}SCoA$

Four different ^{13}C signals will be seen, for the indicated carbons.

34.25

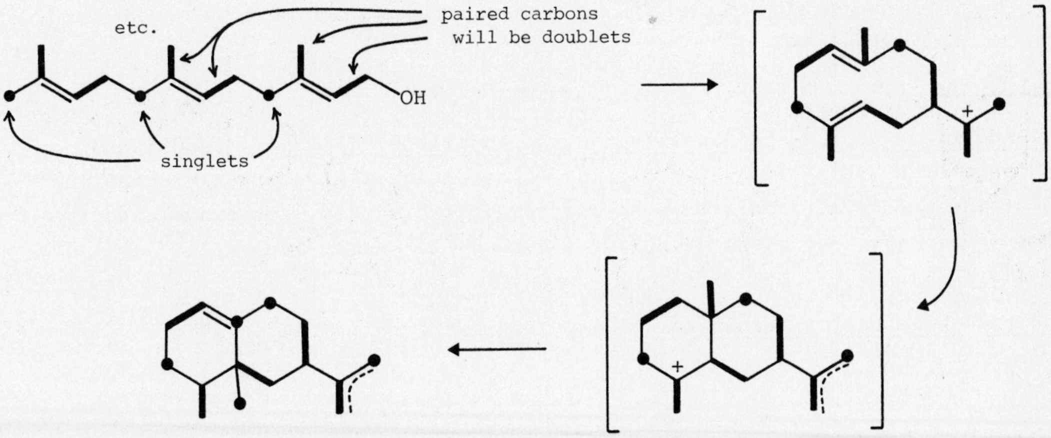

etc.

paired carbons
will be doublets

singlets

APPENDIX I: GLOSSARY

This glossary provides definitions, brief explanations, and comparisons for many of the words and concepts introduced in the text. After each entry, the section(s) in the text where the term can be found or was first introduced is given in parentheses. Many of the explanations are cross-referenced; terms which appear in italics in the explanations are themselves defined in this glossary.

Most of the bold-faced terms in the text have been included, except those whose definition is given explicitly in the text and which you can find directly through the index. This glossary also does not include name reactions, which again you can find through the index in the text.

Absolute configuration (7.3). Actual 3-dimensional relationship of substituents on a *chiral center*. Named according to the *R-S convention*, or in sugar and amino acid chemistry, by the *"D-L" terminology*.
See *Relative configuration*.

Acene (30.5). Linear, fused polybenzenoid hydrocarbon.

Acetal, ketal (14.7.B).

$$R-\underset{\underset{R'}{|}}{\overset{\overset{OR''}{|}}{C}}-OR''$$

acetal: R,R" = alkyl, R' = H
ketal: R,R',R" = alkyl

These are in equilibrium with the aldehyde or ketone plus alcohol only under acidic conditions. The equilibrium is usually driven to the side of acetal or ketal by removing the water by *azeotropic distillation* using a *Dean-Stark trap*. Ketals and acetals are stable to base and are often used as *protecting groups*.

Achiral (7.1). See *Chiral*.

Activating (22.5). An activating substituent on an aromatic ring increases the electron density of the ring so that it undergoes electrophilic aromatic substitution more readily.

Acylammonium salts (18.7.B). Unstable products of the reaction of acyl halides with tertiary amines:

$$R\overset{\overset{O}{||}}{C}NR_3'^+ \ X^-.$$

Acylation (22.4.A). The replacement of a hydrogen (usually) with an acyl group, as in Friedel-Crafts acylation of aromatic rings or acylation of an alcohol with an acid chloride, etc.

Acylium ion (18.6, 22.4.A). [$R-C\equiv O^+ \longleftrightarrow R-\overset{+}{C}=O$]

1,2-Additions vs 1,4-additions (conjugate additions) (19.3.A). Additions across one π-bond are called *1,2-additions*, regardless of the actually numbering scheme of the molecule. Addition across a *conjugated* system, for example to the two ends of a *conjugated diene* or across a *conjugated enone*, are called *conjugate* or *1,4-additions*.

Addition-elimination mechanism (18.6). See *Nucleophilic addition-elimination mechanism*.

Aglycon (28.10). The non-sugar part of a *glycoside*.

Alditol (28.5.D). The polyalcohol resulting from reduction of the carbonyl group of a sugar.

Aldonic acid (28.5.E). The monocarboxylic acid resulting from oxidation of the aldehyde carbon of an *aldose*.

Alkylation (22.4.B). The replacement of a hydrogen (usually) with an alkyl group, as in Friedel-Crafts alkylation of an aromatic ring, or alkylation of a ketone via its enolate, etc.

Allyl, allylic (19.1). An *allylic system* is one involving 3 adjacent, over-lapping p-orbitals, making 3 molecular orbitals, and filled with 2 (*allyl cation*), 3 (*allyl radical*), or 4 (*allyl anion*) electrons. It is an example of *conjugation*.

An *allylic position* is one next to a double bond.

Reactions of *allyl systems* are said to proceed with *allylic rearrangement* if the double bond moves in the course of the reaction.

Amphoteric (29.1, 29.3). Having both acidic and basic character in the same molecule.

Angle of rotation, α (7.2). The amount by which plane polarized light is rotated by an *optically active* sample.

Anisotropic (7.2, 13.9, 20.3.A). Not having the same effect in all directions. *Diamagnetic anisotropy* refers to the *deshielding* effect of electron density which is adjacent to but not surrounding the nucleus being observed in the NMR. (See *chemical shift* and *ring current*)

Anomers, anomeric (28.3). *Anomers* are stereoisomeric sugars which differ in configuration only at the *hemiacetal* or *hemiketal* carbon, also known as the *anomeric* carbon.

Antarafacial (21.5.B). On opposite faces of a π system. See *suprafacial*.

Anti, Gauche, Syn, Eclipsed, Staggered (5.2). These are all terms used to describe three-dimensional relationships of substituents at opposite ends of a single bond.

When the substituents at one end are "lined up" with the substituents at the other end, the molecule is said to have an eclipsed conformation of the single bond. The molecules drawn below are shown in eclipsed conformations.

Eclipsed

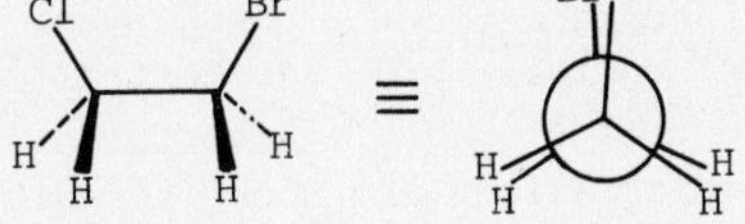

A

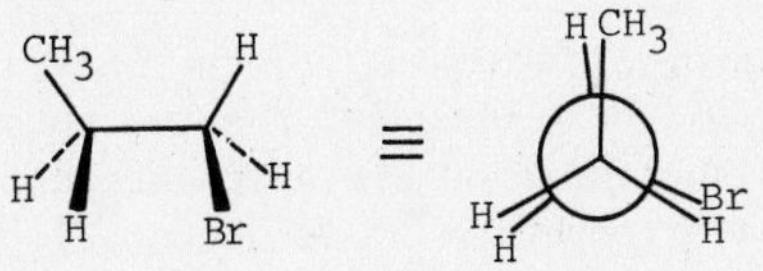

B

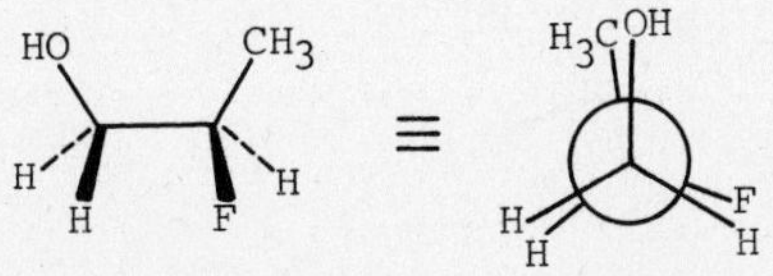

C

In the eclipsed conformation A, the chlorine and bromine atoms are *syn* to each other (coplanar and "pointing in the same direction"). Similarly, the methyl and the hydroxy groups in the eclipsed conformation C are *syn*.

When the substituents at one end are "in between" those at the other end, the molecule is in a *staggered* conformation, as shown for the molecules below. The staggered conformations are more stable (lower potential energy) than the eclipsed.

Staggered

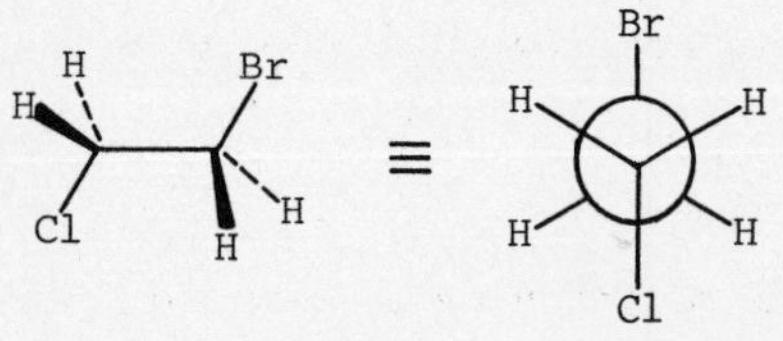

D   ≡   E   ≡

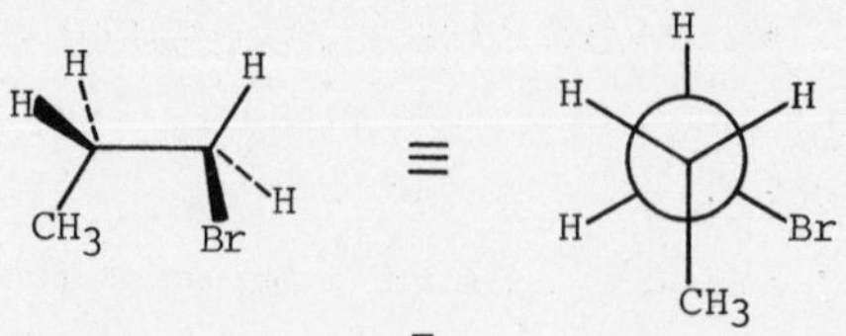

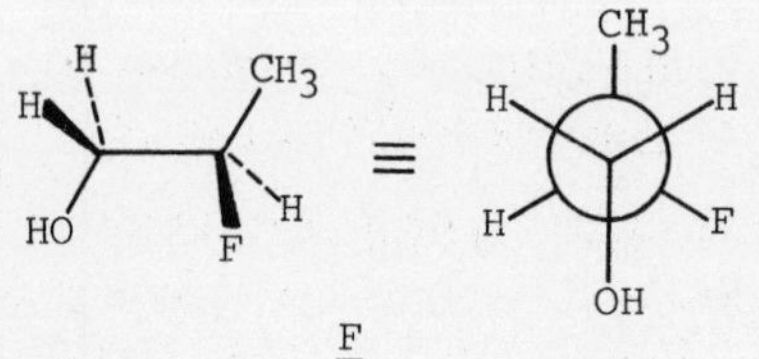

F   ≡

In the staggered conformations D and F, the bromine and the chlorine, and the methyl and hydroxy groups, respectively, are *anti* to each other (coplanar, but "pointing in opposite directions"). In the staggered conformation E, the bromine and the methyl group are said to be *gauche* to each other (dihedral angle = 60°); the staggered conformation F has a *gauche* relationship between the fluorine and hydroxy substituents.

Anti-aromatic (21.3.A). See *Aromatic*.

Antibonding orbital (2.7). See *Orbital*.

Anti-Markovnikov (11.6.C). An orientation opposite to that predicted by *Markovnikov's rule* for electrophilic addition to an alkene. It is the overall result of the free-radical addition of HBr to an alkene or alkyne, or of their hydration via hydroboration/oxidation (11.6.D).

Annulene (21.3.E). A monocyclic $(CH)_n$ hydrocarbon, for example cyclodeca-pentaene is [10]annulene.

Apical, **Equatorial** (25.11.A). In the trigonal bipyramidal conformation of pentavalent phosphorus and silicon compounds, the two substituents which are colinear with the central atom are **apical**, and the three others which are coplanar with the central atom are **equatorial**. These positions are interconverted by **pseudorotation**. The favored conformations are those in which the more electronegative substituents occupy the **apical** positions and the less electronegative groups are **equatorial**.

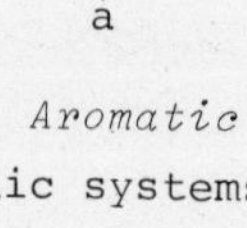

a = *apical*
e = *equatorial*

Aromatic (20.1.A, 20.1.C, 21.3). *Aromatic* compounds are those which have a special stabilization of their electronic systems due to a cyclic arrangement of $4n + 2$ π-electrons. See *Hückel 4n + 2 rule*, *resonance energy*, and *delocalization energy*. Compounds with cyclic π-systems of 4n electrons appear to have a special destabilization and are called *antiaromatic*.

An *aromatic* hydrogen or other substituent is one which is directly attached to an aromatic ring.

Aromatization (30.3.B). Formation of an *aromatic* ring from a less unsaturated precursor, usually by a *dehydrogenation* process.

Asymmetric center or carbon (7.1). See *Stereocenter*.

Asymmetric induction (7.8). *Asymmetric induction* is said to occur when a *chiral center* is formed with a preference for one *absolute configuration* over the other.

Atomic orbital (2.5). See *Orbital*.

Autocatalytic (14.6.D). If one of the products of a reaction is a catalyst for the reaction, the reaction is said to be *autocatalytic*. Often such reactions exhibit an *induction period*.

Autoxidation (10.10.B, 14.9.A). Reaction with atmospheric oxygen, usually to generate an *alkylperoxide*, ROOH, or a peroxycarboxylic acid, $\overset{\overset{\text{O}}{\|}}{\text{RCOOH}}$.

Average bond energy (6.5). The average energy required to dissociate each of the bonds of a certain type in a molecule. It differs from the *bond dissociation energy*, which refers to a specific, instead of an average, bond of a given type.

Axial and equatorial (5.6). In the most stable conformation for the cyclo-hexane ring, called the "chair" form, there are two orientations which substitu-ents can adopt. If they point up and down, perpendicular to the average plane of the six-membered ring, they are *axial*; if they point out somewhat horizontally relative to the ring, they are called *equatorial*, as drawn below:

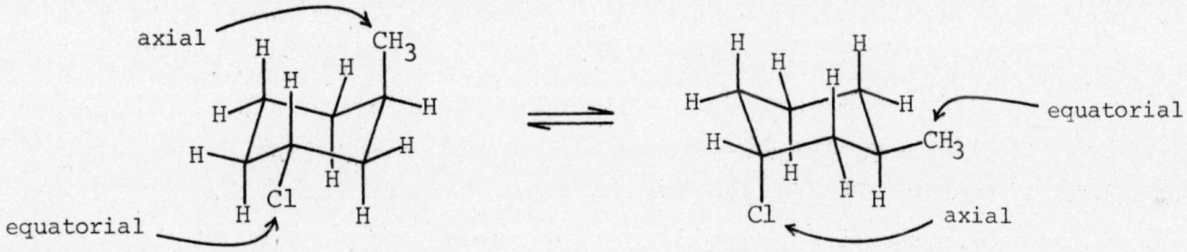

Note that when the cyclohexane ring flips between the two chair conformations, the axial substituents become equatorial and vice versa. You can see this easily if you have a set of models.

The equatorial positions are less *sterically hindered* and therefore more stable for substituents to occupy than the axial ones.

Azeotropic distillation (14.7.B). Two immiscible solvents will distill as a mixture. This forms the basis for removing water from an equilibrium process by distilling with benzene or toluene. The distillate separates into two phases, with the water being drawn off in a *Dean-Stark trap* and the benzene or toluene returned to the reaction flask.

Beer's law (21.5.C). In ultraviolet *spectroscopy*: $\log \frac{I_o}{I} = \varepsilon c d$, where I_o, I = light intensity before and after passing through cell, ε = *extinction coefficient*, c = concentration in moles liter^{-1}, and d = path length in cm.

Bent bonds (5.7, 11.1.A). When geometric constraints force the bond angles around an atom to be smaller than the preferred angles between the orbitals, the single bonds "bend", which is to say the atomic orbitals do not overlap in their normal end-to-end fashion. Instead, the center of electron density in the bonding orbital lies off to the side of the internuclear axis, and the bond is weaker (see Figure 2.9). This behavior is most important for cyclopropane.

·Benzyl, benzylic (20.5). A *benzylic* radical is one involving a carbon radical directly attached to an aromatic ring. Benzylic cations and anions are analogous. A benzylic position is one immediately adjacent to an aromatic ring.

Benzyne (26.3.A). A highly reactive intermediate in the *elimination-addi-tion mechanism* for nucleophilic aromatic substitution:

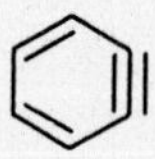

Betaine (14.8.E). A *zwitterionic* intermediate. In the Wittig reaction, the betaine may be in equilibrium with an *oxaphosphetane*.

Bimolecular (9.1, 9.2). See *Molecularity*.

Biosynthesis (25.7, 34.8). The synthesis of compounds by living organisms.

Bond (2.7). A net attractive interaction between two atoms. The most impor-tant bonds in organic chemistry are *covalent bonds*, which result when two atoms share electrons. The behavior of the shared electrons is described by a *molecular orbital*, and the means by which the sharing is accomplished is overlap of the appropriate *atomic orbitals* on each atom. A *single bond* results from the sharing of two electrons in one molecular orbital; a *double* (triple) bond results from the sharing of four (six) electrons in two (three) molecular orbitals.

A *dative* or *donor bond* usually involves the interaction between a vacant metal orbital and a filled orbital (often a *lone pair*) of a *ligand*.

Bond dissociation energy (D or DH°) (6.1). The energy required to break a bond *homolytically* and separate the two radicals.

α- and β-Branching (9.3). Alkyl groups attached to the carbon undergoing a substitution reaction are α-branches; those on an adjacent carbon are β-branches. Both contribute to *steric hindrance* in S_N2-reactions.

Bridged, fused, and spiro ring systems.

A *bridged* compound is a bicyclic compound in which the rings share more than two atoms.

A *fused* compound is one in which the two rings share two adjacent atoms.

A *spiro* compound is one in which the rings share only one atom.

Carbenoid (11.6.F). An organometallic complex which behaves like a carbene (R-C̈-R') source in its reactions.

Carbinolamine (14.7.C). A *hemiaminal*: $R_2C \stackrel{\displaystyle OH}{\underset{\displaystyle NR_2'}{\big<}}$

Carbocation (2.4). A molecule in which a carbon atom is only trivalent and has only six *valence* electrons. The simplest carbocation is the methyl cation The positively charged carbon is sp^2 *hybridized*, bonding to the hydrogens via the three sp^2 orbitals and leaving the remaining p orbital vacant.   H:C̈:H .
                                                                                          +

Carbocation rearrangement (10.6.C). Migration of a substituent, with its bonding electron pair, from an adjacent carbon to a cationic carbon so as to generate a more stable *carbocation*.

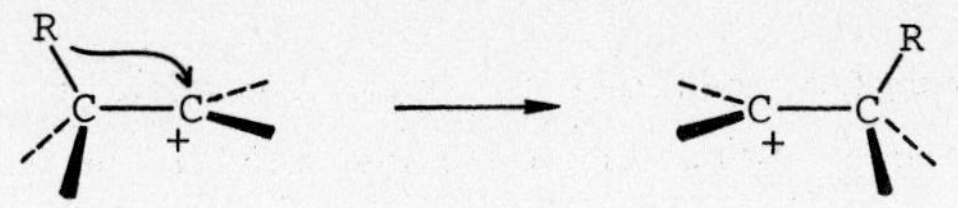

e.g., 2° carbocation → 3° carbocation, or ring-expansion of a four- to a five-membered ring.

Center of symmetry (7.5). An object has a center of symmetry when the exact same environment is encountered at the same distance in both directions along any line through a particular point, which is called the center of symmetry. Such an object is *achiral*.

Chain reaction (6.3). A chain reaction is one in which (relatively few) *initiation* steps take place, followed by (many) *propagation* steps which convert the starting materials to products, and finally, by (again relatively few) *termination* steps. These reactions usually involve radical intermediates, and transformations involving radical intermediates are usually chain reactions. A chain reaction process is shown below:

$$I\text{-}I \xrightarrow[\text{or } \Delta]{h\nu} 2\ I\cdot \qquad\qquad \textit{Initiation}$$

$$I\cdot\ +\ A \longrightarrow I'\ +\ A\cdot$$

$$A\cdot\ +\ B \rightarrow A'\ +\ B\cdot$$
$$B\cdot\ +\ A \rightarrow A\cdot\ +\ B' \qquad \begin{array}{l}\textit{Propagation:}\quad\text{overall process is}\\ \qquad\qquad\qquad A + B \rightarrow A' + B'\end{array}$$

$$A\cdot\ +\ B\cdot,\ A\cdot\ +\ A\cdot,\ \text{or}\ B\cdot\ +\ B\cdot \rightarrow AB,\ AA,\ \text{or}\ BB \quad \textit{Termination}$$

Chair conformation (7.7). The most stable conformation of a cyclohexane ring. In the chair conformation (depicted under *axial*, above), all of the C-C bonds have the staggered conformation and each carbon is free to adopt its preferred tetrahedral geometry.

Characterization (3.4). Determination of the physical and chemical properties of a compound. For example, you could characterize 1-tetradecene ($CH_3(CH_2)_{11}CH=CH_2$) by determining its melting point (-12 °C), boiling point (232 °C), reaction with $KMnO_4$ (to give a carboxylic acid, $CH_3(CH_2)_{11}COOH$), combustion analysis (85.7% C, 14.3% H), and by recording its nmr, ir, and mass *spectra*, etc.

Charge-transfer complex (26.8.D). A complex formed by the face-to-face interaction of two π-systems, one electron-rich and the other electron-poor. There is a certain amount of electron density transferred from the electron-rich (donor) to the electron-poor (acceptor) system.

Chemical shift (13.4). The difference in resonant frequency in the nmr between a reference compound (usually tetramethylsilane, *"TMS"*) and the nucleus of interest, usually measured in parts per million (*ppm*) *downfield* from TMS; this is the so-called "δ scale".

   Downfield = *deshielded* = higher frequency = lower field = "to the left" in most spectra.
   Upfield = the opposite of downfield.

The presence of electron density *around* a nucleus is *shielding*; the withdrawal of electron density or the presence of electron density *next to* a nucleus (*diamagnetic anisotropy*) is *deshielding*.

Chiral (7.1). A molecule is *chiral* if it is not superimposable on its mirror image; the two mirror image molecules are *enantiomers*. A carbon atom with four different substituents is a *stereocenter* or *chiral center*. A molecule with an odd number of *chiral centers* is *chiral*, but with an even number there exists the possibility of *achiral*, *meso* compounds. *Achiral* molecules are *optically inactive*, but *chiral* molecules are not necessarily *optically active*, they could be present as a *racemic* mixture (equal amounts of both *enantiomers*).

Chloromethylation (22.4.B). Replacement of an aromatic hydrogen (usually) with a chloromethyl group, usually using CH_2O, HCl, and $ZnCl_2$.

Combination bands (15.2). See *Overtone*.

Condensation (14.7.C). Combination of two molecules with elimination of water or other small molecule, as in the formation of an *imine* or in the aldol condensation (14.8.C).

Condensed formulas (3.1). See *Structural formulas*.

Configuration:

Electronic: The specific distribution of electrons in *atomic* or *molecular orbitals*.

Stereochemical: The arrangement in 3 dimensions of the substituents on a *chiral center*. See *Absolute configuration*.

Configurational isomers (11.1.A). See *conformation*.

Conformation (5.2), Conformational isomers (11.1.B) = conformers (5.3). There is a fine distinction between *conformers* and other types of *isomers* which is confusing at times. Anytime there are molecules which have the same formula but are put together differently in three dimensions, we can call them isomers. A distinction is drawn between those isomers which interconvert rapidly at ordinary temperatures (without breaking any bonds usually), and those which interconvert very slowly or not at all (and which usually require bonds to be broken and remade during the process). The former are *conformers*, and the different arrangements in three dimensions which a molecule can adopt easily (without breaking bonds) are called different *conformations*. Those which interconvert slowly are called *configurational isomers*.

Conrotatory and disrotatory (21.5.A). In an *electrocyclic* reaction, if the two ends of the *conjugated* system rotate in the same direction (e.g., clockwise) during ring closure the reaction is said to be *conrotatory*; if they rotate in opposite directions (one clockwise, one counterclockwise) it is a *disrotatory* ring closure. *Electrocyclic* ring opening reactions are evaluated the same way.

Coordinatively saturated (34.2). A transition metal which has achieved the *18-electron configuration* is *coordinatively saturated*.

Conjugate acid, (conjugate base)(4.5). The species which results from loss of a proton   from a molecule is its *conjugate base*; the species which results from protonation of a molecule is its *conjugate acid*;

$$HA \rightleftharpoons A^- + H^+$$
$$B: + H^+ \rightleftharpoons B\overset{+}{H}$$

A^- and B: are conjugate bases of HA and $B\overset{+}{H}$, respectively; HA and $B\overset{+}{H}$ are conjugate acids of A^- and B:, respectively.

Conjugation (18.5,19). π-Orbital overlap from more than two atoms. Two double bonds are conjugated if they are adjacent to each other (C = C - C = C, *conjugated diene*) and are *unconjugated* if there is one or more sp^3 hydridized carbons in between (C = C - C - C = C , *unconjugated diene, isolated double bonds*).

A *conjugated enone* is one in which the carbonyl group and double bond are adjacent (C = C - C = O).

Coupling constant, J (13.6). See *Spin-spin splitting*.

Covalent bond (2.7). See *Bond*.

Cracking (6.2). *Pyrolysis* of alkanes to give shorter-chain alkanes and alkenes.

Cross-conjugation (19.3.B). A *conjugated* system which is branched rather than linear is *cross-conjugated*.

Crown ethers (10.11.B). Cyclic polymers of ethylene oxide:

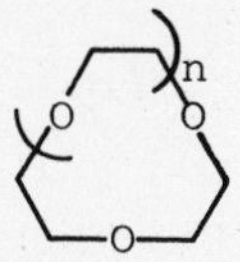

These are important as *phase-transfer catalysts*.

Cumulated double bonds (19.2.C). Double bonds which share the same carbon atom (C = C = C).

Cycloaddition reaction (19.5, 21.5.B, 31.5.B). A reaction in which electron movement occurs in a cyclic manner during the course of addition of a conjugated molecule to a π-bond (for example, the Diels-Alder reaction or *1,3-dipolar cyclo-addition*).

D-L convention (28.2). Systems of nomenclature for indicating the *absolute configuration* of *amino acids* and *sugars*: the molecule is drawn in a *Fischer projection* with the carbon chain written vertically and the most oxidized end at the top. If the *heteroatom* substituent (hydroxy or amino group) projects to the right, that *chiral center* is D, if it's on the left it's L. Whether a sugar belongs to the D- or the L-series is determined by the last *chiral center* in the chain. The configuration of an amino acid is determined by the α-carbon.

Deactivating (22.5). The opposite of *Activating*.

Dean-Stark trap (14.7.B). See *Azeotropic distillation*.

Decarbonylation (34.2). Loss of carbon monoxide, usually referring to the reaction catalyzed by transition metal complexes like Wilkinson's catalyst ([(C$_6$H$_5$)$_3$P]$_3$RhCl).

Decarboxylation (27.6.C,   27.7.C).   Loss of carbon dioxide.

Decoupling (13.7). Strong electromagnetic irradiation of a nucleus at its resonant frequency in an NMR spectrometer causes it to change its allowed *quantized* orientation in the magnetic field rapidly on the *NMR time scale*, averaging out its effect on nuclei to which it is *coupled*. This reduces the observed *coupling constant* J to O. It is useful in proton NMR for interpreting splitting patterns, and is routinely used in CMR to simplify the spectra and improve the signal-to-noise ratio.

Off-resonance decoupling in CMR is a partial decoupling of the protons from the carbons, leaving a small, residual coupling so that the number of hydrogens attached to each carbon can be determined.

Degenerate (15.2, 20.1.C). Energy levels which are different but equal in energy are *degenerate*.

Degree of association (14.6.B). How tightly bound an *ion-pair* is. In non-polar solvents, ions are poorly *solvated* and the *ion pairs* are tightly associated. In polar, particularly hydroxylic solvents, *solvation energies* are high, and ions are only loosely associated. The association of ions usually reduces their reactivity.

Dehydration (11.5.B). Loss of water, usually with reference to an alcohol losing a molecule of water to give an alkene.

Dehydrogenation (20.1.D). The opposite of *hydrogenation*. *Dehydrogenation* involves the removal of hydrogen from a molecule and the introduction of *unsaturation*.

Dehydrohalogenation (11.5.A). Removal of HX, usually referring to E2 reaction of an alkyl halide.

Deinsertion (34.2). See *Insertion*.

Delocalization energy (20.1.B). The hypothetical difference in energy between the actual distribution of electrons in a *conjugated* system and a system of identical geometry with electronic isolation of the π-bonds from each other. Contrast with *empirical resonance energy*, (See *Resonance energy*).

Deshielded, shielded (13.4). See *Chemical Shift*.

Deuteration (8.9.A). Introduction of deuterium into a molecule. It can be accomplished by *deuterium exchange* or by reaction of an organometallic reagent with D_2O, among other methods.

Deuterium exchange (14.6.A). Equilibration of ionizable hydrogens with deuterium atoms from the solvent, usually used to determine how many α-hydrogens (enolizable hydrogens) are present in a ketone or other carbonyl compound.

Dextrorotatory, levorotatory (7.2). A sample which rotates plane polarized light clockwise (+ direction) is *dextrorotatory* (counterclockwise is *levorotatory* (−)).

Diagmagnetic shielding and deshielding (13.4). See *Chemical Shift*, *Anisotropy*, and π-*Electron circulation*.

Diastereomer (7.5). *Stereoisomers* which are not *enantiomers*. If more than one *chiral center* is present in a molecule, changing the *configuration* of all of them gives the *enantiomer*. Changing the configuration of *less* than all of them gives a *diastereomer*.

Diastereomeric salts (29.4.F). See *Resolution*.

Diaxial (11.6.B). This is equivalent to *anti* in a cyclohexane system.

Diazotization (23.7.B, 24.5). Conversion of an amino into a diazonium group:
$$NH_2 + HONO + H^+ \longrightarrow RN_2^+ + 2 H_2O$$

Dienophile (19.5). The "monoene" component of the Diels-Alder reaction. Electron-withdrawing groups on a dienophile usually increase its reactivity.

Dilution principle (19.1.C). A *bimolecular* reaction is slowed down more on dilution than a *unimolecular* reaction.

Dimer, trimer (34.5). See *Polymer*.

1,3-Dipolar cycloaddition (32.5.B). A *cycloaddition reaction* in which the *conjugated* component is 3 atoms long and is *zwitterionic* or with *zwitterionic* character.

Dipole moment, μ(8.1). A dipole moment arises whenever positive and negative charges are separated. The magnitude depends on separation, d, and charge, q: μ = q·d. The general quality of "polarity" depends in part on the presence of a dipole moment in a molecule.

Dispersion force = London force = Van der Waals attraction (5.1). These three terms all describe a very weak interaction which results in an attraction between two molecules. It is different from the more easily understood ionic or dipole interactions, and depends instead on differences in the "instantaneous" distribution of electrons. The most important features to remember for this force are: (1) it is the primary force of attraction between hydrocarbon molecules; (2) it decreases very rapidly with distance; and (3) its magnitude is proportional to the "surface area" of a molecule.

Disproportionation (6.2). *Disproportionation* involves two of the same or similar molecules reacting with each other to produce different products: $2\,A \longrightarrow B + C$ The *cracking* of alkanes provides an example of this.

Disrotatory (21.5.A). See *Conrotatory*.

Donor-acceptor complex (26.8.D). See *Charge-transfer complex*.

Double bond (2.3). See *Bond*.

Double bond character (18.1). Degree of π-bonding character, often evaluated as amount of contribution from a resonance structure containing a double bond, as in the amide linkage.

$$ \underset{|}{\overset{O}{\underset{C}{\|}}} \overset{}{N} \quad \longleftrightarrow \quad \underset{|}{\overset{O^{-}}{\underset{C}{|}}} \overset{+}{N} $$

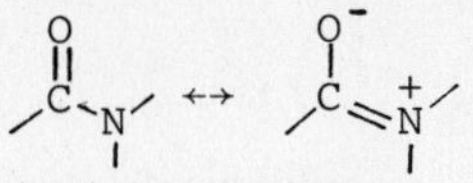

Doublet (13.6). See *Spin-spin splitting*.

Downfield, upfield (13.4). See *Chemical Shift*.

E (entgegen) and Z(zusammen)(11.2). Nomenclature for describing the configuration of a double bond.

E2 (Elimination-bimolecular) 9.6, 11.5.A). The most common mechanism for an elimination reaction. It involves simultaneous removal of the proton by a base, formation of the π-bond, and departure of the leaving group. All the orbitals involved must be coplanar, and this is usually accomplished in an *anti* relationship:

$$ \text{B-H} + \text{alkene} + \text{X}^{-} $$

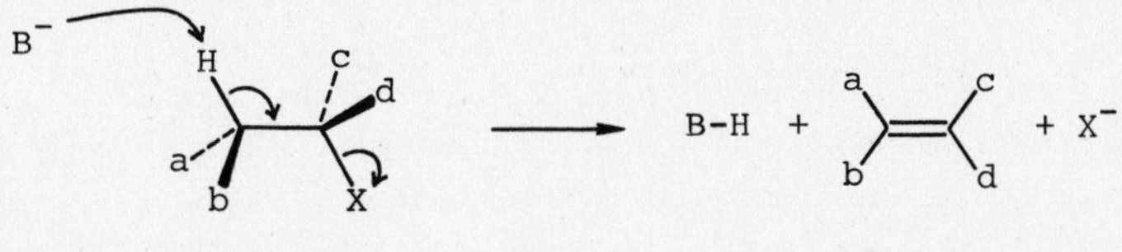

Eclipsed (5.2). See *Anti*.

Edman degradation (29.6.C). A method for the stepwise removal and identification of the N-terminal amino acids from a *peptide* chain.

α-, β-, and γ-effects (13.12). Characteristic effects on *chemical shift* in cmr spectroscopy which depend on specific substituents and their position relative to the nucleus observed.

Eighteen electron rule (34.2). Just as a 2nd or 3rd period element tries to achieve an octet of *valence electrons* in its bonding arrangement, so does a transition metal try to achieve a filled shell of 2s + 10d + 6p = 18 electrons through its bonds to *ligands* and other groups. A metal which has achieved an *18-electron configuration* is *coordinatively saturated*.

Electrocyclic reaction (21.5).   A reaction in which a conjugated molecule undergoes a cyclic rearrangement of electrons to form a molecule with one less π-bond and one more ring, or the reverse of this process.

Electron affinity (2.2). (See definition on page 6 in text.)

Electron-attracting and -donating (10.4). See *Inductive effect*.

π-Electron circulation (13.9.A). The motion of all electrons is altered by a magnetic field. The electron motion induced in the π-electrons of alkenes and aromatic rings causes a *downfield (deshielding)* effect on the *chemical shifts* of nuclei attached to them. This effect is known as *diagmagnetic deshielding*.

Electron count (2.2, 34.2). The number of electrons in the valence shell of an atom or metal is determined for the purpose of evaluating *formal charges, filled octets, 18-electron* configurations, etc.

Electron density (2.5). Refers to the *probability* of finding an electron in a given region of space. This probability is given by the square of the *wavefunction* for the electron; high probability corresponds to high electron density.

Electronegative (2.2). Exerting a strong attraction for electrons. The electronegativity of the elements increases as one goes up and to the right in the periodic table. The more electronegative a group is, the better it is able to stabilize a negative charge, within the constraints of the *octet rule*. Electronegative elements usually need only one or two additional electrons to complete their filled octet.

Electronic transition (21.6). Change of the electronic state of a molecule or atom, usually from the *ground electronic state* to an *excited electronic state* or vice versa. Such transitions are important in ultraviolet *spectroscopy* and photochemistry (21.6.G, 34.4).

Electrophile, electrophilic reagent. The opposite of *nucleophile* and *nucleophilic reagent*. An electrophile contributes the vacant *orbital* when a bond is formed by the reverse of a *heterolytic* process:

$$E^{+} + \ ^{-}\!:Nu \rightarrow E\text{-}Nu$$

electrophile   nucleophile

A proton is the simplest electrophile.

Electropositive (2.2). The opposite of *electronegative*. Electropositive elements are those at the left of the periodic table, which achieve a complete *valence* shell (filled *octet*) by losing rather than gaining one or two electrons.

Elimination-addition mechanism (26.3.A).   For nucleophilic aromatic substitution via a *benzyne* intermediate.

Empirical formula (3.4). The empirical formula of a compound expresses the ratio of elements present. Compare with *molecular formula*.

Enantiomers (7.1). *Stereoisomers* which differ only by being mirror images of each other. See *Chiral* and *Diastereomer*.

Endo and exo (19.5). In a bicyclic compound, the configuration of a non-bridgehead substituent can be specified by its relationship to the other bridges. If it points in the same direction as the longer bridge, it is *endo*; if it points toward the shorter bridge, it is *exo*: e.g.,

shorter bridge

longer bridge

exo

endo

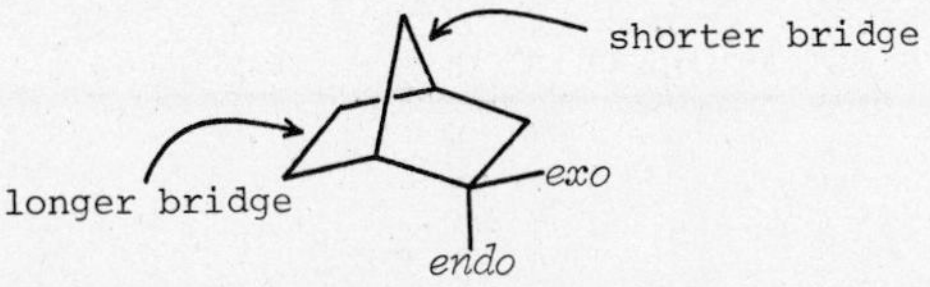

In the transition state of the Diels-Alder reaction, if a substituent on the *dienophile* points toward the diene, it is *endo*; if it points away it is *exo*.

Envelope (5.6). The most favorable conformation for a cyclopentane ring, in which one carbon is pushed out of the plane of the other four in order to minimize the eclipsing interactions of all of the hydrogens. This conformation is not

out-of-plane

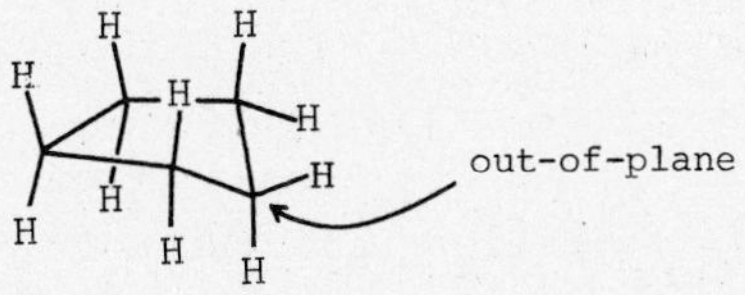

fixed, and all five carbons of a cyclopentane ring can take the out-of-plane position interchangeably. In this instance, the interconversion is referred to as *pseudorotation*.

Enzyme (28.3, 29.7.E). A *protein* that catalyzes a chemical reaction.

Equatorial (5.6, 25.11.A). See definitions under Axial and Apical.

Equilibrium (4.1). Although the term equilibrium is defined in the text, it is important that you understand the distinction between *equilibrium* and rate. The rate constant for a reaction is a measure of how *fast* it goes; the equilibrium constant is a measure of how *far* it goes. There is not necessarily any connection between these two constants: there are many highly *exothermic* reactions which go very slowly (for instance, the decomposition of TNT in the absence of a detonation), and many reactions which are only slightly exothermic but which go very rapidly (for instance, the neutralization of a weak acid with a weak base).

Erythro and threo (27.3.A). A controversial nomenclature system for specifying the relative *configuration* of two *chiral centers*. It arose from carbohydrate chemistry, and is used with Fischer projections in the following way: with the carbon chain written vertically, if the "similar" substituents on two chiral centers are on the same side, the relationship between those carbons is *erythro*. If they are on opposite sides, the relationship is *threo*. Complications arise in systems other than carbohydrates and when it is difficult to decide what the "similar" substituents are.

```
        CHO                      CHO
   H ────── OH             HO ────── H
   H ────── OH              H ────── OH
       CH₂OH                    CH₂OH
```

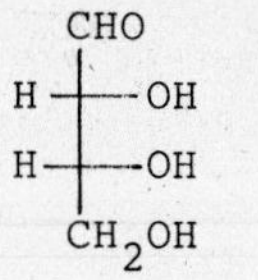

D-*erythrose*   D-*threose*

Ester, esterification (10.6.B, 17.7.C, 25.4, 25.7).   The compound formed from the loss of water (formally) between an alcohol and an acid is an *ester*:

$$ROH + HO\overset{\overset{O}{\|}}{C}R' \rightarrow RO\overset{\overset{O}{\|}}{C}R', \text{ a carboxylic ester}$$

$$2\,ROH + HO\overset{\overset{O}{\|}}{\underset{\underset{O}{\|}}{S}}OH \rightarrow RO\overset{\overset{O}{\|}}{\underset{\underset{O}{\|}}{S}}OR, \text{ a sulfate diester}$$

$$3\,ROH + HO-\overset{\overset{OH}{|}}{P}-OH \rightarrow (RO)_3P: , \text{ a phosphite triester}$$

(but: $ROH + HBr \rightarrow RBr$, an alkyl halide)

Exact mass (32.3). The actual mass, to at least 0.0001 atomic mass unit accuracy, of a molecule or molecular fragment, which allows you to distinguish between *molecular formulas* of the same *nominal mass*.

Excited electronic state (21.6.A). See *Ground electronic state*.

Exo (19.5). See *Endo*.

Extinction coefficient, ε (21.6.C). A measure of the probability that a quantum of electromagnetic radiation with the correct energy will be absorbed and result in an *electronic transition*. It is related to the amount of light transmitted by a sample by *Beer's law*.

First-order vs non-first order nmr spectra (13.7).   When the magnitude of the difference in *chemical shift* ($\Delta\nu$) of two nuclei is much greater than their *coupling constant*, J, the spectrum is said to be *first-order*, and the *spin-spin splitting* patterns follow the usual rules. When $\Delta\nu \simeq J$, the spectrum is *non-first-order*, and the splitting patterns are very complex.

First order reaction (4.3). A true first order reaction is one in which the *rate-determining step* involves only *one* molecule. Therefore the equation for the rate of reaction includes only the concentration of that molecule. If the reaction actually involves two molecules, but one is in large excess (for instance, solvent), the reaction is called a *pseudo first order reaction* because the rate equation still has only one concentration as a variable.

Fischer projection (28.2). A system for indicating 3-dimensional structures in two dimensions. In a Fischer projection the horizontal bonds are understood to project forward and the vertical bonds back:

```
        b                      b
        |                      ┊
   a ───┼─── c      ≡     a ╍╍╍┊╍╍╍ c
        |                      ┊
        d                      d
```

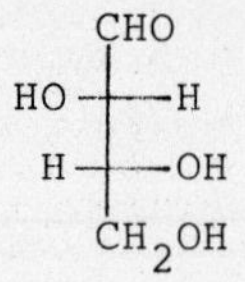

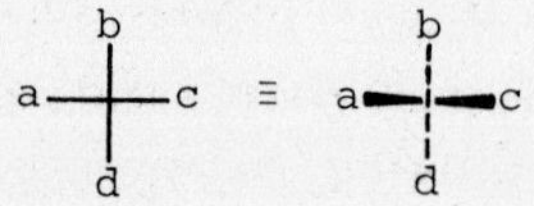

In a Fischer projection, exchange of the positions of any pair of substituents or a 90° rotation of the whole picture leads to a representation of the other *configuration* at that chiral center. Any even combination of these changes (for example 2 pair-wise exchanges, 3 pair-wise exchanges and a 90° rotation, or a 180° rotation) lead to a picture of the same molecule again.

Fluorescence (34.4).   Loss of a photon from the first *excited singlet state* and transition of the molecule to the *ground state*.

Formal charges (2.2).   The difference between the number of *valence* electrons controlled by an atom in the elemental state and in its bonding arrangement in a molecule. The number of valence electrons in the elemental state corresponds to its column in the periodic table; in a molecule, an atom is considered to control all the valence electrons it does not share, and half of those it does share.

Franck-Condon transition (34.4).   An *electronic transition* which occurs more rapidly than atomic (vibrational) motions in a molecule; also called a *vertical transition*.

Free radical (6.1).   Any molecule having unpaired electrons. Usually refers to carbon atoms with only three substituents and seven *valence electrons*, such

as

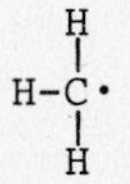

Front side attack (9.1).   A possible mode of substitution stereochemistry. It occurs only in rare instances in nucleophilic displacement reactions (which ordinarily involve *inversion* (S_N2) or *racemization* (S_N1)), but is seen in some electrophilic displacement reactions.

Functional groups (3.3).   The reactive parts of molecules. These are small, frequently-occurring groups of atoms, such as the hydroxy group or carboxy group, which exhibit a typical reactivity in a wide variety of molecules. For example,

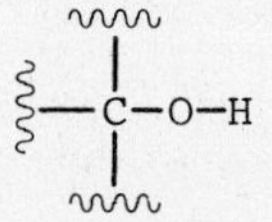

hydroxy group   *carboxy group*

all molecules having a carboxy group are acidic. A list of the most important functional groups is found in Table 3.1 of the text.

Fundamental vibrational modes (15.2).   Modes of vibration which involve more than one bond; all vibrational modes of molecules larger than two atoms are fundamental modes.

Fused ring system (31.1).   See *Bridged*.

Gauche (5.2).   See definition under *Anti*.

Geminal (12.5.C).   Attached to the same carbon. See *Vicinal*.

Gibbs Standard Free Energy Change, $\Delta G°$ (4.2).   This represents the amount of energy available for work that would be released during a reaction if all of the starting material in its standard state were converted to all of the product in its standard state. (In solution, the standard state is about 1 <u>M</u>.) Important equations to remember are $\Delta G° = \Delta H° - T\Delta S°$, which indicates how the *enthalpy* ($\Delta H°$) and the *entropy* ($\Delta S°$) of the reaction contribute to the free energy ($\Delta G°$); and $\Delta G° = -RT \ln K$, which relates the free energy change to the equilibrium constant K.

Glycoside (28.3).   Cyclic *acetals* or *ketals* of a sugar with another alcohol, called the *aglycon*.

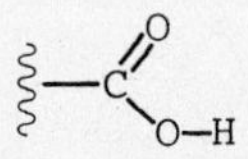

Glyme(s) (10.11.A).   Dimethyl ethers of short ethylene oxide polymers: $CH_3 \text{-} (OCH_2CH_2)_n OCH_3$.   See *Crown ethers*.

Ground electronic state (21.6.A). The lowest energy distribution of electrons in the molecular orbitals of a molecule or the atomic *orbitals* of an atom.   Any higher energy distribution, for example, one resulting from promotion of one of the electrons from a *bonding* to an *antibonding orbital*, is an *excited electronic state*.

Halonium ion (11.6.B).   A divalent halogen cation, usually resulting from the addition of electrophilic halogen to a π-bond.

Harmonic oscillator approximation (15.2).   The approximation of a bond vibration as a system which obeys *Hooke's Law*.

Haworth projection (28.3).   A semi-perspective drawing of the cyclic acetal or ketal form of a sugar to indicate its stereochemistry.   Useful for making the transition from *Fischer projections* to perspective drawings of chair conformations.

Heat of combustion (6.4).   Enthalpy released on complete oxidation of a compound: $C_nH_m \longrightarrow n\ CO_2 + m/2\ H_2O$.   This number provides the same information on the thermodynamic stability of a molecule as the *heat of formation*, but references it to a different standard state. *Heats of combustion* are in fact the values which are obtained experimentally; *heats of formation* are then calculated using the known heats of combustion of the elements.

Heat of formation (5.5).   The *enthalpy* released on forming a compound from its elements.   Comparison of the heats of formation of isomers is an indication of their relative thermodynamic stability.   Compare with *Heat of combustion* (6.4).

Heisenberg Uncertainty Principle (2.5).   The only part of chemistry the philosophers really like.   It sets a lower limit on the accuracy with which we can know both the position and momentum of a particle.   For instance, the more precisely we define how an electron is moving, the less accurately we can know where it is, and vice versa.

Hetero (3.2).   Not carbon, hydrogen (or a metal, usually).   For example, O, N, F, S etc. are all *heteroatoms*, and cyclic compounds in which there are ring atoms other than carbon are called *heterocycles*.

Heterolysis, heterolytic cleavage (6.3).   Cleavage of a bond in which both electrons in the bonding orbital depart with one of the pieces: $A{:}B \rightarrow A^+ + {:}B^-$. There will always be a change in formal charge on the two atoms involved in such a process.   Contrast with *Homolysis*.

Hofmann rule (23.7.E). "In the decomposition of quaternary ammonium hydroxides, the hydrogen is lost most easily from CH_3 , next from RCH_2, and least easily from R_2CH."

HOMO = <u>H</u>ighest <u>O</u>ccupied <u>M</u>olecular <u>O</u>rbital (21.7).   In a molecule, the highest energy molecular <u>orbital</u> that is occupied by a pair of electrons.   Contrast with the <u>LUMO</u>, which is the <u>L</u>owest <u>U</u>noccupied <u>M</u>olecular <u>O</u>rbital.   The interaction between the <u>HOMO</u> of one molecule and the <u>LUMO</u> of another can be used to predict the manner in which the two molecules might react [<u>Perturbational molecular orbital theory</u> (21.7)].

Homolysis, homolytic cleavage (6.3).   Cleavage of a bond in which one of the two bonding electrons departs with each of the pieces: $A{:}B \rightarrow A{\cdot} + {\cdot}B$. There is no change in formal charge when this happens.   Contrast with *Heterolysis*.

Hooke's law (15.2). States that the force needed to stretch or compress a spring (or bond) is directly proportional to the distance it is stretched or compressed.

Hückel 4n + 2 rule (21.3.A). "Monocyclic π-systems with 4n + 2 electrons show relative stability compared to acyclic analogs."

Hückel molecular orbital (21.4).   See *Orbital*.

Hybridization (2.8). A recombination of the *orbitals* of a free atom to enable it to make stronger bonds when it is in a molecule. Whereas the atomic state of carbon has one 2s and three 2p orbitals, carbon is hybridized to provide four $2sp^3$ orbitals (sp^3-hybridized), one 2p and three $2sp^2$ orbitals (sp^2-hybridized), or two 2p and two 2sp orbitals (sp-hybridized) in its molecules. The hybridized orbitals have a characteristic spatial relationship which is reflected in the geometry of the molecule. The exponents correspond to the fractional character of a given atomic orbital in the hybrid; for example, in sp^3, the fractional p-character is $3/(3+1)$, or 0.75. Note that the exponent of s is always unity. (N.B. Don't confuse *hybrid orbitals* with *resonance hybrids*.)

Hydration. The opposite of *dehydration*. Usually the addition of water across the π-bond of an alkene to give an alcohol (11.6.C), of an alkyne to give a ketone (12.6.B), or of a carbonyl compound to give a gem-diol (carbonyl hydrate) (14.7.A).

Hydrogen bond (4.5, 10.3). A dipole-dipole interaction between a hydrogen atom bonded to an electronegative element and an electron *lone pair* on another electronegative atom. It is a weak bond (~5 kcal $mole^{-1}$) but important in the chemistry of alcohols, carboxylic acids, amines and similar compounds.

Hydrogenolysis (20.6.B).   **Cleavage of a single bond by hydrogenation:**

$$A\!-\!B \;+\; H_2 \;\xrightarrow{\text{catalyst}}\; AH \;+\; HB$$

Usually encountered in Raney-nickel desulfurization or in hydrogenation of benzyl alcohols, etc.

Hydrolysis (10.5, 18.6).   See *Solvolysis reaction*.

Hydrophilic (29.7.B).   The opposite of *hydrophobic*: polar, often ionic, well-*solvated* by water, water soluble.

Hydrophobic (29.7.B).   Repelling water. Nonpolar, hydrocarbon chains are poorly *solvated* by water molecules and are excluded from aqueous solution. They form *lipid* bilayers, *micelles*, or separate phases in which they provide their own *solvation*.

Hydroxylation (27.3.A). Usually, addition of two hydroxyl groups to a double bond to give a 1,2-diol.

Hyperconjugation (9.7, 21.6.D).   The mechanism by which a *carbocation* is stabilized by sharing the electron density of bonds to the adjacent carbon. This results in the stability sequence: $3^o > 2^o > 1^o > CH_3^+$ for carbocations.
It is also important in characterizing the interaction of the σ bonds of an alkyl group with an adjacent π-system, as in ultraviolet spectroscopy.

Induction period (14.6.D). If a reaction is *autocatalytic* it will accelerate as it proceeds. The time *before* the reaction gets itself going is called the *induction period*.

Inductive effect (10.4, 17.4.B). The *electron attracting* or *donating* effect of a nearby dipole. For instance, *electronegative* elements like halogens are *electron attracting*; alkyl groups are *electron donating*.

Infrared active, inactive (15.2). See *Selection rule*.

Initiation steps, Initiator (6.3). See *Chain reaction* (6.3).

Inner Salt (29.1). See *Zwitterion*.

Insertion (34.2). A type of reaction in transition metal chemistry in which a donor *ligand* undergoes insertion into a σ-bond between the metal and another group. The reverse of this process is called *deinsertion*. The *electron count* of the metal decreases by two on insertion.

Integrated intensity (13.5). The area under the curve of a given peak in the nmr. For proton nmr, this usually corresponds to the relative number of protons which resonate at that frequency. In *cmr*, *saturation* and *relaxation* effects affect the integrated intensities of different peaks differently, and the area ratios do not correspond to the relative number of carbons.

Interference (2.6). An addition of *wave functions (orbitals)* which results in their cancellation in a certain region of space. This occurs during the formation of an *antibonding* orbital, for instance, in which an atomic orbital wavefunction of one sign overlaps with an orbital of opposite sign on the other atom. The opposite of interference is *reinforcement*.

Intermolecular, intramolecular (9.8). *Intermolecular* = between two or more molecules; *intramolecular* = within the same molecule.

Internal conversion (34.4). Relaxation of an *excited* vibrational *state* to a *ground* vibrational *state*.

Intersystem crossing (34.4). Conversion of the first *excited singlet state* to the first *excited triplet state*.

Inversion (9.1). The normal stereochemistry seen in displacement reactions occurring by the S_N2 *mechanism*. It arises from simultaneous bonding of the incoming *nucleophile* and the departing *leaving group* to opposite lobes of the *orbital* on carbon:

$$\delta^-\ Nu \longleftrightarrow \overset{|}{\underset{|}{C}} \longleftrightarrow L\ \delta^-$$

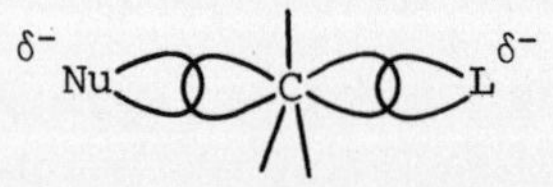

Ionic character 8.6). A highly polarized bond, one between an *electronegative* and an *electropositive* element, has a lot of ionic character. A symmetrical, *covalent* bond between identical groups has no ionic character (e.g., the C-C bond of ethane).

Ionization potential (2.2, 32.4.A). The energy required to remove an electron from an atom or molecule.

Isoelectric point (29.3). The pH at which the average charge on a molecule (usually a *zwitterionic* amino acid or *peptide*) is zero. For the simple amino acids (with only one acidic and one basic group), this is the average of pK_1 and pK_2.

Isolated double bonds (19.2.A). See *Conjugation*.

Isomers (3.6). Compounds which have the same molecular formula but different structures. See *Structural Formulas* and *Stereoisomers*, and the table at the beginning of Chapter 3 in this Study Guide.

J (13.6). See *Coupling Constant*.

positions *meta* to themselves. See *ortho, para-directors*.

All *m-directors* are *deactivating*.

Metallation (26.3.B). Replacement of a hydrogen or a halogen with a metal cation. Deprotonation is usually accomplished with a strong base like lithium diisopropylamide, alkyllithiums, or sodium amide; halogens are replaced with metals using alkyllithiums (*transmetallation*) or the metals themselves.

Micelle (17.4.D). Molecules with both *hydrophilic* and *hydrophobic* regions often cluster together in aqueous solution in *micelles*, in which the non-polar chains are in the interior and the polar regions are on the exterior.

Migratory aptitude (14.9.A). Relative ease with which a particular substituent moves over to an adjacent atom in rearrangements like carbocation rearrangements, the Baeyer-Villiger reaction, or acylnitrene or -carbene rearrangements. Usually H > phenyl > 3° > 2° > 1° > CH_3.

Mixed Claisen condensation (27.7.A). Claisen condensation between a ketone and an ester to give a β-diketone.

Möbius molecular orbital (21.5).   See *Orbital*.

Molecular formula (3.4). The molecular formula of a compound expresses the total number of atoms of each element present. It is always the same as, or a multiple of, the *empirical formula*. For instance, the *empirical formula* for glucose is CH_2O, but the *molecular formula* is $C_6H_{12}O_6$.

Molecular ion, M^+ (32.3). The ion produced in a mass spectrometer on ejection of an electron from a molecule.

Molecular orbital (2.7). See *Orbital*.

Molecularity (9.1). The molecularity of a reaction is the number of molecules involved in the rate-determining transition state. For instance, an S_N2 displacement reaction is a typical *bimolecular* reaction; an S_N1 displacement is a typical *unimolecular* reaction. *Termolecular* reactions, and higher, are very rare.

Monochromator (15.1).   An instrument which disperses a beam of light into its component frequencies, so that a narrow range of frequencies can be focused on the sample. It is an important component of infrared and ultraviolet/visible spectrophotometers.

Monomer (34.5).   See *Polymer*.

Multiplet (13.6). See *Spin-spin splitting*.

Mutarotation (28.3). A change in *optical rotation* which results from the equilibration of *anomers*.

Nitrogen inversion (23.1).

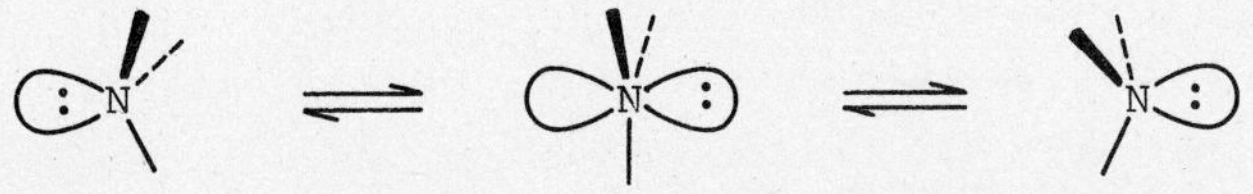

NMR Time Scale (13.10). About 10^{-3} sec, the length of time a molecule must exist in a discrete state for it to be observable by nmr.

Node (2.5). A surface which separates regions of an *orbital* which have opposite signs. For instance, a 2p orbital aligned with the z axis has as its node the xy plane, and the antibonding orbital of a hydrogen molecule has as its node a plane perpendicular to the internuclear axis.

Nominal mass (32.3). The integral mass of a molecule or molecular fragment. See *Exact mass*.

Non-bonded electrons (2.2, 23.1). *Valence electrons* not involved in a *covalent bond*. Oxygen normally has two pairs of non-bonded electrons and nitrogen one, for example: $H\ddot{O}H$, $H_3N:$. These *non-bonded electrons* are also called *lone pair* electrons, and they are the electrons involved when these molecules act as *Lewis bases* or *nucleophiles*.

Nuclear spin (13.3). See *Magnetic moment*.

Nucleophile, nucleophilic reagent (9.1). A *Lewis base*. In its most general sense, any species which can furnish a pair of electrons to make a bond can be considered a nucleophile: any time a bond is formed by the reverse of a heterolytic process, the species that contributes the electrons is a nucleophile. In discussing displacement reactions, those which involve attack by a nucleophile and loss of a *leaving group* are called nucleophilic displacement reactions.

Nucleophilic addition-elimination mechanism (18.6). The most important mechanism whereby substitution reactions occur in carboxylic acid derivatives. In its general form:

$$\underset{\overset{\displaystyle \|}{R-C-X}}{\overset{\displaystyle O}{}} + H\text{-}Nu \rightleftharpoons \underset{\overset{\displaystyle |}{\underset{X}{R-C-Nu}}}{\overset{\displaystyle OH}{}} \rightleftharpoons \underset{\overset{\displaystyle \|}{R-C-Nu}}{\overset{\displaystyle O}{}} + H\text{-}X$$

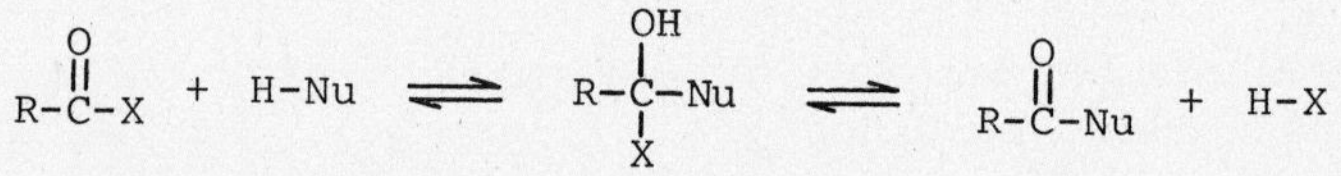

Nucleophilic aromatic substitution can also occur via an addition-elimination mechanism (26.3.A).

Octet (2.2). A filled *valence* shell for elements in the second and third periods of the periodic table. This arrangement for electrons is very stable, and achieving a filled octet is the most important factor in determining how many and what kinds of bonds an element will form in its molecules.

Off-resonance decoupling (13.12). See *Decoupling*.

Optically active (7.2). Capable of rotating the *plane of polarization* of *plane polarized light*. An *optically active* sample must be composed of *chiral* molecules, but the converse is not always true: a *racemic* mixture of chiral molecules is *optically inactive*.

Orbital (2.5). An equation which describes the behavior of an electron. The term is synonymous with *wavefunction*, although conceptually chemists envision a volume having specific shape and orientation when they think of orbitals and a mathematical equation when they think of wavefunctions. An *atomic orbital* describes the behavior of an electron in the vicinity of a single nucleus. *Molecular orbitals* result from the combination (overlap) of two or more atomic orbitals and describe an electron which is shared by several nuclei. Molecular orbitals can be further classified into *bonding*, *nonbonding*, and *antibonding* orbitals, depending on whether the electron distribution in the molecular orbital is more favorable (lower energy), unchanged (same energy), or less favorable (higher energy) than in the component atomic orbitals. Bonding orbitals result from the *reinforcing* overlap of atomic orbitals, antibonding orbitals from their *interfering* overlap.

Cyclic molecular orbitals are classified as *Hückel* if they have an even number (or zero) of positive/negative overlaps around the ring; they are classified as *Möbius* if there is an odd number of such interactions.

    <u>Ortho, meta, and para</u> (20.2.A). Positions on a benzene ring relative to a substituent.

    <u>Ortho, para-directors</u> (22.5). Substituents on an aromatic ring which stabilize adjacent positive charge and thereby favor electrophilic aromatic substitution at positions *ortho* and *para* to themselves. See *meta-directors*.

    o,p-Directors can be either *activating* or *deactivating*.

    <u>Overlap</u> (in NMR spectroscopy) **(13.7)**. When two nuclei resonate at similar *chemical shifts*, their peaks *overlap* (fall on top of one another).

    <u>Overtones, combination bands</u> (15.2). Bands which result in an infrared spectrum from simultaneous change of more than one energy level.

    <u>Oxaphosphetane</u> (14.8.E). A cyclic intermediate in the Wittig reaction (see *betaine*):

    <u>Oxidative addition</u> (34.2). A type of reaction in transition metal chemistry in which the two groups at the ends of a σ-bond both become bonded to the metal. The reverse process is called *reductive elimination*. The *electron count* of the metal decreases by two on oxidative addition.

    <u>**Oxidative coupling**</u> (26.3). **Joining two molecules with overall loss of two protons and two electrons, as in the oxidative coupling of arylcopper compounds to give biphenyls.**

    <u>Oxidative deamination</u> (29.5.C). The opposite of *reductive amination*.

    <u>Oxonium ion structure</u> (2.4). A structure which involves three bonds to an oxygen atom, and therefore a positive *formal charge* on the oxygen. Although localization of a positive charge on the *electronegative* element oxygen would appear to be difficult, the atom still retains a filled *octet valence* shell (compare with a *carbocation*), and this consideration is the most important. The simplest oxonium ion is the hydronium ion: $H:\overset{..}{\underset{+\ H}{O}}:H$.

    <u>Partial rate factors</u> (22.7). In electrophilic aromatic substitution, the partial rate factor is the reactivity of a given position on a substituted aromatic ring relative to benzene, corrected for the number of equivalent positions.

    <u>Peptide</u> (29.1). A *peptide bond* is an amide linkage between two amino acids. *Peptides* are dimers, trimers, oligomers, etc. (*condensation polymers*) of amino acids.

    <u>"Peroxides"</u> (11.6.G). Usually *alkylperoxides* (ROOH) present in impure materials as a result of *autoxidation*. They are often initiators of free radical chain reactions, and are distinctly different from the reagents hydrogen peroxide (HOOH) or peracids (RCO_3H).

    <u>Phase-transfer catalysis</u> (23.5.B). Transfer of ionic reagents from an aqueous

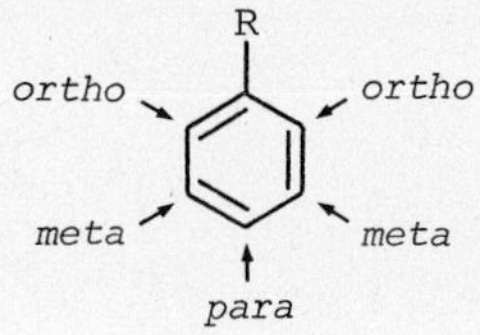

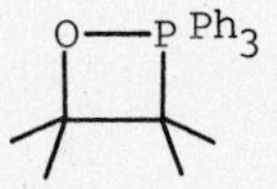

or solid phase into an organic solvent, where they show enhanced reactivity. Phase-transfer catalysts are either *quaternary ammonium salts* or *crown ethers*.

Phosphorane (14.8.E). See *Ylide*.

pK = -log K (4.5).

$$K_a = \frac{[H^+][A^-]}{[HA]} \qquad pK_a = \text{measure of acidity}$$

$$K_b = \frac{[HA][OH^-]}{[A^-]}$$

$$pK_a + pK_b = 14$$

The lower the pK_a, the more acidic HA is and the less basic the *conjugate base* A^- is. When pH = pK_a, $[A^-] = [HA]$.

Plane of symmetry (7.5). An object has a plane of symmetry if it can be divided into two halves which are mirror images of each other. Such objects are *achiral*.

Plane polarized light (7.2). Light in which the electric field vectors of all the light waves lie in the same plane, called the *plane* of *polarization*. An *optically active* sample rotates the plane of polarization of a beam of plane polarized light which passes through it.

Poisoned catalyst (12.6.A). A catalyst whose efficiency and activity have been reduced with a "poison". Lindlar's catalyst ($Pd/BaSO_4$, poisoned with quinoline) is an example.

Polarimeter (7.2). An instrument for measuring *optical activity*.

Polarizability (8.2). Often thought of in an intuitive sense as "softness" or "mushiness" of an atom, polarizability refers to the ease of deforming the electron density around an atom. It increases as one descends in the periodic table because the valence orbitals lie further from the nucleus and the electrons are held less tightly. In general, in protic solvents, the more polarizable a *nucleophile* is the more potent it is as a nucleophile.

Polarized light (7.2). See *Plane polarized light*.

Polymer, polymerization (34.5). **The sequential linking of** *monomers* **to produce** *dimers*, *trimers*, **molecules of intermediate size (***telomers* **or** *oligomers***), and then of very large size (polymers) is called** *polymerization*.

In the formation of an *addition polymer*, the bonds between the monomers are made by addition to a double bond, by a cationic, radical, or anionic process.

In the formation of *condensation polymers*, the bonds are made with the elimination of a small by-product molecule.

Copolymers incorporate more than one *monomer* in the chain, in contrast to *homopolymers* in which all the units are the same.

PPM = parts per million (13.4). See *Chemical Shift*.

Primary, Secondary, Tertiary, Quaternary (6.1, 23.1, 23.5.A). R is understood to be a carbon substituent, such as an alkyl group.

	Carbon	Hydrogen	Radical	Carbocation	Carbanion	Halide	Alcohol	Amine
Primary:	$R-CH_3$	$R-\overset{H}{\underset{H}{C}}-H$	$H\overset{..}{C}H$ (R)	$H\overset{+}{C}H$ (R)	$H\overset{-}{C}H$ (R)	RCH_2X	RCH_2OH	$R-\ddot{N}H_2$
Secondary:	$R-\overset{H}{\underset{H}{C}}-R'$	$R-\overset{H}{\underset{H}{C}}-R'$	$R\overset{..}{\underset{H}{C}}R'$	$R\overset{+}{\underset{H}{C}}R'$	$R\overset{-}{\underset{H}{C}}R'$	$R-\overset{X}{\underset{H}{C}}-R'$	$R-\overset{OH}{\underset{H}{C}}-R'$	$R-\ddot{N}H-R'$
Tertiary:	$R-\overset{H}{\underset{R''}{C}}-R'$	$R-\overset{H}{\underset{R''}{C}}-R'$	$R\overset{..}{\underset{R''}{C}}R'$	$R\overset{+}{\underset{R''}{C}}R'$	$R\overset{-}{\underset{R''}{C}}R'$	$R-\overset{X}{\underset{R''}{C}}-R'$	$R-\overset{OH}{\underset{R''}{C}}-R'$	$R-\underset{R''}{\overset{..}{N}}-R'$
Quaternary:	$R-\overset{R''}{\underset{R''}{C}}-R'$							$R-\underset{\overset{+}{R}}{\overset{R'}{N}}-R''$

(ammonium salt)

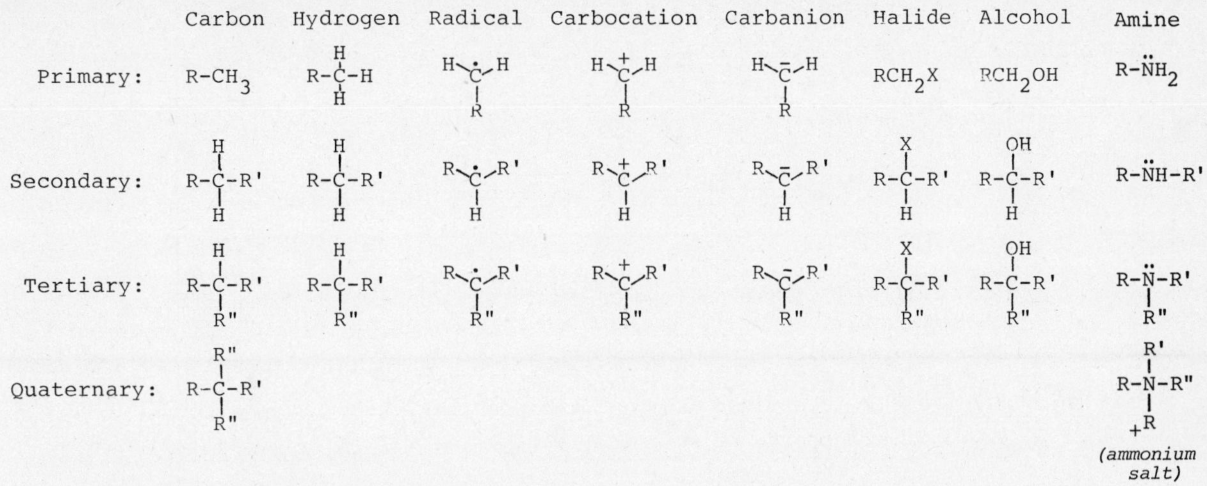

Principle of microscopic reversibility (6.3). "If the easiest way to get from Yosemite Valley to Mono Lake is through Tuolomne Meadows and over Tioga Pass, then the easiest way from Mono Lake to Yosemite Valley is over Tioga Pass and through Tuolomne Meadows", which is to say that the transition state for the forward reaction will be identical to the transition state for the back reaction.

Probability function (2.5). Squaring the value of a *wave function* at each point in space gives a probability function, which describes the likelihood that the electron will be found at that point. Whereas the wave function itself will have regions in which its value is negative and regions in which it is positive, the probability function is always positive (or zero).

Propagation step (6.3). See *Chain reaction*.

Protecting group (16.4). A functional group introduced to mask the reactivity of another functional group so that an otherwise interfering reaction can be carried out elsewhere on the molecule. It is later removed and the original functional group is regenerated.

functional group	protecting group
alcohols	t-butyl ethers (10.10.A)
	silyl ethers (25.11.C)
ketones and aldehydes	*acetals* and *ketals* (14.7.B)
anomeric carbons	*glycoside* formation (28.5.B)
amino acids	carbobenzoxy (Cbz) and
	t-butoxycarbonyl (Boc) groups (29.6.B)

Proteins (29.7). High molecular weight poly*peptides*.

Proton decoupled (13.12). See *Decoupling*.

Pseudo first-order reaction (4.3). See *First-order reaction*.

Pseudorotation (25.11.A). Interconversion of the trigonal bipyramidal intermediates that are involved in substitution reactions of phosphorus and silicon derivatives. In one step of pseudorotation, the apical substituents become equatorial, and two (of the three) equatorial substituents become apical; the other equatorial substituent is the pivot. Pseudorotation is involved in substitution reactions that occur with retention of configuration in these systems.

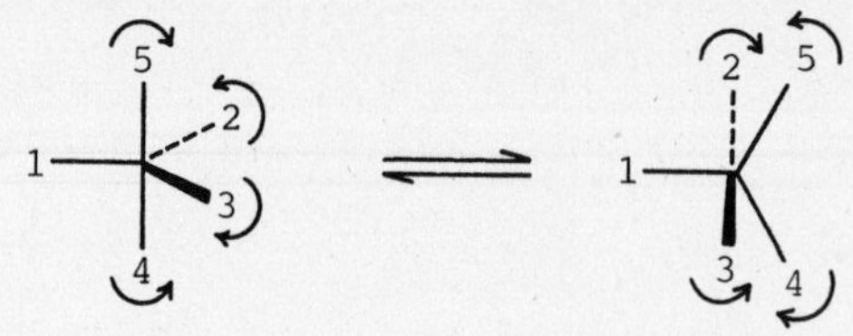

Pseudorotation is also used to describe the interconversions of the cyclopentane envelope conformations.

Pyrolysis (6.2, 18.11). Cleaving a bond or a molecule simply by heating it to a sufficiently high temperature, as in the *cracking* of alkanes, the pyrolytic elimination of acetate or xanthate esters (18.11) or of sulfoxides (25.3).

Quantum numbers (2.5), **Quantized** (13.2). At the atomic level, only certain *electronic configurations*, speeds of rotation, degrees of vibration, orientations in a magnetic field, etc., are possible. These are said to be *quantized*, and their specific value is indicated by the *quantum numbers*.

Quantum yield (34.4). The fraction of molecules which proceed to products after absorbing a photon in a photochemical reaction.

Quartet (13.6). See *Spin-spin splitting*.

Quaternary (6.1). See *Primary*.

R-S Convention (7.3). System of nomenclature for indicating the *absolute configuration* of a *chiral center*. Involves use of the "*sequence rule*".

Racemic mixture, racemate, racemic compound (7.4). An equimolar mixture of the two *enantiomers* of a compound. It is *optically inactive*. A *racemic compound* is a *racemic mixture* in which both *enantiomers* are present in the same crystal structure.

Racemization (7.4, 14.6.C). The equilibration of one *enantiomer* with the other, to produce a *racemic, optically inactive* mixture consisting of equal amounts of both *enantiomers*.

Radical (3.5). From the point of view of nomenclature, a *radical* is a piece of a molecule which is considered as a unit. For instance, "methyl", "phenyl", and "1-chloroethyl" are radicals used as part of the name: 2-(1-chloroethyl)-1-methyl-4-phenylcyclohexane.

In chemical reactions, *radicals* are usually present only as short-lived, unstable intermediates, because they have unpaired electrons and lack valence octets. Free radical halogenation (section 6.3) is a good example of a type of reaction which involves radical intermediates.

Radical anion (12.6.A). An anion with an odd number of electrons; usually obtained by addition of an electron to a neutral, even-electron molecule.

Radical cation (32.1). A cation with an odd number of electrons; usually formed from a neutral, even-electron molecule by ejection of an electron, as in the ionization chamber of a *mass spectrometer* on electron impact.

Reducing vs non-reducing sugar (28.5.E). A sugar in equilibrium with its open chain form in alkaline solution (that is, a *hemiacetal* or *hemiketal*) is a *reducing sugar* because it can be oxidized by Fehling's or Tollen's reagents. If the sugar exists as a *glycoside*, it is a *non-reducing sugar*.

Reduction potential: see *Standard reduction potential*.

Reductive amination (23.6.F). Conversion of a carbon-oxygen double bond to a carbon-nitrogen single bond by reduction of an imine or immonium ion intermediate.

Reductive elimination (34.2). The reverse of *oxidative addition*.

Reinforcement (2.7). The overlap of *orbitals* having the same sign, so that their *wavefunctions* add together; the opposite of *interference*. The overlap of two atomic orbitals to make a bonding molecular orbital is an example of reinforcement.

Relative configuration (28.6). This term refers to a *stereochemical* relationship between two or more *chiral centers*. If the *absolute configuration* of two chiral centers is known, so is their *relative configuration*, but it is possible to know their *relative configuration* without knowing their *absolute configuration*.

Terms such as *meso*, *erythro* and *threo*, and *cis* and *trans* (in cyclic systems) all describe *relative configurations*.

Relaxation (13.5, 14.4). In NMR spectroscopy, *relaxation* is the restoration of the spin distribution of the sample to its equilibrium value. For a ^{13}C nucleus, relaxation is accelerated by hydrogens directly attached to it. If relaxation is slow (for example, for *quaternary* or carbonyl carbons), *saturation* of the NMR signal occurs easily and only a weak resonance peak is seen. See *Integrated intensity*.

Resolution (29.4.F). Separation of the *enantiomers* of a *racemic mixture*, usually by the formation and separation of *diastereomeric salts* or other derivatives, and regeneration of the *enantiomers*.

Resonance (in *Spectroscopy*) (13.4). When the energy of electromagnetic radiation matches the energy difference between two quantum states, as given by the relationship E = hν, absorption or emission of radiation by the sample is possible, and the system is said to be in *resonance*.

Resonance energy (20.1.B). The special stabilization that an *aromatic* π-system has over a hypothetical system of similar electronic *configuration*, but which lacks the *delocalization* of the aromatic system.

The *empirical resonance energy* is determined by experimental comparison of actual molecules. It differs from *delocalization energy*, which results from comparison with theoretical models.

Resonance hybrid (2.4). A molecule which cannot be adequately represented by a single written structure, but can be understood as a hybrid of two or more *resonance structures*.   (N.B. Don't confuse *resonance hybrids* with *hybrid orbitals*.)

Resonance structures (2.4). Structures depicting a molecule which differ only in the distribution of electrons (as opposed to nuclei). They are most important and useful when the alternative bonding arrangements they represent are of similar energy, in which case the molecule they describe is said to be a *resonance hybrid* of the two structures.

Retention (12.6.D). The opposite of *inversion*.

Ring current (20.3.A). The π-*electron circulation* induced in an *aromatic* system by an external magnetic field. See *Anisotropic* and *Chemical shift*.

S$_N$1 (Substitution Nucleophilic Unimolecular) (9.7). A description of the mechanism of a displacement reaction which involves only one molecule in the rate determining step and which takes place first with ionization of the carbon-leaving group bond (slow) and then attack by the nucleophile (fast). Usually goes with loss of configuration at the carbon atom, i.e., racemization if that is the only chiral center present. The rate depends on carbocation stability ($3° > 2° > 1°$).

S_N2 (Substitution <u>Nucleophilic</u> <u>Bimolecular</u>) (9.2). A description of a mechanism of a displacement reaction, as the expanded name above implies. These reactions usually occur with inversion of configuration at the carbon undergoing attack. The rate depends on lack of steric hindrance, and is slowed either by α-*branching* ($1° > 2° > 3°$ in rate) or β-*branching* (e.g., "neopentyl" systems *very* slow).

<u>Sanger method</u> (29.6.C). A method for determining the N-terminal amino acid of a *peptide* by labeling it with a dinitrophenyl group followed by hydrolysis of the peptide and identification of the derivatized amino acid.

<u>Saponification</u> (18.12.B). Alkaline hydrolysis.

<u>Saturated</u> (3.3). From the point of view of *molecular formula*, *saturated* means that there are 2n + 2 hydrogens for every carbon present in the molecule, after a hydrogen has been added for every halogen atom present and subtracted for every nitrogen atom present. For instance, ethane (C_2H_6), 1,2-dichloroethane ($C_2H_4Cl_2$), and ethylamine (C_2H_7N) are all counted as $C_2H_6 = C_nH_{2n+2}$, where n = 2.

From the point of view of structure, *saturated* means containing only single bonds (σ bonds). It differs from the definition above only for cyclic compounds. For instance, cyclohexane (C_6H_{12}) has only single bonds, but the formula is C_nH_{2n}.

See *Unsaturated*.

<u>Saturation</u> (in the NMR (13.5, 14.4). Equalization of the populations of the α- and β-spin states, which leads to disappearance of the nmr signal. (The strength of the signal depends on the difference in population of these spin states.) Saturation is opposed by *relaxation*. (See *Integrated intensity*).

<u>Schiff base</u> (14.7.C). A substituted *imine*: $\underset{/}{\overset{\backslash}{C}}=\underset{\backslash_R}{\overset{..}{N}}$

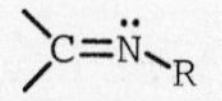

<u>Second-Order kinetics</u> (9.1). See *Kinetic Order*.

<u>Second-Order reaction</u> (4.3). Usually, one in which two molecules are involved in the rate-determining step, and in which, therefore, the rate equation has the concentration of both molecules as variables.

<u>Secondary</u> (6.1). See *Primary*.

<u>Selection rule</u> (15.2). A quantum mechanical requirement for a transition between two energy levels to be allowed. In infrared spectroscopy, the transition must result in a change in the dipole moment of the molecule. Such transitions are *infrared active*.

In ultraviolet-visible spectroscopy, the two electronic states are subject to other quantum mechanical constraints for the *electronic transition* to be allowed.

<u>Sequence rule</u> (7.3). See *R-S convention*.

<u>Sigmatropic rearrangement</u> (20.7).   See definition in text.

<u>Single bond</u> (2.3). See *Bond*

<u>Singlet state</u> (34.4).   An electronic state in which all the electron spins are paired, that is, in which the molecule has a net electronic spin of zero.

Solid phase technique (29.6.B). A method for the synthesis of poly**peptides** on a polymer support.

Solvation (4.3), **Solvation energy** (9.2, 9.4). *Solvation* refers to the interactions between solvent molecules and the molecules dissolved in them (the solute). These interactions often influence the mechanism and rate of a reaction in solution, and therefore frequently make it difficult to compare liquid and gas phase data.

The *solvation energy* is an indication of the strength of these interactions, and is the energy released on transferring a solute from the gas phase into a solvent. It reflects how well the solvent molecules stabilize ions, neutral molecules, or transition states, etc. Difficulties in estimating solvation energies often hinders detailed understanding of reaction kinetics.

Solvolysis reaction (9.7). A substitution reaction in which the nucleophile is the solvent. If the nucleophile is water it is called *hydrolysis:*

$$A-B + RO-H \rightarrow A-O-R + H-B$$

Specific deuteration (8.9.A). See *Deuteration.*

Specific rotation, [α] (7.2). $[\alpha]_D = \dfrac{\alpha}{l \cdot c}$ ← *angle of rotation*

length in   concentration in g/mL
decimeters

Spectra, spectroscopy (3.4, 15.1). *Spectroscopy* is the experimental evaluation of the way in which a substance interacts with electromagnetic radiation, usually for the purpose of structure determination. More detailed descriptions can be found in the Chapters on Nuclear Magnetic Resonance Spectroscopy (Chapter 13), Infrared Spectroscopy (Chapter 15), and Ultraviolet Spectroscopy (Chapter 21). Mass spectrometry (Chapter 32) is another experimental technique for structure determination, although it is not truly a "spectroscopy".

Spin-spin splitting (13.6). Results from the *coupling* of the *magnetic moments* of two nearby, *magnetically nonequivalent* nuclei, so that the orientation of one of them (with or against an external magnetic field) affects the *chemical shift* of the other. The amount that nucleus A affects the chemical shift of nucleus B is called the *coupling constant*, J, and is equal to the amount that nucleus B affects nucleus A, too.

In simple cases, n adjacent protons cause a splitting into n+1 peaks (*doublets, triplets, quartets*, etc.), but the situation can easily become complicated by nonequivalent coupling constants (two *different* adjacent nuclei) and *non-first-order* effects (*multiplets*). *Magnetically equivalent* nuclei do not split each other.

Spiro ring system (27.3.B). See *Bridged.*

Staggered (5.2). See definition under *Anti.*

Standard reduction potential (8.8.B, 26.8.C). An indication of the *electron affinity* of an atom, ion, or molecule: the more *electropositive* a metal is, for example, the more easily it gives up its electron to form the cation, and the more negative the *standard reduction potential* of the cation is. The more positive the *reduction potential* of a quinone is, the stronger an oxidizing agent it is.

Stationary state (34.4). A reaction at equilibrium, usually in reference to a photochemical equilibration.

Stereoaxis (7.1, 19.2). *Chiral* molecules such as some allenes and biphenyls, in which formal rotation about a bond interconverts stereoisomers, are said to have a *stereoaxis.*

Stereocenter (7.1).   If interchanging two substituents on an atom produces a *stereoisomer*, that atom is said to be a *stereocenter*.   Examples of *stereocenters* are carbon atoms with four different substituents, as well as the sp^2-hybridized carbons of an alkene which is capable of E and Z isomerism.   The term *stereocenter* replaces the older term *asymmetric center*. See *Chiral*.

Stereoisomers (7.1).   Molecules which differ only in the three-dimensional relationship between their atoms.

Stereospecific (11.5.A, 16.2, 27.3.A).   Requiring or generating a particular three-dimensional relationship.   For example, the S_N2 reaction proceeds *stereospecifically* with *inversion*, and the *E2* reaction is usually stereospecific for the *anti* relationship between the *leaving group* and the proton which is being removed.

Stereospecific is also used in the sense of giving only one *stereoisomer*, and is a desirable goal in planning the synthesis of a molecule with chiral centers or *cis* or *trans* double bonds.

Steric hindrance (9.3).   An effect which arises when two molecules or parts of molecules try to occupy the same space at the same time.   It is responsible for the γ-*effect* in *CMR* (13.12), preference for *equatorial* versus *axial*-substitution on cyclohexane rings (5.6), the slowing of S_N2 displacement reactions by α- or β-*branching* (9.3), the greater stability of *trans* over *cis* alkenes (11.4), etc.

Structural formulas (3.1).   Drawings of molecules which show how the atoms are connected.   They contrast with *empirical formulas* and *molecular formulas* because a given structural formula represents only one of all possible structural *isomers*.   Even more specific are stereo formulas (Chapter 7).   Structural formulas may be very detailed
(e.g., H-C-C-C-O-H for 1-propanol)   or condensed   ($CH_3CH_2CH_2OH$).

As you become more familiar with organic structures, you will use line formulas to save time.   In these simple structural formulas, the C's and H's on carbon are omitted, and only the bonds between carbon and non-hydrogen atoms are drawn (for example, 1-propanol is drawn: OH).

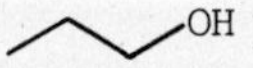

Suprafacial (21.5.B).   On the same face of a π-system.   See *Antarafacial*.

Tautomers, tautomerism (14.6.A).   *Isomers* which differ only in the placement of the protons; refers only to systems involving heteroatoms and which interconvert fairly rapidly.

Telomer (34.5).   See *Polymer*.

Termination (6.3).   See *Chain reaction*.

Tertiary (6.1).   See *Primary*.

Thermodynamic control (19.2.B, 25.5.B).   A reaction in which the products are in equilibrium with the starting materials is said to be under thermodynamic control.   That is, the product obtained is the most stable one.   See *Kinetic control*.

Three center two-electron bond (8.6).   A bond between three atoms, incorporating three *orbitals* in the *bonding molecular orbital*, which is occupied by two electrons.

Tracer isotope (22.2).   A radioactive isotope (e.g., tritium (^3H) or ^{14}C)

used in labeling studies. Only a small fraction of the atoms at a position labeled with a *tracer isotope* are actually the radioactive isotope itself. The presence of a radioactive isotope is determined with an instrument known as a liquid scintillation counter.

Transesterification (18.7.A). Exchange of alkyl groups in an ester by acid- or base-catalysis, usually via the *nucleophilic addition-elimination mechanism*.

Transmetallation (26.3.B). See *Metallation*.

Triplet (in NMR spectroscopy) (13.6). See *Spin-spin splitting*.

Triplet sensitizer (34.4). A molecule which is readily converted to its excited *triplet state* photochemically, and which will react with a different *ground state* molecule to convert it to its *triplet state*.

Triplet state (in photochemistry) (34.4). A molecule or atom in which two electron spins are unpaired, resulting in a net electronic spin of 1.

Unsaturated (3.5). An *unsaturated* molecule contains double or triple bonds (π-bonds). This is reflected in the formula of a hydrocarbon: for every π bond, there are two fewer hydrogens. Compare ethane (C_2H_6), ethylene (C_2H_4), and acetylene (C_2H_2). From the point of view of *molecular* formula, however, a ring results in the same differences: 1-butene ($CH_3CH_2CH{=}CH_2 = C_4H_8$) or cyclobutane

$$\begin{matrix} CH_2-CH_2 \\ | \qquad\ | \\ CH_2-CH_2 \end{matrix} = C_4H_8 \quad .$$ Each π-bond *and* ring in a compound, therefore, is considered to be a *degree of unsaturation* from the point of view of molecular formula.

See *Saturated*.

Valence electrons (2.2). Those in the outermost shell of an atom. The attempt by an atom to achieve a filled *octet* of valence electrons is chiefly responsible for the bonding arrangements it undergoes.

Van der Waals forces (5.1). See *Dispersion force*.

Vertical transition (34.4). See *Franck-Condon transition*.

Vicinal (11.6.E, 12.5.C). Attached to adjacent carbons. See *Geminal*.

Vinylogy (27.7.B). The similarity of a compound in which two functional groups are separated but conjugated by a double bond, with that in which the two groups are directly connected. For example, 4-methoxy-3-penten-2-one is a *vinylogous* ester.

Wavefunction (2.5). The equation which describes the behavior of an electron. The wavefunction can have regions in which its value is positive and regions in which it is negative, just as an ocean wave has peaks and troughs. These signs have no connection with the electron charge, which is always negative. The square of the wavefunction is a *probability function*.

Ylide (14.8.E, 25.8). A neutral molecule which has a formal negative charge on carbon as in *phosphoranes* ($R_3\overset{+}{P}{-}\bar{C}H_2$) and sulfur ylides ($R_2\overset{+}{S}{-}\bar{C}H_2$).

Z (11.2). See *E*.

Zero point energy (6.1). The difference between the lowest point on a potential energy diagram for a bond and the lowest energy attainable (at $0°K$) within the constraints of the *Heisenberg Uncertainty Principle*.

Zwitterion (29.1). A molecule which is an *inner salt*, that is, in which both the cation and anion are part of the same molecule.

APPENDIX II: SUMMARY OF FUNCTIONAL GROUP PREPARATIONS

Functional group interconversions can be discussed as reactions of one function or preparations of another. The following summary lists the preparations of various functional groups discussed in this textbook with reference to each place the reaction is used. Products shown are those for normal work-up of the reaction. Although examples are included with more than one functional group, specific reactions of polyfunctional compounds are not included. Abbreviations used are:

R = alkyl and cycloalkyl; for some cases may also apply to R = H or R = Ar
Ar = aryl
X = halide
Y = leaving group; may be X, sulfonate, and so on
[H] = several reducing agents
[O] = several oxidizing agents

The importance of a given type of reaction or functional group transformation can be gauged roughly by the number of times it is cited.

Acetals and Ketals

Aldehydes or ketones

$$\underset{\text{RCR'}}{\overset{O}{\parallel}} + R''OH \xrightarrow{H^+} \underset{\overset{|}{OR''}}{\overset{OR''}{\overset{|}{RCR'}}}$$

379–383, 446 (763), 848, 855–856, 893–895, 898–900

Acid Anhydrides

Acyl Halides

$$\underset{\text{RCCl}}{\overset{O}{\parallel}} + R'CO_2^- \longrightarrow \underset{\text{RCOCR'}}{\overset{O\;\;\;O}{\parallel\;\;\parallel}}$$

496

Carboxylic acids

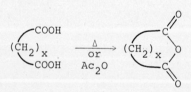

$$x = 2 \text{ or } 3$$

495, 864, 866

Acyl Halides

Carboxylic acids

$$RCOOH + SOCl_2 \longrightarrow RCOCl$$

467–468, 493

$$RCOOH + PCl_5 \longrightarrow RCOCl$$

467

$$RCOOH + PBr_3 \longrightarrow RCOBr$$

464, 467, 546

Alcohols

Aldehydes and ketones: Carbanion additions

$$\underset{\text{RCR'}}{\overset{O}{\parallel}} + R''MgX \text{ or } R''Li \longrightarrow \xrightarrow{H^+} RR'R''COH$$

386–388, 394–395, 435, 440, 445, 496–497, 540–541, 781, 806, 978

$$\underset{\text{RCR'}}{\overset{O}{\parallel}} + R''C\equiv C^- \longrightarrow \xrightarrow{H^+} \underset{RR'CC\equiv CR''}{\overset{OH}{\overset{|}{}}}$$

388, 533

Aldehydes and ketones: Reductions

$$\underset{\substack{\| \\ \text{RCR'}}}{\overset{O}{}} + \text{LiAlH}_4 \text{ or NaBH}_4 \longrightarrow \text{RCHOHR'}$$

267, 400-401, 436, 446, 542, 841, 848, 856, 889, 900, 902, 987

$$\underset{\substack{\| \\ \text{RCR'}}}{\overset{O}{}} \xrightarrow{\text{H}_2/\text{catalyst}} \text{RCHOHR'}$$

402, 436, 590, 901

$$\underset{\substack{\| \\ \text{RCR'}}}{\overset{O}{}} \xrightarrow{\text{Mg}} \xrightarrow{\text{H}^+} \underset{\substack{| \quad | \\ \text{OH OH}}}{\overset{\text{R'} \quad \text{R'}}{\text{RC}-\text{CR}}}$$

848

Alkenes

$$\text{C=C} + \text{H}_2\text{O} \xrightarrow{\text{H}^+} \underset{\substack{| \quad | \\ }}{\overset{\text{H OH}}{-\text{C}-\text{C}-}}$$

260, 765

$$\text{C=C} + \text{HOX} \longrightarrow \underset{\substack{| \quad | \\ }}{\overset{\text{X OH}}{-\text{C}-\text{C}-}}$$

218, 258, 268, 437, 1000

$$\text{C=C} \xrightarrow[\text{H}_2\text{O}]{\text{Hg}^{2+}} \underset{\substack{| \quad | \\ }}{\overset{\text{Hg}^+ \text{ OH}}{-\text{C}-\text{C}-}} \xrightarrow{\text{NaBH}_4} \underset{\substack{| \quad | \\ }}{\overset{\text{H OH}}{-\text{C}-\text{C}-}}$$

260-262

$$\text{C=C} \xrightarrow[]{\text{B}_2\text{H}_6} \xrightarrow{\text{H}_2\text{O}_2} \underset{\substack{| \quad | \\ }}{\text{H}-\text{C}-\text{C}-\text{OH}}$$

262-265, 437

$$\text{RCH=CHR} \xrightarrow{\text{O}_3} \xrightarrow{\text{NaBH}_4} \text{RCH}_2\text{OH}$$

267

$$\text{C=C} \xrightarrow{\text{KMnO}_4} \underset{\substack{| \quad | \\ }}{\text{HO}-\text{C}-\text{C}-\text{OH}}$$

265-266, 846-847

$$\text{C=C} \xrightarrow[\text{H}_2\text{O}_2]{\text{OsO}_4} \underset{\substack{| \quad | \\ }}{\text{HO}-\text{C}-\text{C}-\text{OH}}$$

266, 436, 845, 850

Amines

$$\text{RNH}_2 \xrightarrow{\text{HNO}_2} \text{ROH}$$

743

Carboxylic acids

$$\text{RCOOH} \xrightarrow{\text{LiAlH}_4} \text{RCH}_2\text{OH}$$

401,470

Esters

$$\text{R'COOR} \xrightarrow[\text{H}_2\text{O}]{\text{H+ or OH}^-} \text{R'COOH} + \text{ROH}$$

58-59, 198, 199, 225-226, 511, 585, 859

$$\text{R'COOR} \xrightarrow[\text{or LiBH}_4]{\text{LiAlH}_4} \text{R'CH}_2\text{OH} + \text{ROH}$$

401, 499, 848

$$\text{RCOOEt} + \text{R'MgX or R'Li} \longrightarrow \xrightarrow{\text{H}^+} \text{RR'}_2\text{COH}$$

496, 497

$$\text{RMgX} + (\text{EtO})_2\text{C=O} \longrightarrow \text{R}_3\text{COH}$$

497

$$\text{R'COOR} \xrightarrow[\text{or H}_2/\text{cat.}]{\text{Na/EtOH}} \text{R'CH}_2\text{OH} + \text{ROH}$$

499

Ethers

$$ROR \xrightarrow{\text{HX}} ROH + RX$$

222, 446, 447, 824, 825

Halides and sulfonates

$$RY \xrightarrow{\text{H}_2\text{O or OH}^-} ROH$$

51, 157, 158, 181, 198, 225, 436, 518–519, 858

Oxiranes

$$\underset{\text{C}\overset{\displaystyle\diagup\text{O}\diagdown}{}\text{C}}{} \xrightarrow[\text{H}_3\text{O}^+]{\text{OH}^- \text{ or}} \underset{\text{C}\;\text{C}}{\overset{\text{HO}}{}}\!\!\text{OH}$$

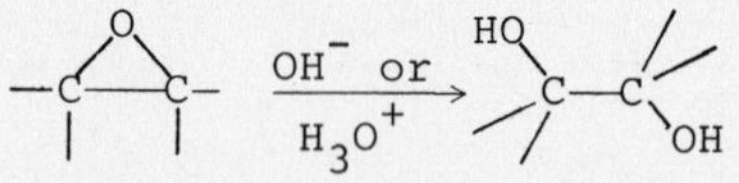

219–220, 437, 846, 1001

$$RM + \underset{\text{CH}_2\!\!-\!\!\text{CH}_2}{\overset{\displaystyle\diagup\text{O}\diagdown}{}} \longrightarrow RCH_2CH_2OH$$

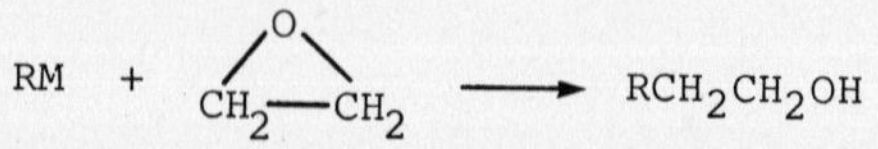

221, 435, 441

Silyl ethers

$$RO\text{-SiR}'_3 \xrightarrow{\text{F}^- \text{ or } \text{H}_3\text{O}^+} ROH$$

792

Aldehydes

Acetals

$$RCH(OR')_2 \xrightarrow{\text{H}^+} RCHO + R'OH$$

382, 446, 886, 895, 898

Acid derivatives

$$RCOCl \xrightarrow[\text{Li}(t\text{-BuO})_3\text{AlH}]{\text{H}_2/\text{cat. or}} RCHO$$

498–499

$$RCONR'_2 \xrightarrow{\text{LiAlH(OEt)}_3} RCHO$$

501

$$\underset{\text{RCHCOOH}}{\overset{\text{OH}}{|}} \xrightarrow[\text{H}_2\text{O}_2]{\text{CaO}} \xrightarrow{\text{Fe}^{+3}} RCHO$$

909

Alcohols

$$RCH_2OH \xrightarrow{\text{[O]}} RCHO$$

210–213, 365, 538

$$\underset{\text{RCHCHR}'}{\overset{\text{HO OH}}{|\;\;|}} \xrightarrow[\text{Pb(OAc)}_4]{\text{HIO}_4 \text{ or}} RCHO + R'CHO$$

850–851, 856, 904–906

$$\underset{\text{R}_2\text{CCH}_2\text{OH}}{\overset{\text{OH}}{|}} \xrightarrow{\text{H}^+} R_2CHCHO$$

1031

Alkenes

$$RCH\!=\!CHR \xrightarrow{\text{O}_3} \xrightarrow[\text{(CH}_3)_2\text{S}]{\text{Zn/AcOH or}} RCHO$$

267, 366

Alkynes

$$RC\!\equiv\!CH \xrightarrow{\text{B}_2\text{H}_6} \xrightarrow[\text{OH}^-]{\text{H}_2\text{O}_2} RCH_2CHO$$

295–296, 366

Arenes

$$ArH + HCON(CH_3)_2 \xrightarrow{\text{POCl}_3} ArCHO$$

713–714, 1015

(Vilsmeier reaction)

Enol ethers

$$R_2C=CHOR' \xrightarrow[H_2O]{H^+} R_2CHCHO$$ 382

Phenols

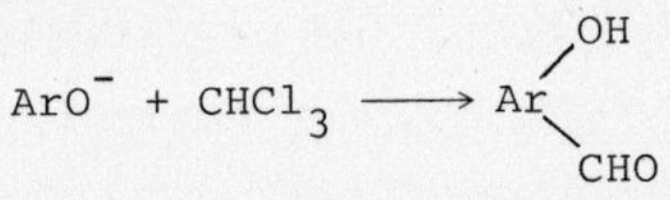

$$ArO^- + CHCl_3 \longrightarrow Ar\begin{array}{c} OH \\ \diagup \\ \diagdown \\ CHO \end{array}$$ 817

(Reimer-Tiemann reaction)

Alkanes and Arenes

Alcohols

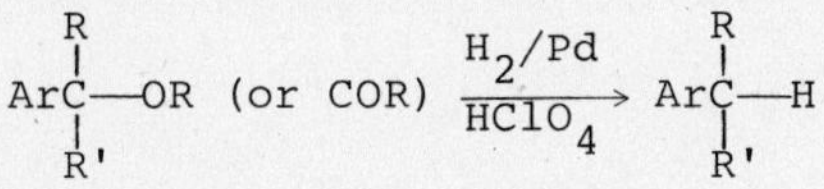

$$\begin{array}{c} R \\ | \\ ArC-OR \ (or \ COR) \\ | \\ R' \end{array} \xrightarrow[HClO_4]{H_2/Pd} \begin{array}{c} R \\ | \\ ArC-H \\ | \\ R' \end{array}$$ 590-591

Aldehyde

$$RCHO \xrightarrow{L_3RhCl} RH$$ 1094

Alkenes

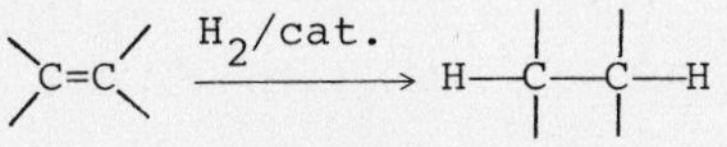

$$\diagup C=C \diagdown \xrightarrow{H_2/cat.} H-\overset{|}{C}-\overset{|}{C}-H$$ 253-255, 436, 444, 445,
                                                   543, 589, 841

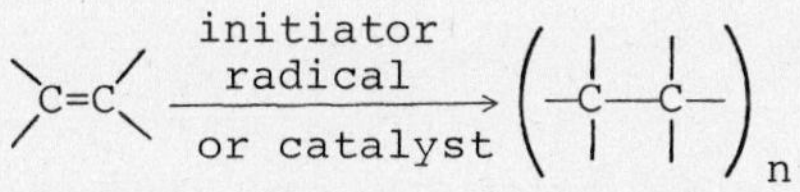

$$\diagup C=C \diagdown \xrightarrow[\text{or catalyst}]{\substack{\text{initiator} \\ \text{radical}}} \left(-\overset{|}{C}-\overset{|}{C}- \right)_n$$ 1110-1115

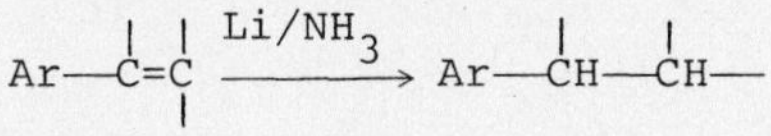

$$Ar-\overset{|}{\underset{|}{C}}=\overset{|}{C} \xrightarrow{Li/NH_3} Ar-\overset{|}{C}H-\overset{|}{C}H-$$ 593

$$-\overset{O}{\overset{||}{C}}-\overset{|}{C}=\overset{|}{C}- \xrightarrow[NH_3]{Li} -\overset{O}{\overset{||}{C}}-\overset{|}{C}H-\overset{|}{C}H-$$ 543-544

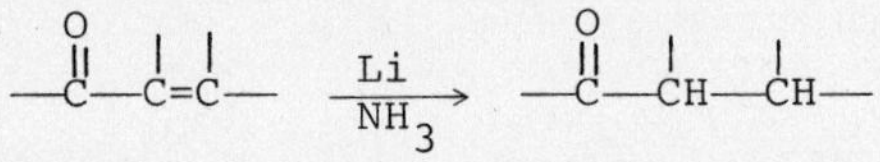

Alkynes

$$RC\equiv CR' \xrightarrow{H_2/cat.} RCH_2CH_2R'$$ 289, 443

Amines

$$ArNH_2 \xrightarrow{HONO} ArN_2^+ \xrightarrow{H_3PO_2} ArH$$ 747, 753, 971

Arenes

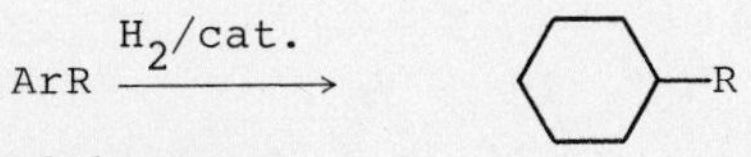

$$ArR \xrightarrow{H_2/cat.} \hexagon-R$$ 589, 863, 983, 988, (1003-1004)

Cyclohexanes

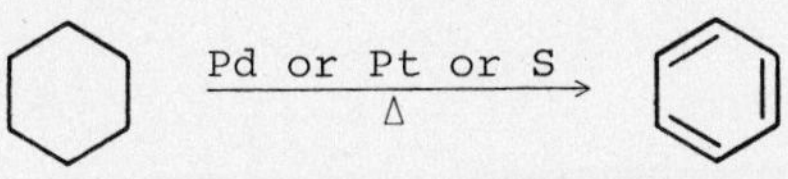

$$\hexagon \xrightarrow[\Delta]{Pd \ or \ Pt \ or \ S} \hexagon$$ 569, 978, 979, 987, 1032,
                                                   1033, 1036, 1037

Halides and sulfonates

$$RX \xrightarrow{\text{LiAlH}_4} RH$$ 401, 590

$$RNa + RX \longrightarrow RR'$$ 175, 522

$$ArLi \text{ or } ArMgX + RX \longrightarrow ArR$$ 579, 807

$$ArX + RX \xrightarrow{\text{Na}} ArR$$
(Wurtz-Fittig reaction)   807

$$ArI + Cu \longrightarrow Ar\text{-}Ar$$
(Ullmann reaction)   807

$$ArH + RX \xrightarrow{\text{AlCl}_3} ArR + ArR'$$
(Friedel-Crafts alkylation)   653-654, 656, 674

$$ArH + \overset{\diagdown}{\underset{\diagup}{C}}{=}\overset{\diagup}{\underset{\diagdown}{C}} \xrightarrow{\text{acid}} Ar{-}\overset{|}{\underset{|}{C}}{-}\overset{|}{\underset{|}{C}}{-}H$$ 655, 771, 812

$$Ar_2CH_2 \text{ (or } Ar_3CH) \xrightarrow{\text{NaNH}_2} \xrightarrow{\text{RX}}$$
$$Ar_2CHR \text{ (or } Ar_3CR)$$ 589

$$ArSO_3H \xrightarrow[100°]{\text{H}_3\text{O}^+} ArH$$ 769-770

Ketones

$$\overset{O}{\overset{\|}{R C R'}} \xrightarrow[\substack{\text{KOH/diethylene glycol} \\ \Delta}]{\text{H}_2\text{NNH}_2} RCH_2R'$$ 402-403, 436, 444, 671, 978
(Wolff-Kishner reduction)

$$\overset{O}{\overset{\|}{R C R'}} \xrightarrow[\text{HCl},\Delta]{\text{Zn(Hg)}} RCH_2R'$$ 403, 444, 671, 987, (988)
(Clemmensen reduction)

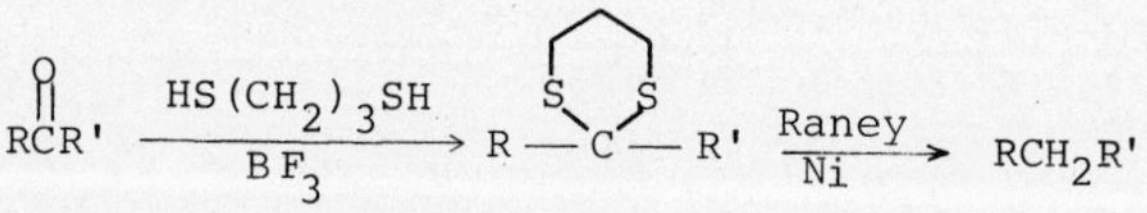

$$\overset{O}{\overset{\|}{R C R'}} \xrightarrow[\text{BF}_3]{\text{HS(CH}_2)_3\text{SH}} R{-}\overset{\text{S}\quad\text{S}}{\underset{|}{C}}{-}R' \xrightarrow{\frac{\text{Raney}}{\text{Ni}}} RCH_2R'$$ 763

$$\overset{O}{\overset{\|}{Ar C R}} \xrightarrow{\text{H}_2\text{-Pd}} ArCH_2R$$ 591

Organometallics

$$RMgX, \ RLi, \ \text{or } R_3Al \xrightarrow{\text{R'OH}} RH$$ 154, 444, 446, 590

$$R_4Si \xrightarrow{\text{HCl}} RH$$ 155

Alkenes

Alcohols

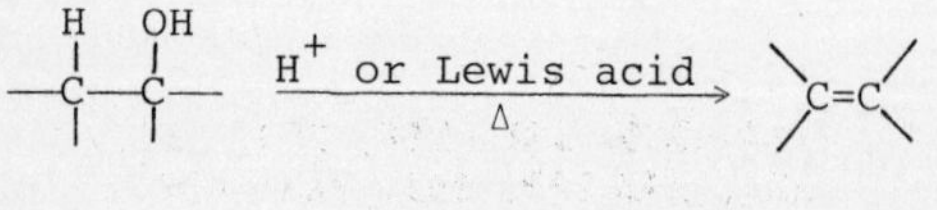

$$\overset{H\quad OH}{{-}\overset{|}{C}{-}\overset{|}{C}{-}} \xrightarrow[\Delta]{\text{H}^+ \text{ or Lewis acid}} \overset{\diagdown}{\underset{\diagup}{C}}{=}\overset{\diagup}{\underset{\diagdown}{C}}$$ 210, 216, 250-252, 398, 435, 436 442, 445, 532, 533, 538, 586, 853-854, 861, 978, 987

$$\overset{H\quad OH}{{-}\overset{|}{C}{-}\overset{|}{C}{-}} \xrightarrow[\substack{\text{NaOH} \\ \text{CH}_3\text{I}}]{\text{CS}_2} \overset{H\quad \overset{S}{\overset{\|}{O C S C H_3}}}{{-}\overset{|}{C}{-}\overset{|}{C}{-}} \xrightarrow{\Delta} \overset{\diagdown}{\underset{\diagup}{C}}{=}\overset{\diagup}{\underset{\diagdown}{C}}$$ 506-508

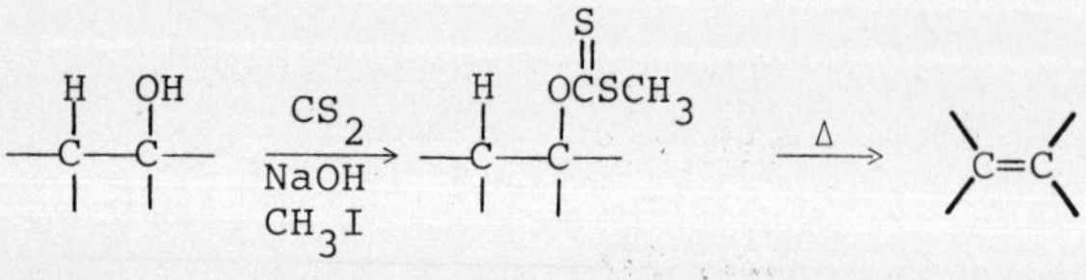

Aldehydes and ketones

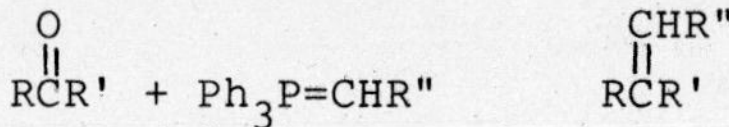

$$\underset{\substack{\| \\ O}}{R\overset{\|}{C}R'} + Ph_3P=CHR'' \longrightarrow \underset{\substack{\| \\ CHR''}}{R\overset{\|}{C}R'}$$
(Wittig reaction)

397-398, 435, 442, 533

Alkynes

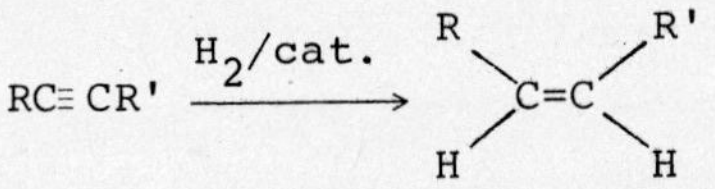

$$RC\equiv CR' \xrightarrow{H_2/cat.} \begin{array}{c} R \\ H \end{array}C=C\begin{array}{c} R' \\ H \end{array}$$

289, 291, 436, 443, 533

$$RC\equiv CR' \xrightarrow[\text{liq. } NH_3]{Na} \begin{array}{c} R \\ H \end{array}C=C\begin{array}{c} H \\ R' \end{array}$$

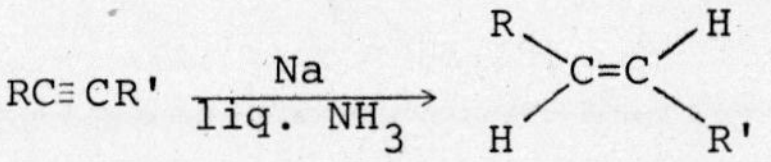

290-291, 436

Amine oxides

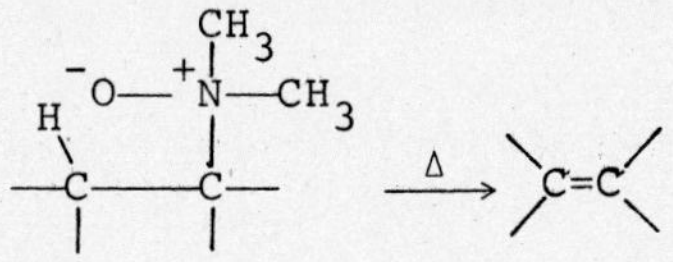

$$\underset{C}{\overset{H}{\underset{|}{\overset{}{\rule{0pt}{0pt}}}}}\underset{C}{\overset{\underset{CH_3}{\overset{O^-\ +N-CH_3}{\rule{0pt}{0pt}}}}{\rule{0pt}{0pt}}} \xrightarrow{\Delta} \quad C=C$$

719

Ammonium hydroxides

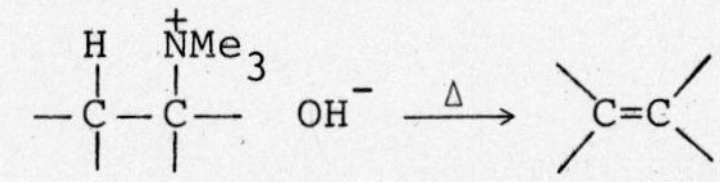

$$\underset{-C-C-}{\overset{H\ \overset{+}{N}Me_3}{\rule{0pt}{0pt}}} OH^- \xrightarrow{\Delta} \quad C=C$$

716-719

Arenes

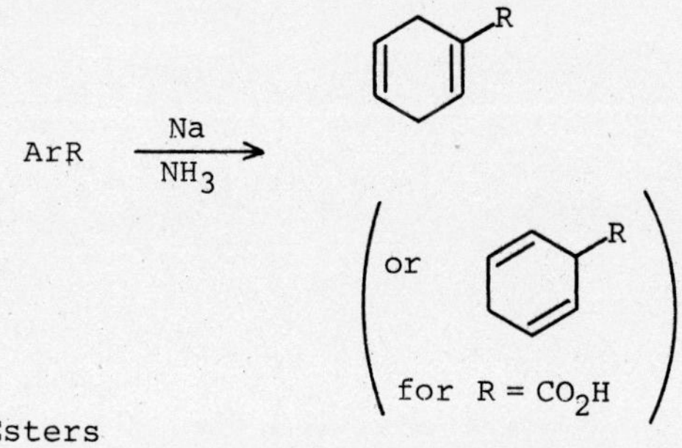

$$ArR \xrightarrow[NH_3]{Na}$$

591-593, 983, 988

(or ... for R = CO$_2$H)

593

Esters

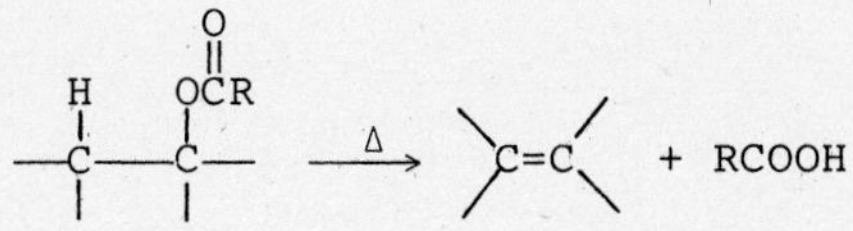

$$\underset{-C-C-}{\overset{H\ O\overset{\|}{C}R}{\rule{0pt}{0pt}}} \xrightarrow{\Delta} \quad C=C \quad + RCOOH$$

506-508, 532

Ethers

$$\underset{-C-C-}{\overset{H\ OR}{\rule{0pt}{0pt}}} \xrightarrow[\Delta]{H^+} \quad C=C$$

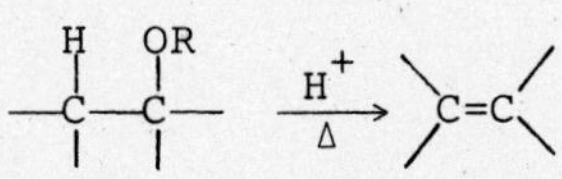

217, 446

Halides and sulfonates (X = halogen; Y = X or sulfonate)

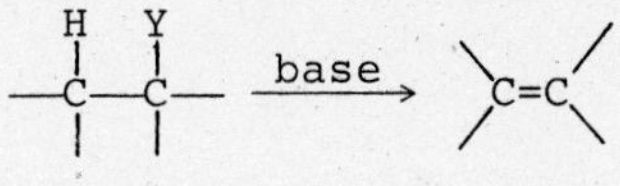

$$\underset{-C-C-}{\overset{H\ Y}{\rule{0pt}{0pt}}} \xrightarrow{base} \quad C=C$$

174, 175, 181, 198, 200, 215,
225, 242-249, 259, 287, 437,
442, 546, 548, 717, 858

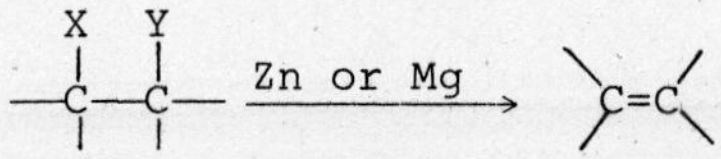

$$\underset{-C-C-}{\overset{X\ Y}{\rule{0pt}{0pt}}} \xrightarrow{Zn\ or\ Mg} \quad C=C$$

548, 612

$$RMgX + CH_2=CHCH_2Y \longrightarrow RCH_2CH=CH_2$$

522, 532

Sulfoxides

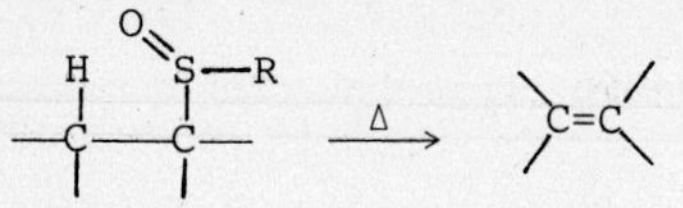

762

Alkynes

$RCX_2CH_2R' \xrightarrow{\text{base}} RC{\equiv}CR'$ 286-288

$RCHXCHXR' \xrightarrow{\text{base}} RC{\equiv}CR'$ 286-288

$RC{\equiv}C^- + R'Y \longrightarrow RC{\equiv}CR'$ 285-286, 381-382, 434, 443

$RCH_2C{\equiv}CH \underset{\longleftarrow}{\xrightarrow{\text{strong base}}} RCH_2C{\equiv}CCH_3$ 287, 288

Amides

Acid anhydrides

$(RCO)_2O + R'NH_2 \longrightarrow RCONHR'$ 495, 701, 708, 749, 753, 935, 940

Acyl halides

$RCOCl + R'NH_2 \longrightarrow RCONHR'$ 494, 707, 938, 940, 946

Carboxylic acids

$RCOOH + R'NH_2 \xrightarrow{\Delta} RCONHR'$

$RCOOH + R'NH_2 \xrightarrow{\text{DCC}} RCONHR'$ 468-469, 707, 715, 944, 947-949, 1117

Esters

$RCOOR' + R''NH_2 \longrightarrow RCONHR''$ 495

Ketones

$R_2C{=}O + HN_3 \xrightarrow{H^+} RCONHR$ 937
   (Schmidt reaction)

Nitriles

$RCN \xrightarrow[\text{or } H_2O_2/OH^-]{H^+} RCONH_2$ 294, 295, 460, 547, 866

Amines

Acyl halides

$RCOCl + N_3^- \longrightarrow RCON_3 \xrightarrow[H_2O]{\Delta} RNH_2$ 705, 707
   (Curtius reaction)

Aldehydes and ketones

702-703

936

Amides

$RCONR'R'' \xrightarrow[OH^-]{H^+ \text{ or}} RCOOH + HNR'R''$ 491, 715, 753, 937, 945, 1001

$$RCONR'R'' \xrightarrow{\text{LiAlH}_4} RCH_2NR'R''$$ 401, 499-500, 704

$$RCONH_2 + Br_2 \xrightarrow{\text{NaOH}} RNH_2$$ 705-706
(Hofmann rearrangement)

Amines

$$RNH_2 \text{ (or } RR'NH) \xrightarrow[\Delta]{\text{CH}_2\text{O, HCOOH}}$$ 703

$$RN(CH_3)_2 \text{ (or } RR'NCH_3)$$
(Eschweiler-Clarke reaction)

Carboxylic acids

$$RCOOH + NaN_3 \xrightarrow[\Delta]{\text{H}^+} RNH_2$$ 705, 707, 738, 937
(Schmidt reaction)

Halides and sulfonates

$$RY + R'NH_2 \text{ (or } NH_3) \longrightarrow RR'NH \text{ (or } RNH_2)$$ 158, 181-182, 698-699, 934, 936, 1001, 1002, 1004

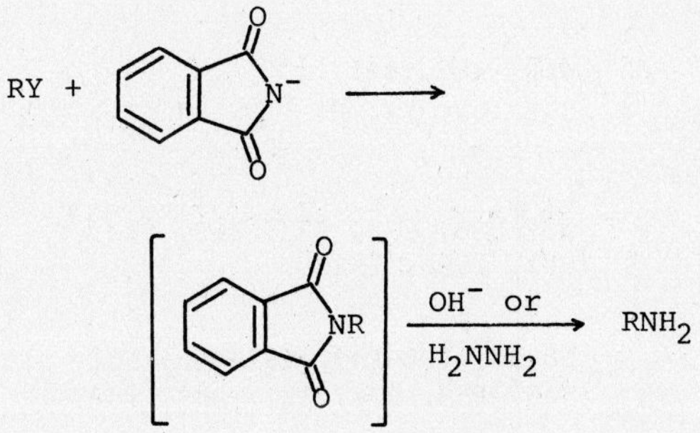

$$RY + \text{ (phthalimide anion)} \longrightarrow$$

$$\left[\text{N-substituted phthalimide} \right] \xrightarrow[\text{H}_2\text{NNH}_2]{\text{OH}^- \text{ or}} RNH_2$$ 699, 934

$$RY + N_3^- \longrightarrow RN_3 \xrightarrow[\text{or LiAlH}_4]{\text{H}_2/\text{cat.}} RNH_2$$ 738

$$ArX + NH_2^- \xrightarrow{\text{liq NH}_3} ArNH_2 + Ar'NH_2$$ 803-804, (1029)

Nitriles

$$RCN \xrightarrow[\text{H}_2/\text{cat.}]{\text{LiAlH}_4 \text{ or}} RCH_2NH_2$$ 292, 401, 701

Nitro compounds

$$RNO_2 \xrightarrow{\text{LiAlH}_4} RNH_2$$ 401

$$RNO_2 \xrightarrow[\text{H}_2/\text{cat.}]{\text{Fe, H}^+ \text{ or}} RNH_2$$ 700, 732, 752, 753, 801

Oximes

$$\overset{\text{NOH}}{\underset{}{R\overset{\|}{C}R'}} \xrightarrow[\text{or LiAlH}_4]{\text{H}_2/\text{cat.}} \overset{\text{NH}_2}{\underset{}{R\overset{|}{C}HR'}}$$ 702, 935

Azides

$$RY + N_3^- \longrightarrow RN_3$$ 158, 705, 737-738, 841

$$\overset{O}{\overset{\diagup \,\diagdown}{RCH-CH_2}} + N_3^- \longrightarrow R\overset{\text{OH}}{\overset{|}{C}H}CH_2N_3$$ 738

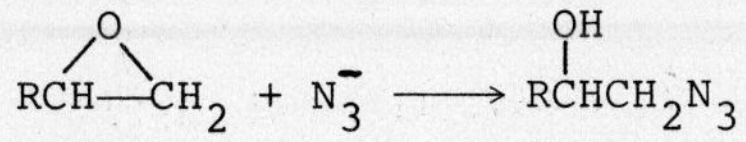

Carboxylic Acids

Acid anhydrides

$(RCO)_2O + H_2O \longrightarrow RCOOH$ **487, 491**

Acyl halides

$RCOCl + H_2O \longrightarrow RCOOH$ **487,491**

Alcohols

$RCH_2OH \xrightarrow{[O]} RCOOH$ **461, 903, 911, 913**

Aldehydes

$RCHO \xrightarrow{[O]} RCOOH$ **398–399, 461–462, 538, 902–904, 908–909, 911, 913, 914**

Alkenes

$RCH=CHR' \xrightarrow{KMnO_4} RCOOH + R'COOH$ **697, 863**

Amides

$RCONH_2 \xrightarrow[\text{or HONO}]{H^+ \text{ or } OH^-} RCOOH$ **460, 487, 491**

Arenes

$ArR \xrightarrow{[O]} ArCOOH$ **587–588, 670, 733, 863, 864, 983, 1025, 1026**

Esters

$RCOOR' \xrightarrow{H^+ \text{ or } OH^-} RCOOH + R'OH$ **58–59, 198–199, 487–490, 511, 546, 859, 874, 877, 945, 1087**

$RCOOCH_2Ar \xrightarrow[Pt]{H_2} RCOOH$ **940, 946**

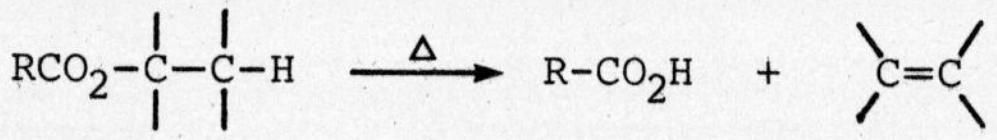

$RCO_2-\overset{|}{\underset{|}{C}}-\overset{|}{\underset{|}{C}}-H \xrightarrow{\Delta} R-CO_2H + \,\,\text{C=C}$ **506–508**

Halides

$RX \xrightarrow{Mg \atop ether} [RMgX] \xrightarrow{CO_2} RCOOH$ **460–461, 806**

Hydroxy ketones

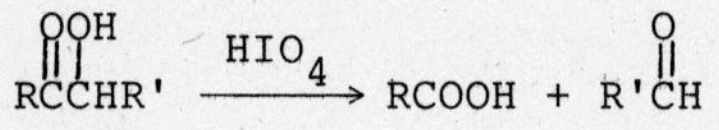

$\underset{RCCHR'}{\overset{OOH}{||\,|}} \xrightarrow{HIO_4} RCOOH + \overset{O}{\underset{R'CH}{||}}$ **856**

$\overset{O}{\underset{RCCH_2R'}{||}} \xrightarrow{[O]} RCOOH + R'COOH$ **400, 863**

Nitriles

$RCN \xrightarrow{H^+ \text{ or } OH^-} RCOOH$ **459–460, 546, 858, 862, 908, 936**

Enamines

$-\overset{|}{\underset{|}{C}}H\overset{O}{\underset{||}{C}}- + R_2NH \longrightarrow \,\,\text{C=C}^{NR_2}$ **719–722, 1024, 1033**

$-\overset{|}{\underset{|}{C}}H-\overset{|}{\underset{|}{C}}H-NR_2 \xrightarrow{Hg(OAc)_2} \xrightarrow{OH^-} \,\,\text{C=C}^{NR_2}$ **772**

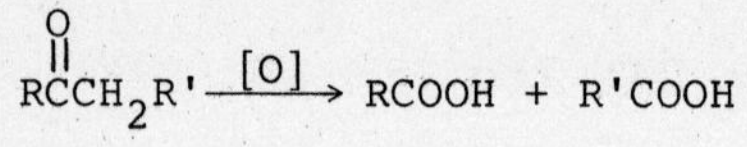

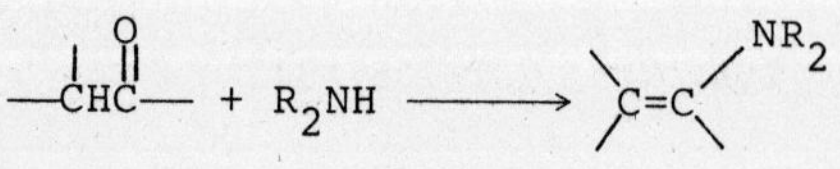

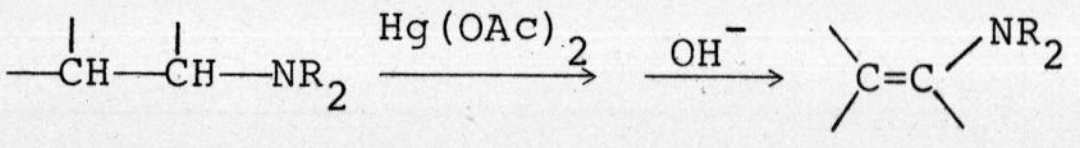

Epoxides (see Oxiranes)

Esters

  Acid anhydrides

    $(RCO)_2O + R'OH \longrightarrow RCOOR'$ **494, 901**

  Acyl halides

    $RCOCl + R'OH \longrightarrow RCOOR'$ **173, 493, 497, 546, 819, 856**

  Alcohols and phenols

    $ROH + R'COOH \xrightarrow{H^+} R'COOR$ **465-467, 859-861**

    $ROH + R'COCl \longrightarrow R'COOR$ **173, 493, 497, 819, 856, 863**

    $ROH + (R'CO)_2O \longrightarrow R'COOR$ **494, 819**

  Amides

    $RCONH_2 + R'OH \xrightarrow{H^+} RCOOR'$ **547**

  Carboxylic acids

    $RCOOH + CH_2N_2 \longrightarrow RCOOCH_3$ **462-463, 739**

    $RCOOH + R'OH \xrightarrow{H^+} RCOOR'$ **465-467, 859-861, 939**

    $RCO_2^- + R'Y \longrightarrow RCOOR'$ **160, 768, 861, 949**

  Esters

    $RCOOR' + R''OH \xrightarrow{H^+ \text{ or } R''O^-} RCOOR'' + R'OH$ **494, 1117**

  Halides and sulfonates

    $RY + R'CO_2^- \longrightarrow R'COOR$ **158-160, 173, 175, 198, 199, 225-226, 462, 585, 768, 802, 861**

  Ketones

     399-400, 859

Ethers

  Alcohols

    $ROH \xrightarrow[\Delta]{H^+} ROR$ **209, 215-216, 250, 766, 849-850**

  Alkenes

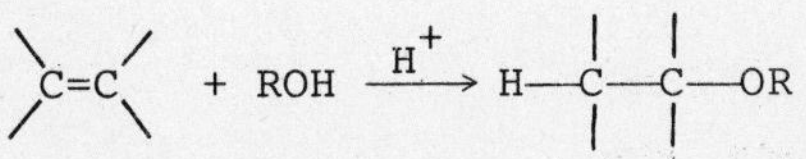

     446

     261

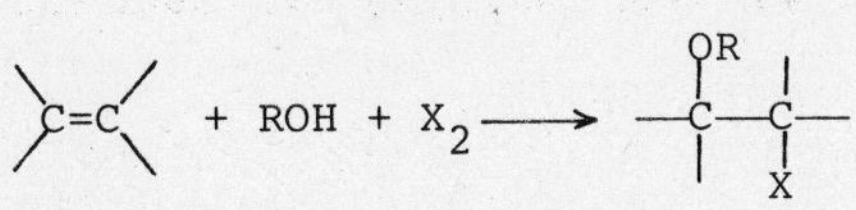

     258

  Alkynes

    $RC{\equiv}CH \xrightarrow[R'OH]{R'O^-} RC{=}CH_2$ **295, 386**

Halides and sulfonates

$$RY + R'O^- \text{ (or R'OH)} \longrightarrow ROR'$$

158, 170, 172, 177, 181, 200, 215, 222-223, 766, 842, 900

$$RY + ArO^- \longrightarrow ROAr$$

814

$$ArX + RO^- \longrightarrow ArOR$$

814

Ketals

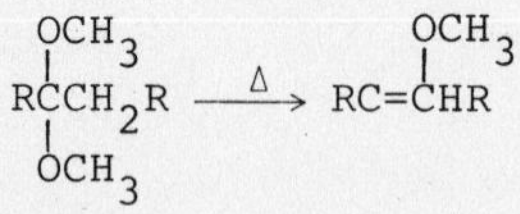

$$\underset{\underset{\overset{|}{OCH_3}}{\overset{\overset{|}{OCH_3}}{|}}}{RCCH_2R} \xrightarrow{\Delta} \underset{\overset{|}{OCH_3}}{RC=CHR}$$

382

Ketones

$$\underset{\overset{\|}{O}}{R-C-CH_2R} \xrightarrow{LDA} \xrightarrow{Me_3SiCl} \underset{\overset{|}{O-SiMe_3}}{R-C=CHR}$$

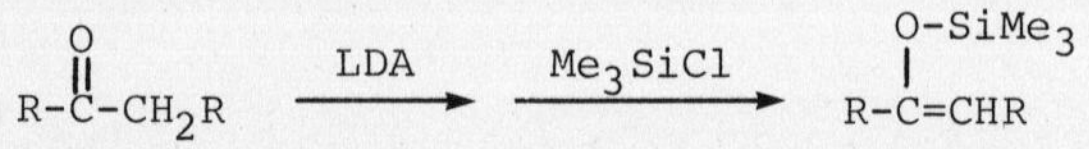

372

Halogen Compounds

Alcohols

$$ROH + HX \longrightarrow RX$$

200-202, 207-209, 518-519

$$ROH + SOCl_2 \longrightarrow RCl$$

203, 209, 440, 521, 586, 590

$$ROH + PBr_3 \longrightarrow RBr$$

203-204, 209, 436

$$ROH + PI_3 \longrightarrow RI$$

204

Alkanes

$$RH + X_2 \xrightarrow{h\nu} RX$$

96-106, 134-136, 225-226, 435, 464, 525-526

Alkenes

$$\underset{}{C=C} + HX \longrightarrow H-\underset{|}{\overset{|}{C}}-\underset{|}{\overset{|}{C}}-X$$

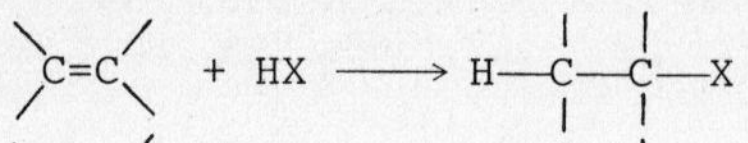

259-260, 270-272, 292-293, 528

$$\underset{}{C=C} + X_2 \longrightarrow X-\underset{|}{\overset{|}{C}}-\underset{|}{\overset{|}{C}}-X$$

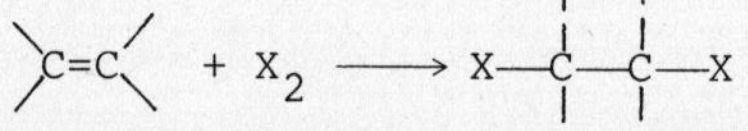

255-258, 437, 528-530, 539, 645, 790, 1001

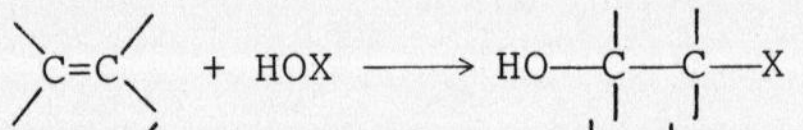

$$\underset{}{C=C} + HOX \longrightarrow HO-\underset{|}{\overset{|}{C}}-\underset{|}{\overset{|}{C}}-X$$

218, 258, 268, 437

$$\underset{}{C=C} + CX_4 \longrightarrow X-\underset{|}{\overset{|}{C}}-\underset{|}{\overset{|}{C}}-CX_3$$

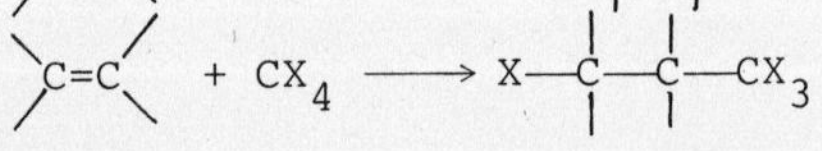

271

$$RCH=CH-SiMe_3 + X_2 \longrightarrow RCH=CHX$$

790

$$CH_2=CH-\underset{|}{\overset{\overset{|}{H}}{C}}- \xrightarrow{NBS} CH_2=CH-\underset{|}{\overset{\overset{|}{Br}}{C}}-$$

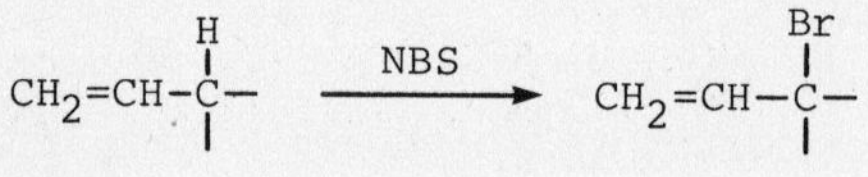

525, 526

Alkynes

$$RC{\equiv}CR' + HX \longrightarrow RCH=CXR'$$

292-293, 296

Amines

$$ArNH_2 \xrightarrow{HONO} ArN_2^+ \xrightarrow{I^-} ArI$$

743, 752

$$ArNH_2 \xrightarrow{HONO} ArN_2^+ \xrightarrow[\Delta]{CuX} ArX \text{ (X = Cl, Br)}$$

743-745, 801

$$ArNH_2 \xrightarrow[BF_3 \text{(or } HPF_6)]{HONO} ArN_2^+ BF_4^- \text{ (or } PF_6^-) \xrightarrow{\Delta} ArF$$

746, 752

Arenes

$$ArH + X_2 \longrightarrow ArX$$

645-649, 657-659, 672, 673, 712, 713, 715, 747, 770, 799-800, 815, 822, 981, 989, 991, 1011, 1022, 1027

$$ArH + CH_2O + HCl \xrightarrow{ZnCl_2} ArCH_2Cl$$

655, 1015

$$ArCH_3 + Cl_2 \xrightarrow{h\nu} ArCH_2Cl$$

582-589

$$ArCHR_2 + Br_2 \xrightarrow{h\nu} ArCBrR_2$$

584

$$ArH + CCl_4 \xrightarrow{AlCl_3} Ar_3CCl$$

656

$$Ar-SiMe_3 + X_2 \longrightarrow Ar-X + X-SiMe_3$$

789

Carboxylic acids

$$RCH_2COOH + Br_2 \xrightarrow{PBr_3} RCHBrCOOH$$
 (Hell-Volhard-Zelinsky reaction)

464-465, 546, 858

$$RCOOH \xrightarrow{Ag^+} \xrightarrow[CCl_4]{Br_2} RBr$$

470

$$RCOOH \xrightarrow[Br_2]{HgO} RBr$$

471

$$RCOOH \xrightarrow[LiCl]{Pb(OAc)_4} RCl$$

471

Ethers

$$ROR' + HX \longrightarrow ROH + R'X \text{ or } RX + R'X$$

216, 222

Halides and sulfonates

$$RY + X^- \longrightarrow RX$$

157, 158, 174, 205, 521

Ketones

374-375

Hemiacetals, Hemiketals: see Acetals and Ketals

Imines

Aldehydes and ketones

383-386, 538, 702, 703, 856, 906-907, 910, (1018-1019), 1036

Amines

$$R_2CHNR'_2 \xrightarrow{Hg(OAc)_2} R_2C \overset{+}{=\!=\!=} NR'_2$$

722

Ketones

Acyl Halides

496

739

Alcohols

$$RR'CHOH \xrightarrow{[O]} R\overset{\overset{\displaystyle O}{\|}}{C}R'$$

210-213, 225-226, 365-366, 436, 587, 868, 900

$$-\overset{\overset{\displaystyle OH}{|}}{C}-\overset{\overset{\displaystyle OH}{|}}{C}- \xrightarrow[\text{Pb(OAc)}_4]{\text{HIO}_4 \text{ or}} -\overset{\overset{\displaystyle O}{\|}}{C} + \overset{\overset{\displaystyle O}{\|}}{C}-$$

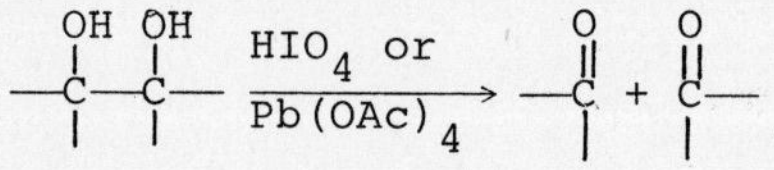

850-851, 904-906

$$R_2\overset{\overset{\displaystyle OH}{|}}{C}-\overset{\overset{\displaystyle OH}{|}}{C}R_2 \xrightarrow{H^+} R_3C\overset{\overset{\displaystyle O}{\|}}{C}R$$

849

Alkenes

$$\overset{}{C}=\overset{}{C} \xrightarrow{O_3} \overset{}{C}=O + O=\overset{}{C}$$

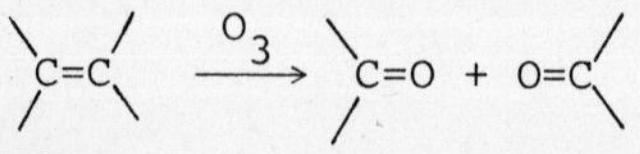

267, 366

Alkynes

$$RC\equiv CR \xrightarrow[\text{Hg}^{2+}]{H^+} R\overset{\overset{\displaystyle O}{\|}}{C}CH_2R$$

294, 368

$$RC\equiv CR \xrightarrow{B_2H_6} \xrightarrow[\text{OH}^-]{H_2O_2} R\overset{\overset{\displaystyle O}{\|}}{C}CH_2R$$

(295-296)

Arenes

$$ArH + RCOCl \xrightarrow{\text{Lewis acid}} Ar\overset{\overset{\displaystyle O}{\|}}{C}R$$

652-653, 673, 713, 790, 982

$$ArH + (RCO)_2O \xrightarrow{\text{AlCl}_3} Ar\overset{\overset{\displaystyle O}{\|}}{C}R$$

822-824, 978, 982, 985, 986, 1011, 1014

$$ArH + RCOOH \xrightarrow[\text{or Lewis acid}]{H^+} Ar\overset{\overset{\displaystyle O}{\|}}{C}R$$

822, 824, 987

$$ArCH_2R \xrightarrow{[O]} Ar\overset{\overset{\displaystyle O}{\|}}{C}R$$

974

Dithioacetals

$$R-\overset{}{C}-R' \xrightarrow[\text{H}_2\text{O}]{\text{HgCl}_2} R\overset{\overset{\displaystyle O}{\|}}{C}R'$$

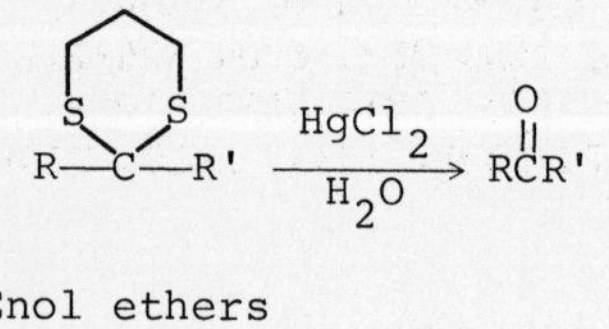

783

Enol ethers

$$R\overset{\overset{\displaystyle OR'}{|}}{C}=CR_2 \xrightarrow[\text{H}_2\text{O}]{H^+} R\overset{\overset{\displaystyle O}{\|}}{C}CHR_2$$

382, 593

Esters

$$RCH_2COOEt + R'COOEt \xrightarrow{\text{base}} R\overset{\overset{\displaystyle COR'}{|}}{CH}COOEt$$

503-505, 867-869

Ketones

$$RCH_2\overset{\overset{\displaystyle O}{\|}}{C}R' \xrightarrow{\text{SeO}_2} R\overset{\overset{\displaystyle O}{\|}}{C}-\overset{\overset{\displaystyle O}{\|}}{C}R'$$

868

Nitriles

Aldehydes and ketones

$$\underset{\underset{\displaystyle RCR' \ (or \ H)}{\overset{\displaystyle O}{\|}}}{} + HCN \longrightarrow \underset{\underset{\displaystyle RR'(or \ H)CCN}{}}{\overset{\displaystyle OH}{|}}$$ 388-390, 435, 547, 701, 858, 908

$$\underset{\underset{\displaystyle RCR' \ (or \ H)}{\overset{\displaystyle O}{\|}}}{} + HCN + NH_3 \longrightarrow \underset{\underset{\displaystyle RR'CCN}{}}{\overset{\displaystyle NH_2}{|}}$$ 936

$$-\underset{|}{C}=\underset{}{C}-\underset{\overset{\displaystyle O}{\|}}{C}- + HCN \longrightarrow -\underset{\underset{|}{|}}{\overset{\displaystyle CN}{C}}-CH-\underset{\overset{\displaystyle O}{\|}}{C}-$$ 539-540, 862

Amides

$$RCONH_2 \xrightarrow[SOCl_2]{P_2O_5 \, or} RCN$$ 506

Amines

$$ArNH_2 \xrightarrow{HONO} ArN_2^+ \xrightarrow{CuCN} ArCN$$ 745, 752
    (Sandmeyer reaction)

Halides and sulfonates

$$RY + CN^- \ (or \ CuCN) \longrightarrow RCN$$ 158, 172, 259, 285, 434, 460,
    546, 585, 862

Oximes

$$RCH=NOH \xrightarrow{Ac_2O} RCN$$ 910

Sulfonic acids

$$ArSO_3H \xrightarrow[\Delta]{NaCN} ArCN$$ 772

Nitro Compounds

Amines

$$ArNH_2 \xrightarrow{HONO} ArN_2^+ \xrightarrow[Cu]{NO_2^-} ArNO_2$$ 746

Arenes

$$ArH + HNO_3 \longrightarrow ArNO_2$$ 650-651, 657-659, 670, 672-673,
    713, 715, 752, 753, 800, 820-821,
    974, 980, 984, 1010-1011, 1021,
    1022, 1026-1028, 1034, 1037, 1038

Halides and sulfonates

$$RY + NO_2^- \longrightarrow RNO_2$$ 171, 732

Ketones

$$\underset{\underset{\displaystyle RCR'}{\overset{\displaystyle O}{\|}}}{} + CH_3NO_2 \xrightarrow{base} \underset{\underset{\displaystyle R'}{|}}{\overset{\displaystyle OH}{\underset{\displaystyle RCCH_2NO_2}{|}}}$$ 732

Organometallics

Boron

$$RCH=CH_2 + B_2H_6 \longrightarrow (RCH_2CH_2)_3B$$ 262-265

$$RC\equiv CR + B_2H_6 \longrightarrow (RCH=CR)_3B$$ 295-296

Cadmium

$$RMgX + CdCl_2 \longrightarrow R_2Cd \, (R = prim.)$$ 153

Copper

$RLi + CuI \longrightarrow R_2CuLi$ — 496, 541, 807

Lithium

$RX + Li \xrightarrow{ether} RLi$ — 153, 806

$ArBr + RLi \longrightarrow ArLi$ — 806

Magnesium (Grignard reagents)

$RX + Mg \xrightarrow{ether} RMgX$ — 152, 444, 446, 460, 522–523, 806, 989

Mercury

RLi or $RMgX + HgCl_2 \longrightarrow R_2Hg$ — 154

$RCH=CH_2 + Hg(OAc)_2 \xrightarrow{R'OH} RCHCH_2HgOAc$, OR' — 261

Silicon

$RMgX + SiCl_4 \longrightarrow R_4Si$ — 153

Silver

$RC\equiv CH + AgNO_3 \longrightarrow RC\equiv CAg$ — 283–284

Sodium

$RX + Na \longrightarrow RNa$ — 175

Oxiranes

Aldehydes and ketones — 784

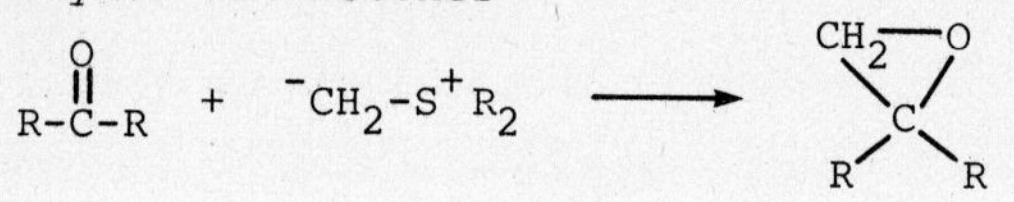

Alkenes

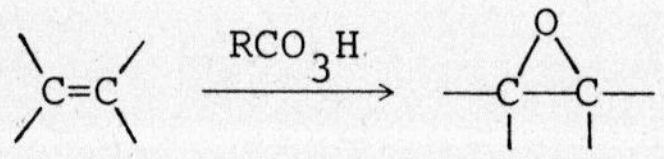

$C=C \xrightarrow{RCO_3H}$ epoxide — 268, 437, 846, 1000

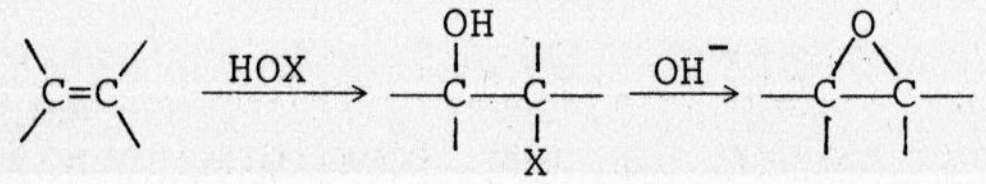

$C=C \xrightarrow{HOX} \xrightarrow{OH^-}$ epoxide — 218–219, 256, 268, 437, 1000

Phenols

Amines

$ArNH_2 \xrightarrow{HONO} ArN_2^+ \xrightarrow{H_2O, \Delta} ArOH$ — 743, 811, 1029

Ethers

$ArOR + HX \longrightarrow ArOH + RX$ — 824, 825

Halides

$ArX \xrightarrow{OH^-} ArOH$ — 801, 803, 811

Hydroperoxides

$R_2C(Ar)OOH \xrightarrow{H^+} RCR + ArOH$ — 812

Sulfonic acids

$$ArSO_3H \xrightarrow[\Delta]{NaOH} ArOH \qquad\qquad\qquad 772, 811, 983$$

Phosphorus Compounds

Phosphate esters

$$nROH + Cl_n\overset{\overset{\textstyle O}{\|}}{P}(OR')_{3-n} \longrightarrow (RO)_n\overset{\overset{\textstyle O}{\|}}{P}(OR')_{3-n} \qquad 777$$

Phosphines

$$RMgX + PCl_3 \longrightarrow R_3P \qquad\qquad\qquad 774$$

Phosphite esters

$$ROH + PCl_3 \xrightarrow{pyridine} (RO)_3P: \qquad\qquad 779$$

Phosphonate esters

$$(RO)_3P: + R'X \longrightarrow (RO)_2\overset{\overset{\textstyle O}{\|}}{P}R' \qquad 779\text{-}780$$

Phosphonium salts

$$R_3P: + R'X \longrightarrow R_3\overset{+}{P}R' \ X^- \qquad 157, 158, 396\text{-}397, 533, 775$$

Ylides

$$R_3\overset{+}{P}CHR'_2 \xrightarrow{n\text{BuLi}} R_3\overset{+}{P}\overset{-}{C}R'_2 \qquad 397, 442, 533, 781$$

Polymers

By addition

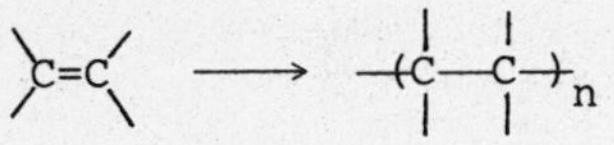

$$\underset{\diagdown}{\overset{\diagup}{C}}=\underset{\diagdown}{\overset{\diagup}{C}} \longrightarrow \left(\!\!\begin{array}{c}|\\ C\\ |\end{array}\!\!-\!\!\begin{array}{c}|\\ C\\ |\end{array}\!\!\right)_{\!n} \qquad\qquad 1111\text{-}1116$$

By condensation

$$HY'\text{-}R\text{-}YH \longrightarrow (Y'\!\!-\!\!R) + HY \qquad\qquad 1116\text{-}1118$$

Quinones

Phenols

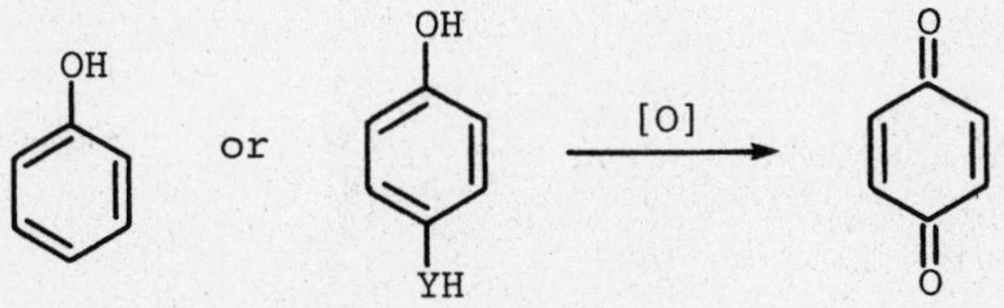

828-829, 982, 988

Silicon Compounds

Silanes

$$RMgX + SiCl_4 \longrightarrow R_4Si \qquad\qquad 153, 786, 787$$

$$R_3SiCl \xrightarrow{LiAlH_4} R_3SiH \qquad\qquad 788\text{-}789$$

Silyl ethers

$$RO^- + R'_3SiCl \longrightarrow RO\text{-}SiR'_3 \qquad 372, 447, 792$$

<u>Sulfur Compounds</u>

Disulfides

$$2 \ RSH \xrightarrow{[O]} RSSR \qquad\qquad 759-760$$

Sulfides

$$RS^- + R'Y \longrightarrow RSR' \qquad\qquad 758-759, \ 1001-1004$$

$$\overset{\displaystyle}{C}{=}\overset{\displaystyle}{C} + RSH \longrightarrow H{-}\overset{|}{C}{-}\overset{|}{C}{-}SR \qquad\qquad 271$$

$$\overset{O}{\underset{\underset{-}{}}{R\overset{\|}{C}CHR'}} \xrightarrow{R''SSR''} \underset{\underset{R'}{|}}{R\overset{O}{\overset{\|}{C}}CHSR''} \qquad\qquad 760$$

Sulfinic acids

$$ArSO_2Cl \xrightarrow[H_2O]{Zn} ArSO_2H \qquad\qquad 773$$

Sulfonamides

$$RSO_2Cl + R'NH_2 \longrightarrow RSO_2NHR' \qquad\qquad 773$$

Sulfonate esters

$$ArSO_2Cl + ROH \xrightarrow{pyridine} ArSO_2OR \qquad\qquad 205, \ 521, \ 767-768, \ 1025$$

Sulfones

$$R_2SO \xrightarrow{R'CO_3H} R_2SO_2 \qquad\qquad 761$$

$$R_2S \xrightarrow[\substack{or \\ R'CO_3H}]{KMnO_4} R_2SO_2 \qquad\qquad 761$$

$$ArSO_2Cl + Ar'H \xrightarrow{AlCl_3} ArSO_2Ar' \qquad\qquad 773$$

$$RSO_2^- + R'X \longrightarrow RSO_2R' \qquad\qquad 774$$

Sulfonic acids

$$RY + SO_3^= \longrightarrow RSO_3^- \qquad\qquad 171, \ 767$$

$$\overset{O}{R\overset{\|}{C}H} + HSO_3^- \longrightarrow \underset{}{R\overset{OH}{\overset{|}{C}H}SO_3^-} \qquad\qquad 767$$

$$ArSO_2Cl \xrightarrow{H_2O} ArSO_3H \qquad\qquad 760$$

$$ArH + H_2SO_4 \longrightarrow ArSO_3H \qquad\qquad 768-770, \ 821-822, \ 981, \ 984, \ 1027$$

Sulfonium salts

$$R_2S + R'X \longrightarrow R_2\overset{+}{S}R' \ X^- \qquad\qquad 158, \ 763, \ 783$$

Sulfonyl halides

$$ArSSAr \xrightarrow[HNO_3]{Cl_2} ArSO_2Cl \qquad\qquad 760$$

$$RSO_3Na \xrightarrow{PCl_5} RSO_2Cl \qquad\qquad 767,\ 773$$

$$ArH \xrightarrow{ClSO_3H} ArSO_2Cl \qquad\qquad 771,\ 773$$

Sulfoxides

$$R_2S \xrightarrow{H_2O_2} R_2SO \qquad\qquad 761,\ 762$$

Thiols

$$RY + HS^- \longrightarrow RSH \qquad\qquad 158,\ 758$$

$$RY + H_2NCSNH_2 \longrightarrow \xrightarrow{OH^-} RSH \qquad\qquad 758\text{-}759$$

$$RX \longrightarrow RMgX \xrightarrow{S} RSH \qquad\qquad 759$$

$$RSSR \xrightarrow[NH_3]{Li} RSH \qquad\qquad 760$$

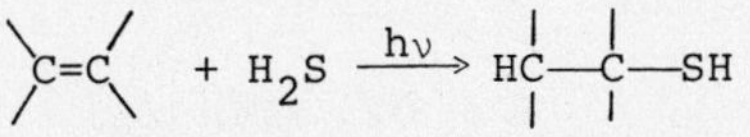

$+ H_2S \xrightarrow{h\nu}$ HC—C—SH $\qquad\qquad$ 271

$$ArNH_2 \xrightarrow{HONO} ArN_2^+ \xrightarrow[EtOCS_2^-;OH^-]{HS^-\ or} ArSH \qquad\qquad 744,\ 752$$

Thiocyanates

$$RX + {}^-SCN \longrightarrow RSCN \qquad\qquad 158,\ 170,\ 697$$

FORMATION OF C–C BONDS

Acyloin and Pinacol Condensations

$$RCOOEt \xrightarrow[ether]{Na} RCOCHOHR \qquad\qquad 851\text{-}852$$

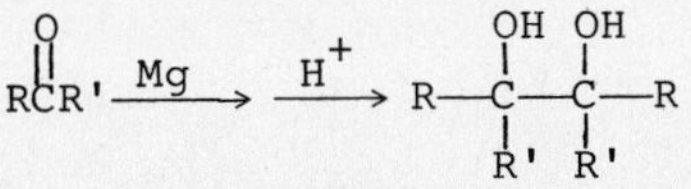

$\qquad\qquad$ 848

Alkene Addition Reactions

Carbenoid additions

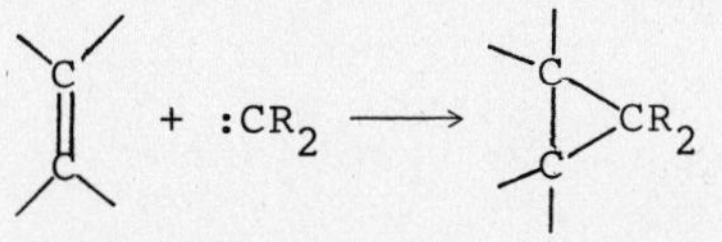

$\qquad\qquad$ 268-270, 437, 697, 740

Carbon tetrahalide addition

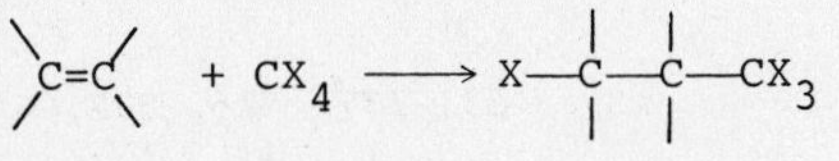

$\qquad\qquad$ 271, 272

Claisen rearrangement

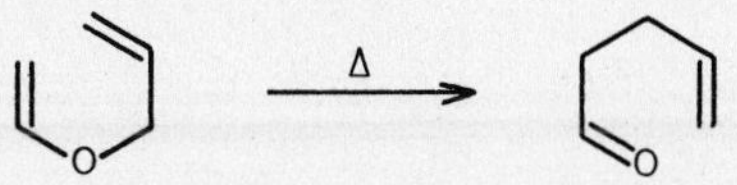

$\qquad\qquad$ 595, 825-826

Cope rearrangement

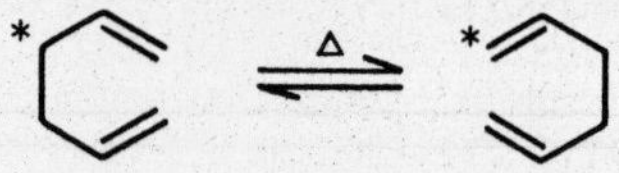

594

Cycloaddition reactions
(see also Diels-Alder cycloaddition)

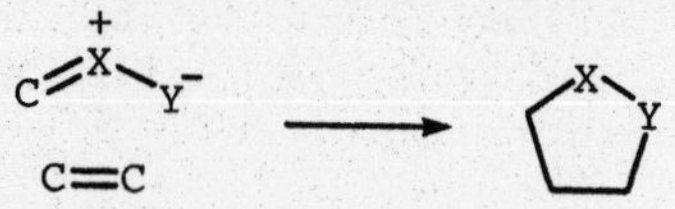

1019, 1020

Diels-Alder cycloaddition

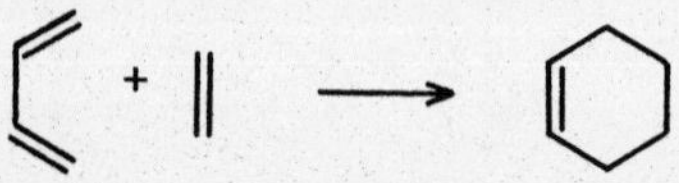

550-554, 612, 616, 623-624,
835, 863, 989, 1040

Michael additions

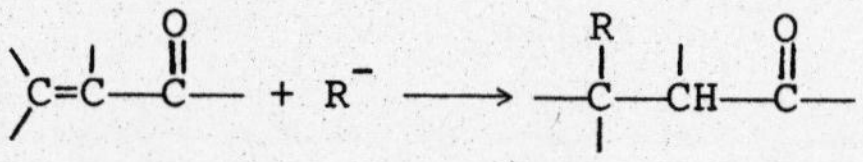

876-878, 935, 1030

(from ketone, β-dicarbonyl or enamine)

Alkylation of Carbon Acids

Acetylides

$RC \equiv C^- + R'Y \longrightarrow RC \equiv CR'$

285-286, 381-382, 434, 443

Benzylic carbanions

Ar_2CH_2 (or Ar_3CH) $\xrightarrow{NaNH_2}$

$\xrightarrow{RX}$ Ar_2CHR (or Ar_3CR)

589, (733), 1030, 1035, 1038

Dithianes

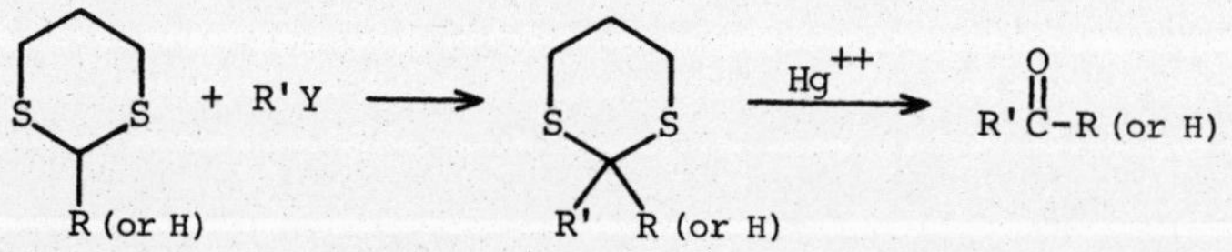

$+ R'Y \longrightarrow \xrightarrow{Hg^{++}}$ $R'\overset{O}{C}$-R (or H)

783

Enamines

$\underset{/}{\overset{\backslash}{C}}=\overset{|}{C}NR_2 + R'Y \longrightarrow$

$R'-\overset{|}{\underset{|}{C}}-\overset{|}{\underset{|}{C}}=NR_2^{\pm} \xrightarrow{H_2O} R'-\overset{|}{\underset{|}{C}}-\overset{O}{\underset{|}{C}}-$

721

Enolates

$\overset{\backslash}{\underset{/}{C}}=\overset{O^-}{C}R + R'CH_2Y \longrightarrow R'CH_2C\overset{O}{-}CR$

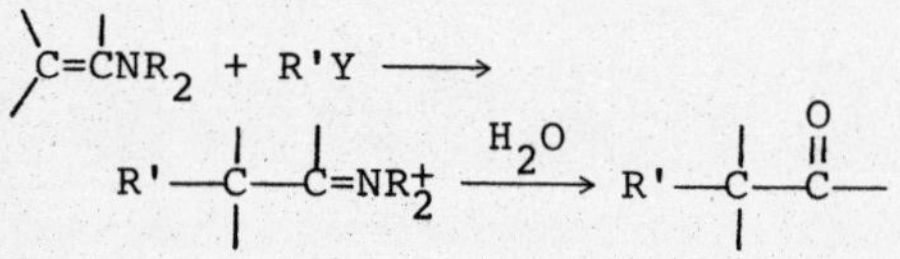

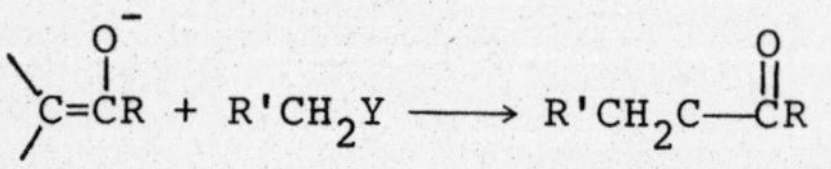

371-372, 435, 502, 697

$(EtOOC)_2CH^- + RY \longrightarrow (EtOOC)_2CHR$

873-874, 934-936

$RCO\overline{C}HCOOEt + R'Y \longrightarrow RCOC\overset{R'}{H}COOEt$

873-875

$R\overline{C}HCOOEt + R'Y \longrightarrow RR'CHCOOEt$

502

Appendix II

Phosphorus- and sulfur-stabilized carbanions

$$RCH_2Z \xrightarrow{n\text{BuLi}} \xrightarrow[\substack{\text{or} \\ R'_2C=O}]{R'X} \underset{R'}{RCHZ} \text{ or } \underset{R_2COH}{RCHZ}$$

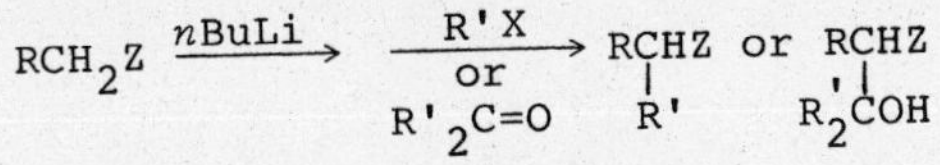

781–784

$$(Z = PO_3R''_2, \ SR'', \ \overset{+}{S}R''_2, \ SO_2R'')$$

Carbonyl Condensation Reactions

Aldol type

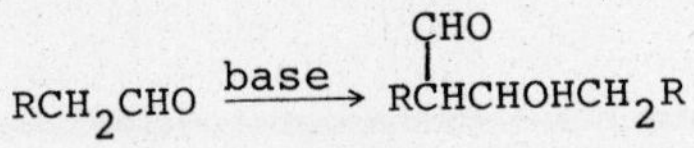

$$RCH_2CHO \xrightarrow{\text{base}} \overset{CHO}{\underset{}{RCHCHOHCH_2R}}$$

390–393, 435, 852–853

$$\overset{O}{\underset{}{RCCH_2R'}} + R''CHO \longrightarrow \overset{O}{\underset{R'}{RCC=CHR''}}$$

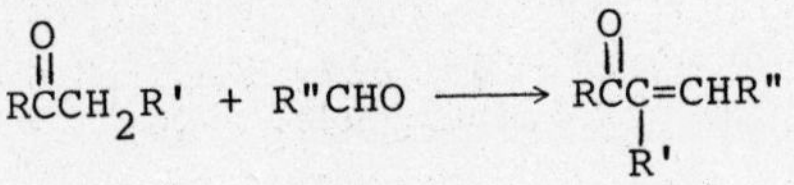

390–393, 435, 443, 538, 852, 878

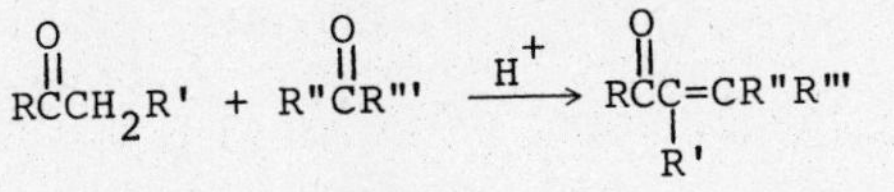

$$\overset{O}{\underset{}{RCCH_2R'}} + \overset{O}{\underset{}{R''CR'''}} \xrightarrow{H^+} \overset{O}{\underset{R'}{RCC=CR''R'''}}$$

536–537, 878

$$RCH_2COOEt \xrightarrow{R'_2NLi} R\bar{C}HCOOEt \xrightarrow{\overset{O}{R''CR'''}}$$

$$\underset{\underset{OH}{R''-C-R'''}}{RCHCOOEt}$$

502, 858

$$\overset{O}{\underset{}{RCR'}} + R''COCH_2COOEt \longrightarrow$$

$$\underset{R'}{\overset{HO\ COOEt}{RC-CHCOR''}} \text{ or } RR'C=C\overset{COOEt}{\underset{COR''}{}}$$

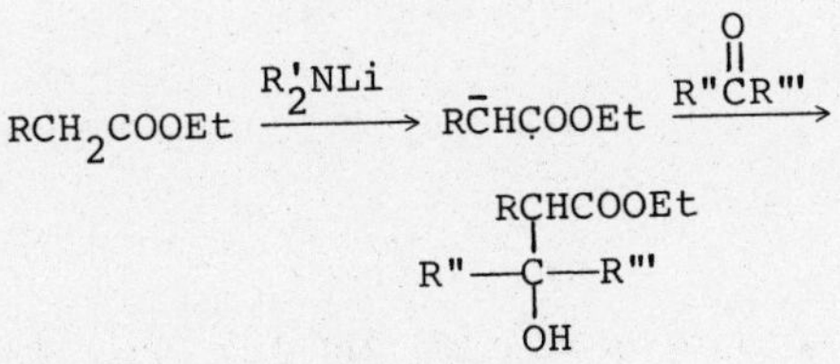

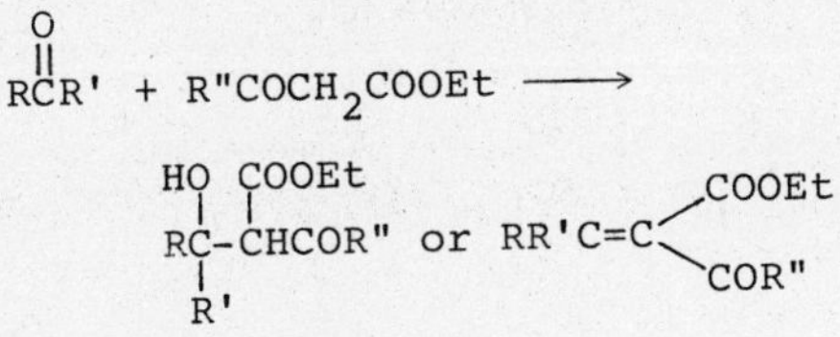

875–876, 1024

Benzoin

$$ArCHO \xrightarrow{CN^-} ArCOCHOHAr$$

852

Claisen and Dieckmann condensations

$$RCOOEt + R'CH_2COOEt \xrightarrow{EtO^-} \overset{COOEt}{\underset{}{R'CHCOR}}$$

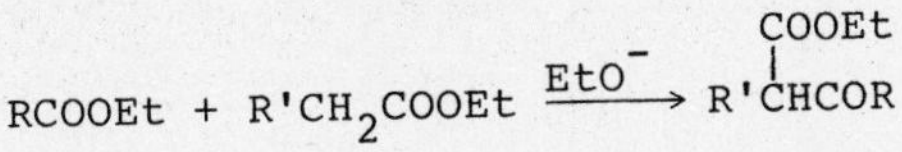

503–505, 867–869, 1039

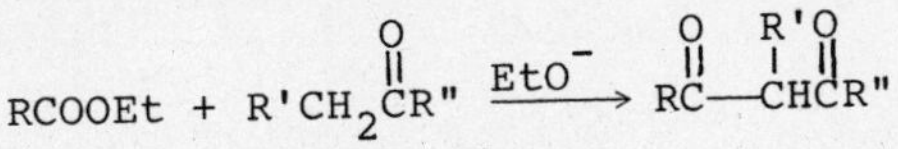

$$RCOOEt + R'CH_2\overset{O}{CR''} \xrightarrow{EtO^-} \overset{O}{RC}\overset{R'O}{-CHCR''}$$

868–869

Henry

$$RCH_2NO_2 + \overset{O}{RCR'} \xrightarrow{\text{base}} \overset{NO_2}{\underset{OH}{RCHCR'_2}} \longrightarrow \overset{NO_2}{R-C=CR'_2}$$

732

Horner-Emmons

$$\overset{O}{RCR} + R'\overset{O}{\underset{}{C}}\underset{}{\bar{C}}HPO_3Et_2 \longrightarrow R_2C=CHCR'$$

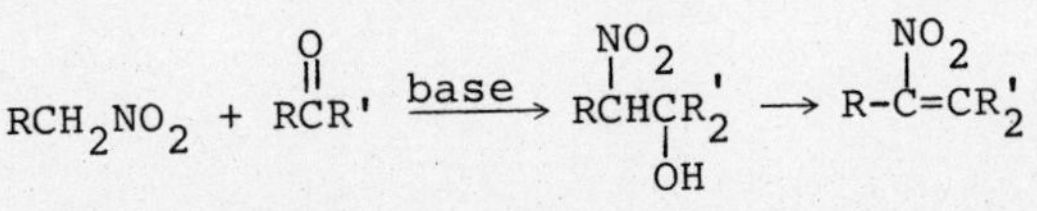

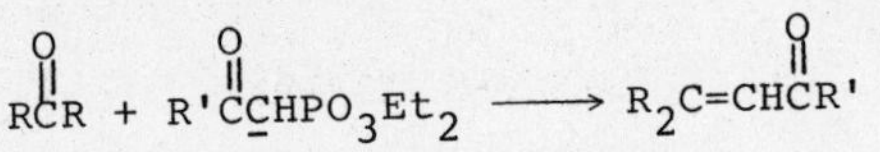

782

Knoevenagel

$$RCHO + CH_2(COOH)_2 \xrightarrow{\text{amine}} RCH=C(COOH)_2$$

875–876

Mannich

$$\underset{\substack{\| \\ O}}{RCCH_2R'} + CH_2O + HNR_2'' \xrightarrow{H^+} \underset{\substack{| \\ R'}}{\underset{\substack{\| \\ O}}{RCCHCH_2NR_2''}}$$

722

Perkin

$$ArCHO + (RCH_2CO)_2O \xrightarrow{RCH_2CO_2^-} \underset{\substack{R \\ \|}}{ArCH=CCOOH}$$

546–547

Reformatsky

$$\underset{\substack{\| \\ O}}{RCR'} \text{ (or H)} + BrCHR''COOEt \xrightarrow{Zn} \underset{\substack{| \\ R' \text{ (or H)}}}{\underset{\substack{OH \\ |}}{RCCHR''COOEt}}$$

503

Wittig

$$Ph_3P=CHR + R_2'C=O \longrightarrow R_2'C=CHR$$

397–398, 435, 442, 533

Cyanide Reactions

$$RY + CN^- \longrightarrow RCN$$

158, 172, 259, 285, 434, 460, 546, 585, 862

$$\underset{\substack{\| \\ O}}{RCR'} + HCN \longrightarrow \underset{\substack{| \\ OH}}{RR'CCN}$$

388–390, 435, 547, 701, 858, 908

$$\underset{\substack{\| \\ O}}{RCR'} + HCN + NH_3 \longrightarrow \underset{\substack{| \\ NH_2}}{RR'CCN}$$

936

$$\underset{\substack{| \quad | \\ }}{C=C}\underset{\substack{\| \\ O}}{-C-} + HCN \longrightarrow \underset{\substack{| \\ CN}}{-C-}\underset{}{CH}\underset{\substack{\| \\ O}}{-C-}$$

539–540, 862

$$ArX + CuCN \longrightarrow ArCN$$

745

Grignard and Related Organometallic Reactions

Acyl halides

$$RCOCl + R'MgX \longrightarrow \underset{\substack{\| \\ O}}{RCR'}$$

496

$$RCOCl + R_2'CuLi \longrightarrow \underset{\substack{\| \\ O}}{RCR'}$$

496

$$RCOCl + CH_2N_2 \longrightarrow \underset{\substack{\| \\ O}}{RCCHN_2} \text{ or } \underset{\substack{\| \\ O}}{RCCH_2Cl}$$

739

Aldehydes and ketones

$$RMgX \text{ (or RLi)} + \underset{\substack{\| \\ O}}{R'CR''} \text{ (or H)} \longrightarrow \underset{\substack{| \\ R'}}{\underset{\substack{OH \\ |}}{RCR''}} \text{(or H)}$$

386–388, 435, 440, 441, 496, 497, 540–541, 806, 856, 978, 1040

$$\underset{\substack{\| \\ O}}{RCR'} \text{ (or H)} + RC\equiv C^- (MgX, Li^+, \text{ or } Na^+) \longrightarrow$$

$$\underset{\substack{| \\ R' \text{ (or H)}}}{\underset{\substack{OH \\ |}}{RCC\equiv CR''}}$$

388, 435, 533

Carbon dioxide

$$RMgX \text{ (or RLi)} \xrightarrow{CO_2} RCOOH$$

460–461

Esters

    $RCOOEt + R'MgX$ (or $R'Li$) $\longrightarrow RR'_2COH$ 496-497

    $RMgX + (EtO)_2C=O \longrightarrow R_3COH$ 497

Halides

    $RMgX + CH_2=CHCH_2X \longrightarrow RCH_2CH=CH_2$ 522, 532

Oxirane

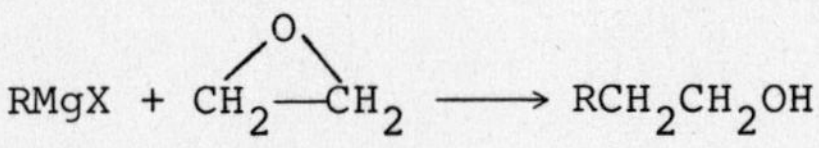

    $RMgX + CH_2\overset{O}{\frown}CH_2 \longrightarrow RCH_2CH_2OH$ 221, 435, 441

Unsaturated ketones

    $RMgX$ (or R_2CuLi) +

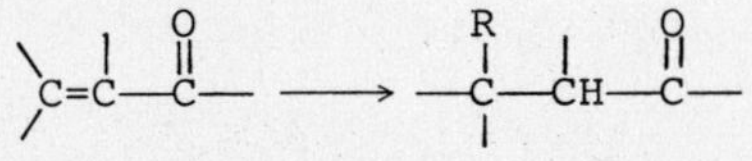

                                            540-541, 841

Formation of C—C Bonds to Aromatic Rings

Amine derivatives

    $ArNH_2 \xrightarrow{HONO} ArN_2^+ \xrightarrow{CuCN} ArCN$ 745, 752

    $ArNH_2 \xrightarrow{HONO} ArN_2^+ \xrightarrow[OH^-]{Ar'H} Ar\text{—}Ar'$ 748-749, 752

    $ArNHNHAr \xrightarrow{H^+} H_2NAr'Ar'NH_2$ 736, 971
    (benzidine rearrangement)

Arenes

    $ArH + RCOCl$ (or $(RCO)_2O$) $\xrightarrow{Lewis\ acid} Ar\overset{O}{\overset{\|}{C}}R$ 652-653, 673, 713, 790, 822-824,
                                            978, 982, 985, 986, 1011, 1014

    $ArH + RCOOH \xrightarrow[Lewis\ acid]{H^+\ or} Ar\overset{O}{\overset{\|}{C}}R$ 822, 824, 987

    $ArH + HCON(CH_3)_2 \xrightarrow{POCl_3} ArCHO$ 713, 1015

    $ArH + CH_2O + HCl \xrightarrow{ZnCl_2} ArCH_2Cl$ 655, 1015

    $ArH + RX \xrightarrow{AlCl_3} ArR$ ($+ Ar'R + ArR'$)   653-654, 656

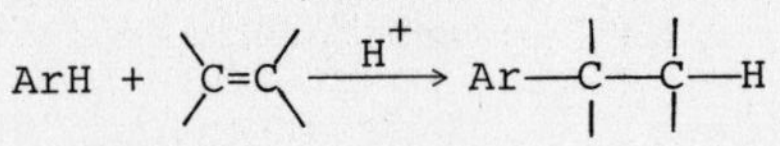

    $ArH + \,\diagdown\!C=C\diagup \xrightarrow{H^+} Ar\text{—}\overset{|}{C}\text{—}\overset{|}{C}\text{—}H$ 655, 771, 811

Aryl halides and organometallics

    $ArX + RX \xrightarrow{Na} ArR$ 807

    $ArX \xrightarrow{Cu} ArAr$ 807

    $ArX \xrightarrow{Mg} \xrightarrow{CO_2} ArCOOH$ 806

    $ArLi \xrightarrow{CuBr} \xrightarrow{O_2} Ar\text{-}Ar$ 807

Phenols

$$ArO^- + RCHO \longrightarrow HOAr'\overset{\overset{\displaystyle OH}{|}}{C}HR \qquad\qquad 815$$

$$ArO^- + CO_2 \longrightarrow Ar\overset{OH}{\underset{COOH}{<}} \qquad\qquad 816$$

$$ArO^- + CHCl_3 \longrightarrow Ar\overset{OH}{\underset{CHO}{<}} \qquad\qquad 817$$

$$Ar\overset{\overset{\displaystyle O}{\|}}{O}CR \xrightarrow{AlCl_3} Ar\overset{OH}{\underset{COR}{<}} \qquad\qquad 824$$

$$ArOCH_2CH=CH_2 \xrightarrow{\Delta} Ar\overset{OH}{\underset{CH_2CH=CH_2}{<}} \qquad\qquad 825\text{-}826$$

(Claisen rearrangement)

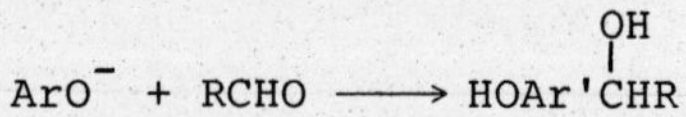

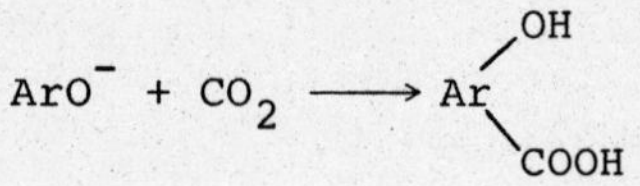

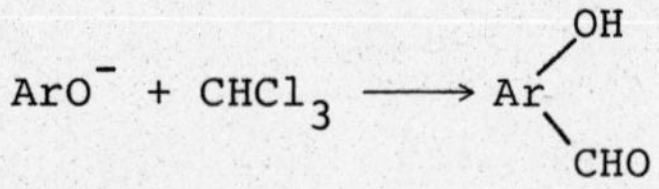

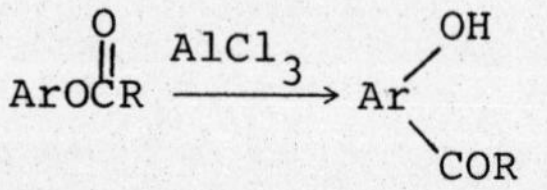

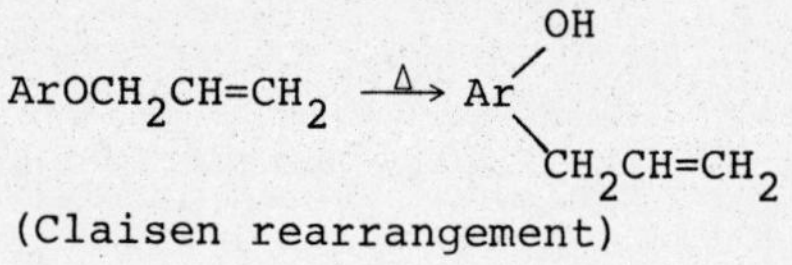